Powerplants for Aerospace Vehicles

THIRD EDITION

Northrop Institute of Technology

James L. McKinley

Ralph D. Bent

McGRAW-HILL BOOK COMPANY

New York   St. Louis   San Francisco
Sydney   Toronto   London

Powerplants for Aerospace Vehicles

Library of Congress Catalog Card Number: 64-25002

47490

7 8 9 HDBP 7 5 4 3 2 1 0 6 9

Northrop Institute of Technology Series

Other Books in the Series
BASIC SCIENCE FOR AEROSPACE VEHICLES, 3/e
ELECTRICITY AND ELECTRONICS FOR AEROSPACE VEHICLES
MAINTENANCE AND REPAIR OF AEROSPACE VEHICLES, 3/e

Powerplants for Aerospace Vehicles

Preface

Powerplants for Aerospace Vehicles is the third edition of the book formerly titled *Aircraft Power Plants*. This text provides the student, mechanic, and aviation technician with a well-rounded background of information on aircraft engines, engine accessories, and powerplant systems. It is one of a series of four texts prepared by the Northrop Institute of Technology. The two which precede this text cover basic science and electricity and electronics; the final volume deals with maintenance and repair. Taken all together, these books are designed to encompass information on all phases of airframe and powerplant technology.

This edition of the powerplant text has been brought up to date by the addition of new descriptive material and illustrations on powerplant electrical systems, fuel systems, fuels, fuel-control devices, ignition systems, modern engines of both piston and turbine types, propellers and propeller controls, and starting systems for both piston and turbine engines. New chapters on electricity, engine overhaul practices, and rocket engines expand the usefulness of the text.

Each topic in *Powerplants for Aerospace Vehicles* has been explained in as much detail as possible so that the reader may become thoroughly familiar with all aspects of modern powerplants. In addition to its use as a classroom text, it is valuable for home study and as a reference book for the mechanic or technician on the job. The subjects are organized so that instructors in public and private technical schools, training divisions of aircraft factories and airlines, vocational schools, high schools, and industrial education divisions of colleges and universities are provided with a wealth of classroom material. Review questions have been added at the end of each chapter so that the student may check his knowledge of the material presented.

RALPH D. BENT

Acknowledgments

The authors wish to express appreciation to the following organizations for their generous assistance in providing illustrations and technical information for this text:

Aerojet General Corporation, Azusa, California

Ahrens Controls, Inc., Chicago, Illinois

AiResearch Manufacturing Division, Garrett Corporation, Los Angeles, California

AiResearch Manufacturing Division of Arizona, Garrett Corporation, Phoenix, Arizona

Allison Division, General Motors Corporation, Indianapolis, Indiana

Beech Aircraft Corporation, Wichita, Kansas

Bendix Products Division, The Bendix Corporation, South Bend, Indiana

Bendix Scintilla Division, The Bendix Corporation, Sidney, New York

Bendix Utica Division, The Bendix Corporation, Utica, New York

Boeing Company, Transport Division, Renton, Washington

Bray Oil Company, Los Angeles, California

Cessna Aircraft Company, Wichita, Kansas

Champion Spark Plug Company, Toledo, Ohio

Continental Motors Corporation, Muskegon, Michigan

Convair–General Dynamics, San Diego, California

Delco-Remy Division, General Motors Corporation, Anderson, Indiana

Douglas Aircraft Company, Santa Monica, California

Douglas Aircraft Company, Long Beach, California

Ethyl Corporation, New York, New York

Exide Industrial Division, Electric Storage Battery Company, Philadelphia, Pennsylvania

Federal Aviation Agency, Washington, D.C.

General Electric Company, Cincinnati, Ohio

General Electric Company, Small Engine Division, West Lynn, Massachusetts

Hamilton Standard Division, United Aircraft Corporation, Windsor Locks, Connecticut

Hartzell Propeller, Inc., Piqua, Ohio

Lycoming Division, Avco Corporation, Williamsport, Pennsylvania

Marvel-Schebler Products Division, Borg-Warner Corporation, Decatur, Illinois

McCauley Industrial Corporation, Dayton, Ohio

Pangborn Corporation, Hagerstown, Maryland

Pesco Products Division, Borg-Warner Corporation, Bedford, Ohio

Piper Aircraft Corporation, Lock Haven, Pennsylvania

Pratt & Whitney Aircraft Division, United Aircraft Corporation, East Hartford, Connecticut

Rajay Company, Inc., Long Beach, California

Rocketdyne Division, North American Aviation, Inc., Canoga Park, California

Shakespeare Products Co., Kalamazoo, Michigan

Sky Store, Inc., Hawthorne, California

Slick Electro, Inc., Rockford, Illinois

Tansey Aircraft Pulley Company, Gardena, California

Timken Roller Bearing Company, Canton, Ohio

Weatherhead Company, Cleveland, Ohio

Western Gear Corporation, Lynwood, California

Westinghouse Electric Corporation, Pittsburgh, Pennsylvania

Woodward Governor Company, Rockford, Illinois

Contents

CHAPTER 1

Powerplant Progress

Early engines

Development of the internal-combustion engine took place largely during the nineteenth century. One of the first such engines was described in 1820 by the Reverend W. Cecil in a discourse before the Cambridge Philosophical Society in England. This engine operated on a mixture of hydrogen and air. In 1838 the English inventor William Barnett built a single-cylinder gas engine which had a combustion chamber at both the top and the bottom of the piston. This engine burned gaseous fuel rather than the liquid fuel used in the modern gasoline engine.

The first practical gas engine was built in 1860 by a French inventor named Jean Joseph Étienne Lenoir. This engine utilized illuminating gas as a fuel, and ignition of the fuel was provided by a battery system. Within a few years approximately 400 of these engines had been built to operate a variety of machinery such as lathes and printing presses.

The first four-stroke-cycle engine was built by August Otto and Eugen Langen of Germany in 1876. As a result, the four-stroke-cycle engine is often called an Otto-cycle engine. Otto and Langen also built a two-stroke-cycle engine.

In America, George B. Brayton, an engineer, built an engine using gasoline as a fuel and exhibited it at the 1876 Centennial Exposition in Philadelphia. The first truly successful gasoline engine operating according to the four-stroke-cycle principle was built in Germany in 1885 by Gottlieb Daimler, who had previously been associated with Otto and Langen. A similar gasoline engine was built by Karl Benz of Germany in the same year. The Daimler and Benz engines were used in early automobiles, and the engines used today are similar in many respects to the Daimler and Benz engines.

The first successful airplane engine

Inasmuch as the first powered flight in an airplane was made by the Wright brothers on December 17, 1903, it is safe to say that the first successful gasoline engine for an airplane was the engine used in the Wright airplane. This engine was designed and built by the Wright brothers and their mechanic Charles Taylor. The engine had the following characteristics: (1) water cooled; (2) four cylinders; (3) bore, 4⅜ in.; stroke, 4 in.; displacement, 240 cu in.; (4) 12 hp; (5) weight, 180 lb; (6) cast-iron cylinders with sheet-aluminum water jackets; (7) valve-in-head with the exhaust valve mechanically operated and the intake valve automatically operated; (8) aluminum-alloy crankcase; (9) carburetion by means of fuel flow into a heated manifold; and (10) ignition by means of a high-tension magneto.

World War I engines

The extensive development and use of airplanes during World War I contributed greatly to the improvement of engines. One of the types of engines which found most extensive use was the air-cooled rotary-type radial engine. In this type of engine the crankshaft is held stationary and the cylinders rotate around the crankshaft. Among the best known rotary engines were the Le Rhône, Gnôme-Monosoupape, and the Bentley. Even though the rotary engines powered many World War I airplanes, they had two serious disadvantages: (1) The torque and gyro effects of the large rotating mass of the engines made the airplane difficult to control, and (2) the engines used castor oil as a lubricant, and since the castor oil was mixed with the fuel of the engine in the crankcase, the exhaust of the engine contained unburned castor oil fumes which were often nauseating to the pilot.

A number of in-line and V-type engines were also developed during World War I. Among these were the Hispano-Suiza, a 90° V-8 engine; the Rolls-Royce V-12 engine; the American-made Liberty V-12 engine; and several German engines including the Mercedes, the Benz, and the BMW.

Following World War I a number of excellent American engines were built, and the results of the postwar development led to the very efficient engines which were employed in World War II. Among the American engines not already mentioned but developed during and after World War I were the Curtiss OX series, the Wright Hisso (an American-built Hispano-Suiza), the Packard V-12, the Curtiss D-12 (a V-12 engine), the Wright Whirlwind engines (radial, air-cooled), and the Pratt & Whitney Wasp and Hornet engines (radial, air-cooled types). Numerous smaller engines were also developed and built including radial, opposed-cylinder, and in-line types.

Progress in design

Engineers who specialize in the design of aircraft powerplants have used light alloy metals for construction of the engines, and they have adopted weight-saving cylinder arrangements, such as placing the cylinders radially in one or more rows around the crankshaft, with the result that today the weight per horsepower on several engines is below 1.2 lb and on some, less than 1 lb.

Airplanes have increased in size, carrying capacity, and speed. With each increase has come a demand for more power, and this has been met by improvements in engine and propeller design and by the use of turbojet and turboprop engines. As piston engines increased in power, they became more complicated. The early powerplant engineers and mechanics had only a few comparatively simple problems to meet, but the modern powerplant specialist must be familiar with the principles of the internal-combustion engine; the classification, construction, and nomenclature of engines; their fuel and carburetion systems; supercharging and induction systems; the lubrication of powerplants; engine-starting systems; ignition systems; valve and ignition timing; engine control systems; and propellers, both wood and metal. If the specialist works with turbine engines, he must be familiar with the construction and operation of these engines and the complex fuel-control units and systems required for such engines. In addition to understanding the design, construction, and operation of powerplants, the specialist must know the proper procedures for inspection, maintenance, overhaul, and repair.

Fundamentally, the reciprocating internal-combustion engine that we know today is a direct descendant of the first Wright engine. It has become larger, heavier, and much more powerful, but the basic principles are essentially the same. However, the modern reciprocating aircraft engine has reached a stage in its development where it is faced with what is commonly called the **theory of diminishing returns.** More cylinders are added to obtain more power, but the resulting increases in size and weight complicate matters in many directions. For example, the modern conventional engine may lose more than 30 percent of its power in dragging itself and its nacelle through the air and in providing necessary cooling.

The improvement in reciprocating engines has be-
come quite noticeable in the smaller engines used for light aircraft. This has been accomplished chiefly with the opposed-type, four- and six-cylinder engines. Among the improvements developed for light engines during and since World War II are geared propellers, superchargers, and direct fuel-injection systems. Whereas light airplanes were once limited to flight at comparatively low altitudes, today many of them are capable of cruising at well over 20,000 ft altitude.

Jet propulsion

During World War II, the demand for increased speed and power expedited the progress which was already taking place in the development of jet-propulsion powerplants. As a result of the impetus given by the requirements of the War and Navy Departments in the United States and similar demands on the part of our British allies, engineers in England and the United States designed, manufactured, and tested in flight an amazing variety of jet-propulsion powerplants. It must be noted also that the German government was not trailing behind in the jet-propulsion race, because the first flight by an airplane powered with a true jet engine was made in Germany on August 27, 1939. The airplane was a Heinkel He 178 and was powered by a Heinkel HeS 3B turbojet engine.

The successful development of jet propulsion is beyond question the greatest single advance in the history of aviation since the Wright brothers made their first flight. The speed of aircraft has increased from below Mach 1 to speeds of Mach 3, or three times the speed of sound. Commercial airliners now operate at more than 600 mph rather than at high speeds of around 350 mph, which is usually about the maximum for conventional propeller-driven airliners.

The reciprocating engine will be retained for many years to come for use in airplanes where low power and relatively low speed are expected. The gas-turbine engine is used both as a jet engine and for driving propellers and helicopter rotors. Small turboprop engines have also been developed for operating luxury-type and business-type light aircraft. Some business aircraft are also equipped with turbojet engines, but the cost of such aircraft is very high compared with conventional types.

The design and construction of jet engines have advanced most rapidly, and it is difficult for any textbook to keep up with all the latest developments. Nevertheless, the basic principles of theory, construction, and operation of gas-turbine and rocket engines are covered in the last few chapters of this text.

CHAPTER 2

Internal-combustion-engine Principles

ENGINE CYCLE AND STROKE

Cycle

A **cycle** is a complete sequence of events returning to the original state. For example, a cycle may be an interval or period of time occupied by one round or course of events repeating in the same order in a series, such as the cycle of the seasons, with spring, summer, autumn, and winter following each other and then recurring.

An **engine cycle** is a series of events that an internal-combustion engine performs while it is operating and delivering power. Since these events occur in a certain sequence, they are said to be **timed.**

Most piston-type engines operate on the **four-stroke five-event-cycle** principle which was originally developed by August Otto in Germany. There are four strokes of the piston, two up and two down, for each engine-operating cycle. The five events consist of these strokes plus the **ignition event.** The theoretical cycles through which a **heat engine** operates are the **Carnot cycle, Otto cycle, Brayton cycle,** and **Diesel cycle.** The nature of these cycles will be explained later.

Stroke

The basic power-developing parts of a typical gasoline engine are the **cylinder, piston, connecting rod,** and **crankshaft.** These are shown in Fig. 2·1. The cylinder has a smooth surface such that the piston can, with the aid of piston rings and a lubricant, create a seal so no gases can escape between the piston and the cylinder walls. The piston is connected to the crankshaft by means of the connecting rod so the rotation of the crankshaft causes the piston to move with a reciprocating motion up and down in the cylinder. The distance through which the piston travels is called the

stroke. The limit of travel to which the piston moves into the cylinder is called **top dead center,** and the limit to which it moves in the opposite direction is called **bottom dead center.** For each revolution of the crankshaft there are two strokes of the piston, one up and one down, assuming that the cylinder is in a vertical position. Figure 2·2 shows that the stroke of the

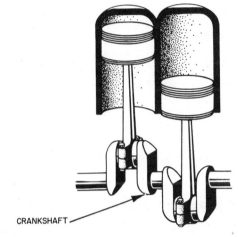

CRANKSHAFT

Figure **2·1** Basic parts of a gasoline engine.

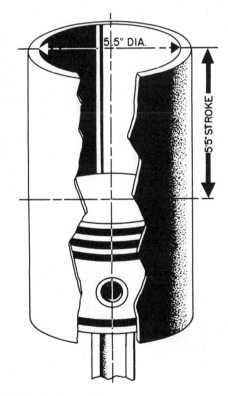

5.5" DIA.

5.5" STROKE

Figure **2·2** Stroke and bore.

3

cylinder illustrated is 5.5 in. and that its **bore** (internal diameter) is also 5.5 in. An engine having the bore equal to the stroke is often called a **square** engine.

It is important to understand the position called **top dead center** (abbreviated TDC) and **bottom dead center** (abbreviated BDC) because these positions of the piston are used in setting the timing and determining the valve overlap. Top dead center may be defined as the point which a piston has reached when it is at its maximum distance from the center line of the crankshaft. In like manner, bottom dead center may be defined as the position which the piston has reached when it is at a minimum distance from the center line of the crankshaft. Figure 2·3 illustrates the piston position at top dead center and at bottom dead center.

The four-stroke five-event cycle

The four strokes of a four-stroke-cycle engine are the **intake** stroke, the **compression** stroke, the **power** stroke, and the **exhaust** stroke. The names of the strokes are descriptive of the nature of each stroke. During the intake stroke the piston starts at top dead center with the intake valve open and the exhaust valve closed. As the piston moves downward, a mixture of fuel and air from the carburetor is drawn into the

cylinder. The intake stroke is illustrated in Fig. 2·4.

When the piston has reached bottom dead center at the end of the intake stroke, the intake valve closes and the piston moves back towards the cylinder head. Since both valves are now closed, the fuel/air mixture is compressed in the cylinder. For this reason the event illustrated in Fig. 2·5 is called the **compression** stroke. A few degrees of crankshaft travel before the piston reaches top dead center on the compression stroke, the **ignition** event takes place. Ignition is caused by a spark plug which produces an electric spark in the fuel/air mixture. This spark ignites the fuel/air mixture, thus creating heat and pressure to force the piston downward toward bottom dead center. The reason ignition is timed to occur a few degrees before top dead center is to allow time for complete combustion of the fuel and to develop maximum pressure. If the ignition occurred at top dead center, the piston would be moving downward as the fuel burned and a maximum pressure would not be developed. Also, the burning gases moving down the walls of the cylinder would heat the cylinder walls and the engine would develop excessive temperature.

The stroke during which the piston is forced down, as the result of combustion pressure, is called the **power** stroke because this is the time that power is developed in the engine. The movement of the piston downward causes the crankshaft to rotate, thus turning the flywheel or propeller being driven by the engine. The power stroke illustrated in Fig. 2·6 is also called the **expansion** stroke because of the gas expansion which takes place at this time.

Shortly before the piston reaches bottom dead center on the power stroke, the exhaust valve opens and the hot gases begin to escape from the cylinder. The pressure differential across the piston drops to zero, and the gases that remain in the cylinder are forced out the open exhaust valve as the piston moves back toward top dead center. This is the **exhaust** stroke and is also called the **scavenging** stroke because the burned gases are scavenged (removed from the cylinder) during the stroke. The exhaust stroke is illustrated in Fig. 2·7.

We may summarize the complete cycle of the four-stroke-cycle engine as follows: **Intake stroke**—the intake valve is open, exhaust valve closed, the piston moves downward and draws the fuel/air mixture into the cylinder, the intake valve closes; **compression stroke**—both valves are closed, the piston moves toward top dead center and compresses the fuel/air mixture, ignition takes place near the top of the stroke; **power stroke**—both valves are closed, the pressure of the expanding gases forces the piston toward bottom dead center, the exhaust valve opens near the bottom of the stroke; **exhaust stroke**—the exhaust valve is open, the intake valve closed, the piston moves toward top dead center and forces burned gases out through the open exhaust valve, the intake valve opens near the top of the stroke.

The five-event sequence of intake, compression, ignition, power, and exhaust is a cycle which must

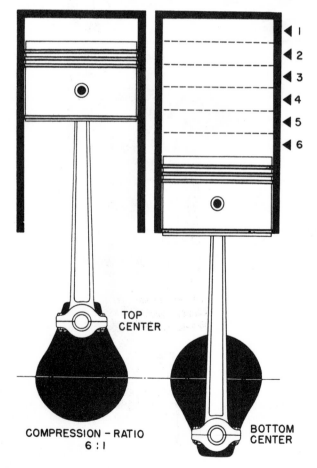

TOP CENTER

BOTTOM CENTER

COMPRESSION – RATIO 6 : 1

Figure **2·3** *Top and bottom center.*

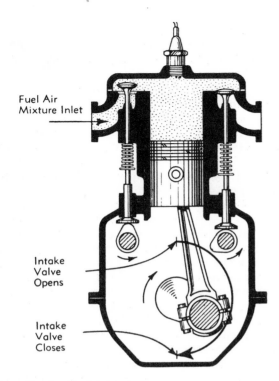

Fuel Air
Mixture Inlet

Intake
Valve
Opens

Intake
Valve
Closes

Figure **2·4**   *The intake stroke.*

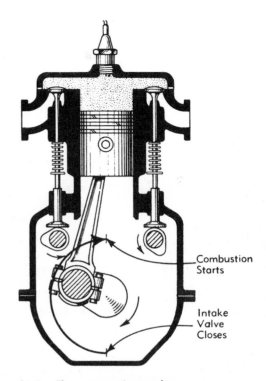

Combustion
Starts

Intake
Valve
Closes

Figure **2·5**   *The compression stroke.*

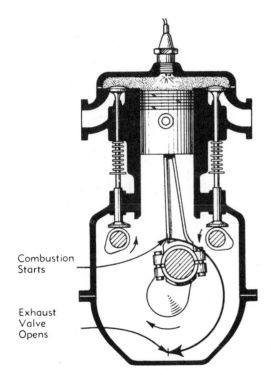

Combustion
Starts

Exhaust
Valve
Opens

Figure **2·6**   *The power stroke.*

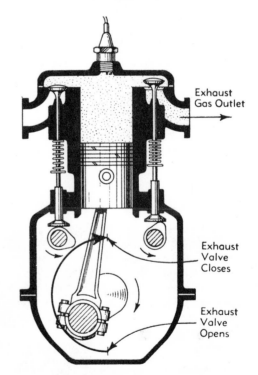

Exhaust
Gas Outlet

Exhaust
Valve
Closes

Exhaust
Valve
Opens

Figure **2·7**   *The exhaust stroke.*

take place in the order given if the engine is to operate at all, and it must be repeated over and over for the engine to continue operation. None of the events can be omitted, and each event must take place in the proper sequence. For example, if the gasoline supply is shut off, there can be no power event. The mixture

of gasoline and air must be admitted to the cylinder during the intake stroke. Likewise, if the ignition switch is turned off, there can be no power event because the ignition must occur before the power event can take place.

An engine cannot normally start itself but requires

rotation of the crankshaft in order to start the sequence of events necessary for operation. For this reason a variety of starting systems has been employed. Among such systems are hand-cranking of the engine, hand-cranked inertia starters, electrical inertia starters, combustion starters, and direct-cranking electrical starters. These systems are described in a later section of this text.

Conversion of heat energy to mechanical energy

Energy is the capacity for performing work. There are two kinds of energy: **kinetic** and **potential. Kinetic** energy is the energy of motion, such as that possessed by a moving cannon ball, falling water, or a strong wind. **Potential** energy is the energy of position, or stored energy. A coiled spring has potential energy. Likewise, the water behind the dam of a reservoir has potential energy and gasoline has potential energy.

Energy can be neither created nor destroyed. A perpetual-motion machine cannot exist because, even if friction and the weight of the parts were eliminated, the machine can never have any more energy than that which has been put into it.

Energy cannot be created, but it can be transformed from one kind into another. When a coiled spring is wound, work is performed. When the spring unwinds, its stored or potential energy becomes kinetic energy. When a mixture of gasoline and air is ignited, the combustion process increases the kinetic energy of the molecules in the gases. When the gas is confined as in a reciprocating-engine cylinder, this results in increased pressure (potential energy) which produces work when the piston is forced downward.

Heat energy can be transformed into mechanical energy, mechanical energy can be transformed into electrical energy, and electrical energy can be transformed into heat, light, chemical, or mechanical energy.

Boyle's law and Charles's law

Boyle's law states that the volume of any dry gas varies inversely with the absolute pressure sustained by it, the temperature remaining constant. In other words, increasing the pressure upon a volume of confined gas reduces its volume correspondingly. In a similar manner, doubling the pressure reduces the volume of the gas to one-half, trebling the pressure reduces the volume to one-third, etc.

Charles's law states that the pressure of a confined gas is directly proportional to its absolute temperature. Therefore, as the temperature of the gas is increased, the pressure is also increased as long as the volume remains constant.

These laws may be used to explain the operation of an engine. The mixture of fuel and air burns when it is ignited and gives off heat. The heat is absorbed by the gases in the cylinder, and they tend to expand. The increase in pressure, acting on the head of the piston, forces it to move, and the motion is transmitted to the crankshaft through the connecting rod.

A further understanding of the engine operation may be gained by examining the theory of the **Carnot cycle,** developed by the French physicist Sadi Carnot (1796–1832). The Carnot cycle explains the operation of an "ideal" heat engine. The engine employs a gas as a working medium, and the changes in pressure, volume, and temperature are in accordance with Boyle's and Charles's laws. A detailed study of the Carnot cycle is not essential to the present discussion; however, if the student desires to pursue the matter further, he can find a complete explanation in any good college text on physics.

As explained previously, the conventional piston engine utilizes a connecting rod to transmit the movement of the piston to the crankshaft in order to produce the rotary motion of the crankshaft. An ordinary sewing-machine band wheel and treadle, illustrated in Fig. 2·8, afford a good example of the conversion of straight-line motion to rotary motion. One end of a connecting rod is fastened at A to the treadle. The other end of the connecting rod is fastened at B, a point on the band wheel which is off center. When the treadle is pushed down with the toe of the foot, the end of the connecting rod marked A moves downward and pulls the other end of the connecting rod B around

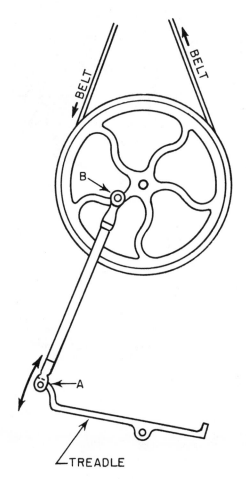

Figure **2·8** *Converting reciprocating motion to rotary motion.*

for a part of a circle. If the operator continues to push down with his toe, the band wheel will stop at **dead center,** but if the operator pauses a moment, the inertia of the band wheel will carry it past the dead-center position. The operator then pushes with his heel on the rear edge of the treadle, and the end of the connecting rod is pushed upward, causing the point *B* on the band wheel to move upward. As the point *B* nears the top-dead-center position, the operator pauses again and allows the band wheel to be carried past the dead-center position by inertia. Thus, to keep the band wheel turning, the operator pushes down with the toe, pauses, pushes down with the heel, pauses, and repeats the process indefinitely. The energy of the operator is exerted up and down; that is, it is a reciprocating motion, but a rotary motion is imparted to the band wheel.

Two-stroke cycle

Although present-day aircraft engines of the reciprocating type usually operate on the four-stroke-cycle principle, a few small auxiliary engines operate on the two-stroke-cycle principle. The differences are the number of strokes per operating cycle and the method of admitting the fuel/air mixture into the cylinder. The two-stroke-cycle engine is mechanically simpler than the four-stroke-cycle engine, but it is less efficient and is more difficult to lubricate and cool properly; hence, its use is restricted. The operating principle of the two-stroke-cycle engine is illustrated in Fig. 2·9.

The two-stroke-cycle engine is constructed with a cylinder, piston, crankshaft, connecting rod, and crankcase, similar to the four-stroke-cycle engine; however, the valve arrangement and fuel intake system are considerably different. The upward movement of the piston in the cylinder of the engine creates low pressure in the crankcase. This reduced pressure causes

a suction which draws the fuel/air mixture from the carburetor into the crankcase through a check valve. When the piston has reached top dead center, the crankcase is filled with fuel/air mixture and the inlet check valve is closed. The piston then moves downward in the cylinder and compresses the mixture in the crankcase. As the piston reaches the lowest point in its stroke, the intake port is opened to permit the fuel/air mixture which is compressed in the crankcase to flow into the cylinder. This is the **intake event.**

The piston then moves up in the cylinder, the intake port is closed, and the fuel/air mixture in the cylinder is compressed. While this is happening, a new charge of fuel and air is drawn into the crankcase. This is the **compression event** and is shown in Fig. 2·9a.

The piston continues to move up in the cylinder, and when it is almost at the top of the stroke, a spark is produced at the gap of the spark plug, thus igniting the fuel/air mixture. This is the **ignition event.** As the fuel/air mixture burns, the gases of combustion expand and drive the piston down. This is the **power event** and is shown in Fig. 2·9b.

When the piston approaches the bottom point of its travel, the exhaust port is opened to allow the hot gases to escape. This occurs a fraction of a second before the intake valve opens to release the cylinder pressure and to reduce the mixing of fuel and air with the burned exhaust gases. As the exhaust gases rush out the exhaust port on one side of the cylinder, the intake port is opened and the fuel/air mixture flows into the other side. A baffle on the top of the piston deflects the incoming mixture toward the top of the cylinder, thus helping to scavenge the exhaust gases and reduce the mixing of the fuel/air mixture with the exhaust gases. It can easily be seen that the **exhaust** and **intake events** take place almost simultaneously, with the exhaust event leading by a small fraction of the piston stroke. This is illustrated in Fig. 2·9c.

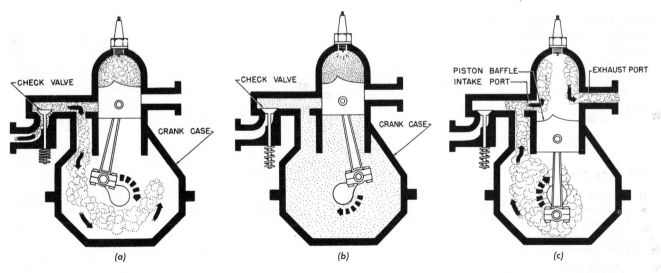

Figure **2·9**   Operation of a two-stroke-cycle engine.   (a) Compression event.   (b) Ignition and power events.   (c) Exhaust and intake events.

It will be noted that there are five events in the two-stroke engine cycle, but at one point, two of the events happen at approximately the same time. During the time that the combined exhaust and intake events are occurring, some of the fuel/air mixture is diluted with burned gases retained from the previous cycle and some of the fresh mixture is discharged with the exhaust gases. The baffle on the top of the piston is designed to reduce the losses as much as possible.

It is important to understand that two strokes of the piston (one complete crankshaft revolution) are required to complete the cycle of operation. For this reason, all cylinders of a multicylinder two-stroke-cycle engine will fire at each revolution of the crankshaft. Remember that the four-stroke-cycle engine cylinder fires only once in two complete revolutions of the crankshaft.

The operation of the two-stroke-cycle engine may be summarized as follows: The piston moves upward and draws a fuel/air mixture into the crankcase through a check valve, the crankcase being airtight except for this valve; the piston moves downward and compresses the mixture in the crankcase; the intake port is opened and the compressed fuel/air mixture enters the cylinder; the piston moves upward and compresses the mixture in the combustion chamber; near the top of the piston stroke, the sparkplug ignites the mixture, thus causing the piston to move down; near the bottom of the stroke, the exhaust port is opened to allow the burned gases to escape and the intake port opens to allow a new charge to enter the cylinder. Note that, as the piston moves down during the power event, the fuel/air mixture is being compressed in the crankcase. As the piston moves upward during the compression event, the fuel/air mixture is being drawn into the crankcase.

The two-stroke cycle has three principal disadvantages: (1) There are a loss of efficiency as a result of the fuel/air charge mixing with the exhaust gases and the loss of some of the charge through the exhaust port; (2) the engine is more difficult to cool than the four-stroke-cycle engine, largely because the cylinder fires at every revolution of the crankshaft; and (3) the engine is somewhat difficult to lubricate properly because the lubricant must be introduced with the fuel/air mixture through the carburetor. This is usually accomplished by mixing the lubricant with the fuel in the fuel tank.

THE DIESEL ENGINE

Operating principle

The operating principle of the diesel four-stroke-cycle engine superficially resembles that of the four-stroke-cycle gasoline engine except that the pure diesel engine requires no electrical ignition. Also, the diesel engine operates on fuel oils that are heavier and cheaper than gasoline.

On the **intake stroke** of the diesel engine, pure air only is drawn into the cylinder. On the **compression** stroke, the piston compresses the air to such an extent that the air temperature is high enough to ignite the fuel without the use of an electric spark. As the piston approaches the top of its stroke, the fuel is injected into the cylinder under a high pressure in a finely atomized state. The highly compressed hot air already in the cylinder ignites the fuel. The fuel burns during the **power stroke,** and the waste gases escape during the exhaust stroke in the same manner as they do in a gasoline engine.

The **compression ratio,** to be discussed more fully later, is the ratio of the volume of space in a cylinder when the piston is at the bottom of its stroke to the volume when the piston is at the top of its stroke. The compression ratio of a diesel engine may be as high as 14:1 as compared with a maximum of 10 or 11:1 for conventional gasoline engines. It is common for a gasoline engine to have a compression ratio of about 7:1; however, certain high-performance engines have a higher ratio. The compression ratio of a conventional gasoline engine must be limited because the temperature of the compressed gases in the cylinder must not be high enough to ignite the fuel. The high-octane and high-performance-number fuels developed in the past few years have made it possible to utilize higher compression ratios for conventional engines. If the compression ratio is too high for the fuel being used, **detonation** (explosion) of the fuel will occur, thus causing overheating, loss of power, and probable damage to the pistons and cylinders. Detonation will be described more fully later in this text.

Like the gasoline internal-combustion engine, the diesel engine may be either a two-stroke-cycle or a four-stroke-cycle engine.

POWER CALCULATIONS

Power

Power is the rate of doing work. A certain amount of work is accomplished when a particular weight is raised a given distance. For example, if a weight of 1 ton is raised vertically 100 ft, we may say that 100 ton-ft of work has been done. Since a ton is equal to 2,000 lb, we can also say that 200,000 ft-lb of work has been done. When we speak of power, we must also consider the time required to do a given amount of work. Power depends upon three factors: (1) the force exerted, (2) the distance the force moves, and (3) the time required to do the work.

James Watt, the inventor of the steam engine, found that an English work horse could work at the rate of 550 ft-lb per sec, or 33,000 ft-lb per min, for a reasonable length of time. From his observations came the **horsepower** (hp), which is the unit of power in the English system of measurements.

When a 1-lb weight is raised 1 ft, 1 ft-lb of work has been performed. When a 1000-lb weight is lifted 33 ft, 33,000 ft-lb of work has been performed. If the 1000-lb weight is lifted 33 ft in 1 min, 1 (hp) has been expended. If it takes 2 min to lift the weight through the same distance, ½ hp has been used. If it requires 4 min, ¼ hp has been used. **One horsepower equals 33,000 ft-lb of work per min, or 550 ft-lb of work per sec.** The capacity of automobile, aircraft, and other engines to do work is measured in horsepower. In the metric system, the unit of power is the **kilowatt,** which is equivalent to 1.34 hp.

Piston displacement

In order to compute the power of an engine, it is necessary to determine how many foot-pounds of work can be done by the engine in a given time. In order to do this, we must know various measurements such as cylinder bore, piston stroke, and piston displacement.

The **piston displacement** of one piston is obtained by multiplying the area of a cross section of the cylinder bore by the total distance the piston moves during one stroke in the cylinder. Since the volume of any true cylinder is its cross-sectional area multiplied by its height, the piston displacement can be stated in terms of cubic inches of volume. The piston displacement of one cylinder can be determined if the bore and stroke are known. For example, if the bore of a cylinder is 6 in. and the stroke is 6 in., we can find the displacement as follows:

Cross-sectional area = πr^2 = 28.274 sq in.
Displacement = 6×28.274 = 169.644 cu in.

The total piston displacement of an engine is the total volume displaced by all the pistons during one revolution of the crankshaft. It equals the number of cylinders in the engine multiplied by the piston displacement of one piston. Other factors remaining the same, the greater the total piston displacement, the greater will be the maximum horsepower that an engine can develop.

Displacement is one of the many factors in power-plant design which are subject to compromise. If the cylinder bore is too large, fuel will be wasted and the intensity of the heat and the restricted flow of the heat may be so great that the cylinder may not be cooled properly. If the stroke (piston travel) is too great, excessive dynamic stresses and too much angularity of the connecting rods will be the undesirable consequences.

It has been found that a "square" engine provides the proper balance between the dimensions of bore and stroke. Remember that a square engine has the bore and stroke equal. Increased engine displacement can be obtained by adding cylinders, thus producing an increase of power output. The addition of cylinders produces what is known as a **closer spacing of power impulses,** which increases the smoothness of engine operation.

In addition to the method shown previously for determining piston displacement using bore and stroke, we can use the formula $\frac{1}{4}\pi D^2 = A$ for determining the cross-sectional area of the cylinder. This formula can also be written $A = \pi D^2/4$, where A is the area in square inches and D is the diameter of the bore.

If a piston has a diameter of 5 in., its area is $\frac{1}{4}\pi \times 25$, or 19.635 sq in. In place of $\frac{1}{4}\pi$ we can use 0.7854, which is the same value.

If the piston mentioned above is used where the stroke is 6 in., the displacement of the piston is 6×19.635, or 117.81 cu in. If the engine has 14 cylinders, the total displacement of the engine is $117.81 \times 14 = 1649.34$ cu in. This engine would be called a **1650** engine.

A typical radial engine has a bore of 5.5 in. and a stroke of 5.5 in. The cross-sectional area of the cylinder is then $5.5^2 \times 0.7854 = 23.758$ sq in. The displacement of one piston is $5.5 \times 23.758 = 130.669$ cu in. The engine has 14 cylinders, so the total displacement is $14 \times 130.669 = 1829.366$ cu in. This is called an **1830** engine.

Compression ratio

The **compression ratio** of a cylinder is the ratio of the volume of space in the cylinder when the piston is at the bottom of its stroke to the volume when the piston is at the top of its stroke. For example, if the volume of the space in a cylinder is 120 cu in. when the piston is at the bottom of its stroke and the volume is 20 cu in. when the piston is at the top of its stroke, the compression ratio is 120:20. Stated in the form of a fraction, it would be $^{120}/_{20}$, or if the larger number is divided by the smaller number, the compression will be shown as 6:1. This is the usual manner for expressing compression ratio.

As stated previously, the compression ratio of any internal-combustion engine is a factor which controls the maximum horsepower which can be developed by the engine, other factors remaining the same. Within reasonable limits, the maximum horsepower increases as the compression ratio increases. However, it has been found by experience that, if the compression ratio of the internal-combustion engine is much greater than 10:1, preignition (premature ignition of the fuel/air charge) or detonation may occur and cause overheating, loss of power, and damage to the engine. If the engine has a compression ratio as high as 10:1, it is necessary that the fuel used for it have a high antiknock characteristic (high octane rating or high performance number).

The **maximum compression ratio** of an engine, as indicated above, is limited by the detonation characteristics of the fuel used. Detonation has been mentioned briefly before and will be discussed more thoroughly in later sections of the text, but it is sufficient to state here that detonation occurs when 75 to 80 percent of the fuel/air mixture burns normally and then the remainder burns with explosive rapidity, or, in effect, it explodes.

In addition to the detonation characteristics of the fuel used, the maximum compression ratio of an aircraft engine is also limited by the design limitations of the engine, the availability of high-octane fuel, and the degree of supercharging.

An increase in the compression ratio of an engine may be accomplished by installing "higher" pistons or by using longer connecting rods. In an engine which has a removable cylinder head, the combustion space in the head may be reduced by "shaving" the surface of the cylinder head where it mates with the top of the cylinder. This, of course, increases the compression ratio.

Increasing the compression ratio of an engine causes a lower specific fuel consumption (pounds of fuel burned per hour per horsepower) and a greater thermal efficiency. **Thermal efficiency** is the ratio of the heat converted to useful work to the heating value of the fuel consumed.

The indicator diagram

Indicated horsepower is based on the theoretical amount of work done according to calculations made from the actual pressure recorded in the form of a diagram on an indicator card, as illustrated in Fig. 2·10. This particular indicator diagram shows the pressure rise during the compression stroke and after ignition. It also shows the pressure drop with the expansion of the gases during the power stroke. It clearly emphasizes the fact that the force acting on the piston during the combustion (power) stroke of the engine is not constant, because the fuel/air mixture burns almost instantaneously, with a resulting high pressure at the top of the stroke and a lowering pressure as the piston descends.

Power computations for indicated horsepower are somewhat simplified by using the average pressure acting on the piston throughout the working stroke. This average pressure, often called the **mean effective pressure,** is obtained from the indicator diagram. The indicator diagram is drawn on the indicator card by a mechanical device attached to the engine cylinder.

Indicated horsepower

If the characteristics of an engine are known, the **indicated horsepower** rating can be calculated. The total force acting on the piston in one cylinder is the product of the **indicated mean effective pressure** P and the area A of the piston head in square inches (found by the formula which states that the area of a circle is πr^2 or $\frac{1}{4}\pi D^2$).

The distance through which this total force acts in 1 min multiplied by the total force gives the number of foot-pounds (ft-lb) of work done in 1 min. The work done in 1 min by one piston multiplied by the number of cylinders in operation gives the amount of work done in 1 min by the entire engine. This product is divided by 33,000 (the number of foot-pounds per minute in 1 hp) to obtain the indicated horsepower rating of the engine.

The length of the stroke in feet is represented by L, the area of the piston in square inches by A, the indicated mean effective pressure in pounds per square inch (psi) by P, the number of working strokes per minute (rpm/2) per cylinder by N, and the number of cylinders by K. Indicated horsepower can then be computed by the formula,

$$\text{ihp} = \frac{PLANK}{33,000}$$

The foregoing formula can be made clear when it is remembered that **work** is equal to **force** times **distance** and **power** is **force** times **distance** divided by **time**. PLA is the product of **pressure, distance,** and **area,** but **pressure** times **area** equals force; hence, $PLA = FD$. In the formula, $PLANK$ is the number of foot-pounds per minute produced by an engine because N repre-

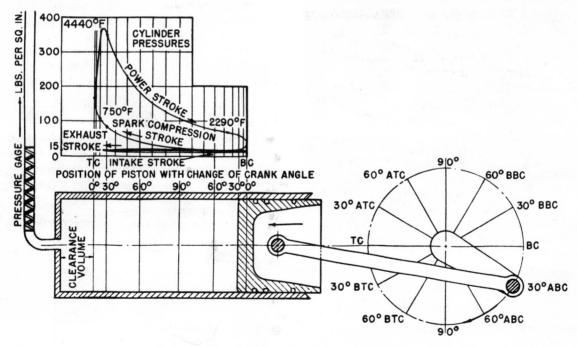

Figure 2·10   Cylinder pressure indicating diagram.

sents the number of working strokes per minute for each cylinder and K is the number of cylinders. To find horsepower, it is merely necessary to divide the number of foot-pounds per minute by 33,000, since 1 hp = 33,000 ft-lb per min.

Indicated horsepower may be defined as the total horsepower converted by the engine from heat energy to mechanical energy. It is usually abbreviated ihp.

Brake horsepower

Brake horsepower (bhp) is the actual horsepower delivered by an engine to a propeller or other driven device. It is the ihp minus the friction horsepower (fhp). Friction horsepower is that part of the total horsepower necessary to overcome the friction of the moving parts in the engine and its accessories. The relationship may be expressed: bhp = ihp − fhp.

It may also be stated that the bhp is that part of the total horsepower developed by the engine which can be used to perform work. On many aircraft engines it is between 85 and 90 percent of the indicated horsepower.

The bhp of an engine can be determined by coupling the engine to any power-absorbing device, such as an electric generator, in such a manner that the power output can be accurately measured. A **dynamometer** is an apparatus for measuring force, which can be used for determining the power output of an engine. If an electric generator is connected to a known electric load and the efficiency of the generator is known, the bhp of the engine driving the generator can be determined. For example, assume that an engine is driving a generator producing 110 volts and the load on the generator is 50 amp. Electrical power is measured in watts and is equal to the voltage multiplied by the amperage. Therefore the electrical power developed by the generator is 50 × 110 or 5,500 watts. Since 1 hp = 746 watts, 5,500 watts = 7.36 hp. If the generator is 60 percent efficient, the power required to drive it is equal to 7.36/0.60 or 12.27 hp. Therefore, we have determined that the engine is developing 12.27 bhp to drive the generator.

The prony brake

The **prony brake**, illustrated in Fig. 2·11, is a device used to measure the torque or turning moment produced by an engine. The scale is read before the force is applied, and the reading is recorded as the **tare**. The force F, produced by the lever arm, equals the weight recorded on the scale minus the tare. The known values are then F, the distance L, and the rpm of the engine driving the prony brake. To obtain the bhp, these values are used in the following formula:

$$\text{bhp} = \frac{F \times L \times 2\pi \times \text{rpm}}{33,000}$$

In the foregoing formula, the distance through which the force acts in 1 revolution is the circumference of the circle of which the distance L is the radius. This circumference is determined by multiplying the radius L by

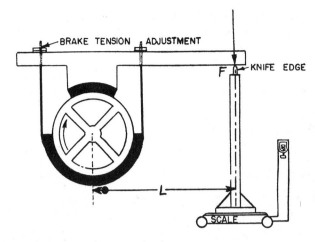

Figure 2·11   The prony brake.

2π. In the formula we see, then, that the force acts through a given distance a certain number of times per minute, and this gives us the foot-pounds per minute. When this is divided by 33,000, the result is bhp.

If a given engine turning at 1800 rpm produces a force of 200 lb on the scales at the end of a 4-ft lever, we can compute the bhp as follows:

$$\text{bhp} = \frac{200 \times 4 \times 2\pi \times 1800}{33,000}$$
$$= 274$$

The torque nose

It has often been the practice with large reciprocating engines used in transport aircraft to equip one or more of the engines with a torque-indicating system. This system consists of a mechanism in the nose section of the engine which applies pressure to oil in a closed chamber in proportion to engine torque. Since the planetary gears of a propeller reduction-gear system must work against a large stationary ring gear, the ring gear can be used to develop an indication of engine torque. The outside of the ring gear is constructed with helical teeth which fit into similar helical teeth in the nose case. When torque is developed, the ring gear tends to move forward. This movement is transmitted to hydraulic pistons which are connected to a pressure gage in the cockpit or on the flight engineer's panel. The gage may be calibrated to read directly in bmep, or **brake mean effective pressure**, which, in turn, is used to compute bhp.

Brake mean effective pressure can be derived mathematically from the bhp and vice versa. When the bhp has been determined by means of a dynamometer, the bmep can be computed by means of the following formula:

$$\text{bmep} = \text{bhp} \times \frac{33,000}{LAN}$$

where L = stroke, ft
    A = area of bore, sq in.
    N = number of working strokes per min

In a four-stroke-cycle engine, $N = \frac{1}{2}$ rpm of the engine multiplied by the number of cylinders.

Power ratings

The **takeoff power** rating of an engine is determined by the maximum rpm and manifold pressure at which the airplane engine may be operated during the process of taking off. The takeoff power may be given a time limitation, such as a period of 1 to 5 min. **Manifold pressure** is the pressure of the fuel/air mixture in the intake manifold between the carburetor or internal supercharger and the intake valve. The pressure is given in inches of mercury (in. Hg) above absolute zero pressure. Standard sea-level pressure is 29.92 in. Hg, so the reading on the manifold pressure gage may be either above or below this figure. As manifold pressure increases, the power output of an engine increases provided that the rpm remains constant. Likewise, the power increases as rpm increases provided that the manifold pressure remains constant.

The takeoff power of an engine may be about 10 percent above the maximum continuous power-output allowance. This is the usual increase of power output permitted in the United States, but in British aviation the increase above maximum cruising power may be as much as 15 percent. It is referred to as the **overspeed** condition. The maximum continuous power is also called the "maximum except takeoff" power and is indicated by the abbreviation METO.

During takeoff conditions with the engine operating at maximum takeoff power, the volume of air flowing around the cylinders is restricted because of the low speed of the airplane during takeoff, and the initial carburetor air temperature may be very high in hot weather. For these reasons the operator of the airplane must exercise great care, especially in hot weather, to avoid overheating the engine and damaging the valves, piston, and piston rings. The overheating may cause detonation or preignition with a resultant loss of power in addition to engine damage.

The **rated power,** also called the **standard engine rating,** is the maximum horsepower output which can be obtained from an engine when it is operated at specified rpm and manifold pressure conditions established as safe for continuous operation. This is the power guaranteed by the manufacturer of the engine under the specified conditions and is the same as METO power.

Maximum power is the greatest power output that the engine can develop at any time under any conditions.

Critical altitude

The **critical altitude** is the highest level at which an engine will maintain a given horsepower output. For example, an aircraft engine may be rated at a certain altitude which is the highest level at which rated power output can be obtained from the engine at a given rpm.

ENGINE EFFICIENCY

Mechanical efficiency

The **mechanical efficiency** of an engine is measured by the ratio of the shaft output or brake horsepower to the indicated horsepower or power developed in the cylinders. For example, if the ratio of the bhp to the ihp is 9:10, then the mechanical efficiency of the engine is 90 percent. In determination of mechanical efficiency, only the losses suffered by the energy that has been delivered to the pistons is considered. The word **efficiency** may be defined as the ratio of output to input.

Thermal efficiency

Thermal efficiency is a measure of the heat losses suffered in converting the heat energy of the fuel into mechanical work. In Fig. 2·12 the heat dissipated by the cooling system represents 25 percent, the heat carried away by the exhaust gases represents 40 percent, the mechanical work on the piston to overcome friction and pumping losses represents 5 percent, and the useful work at the propeller shaft represents 30 percent of the heat energy of the fuel.

The **thermal efficiency** of an engine is the ratio of the heat developed into useful work to the heat energy of the fuel. It may be based on either bhp or ihp and is represented by a formula in this manner:

Indicated thermal efficiency

$$= \frac{\text{ihp} \times 33{,}000}{\text{wt of fuel burned per min} \times \text{heat value (Btu)} \times 778}$$

The formula for brake thermal efficiency is the same as that given above with the word "brake" inserted in place of "indicated" in both sides of the equation.

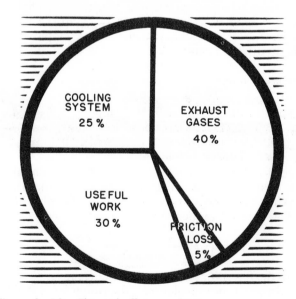

Figure **2·12** *Thermal efficiency chart.*

If we wish to find the brake thermal efficiency of a particular engine, we must first know the following quantities: bhp, fuel consumption in pounds per minute, and the heat value of the fuel in Btu (British thermal units). In this case, let us suppose that the engine develops 104 bhp at 2600 rpm and burns 6.5 gal per hr of gasoline. The heat value of the fuel is 19,000 to 20,000 Btu.

First we must convert gallons per hour to pounds per minute. Since there are 60 min per hr, we divide 6.5 by 60 to obtain 0.108 gpm. Since each gallon of fuel weights approximately 6 lb, we multiply 0.108 by 6 to obtain 0.648 lb per min. The formula then becomes:

$$bte = \frac{104 \times 33,000}{0.648 \times 20,000 \times 778}$$

$$= \frac{3,432,000}{10,080,000} = 0.34$$

Hence the brake thermal efficiency is 34 percent.

To explain the formula, we must know only that the energy of 1 Btu is 778 ft-lb. $104 \times 33,000$ provides us with the total foot-pound output. The figures in the denominator give us the total input energy of the fuel. The fraction then represents the ratio of input to output.

In the foregoing problem, if the engine burns 100 gal of gasoline, only 34 gal is converted to useful work. The remaining 66 percent of the heat produced by the burning fuel in the engine cylinders is lost by being exhausted through the exhaust manifold or through the cooling of the engine. This is an excellent value for many modern aircraft engines running at full power. At slightly reduced power, the thermal efficiency may be a little greater, and by the use of high compression with high-octane fuels, an engine may be made to produce as high as 40 percent brake thermal efficiency. This is not normal, however, and is not necessarily desirable for mechanical reasons.

Although a thermal efficiency of 34 percent may not appear high, it is excellent when compared with other types of engines. For example, the old steam locomotive had a thermal efficiency of not much more than 5 percent. The thermal efficiency of many diesel engines is 35 percent if run at an output of one-half to three-fourths full power, but when the output is increased to full power, the thermal efficiency of the diesel drops to less than one-half that of the usual carburetor-type engine. This is because of an incomplete combustion of fuel when large amounts of excess air are no longer present. Thermal efficiencies as high as 45 percent have been obtained under favorable conditions in low-speed stationary or marine engines. The diesel engine has been used successfully in airplanes, but in its present state of development it lacks many of the advantages of the carburetor-type aircraft engine.

Volumetric efficiency

Volumetric efficiency is the ratio of the volume of fuel/air charge, burned by the engine, at atmospheric pressure and temperature to the piston displacement. If the cylinder of an engine draws in a charge of fuel and air having a volume at standard atmospheric pressure and temperature which is exactly equal to the piston displacement of the cylinder, the cylinder has a volumetric efficiency of 100 percent.

In a similar manner, if a volume of 95 cu in. of fuel and air mixture is admitted into a cylinder of 100-cu-in. displacement, the volumetric efficiency is 95 percent. Volumetric efficiency may be expressed as a formula thus:

$$Vol\ eff = \frac{vol\ of\ charge\ at\ atm\ pressure}{piston\ displacement}$$

Factors which tend to decrease volumetric efficiency are an improper timing of the valves, fuel/air manifolds having too small a diameter and many bends, the use of air which has been raised to too high a temperature from any cause, too high a temperature in the combustion chamber, incomplete scavenging of the burned gases during the exhaust stroke, and excessive speed. One or more of these factors may exist at various times.

A **naturally aspirated** (unsupercharged) engine always has a volumetric efficiency of less than 100 percent. On the other hand, the supercharged engine often is operated at a volumetric efficiency of more than 100 percent because the supercharger compresses the air before it enters the cylinder. The volumetric efficiency of a naturally aspirated engine is less than 100 percent for two principal reasons: (1) The bends, obstructions, and surface roughness inside the intake system cause substantial resistance to the air flow, thus reducing air pressure below atmospheric in the intake manifold; (2) the throttle and the carburetor venturi provide restrictions across which a pressure drop occurs.

ENGINE REQUIREMENTS

To be satisfactory for use in an airplane, the engine must possess certain characteristics. The most important of these are light weight, reliability, economy of operation, flexibility, and balance. Each of these characteristics is important and will be discussed individually.

Weight

The weight of an engine must be related to its power output in order to determine its desirability for use in an airplane. The weight is therefore included in the factor called the **weight/power ratio,** which may be defined as the weight in pounds per horsepower output. If an engine weighs 2400 lb and the METO horsepower is 2200, then the weight/power ratio is 2400/2200 or 1.09 lb per hp. The overall usefulness of an engine must be considered with the necessary accessories and systems required for operation. When all the items of the powerplant are included, we have the all-up or flying weight of the powerplant.

Powerplant weight must be kept as low as possible to leave a reasonable amount of the gross weight of the airplane available for a useful load and also to provide a margin of safety.

The weight per horsepower depends in part upon the size of the engine, but this, in turn, depends upon the choice of metals and alloys, the engine accessories that are added, the stress analysis factors, the use of high-performance fuels, and the absence or presence of a supercharger to give a better performance with a lower fuel consumption. The use of the power recovery turbine by which a portion of the exhaust energy is returned to the crankshaft on the Wright R-3350 engine has proved to be a most effective method for improving the weight/power ratio and also the specific fuel consumption.

Small engines are usually built for small airplanes which are operated by private pilots who have a limited budget. To keep down costs, the manufacturer may select less expensive materials and follow cheaper manufacturing processes, with the result that the typical small engine has a greater weight per horsepower than the larger engines.

Large engines are normally built for airplanes operated by the airlines or by the government; hence the original cost of the engine is not so important to the buyer as the efficiency of its performance over a long period of time. Horsepower can be increased by the use of superchargers, higher crankshaft speeds, and other devices and methods. The selection of lighter weight but more expensive materials lowers the weight; consequently the ratio of horsepower to weight is greater than in the case of the typical small engine. In recent years, the use of direct fuel injection and supercharging on small engines has greatly increased their efficiency, weight/power ratio, and specific fuel consumption.

Reliability

An aircraft engine is **reliable** when it can be depended upon to do what it is rated to do by the manufacturer. It should not fail if properly inspected, maintained, and operated by skilled personnel. It should have a long life, with the maximum of time between overhaul periods. It should also have a low fuel consumption at cruising speeds. Its units, parts, and accessories should serve well for a long period of time, and they should be easily, quickly, and inexpensively replaced after a reasonable time of service.

Economy of operation

It is apparent that, if an airplane engine is mechanically reliable, it costs less to operate than one which constantly needs overhauling or other maintenance. In addition, low fuel and oil consumption must be considered, not only from the viewpoint of their direct cost, but also from the standpoint of reducing weight in flight.

As previously mentioned, **specific fuel consumption** is a measure of the power developed to fuel consumed; hence it is also a measure of fuel economy. Specific fuel consumption is obtained by dividing the weight of the fuel burned per hour by the horsepower developed.

Flexibility

Flexibility is the ability of the engine to run smoothly and perform in the desired manner at all speeds from idling to full power output and through all variations of atmospheric conditions. Flexibility also includes the ability to operate efficiently at all altitudes at which the aircraft is designed to fly.

Balance

Balance has several possible meanings in a discussion of the fundamental requirements for aircraft engines, but the principal factor is **freedom from vibration.** Since the airplane is light and rather flexible, engine vibrations may reduce the life of certain parts or units and may cut down the life of the airplane as a whole. In addition, vibration is fatiguing to the pilot and passengers, thus reducing the desirability of flight. Tubing, cables, conduits, instruments, and accessories may be severely damaged and, at least, their functions may be impaired by excessive engine vibration.

One of the methods of reducing vibration is to design the engine with a large number of cylinders, thus reducing the total effect of the pulsating torque delivered by the separate cylinders. Rotating masses, such as crankshafts, may be balanced by the use of counterweights and dynamic dampeners.

In addition to proper balancing of the engine and its parts, the engine mounting structure attached to the airplane is designed to reduce the effects of vibration. This is accomplished by the use of rubber or synthetic-rubber mounting attachments which prevent the engine vibration from being transmitted to the engine mount and thence to the aircraft structure.

REVIEW QUESTIONS

1. Define *cycle*.
2. Explain the four-stroke five-event cycle of a piston engine.
3. Describe the function of each of the basic parts of a typical gasoline engine.
4. Explain the measurements *bore* and *stroke*.
5. Why are the positions TDC and BDC of the piston important?
6. What are the positions of the intake and exhaust valves at the end of the power stroke?
7. At what point in the cycle does the ignition event take place?
8. Why is ignition timed to take place at this point?
9. Explain the energy conversion in a gasoline engine.
10. What is the function of the connecting rod?
11. Describe the operation of a two-stroke-cycle engine through the complete cycle.
12. How does the valve action in a two-stroke-cycle engine differ from the valve action in a four-stroke-cycle engine?
13. Why is a two-stroke-cycle engine less efficient than a four-stroke-cycle engine?

14. Describe the operation of a diesel engine.
15. Compare the compression ratio of a diesel engine with that of a conventional gasoline engine.
16. Compute the horsepower output of the following described engine operating at 2000 rpm: bore, 3.5 in.; stroke, 4 in.; number of cylinders, 6; bmep, 140 psi.
17. What is meant by *indicated horsepower?*
18. Compute the piston displacement of a radial engine having nine cylinders, a bore of 5 in., and a stroke of 5 in.
19. Compute the compression ratio of an engine which has a bore of 5 in. and a stroke of 5 in. when the volume of the combustion chamber is 16.36 cu in. with the piston at top dead center.
20. Discuss the relationship between compression ratio and fuel octane rating.
21. In what way are indicated horsepower, friction horsepower, and brake horsepower related?
22. Explain the operation of a dynamometer.
23. How can horsepower be determined with a prony brake?
24. Explain the function of a *torque nose* on an engine.
25. Compute the bmep of an engine when the output is 450 hp, the rpm is 2300, the bore and stroke are each 5.5 in., and the number of cylinders is nine.
26. How is the power output of an engine affected by manifold pressure?
27. Explain *rated power* of an engine.
28. What is the *critical altitude* of an engine?
29. Explain *mechanical efficiency, thermal efficiency, volumetric efficiency.*
30. List the most important requirements for an aircraft engine.

CHAPTER 3

Engine Classification, Construction, and Nomenclature

In-line engines

The cylinders of the **in-line** engines are arranged in a single row on the crankcase in either an upright or an inverted position, although practically all in-line aircraft engines are of the inverted type. The number of cylinders is usually limited to six in order to facilitate cooling and to avoid excessive weight per horsepower. There is generally an even number of cylinders in order to provide for better balance of firing impulses. The in-line engine has only one crankshaft, which is located above the cylinders in the inverted engine. This engine may be either air cooled or liquid cooled, but the liquid-cooled types are seldom found in the United States.

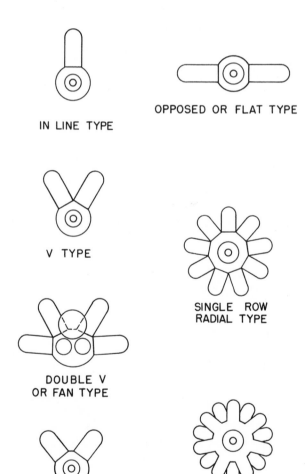

IN LINE TYPE

OPPOSED OR FLAT TYPE

V TYPE

SINGLE ROW RADIAL TYPE

DOUBLE V OR FAN TYPE

X TYPE

DOUBLE ROW RADIAL TYPE

Figure **3·1** Engines classified according to cylinder arrangement.

Conventional piston engines are classified according to a variety of characteristics including cylinder arrangement, cooling method, and number of strokes per cycle. The most satisfactory classification, however, is by cylinder arrangement. This is the method usually employed because it is more completely descriptive than the other classifications. Gas-turbine engines are classified according to construction and function, and these classifications will be discussed in a later section.

Cylinder arrangement

Although some engine designs have become obsolete, we shall mention the types most commonly constructed throughout the history of powerplants. Aircraft engines may be classified according to cylinder arrangement with respect to the crankshaft as follows: (1) in-line, upright; (2) in-line, inverted; (3) V-type, upright; (4) V-type, inverted; (5) double-V or fan type; (6) opposed or flat type; (7) X type; (8) radial type, single row; (9) radial type, double row; (10) radial type, multiple row or "corncob." The simple drawings of Fig. 3·1 illustrate some of these arrangements.

The double-V and fan-type engines have not been in use for many years, and the only piston engines in extensive use in the United States at the present time are the opposed and radial types. A few V-type and in-line engines may still be found in operation, but these engines are no longer manufactured in the United States for general aircraft use.

Use of the in-line type of engine is largely confined to low- and medium-horsepower engines for light airplanes. This engine presents a small frontal area and is therefore adapted to streamlining and a resultant low-drag nacelle configuration. When the cylinders are mounted in the inverted position, greater pilot visibility and a shorter landing gear are possible. However, the in-line engine has a greater weight-to-horsepower ratio than other types. When the size of an aircraft engine is increased, it becomes increasingly difficult to cool it if it is of the air-cooled in-line type; hence, this engine is not suitable for a high horsepower output.

V-type engines

The V-type engine has the cylinders arranged on the crankcase in two rows or banks forming the letter V with an angle between the banks of 90, 60, or 45°. There is always an even number of cylinders in each row.

Since the two banks of cylinders are opposite each other, two sets of connecting rods can operate on the same crankpin, thus reducing the weight per horsepower as compared with the in-line engine. The frontal area is only slightly greater than that of the in-line type; hence, the engine cowling can be streamlined to reduce drag. If the cylinders are above the crankshaft, the engine is known as the **upright-V type,** but if the cylinders are below the crankshaft, it is known as an **inverted-V** type. Better pilot visibility and a short landing gear are possible if the engine is inverted.

Opposed, flat, or O-type engine

The opposed-type engine is most popular for light conventional aircraft and helicopters and is manufactured in sizes delivering less than 100 to more than 400 hp. These engines are the most efficient, dependable, and economical types available for light aircraft. Gas-turbine engines are being installed in some light aircraft, but their cost is still prohibitive for the average airplane owner.

The opposed-type engine is usually mounted with the cylinders horizontal and the crankshaft horizontal; however, in some helicopter installations the crankshaft is vertical. The engine has a low weight-to-horsepower ratio, and because of its flat shape it is very well adapted to streamlining and horizontal installation in the nacelle. Another advantage is that it is reasonably free from vibration. Figure 3·2 illustrates a typical opposed engine for light aircraft.

Radial engines

The radial engines have been the "work horse" of military and commercial aircraft ever since the 1920s, and during World War II they were used in all United States bombers and transport aircraft and in most of the other categories of aircraft. They were developed to a peak of efficiency and dependability, and even today, in the jet age, many of them are still in operation throughout the world in all types of duty.

A **single-row radial** engine has an odd number of

Figure 3·2   Opposed-type aircraft engine. (Lycoming Div., Avco Corp.)

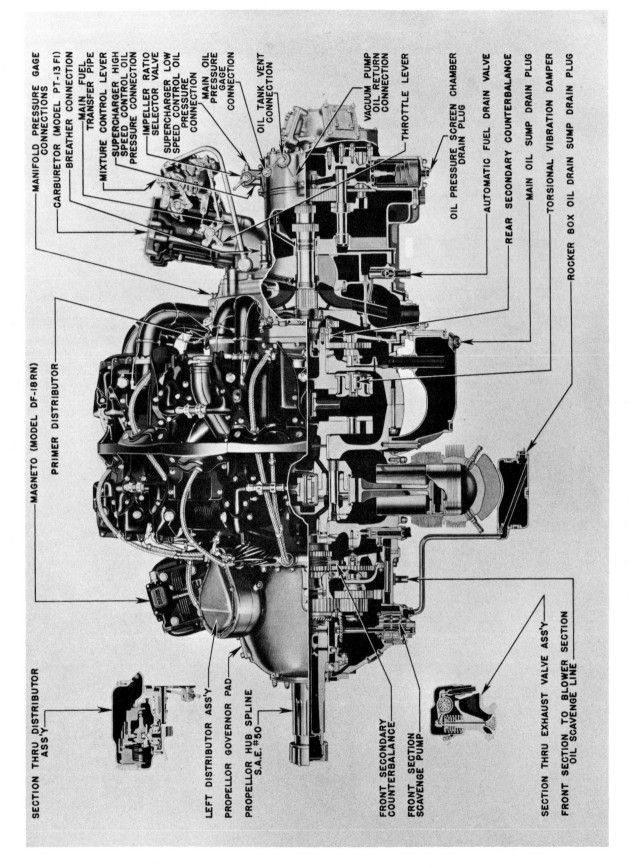

MANIFOLD PRESSURE GAGE CONNECTIONS

CARBURETOR (MODEL PT-13 FI)

BREATHER CONNECTION

MAIN FUEL TRANSFER PIPE

MIXTURE CONTROL LEVER

SUPERCHARGER HIGH SPEED CONTROL OIL PRESSURE CONNECTION

IMPELLER RATIO SELECTOR VALVE

SUPERCHARGER LOW SPEED CONTROL OIL PRESSURE CONNECTION

MAIN OIL PRESSURE GAGE CONNECTION

OIL TANK VENT CONNECTION

VACUUM PUMP OIL RETURN CONNECTION

THROTTLE LEVER

OIL PRESSURE SCREEN CHAMBER DRAIN PLUG

AUTOMATIC FUEL DRAIN VALVE

REAR SECONDARY COUNTERBALANCE

MAIN OIL SUMP DRAIN PLUG

TORSIONAL VIBRATION DAMPER

ROCKER BOX OIL DRAIN SUMP DRAIN PLUG

MAGNETO (MODEL DF-18RN)

PRIMER DISTRIBUTOR

SECTION THRU DISTRIBUTOR ASS'Y

LEFT DISTRIBUTOR ASS'Y

PROPELLOR GOVERNOR PAD

PROPELLOR HUB SPLINE S.A.E. #50

FRONT SECONDARY COUNTERBALANCE

FRONT SECTION SCAVENGE PUMP

SECTION THRU EXHAUST VALVE ASS'Y

FRONT SECTION TO BLOWER SECTION OIL SCAVENGE LINE

Figure 3 · 3   Double-row radial engine. (*Pratt & Whitney Aircraft*)

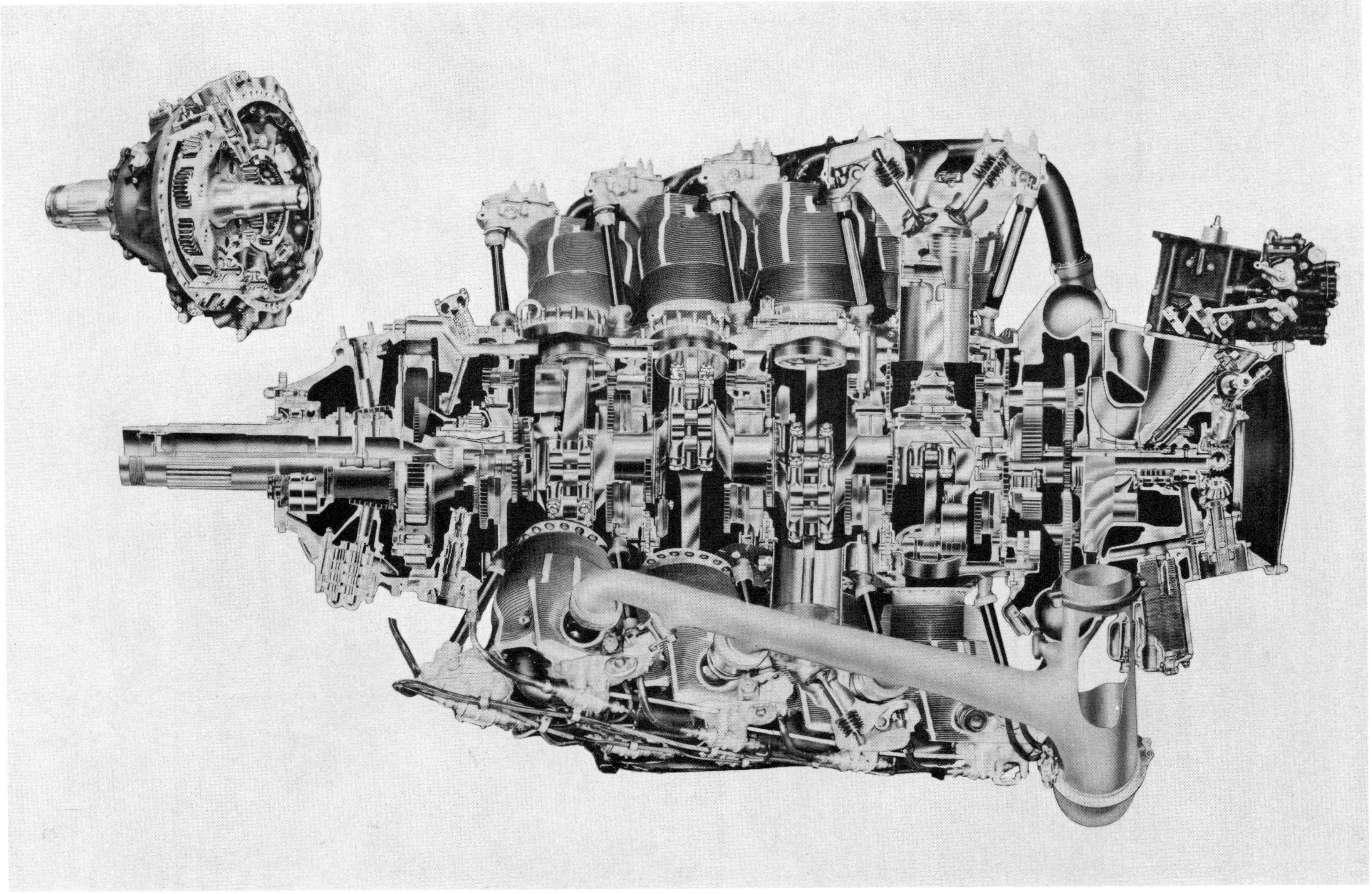

Figure 3·4 Pratt & Whitney R-4360 engine. (Pratt & Whitney Aircraft)

cylinders extending radially from the center line of the crankshaft. The number of cylinders is usually from five to nine. The cylinders are arranged evenly in the same circular plane, and all the pistons are connected to a single-throw, 360° crankshaft, thus reducing the number of working parts and also reducing the weight.

A **double-row radial** engine resembles two single-row radial engines combined on a single crankshaft as shown in Fig. 3·3. The cylinders are arranged radially in two rows, and each row has an odd number of cylinders. The usual number of cylinders used is either 14 or 18, which means that the same effect is produced as having either two seven-cylinder engines or two nine-cylinder engines joined on one crankshaft. A two-throw, 180° crankshaft is used to permit the cylinders in each row to be alternately staggered on the common crankcase. That is, the cylinders of the rear row are located directly behind the spaces between the cylinders in the front row. This allows the cylinders in both rows to receive ram air for the necessary cooling.

The radial engine has the lowest weight-per-horse-power ratio of all the different types of piston engines. It has the disadvantage of greater drag because of the area presented to the air, and it also has some problems in cooling. Nevertheless, the dependability and efficiency of the engine have made it the most widely used type for large aircraft equipped with reciprocating engines.

Multiple-cylinder radial engine

The 28-cylinder Pratt & Whitney R-4360 engine was used extensively at the end of World War II and afterward for both bombers and transport aircraft. This was the largest and most powerful piston-type engine built and used successfully in the United States. A photograph of this engine is shown in Fig. 3·4. Because of the development of the gas-turbine engine, the very large piston engine has been replaced by the more powerful, lighter weight turboprop and turbojet engines. Since it has few moving parts compared with the piston engine, the gas-turbine engine is more trouble free and the maintenance cost is reduced.

Engine cooling

Aircraft engines may be cooled either by air or by liquid; however, there are few liquid-cooled engines still in operation in the United States. We shall therefore devote most of our discussion to the air-cooled types.

Excessive heat is undesirable in any internal-combustion engine for three principal reasons: (1) It adversely affects the behavior of the combustion of the fuel/air charge, (2) it weakens and shortens the life of the engine parts, and (3) it impairs lubrication.

If the temperature inside the engine cylinder is too great, the fuel mixture will be preheated and combustion will occur before the proper time. Premature combustion causes detonation, "knocking," and other undesirable conditions. It will also aggravate the overheated condition and is likely to result in failure of pistons and valves.

The strength of many of the engine parts depends upon their heat treatment. Excessive heat weakens such parts and shortens their life. Also, the parts may become elongated, warped, or expanded to the extent that they freeze or lock together and stop the operation of the engine.

Excessive heat "cracks" the lubricating oil, lowers its viscosity, and destroys its lubricating properties.

Air cooling

In an air-cooled engine, thin metal fins project from the outer surface of the walls and heads of the engine cylinders. When air flows over the fins, it absorbs the excess heat from the cylinders and carries it into the atmosphere. Deflector baffles fastened around the cylinders direct the flow of air to obtain the maximum cooling effect. A cylinder with baffles is shown in Fig. 3·5. The operating temperature of the engine can be controlled by movable **cowl flaps** located on the engine

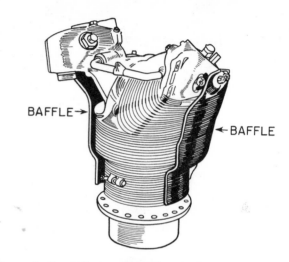

Figure 3·5   Cylinder with cooling baffles.

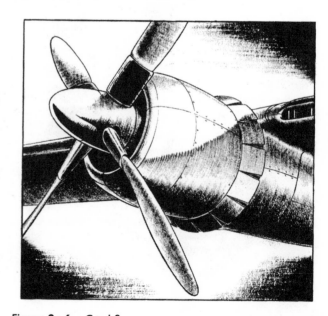

Figure 3·6   Cowl flaps.

cowling. On some airplanes, these cowl flaps are manually operated, and on other airplanes they can be operated either manually or by means of a thermostatically controlled actuator. Cowl flaps are illustrated in Fig. 3·6.

In the assembly of the engine baffling system, great care must be taken to see that the pressure baffles around the cylinders are properly located and secured. An improperly installed or loose baffle can cause a hot spot to develop with the result that the engine may fail. The proper installation of baffles around the

cylinders of a twin-row radial engine is illustrated in Fig. 3·7. Baffling for an opposed-type engine is shown in Fig. 3·8. It will be observed that the baffling maintains a high-velocity airstream close to the cylinder and through the cooling fins.

Cylinder cooling is accomplished by carrying the heat from the inside of the cylinders to the air outside the cylinders. Heat passes by conduction through the metal walls and fins of the cylinder assembly to the cooling airstream which is forced into contact with the fins by the baffles and cowling. The fins on the cylinder head are made of the same material as the head and are forged or die-cast as part of the head. Fins on the steel cylinder barrel are of the same metal as the barrel in most instances and are machined from the same forging as the barrels. In some cases the inner part of the cylinder is a steel sleeve and the cooling fins are made as a part of a muff or sleeve shrunk on the outside of the inner sleeve. A large amount of the heat developed in an engine cylinder is carried to the atmosphere with the exhaust. This amount varies from 40 to 50 percent, depending upon the design of the engine. The proper adjustment of valve timing is the most critical factor in heat rejection through the exhaust.

Since air-cooled cylinder assemblies are exposed to conditions leading to corrosion, they must be protected against this form of deterioration. One method is to apply a coating of baked, heat-resistant black enamel. A better method is to "metallize" the cylinders by means of a thin layer of molten aluminum which is sprayed on the cylinder with a special metallizing gun. The aluminum coating is preferred because (1) it provides more protection against the corrosive action of saltwater spray and salt air and (2) it resists the blasting effect of sand and other gritty particles carried by the cooling stream of air better than enamel.

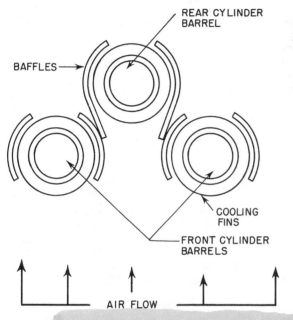

Figure **3·7** *Baffles around the cylinders of a twin-row radial engine.*

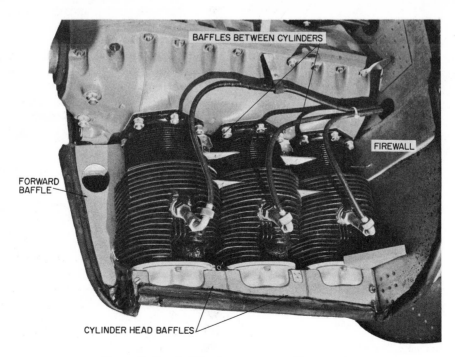

Figure **3·8** *Baffling for an opposed-type engine.*

The principal advantages of air cooling are that (1) the weight of the air-cooled engine is usually less than that of a liquid-cooled engine of the same horsepower because the air-cooled engine does not need a radiator, connecting hoses and lines, and the coolant liquid; (2) the air-cooled engine is less affected by cold-weather operations; and (3) the air-cooled engine in military airplanes is less vulnerable to gunfire. If an enemy bullet or bomb fragment strikes the radiator, hose, or lines of a liquid-cooled engine, it is obvious that its cooling system will leak and soon cause a badly overheated engine.

Liquid cooling

Liquid-cooled engines are rarely found in United States aircraft today; however, the powerplant technician should have some understanding of the principal elements of such systems.

A liquid cooling system consists of the liquid passages around the cylinders and other hot spots of the engine (see Fig. 3·9), a radiator by which the liquid is cooled, a thermostatic element to govern the amount of cooling applied to the liquid, a coolant pump for circulating the liquid, and the necessary connecting pipes and hoses. If the system is sealed, a relief valve is required to prevent excessive pressure and a sniffler valve is necessary to allow the entrance of air to prevent negative pressure when the engine is stopped and cooled off.

Water was the original coolant for liquid-cooled engines. Its comparatively high freezing point (32°F) and its relatively low boiling point (212°F) made it unsatisfactory for the more powerful engines used in military applications. The liquid most commonly used for liquid-cooled engines during World War II was **ethylene glycol** or a mixture of ethylene glycol and water. Pure ethylene glycol has a boiling point of about 350°F and a slush-forming freezing point of about 0°F at sea level. This combination of high boiling point and low freezing point made it a satisfactory coolant for aircraft engines.

THE CRANKCASE

The **crankcase** of an engine is the housing that encloses the various mechanisms surrounding the crankshaft; hence it is the foundation of the engine. The functions of the crankcase are as follows: (1) the crankcase must support itself, (2) it contains the bearings in which the crankshaft revolves, (3) it provides a tight enclosure for the lubricating oil, (4) it supports the various internal and external mechanisms of the powerplant to the airplane, (6) it provides support for the attachment of the cylinders, and (7) by reason of its strength and rigidity, it prevents the misalignment of the crankshaft and its bearings.

Construction

Crankcases are of many sizes and shapes and may be of one-piece or multipiece construction. Most aircraft engine crankcases are made of aluminum alloy because it is both light and strong, but some engines which develop a great power output have crankcases made of forged steel. Although the variety of crankcase designs makes any attempts at classification difficult, they may be divided into three broad groups for discussion: (1) in-line and V-type crankcases, (2) opposed-engine crankcases, and (3) radial-engine crankcases.

In-line and V-type engine crankcases

Large in-line and V-type engine crankcases usually have four major sections: (1) the front or nose section, (2) the main or power section, (3) the fuel-induction and -distribution section, and (4) the accessory section.

The front or nose section is directly behind the propeller in most tractor-type airplanes. A **tractor-type** airplane is one in which the propeller "pulls" the airplane forward. The **nose section** may be cast as part of the main or power section, or it may be a separate construction with a dome or conical shape to reduce drag. Its function is to house the propeller shaft, the propeller thrust bearing, the propeller reduction-gear train, and sometimes a mounting pad for the propeller governor. In a very few arrangements where the nose section is not located close to the engine, the propeller is connected to the engine through an extension shaft and the reduction-gear drive has its own lubricating system. This same arrangement is found in some turboprop engines.

The **main** or **power section** varies greatly in design for different engines. When it is made up of two parts, one part supports one half of each crankshaft bearing and the other supports the opposite half of each bearing. The cylinders are normally mounted on and bolted to the heavier of the two parts of this section on an in-line engine, and the crankshaft bearings are usually supported by reinforcing weblike partitions.

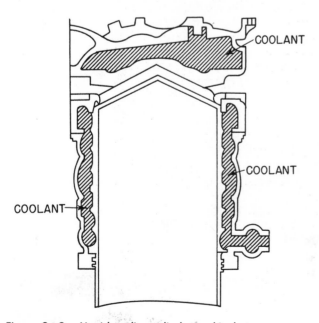

Figure 3·9 Liquid cooling cylinder and jacket.

COOLANT

COOLANT

COOLANT

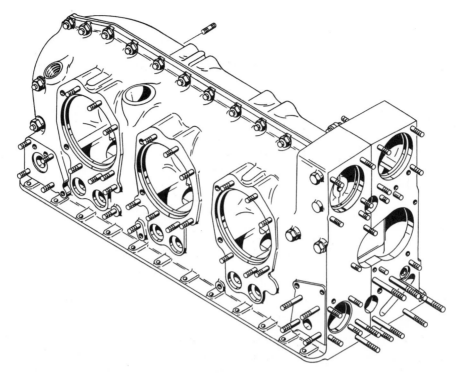

Figure 3·10   Crankcase for a six-cylinder opposed engine. (Continental Motors Corp.)

External mounting lugs and bosses are often provided for attaching the engine to the engine mount.

The **fuel-induction and -distribution section** is normally located next to the main or power section. This section houses the diffuser vanes and supports the internal blower impeller when the engine is equipped with an internal blower system. The induction manifold is located between the fuel-induction and -distribution section and the cylinders. The housing of this section has an opening for the attachment of a manifold-pressure gage line, and it also has internal passages for the fuel drain valve of the blower case. The **fuel drain valve** is designed to permit the automatic drainage of excess fuel from the blower case.

The **accessory section** may be a separate unit mounted directly on the induction and fuel-distribution section, or it may form a part of the induction and fuel-distribution section. It contains the accessory drive-gear train and has mounting pads for the fuel pump, coolant pump, vacuum pump, lubricating-oil pumps, magnetos, tachometer generator, and similar devices operated by engine power. The material used in constructing this section is generally either an aluminum-alloy casting or a magnesium-alloy casting.

Opposed-engine crankcase

The crankcase for a six-cylinder opposed engine is shown in Fig. 3·10. This assembly consists of two reinforced aluminum-alloy castings divided vertically at the center line of the engine and fastened together by means of a series of studs and nuts. The mating surfaces of the crankcase are joined without the use of a gasket, and the main bearing bores are machined for the use of precision-type main bearing inserts. Machined mounting pads are incorporated into the crankcase for attaching the accessory housing, cylinders, and oil sump.

The crankcase of the opposed engine contains bosses and machined bores to serve as bearings for the camshaft. During overhaul it is important to inspect these areas for excessive wear. On the camshaft side of each crankcase half are the tappet bores which carry the hydraulic valve tappet bodies.

Essential portions of the lubricating system are contained in the crankcase. Oil passages and galleries are drilled in the sections of the case to supply the crankshaft bearings, camshaft bearings, and various other moving parts which require lubrication. During overhaul, the technician must make sure that all oil passages are free of foreign matter.

Radial-engine crankcase

Radial-engine crankcases (see Fig. 3·11) may have as few as three or as many as seven principal sections, the number depending upon the size of the engine and its type, although the large engines usually have more sections than the small ones. For the purpose of describing radial-engine crankcases, it is customary to assume that the typical radial-engine crankcase has four major sections, although this is not necessarily true.

The **front or nose section** is usually made of aluminum alloy, its housing is approximately bell-shaped, and it is fastened to the power section by studs and nuts or cap screws. In most cases, this section supports a propeller thrust bearing, a propeller-gover-

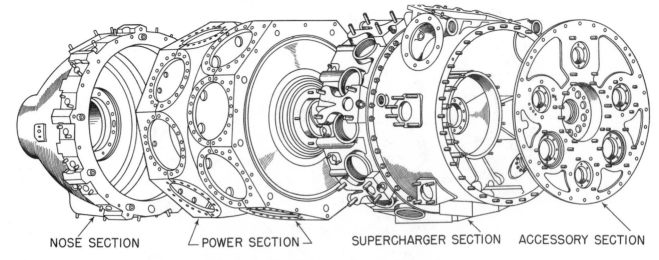

NOSE SECTION   POWER SECTION   SUPERCHARGER SECTION   ACCESSORY SECTION

Figure **3·11** *Crankcase for a radial engine.*

nor drive shaft, and a propeller reduction-gear assembly if the engine provides for propeller speed reduction. It may also include an oil-scavenging pump and a cam plate or cam-ring mechanism.

This section also may provide mounting for a propeller-governor control valve, a crankcase breather, an oil sump, magnetos, and magneto distributors. The engines which have magnetos mounted on the nose case are usually of the higher power ranges. The advantage of mounting the magneto on the nose section is in cooling. When the magnetos are on the nose section of the engine, they are exposed to a large volume of ram air; thus they are kept much cooler than is the case when they are mounted on the accessory section.

The **main or power section** may be of one-piece or two-piece construction and usually consists of one, two, or possibly three pieces of high-strength heat-treated aluminum-alloy or steel forging, bolted together if there is more than one piece. The cam-operating mechanism is usually housed and supported by the main crankcase section. At the center of each main crankcase web section are crankshaft bearing supports. Cylinder mounting pads are located radially around the outside circumference of the power section. The cylinders are fastened to the pads by means of studs and nuts or cap screws. Oil seals are located between the front crankcase section and the main crankcase. Similar seals are installed between the power section and the fuel-distribution section.

The **fuel-induction and -distribution section** is normally located immediately behind the main power section and may be of either one-piece or two-piece construction. It is sometimes called the **blower section** or the **supercharger section** because its principal function is to house the blower or supercharger impeller and diffuser vanes. There are openings on the outside circumference of the housing for attaching the individual induction pipes, a small opening for the attachment of the manifold pressure line, and internal passages which lead to the supercharger drain valve.

The **accessory section** provides mounting pads for the accessory units such as the fuel pumps, vacuum pumps, lubricating-oil pumps, tachometer generators, generators, magnetos, starters, two-speed supercharger control valves, oil-filtering screens, Cuno filters, and other items of accessory equipment. In some aircraft powerplants, the cover for the supercharger rear housing is made of an aluminum-alloy or a magnesium-alloy casting in the form of a heavily ribbed plate that provides the mounting pads for the accessory units, but in other powerplants, the housings for the accessory units may be mounted directly on the rear of the crankcase. Regardless of the construction and location of the accessory housing, it contains the gears for driving those accessories which are operated by engine power.

CYLINDERS

The **cylinder** of an internal-combustion engine converts the chemical heat energy of the fuel to mechanical energy and transmits it through pistons and connecting rods to the rotating crankshaft. In addition to developing the power from the fuel, the cylinder dissipates a substantial portion of the heat produced by the combustion of the fuel, houses the piston and connecting-rod assembly, supports the valves and a portion of the valve actuating mechanism, and supports the spark plugs.

The cylinder assembly used for present-day engines usually includes the following components: (1) cylinder barrel, (2) cylinder head, (3) valve guides, (4) valve rocker arm supports, (5) valve seats, (6) spark-plug bushings, and (7) cooling fins. The cylinder assemblies together with pistons, connecting rods, and the crankcase section to which they are attached may be regarded as the main power section of the engine.

The two major units of the cylinder assembly are the cylinder barrel and cylinder head. These are shown in the illustration of Fig. 3·12. The principal requirements for this assembly are (1) strength to withstand the internal pressures developed during operation at the temperatures which are normally developed when the engine is run at maximum design loads, (2) light weight, (3) heat-conducting properties to obtain efficient cooling, and (4) a design which makes possible easy and inexpensive manufacture, inspection, and maintenance.

Cylinder barrel

In general, the barrel in which the piston reciprocates must be made of high-strength steel alloy, be constructed to save weight as much as possible, have the proper characteristics for operating under high temperatures, be made of a good bearing material, and have high tensile strength. The barrel is usually made of chrome-molybdenum (SAE 4130 or 4140) steel or chrome-nickel-molybdenum steel which is initially forged to provide maximum strength. The forging is machined to design dimensions with external fins and a smooth cylindrical surface inside. After machining, the inside surface is honed to a specific finish to provide the proper bearing surface for the piston rings. The roughness of this surface must be carefully controlled. If it is too smooth, it will not hold sufficient oil for the break-in period, and if it is too rough, it will lead to excessive wear or other damage to both the piston rings and the cylinder wall. The inside of the cylinder barrel may be surface-hardened by means of **nitriding**, or it may be chrome-plated to provide a long-wearing surface. Nitriding is a process whereby the nitrogen from anhydrous ammonia gas is caused to penetrate the surface of the steel by exposing the barrel to the ammonia gas for 40 hr or more while the barrel is at a temperature of about 975°F.

The base of the cylinder barrel incorporates a machined mounting flange by which the cylinder is attached to the crankcase. The flange is drilled to provide holes for the mounting studs or bolts. The holes are reamed for accurate dimensioning. The cylinder **skirt** extends beyond the flange into the crankcase and makes it possible to use a shorter connecting rod. It also makes it possible to reduce the external dimensions of the engine.

The outer end of the cylinder barrel is usually provided with threads so it can be screwed and shrunk into the cylinder head, which is also threaded. The cylinder head is heated in an oven to 575 to 600°F and is then screwed onto the cool cylinder barrel.

As mentioned previously, cooling fins are generally machined directly on the outside of the barrel. This method provides the best conduction of heat from the inside of the barrel to the cooling air. On some cylinders, the cooling fins are on aluminum-alloy muffs or sleeves shrunk on the outside of the barrel.

Cylinder heads

The cylinder head encloses the combustion chamber for the fuel/air mixture and contains the intake and exhaust valves, valve guides, and valve seats. The cylinder head also provides the support for the rocker shafts upon which the valve rocker arms are mounted. The openings into which the spark plugs are inserted are provided in the cylinder head at positions designed to provide the best burning pattern. The spark-plug openings may contain bushings shrunk and staked into the head, and in some cylinders the threads are reinforced with steel inserts called Heli-Coils. The Heli-Coil inserts make it possible to restore the threads by replacement of the inserts.

Cylinder heads are usually made of cast-aluminum alloy (AMS 4220) to provide a maximum of strength with minimum weight. The cooling fins are cast or machined on the outside of the head in a pattern to provide the most efficient cooling and to take advantage of cylinder-head cooling baffles. The area surrounding the intake passage and valve does not usually have cooling fins because the fuel/air mixture entering the cylinder carries the heat away. The intake side of the cylinder head can be quickly identified by noting which side is not finned.

As shown in the illustration of Fig. 3·13, the valve guides are positioned to support and guide the stems of the valves. The valve guides are shrunk into bored bosses with 0.001- to 0.0025-in. tight fit. Before the valve guides are installed, the cylinder head is heated to expand the holes into which the guides are to be installed. The guides are then pressed into place or driven in with a special drift. When the cylinder head cools, the guide is gripped so tightly that it will not become loose even under severe heating conditions.

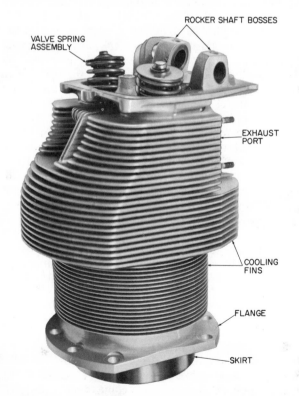

VALVE SPRING
ASSEMBLY

ROCKER SHAFT BOSSES

EXHAUST
PORT

COOLING
FINS

FLANGE

SKIRT

Figure 3·12   A cylinder assembly.

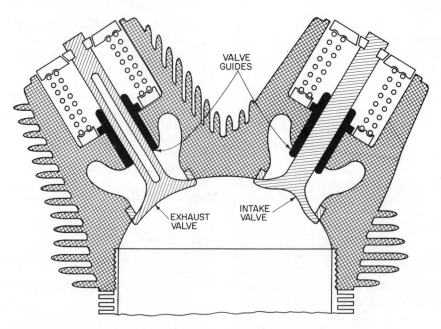

Figure **3·13** *Installation arrangement of valve guides.*

It is common practice when valve guides are replaced to install new guides which are approximately 0.002 in. larger than the holes in which they are to be installed. Valve guides are made of aluminum bronze, tin bronze, or steel, and in some cylinders the exhaust-valve guide is steel while the intake-valve guide is made of bronze.

Because the aluminum-alloy cylinder-head material does not provide serviceable valve seats, valve-seat inserts are shrunk into place for both the intake and exhaust valves. These inserts are made of forged chrome-molydenum steel or bronze and are installed in the heated head just before the head is screwed onto the barrel. In some cases the exhaust-valve seat is made of steel with a layer of Stellite (a very hard, heat-resisting alloy) bonded on the seat surface to provide a more durable seat. Valve-seat inserts are replaceable when they have been reground to the extent that they are no longer within approved dimension limits.

The interior shape of the cylinder head may be flat, peaked, or hemispherical, but the last shape is preferred because it is more satisfactory for scavenging the exhaust gases rapidly and thoroughly. Figure 3·14 shows the internal shapes of three different cylinder heads. In actual construction, they are not shaped exactly as shown.

The three methods used for joining the cylinder barrel to the cylinder head are (1) the threaded joint, (2) the shrink fit, and (3) the stud-and-nut joint. The method most commonly employed for modern engines is the threaded joint.

The threaded joint is accomplished by chilling the cylinder barrel which has threads at the head end and heating the cast cylinder head to about 575°F as previously explained. The cylinder head is threaded to receive the end of the barrel. A **jointing compound** is placed on the threads to prevent compression leakage, and then the barrel is screwed into the cylinder head. When the cylinder head cools, it contracts and grips the barrel tightly.

The cylinder head is provided with machined surfaces at the intake and exhaust openings for the attachment of the intake and exhaust manifolds. The manifolds are held in place by means of bolted rings which fit against the flanges of the manifold pipes. The intake pipes are usually provided with synthetic-rubber gaskets which seal the joint between the pipe and the cylinder. Exhaust pipes are usually sealed by means of metal or metal and asbestos gaskets. The mounting studs are threaded into the cast cylinder heads and are not usually removed except in case of damage.

PISTONS

Construction

The **piston** is a plunger that moves back and forth or up and down within an engine cylinder barrel. It transmits the force of the burning and expanding gases in the cylinder through the **connecting rod** to the engine crankshaft. As the piston moves down (toward

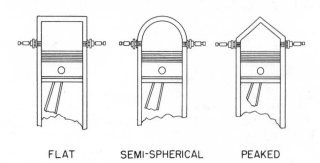

FLAT   SEMI-SPHERICAL   PEAKED

Figure **3·14** *Internal shapes of cylinder heads.*

the crankshaft) in the cylinder, during the intake stroke, it draws in the fuel/air mixture. As it moves upward (toward the cylinder head), it compresses the charge. Ignition takes place, and the expanding gases cause the piston to move toward the crankshaft. On the next stroke (toward the head), it forces the burned gases out of the combustion chamber.

In order to obtain maximum engine life, the piston must be able to withstand high operating temperatures and pressures; hence, it is usually made of aluminum alloy which may be either forged or cast. Aluminum alloy AMS 4140 is often used for forged pistons. Cast pistons may be made of Alcoa 132 alloy. Aluminum alloy is used because it is light in weight, it has a high heat conductivity, and it has excellent bearing characteristics.

A typical piston is illustrated in Fig. 3·15. The top of the piston is the **head.** The sides form the **skirt.** The underside of the piston often contains ribs or other means of presenting maximum surface area for contact with the lubricating oil which is splashed on it. This oil carries away part of the heat which is conducted through the piston head.

Grooves are machined around the outer surface of the piston to provide support for the **piston rings.** The metal between the grooves is called a **groove land** or simply a **land.** The grooves must be accurately dimensioned and concentric with the piston.

The piston and ring assembly must form as nearly a perfect seal with the cylinder wall as possible. It must slide along the cylinder wall with very little friction. All the piston assemblies in any one engine must be balanced. This means that each piston must weigh within ¼ oz of each of the others. This balance is most important in order to avoid vibration while the engine is operating.

Figure 3·16 is a drawing to illustrate the cross section of an assembled piston. This particular piston has five piston rings; however, some pistons are equipped with only four rings and many use three rings.

The parts of a complete piston assembly are shown in Fig. 3·17. This illustration shows the piston, piston pin, pin retainer plugs, oil rings, and compression rings.

Piston speed

In order to appreciate the loads imposed on a piston and connecting-rod assembly it is helpful to consider the speed at which the piston must travel in the cylinder. In order to move at high speeds with a minimum of stress the piston must be as light as possible. If an engine operates at 2000 rpm, the piston will start and stop 4000 times in 1 min, and if the piston has a 6-in. stroke, it may reach a velocity of more than 35 mph during the first and fourth quarters of crankshaft rotation.

Piston temperature and pressure

The temperature inside the cylinder of an airplane engine may exceed 4000°F, and the pressure against the piston during operation may be as high as 500 psi or higher. Since aluminum alloy is light and strong and conducts the heat away rapidly, it is generally used in piston construction. The heat in the piston is carried to the cylinder wall through the outside of the piston

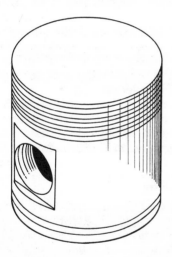

Figure 3·15   A piston.

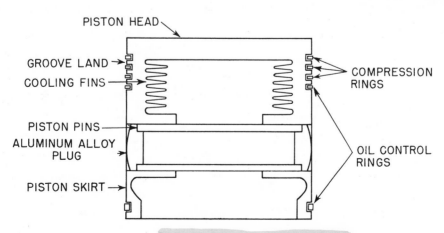

Figure 3·16   Cross section of an assembled piston.

27

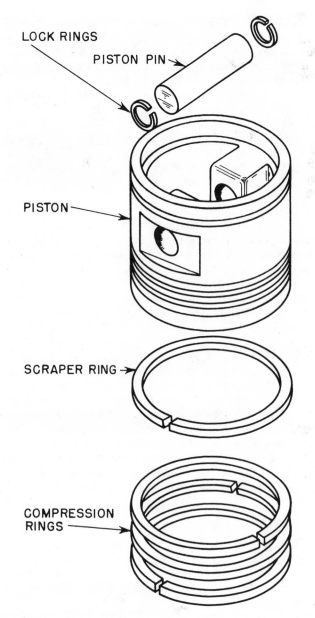

LOCK RINGS

PISTON PIN →

PISTON →

SCRAPER RING →

COMPRESSION RINGS →

Figure 3·17   Complete piston assembly.

and is transmitted to the engine oil in the crankcase through ribs or other means on the inside of the piston head. Fins increase the strength of the piston and are more generally used than other methods of cooling.

Piston and cylinder wall clearance

Piston rings are used as seals to prevent the loss of gases between the piston and cylinder wall during all strokes. It would be desirable to eliminate piston rings by having pistons large enough to form a gastight seal with the cylinder wall, but in that case the friction between the piston and the cylinder wall would be too great and there would be no allowance for expansion and contraction of the metals. The piston is actually made a few thousandths of an inch smaller than the cylinder, and the rings are installed in the pistons to seal the space between the piston and cylinder wall.

Types of pistons

Pistons may be classified according to the type of head used. These are flat, recessed, concave, convex, or truncated cone and are illustrated in Fig. 3·18. Pistons in modern engines are usually of the flat-head type. The skirt of the piston may be of the **trunk type, trunk type relieved at the piston pin,** or **slipper type.** Typical pistons for modern engines are shown in Fig. 3·19. It will be noted that some pistons have the skirt cut out at the bottom to clear the crankshaft counterweights. Slipper-type pistons are no longer used in modern engines because they do not provide adequate strength and wear resistance.

The horsepower ratings of engines of the same basic design are changed merely by the use of different pistons. A domed piston increases the compression ratio and the bmep when the engine is operating at a given rpm.

Piston-ring construction

Piston rings are usually made of high-grade gray cast iron. This material provides the spring action necessary to maintain a steady pressure against the cylinder wall, thus retaining the necessary seal. Cast-iron rings do not lose their elasticity even though they are exposed to rather high temperatures. The rings are split so they can be slipped over the outside of the

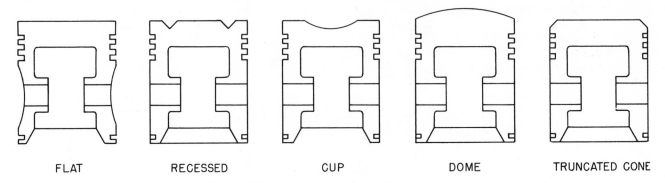

FLAT   RECESSED   CUP   DOME   TRUNCATED CONE

Figure 3·18   Types of piston heads.

Figure 3·19   Several types of pistons.

piston and into the ring grooves which are machined on the circumference of the piston. Some compression rings are given a chrome-plated surface on the face of the ring. This type of ring must never be used in a chrome-plated cylinder.

The piston-ring gap may be a plain butt joint, a step joint, or an angle joint as shown in Fig. 3·20. The butt joint is commonly used in modern aircraft engines. When a piston ring is installed in a cylinder, there must be a specified gap clearance between the ends of the joint to allow for expansion during the operation of the engine. This gap is given in the **Table of Limits** for the engine. If a piston ring does not have sufficient gap clearance, it may seize and cause scoring of the cylinder or failure of the engine. The joints of the piston rings must be staggered around the circumference of a piston when they are installed in the cylinder to reduce **blowby,** that is, to prevent the escape of gases. The side clearance of piston rings in the piston grooves is important to allow free movement of the ring in the groove, but it should not be great enough to allow appreciable leakage of gases. The side clearance for the various rings is specified in the Table of Limits for the engine.

Functions of piston rings

The importance of the piston rings in a reciprocating engine cannot be overemphasized. The three principal functions are (1) to provide a seal to hold the pressures in the combustion chamber, (2) to prevent excessive oil from entering the combustion chamber, and (3) to conduct the heat from the piston to the cylinder walls. Worn or otherwise defective piston rings will cause loss of compression and excessive oil consumption. Defective piston rings will usually cause excessively high oil discharge from the crankcase breather and an excessive amount of blue smoke from the exhaust of

the engine during normal operation. The smoke is normal when an engine is first started, but it should not continue for more than a few moments.

Types of piston rings

Piston rings in general may be of the same thickness throughout the circumference or they may vary, but aircraft-engine piston rings are almost always of the same thickness all the way around. Piston rings may be classified to function as (1) compression rings and (2) oil rings.

The purpose of **compression rings** is to prevent gases from escaping past the piston during engine operation. They are placed in the ring grooves immediately below the piston head. The number of compression rings used on a piston is determined by the designer of the engine, but most aircraft engines have three or four piston rings for each piston.

The cross section of the compression ring may be rectangular, tapered, or wedge-shaped. The rectangu-

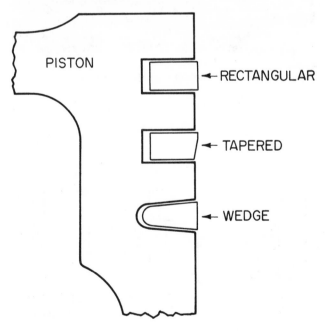

Figure 3·21   Cross sections of compression rings.

Figure 3·20   Piston ring joints.

lar cross section provides a straight bearing edge against the cylinder wall. The tapered and wedge-shaped cross sections present a bearing edge which is supposed to hasten the seating of a new ring against the hardened surface of the cylinder wall. Figure 3·21 illustrates cross sections of rectangular, tapered, and wedge-shaped compression rings.

The principal purpose of **oil rings** is to control the quantity of lubricant supplied to the cylinder walls and prevent this oil from passing into the combustion chamber. The two types of oil rings are **oil-control rings** and **oil-wiper rings** (sometimes called **oil-scraper rings.)**

Oil-control rings are placed in the grooves immediately below the compression rings. There may be only one oil-control ring to a piston, or there may be two or three. The purpose of the oil-control ring is to control the thickness of the oil film on the cylinder wall. The oil-control ring groove is often provided with drilled holes to the inside of the piston to permit excess oil to be drained away. The oil flowing through the drilled holes provides additional lubrication for the piston pins.

If too much oil enters the combustion chamber, it will burn and may leave a coating of carbon on the combustion chamber walls, the piston head, and the valve heads. This carbon can cause the valves and piston rings to stick if it enters the valve guides and the ring grooves. In addition, the carbon may cause detonation, preignition, and increased oil consumption.

Oil-wiper or -scraper rings are placed on the skirts of the pistons to regulate the amount of oil passing between the piston skirts and the cylinder walls during each of the piston strokes. The cross section is usually beveled, and the beveled edge is installed in either of two positions. If the beveled edge is installed nearest the piston heads, the ring scrapes oil toward the crankcase. If installed with the beveled edge away from the piston head, the ring serves as a pump to keep up the flow of oil between the piston and the cylinder wall. Figure 3·22 shows cross sections of oil-control, oil-wiper, and bottom oil ring installations. The engine technician must make sure that he installs the piston rings according to the manufacturer's overhaul instructions.

Piston-ring cross sections

In addition to the cross sections of compression rings described previously, we must consider the shapes of oil rings. Oil-control rings usually have one of three cross sections: (1) ventilated, (2) oil wiper (tapered with narrow edge up), or (3) uniflow effect (tapered with wide edge up). The choice of the cross section to be used is normally determined by the manufacturer. In some cases the upper oil-control ring is made up of two or more parts. The **ventilated-type** oil-control rings are usually of a two-piece construction, made with a number of equally spaced slots around the entire circumference of the ring to allow the oil to drain through to the holes in the ring groove and then into the crankcase. Another ring assembly consists of two thin steel rings, one on each side of a cast-iron ring. The cast-iron ring has cutouts along the sides to permit the flow of oil into the groove and through drilled holes to the inside of the piston. The choice of the particular ring to be used with an engine is normally determined by the manufacturer. Where there is more than one position in which a ring may be installed, it should be marked to show the correct installation.

Narrow surfaced rings are preferred to wide ones because they adapt themselves better to the wall of the cylinder. Regardless of the cross section or the width, all modern piston rings are constructed to withstand wear and deterioration. Wear is generally caused by fine abrasive particles in the lubricating oil and by the friction existing between the rings, ring grooves, and cylinder walls.

Wedge-shaped piston rings are fitted to beveled-edge grooves to obtain a sliding, self-cleaning action that will prevent sticking between the ring and the groove. Also, the ring lands remain stronger where beveled-edge grooves are between them. Since compression rings operate at the highest temperatures and are a greater distance from the oil source, they receive less lubrication than other rings and have the greatest tendency to stick; therefore, wedge-shaped rings are installed as compression rings; that is, they are placed in the ring grooves immediately below the piston head.

On certain radial-type aircraft engines, the oil-wiper rings on the upper cylinders are faced toward the piston head or dome to carry more oil to the top piston rings; hence the oil rings above the top ring serve as wiper rings. In that case, the oil-control rings on the lower cylinders are normally faced toward the crankshaft to prevent overlubrication.

Piston pins

A **piston pin,** sometimes called a **wrist pin,** is used to attach the piston to the connecting rod. It is made of steel (AMS 6274 or AMS 6322) hollowed for lightness and surface-hardened or through-hardened to resist wear. The pin passes through the piston at right angles to the skirt so that the piston can be anchored to the connecting-rod assembly. A means is provided to prevent the piston pin from moving sideways in the piston and damaging the cylinder wall. The piston pin is

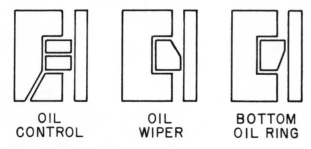

OIL CONTROL   OIL WIPER   BOTTOM OIL RING

Figure 3·22   Piston-ring installations.

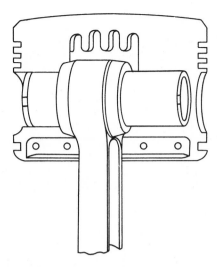

Figure **3·23** *Piston pin in a piston-pin boss.*

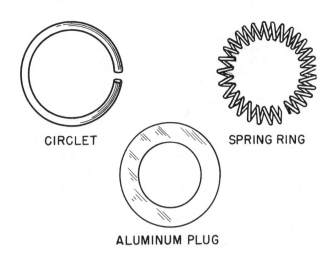

Figure **3·24** *Piston-pin retainers.*

mounted in bosses and bears directly on the aluminum alloy of which the pistons are made. When the piston is made of aluminum alloy, however, the bosses may or may not be lined with some nonferrous (no iron or steel) metal such as bronze. Figure 3·23 shows a piston pin in a piston-pin boss. The piston pin passes through the piston bosses and also through the small end of the connecting rod which rides on the central part of the pin.

Piston pins are usually classified as **stationary** (rigid), **semifloating,** or **full-floating.** The stationary type is not free to move in any direction and is securely fastened in the boss by means of a set screw. The semifloating piston pin is securely held by means of a clamp screw in the end of the connecting rod and a half slot in the pin itself. The full-floating type is free to run or slide in both the connecting rod and the piston and is used in most modern aircraft engines.

Piston-pin retainers

The three devices used to prevent contact between the piston-pin ends and the cylinder wall are **circlets, spring rings,** and **nonferrous-metal plugs.** Figure 3·24 shows these three retainers.

Circlets resemble piston rings and fit into grooves at the outside end of each piston boss.

Spring rings are circular spring steel coils which fit into circular grooves cut into the outside end of each piston boss to prevent the movement of the pin against the cylinder wall.

Nonferrous-metal plugs, usually made of aluminum alloy, are called **piston-pin plugs** and are used in most aircraft engines. They are inserted in the open ends of a hollow piston pin to prevent the steel pin end from bearing against the cylinder wall. The comparatively soft piston-pin plugs may bear against the cylinder walls without damage to either the plug or the wall.

Piston pins are fitted into the pistons and the connecting rod with clearances of less than 0.001 in. This is commonly called a "push fit" because the pin can be inserted in the piston boss by pushing with the palm of the hand. The proper clearances for piston pins, bosses, and connecting rods are listed in the Table of Limits for any particular engine.

Since the piston-pin bearing surfaces are not pressure-lubricated, it is a common practice to drill holes through the piston-pin bosses to supply oil to the bearing surfaces.

CONNECTING-ROD ASSEMBLIES

A variety of connecting-rod assemblies have been designed for the many different types of engines. Some of the arrangements for such assemblies are shown in Fig. 3·25. The **connecting rod** is defined as the link which transmits forces between the piston and the crankshaft of an engine. It furnishes the means of converting the reciprocating motion of the piston to a rotating movement of the crankshaft in order to drive the propeller.

Construction

A tough steel alloy (SAE 4340) is the material used for manufacturing most connecting rods, but aluminum alloy has been used for some low-power engines. The cross-sectional shape of the connecting rod is usually like either the letter H or the letter I, although some have been made with a tubular cross section. The end of the rod which connects to the crankshaft is called the **large end** or **crankpin end,** and the end which connects to the piston pin is called the **small end** or the **piston-pin end.** Connecting rods, other than tubular types, are manufactured by forging in order to provide maximum strength.

Connecting rods stop, change direction, and start at the end of each stroke; hence, they must be light in weight to reduce the inertia forces produced by these changes of velocity and direction. At the same time, they must be strong enough to remain rigid under the severe loads imposed under operating conditions.

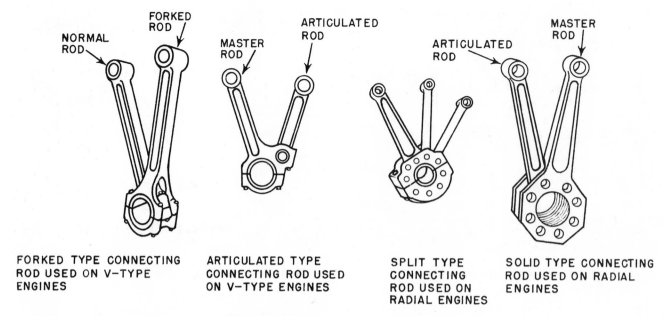

FORKED TYPE CONNECTING ROD USED ON V-TYPE ENGINES

ARTICULATED TYPE CONNECTING ROD USED ON V-TYPE ENGINES

SPLIT TYPE CONNECTING ROD USED ON RADIAL ENGINES

SOLID TYPE CONNECTING ROD USED ON RADIAL ENGINES

Figure 3·25   Connecting-rod assemblies.

There are three principal types of connecting-rod assemblies: (1) the plain type, shown in Fig. 3·26; (2) the fork-and-blade type, shown in Fig. 3·27; and the master-and-articulated type, shown in Fig. 3·28.

Plain connecting rod

The plain connecting rod is used on in-line engines and opposed engines. The small end of the rod usually has a bronze bushing to serve as a bearing for the piston pin. This bushing is pressed into place and then reamed to the proper dimension. The large end of the rod is made with a cap, and a two-piece shell bearing is installed. The bearing is held in place by the cap. The outside of the bearing flange bears against the sides of the crankpin journal when the rod assembly is installed on the crankshaft. The bearing inserts are often made of steel and lined with a nonferrous bearing material such as lead bronze, copper lead, lead silver, or babbitt (a soft bearing alloy, silver in color and composed of tin, copper, and antimony). Another type of bearing insert is made of bronze and has a lead

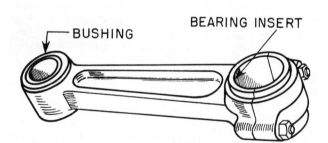

Figure 3·26   Plain-type connecting rod.

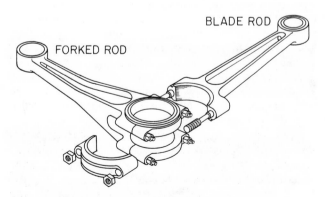

Figure 3·27   Fork-and-blade connecting rod.

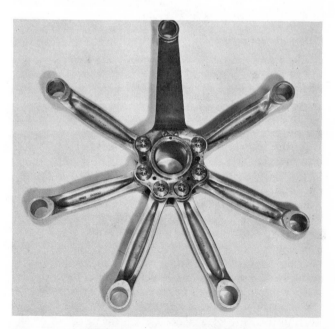

Figure 3·28   Master-and-articulated rod assembly.

plating for the bearing surface against the crankpin.

The two-piece bearing shell fits snugly in the large end of the connecting rod and is prevented from turning by dowel pins or by tangs which fit into slots cut into the cap and the connecting rod. The cap is usually secured on the end of the rod by bolts; however, some rods have been manufactured with studs for holding the cap in place.

During inspection, maintenance, repair, and overhaul, the proper fit and balance of connecting rods are obtained by always replacing the connecting rod in the same cylinder and in the same relative position as it was before removal. The connecting rods and caps are usually stamped with numbers to indicate their position in the engine. The rod assembly for the No. 1 cylinder is marked with a 1, the assembly for the No. 2 cylinder is marked with a 2, and so on.

The fork-and-blade connecting-rod assembly

The fork-and-blade connecting rod, illustrated in Fig. 3·27, is generally used in V-type engines. The **forked rod** is split on the large end to provide space for the **blade rod** to fit between the prongs.

One two-piece bearing shell is fastened by lugs or dowel pins to the forked rod. Between the prongs of the forked rod, the center area of the outer surface of this bearing shell is coated with a nonferrous bearing metal to act as a journal for the blade rod and cap.

During overhaul or maintenance, the fork-and-blade connecting rods are always replaced on the crankshaft in the same relative positions as they occupied in their original installation. This ensures the proper fit and engine balance. Specific instructions for overhaul operations are given in the manufacturer's overhaul manual, and such instructions must be followed carefully in order to obtain the best results. This applies to all aircraft engines.

Master-and-articulated connecting-rod assembly

The **master-and-articulated rod assembly** is used primarily for radial engines, although some V-type engines have employed this type of rod assembly. The complete rod assembly for a seven-cylinder radial engine is shown in Fig. 3·28.

The **master rod** in a radial engine is subjected to some stresses not imposed upon the plain connecting rod; hence its design and construction must be of the highest quality. It is made of an alloy-steel forging, machined and polished to final dimensions and heat-treated to provide maximum strength and resistance to vibration and other stresses. The surface must be free of nicks, scratches, or other surface damage which may produce a stress concentration and ultimate failure.

The master rod is similar to other connecting rods except that it is constructed to provide for the attachment of the articulated rods (link rods) on the large end. The large end of the master rod may be a two-piece type or a one-piece type, as shown in Fig. 3·29.

If the large end of the master rod is made of two pieces, the crankshaft is one solid piece. On the other

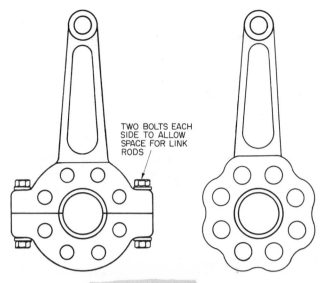

Figure **3·29** *Types of master rods.*

hand, if the rod is one piece, then the crankshaft may be of either two-piece or three-piece construction. Regardless of the type of construction, the usual bearing surfaces must be supplied.

Master-rod bearings are generally of the plain type and consist of a split shell or a sleeve, depending upon whether the master rod is of the two-piece type or the one-piece type. The bearing usually has a steel or bronze backing with a softer nonferrous material bonded to the backing to serve as the actual bearing material. In low-power engines, babbitt material was suitable for the bearing surface, but it was found to be lacking in the durability necessary for the higher power engines. For this reason, bronze, leading bronze, and silver are used in later engines. The actual bearing surface is usually plated with lead in order to reduce the friction as much as possible. During operation the bearing is cooled and lubricated by a constant flow of lubricating oil.

The **articulated rods** (link rods) are hinged to the master rod flanges by means of steel **knuckle pins.** Each articulated rod has a bushing of nonferrous metal, usually bronze, pressed or shrunk into place to serve as a knuckle-pin bearing. Aluminum-alloy link rods have been used successfully in some lower power radial engines. When these are employed, it is not necessary to provide bronze bushings at the ends of the rod because the aluminum alloy furnishes a good bearing surface for the piston pins and knuckle pins.

Articulated rods, when made of steel, are usually constructed in an I or H cross section. These configurations give the greatest strength and resistance to distortion with the lightest weight.

The knuckle pin, mentioned previously, resembles a piston pin. It is usually made of nickel steel, hollowed for lightness and to permit the passage of lubricating oil and surface-hardened to reduce wear.

The articulated rod is bored and supplied with bushings at each end. One end receives the piston pin,

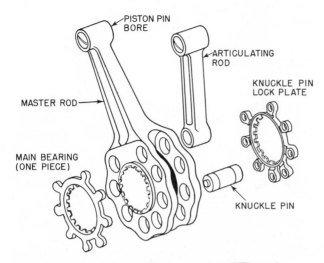

Figure **3·30** *Knuckle-pin and lock-plate assembly.*

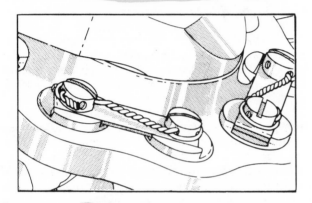

Figure **3·31** *Stationary knuckle pin and lock plate.*

and the other end receives the knuckle pin. The knuckle-pin bore in the articulated rod includes a bushing of nonferrous metal, which is usually bronze. It is pinned, pressed, shrunk, or spun into place. The bushing must be bored to precise dimension and alignment.

Knuckle pins installed with a loose fit so that they can turn in the master-rod flange holes and also turn in the articulated rod bushings are called **full-floating knuckle pins.** Knuckle pins also may be installed so that they are prevented from turning in the master rod by means of a tight press fit. In either type of installation a lock plate on each side bears against the knuckle pin and prevents it from moving laterally (sideways).

Figure 3·30 shows a knuckle-pin and lock-plate assembly for a full-floating arrangement, and in Fig. 3·31 a stationary knuckle-pin and lock-plate assembly is illustrated.

CRANKSHAFT

The **crankshaft** transforms the reciprocating motion of the piston and connecting rod into rotary motion for turning the propeller. It is a shaft composed of one or more cranks located at definite places between the

ends. These **cranks,** sometimes called **throws,** are formed by forging offsets into a shaft before it is machined. Since the crankshaft is the backbone of an internal-combustion engine, it is subjected to all the forces developed within the engine and must be of very strong construction. For this reason, it is usually forged from some extremely strong steel alloy, such as chromium-nickel-molybdenum steel (SAE 4340).

A crankshaft may be constructed of one or more pieces. Regardless of whether it is of one-piece or multipiece construction, the corresponding parts of all crankshafts have the same names and functions. The parts are (1) the main journal, (2) the crankpin, (3) the crank cheek or crank arm, and (4) the counterweights and dampers. Figure 3·32 shows the nomenclature of a typical crankshaft. This particular shaft is used in a six-cylinder opposed engine.

The main journal

The **main journal** is that part of the crankshaft which is supported by and rotates in a **main bearing.** Because of this it may also properly be called a **main-bearing journal.** This journal is the center of rotation of the crankshaft and serves to keep the crankshaft in alignment under all normal conditions of operation. The main journal is surface-hardened by nitriding for a depth of 0.015 to 0.025 in. to reduce wear. Every aircraft-engine crankshaft has two or more main journals to support the weight and operational loads of the entire rotating and reciprocating assembly in the power section of the engine.

Crankpin

The **crankpin** can also be called a **connecting-rod bearing journal** simply because it is the journal for a connecting-rod bearing. Since the crankpin is off center from the main journals, it is sometimes called a **throw.** The crankshaft will rotate when a force is applied to the crankpin in any direction other than parallel to a line directly through the center line of the crankshaft.

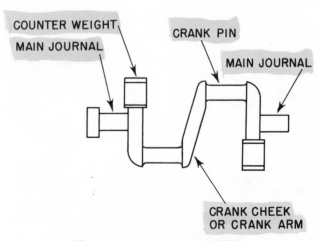

Figure **3·32** *Crankshaft with nomenclature.*

The crankpin is usually hollow for three reasons: (1) It reduces the total weight of the crankshaft, (2) it provides a passage for the lubricating oil, and (3) it serves as a chamber for collecting carbon deposits, sludge, and other foreign substances which are thrown by centrifugal force to the outside of the chamber where they will not reach the connecting-rod bearing surface. For this reason the chamber is often called the **sludge chamber.** On some engines a drilled passage from the sludge chamber to an opening on the exterior surface of the connecting rod makes it possible to spray clean oil on the cylinder walls.

Lubrication of the crankpin bearings is accomplished by oil taken through drilled passages from the main journals. The oil reaches the main journals through drilled passages in the crankcase and the crankcase webs which support the main bearings. During overhaul the technician must see that all oil passages and sludge chambers are cleaned in accordance with manufacturer's instructions.

Crank cheek

The **crank cheek,** sometimes called the **crank arm,** is that part of the crankshaft which connects the crankpin to the main journal. It must be constructed to maintain rigidity between the journal and the crankpin. On many engines, the crank cheek extends beyond the **main journal** and supports a counterweight used to balance the crankshaft. The crank cheeks usually are provided with drilled oil passages through which lubricating oil passes from the main journals to the crankpins.

Counterweights and dampeners

The purpose of **counterweights** and **dampers** is to relieve the whip and vibration caused by the rotation of the crankshaft. They are suspended from or installed in specified crank cheeks at locations determined by the design engineers. Crankshaft vibrations caused by power impulses may be reduced by placing floating dampers in a counterweight assembly. The need for counterweights and dampers is not confined to air-craft engines. Any machine with rotating parts may reach a speed at which so much vibration occurs in the revolving mass of metal that it must be reduced or the machine will eventually destroy itself.

The purpose of the counterweight is to provide static balance for a crankshaft. If a crankshaft has more than two throws, it does not always require counterweights because the throws, being arranged symmetrically opposite each other, balance each other. A single-throw crankshaft, such as that used in a single-row radial engine, must have counterbalances to offset the weight of the single throw and the connecting rod and piston assembly attached to it. This crankshaft is illustrated in Fig. 3·33.

Dampers or **dynamic balances** are required to overcome the forces which tend to cause deflection of the crankshaft and torsional vibration. These forces are generated principally by the power impulses of the pistons. If we compute the force exerted by the piston of an engine near the beginning of the power stroke, we shall find that 8000 to 10,000 lb is applied to the throw of a crankshaft. As the engine runs, this force is applied at regular intervals to the different throws of the crankshaft on an in-line or opposed engine and to the one throw of a single-row radial engine. If the frequency of the power impulses is such that it matches the natural vibration frequency of the crankshaft and propeller as a unit or of any moving part of the engine, then severe vibration will take place. The dynamic balances may be pendulum-type weights mounted in the counterweight as shown in Fig. 3·34, or they may be straddle mounted on extensions of the crank cheeks. In either case, the weight is free to move in a direction and at a frequency which will dampen out the natural vibration of the crankshaft.

The effectiveness of a dynamic dampener can be understood by observing the operation of a pendulum.

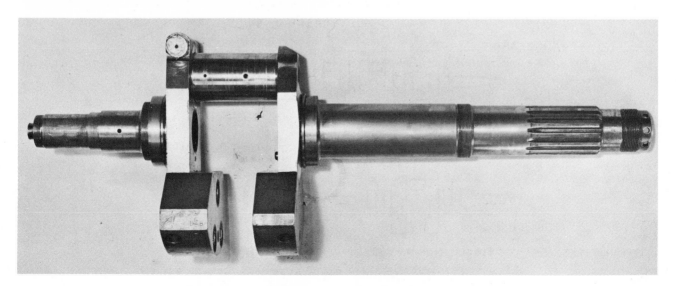

Figure 3·33   Single-throw crankshaft with counterweight.

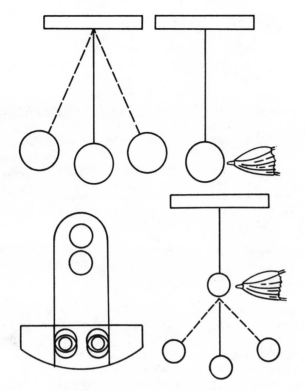

Figure 3·34 *Dynamic balances and principle of operation.*

If a simple pendulum is given a series of regular impulses at a speed corresponding to its natural frequency, using a bellows to simulate a modified power impulse in an engine, it will begin swinging or vibrating back and forth from the impulses, as shown in the upper half of Fig. 3·34.

Another pendulum, suspended from the first will absorb the impulse and swing itself, leaving the first pendulum stationary, as shown in the lower portion of Fig. 3·34. The dynamic dampener, then, is a short

pendulum hung on the crankshaft and tuned to the frequency of the power impulses to absorb vibration in the same manner as the pendulum illustrated in the lower part of the illustration.

Types of crankshafts

The four principal types of crankshafts are (1) the **single-throw,** (2) the **double-throw,** (3) the **four-throw,** and (4) the **six-throw.** Figure 3·35 shows the crankshaft for an in-line engine, a single-row radial engine, and a double-row radial engine. Each individual type of crankshaft may have several configurations depending upon the requirements of the particular engine for which it is designed. An engine which operates at a high speed and power output requires a crankshaft more carefully balanced and with greater resistance to wear and distortion than an engine which operates at slower speeds.

Single-throw crankshaft

The type of crankshaft and the number of crankpins it contains correspond in every case to the engine cylinder arrangement. The position of a crank on any crankshaft in relation to other cranks on the same shaft is given in degrees.

The single-throw or 360° type of crankshaft is used in single-row radial engines. It may be of single-piece or two-piece construction with two main bearings, one on each end. A single-piece crankshaft is shown in Fig. 3·36. This crankshaft must be used with a master rod having the large end split.

Two-piece single-throw crankshafts are shown in Fig. 3·37. The first of these is a clamp-type shaft. The front section of this shaft includes the main bearing journal, the front crank-cheek and counterweight assembly, and the crankpin. The rear section contains the clamp by which the two sections are joined, the rear crank-cheek and counterweight assembly, and the rear main bearing journal. The spline-type crankshaft

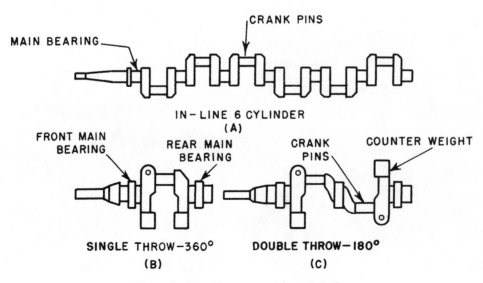

Figure 3·35 *Three types of crankshafts.*

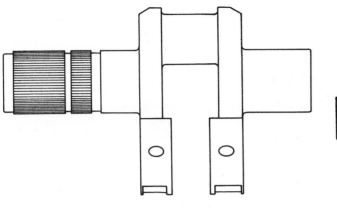

Figure 3·36   A single-piece crankshaft.

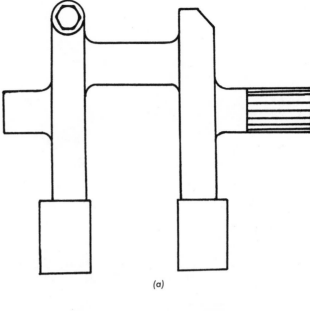

(a)

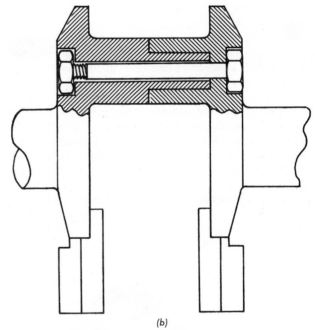

(b)

Figure 3·37   Two-piece single-throw crankshafts.

shown in Fig. 3·37 has the same parts as the clamp-type with the exception of the device by which the two sections are joined. In this shaft, the crankpin is divided, one end having a female spline and the other having a male spline to match. When the two parts are joined, they are held securely in place by means of an alloy-steel bolt.

Double-throw crankshaft

The double-throw or 180° crankshaft is generally used in a double-row radial engine. When used in this type of engine, the crankshaft has one throw for each row of cylinders. The construction may be one-piece or three-piece, and the bearings may be of the ball type or roller type.

Four-throw crankshaft

Four-throw crankshafts are used in four-cylinder opposed engines, four-cylinder in-line engines, and V-8 engines. In the four-throw crankshaft for an in-line or opposed engine two throws are placed 180° from the other two throws. There may be three or five crank-shaft main journals, depending upon the power output and the size of the engine. The bearings for the four-cylinder opposed engine are of the plain, split-shell type. In the four-throw crankshaft, illustrated in Fig. 3·38, lubrication for the crankpin bearings is provided through passages drilled in the crank cheeks. During operation, oil is brought through passages in the crank-

Figure 3·38   Four-throw crankshaft.

Figure **3·39**   Crankshaft for six-cylinder opposed engine.

case webs to the main-bearing journals. From the main-bearing journals the oil flows through the crank-cheek passages to the crankpin journals and the sludge chambers in the journals.

Six-throw crankshaft

Six-throw crankshafts are used in six-cylinder in-line engines, twelve-cylinder V-type engines, and six-cylinder opposed engines. Since the in-line and V-type engines are not in general use in the United States, we shall limit our discussion to the type of shaft used in the six-cylinder opposed engine.

A crankshaft for a Continental, six-cylinder opposed air-craft engine is shown in Fig. 3·39. This is a one-piece, six-throw, 60° crankshaft machined from an alloy-steel (SAE 4340) forging. It has four main journals and one double-flanged main-thrust journal. The shaft is heat-treated for high strength and nitrided to a depth of 0.015 to 0.025 in., except on the propeller

splines, for maximum wear. The crankpins and main bearing journals are ground to close limits of size and surface roughness. After grinding, nitriding, and polishing the crankshaft is balanced statically and dynamically. Final balance is attained after the assembly of the counterweights and other parts.

As shown in the illustration of Fig. 3·39, the crankshaft is provided with dynamic counterweights. Since the selection of the counterweights is necessary to preserve the dynamic balance of the complete assembly, they cannot be interchanged on the shaft or between crankshafts. For this reason, neither counterweights nor bare crankshafts are supplied alone.

The crankshaft is line bored the full length to reduce weight. Splined shafts have a threaded plug installed at the front end. The crankpins are recessed at each end to reduce weight. Steel tubes permanently installed in holes drilled through the crank cheeks provide oil passages across the lightening holes to all crankpin

Figure **3·40**   Plain bearings.

surfaces from the main journals. A U-shaped tube, permanently installed inside the front end of the shaft bore, conducts oil from the second main journal to the front main-thrust journal.

BEARINGS

A **bearing** is any surface that supports or is supported by another surface. Another definition is that a bearing is a part in which a journal, pivot, pin, shaft, or similar device turns or revolves. The bearings used in aircraft engines are designed to produce a minimum of friction and a maximum of wear resistance.

A good bearing has two broad characteristics: (1) It must be made of a material that is strong enough to withstand the pressure imposed on it and yet permit the other surface to move with a minimum of wear and friction, and (2) the parts must be held in position within very close tolerances to provide quiet and efficient operation and at the same time permit freedom of motion.

Bearings must reduce the friction of moving parts and also take thrust loads, radial loads, or a combination of thrust and radial loads. Those which are designed primarily to take thrust loads are called **thrust bearings.**

Bearing surfaces may move in relation to each other in either of two ways: (1) There may be a sliding movement of one metal surface against the other, or (2) one surface may roll over the other. The three types of bearings are (1) **plain,** (2) **roller,** and (3) **ball.**

Plain bearings

Plain bearings are illustrated in Fig. 3·40. These bearings are usually designed to take radial loads; however, plain bearings with flanges are often used as thrust bearings in opposed aircraft engines. Plain bearings are used for connecting rods, crankshafts, and camshafts of low-power aircraft engines. The metal used for plain bearings may be silver, lead, an alloy (such as bronze or babbitt), or a combination of metals. Bronze withstands high compressive pressures but offers more friction than babbitt. On the other hand, babbitt offers less friction but cannot withstand high compressive pressures as well as bronze. Silver withstands compressive pressures and is an excellent conductor of heat, but its frictional qualities are not dependable.

Plain bearings are made with a variety of metal combinations. Some bearings in common use are steel-backed with silver or silver-bronze on the steel, and then a thin layer of lead is applied for the actual bearing surface. Other bearings are bronze-backed and have a lead or babbitt surface.

Roller bearings

The **roller bearings** shown in Fig. 3·41 are one of the two types known as "antifriction" bearings because the rollers eliminate friction to a large extent. These bearings are made in a variety of shapes and sizes and

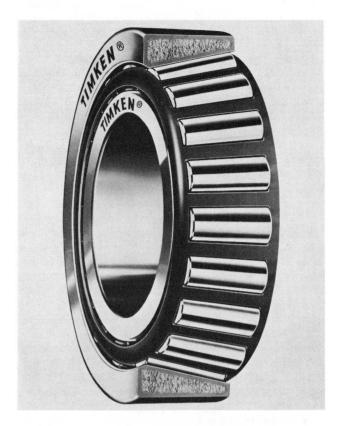

(a)

(b)

Figure 3·41   Roller bearings. (Timken Roller Bearing Co.)

can be adapted to both radial and thrust loads. Straight roller bearings are used only for radial loads; however, tapered roller bearings will support both radial and thrust loads.

The bearing **race** is the guide or channel along which the rollers travel. In a roller bearing, the roller is situated between an inner and an outer race, both of which are made of casehardened steel. When a roller is tapered, it rolls on a cone-shaped race inside an outer race.

Roller bearings are used in high-power aircraft engines as main bearings to support the crankshaft. They are also used in other applications where radial loads are high.

Ball bearings

Ball bearings provide less friction than any other type. A ball bearing consists of an inner race and an outer race, a set of polished steel balls, and a ball retainer. Some ball bearings are made with two rows of balls and two sets of races. The races are designed with grooves to fit the curvature of the balls to provide a large contact surface for carrying high radial loads.

A typical ball bearing used in an aircraft engine is shown in Fig. 3·42. In this bearing, the balls are controlled and held in place by means of the ball retainer. This retainer is necessary to keep the balls properly spaced, thus preventing them from contacting one another.

Ball bearings are commonly used for thrust bearings in large radial engines and in gas-turbine engines. Because of their construction, they can withstand heavy thrust loads almost as well as they support radial loads. A ball bearing designed especially for thrust

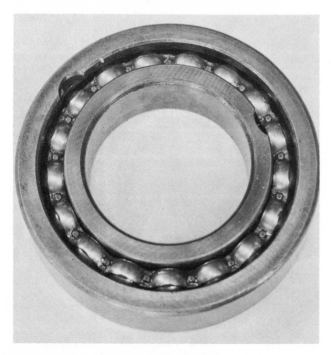

Figure 3·42 A ball-bearing assembly.

loads is made with exceptionally deep grooves in the races.

In addition to the large ball bearings used as main bearings and thrust bearings, many smaller ball bearings will be found in generators, magnetos, starters, and other accessories used on aircraft engines. For this reason the engine technician should be thoroughly familiar with the inspection and servicing of such bearings.

VALVES AND ASSOCIATED PARTS

Definition and purpose

In general, a **valve** is any device for regulating or determining the direction of flow of a liquid, gas, etc., by a movable part which opens or closes a passage. The word **valve** is also applied to the movable part itself.

The main purpose of valves in an internal-combustion engine is to open and close **ports,** which are openings into the combustion chamber of the engine. One is called the **intake port,** and its function is to allow the fuel/air charge to enter the cylinder. The other is called the **exhaust port** because it provides an opening through which burned gases are expelled from the cylinder.

Each cylinder must have at least one intake port and one exhaust port. On some liquid-cooled engines of high power output, two intake and two exhaust ports are provided for each cylinder. The shape and form of all valves are determined by the design and specifications of the particular engine in which they are installed.

Poppet-type valves

The word **poppet** comes from the popping action of the valve. This type of valve is made in four general configurations with respect to the shape of the valve head. These are (1) the flat-headed valve, (2) the semi-tulip valve, (3) the tulip valve, and (4) the mushroom valve. These are illustrated in Fig. 3·43.

Valves are subjected to high temperatures and a corrosive environment; hence they must be made of metals which resist these deteriorating influences. Since **inlet** or **intake** valves operate at lower temperatures than **exhaust** valves, they may be made of chrome-nickel steel. Exhaust valves, which operate at higher temperatures, are usually made of nichrome, silchrome, or cobalt-chromium steel. Poppet valves are made from these special steels and forged in one piece.

A valve **stem** is surface-hardened to resist wear. Since the **tip** of the valve must resist both wear and pounding, it is made of hardened steel and welded to the end of the stem. There is a machined **groove** on the stem near the tip to receive split-ring stem keys. These stem keys form a lock ring to hold the valve spring retaining washer in place.

The stems of some valves have a narrow groove below the lock-ring groove for the installation of **safety circlets** or **spring rings** which are designed to prevent the valves from falling into the combustion chambers if

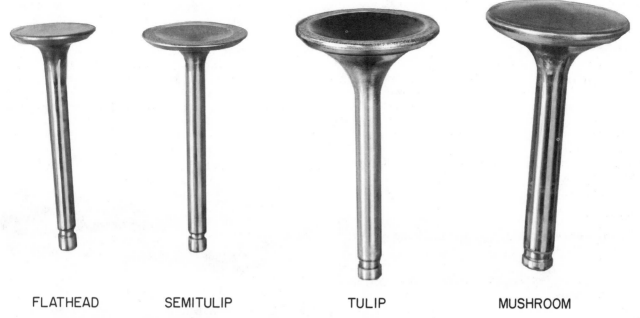

FLATHEAD   SEMITULIP   TULIP   MUSHROOM

Figure **3·43**   *Types of valves.*

the tip should break during engine operation and on the occasion of valve disassembly and assembly. A poppet-valve installation for a radial engine is shown in Fig. 3·44.

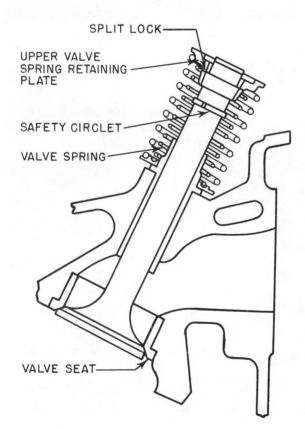

SPLIT LOCK

UPPER VALVE
SPRING RETAINING
PLATE

SAFETY CIRCLET

VALVE SPRING

VALVE SEAT

Figure **3·44**   *Poppet valve installation.*

Exhaust valves

Exhaust valves operate at high temperatures, and they do not receive the cooling effect of the fuel/air charge; hence, they must be designed to dissipate heat rapidly. This is accomplished by making the exhaust valve with a hollow stem and, in some cases, a hollow mushroom head and partly filling the hollow portion with metallic sodium. The sodium melts at a little over 200°F, and during operation it flows back and forth in the stem, carrying heat from the head and dissipating it through the valve guides into the cylinder head. The cylinder head is cooled by means of fins as explained previously. In some engines, exhaust valve stems contain a salt as the cooling agent.

Lower power engines are not all equipped with sodium-filled exhaust valves. It is important, however, for the technician to determine whether the exhaust-valve stems upon which he may be working are of this type. Under no circumstances should a sodium valve be cut open, hammered, or otherwise subjected to treatment which may cause it to rupture.

The faces of high-performance exhaust valves are often made more durable by the application of about 1/16 in. of a material called Stellite. This alloy is welded to the face of the valve and then ground to the correct angle. Stellite is resistant to high-temperature corrosion and also withstands the shock and wear associated with valve operation exceptionally well.

The face of the valve is usually ground to an angle of either 30 or 45°. In some engines, the intake-valve face is ground to an angle of 30° and the exhaust-valve face is ground to 45°.

The tip of the valve stem is often made of high-carbon steel or Stellite so it can be hardened to resist wear. It must be remembered that the tip of the valve stem is continuously receiving the impact of the rocker arm which causes the valve to open and close.

Intake valves

Specially cooled valves are not generally required for the intake port of an engine because the intake valves are cooled by the fuel/air mixture. For this reason, the most commonly used intake valves have solid stems and the head may be flat or of the tulip type. The valve is forged from one piece of alloy steel and then machined all over to produce a smooth finish. The stem is accurately dimensioned to provide the proper clearance in the valve guide. The intake valve stem has a hardened tip similar to that of the exhaust valve.

Intake valves for low-power engines usually have flat heads. Tulip-type heads are often used on the intake valves for high-power engines because the tulip shape places the metal of the head more nearly in tension, thus reducing the stresses where the head joins the stem.

Valve seats

The aluminum alloy used for making engine cylinder heads is not hard enough to withstand the constant hammering given by the opening and closing of the valves. For this reason, bronze or steel valve seats are shrunk or screwed into the circular edge of the valve openings in the cylinder head. A typical six-cylinder opposed engine has forged aluminum-bronze intake-valve seats and forged chrome-molybdenum steel seats for the exhaust valves. The engines in common use

today usually have the valve seats shrunk into the seat recesses as shown in Fig. 3·45. Before the seat is installed, its outside diameter is from 0.007 to 0.015 in. larger than the recess in which it is to be installed. In order to install the seats, the cylinder head must be heated to 575° or more. The seat is chilled and pressed or drifted into place while the cylinder head is hot. Upon cooling, the head recess shrinks and grips the seat firmly.

It is necessary to replace valve seats only after they have worn beyond the limits specified by the manufacturer. Repeated grinding of the seats eventually makes it necessary to replace them.

Valve seats are ground to the same angle as the face of the valve, or they may have a slightly different angle to provide an "interference fit." In order to obtain good seating at operating temperatures, valve faces are sometimes ground to an angle ¼ to 1° less than the angle of the valve seats.

Valve springs

Valves are closed by helical-coiled springs. Two or more springs, one inside the other, are installed over the stem of each valve. If only one spring were used on each valve, the valve would surge and bounce because of the natural vibration frequency of the spring. Each spring of a pair of springs is made of round spring steel wire of a different diameter, and the two coils differ in pitch. Since each spring has a different frequency, the two springs rapidly damp out all spring-surge vibrations during engine operation. A second reason for the use of two (or more) valve springs

Figure **3·45** *Valve seat in the cylinder head.*

on each valve is that it reduces the possibility of failure by breakage from heat and metal fatigue.

The valve springs are held in place by means of steel **valve-spring retainers,** which are special washers shaped to fit the valve springs. The lower retainer seats against the cylinder head, and the upper retainer is provided with a conical recess into which the split stem keys fit. The valve-spring retainers are sometimes called the upper and lower **valve-spring seats.**

VALVE OPERATION AND MECHANISMS

Principles

In order to understand valve operation and timing, it is essential that the fundamental principles of engine operation be kept in mind. It will be remembered that most modern aircraft engines of the piston type operate on the four-stroke-cycle principle. This means that the piston makes four strokes during one cycle of operation. During the four strokes, five events take place. These are (1) intake, (2) compression, (3) ignition, (4) combustion, and (5) exhaust. During these events the operation of the valves direct the flow of the fuel/air mixture and the burned gases. At the intake stroke the intake valve must be open and the exhaust valve closed. The valves are both closed during the compression, ignition, and combustion events, and then the exhaust valve opens at the end of the power stroke. This is illustrated in Fig. 3·46.

During one cycle of the engine operation, the crankshaft makes two revolutions and the valves each perform one operation. It is therefore apparent that the valve-operating mechanism for an intake valve must make one operation for two turns of the crankshaft. On an opposed or in-line engine which has single lobes on the camshaft, the camshaft is geared to the crankshaft to produce one revolution of the camshaft for two revolutions of the crankshaft. The cam drive gear on the crankshaft has one-half the number of teeth that the camshaft gear has, thus producing the 1:2 ratio.

On radial engines which utilize **cam rings** or **cam plates** to operate the valves, there may be three, four, or five cam lobes on the cam ring. The ratio of crankshaft to cam-ring rotation is then 1:6, 1:8, 1:10, respectively.

Piston position

In any complete discussion of valve operation and timing, it is necessary that we take into consideration the position of the piston. A piston has two extreme positions, **top dead center** (TDC) and **bottom dead center** (BDC). These positions are often called **top center** and **bottom center.**

Top dead center occurs when the piston is at the exact top of its stroke with the crank throw and connecting rod in perfect alignment. The piston is at bottom dead center when the crankshaft has turned 180° from top dead center. At this time the piston is

at the bottom of its stroke and the crank throw is aligned with the connecting rod.

During the operation of an engine, as the piston approaches and leaves the top- or bottom-center positions, its linear or up-and-down motion becomes small in comparison with crankshaft angular travel. This is illustrated in the diagram of Fig. 3·47.

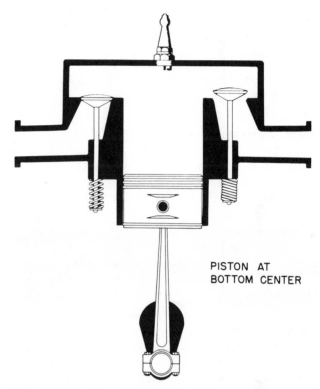

Figure **3·46**   Operation of valves.

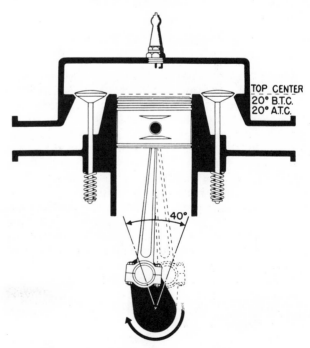

Figure **3·47**   Crankshaft and piston travel.

As the piston leaves the top-center position, it accelerates and attains its maximum speed when the connecting rod and crank throw are at right angles. From this position, the piston loses speed, passes through the halfway position, and reaches bottom center. Leaving the bottom-center position, the piston travel action is reversed until the piston again reaches top center.

During the first 90° of crankshaft rotation from top center, the piston moves more than half the stroke. Also, when the crankshaft rotates from 90° before top center (BTC) to top center, the piston moves through more than half of its stroke. The piston travel is comparatively slow around top center; hence, all instructions for timing emphasize the importance of locating the top-center position exactly.

Abbreviations for valve timing positions

In a discussion of the timing points for an aircraft engine it is convenient to use abbreviations. The abbreviations commonly used in describing crankshaft and piston positions for the timing of valve opening and closing are as follows:

After bottom center	ABC	Exhaust closes	EC
After top center	ATC	Exhaust opens	EO
Before bottom center	BBC	Intake closes	IC
Bottom center	BC	Intake opens	IO
Bottom dead center	BDC	Top center	TC
Before top center	BTC	Top dead center	TDC

Engine timing diagram

To provide a visual concept of the timing of valves for an aircraft engine, a valve timing diagram is used. The diagram for the Continental Model E-165 and E-185 engines is shown in Fig. 3·48. A study of this diagram reveals the following specifications for the timing of the engine.

IO	15° BTC	EO	55° BBC
IC	60° ABC	EC	15° ATC

Reason suggests that the intake valve should open at top center and close at bottom center. Likewise, it seems that the exhaust valve should open at bottom center and close at top center. This would be true except for the inertia of the moving gases and the time required for the valves to open fully. Near the end of the exhaust stroke, the gases are still rushing out the exhaust valve. The inertia of the gases causes a low-pressure condition in the cylinder at this time. Opening of the intake valve a little before top center takes advantage of the low-pressure condition to start the flow of fuel/air mixture into the cylinder, thus bringing a greater charge into the engine and improving volumetric efficiency. The exhaust valve closes shortly after the piston reaches top center and prevents reversal of the exhaust flow back into the cylinder. The angular distance through which both valves are open is called **valve overlap** or **valve lap.**

In the diagram of Fig. 3·48, the intake valve remains open 60° after bottom center. This is to take advantage

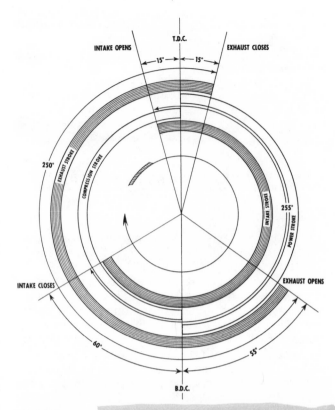

Figure 3·48 Diagram for valve timing. (Continental Motors Corp.)

of the inertia of the fuel/air mixture rushing into the cylinder because the mixture will continue to flow into the cylinder for a time after the piston passes bottom center. The total period during which the intake valve is open is designed to permit the greatest possible charge of fuel/air mixture into the cylinder.

The exhaust valve opens before bottom center for two principal reasons: (1) more thorough scavenging of the cylinder and (2) better cooling of the engine. Most of the energy of the burning fuel is expended by the time the crankshaft has moved 120° past top center on the power stroke and the piston has moved almost to its lowest position. Opening the exhaust valve at this time allows the hot gases to escape early, and less heat is transmitted to the cylinder walls than would be the case if the exhaust valve were closed until the piston reached bottom center. The exhaust valve is not closed until after top center because the inertia of the gases aids in removing additional exhaust gas after the piston has passed top center.

The opening or closing of the intake or exhaust valves after top or bottom center is called **valve lag.** The opening or closing of the intake or exhaust valves before bottom or top center is called **valve lead.** Both valve lag and valve lead are expressed in degrees of crankshaft travel. For example, if the intake valve opens 15° before top center, the valve lead is 15°.

It will be noted from the diagram of Fig. 3·48 that the valve lead and valve lag are greater in relation to the bottom-center position than they are to the top-center position. One of the reasons for this is that the piston travel per degree of crankshaft travel is less near bottom center than it is near top center. This is illustrated in Fig. 3·49. In the diagram, the circle represents the path of the crank throw and the point C represents the center of the crankshaft. TC is the position of the piston pin at top center, and BC is the position of the piston pin at bottom center. The numbers show positions of the piston pin and the crank throw at different points through 180° of crankshaft travel. It will be noted that the piston travels much farther during the first 90° of crankshaft travel than it does during the second 90°.

Firing order

In any discussion of valve or ignition timing, it is essential that we consider the **firing order** of various engines because all parts associated with the timing

of the engine must be designed and timed to comply with the firing order. As the name implies, the firing order of an engine is the order in which the cylinders fire.

The firing order of in-line, V-type, and opposed engines is designed to provide for balance and to eliminate vibration to the extent that this is possible. The firing order is determined by the relative positions of the throws on the crankshaft and the positions of the lobes on the cam shaft.

The firing order of a single-row radial engine which operates on the four-stroke cycle must always be by alternate cylinders, and the engine must have an odd number of cylinders. Twin-row radial engines are essentially two single-row engines joined together. This means that alternate cylinders in each row must fire in sequence. For example, an 18-cylinder engine consists of two single-row 9-cylinder engines. The rear row of cylinders has the odd numbers 1, 3, 5, 7, 9, 11, 13, 15, and 17. Alternate cylinders in this row are 1, 5, 9, 13, 17, 3, 7, 11, and 15. The front row has the numbers 2, 4, 6, 8, 10, 12, 14, 16, and 18, and the alternate cylinders for this row are 2, 6, 10, 14, 18, 4, 8, 12, and 16. Since the firing of the front and rear rows of cylinders is started on opposite sides of the engine, the first cylinder to fire after No. 1 is No. 12. Starting with No. 12 cylinder, the front-row firing sequence is then 12, 16, 2, 6, 10, 14, 18, 4, and 8. By combining the rear row firing with the front row firing, we obtain the firing order for the complete engine, thus: 1, 12, 5, 16, 9, 2, 13, 6, 17, 10, 3, 14, 7, 18, 11, 4, 15, and 8.

The following table gives the firing orders for the majority of engine types:

Table 3·1

Type	Firing order
4-cyl. in-line	1-3-4-2 or 1-2-4-3
6-cyl. in-line	1-5-3-6-2-4
8-cyl. V-type (CW)	1R-4L-2R-3L-4R-1L-3R-2L
12-cyl. V-type (CW)	1L-2R-5L-4R-3L-1R-6L-5R-2L-3R-4L-6R
4-cyl. opposed	1-3-2-4 or 1-4-2-3
6-cyl. opposed	1-4-5-2-3-6
9-cyl. radial	1-3-5-7-9-2-4-6-8
14-cyl. radial	1-10-5-14-9-4-13-8-3-12-7-2-11-6
18-cyl. radial	1-12-5-16-9-2-13-6-17-10-3-14-7-18-11-4-15-8

Purpose of valve-operating mechanism

The purpose of a valve-operating mechanism in an aircraft engine is to control the timing of the valves of the engine so that each valve will open at the correct time, remain open for the required length of time, and close at the proper time. The mechanism should be simple in design, be ruggedly constructed, and give satisfactory service for a long time with a minimum of inspection and maintenance.

The two types of valve-operating mechanisms most

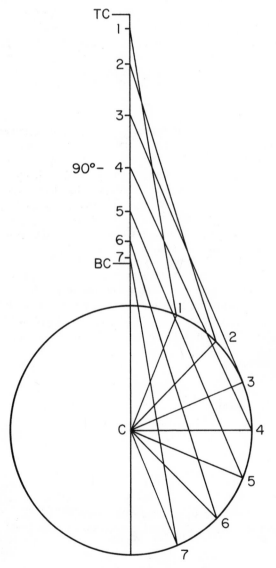

Figure 3·49 Relationship between piston travel and crankshaft travel.

generally used today are the type found in the opposed engine and the type used in a typical radial engine. Since both of these engines are equipped with overhead valves (valves in the cylinder head), the valve-operating mechanisms for each are quite similar.

Valve mechanism components

A standard valve-operating operating mechanism includes certain parts which are found in both opposed and radial engines. These parts may be described briefly as follows:

Cam. A device for actuating the valve lifting mechanism.

Valve lifter or tappet. A mechanism to transmit the force of the cam to the valve push rod.

Pushrod. A steel or aluminum-alloy rod or tube situated between the valve lifter and the rocker arm of the valve operating mechanism to transmit the motion of the valve lifter.

Rocker arm. A pivoted arm mounted on bearings in the cylinder head to open and close the valves. One end of the arm presses on the stem of the valve and the other end receives motion from the pushrod.

The valve-operating cam in an opposed or in-line engine consists of a shaft with a number of cam lobes sufficient to operate all the intake and exhaust valves of the engine. In a typical six-cylinder opposed engine, the camshaft has three groups of three cam lobes as shown in Fig. 3·50. In each group, the center lobe actuates the valve lifters for the two opposite intake valves while the outer lobes of each group actuate the lifters for the exhaust valves.

In a radial engine, the valve-actuating device is a cam plate or cam ring with three or more lobes. In a five-cylinder radial engine, the cam ring usually has three lobes; in a seven-cylinder radial engine, the cam ring has three or four lobes; and in a nine-cylinder radial engine, the cam ring has four or five lobes.

Valve-operating mechanisms for in-line and V-type engines utilize a camshaft similar to the type installed in an opposed engine. The shaft incorporates single cam lobes placed at positions along the shaft which will enable them to actuate the valve lifters or rocker arms at the correct time. Some in-line and V-type engines have overhead camshafts. In such cases the actuating mechanism may be arranged as shown in Fig. 3·51. The camshaft is mounted along the top of the cylinders and is driven by a system of bevel gears through a shaft leading from the crankshaft drive gear.

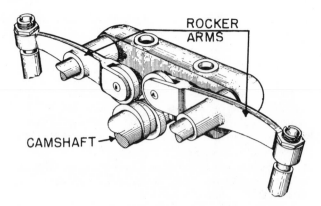

Figure 3·51 Overhead camshaft arrangement.

Valve mechanism for opposed engines

A simplified drawing of a valve-operating mechanism is shown in Fig. 3·52. The valve action starts with the crankshaft timing gear which meshes with the camshaft gear. As the crankshaft turns, the camshaft also turns, but at one-half the rpm of the crankshaft. This is because a valve operates only once during each cycle and the crankshaft makes two revolutions per cycle. A cam lobe on the camshaft raises the cam roller and hence the pushrod to which the cam roller is attached. In opposed engines, a cam roller is not employed, and in its place is a tappet or a hydraulic lifter. The pushrod raises one end of the rocker arm and lowers the other end, thus depressing the valve, working against the tension of the valve spring which normally holds the valve closed. When the cam lobe has passed by the valve lifter, the valve will close by the action of the valve spring or springs.

The valve-operating mechanism for a modern opposed-type aircraft engine is shown in Fig. 3·53. The valve-actuating mechanism starts with the drive gear on the crankshaft. This gear may be called the **crankshaft timing gear** or the **accessory drive gear.** Mounted on the end of the camshaft is the **camshaft gear,** which has twice as many teeth as the crankshaft gear. In some engines the mounting holes in the camshaft gear are spaced in such a manner that they will line up with the holes in the camshaft flange in only one position. In other engines, a dowel pin in the end of the crankshaft mates with a hole in the crankshaft gear to assure correct position. Thus, when the timing marks on the camshaft and the crankshaft gear are aligned, the

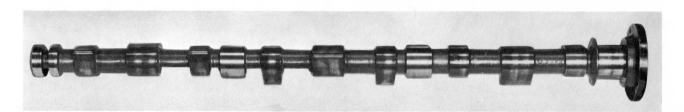

Figure 3·50 Camshaft for six-cylinder opposed engine.

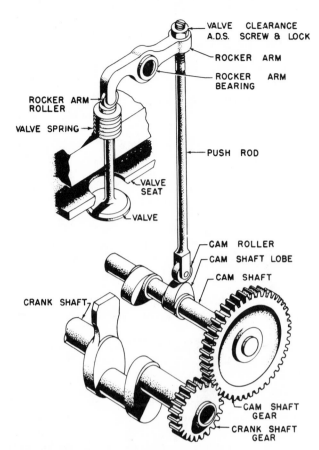

Figure 3·52 Valve-operating mechanism.

camshaft will be properly timed with the crankshaft.

Adjacent to each cam lobe is the **cam follower face** which forms the base of the **hydraulic valve lifter** or tappet assembly. The outer cylinder of the assembly is called the **lifter body.** Inside the lifter body is the **hydraulic unit assembly** consisting of the following parts: **cylinder, plunger, plunger springs, ball check valve,** and **oil inlet tube.** Figure 3·54 is an illustration of the complete lifter assembly. During operation, engine oil under pressure is supplied to the oil reservoir in the lifter body through an inlet hole in the side. Since this oil is under pressure direct from the main oil gallery of the engine, it flows into the oil inlet tube, through the ball check valve, and into the cylinder. The pressure of the oil forces the plunger against the **pushrod socket** and takes up all the clearances in the valve-operating mechanism. For this reason, a lifter of this type has been called a "zero-lash lifter." When the cam is applying force to the cam follower face, the oil in the cylinder tends to flow back into the oil reservoir, but this is prevented by the ball check valve.

During overhaul of the engine, the hydraulic valve lifter assembly must be very carefully inspected. All the parts of one assembly must be reassembled together in order to assure proper operation.

The ball end of the hollow valve pushrod fits into the pushrod socket or cup which bears against the plunger in the lifter. Both the socket and the ball end of the pushrod are drilled to provide a passage for oil to

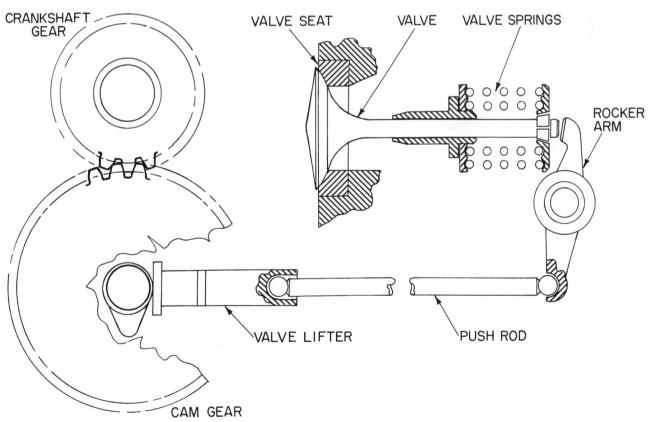

Figure 3·53 Valve mechanism for opposed engine.

Figure 3·54   Hydraulic valve lifter assembly.

cam track operates the intake valves, and the other track operates the exhaust valves. In addition, there are the necessary pushrods, rocker-arm assemblies, and tappet assemblies that make up the complete mechanism.

A **cam ring** (or cam plate), such as the one shown in Fig. 3·55, serves the same purpose in a radial engine as a camshaft serves in other types of engines. The cam ring is a circular piece of steel with a series of cam lobes on the outer surface. The **cam track** includes both the lobes and the surface between the lobes. The **cam rollers** ride on the cam track.

Figure 3·56 illustrates the gear arrangement for driving a cam plate (or ring). This cam plate has four lobes on each track; hence it will be rotated at one-

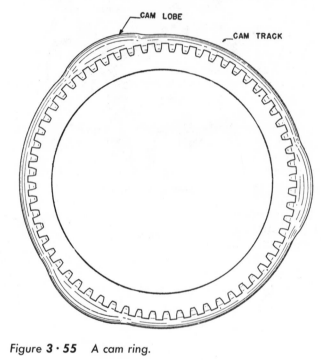

Figure 3·55   A cam ring.

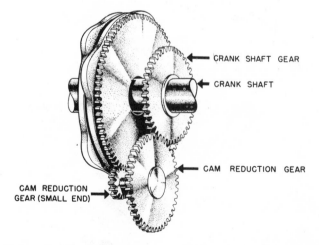

Figure 3·56   Drive gear arrangement for radial engine cam.

flow into the pushrod. This oil flows through the pushrod and out a hole at the end which fits the pushrod socket in the **rocker arm,** thus providing lubrication for the rocker-arm bearing (bushing) and valves. The rocker arm is drilled to permit oil flow to the bearing and valve mechanism.

The rocker arm is mounted on a steel shaft which, in turn, is mounted in rocker-shaft bosses in the cylinder head. The rocker-shaft bosses are cast integrally with the cylinder head and then are machined to the correct dimension and finish for the installation of the rocker shafts. The rocker-shaft dimension provides a push fit in the boss. The shafts are held in place by the rocker box covers or by covers over the holes through which they are installed. The steel rocker arms are fitted with bronze bushing to provide a good bearing surface. These bushings may be replaced at overhaul if they are worn beyond acceptable limits.

One end of each rocker arm bears directly against the hardened tip of the valve stem. Thus when the rocker arm is rotated by the pushrod, the valve is depressed against valve spring pressure. The distance the valve opens and the time it remains open are determined by the height and contour of the cam lobe.

Valve mechanism for radial engines

Depending upon the number of rows of cylinders, the valve-operating mechanism of a radial engine is operated by either one or two cam plates (or cam rings). Only one plate (or ring) is used with a single-row radial engine, but a double cam track is required. One

48

eighth crankshaft speed. Remember that a valve operates only once during each cycle and the crankshaft makes two revolutions for each cycle. Since there are four lobes on each cam track, the valve operated by one set of lobes will open and close four times for each revolution of the cam plate. This means that the cylinder has completed four cycles of operation and the crankshaft has made eight revolutions.

In the illustration it will be noted that the crankshaft gear and the large cam reduction gear are the same size; hence the cam reduction gear will turn at the same rpm as the crankshaft. The small cam reduction gear is only one-eighth the diameter of the cam plate gear, and this provides the reduction to make the cam plate turn at one-eighth crankshaft speed. The rule for cam-plate speed with respect to crankshaft speed may be given as a formula thus:

$$\text{cam-plate speed} = \frac{1}{\text{no. of lobes} \times 2}$$

Figure 3·57 illustrates a cam plate driven by an internal gear. In an arrangement of this type the cam plate turns opposite the direction of engine rotation. A study of the operation of the cam will lead us to the conclusion that a four-lobe cam turning in the opposite direction from the crankshaft will be used in a nine-cylinder radial engine. In the diagrams of Fig. 3·58 the numbers on the large outer ring represent the cylinders of a nine-cylinder radial engine. The firing order of such an engine is always 1-3-5-7-9-2-4-6-8. The small ring in the center represents the cam ring. In diagram a we note that No. 1 cam is opposite No. 1 cylinder. We may assume that the cam is operating No. 1 intake valve. In moving from No. 1 cylinder to No. 3 cylinder, the next cylinder in the firing order, we see that the crankshaft must turn 80° in the direction shown. Since the cam is turning at one-eighth crank-

shaft speed, a lobe on the cam will move 10° while the crankshaft is turning 80°. Thus, we see that No. 2 cam lobe will be opposite No. 3 cylinder. When the crankshaft has turned another 80° to the intake operation of the No. 5 cylinder, No. 3 cam lobe is opposite No. 5 cylinder.

If we draw a similar diagram for a nine-cylinder radial engine with a five-lobe cam, we will note that the cam must travel in the same direction as the crankshaft. This is because there will be 72° between the centers of the cam lobes and 80° between the cylinders firing in sequence. The cam plate will turn one-tenth crankshaft rpm; hence as the crankshaft turns 80°, the cam plate will turn 8°, and this will align the next operating cam with the proper valve mechanism.

The valve-operating mechanism for a radial engine is shown in Fig. 3·59. All the main parts are labeled and should be carefully studied. Since the cam in this illustration has three lobes and is turning opposite the direction of the crankshaft, we can determine that the valve mechanism must be designed for a seven-cylinder radial engine.

The valve **tappet** in this mechanism is spring loaded to reduce shock and is provided with a cam roller to bear against the cam track. The tappet is enclosed in a tube called the **valve tappet guide.** The valve tappet is drilled to permit the passage of lubricating oil into the hollow pushrod and up to the rocker-arm assembly. The rocker arm is provided with a **clearance-adjusting screw** so proper clearance can be obtained between the rocker arm and valve tip. This clearance is very important because it determines when the valve will start to open, how far it will open, and how long it will stay open.

This pushrod transmits the lifting force from the valve tappet to the rocker arm in the same manner as that described for the opposed-type engines. The rod may be made of steel or aluminum alloy. Although it is called a rod, it is actually a tube with steel balls pressed into the ends. The length of the pushrod depends upon the distance between the tappet and the rocker-arm sockets.

An aluminum-alloy tube, called a **pushrod housing,** surrounding each pushrod provides a passage through which the lubricating oil can return to the crankcase, keeps dirt away from the valve-operating mechanism, and otherwise provides protection for the pushrod.

The rocker arm in the radial engine serves the same purpose as it does in the opposed engine. Rocker-arm assemblies are usually made of forged steel and are supported by a bearing which serves as a pivot. This bearing may be a plain, roller, or ball type. One end of the arm bears against the pushrod, and the other end bears on the valve stem. The end of the rocker arm bearing against the valve stem may be plain, or it may be slotted to receive a steel **rocker-arm roller.** The other end of the rocker arm may have either a threaded split clamp and locking bolt or a tapped hole in which is mounted the valve clearance-adjusting screw. The adjusting ball socket is often drilled to permit the flow of lubricating oil.

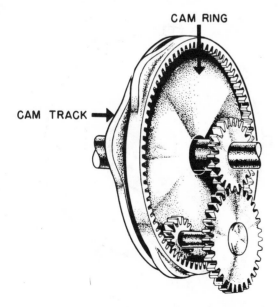

CAM RING

CAM TRACK

Figure 3·57   Cam plate driven by internal gear.

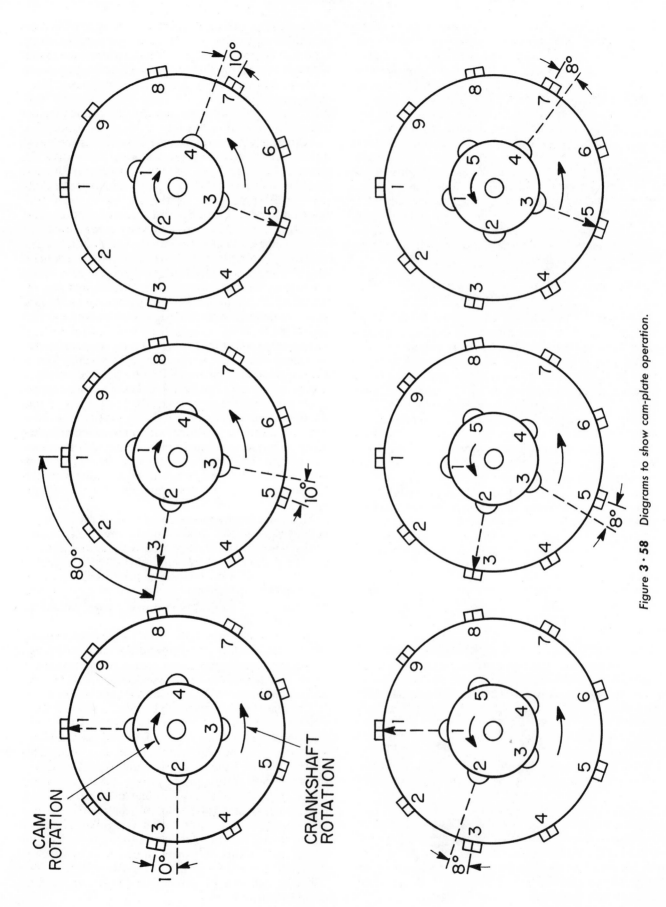

CAM ROTATION

CRANKSHAFT ROTATION

10°

80°

10°

8°

8°

10°

8°

Figure 3·58 Diagrams to show cam-plate operation.

50

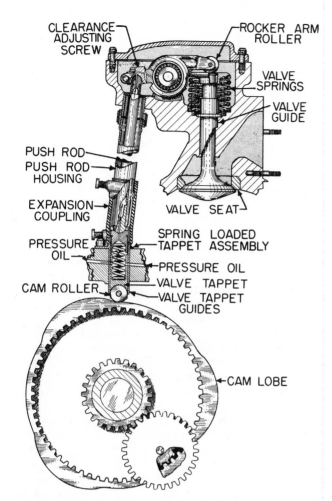

Figure 3·59 Valve-operating mechanism for a radial engine.

Typical rocker arms are illustrated in Fig. 3·60. Rocker arms shown at *b* and *c* are designed for opposed-type engines. The rocker arm at *a* is used in a Pratt & Whitney R-985 radial engine.

Valve clearance

Every engine must have a slight clearance between the rocker arm and the valve stem. When there is no clearance, the valve may be held off its seat when it should be seated (closed). It is apparent that this will cause the engine to operate erratically and eventually the valve will be damaged.

The cold clearance for the valves on an engine is usually much less than the "hot" or operating clearance. This is true except when the engine is equipped with an overhead cam. The reason for the difference in hot and cold clearances is that the cylinder of an engine becomes much hotter than the pushrod and therefore expands more than the pushrod. In effect, this shortens the pushrod and leaves a gap between the pushrod and the rocker arm or between the rocker arm and the valve stem. The hot valve clearance of an engine can be as much as 0.070 in., while the cold clearance may be 0.010 in.

In adjusting the valve clearance of an engine, the technician must make sure that the cam is turned to a position where it is not applying any pressure to the pushrod. For any particular cylinder, it is good practice to place the piston in the position for the beginning of the power stroke. At this point both cams are well away from the valve tappets for the valves being adjusted.

On an adjustable rocker arm, the locknut is loosened and a feeler gage of the correct thickness is inserted between the rocker arm and the valve stem. The adjusting screw is turned to a point where a slight drag is felt on the feeler gage. The lock screw or nut is then tightened to the proper torque while the adjusting screw is held in place. After the adjusting screw has been locked, a feeler gage 0.001 in. thicker than the gage used for adjusting the clearance cannot be inserted in the gap if the clearance is correct.

When it is necessary to adjust the valves for an engine which is designed with a floating cam ring, special procedures must be followed. The floating cam ring for an R-2800 engine may have a clearance at the bearing of 0.013 to 0.020 in., and this will affect the value adjustment if it is not eliminated at the point where the valves are being adjusted. The clearance is called **cam float** and is eliminated by depressing certain valves while others are being adjusted.

Each valve tappet which is riding on a cam lobe applies pressure to the cam ring because of the valve springs. Therefore, if the pressure of the valves on one

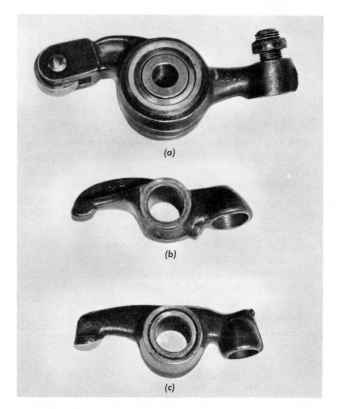

Figure 3·60 Rocker arms.

side of the cam ring is released, the ring will tend to move away from the tappets which are applying pressure. This will eliminate the cam float on that side of the cam ring. The valves whose tappets are resting on the cam ring at or near the point where there is no clearance between the ring and the bearing surface, and which are between lobes, are adjusted, and then the crankshaft is turned to the next position. Certain valves are depressed, and other valves on the opposite side of the engine are adjusted. Table 3·2 is a chart showing

Table 3·2 Valve adjusting chart

Set piston at top center of its exhaust stroke	Depress rockers		Adjust valve clearances	
	Inlet	Exhaust	Inlet	Exhaust
11	7	15	1	3
4	18	8	12	14
15	11	1	5	7
8	4	12	16	18
1	15	5	9	11
12	8	16	2	4
5	1	9	13	15
16	12	2	6	8
9	5	13	17	1
2	16	6	10	12
13	9	17	3	5
6	2	10	14	16
17	13	3	7	9
10	6	14	18	2
3	17	7	11	13
14	10	18	4	6
7	3	11	15	17
18	14	4	8	10

the proper combinations for adjusting the valves on an R-2800 engine.

According to the chart, the valve adjustment begins with No. 1 inlet and No. 3 exhaust valves. Number 11 piston is placed at top center on its exhaust stroke. In this crankshaft position, the No. 15 exhaust tappet and the No. 7 inlet tappet are riding on top of cam lobes and applying pressure to the cam ring. When these two valves are depressed, the pressure is released from this side of the cam ring and the pressure of the tappets on opposite side of the ring eliminates the cam ring float. The No. 1 inlet and the No. 3 exhaust valves are then adjusted for proper clearance. The adjustment is made only when the engine is cold.

Care must be exercised when depressing the valves on the engine. If a valve which is closed is completely depressed, the ball end of the pushrod may fall out of its socket. If the valve-adjusting chart is followed closely, only the valves which are open will be depressed.

On modern opposed-type engines the rocker arm is not adjustable and the valve clearance is adjusted by changing the pushrod. If the clearance is too great, a longer pushrod is used. When the clearance is too small, a shorter pushrod is installed. A wide range of clearances is allowable because the hydraulic valve lifters take up the clearance when the engine is operating. Valve clearance in these engines is normally checked only at overhaul.

Valve timing

The manufacturer of an engine specifies in the maintenance and overhaul instructions the exact timing of the valves that will obtain the best performance. These instructions must be carefully followed and can be disregarded only when such deviation from the manufacturer's instructions is specifically approved by manufacturers' bulletins, FAA Airworthiness Directives, or similar authority.

When a new engine is designed, there are many theoretical calculations before even the first engine of the new model is constructed. When the prototype engine leaves the factory, it is placed on a test block and operated at various speeds; with different grades of fuel; at different conditions of temperature, pressure, and humidity; and with various adjustments of valve and ignition timing. The horsepower developed by the engine under every conceivable set of conditions is accurately indicated and recorded. Finally, the manufacturer is able to state positively what adjustments will be permitted in the valve and ignition timing.

The power delivered by an engine at a given speed depends to a great extent upon the valve timing. If the best performance is obtained at high speeds, the performance is less efficient at low speeds. The reverse is also true. For this reason, valve timing is usually specified to obtain the best average results throughout the usual speed range of the airplane in which the engine is installed. Generally, it may be expected that the engine is timed to give the most efficient performance at or near normal cruising speed.

The valve timing on modern aircraft engines is designed to remain the same under all conditions of operation after it is originally assembled with correct timing. On a few airplane engines the valve mechanisms have drives which may fail, but these are not in common use.

The basic principle of valve timing is to make sure that one of the valves is opening at the correct time. Since all cams are normally on one shaft or one cam plate, if one valve is in time, the others must be in time also. In V-type engines, two cams must be timed. In an opposed engine, the crankshaft gear can be installed in only one position and the camshaft gear can be installed on the camshaft in only one position. If the two gears are meshed with the mark gear teeth together, then the camshaft is properly timed. This is illustrated in Fig. 3·61.

The valve timing of a V-type engine with an overhead cam is accomplished by adjusting the position of a vernier gear until the camshaft is in the correct position. The No. 1 piston is placed in the position where the intake valve is required to begin opening. The camshaft is turned in the normal direction of rotation until the cam lobe for the intake valve of No. 1

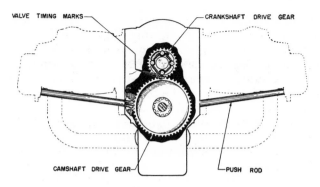

Figure 3·61 *Meshing of marked teeth on cam drive gears.*

cylinder is starting to apply pressure to the rocker arm and valve. At this time the gears are meshed with all clearance or backlash taken up. When this is accomplished, the camshaft is timed. On a V-type engine it is necessary to time each camshaft separately.

In order to determine the position of a piston for valve timing, certain special tools and instruments are used. One of these is the **top-center indicator** which determines the top-dead-center position of the piston in the cylinder. Another is the **timing disk** which is used to measure the crankshaft rotation in degrees and to aid in determining when the crankshaft is in the correct position for timing the valves. Figure 3·62 shows how these tools are used.

The top-center indicator is a hinged lever mounted in an adapter which fits the spark-plug opening. One end of the lever extends into the cylinder where it may bear against the top of the piston, and the other end of the lever is a pointer which moves along a scale. When the piston approaches top center, it presses upward on the end of the indicator lever and moves the pointer along the scale.

The timing-disk indicator consists of two parts, the disk itself and a pointer. The timing disk is fastened to the nose case of the engine in such a manner that the propeller shaft extends through the center of the disk. The pointer is clamped or otherwise fastened to the propeller shaft. A timing handle (propeller shaft wrench) is made to fit the splines of the shaft and is used to turn the crankshaft.

To locate the top dead center of a cylinder, the tools are installed as shown in the drawing. The crankshaft is then turned in the normal direction of rotation until the top-center indicator starts to move. At this point, a mark is placed at the pointer position on the scale of

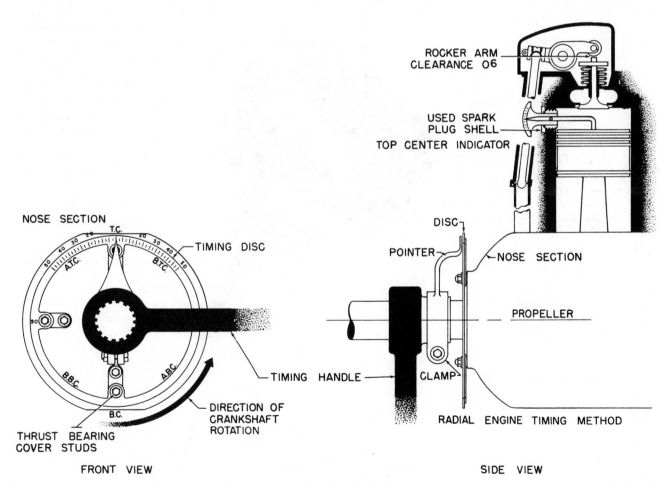

Figure 3·62 *Use of timing disk and pointer.*

the top-center indicator and also at the position of the pointer on the timing disk. The crankshaft is turned farther in the direction of rotation until the top-center indicator pointer has moved to its limit and back to the mark previously placed on the scale. The turning is stopped at this point, and another mark is placed on the timing disk. The crankshaft is then turned in reverse to a point where the piston has moved away from the arm of the top-center indicator. The top-center position of the piston is found by turning the crankshaft again in the direction of normal rotation until the pointer on the crankshaft is exactly halfway between the marks on the timing disk. The reason that the engine is turned in reverse and then turned in the direction of normal rotation is to take up any clearance or slack that may exist in the various parts.

It is possible to find approximate top center by turning the crankshaft until the pointer of the top-center indicator moves to its extreme position. It will be noted, however, that the crankshaft can be moved back and forth a small amount when the piston is at top center without showing appreciable movement on the top-center indicator. This means that the top-center position cannot be located precisely in this manner. When the method described with the timing disk is used, the top-center position is located very accurately.

After the position of the top dead center is located,

the timing disk may be adjusted to show this position as 0° as indicated in the drawing. Thereafter, the indication on the timing disk may be used to show the number of degrees the crankshaft is turned before or after top center. When the crankshaft is placed in any given position, it should be turned in reverse first and then brought to the desired position while turning in the normal direction of rotation. As explained above, this will eliminate any backlash that may exist in the mechanism. This is particularly important when timing the ignition.

TIME-RITE PISTON-POSITION INDICATOR

A very useful and popular timing device is called the Time-Rite piston-position indicator. This device, manufactured by the Gabb Special Products Division of the E. Horton & Son Company, is illustrated in Fig. 3·63. The Time-Rite instrument is designed to afford precision timing for all reciprocating aircraft engines by direct measurement of piston travel.

Description

The Time-Rite consists principally of a body which screws into the spark-plug hole, a pivot arm which contacts the head of the piston, an automatically

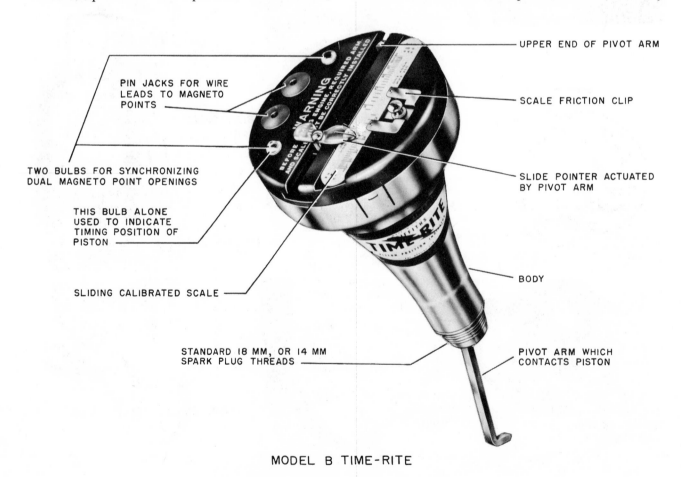

PIN JACKS FOR WIRE LEADS TO MAGNETO POINTS

TWO BULBS FOR SYNCHRONIZING DUAL MAGNETO POINT OPENINGS

THIS BULB ALONE USED TO INDICATE TIMING POSITION OF PISTON

SLIDING CALIBRATED SCALE

STANDARD 18 MM, OR 14 MM SPARK PLUG THREADS

UPPER END OF PIVOT ARM

SCALE FRICTION CLIP

SLIDE POINTER ACTUATED BY PIVOT ARM

BODY

PIVOT ARM WHICH CONTACTS PISTON

MODEL B TIME-RITE

Figure 3·63 Time-Rite piston-position indicator.

referenced slide pointer, and an adjustable calibrated scale. These design features eliminate the need for finding top dead center and compensate for the variables involved in accurate piston positioning.

Calibrated scales are available for all types of engines, and all scale calibrations are obtained in cooperation with and are approved by the engine manufacturers.

Because of the difference in spark-plug locations and piston-dome shapes, several different pivot arms are available to adapt the Time-Rite to all aircraft engines. All arms are easily interchanged in accordance with instruments furnished with each instrument.

Use of the Time-Rite

The proper use of the Time-Rite piston-position indicator is best described in steps, as illustrated in Fig. 3·64.

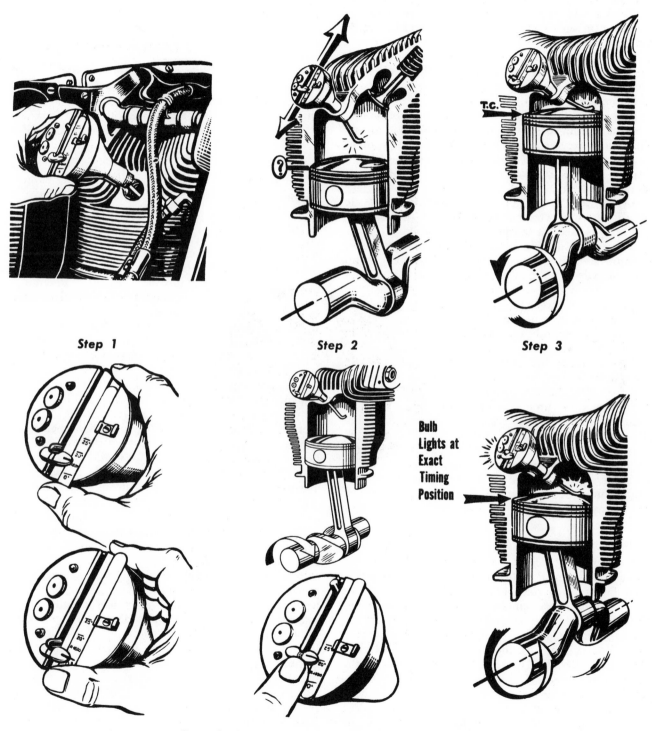

Step 1   Step 2   Step 3

Bulb Lights at Exact Timing Position

Figure 3·64   Steps in the use of the Time-Rite indicator.

Step 1. Remove the front spark plug and gasket from cylinder No. 1. Screw the Time-Rite into the spark-plug bushing after making sure that the piston is not near top center. The instrument cannot be installed readily with the piston at or near the top of the stroke.

With some engines it may not be possible to screw the Time-Rite into the spark-plug bushing when using a hooked pivot arm, since the arm hits either the cylinder wall or the top of the cylinder head. In this case simply hold the cap so that it will not rotate, and screw the body into the bushing. Be sure that the correct arm and scale are installed properly before timing the engine.

Step 2. Turn the cap so that the slot is parallel with the vertical axis of the cylinder. The scale should be to the right of the slot when the indicator is installed in radial engines.

Step 3. Turn the engine in the direction of rotation so that the piston goes through the top-center position. This will leave the slide pointer at the highest point of piston travel. This operation takes the place of finding top dead center, as is required with other methods of engine timing.

Step 4. Set the zero position of the scale opposite the slide-pointer reference mark. Be sure that the correct scale is used for the engine being timed.

Step 5. Turn the engine back through the top-center position so that the piston has reached some point before the desired timing position. Set the slide pointer opposite the desired timing position on the scale.

Step 6. Turn the engine in the direction of rotation until the pivot arm just touches the slide pointer. The bulb will light to indicate that the piston is at the exact timing position.

As with many instruments, there are variations in the methods used to obtain the same results. For example, after the zero position of the scale is located as in Step 4, the timing position of the engine can be found by using the slide pointer. In Step 5, instead of the pointer being placed opposite the desired timing position on the scale, it is placed well above any of the scale marks. Then the engine is turned in the normal direction slowly until the pivot arm moves the pointer to the timing position on the scale. This method must be employed if the light is inoperative.

Checking valve timing

The correct procedure for checking or adjusting the valve timing on a particular engine is given in the manufacturer's overhaul and maintenance manual. For best results, the manufacturer's recommendations should always be followed. The proper timing for the valves of an engine is often shown on the engine data plate. For example, the indication may read: **I.O. 15° BTC, E.C. 20° ATC.** These instructions mean that the intake valve opens 15° before top center and the exhaust valve closes 20° after top center. To check the timing of the valves it is merely necessary to place the piston in the position called for and then see if the required valve action is taking place.

It must be remembered that the piston makes four strokes per cycle and it must be on the correct stroke when valve timing is being checked. Since the intake valve must open at or near the end of the exhaust stroke, the proper stroke of the piston can be determined by watching the valve action. By rotating the engine in the normal direction of rotation and noting when the exhaust valve begins to close, the technician will at the same time see that the intake valve is beginning to open. At this time the piston is near top center at the end of the exhaust stroke and the beginning of the intake stroke. If it is desired to find top center at the end of the compression stroke, the engine should be turned to a position near midway between the point where the intake valve closes and the exhaust valve opens. Top center is not usually exactly halfway between these points, but this will serve to place the piston on the correct stroke for compression.

THE ACCESSORY SECTION

The **accessory section** of an engine provides mounting pads for the accessory units such as the fuel pressure pumps, fuel-injector pumps, vacuum pumps, oil pumps, tachometer generators, electrical generators, magnetos, starters, two-speed supercharger control valves, oil screens, hydraulic pumps, and other units. Regardless of the construction and location of the accessory housing, it contains the gears for driving those accessories which are operated by engine power.

Accessory sections for aircraft engines vary widely in shape and design because of the engine and aircraft requirements. The illustrations in the accompanying text show accessory sections designed for a radial engine and an opposed engine.

The accessory section which is shown in Fig. 3·65 is designed for the Pratt & Whitney R-985 Junior Wasp radial engine and is called the **rear case.** This case section attaches to the rear of the supercharger case and supports the accessories and accessory drives. The front face incorporates a vaned diffuser, and the rear face contains an intake duct with three vanes in the elbow. The case also includes an oil pressure chamber containing an oil strainer and check valve, a three-section oil pump, and an oil pressure relief valve. Mounting pads are provided for the carburetor adapter, two magnetos, a fuel pump, starter vacuum-pump adapter, tachometer, and generator. The accessories are driven by three shafts which extend entirely through the supercharger and rear sections. Each shaft carries a spur gear at its forward end which meshes with a gear coupled to the rear of the crankshaft. The upper shaft provides a drive for the starter and for the generator. Each of the two lower shafts drives a magneto through an adjustable, flexible coupling. Four vertical drives are provided for by a bevel gear keyed to each magneto drive shaft. Two vertical drive shafts are for operating accessories, and two tachometers are driven from the upper side of the bevel gears. The undersides of the bevel gears drive an oil pump on the right side and a fuel pump on the left.

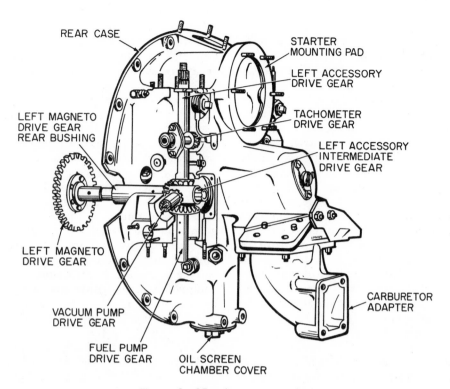

Figure **3 · 65** *Accessory section.*

REAR CASE

STARTER MOUNTING PAD

LEFT ACCESSORY DRIVE GEAR

LEFT MAGNETO DRIVE GEAR REAR BUSHING

TACHOMETER DRIVE GEAR

LEFT ACCESSORY INTERMEDIATE DRIVE GEAR

LEFT MAGNETO DRIVE GEAR

VACUUM PUMP DRIVE GEAR

FUEL PUMP DRIVE GEAR

OIL SCREEN CHAMBER COVER

CARBURETOR ADAPTER

An additional drive, for a vacuum pump, is located at the lower left of the left magneto drive.

Accessory section for opposed engine

The **accessory case** for a Continental six-cylinder opposed engine is shown in Fig. 3 · 66. This case is constructed of magnesium and is secured to the crankcase rear flange by 12 hex-head screws.

The accessory case conforms to the shape of the crankcase rear flange and is open at its front side within the height of the crankcase. The accessory case extends below the crankcase, forming a closed compartment which serves as the oil sump in dry sump engines.

The rear surface of the accessory case is provided with raised, machined pads for mounting of the starter, generator, magnetos, left- and right-side accessory drive adapters, oil screen housing, tachometer drive housing, and accessory drive idler gear shaft. Tapped holes and studs provide attachments for adapters, housings, and accessories.

The pressure oil screen assembly is screwed into a housing which is attached by five hex-head screws to the rear surface of the accessory case below the right magneto. The open front end of the tubular screen assembly fits closely into a counterbore in the cases of wet sump engines, while the cases of dry sump models are equipped with a check-valve assembly which fits in the same counterbore and receives a slightly different screen over its rear shoulder. The check valve offers no resistance to oil leaving the front end of the screen, but it prevents return flow during periods of idleness. The cavity surrounding the oil screen is connected by a pas-

Figure **3 · 66** *Accessory case for six-cylinder opposed engine.*

sage to the pressure oil pump outlet port. The pressure oil screen exit cavity of cases for wet sump engines is drilled and tapped through from the right side of the case for an outlet oil line elbow fitting. In dry sump engines the screen exit is connected to the rear end of the crankcase right oil gallery.

The housing for a gear-type pressure oil pump is attached to the front surface of the accessory case rear wall by five screws. One screw is installed from the rear and lies within the generator pilot counterbore of the case rear surface. Two of the pressure oil screen housing attaching screws pass through the case rear wall and into pump housing tapped holes. The other two points of pump housing attachment are the two tachometer drive housing attaching screws. The lower, or driving, impeller of the pressure pump has a squared hole in the center of the camshaft gear web. A rearward extension of the upper, or driven, pump impeller passes through the rear wall of the case and through a small cast housing provided with a shaft oil seal and threaded to receive the tachometer drive conduit nut. The tachometer drive cable end enters and is driven by a slotted hole in the impeller shaft.

Accessory cases for wet sump engines of this model are equipped with an oil suction tube attached to the inlet port of the pressure oil pump and extending downward through a hole in the bottom case surface. The oil sump bypass tube is installed in the case hole surrounding the suction tube and is sealed to the case and to the oil sump inlet opening by two hydraulic O rings installed in grooves in the outer surface of the tube. The suction tube is attached to the left side wall of the accessory case by a clip, a speed nut, and a roundhead screw. Accessory cases for dry sump engines do not have the large bottom hole for the bypass tube, but they are tapped to receive a ⅝-18 drain plug. Instead of the suction tube, cases of dry sump engines are equipped with an oil inlet tube connected to the pressure pump inlet port and extending through the left side of the case for connection of the oil inlet hose.

The generator is mounted on a pad below the left magneto and is centered by a pilot which fits in a case counterbore. Three studs attach the assembly. Below the generator a pad is provided for mounting the left-side accessory drive adapter. The adapter is bored lengthwise for a shaftgear bearing. The rear end of the left-side accessory drive shaftgear is splined to receive and drive the accessory drive shaft. A fuel pump is normally mounted on this drive. The left-side accessory drive shaftgear installed in all dry sump engines of this model has a forward projection through the front wall of the case which drives a gear-type oil scavenge pump. The scavenge pump is mounted on a pad machined on the front side of the case at the lower left corner. It is retained by six hex-head screws. The left-side accessory drive shaftgear is driven by an idler gear which rotates on a shaft installed from the rear side of the case and retained by two screws. The right-side accessory drive, consisting of a shaftgear and an adapter, is installed on a mount pad below the oil pressure screen housing.

Magnetos are mounted on pads at left and right sides of the accessory case rear surface and are attached by two studs and nuts each. Magneto drive gears are independently mounted on supports attached to the rear of the crankcase and are engaged to the magnetos through rubber-padded couplings.

The starter mount pad is at the upper rear of the accessory case. The adapters used depend upon the type of starter to be installed on the engine.

A vertical oil passage is drilled from the right side of the accessory case bottom surface to the outlet of the pressure oil screen. It is plugged at the case bottom surface. An intersecting diagonal passage is drilled from the right side of the case through a rib along the front case wall to outlets in the front bearings of the idler gear shaft and the left side accessory drive shaftgear. For use with dry sump engines this passage is always plugged with a plain ⅛-in. pipe plug at the right-side surface of the case. For wet sump engines which are not equipped with a left-side accessory drive, the diagonal passage must be closed with a special extension plug which fits closely in the drilled hole to prevent escape of oil through the open shaft bearings. A small hole drilled from the right-side accessory drive mounting pad into the vertical oil passage registers with an oil hole in the drive adapter leading to the shaftgear bearing.

The upper of two bronze acorn caps below the left magneto guides and covers the oil pressure relief valve and spring. The relief valve seat registers with the rear end of the left oil gallery.

REVIEW QUESTIONS

1. Name four of the most common engine classifications by cylinder arrangement.
2. What types of engines provide the best power/weight ratio?
3. What types of engines provide the least drag in flight?
4. Discuss the comparative advantages and disadvantages of air cooling and liquid cooling for aircraft engines.
5. Describe some of the effects of excessive heat in an aircraft engine.
6. Describe how cylinders are designed for air cooling.
7. Explain the use of baffles in air cooling.
8. What may happen if baffles are not properly installed?
9. What liquid is used as the coolant in a liquid-cooled engine?
10. Describe the functions of a crankcase.
11. Describe the construction of a crankcase for a six-cylinder opposed engine.
12. Of what material is a crankcase usually made?
13. Name the principal sections of the crankcase for a radial engine. Describe the function of each.
14. What accessories may be found mounted on the nose section of a radial engine?
15. What principal parts are supported by the power section?
16. Describe the arrangement of the fuel induction system.
17. Name the accessories which may be mounted on the accessory section.
18. Name the parts of a cylinder assembly.
19. What are the principal requirements for a cylinder assembly?

20. Of what material is a cylinder-barrel construction and by what process is it manufactured?
21. Why is a cylinder barrel manufactured with a skirt?
22. What is meant by nitriding?
23. By what two methods are cooling fins provided for cylinder barrels?
24. Describe the construction of a cylinder head.
25. Why are valve guides installed in a cylinder head?
26. What is the purpose of a Heli-Coil insert?
27. How is a cylinder head attached to a cylinder barrel?
28. What type of fit is required for the installation of valve guides in the cylinder head?
29. How can the intake-valve side of a cylinder head be distinguished from the exhaust-valve side?
30. Explain the reason for valve seats in a cylinder head, and describe the method of installation.
31. What is the principal function of a piston?
32. Why are pistons made of aluminum alloy?
33. How is a piston cooled?
34. What is the weight limitation with respect to pistons installed in the same engine?
35. Discuss the requirements of piston rings and their installation on the piston.
36. What is the purpose of the holes drilled through the piston wall in the oil ring grooves?
37. Why is piston-ring gap clearance important?
38. Describe the difference in the construction of different types of piston rings, and explain the function of each.
39. At what location on the piston are compression rings installed?
40. Describe the construction of a piston pin.
41. What means is employed to prevent the ends of piston pins from contacting and scoring the cylinder walls?
42. What is the function of a connecting rod?
43. Describe the construction of a connecting rod.

44. What are the three principal types of connecting-rod assemblies?
45. Describe the master-and-articulated connecting-rod assembly.
46. Describe the construction of a master rod bearing.
47. What device is used to hold knuckle pins in place?
48. Name the parts of a crankshaft.
49. Describe the oil passages and sludge chambers in a crankshaft.
50. Why are counterweights needed on some crankshafts?
51. Why is a plain bearing faced with a soft metal such as lead, silver, or babbitt?
52. Describe the two types of antifriction bearings.
53. By what means may an exhaust valve be cooled?
54. Describe the use of Stellite in the construction of exhaust valves.
55. Why are two coiled springs used to hold valves in the closed position?
56. Describe the valve-operating mechanism for an opposed engine.
57. Explain *valve lap, valve lead,* and *valve lag.*
58. What is the speed of rotation for the camshaft in an opposed engine relative to crankshaft speed?
59. How is correct valve timing assured when an opposed-type engine is assembled?
60. Name the parts of a typical hydraulic valve lifter.
61. Describe the operation of the hydraulic valve lifter.
62. Give the speed and direction of rotation of a four-lobe cam plate with respect to the crankshaft in a seven-cylinder radial engine.
63. Explain the difference between *hot* and *cold* valve clearances.
64. Describe the procedure for locating the top-dead-center position of a particular cylinder.
65. Describe the use of the Time-Rite piston-position indicator.

CHAPTER 4

Float-type Carburetors

PRINCIPLES OF CARBURETION

From the discussion of heat-engine principles, it will be remembered that a heat engine converts a portion of the heat of a burning fuel to mechanical work. In order to obtain heat from fuel it is necessary that the fuel be burned, and the burning of fuel requires a combustible mixture. The purpose of **carburetion** is to provide the combustible mixture of fuel and air necessary for the operation of an engine.

Since gasoline and many other petroleum fuels consist of carbon (C) and hydrogen (H) chemically combined to form hydrocarbon molecules (CH), it is possible to burn these fuels by adding oxygen (O) to form a gaseous mixture. The carburetor mixes the fuel with the oxygen of the air to provide a combustible mixture which is supplied to the engine through the induction system. The mixture is ignited in the cylinder with the result that the heat energy of the fuel is released and the fuel air mixture is converted to carbon dioxide (CO_2), water (H_2O), and possibly some carbon monoxide (CO).

The carburetors used on aircraft engines are comparatively complicated because they play an extremely important part in engine performance, mechanical life, and the general efficiency of the airplane. This is caused by the widely diverse conditions under which airplane engines are operated. The carburetor must deliver an accurately metered fuel/air mixture for engine loads and speeds between wide limits, it must provide for automatic or manual mixture correction under changing conditions of temperature and altitude, and it is subjected to continuous vibration that tends to upset the calibration and adjustment. For these reasons, many accurately constructed and delicately adjusted parts are included in an aircraft carburetor assembly. A knowledge of the functions of these parts is essential to the understanding of carburetor operation.

Fluid pressure

In the carburetor system of an internal-combustion engine, liquids and gases, collectively called **fluids,** flow through various passages and orifices (holes). The volume and density of liquids remain fairly constant, but gases expand and contract as a result of surrounding conditions.

The atmosphere surrounding the earth is like a great pile of blankets pressing down on the earth's surface. **Pressure** may be defined as force acting upon an area. It is commonly measured in pounds per square inch (psi), inches of mercury (in. Hg), or centimeters of mercury (cm Hg). The atmospheric pressure at any place is equal to the weight of a column of water or mercury a certain number of inches, centimeters, or millimeters in height. For example, if the cube-shaped box shown in Fig. 4·1, each side of which is 1 sq in. in area, is filled with mercury, that quantity of mercury will weigh 0.491 lb and a force of 0.491 lb is acting on the bottom square inch of the box. If the same box were 4 in. high, the weight of the mercury would be 4 × 0.491 or 1.964 lb; hence, the downward force on the bottom of the box would be 1.964 lb. Therefore, each inch of height of a column of mercury represents 0.491 psi pressure. To change inches of mercury to pounds per square inch, simply multiply by 0.491. For example, if the height of a column of mercury is 29.92 in., multiply 29.92 by 0.491 and the product is 14.69, hence 14.69 psi.

Referring again to Fig. 4·1, a glass tube about 36 in. long, with one end sealed and the other end open, is

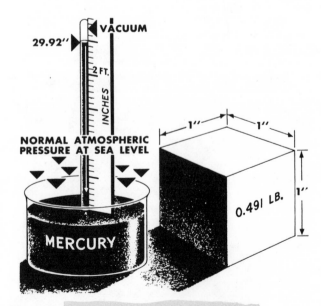

Figure 4·1 Measuring atmospheric pressure.

60

filled completely with mercury. The tube is then placed in a vertical position with the open end submerged in a small container partly filled with mercury. If this experiment is performed at sea level under standard conditions, the mercury will sink and come to rest at a level of 29.92 in. above the mercury in the container. There is then a vacuum above the mercury in the tube; hence, there is no atmospheric pressure above the mercury in the tube.

The atmospheric pressure acts on the surface of the mercury in the container of Fig. 4·1. The weight of the mercury column above the surface of the mercury in the container must therefore equal the weight of the air column above the same surface. The length of the mercury column in the tube indicates the atmospheric pressure and is measured by means of a scale placed beside the tube or marked on its surface.

Atmospheric pressure is expressed in per square inch, inches of mercury, centimeters of mercury, millimeter of mercury, or **millibars** (mb). Standard sea-level pressure is 14·7 psi, 29.92 in. Hg, 76 cm Hg, 760 mm Hg, or 1013 mb. It is well to remember these quantities because they may be encountered often in discussions of pressures in general or especially atmospheric pressures.

From observations such as those described above, the National Aeronautic and Space Administration (NASA) and the International Committee for Aeronautical Operations (ICAO) have established a **standard atmosphere** for comparison purposes. Standard atmosphere is defined as a pressure of 29.92 in. Hg at sea level with a temperature of 15°C (59°F) when the air is perfectly dry at lat 40°N. This is a purely fictitious and arbitrary standard, but it has been accepted and should be known to pilots, technicians, and others engaged in aircraft work.

The pressure of the atmosphere varies with the altitude. At 5,000 ft, it is 24.89 in. Hg; at 10,000 ft, it is 20.58 in. Hg; at 20,000 ft, it is 13.75 in. Hg; at 30,000 ft, it is 8.88 in. Hg; and at 50,000 ft, it is only 3.436 in. Hg.

Expressing the same principle in different terms, the pressure of the atmosphere at sea level is 14.7 psi, but at an altitude of 20,000 ft, the pressure is only about 6.74 psi.

The pressure exerted on the surface of the earth by the weight of the atmosphere is called **absolute pressure** and can be measured by a barometer. A **relative pressure** assumes that the atmospheric pressure is zero. Relative or differential pressures are usually measured by fuel pressure gages, steam gages, etc. This means that, when a pressure is indicated by such a gage, the pressure actually shown is so many pounds per square inch above atmospheric pressure. This pressure is often indicated as *psig* meaning psi gage. When absolute pressure is indicated it is shown as *psia,* meaning psi absolute.

The effect of atmospheric pressure is important to the understanding of all aircraft fluids, including fuel, oil, water, hydraulic fluid, etc. The effect of atmospheric pressure on liquids can be demonstrated by a simple experiment. Place a tube in a glass of water, place your finger over the open end of the tube, and take the tube out of the water, retaining your finger at the end. The water will not run out of the tube until your finger is removed. This shows the importance of providing and maintaining open vents to the outside atmosphere for tanks, carburetor chambers, and other parts or units depending upon atmospheric venting for their operation.

The venturi tube

Figure 4·2 shows the operation of a **venturi tube** used originally for the measurement of the flow of water in pipes. This device consists of a conical nozzle-like reducer through which the air enters, a narrow section called the **throat,** and a conical enlargement for the outlet which attains the same size as the inlet but more gradually. The operation is based upon Bernoulli's principle.

The quantity of water or air drawn through the inlet will be discharged through the same size opening at the outlet. The velocity of the fluid must, therefore, increase as it passes through the inlet cone, attain a maximum value in the throat, and thereafter gradually slow down to its initial value at the outlet. The pressure at the throat is consequently less than that at either the entrance or the exit.

Figure 4·3 shows a venturi tube with manometers, which are gages for measuring pressure similar in principle to barometers. Bernoulli's principle states that the total energy of a particle in motion is constant at all points on its path in a steady flow; therefore, at a higher velocity the pressure must decrease. The pressure in the throat of the venturi tube is less than the pressure in either end of the tube because of the increased velocity in the constricted portion. This is explained by the fact that the same amount of air passes all points in the tube in a given time.

An analogy can be found in the case of men march-

Figure **4·2**   *Operation of a venturi tube.*

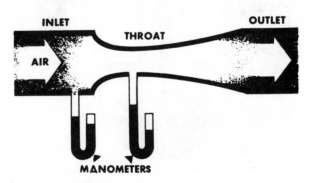

Figure **4·3**   *Venturi tube with manometers.*

ing down a street. If the street is wide enough for the men to march 20 abreast and then narrows to an alley where they can march only 10 abreast, the men marching through the alley must walk twice as fast as they did in the street for the same number of men to pass a point in the alley in a given period of time. If they did not increase their marching speed in the alley, there would soon be a traffic jam at the entrance to the alley.

The venturi illustrates the relationship existing between pressure (force per unit area) and velocity in a moving column of air. In equal periods of time, equal amounts of air flow through the inlet, which has a large area; through the throat, which has a small cross-sectional area; and then out through the outlet, which also has a large area.

If any body, fluid or solid, is at rest, force must be applied to set it in motion. If the body is already in motion, force must be applied to increase its velocity. If a body in motion is to have its velocity decreased, or if the body is to be brought to a state of rest, an opposing force must be applied.

In Fig. 4·3, if the cross-sectional area of the inlet is twice that of the throat, the air will move twice as fast in the throat as it does in the inlet and outlet. Since we have agreed that the velocity of any moving object cannot be decreased without applying an opposing force, the pressure of the air in the outlet portion of the tube must be greater than it is in the throat. From this it can be understood that the pressure in the throat must be less than it is at either end of the tube.

Figure 4·4 shows an ordinary atomizer. When the rubber bulb is squeezed, air is forced through a horizontal tube which is wide where it joins the bulb, narrow in the middle, and wide again where it approaches the nozzle. At the narrowed portion of this tube (throat), there is a vertical tube called a **riser,** which extends from the lower portion of the throat into the liquid. When air passes through the horizontal tube, the velocity is high in the throat; consequently the pressure there is reduced to less than the atmos-

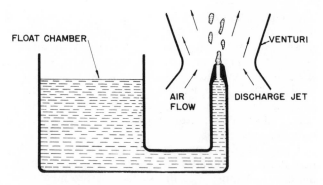

Figure 4·5   Venturi applied to a carburetor.

pheric pressure acting on the surface of the liquid in the container. The difference in pressure forces the liquid to ascend in the vertical riser, from the top of which it is expelled by the airstream through the nozzle. This is merely an application of the venturi-tube principle.

Venturi tube in a carburetor

Figure 4·5 shows the venturi principle applied in a simplified carburetor. The amount of fluid which flows through a given passage in any unit of time is directly proportional to the velocity at which it is moving. The velocity is directly proportional to the difference in applied forces. If a fuel discharge nozzle is placed in the venturi throat of a carburetor, the effective force applied to the fuel will depend upon the velocity of air going through the venturi. The rate of flow of fuel through the discharge nozzle will be proportional to the amount of air passing through the venturi, and this will determine the supply of the required fuel/air mixture delivered to the engine. The ratio of fuel to air should be varied within certain limits; hence, a mixture-control system is provided for the venturi-type carburetor.

Review of the engine cycle

The conventional aircraft internal-combustion engine is a form of heat engine in which the burning of the fuel/air mixture occurs inside a closed cylinder and in which the heat energy of the fuel is converted into mechanical work to drive the propeller.

The **engine cycle** must be understood and remembered in order to learn the process of carburetion. The fuel and air must be mixed and inducted into the cylinder during the **intake stroke;** the fuel/air charge must be compressed during the **compression stroke;** the charge must be ignited, it must burn, and it must expand to drive the piston downward and cause the crankshaft to revolve during the **power stroke;** and finally, the burned gases must be exhausted or scavenged during the **exhaust stroke.**

The quantity and the nature of the charge of fuel and air inducted into the engine cylinder must be given considerable attention because the power, speed, and operating efficiency of the engine are governed largely by this charge.

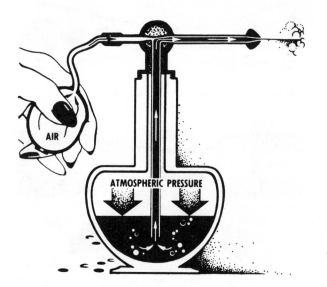

Figure 4·4   Operation of an atomizer.

Fuel and fuel mixtures

Gasoline and other liquid fuels will not burn in the liquid state, but when air is united with the fuel by atomization, the spray or vapor thus formed is highly combustible. The mixture of fuel and air is described as **chemically correct** when there is just enough oxygen present to burn the fuel completely. Since air is approximately 23.15 percent oxygen by weight, we use air for the burning of fuel. If there is not quite enough air, combustion may occur but it will not be complete. If there is too much air, or if there is not enough air, the mixture will not burn.

As mentioned previously, burning is a chemical process. Gasoline is composed of carbon and hydrogen, and a gasoline called isooctane has the formula C_8H_{18}. During the burning process this molecule must be combined with oxygen to form carbon dioxide (CO_2) and water (H_2O). The equation for the process may be

$$2C_8H_{18} + 25\,O_2 \longrightarrow 16CO_2 + 15H_2O$$

Thus we see that 2 molecules of this particular gasoline require 50 atoms of oxygen for complete combustion. The burning of fuel is seldom as complete as this, and the resulting gases would likely contain carbon monoxide (CO). In such a case the equation could be

$$C_8H_{18} + 12\,O_2 \longrightarrow 7CO_2 + 9H_2O + CO$$

Gasoline will burn in a cylinder if mixed with air in a ratio between 8 parts of air to 1 part of fuel and 18 parts of air to 1 part of fuel. That is, the air/fuel (A/F) ratio would be 8:1 to 18:1 for combustion. This means that the air/fuel mixture can be ignited in a cylinder when the ratio is as rich as 8 parts of air by weight to 1 part of fuel by weight, as lean as 18 parts of air by weight to 1 part fuel by weight and when ratios between these two extremes are present. In fuel/air (F/A) mixtures, the proportions are expressed on the basis of weight because a ratio based on volumes would be subject to inaccuracies resulting from variations of temperature and pressure.

Air is a mechanical mixture containing about 75.3 percent nitrogen, 23.15 percent oxygen by weight, and a small percentage of other gases. The nitrogen is an inert gas which has no chemical effect on combustion. The oxygen is the only gas in the mixture which serves any useful purpose as far as the combustion of fuel is concerned.

Although the fuel/air mixture will burn at the ratios given, the best power range is usually considered to be between 1:12 and 1:16, but this is a broad general statement subject to exceptions. Internal-combustion engines are so sensitive to the proportioning of the fuel and air that the mixture ratios must be maintained within a definite range for any given engine.

The proportions of fuel and air may be expressed as a direct ratio, written 1:12 or as a decimal fraction. If the ratio is 1:12, the decimal ratio may be written 0.083. The decimal expression of the fuel/air ratio is often found in the instructions given for the calibration of aircraft-engine instruments which indicate fuel/air ratios.

In many airplane engines, the most practical fuel/air ratios vary from 1:11.5 (or 0.087), called the **rich, best-power mixture,** to 1:13.5 (or 0.074), called the **lean, best-power mixture.** Specific instructions concerning mixture ratios are given in detail for each make, type, and model of engine, but the rich mixtures are generally used at high power output, and the leaner mixtures are customarily used at a lower cruising power. This information may be given in an engine-operating manual in words and also in the form of a chart, graph, or curve, having the mixture ratios plotted horizontally and the indicated horsepower output plotted vertically.

Incorrect mixtures cause variations in engine performance that may lead to serious engine damage. Black smoke (free carbon) appears in the exhaust when a rich mixture is burned, and there is a loss of power.

We have already stated that, if there is too much air or too much fuel, the mixture will not burn. In other words, when the mixture is excessively rich or excessively lean, it approaches the limit of flammability, and the rate of burning decreases until it finally reaches zero. This is much more pronounced on the lean side than it is on the rich side of the correct proportion of fuel and air.

It has been shown that very lean mixtures cause a loss of power. Under certain conditions the engine cylinders may be seriously overheated as a result of using a very lean mixture. Pilots are always instructed to avoid lean mixtures when operating their engines near maximum output and to watch carefully the cylinder-head temperature indications to guard against overheating the cylinders.

If the engine is operated with an excessively lean mixture, detonation will probably occur. This is indicated by a sharp rise in cylinder-head temperature, the emission of puffs of black smoke from the exhaust, and, of course, loss of power.

The chart of Fig. 4·6 was derived from a test run to determine the effect of fuel/air ratios. It will be observed that the lowest specific fuel consumption in this case occurred with a fuel/air ratio of approximately 0.067 and that maximum power was developed at F/A ratios between 0.074 and 0.087. For this particular engine, we may say that lean best power is at point A on the chart (F/A ratio 0.074) and rich best power is at point B (F/A ratio 0.087).

It will be noted further that specific fuel consumption increases substantially as the mixture is leaned or enriched from the point of lowest specific fuel consumption. From this observation it is quite apparent that excessive leaning of the mixture in flight will not produce maximum economy.

If detonation is allowed to continue, the result will be mechanical damage or failure of the top of the pistons and rings. In severe cases cylinder heads may be fractured. It is therefore important to follow the engine-operating instructions regarding mixture-control settings, thereby avoiding detonation and its unfavorable consequences. A careful observance of cylinder-head temperature will enable the pilot to take

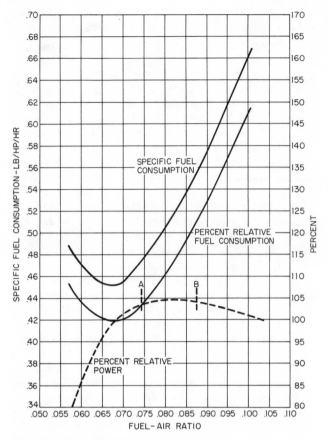

Figure **4·6** *Effects of fuel/air ratios and power settings on fuel consumption.*

short periods that its high rate of fuel consumption is generally not a serious problem. The rich mixture aids in cooling the engine because the vaporization of the extra fuel absorbs heat and the unburned fuel helps to carry heat away through the exhaust. Medium speeds, which account for more than half the whole range of engine speed, make it possible to use lean mixtures which provide a low rate of fuel consumption and still give good performance.

Effect of pressure differential in a U-shaped tube

Figure 4·7 shows two cross-sectional views of a U-shaped glass tube. In the upper view, the liquid surfaces in the two arms of the tube are even because the pressures above them are equal. In the lower view, the pressure in the right arm of the tube is reduced while the pressure in the left arm of the tube remains the same as it was before. This causes the liquid in the left arm to be pushed down while the liquid in the right arm is raised until the differences in the weights of the liquid in the two arms is exactly proportional to the difference in the forces applied on the two surfaces.

Pressure differential in a simple carburetor

The principle explained in the preceding paragraph is applied in a simple carburetor, such as the one shown in Fig. 4·5. The rapid flow of air through the venturi reduces the pressure at the discharge nozzle so that the pressure in the fuel chamber can force the fuel out into the airstream. Since the airspeed in the tube is comparatively high and there is a relatively great reduction in pressure at the nozzle during medium and high engine speeds, there is a reasonably uniform fuel supply at those speeds.

When the engine speed is low and the pressure drop in the venturi tube is slight, the situation is different.

corrective action before damage occurs in most cases. A reduction of power and enrichment of the mixture will usually suffice to eliminate detonation.

An excessively lean mixture may cause an engine to **backfire** through the induction system or to stop completely. A backfire is caused by slow flame propagation. This happens because the fuel/air mixture is still burning when the engine cycle is completed. The burning mixture ignites the fresh charge when the intake valve opens, the flame travels back through the induction system, the combustible charge is burned, and often any gasoline that has accumulated near the carburetor is burned. This occurs because flame propagation speed decreases as the mixture is leaned. Thus, a mixture which is lean enough will still be burning when the intake valve opens.

Backfiring is not the same as **kickback.** Kickback occurs when the ignition is advanced too far at the time that the engine is to be started. If the mixture is ignited before the piston reaches top center, the combustion pressure may cause the piston to reverse its direction and turn the crankshaft against the normal direction of rotation.

Rich mixtures are required at both low and high speeds. An engine operating at almost full power requires a very rich mixture to prevent detonation and overheating, but full power is used for such relatively

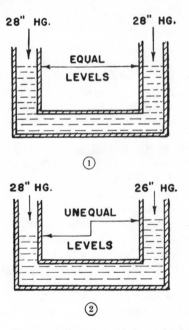

Figure **4·7** *Pressure effects in a U-shaped tube.*

64

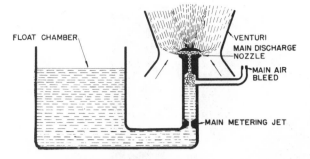

Figure 4·8   Basic carburetor.

This simple nozzle, otherwise known as a **fuel discharge nozzle,** in a carburetor of fixed size does not deliver a continuously richer mixture as the engine suction and airflow increase. Instead, a plain discharge nozzle will give a fairly uniform mixture at medium and high speeds, but at low speeds and low suction, the delivery falls off greatly in relation to the airflow.

This is partly because some of the suction force is consumed in raising the fuel from the float level to the nozzle outlet, which is slightly higher than the fuel level in the fuel chamber to prevent the fuel from overflowing when the engine is not operating. It is also caused by the tendency of the fuel to adhere to the metal of the discharge nozzle and break off intermittently in large drops instead of forming a fine spray. The discharge from the plain fuel nozzle is, therefore, retarded by an almost constant force which is not important at high speeds with high suction but which definitely reduces the flow when the suction is low on account of reduced speed.

Figure 4·8 shows how the problem is overcome in the design and construction of the venturi-type carburetor. Air is **bled** from behind the venturi and passed into the **main discharge nozzle** at a point slightly below the level of the fluid, causing the formation of a finely divided fuel/air mixture which is fed into the airstream at the venturi. A metering jet between the fuel chamber and the main discharge nozzle controls the amount of fuel supplied to the nozzle. A **metering jet** is an orifice, or opening, which is carefully dimensioned to meter, or "measure," fuel flow accurately in accordance with the pressure differential existing between the float chamber and the discharge nozzle.

The air bleed

The **air bleed** in a carburetor lifts an emulsion of air and liquid to a level higher above the liquid level in the float chamber than would be possible with unmixed fuel. Figure 4·9 shows a person sucking on a straw placed in a glass of water. The suction is great enough to lift the water above the level in the glass without drawing any into the mouth. In Fig. 4·10, a tiny hole has been pricked in the side of the straw above the surface of the water in the glass and the same suction is applied as before. The hole causes bubbles of air to enter the straw, and the liquid is drawn up in a series of small drops or slugs.

In Fig. 4·11 the air is taken into the main tube through a smaller tube which enters the main tube below the level of the water, and there is a restricting orifice at the bottom of the main tube; that is, the size of the main tube is reduced at the bottom. Instead of a continuous series of small drops or slugs being drawn up through the tube when the person sucks on it, there is a finely divided mixture of air and water formed in the tube.

Since there is a distance through which the water must be lifted from its level in the glass before the air begins to pick it up, the free opening of the main tube at the bottom prevents a very great suction being exerted on the air-bleed hole or vent. If the air openings were too large in proportion to the size of the main tube, the suction available to lift the water would be reduced.

In Fig. 4·11, the ratio of water to air could be modified for high and low airspeeds (produced by sucking on the main tube) by changing the dimensions of the air bleed, the main tube, and the opening at the bottom of the main tube.

In Fig. 4·8, the carburetor nozzle has an air bleed as explained previously. We can summarize our discussion by stating that the purpose of this air bleed

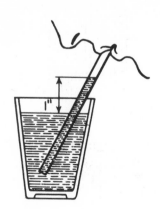

Figure 4·9   Suction lifting a liquid.

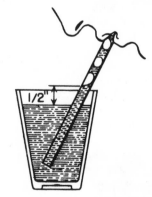

Figure 4·10   Effect of air bleed.

Figure 4·11   Air bleed breaking up a liquid.

Figure **4·12**   *A throttle valve.*

in the discharge nozzle is to assist in the production of a more uniform mixture of fuel and air throughout all operating speeds of the engine.

Vaporization of fuel

The fuel leaves the discharge nozzle of the carburetor in a stream which breaks up into various sizes of drops suspended in the airstream, and then they are even more finely divided. Vaporization occurs on the surfaces of each drop, causing very fine particles to disappear and the large particles to decrease in size. The problem of properly distributing the particles would be simple if all the particles in each drop vaporized completely before the mixture left the intake pipe, but some particles of the fuel enter the engine cylinders while they are still in a liquid state; hence they must be vaporized and mixed in the cylinder during the compression stroke.

The completeness of vaporization depends upon the volatility of the fuel, the temperature of the air, and the degree of atomization. **Volatile** means readily vaporized; hence, the more volatile fuels evaporate more readily. Higher temperatures increase the rate of vaporation; hence, carburetor air-intake heaters are sometimes provided. Some engines are equipped with "hot-spot" heaters which utilize the heat of exhaust gases to heat the intake manifold between the carburetor and the cylinders. This is usually accomplished by routing a portion of the engine exhaust through a jacket surrounding the intake manifold. In another type of hot-spot heater, the intake manifold is passed through the oil reservoir of the engine. The hot oil supplies heat to the intake manifold walls, and this heat is transferred to the fuel/air mixture.

The degree of atomization is the extent to which fine spray is produced; the more fully the mixture is reduced to fine spray and vaporized, the greater is the efficiency of the combustion process. The air bleed in the main discharge nozzle passage aids in the atomization and vaporization of the fuel. If the fuel is not fully vaporized, the mixture may run "lean" even though there is an abundance of fuel present.

Throttle valve

A **throttle valve**, usually a **butterfly-type** valve, is incorporated in the fuel/air duct to regulate the fuel/air output. The throttle valve is usually an oval-shaped metal disk mounted on the throttle shaft in such a manner that it can completely close the throttle bore. In the closed position, the plane of the disk makes an angle of about 70° with the axis of the throttle bore. The edges of the throttle disk are shaped to fit closely against the sides of the fuel/air passage. The arrangement of such a valve is shown in Fig. 4 · 12. The amount of air flowing through the venturi tube is reduced when the valve is turned toward its closed position. This reduces the suction in the venturi tube; hence less fuel is delivered to the engine. When the throttle valve is opened, the flow of the fuel/air mixture to the engine is increased. Thus opening or closing the throttle valve regulates the power output of the engine. In Fig. 4 · 13, the throttle valve is shown in the open position.

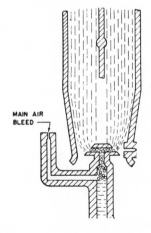

Figure **4 · 13**   *Throttle valve in open position.*

FLOAT-TYPE CARBURETORS

Essential parts of a carburetor

The carburetor consists essentially of a main air passage through which the engine draws its supply of air, mechanisms to control the quantity of fuel discharged in relation to the flow of air, and a means for regulating the quantity of fuel/air mixture delivered to the engine cylinders.

The essential parts of a float-type carburetor are (1) the float mechanism and its chamber, (2) the strainer, (3) the main metering system, (4) the idling system, (5) the economizer system, (6) the accelerating system, and (7) the mixture-control system.

In the float-type carburetor, atmospheric pressure in the fuel chamber forces fuel from the discharge nozzle when the pressure is reduced at the venturi tube. The intake stroke of the piston reduces the pressure in the engine cylinder, thus causing air to flow through the intake manifold to the cylinder. This flow of air passes through the venturi of the carburetor and causes the reduction of pressure in the venturi which, in turn, causes the fuel to be sprayed from the discharge nozzle.

The float mechanism

As previously explained, the float in a carburetor is designed to control the level of fuel in the float chamber. This fuel level must be maintained slightly below the discharge nozzle outlet holes in order to provide the correct amount of fuel flow and to prevent leakage of fuel from the nozzle when the engine is not running. The arrangement of a float mechanism in relation to the discharge nozzle is shown in the diagram of Fig. 4·14. In the diagram it will be noted that the float is attached to a lever which is pivoted, and one end of the lever is engaged with the float needle valve. When the float rises, the needle valve closes and stops the flow of fuel into the chamber. At this point, the level of the fuel is correct for proper operation of the carburetor provided that the needle valve seat is at the correct level.

As shown in Fig. 4·14, the float-valve mechanism includes a needle and a seat. The needle valve is constructed of hardened steel, or it may have a synthetic-rubber section which fits the seat. The needle seat is usually made of bronze. There must be a good fit between the needle and seat to prevent fuel leakage and overflow from the discharge nozzle.

During the operation of the carburetor, the float assumes a position slightly below its highest level to allow a valve opening sufficient for replacement of the fuel as it is drawn out through the discharge nozzle. If the fuel level in the float chamber is too high, the mixture will be rich, and if the fuel is too low, the mixture will be lean. In order to adjust the fuel level for the carburetor shown in Fig. 4·14, washers are placed under the float needle seat. If the fuel level (float level) needs to be raised, washers are removed from under the seat. If the level needs to be lowered, washers are added. The specifications for the float level are given in the manufacturer's overhaul manual.

For some carburetors, the float level is adjusted by bending the float arm. This is true of many automobile carburetors as well as some aircraft carburetors.

Figure 4·15 shows two additional types of float mechanisms. The upper drawing illustrates the **concentric** (having a common center) float and valve, while the lower drawing illustrates an **eccentric** (off-center) float and valve.

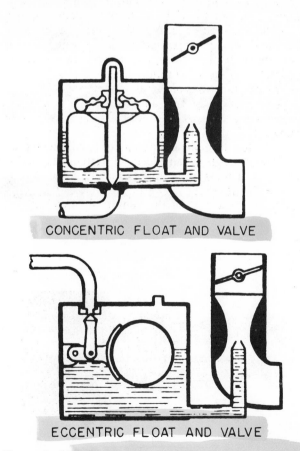

CONCENTRIC FLOAT AND VALVE

ECCENTRIC FLOAT AND VALVE

Figure 4·15 Concentric and eccentric float mechanisms.

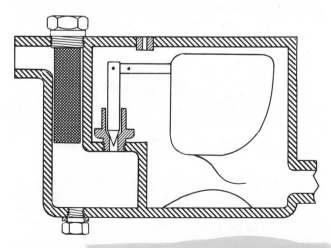

Figure 4·14 Float and needle-valve mechanism in a carburetor.

The fuel strainer

In most carburetors, the fuel supply must first enter a strainer chamber, where it passes through a strainer screen. The **strainer,** then, consists of a fine wire mesh or other type of filtering device, cone-shaped or cylindrically shaped, located so that it will intercept any dirt particles which might clog the needle valve opening or, later, the metering jets. The strainer is usually removable so that it can be taken out and thoroughly drained and flushed. It is retained by a strainer plug or a compression spring. A typical strainer is shown in Fig. 4·16.

The main metering system

The **main metering system** controls the fuel feed in the upper half of the engine speed range as used for cruising and full-throttle operations. It consists of three principal divisions or units: (1) the **main metering jet** through which fuel is drawn from the float chamber; (2) the **main discharge nozzle,** which may be any one of several types; and (3) the **passage leading to the idling system.**

Although the previous statement is correct, it should be understood that some authorities state that the purpose of the main metering system is to maintain a constant fuel/air mixture at all throttle openings throughout the power range of engine operation. The same authorities divide the main metering system into four parts, as follows: (1) the venturi, (2) a metering jet which measures the fuel drawn from the float chamber, (3) a main discharge nozzle including the main air bleed, and (4) a passage leading to the idling system. It is apparent that these are merely two different approaches to the same thing.

The three functions of the main metering system are (1) to proportion the fuel/air mixture, (2) to decrease the pressure at the discsarge nozzle, and (3) to limit the airflow at full-throttle.

The airflow through an opening of fixed size and the fuel flow through an air-bleed jet system respond to variations of pressure in approximately equal proportions. If the discharge nozzle of the air-bleed system is located in the center of the venturi so that both the air-bleed nozzle and the venturi are exposed to the suction of the engine in the same degree, it is possible to maintain an approximately uniform mixture of fuel and air throughout the power range of engine operations. This is illustrated in Fig. 4·17, which shows the air-bleed principle and the fuel level of the float chamber in a typical carburetor.

The full power output from the engine makes it necessary to have a manifold suction (reduced pressure or "partial vacuum") above the throttle valve which is between 0.4 and 0.8 psi at full engine speed. However, more suction is desired for metering and spraying the fuel, and this is obtained from the venturi. When a discharge nozzle is located in the central portion, the suction obtained is several times as great as the suction found in the intake manifold.

Thus, it is possible to maintain a relatively low manifold vacuum (high manifold pressure) which results in high volumetric efficiencies as contrasted to high manifold vaccums which result in low volumetric efficiencies.

We have previously stated that the venturi tube affects the air capacity of the carburetor. Hence, it is apparent that it should be obtainable in various sizes which are selected according to the requirements of the particular engine for which the carburetor is designed.

By itself, the main metering system does not accomplish all its functions unaided, but when the other essential parts of a carburetor are examined, the whole system of carburetion becomes apparent. The main metering system for a typical carburetor is shown in Fig. 4·18.

Idling system

At idling speeds, the airflow through the venturi of the carburetor is too low to draw sufficient fuel from the discharge nozzle, so the carburetor cannot deliver enough fuel to the engine to keep it running. At the same time, with the throttle nearly closed, the air velocity is high and the pressure is low between the edges of the throttle valve and the walls of the air passages. Furthermore, there is very high suction on the intake side of the throttle valve. Because of this situation, an idling system is added with an outlet at the throttle valve. This idling system delivers fuel only when the throttle valve is nearly closed and the engine is running slowly. An **idle cutoff** valve stops the flow of fuel through this idling system on some carburetors, and this is used for stopping the engine. An increased amount of fuel (richer mixture) is used in the idle range because, at idling speeds, the engine may not have enough air flowing past its cylinders to provide proper cooling.

Figure 4·19 is a drawing of a three-piece main discharge assembly, showing the main discharge nozzle, the main air bleed, the main discharge-nozzle stud, the idle feed passage, the main metering jet, and the accelerating well screw. This is one of the two types of main discharge-nozzle assemblies used in modern updraft, float-type carburetors. An **updraft** carburetor is

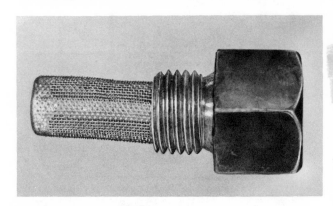

Figure 4·16 *Carburetor fuel strainer.*

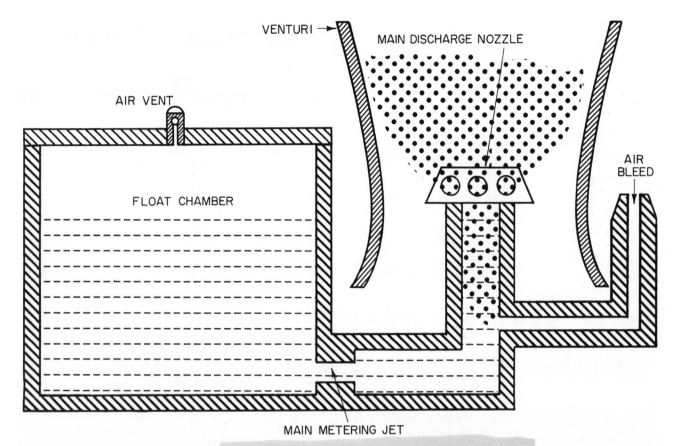

Figure **4·17**   *Location of air-bleed system and main discharge nozzle.*

one in which the air flows upward through the carburetor to the engine. The other type has the main discharge nozzle and the main discharge-nozzle stud combined in one piece screwed directly into the discharge-nozzle boss, which is part of the main body casting, thereby eliminating the necessity of having a discharge-nozzle screw.

Figure 4·20 is a drawing of a conventional idle system, showing the idling discharge nozzles, the mix-

ture adjustment, the idle air bleed, the idle metering jet, and the idle tube. It will be noted that the fuel for the idling system is taken from the fuel passage for the main discharge nozzle and the idle air-bleed air is taken from a chamber outside the venturi section. Thus the

Figure **4·18**   *Main metering system. (Bendix Products Division)*

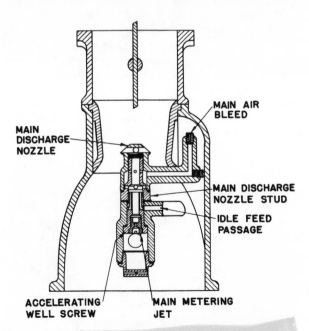

Figure **4·19**   *Three-piece main discharge assembly.*

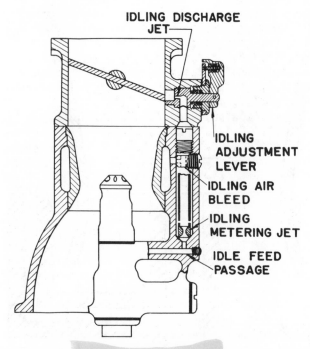

Figure **4·20** *Conventional idle system.*

IDLING DISCHARGE JET

IDLING ADJUSTMENT LEVER

IDLING AIR BLEED

IDLING METERING JET

IDLE FEED PASSAGE

throttle valve. This chamber or slot has openings into the barrel of the carburetor, both above and below the throttle.

In the drawings of Figs. 4·20 and 4·21, it will be noted that there is a small chamber surrounding the main discharge-nozzle passage just below the main

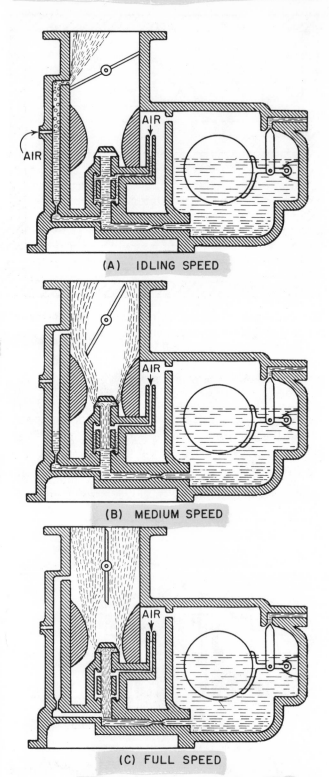

(A) IDLING SPEED

AIR

AIR

(B) MEDIUM SPEED

AIR

(C) FULL SPEED

AIR

Figure **4·21** *Float-type carburetor at different speeds.*

idle air is at air inlet pressure. The idle discharge is divided between two discharge nozzles, and the relative quantities of fuel flowing through these nozzles are dependent upon the position of the throttle valve. At very low idle, all the fuel passes through the upper orifice, since the throttle valve covers the lower orifice. In this case, the lower orifice acts as an additional air bleed for the upper orifice. As the throttle is opened further, exposing the lower orifice, additional fuel passes through this opening.

Since the idle mixture requirements vary with climatic conditions and altitude, a needle-valve-type mixture adjustment is provided to vary the orifice in the upper idle discharge hole. Moving this needle in or out of the orifice varies the idle fuel flow accordingly to supply the correct fuel/air ratio to the engine.

The idling system described above is used in the Bendix-Stromberg NA-S3A1 carburetor and will not necessarily be employed in other carburetors. The principles involved are similar in all carburetors, however.

Figure 4·21 shows a typical float-type carburetor at (*A*) idling speed, (*B*) medium speed, and (*C*) full speed. The greatest suction (pressure reduction) in the intake manifold above the throttle is at the lowest speeds, when the smallest amount of air is received, which is also the condition requiring the smallest amount of fuel. When the engine speed increases, more fuel is needed but the suction in the manifold decreases. For this reason, the metering of the idling system is not accomplished by the suction existing in the intake manifold. Instead, it is controlled by the suction existing in a tiny intermediate chamber or slot formed by the idling discharge nozzle and the wall of the carburetor at the edge of the air-bleed inlet. This chamber serves as an **accelerating well** to store extra fuel, which is drawn out when the throttle is suddenly opened. This extra fuel is necessary to compensate for a sudden increase of airflow in order to maintain a correct fuel/air ratio.

When the engine is operating at intermediate speed, it will be observed that the accelerating well still has some fuel. However, when the throttle is wide open, all the fuel from the well is drawn out. At full power, all fuel is supplied through the main discharge and the economizer system, and the idling system then acts as an auxiliary air bleed to the main metering system. The main metering jet provides an approximately constant mixture ratio for all speeds above idling, but it has no effect during idling.

Economizer system

An **economizer** is essentially a valve which is closed at cruising speed but is opened to provide an enriched mixture for high-speed operation. In other words, it supplies and regulates the additional fuel required for all speeds above the cruising range. It is also correct to say that an economizer is a device for enriching the mixture at increased throttle settings. However, the economizer must close properly at cruising speed. If it does not, the engine may operate satisfactorily at full throttle but it will "load up" at all speeds below cruising on account of the extra fuel being fed into the system. The extra-rich condition will be indicated by rough running and black smoke emanating from the exhaust.

The economizer system gets its name from the fact that it enables the pilot to obtain maximum economy in fuel consumption by providing for a lean mixture during cruising operation and a rich mixture for full-power settings. Most economizers in their modern form are merely enriching devices. The carburetors equipped with economizers are normally set for their leanest practical mixture delivery at cruising speeds, and enrichment takes place as required for higher power settings.

Three types of economizers for float-type carburetors are (1) the needle-valve type, (2) the piston type, and (3) the manifold-pressure-operated type. Figure 4·22 illustrates the needle-valve type of economizer. This mechanism utilizes a needle valve which is opened by the throttle linkage at a predetermined throttle position. This permits a quantity of fuel, in addition to the fuel from the main metering jet, to enter the discharge-nozzle passage. As shown in the diagram, the economizer needle valve permits fuel to bypass the cruise valve metering jet.

The **piston-type economizer,** illustrated in Fig. 4·23, is also operated by the throttle. The lower piston serves as a fuel valve, preventing any flow of fuel through the system at cruising speeds. The upper piston functions as an air valve, allowing air to flow through the separate economizer discharge nozzle at part throttle. As the throttle is opened to higher power positions, the lower piston uncovers the fuel port leading from the economizer metering valve and the upper piston closes the air ports. Fuel fills the economizer well and is discharged into the carburetor venturi where it adds to the fuel from the main discharge nozzle. The upper piston of the economizer permits a small amount of air to bleed into the fuel, thus assisting in the atomization of the fuel from the economizer system. The space below the lower piston of the economizer acts as an accelerating well when the throttle is opened.

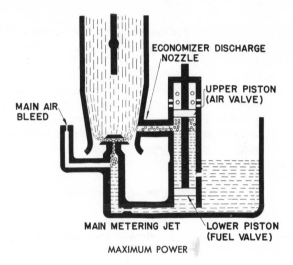

MAXIMUM POWER

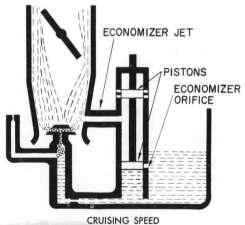

CRUISING SPEED

Figure **4·23** *Piston-type economizer.*

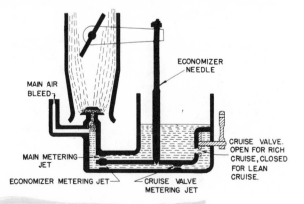

Figure **4·22** *Needle-type economizer.*

The **manifold-pressure-operated economizer,** illustrated in Fig. 4·24, has a bellows which is compressed when the pressure from the engine blower rim produces a force greater than the compression spring in the bellows chamber. As engine speed increases, the blower pressure will also increase. This pressure collapses the bellows and causes the economizer valve to open. Fuel then flows through the economizer metering jet to the main discharge system. The operation of the bellows and spring is stabilized by means of a dashpot as shown in the drawing.

Accelerating system

When the throttle controlling an engine is suddenly opened, there is a corresponding increase in the airflow, but because of the inertia of the fuel, the fuel flow does not accelerate in proportion to the airflow increase. Instead, the fuel lags behind and causes a temporary lean mixture. This, in turn, may cause the engine to miss or backfire, and it is certain to cause a temporary reduction in power. To prevent this condition, all modern carburetors are equipped with an **accelerating system.** This is either an accelerating pump or an accelerating well, which has been mentioned previously. The function of the accelerating system is to discharge an additional quantity of fuel into the carburetor airstream when the throttle is suddenly opened, thus causing a temporary enrichment of the mixture and producing a smooth and positive acceleration of the engine.

It has been explained that the accelerating well is a space around the discharge nozzle connected by holes to the fuel passage leading to the discharge nozzle. The upper holes are located near the fuel level and are uncovered at the lowest pressure that will draw fuel from the main discharge nozzle; hence, they receive air during the entire time that the main discharge nozzle operates.

Very little throttle opening is required at idling speeds. When the throttle is suddenly opened, air is drawn in to fill the intake manifold and whichever cylinder is on the intake stroke. This sudden rush of

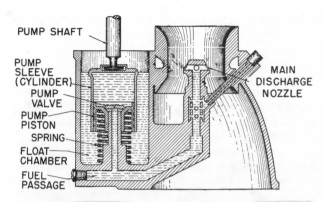

Figure **4·25**   A movable-piston-type accelerating pump.

air temporarily creates a high suction at the main discharge nozzle, brings into operation the main metering system, and draws additional fuel from the accelerating well. Because of the throttle opening, the engine speed increases and the main metering system continues to function.

The **accelerating pump** illustrated in Fig. 4·25, is a sleeve-type piston pump operated by the throttle. The piston is mounted on a stationary hollow stem screwed into the body of the carburetor. The hollow stem opens into the main fuel passage leading to the discharge nozzle. Mounted over the stem and piston is a movable cylinder or sleeve which is connected by the pump shaft to the throttle linkage. When the throttle is closed, the cylinder is raised and the space within the cylinder fills with fuel through the clearance between the piston and the cylinder. If the throttle is quickly moved to the open position, the cylinder is forced down as shown in Fig. 4·26, and the increased fuel pressure also forces the piston part way down along the stem. As the piston moves down, it opens the pump valve and permits the fuel to flow through the hollow stem into the main fuel passage. With the throttle fully open and the accelerating pump cylinder all the way down, the spring pushes the piston up and forces most of the fuel out of the cylinder. When the piston reaches its highest position, it closes the valve and no more fuel flows toward the main passage.

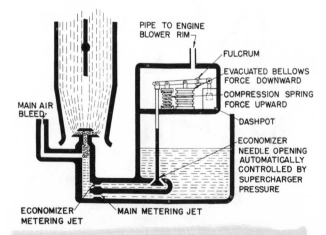

Figure **4·24**   Manifold-pressure-operated economizer.

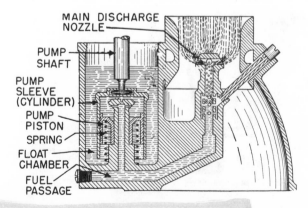

Figure **4·26**   Accelerating pump in operation.

There are several types of accelerating pumps, but each serves the purpose of providing extra fuel during rapid throttle opening and acceleration of the engine. When a throttle is moved slowly toward the open position, the accelerating pump does not force extra fuel into the discharge system. This is because the spring in the pump holds the valve closed unless the fuel pressure is great enough to overcome the spring pressure. When the throttle is moved slowly, the trapped fuel seeps out through the clearance between the piston and the cylinder and the pressure does not build up enough to open the valve.

Mixture-control systems

At higher altitudes, the air has less pressure, density, and temperature. The weight of the air taken into an unsupercharged engine decreases with the decrease in air density, and the power is reduced in approximately the same proportion. Since the quantity of oxygen taken into the engine decreases, the fuel/air mixture becomes too rich for normal operations. The mixture proportion delivered by the carburetor becomes richer at a rate inversely proportional to the square root of the increase in density of the air.

It must be remembered that the density of the air changes with temperature and pressure. If the pressure remains constant, the density of the air will vary according to temperature, increasing as the temperature drops. This will cause a leaning of the fuel/air mixture in the carburetor because the denser air contains more oxygen. The change in air pressure due to altitude is considerably more of a problem than the change in density due to temperature changes. At 18,000 ft altitude, the air pressure is approximately one-half the pressure at sea level. Hence, in order to provide a correct mixture, the fuel flow would have to be reduced to almost one-half what it would be at sea level. The adjustment of fuel flow to compensate for changes in air pressure and temperature is a principal function of the mixture control.

Briefly, the **mixture-control system** can be described as a mechanism or device by means of which the richness of the mixture entering the engine during flight can be controlled to a reasonable extent. This control should exist through all normal altitudes of operation.

The functions of the mixture-control system are (1) to prevent the mixture from becoming too rich at high altitudes and (2) to economize on fuel during engine operation in the low-power range where cylinder temperature will not become excessive with the use of the leaner mixture.

Mixture-control systems may be classified according to their principles of operation as (1) **back-suction** type, which reduces the effective suction on the metering system; (2) **needle** type, which restricts the flow of fuel through the metering system; and (3) the **air-port** type, which allows additional air to enter the carburetor between the main discharge nozzle and the throttle valve. Figure 4·27 shows two views of a back-suction mixture-control system. The left view shows the mixture-control valve in the closed position. This cuts off the atmospheric pressure from the space above the fuel in the fuel chamber. Since the float chamber is connected to the low-pressure area in the venturi of the carburetor, the pressure above the fuel in the float chamber will be reduced until fuel is no longer delivered from the discharge nozzle. This acts as an **idle cutoff** and stops the engine. The end of the back-suction tube, in actual construction, is located where the pressure is somewhat higher than that at the nozzle, thus making it possible for the mixture-control valve to be completely closed without stopping the flow of fuel. The fuel flow is varied by adjusting the opening of the mixture-control valve. To lean the mixture, the valve is moved toward the **closed** position, and to enrich the mixture, the valve is moved toward the **open** position. The righ-hand drawing in Fig. 4·27 shows the valve in the full rich position.

In order to reduce the sensitivity of the back-suction mixture control, a disk-type valve is used. This valve is constructed so that a portion of the valve opening can be closed rapidly at first and the balance of the opening is closed gradually. A drawing of the disk-type valve is shown in Fig. 4·28. This assembly is called an **altitude-control valve disk and plate.** The arrangement of the mixture control for an NA-S3A1 carburetor is shown in Fig. 4·29.

A needle-type mixture control is shown in Fig. 4·30. In this control, the needle is used to restrict the fuel passage to the main metering jet. When the mixture

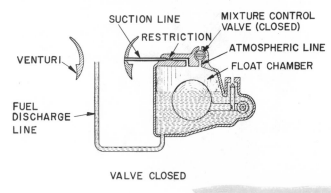

VALVE CLOSED

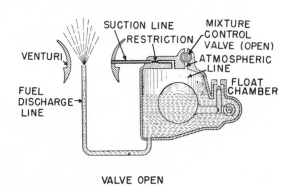

VALVE OPEN

Figure **4·27** *Back-suction-type mixture control.*

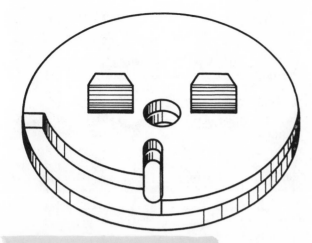

Figure 4·28   Disk-type mixture control.

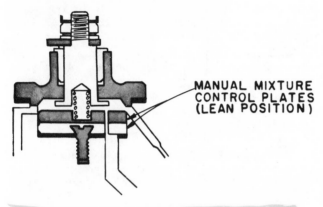

MANUAL MIXTURE
CONTROL PLATES
(LEAN POSITION)

Figure 4·29   Mixture control for NA-S3A1 carburetor.

control is in the FULL RICH position, the needle is in the fully raised position and the fuel is accurately measured by the main metering jet. The needle valve is lowered into the needle-valve seat to lean the mixture, thus reducing the supply of fuel to the main discharge nozzle. Even though the needle valve is completely closed, a small bypass hole from the float chamber to the fuel passage allows some fuel to flow; hence, the size of this bypass hole determines the control range.

The air-port type of mixture control, illustrated in Fig. 4·31, has an air passage leading from the region between the venturi tube and the throttle valve to atmospheric pressure and a butterfly valve in the air passage, manually controlled by the pilot in the cockpit. It is apparent that, when the pilot opens the butterfly valve in the air passage, air which has not been mixed with fuel will be injected into the fuel/air mixture. At the same time, the suction in the intake manifold will be reduced, thereby reducing the velocity of the air coming through the venturi tube. This will further reduce the amount of fuel being drawn into the intake manifold.

Automatic mixture control

Originally, the mixture control was manually operated on all airplane engines, but the more modern aircraft carburetors are often equipped with a device for automatically controlling the mixture as altitude changes. **Automatic mixture-control systems** may be operated on the back-suction principle, the needle-valve principle, or by throttling the air intake to the carburetor. In the last type of automatic mixture control, the control regulates power output within certain

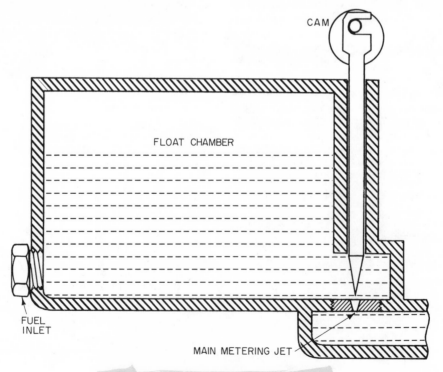

CAM

FLOAT CHAMBER

FUEL
INLET

MAIN METERING JET

Figure 4·30   Needle-type mixture control.

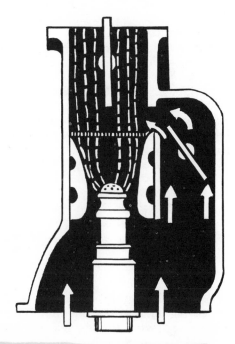

Figure **4 · 31** Air-port-type mixture control.

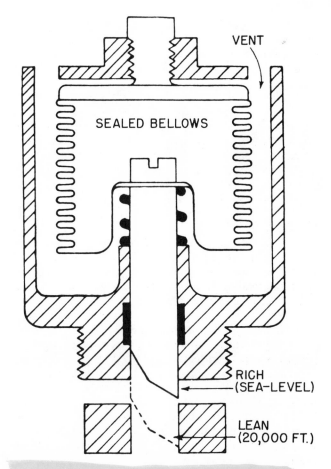

Figure **4 · 32** Automatic mixture-control mechanism.

limits in addition to exercising its function as a mixture control.

In automatic mixture-control systems operating on the back-suction and needle-valve principles, the control may be directly operated by the expansion and contraction of a pressure-sensitive evacuated bellows through a system of mechanical linkage. This is the simplest form of automatic mixture control and is generally found to be accurate, reliable, and easy to maintain. Some mixture-control valves, such as the one illustrated in Fig. 4 · 32, are operated by bellows vented to the atmosphere; hence, the fuel flow is proportional to the atmospheric pressure. Figure 4 · 33 shows the bellows type of mixture-control valve installed on a carburetor as a back-suction control device. As atmospheric pressure decreases, the bellows will expand and begin to close the opening into the fuel chamber. This will cause a reduction of pressure in the chamber, thus resulting in a decreased flow of fuel from the discharge nozzle. In some systems, not illustrated here, having external superchargers, both the fuel chamber and the bellows may be vented to the carburetor intake to obtain the correct mixtures of fuel and air.

Automatic controls often have more than one setting in order to obtain the correct mixtures for cruising and high-speed operation. In addition to the automatic control feature, there is usually a provision for manual control if the automatic control fails.

When the engine is equipped with a fixed-pitch propeller which allows the engine speed to change as the mixture changes, a manually operated mixture control can be adjusted by observing the change in engine rpm as the control is moved. Obviously, this will not succeed with a constant-speed propeller.

If a constant-speed propeller cannot be locked into

fixed-pitch position, and if the extreme pitch positions cause engine speeds outside the normal operating range in flight, it is necessary to have an instrument of some type to indicate fuel/air ratio or power output.

If the propeller can be locked in a fixed-pitch position, and if this does not lead to engine speeds outside

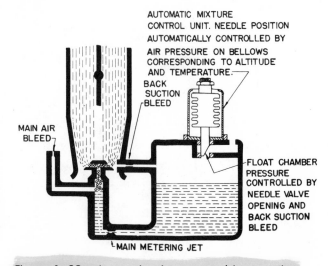

Figure **4 · 33** Automatic mixture-control in operation.

the normal flight operating range, the following expressions may be employed to describe the manual adjustments of the mixture control:

Full rich is the mixture-control setting in the position for maximum fuel flow.

Rich best power is the mixture-control setting which, at a given throttle setting, permits maximum engine rpm with the mixture control as far toward full rich as possible without reducing rpm.

Lean best power is the mixture-control setting which, at a given throttle setting, permits maximum engine rpm with the mixture control as far toward "lean" as possible without reducing rpm.

Downdraft carburetors

Thus far in our discussion, we have discussed **updraft** carburetors principally. "Updraft" means that the air through the carburetor is flowing upward. A **downdraft carburetor,** such as the one illustrated in Fig. 4·34, takes air from above an engine and causes it to flow down through the carburetor. Those who favor downdraft carburetors claim that this type reduces fire hazard, provides a better distribution of mixture to the cylinders of an upright engine, and has less tendency to pick up sand and dirt from the ground.

Downdraft carburetors are very similar in function and systems to the updraft types. The drawing of Fig. 4·34 illustrates one of the several types of downdraft carburetors used for aircraft. This particular model has two float chambers, two throttle valves, and an automatic mixture-control unit.

Figure 4·35 illustrates a portion of a downdraft

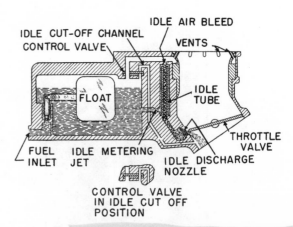

Figure 4·35 Downdraft carburetor showing idling system.

carburetor and its idling system, emphasizing the path of the fuel leaving the float chamber and the position of the idle air bleed. When the engine is not operating, this air bleed, in addition to its other functions, prevents the siphoning of fuel. An average intake pressure to the mixture-control system is supplied by the series of vents at the entrance to the venturi.

Model designation

All Bendix-Stromberg float-type aircraft carburetors carry the general model designation NA followed by a hyphen; the next letter indicates the type as shown in Table 4·1.

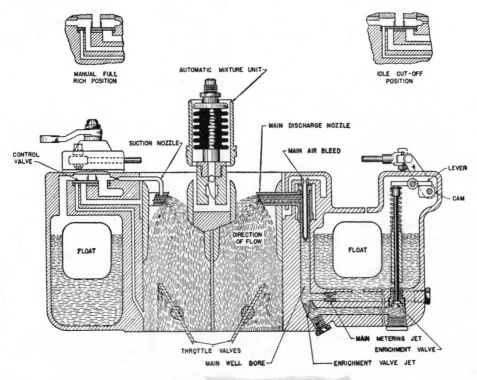

Figure 4·34 A downdraft carburetor.

Table 4·1

Type letter	Type description
S and R	Single barrel
D	Double barrel, float chamber to rear (obsolescent)
U	Double barrel, float chamber between barrels
Y	Double barrel, double chamber fore and aft of barrels
T	Triple barrel, double float chamber fore and aft of barrels
F	Four barrel, two separate float chambers

The final numeral indicates the nominal rated size of the carburetor, the size starting from 1 in., which is No. 1, and increasing in ¼-in. steps. For example, a 2-in. carburetor is No. 5. The actual diameter of the carburetor barrel opening is ³⁄₁₆ in. greater than the nominal rated size in accordance with the standards of the Society of Automotive Engineers. A final letter is used to designate various models of a given type. This system of model designation applies to inverted or downdraft as well as to the updraft carburetors. The model designation and serial number are found on an aluminum tag riveted to the carburetor. There are so many Bendix-Stromberg carburetors that it is necessary to consult the publications of the manufacturer to learn the details of the designation system, but the above explanation is ample for ordinary purposes.

Typical float-type carburetors

A comparatively simple float-type carburetor is illustrated in the drawing of Fig. 4·36. This is the NA-S3A1 Bendix-Stromberg carburetor used on a number of small aircraft engines. The NA-S3A1 carburetor is a single-barrel updraft model with a single hinge-type float, a main metering system of the plain tube type with an air bleed to the main discharge nozzle, an idling system, and a back-suction-type mix-

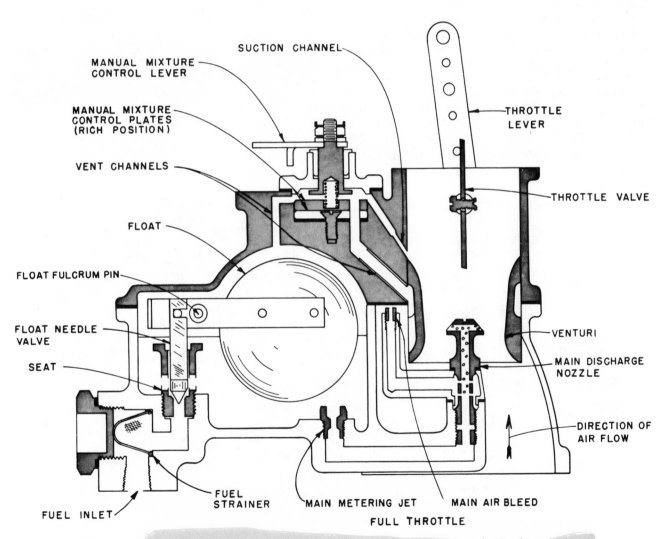

Figure 4·36 Diagram of Bendix-Stromberg NA-S3A1 carburetor. (Bendix Products Division)

Figure 4·37 Photograph of NA-S3A1 carburetor. (Sky Store, Hawthorne, Calif.)

Figure 4·38 Marvel-Schebler MA-3 carburetor.

ture control, manually operated. An external view of the carburetor is shown in Fig. 4·37.

A careful examination of the drawing of Fig. 4·36 will show how the principles explained in previous sections are utilized in this carburetor to control fuel flow and to provide a suitable mixture for engine operation.

Another carburetor commonly used for light air-craft engines is the Marvel-Schebler MA-3, shown in Fig. 4·38. This carburetor is somewhat more complex than the Bendix-Stromberg NA-S3A1 mentioned previously. The MA-3 carburetor has a double float

assembly hinged to the upper part of the carburetor. This upper part is called the **throttle body** because it contains the throttle assembly. The fuel inlet, the float needle valve, and two venturis are also contained in the throttle body.

The carburetor body and bowl assembly contains a crescent-shaped fuel chamber surrounding the main air passage. The main fuel discharge nozzle is installed

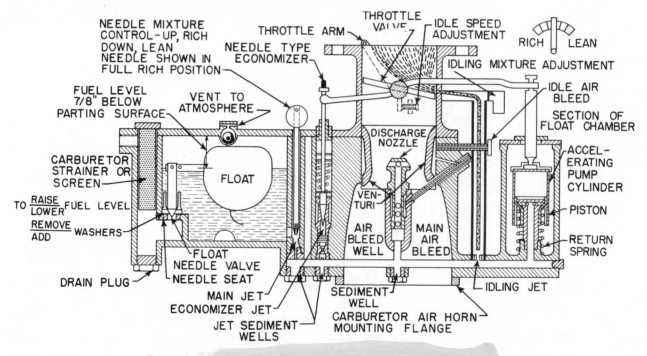

Figure 4·39 Diagram of Bendix-Stromberg NAR series carburetor.

78

at an angle in the air passage with the lower end leading into the main fuel passage. An accelerating pump is incorporated in one side of the body and bowl assembly. The pump receives fuel from the fuel chamber and discharges accelerating fuel through a special **accelerating pump discharge tube** into the carburetor bore adjacent to the main discharge nozzle. The carburetor also includes an altitude mixture-control unit.

The principal features of a more complex carburetor are illustrated in Fig. 4·39. This is a Bendix-Stromberg NAR-type carburetor, and it includes all the systems explained previously. The operation of these systems can be easily understood through a careful study of the drawing. Observe particularly the float and needle valve, the needle-type mixture control, the economizer system, the accelerating pump, the idle system, the main metering system, and the air bleeds. The names of all the principal parts are included in the illustration, and these should be memorized by the student.

Disadvantages of float-type carburetors

Float-type carburetors have been improved steadily by their manufacturers, but they have two important disadvantages or limitations: (1) the fuel-flow disturbances in maneuvers may interfere with the functions of the float mechanism, resulting in erratic fuel delivery, sometimes causing engine failure, and (2) when icing conditions are present, the discharge of fuel into the airstream ahead of the throttle causes a drop of temperature and a resulting formation of ice at the throttle valve.

CARBURETOR ICING

Water vapor in air

In addition to gases, the air always contains some water vapor, but there is an upper limit to the amount of water vapor (as an invisible gas) that can be contained in any space at a given temperature. The capacity of air to hold water increases with the temperature. When air contains the maximum possible amount of moisture at a given temperature in a given space, the pressure exerted by the water vapor is also at a maximum and the space is then said to be **saturated.**

Humidity

Humidity, in simple terms, is moisture or dampness. The **relative humidity** of air is the ratio of the amount of moisture which the air does have to what it could contain, usually expressed as percent relative humidity. For example, if we have saturated air at 20°F and the temperature is increased to 40°F, the relative humidity will drop to 43 percent if the barometric pressure has remained unchanged. If this same air is heated further without removing or adding moisture, its capacity for holding water vapor will increase and its relative humidity will be less.

Lowering the temperature of air reduces its capacity to hold moisture. For example, if air at 80°F has a relative humidity of 49 percent and it is suddenly cooled to 62°F, it will be found that the relative humidity is then 100 percent because cooling the air has increased its relative humidity.

In the case just mentioned, a relative humidity of 100 percent means that the air is saturated; that is, it contains all the moisture that it can hold. If it should be cooled still more and its moisture capacity decreases, some of the water vapor will condense. The temperature at which the moisture in the air begins to condense is called the **dew point.**

Vaporization

The addition of heat changes a solid into a liquid, and it can change a liquid into a gas or vapor. The process of converting a liquid into a vapor is called **vaporization.** As the liquid is heated, the more rapidly moving molecules escape from the surface in a process called **evaporation.** Thus, when a pan of water is put on a hot stove, bubbles of water vapor begin to form at the bottom of the pan, they rise through the cooler water above them and then collapse, causing the "singing" noise associated with boiling liquids. When all the water in the pan is hot enough for the bubbles to reach the surface easily, vaporization takes place throughout the water, accompanied by a violent disturbance. This vaporization is commonly called **boiling.**

Latent heat of vaporization

When a liquid evaporates, it uses heat. If one gram of water is raised in temperature from 0°C (32°F) to 100°C (212°F) 100 calories are required. (A **calorie** is defined as the quantity of heat required to raise the temperature of one gram of water from 14.5 to 15.5°C.)

More heat is applied, and the liquid water at 100°C is changed to water vapor of 100°C. This evaporation requires 539 cal. The temperature of the water does not rise during this process of changing from a liquid to a gaseous state; hence, it is evident that 539 cal are required for the change of state. The reverse is also true; that is, when 1 g of water vapor is condensed to liquid water, 539 cal are given off. This energy, 539 cal, required for the change of state from liquid to vapor or from vapor to liquid, is called the **latent heat of vaporization or condensation.**

Laws of evaporation

There are six so-called **laws of evaporation** which have a bearing on the formation of ice in carburetors, as follows:

1. **The rate of evaporation increases as the temperature increases.** Heat increases the rate at which molecules move; hence, hot water evaporates faster than cold water.
2. **The rate of evaporation increases with an increase of the surface area of the liquid.** More molecules can escape in a given time from a large surface than from a small surface; hence, water in a big pan will evaporate faster than it will in a small vase.
3. **The rate of evaporation increases when the atmospheric pressure decreases.** If the weight of the air above water is less, the escaping molecules encounter less resistance. In

other words, evaporation is faster under low pressure than it is under high pressure. For example, it is possible to freeze water by the cooling effect of evaporation if a stream of dry air is passed over water in a partial vacuum.

4. **The rate of evaporation varies with the nature of the exposed liquid.** For example, alcohol evaporates faster than water.

5. **The rate of evaporation of water is decreased when the humidity of the air is increased.** The escaping molecules of water can get away more easily if there are only a few molecules of water already in the air above the water. Conversely, if the humidity is high, the escaping molecules encounter more resistance to their departure from the water.

6. **The rate of evaporation increases with the rate of change of the air in contact with the surface of the liquid.** Wet clothes dry faster on a windy day than on a day when the air is calm.

The cooling effect of evaporation

Every gram of water that evaporates from the skin takes heat from the skin and the body is cooled. That is the reason for human perspiration. If a person stands in a breeze, the perspiration evaporates more rapidly and the body is cooled faster. If the relative humidity is great, a person suffers from the heat on a hot day because the perspiration does not evaporate fast enough to have a noticeable cooling effect. Even the commercial production of ice depends upon the cooling effect of evaporation.

Carburetor ice formation

When fuel is discharged into the low-pressure area in the carburetor venturi, it evaporates rapidly. This evaporation of the fuel cools the air, the walls, and the water vapor. If the humidity (moisture content) of the air is high and the metal of the carburetor is cooled below 32°F, ice forms and interferes with the operation of the engine. The fuel/air passages are clogged up, the mixture flow is reduced, and the power output drops. Eventually, if the condition is not corrected, the drop in power output may cause engine failure. The formation of ice in the carburetor may be indicated by a gradual loss of engine speed, a loss of manifold pressure, or both, without change in the throttle position.

It is of extreme importance that a pilot recognize the symptoms of carburetor icing and the weather conditions which may be conducive to icing. The principal effects of icing are the loss of power (drop in manifold pressure without a change in throttle position), engine roughness, and backfiring. The backfiring is caused when the discharge nozzle is partially blocked to cause a leaning of the mixture.

Standard safety procedures with respect to icing are (1) a check of carburetor heater operation before take-off, (2) turning on the carburetor heater when reducing power for gliding or landing, and (3) use of carburetor heat whenever icing conditions are believed to exist.

If the mixture temperature is slightly above freezing, there is little danger of carburetor icing. For this reason, a **mixture thermometer** is sometimes installed between the carburetor and the intake valve. This instrument not only indicates low temperatures in the carburetor venturi which would lead to icing conditions but also indicates high temperatures when a carburetor air-intake heater is used in order to avoid excessively high temperatures which would cause detonation, preignition, and loss of power.

In general, ice may form in a carburetor system in any one of three processes as follows: (1) the cooling effect of the evaporation of the fuel after being introduced into the air stream may produce what is called **fuel ice** or **fuel evaporation ice**; (2) water in suspension in the atmosphere coming in contact with engine parts at a temperature below 32°F may produce what is called **impact ice** or **atmospheric ice**; (3) the freezing of the condensed water vapor of the air at or near the throttle forms what is known as **throttle ice** or **expansion ice**. This classification of carburetor ice in three groups is purely arbitrary. The pilot bothered by carburetor icing is not particularly interested in the name to give the ice; he wants to know how to get rid of it, avoid its repetition, and take measures on the ground to remedy the condition producing it.

The pilot confronted by carburetor icing can take several measures to get rid of it. He can fly slower, fly at an altitude where the air is warmer, turn on the carburetor air heater, and do other things beyond the scope of this discussion. However, it is better to avoid icing conditions in the first place.

Some pilots erroneously believe that carburetor icing does not take place when the free air temperature is above the freezing point. Ice can be formed when the inlet-air temperature is above the freezing point and when relative humidity is below 100 percent. Water condensation takes place, and since heat is absorbed from the air/vapor mixture by the evaporating fuel, the mixture drops below 32°F, thus freezing the condensed water vapor. The most severe carburetor icing conditions may occur with the temperature between 50 and 60°F with a humidity above 60 percent. Under these conditions, the moisture in the air is frozen and deposited in the carburetor, where it continues to grow in size until it may lock the throttle valve or restrict the amount of air entering the system to a degree that will cause engine failure.

When the fuel is vaporized in the carburetor as the fuel sprays out of the nozzle, the temperature of the incoming air usually drops at least 30°F and may drop as much as 70°F, depending on several factors. As the throttle is opened, the temperature of the incoming air drops even further.

The variable-venturi carburetor and the pressure-injection carburetors are relatively free from carburetor icing troubles, but even in these carburetors ice or snow already formed in the atmosphere may get into the carburetor induction system unless the powerplant is provided with an air intake or scoop which is located where it can receive air free from ice or snow.

Carburetor air-intake heaters

The exhaust-type carburetor air-intake heater is essentially a jacket or tube through which the hot exhaust gases of the engines are passed to warm the air flowing over the heated surface before the air enters the carburetor system. The amount of warm air entering the system can be controlled by an adjustable valve.

The **alternate air-inlet** heating system has a two-position valve and an air scoop. When the passage from the scoop is closed, warm air from the engine compartment is admitted to the carburetor system. When the passage from the scoop is open, cold air comes from the scoop. Since the heating of the air for the carburetor depends upon the free-air temperature, the engine temperature, the cowl-flap position, and other variable factors, this system is not always very dependable.

In a third type of carburetor air-intake heater, the air is heated by the compression which occurs in the external supercharger, but it becomes so hot that it is passed through an **intercooler** to reduce its temperature before entering the carburetor. Shutters at the rear of the intercooler can be opened or closed to regulate the degree of cooling to which the air warmed by the supercharger is subjected.

Excessively high carburetor air temperatures

At first thought, it seems foolish to heat the air first and then cool it when the purpose is to raise its temperature to avoid icing the carburetor. However, it has been stated before in this text that excessively high carburetor air temperatures are not wanted. Air expands when heated, and its density is reduced. Lowering the density of the air reduces the mass; that is, it cuts down the **weight** of the fuel/air charge in the engine cylinder. This results in a loss of power because power depends upon the weight of fuel/air mixture burned in the engine.

Another danger inherent in a high fuel/air temperature is detonation. If the air temperature is such that further compression in the cylinder raises the temperature to the combustion level of the fuel, detonation will occur. As explained previously, detonation causes excessive cylinder-head temperatures and may lead to piston damage and engine failure. This is one of the reasons why it is necessary to employ an intercooler with a high-pressure supercharger, especially at low altitudes where the air is dense.

INSPECTION AND OVERHAUL OF FLOAT-TYPE CARBURETORS

Inspection in airplane

Remove the carburetor strainer and clean it frequently. Flush the strainer chamber with gasoline to remove any foreign matter or water. Inspect the fuel lines to make certain that they are tight and in good condition. Inspect the carburetor to be sure that all safety wires, cotter pins, etc., are in place and that all parts are tight. On those models having economizer or accelerating pumps, clean the operating mechanism frequently and put a small quantity of oil on the moving parts.

It is particularly important, when inspecting the carburetor and associated parts, to examine the mounting flange closely for cracks or other damage. The mounting studs and safetying devices should be checked carefully for security. If there is an air leak between the mounting surfaces or because of a crack, the fuel/air mixture may become so lean that the engine will fail. A very small leak can cause overheating of the cylinders and power loss.

Disassembly

Great care must be used when disassembling a float-type carburetor to make sure that parts are not damaged. The sequence described in the manufacturer's overhaul manual should be used if a manual is available. This sequence is designed to disassemble the carburetor in such an order that parts still on the assembly will not interfere with parts to be removed. As parts are removed, they should be placed in a tray with compartments to keep the components of each assembly together. When this is done, there is much less likelihood of installing parts in the wrong position when the carburetor is reassembled.

The tools used in the disassembly of a carburetor should be of the proper type. Screwdrivers should have the blades properly ground to avoid slipping in screw slots and damaging the screw heads or gouging the aluminum body of the carburetor. Metering jets and other specially shaped parts within the carburetor should be removed with the tools designed for the operation. A screwdriver should not be used for prying except where specific instructions are given that this should be done.

Cleaning

The cleaning of carburetor parts is usually described in the manufacturer's overhaul manual, but there are certain general principles which may be followed satisfactorily. The first step in cleaning parts is to remove oil and grease. This can be done by using a standard petroleum solvent such as Stoddard Solvent (Federal Specification P-S-661 or the equivalent). The parts to be cleaned should be immersed in the solvent for 10 to 15 min, rinsed in the solvent, and then dried.

To remove carbon and gum from the carburetor parts, a suitable carbon remover should be employed. Carbon remover MIL-C-5546A or the equivalent may be used. The remover should be heated to about 60°C, and the parts immersed in it for 30 min. The parts should then be rinsed thoroughly in hot water (about 80°C) and dried with clean, dry compressed air, particular attention being paid to internal passages and recesses.

Wiping cloths or rags should never be used to dry carburetor parts because of the lint which will be deposited on the parts. Small particles of lint can obstruct jets, jam close-fitting parts, and cause valves to leak.

If aluminum parts are not corroded but still have some deposits of carbon, these deposits may be removed with No. 600 wet-or-dry paper used with water. After this the parts should be rinsed with hot water and dried.

Aluminum parts that are corroded can be cleaned by immersion in an alkaline cleaner Formula T or an equivalent inhibited against attack on aluminum. The parts should be immersed for 10 to 15 min with the cleaner temperature at 88 to 100°C. The cleaning solution can be made by mixing ingredients as follows:

Sodium phosphate dibasic	2 lb
Sodium metasilicate	1 lb
Soap (Fed. Spec. P-S-598)	0.8 lb
Sodium dichromate	0.2 lb
Water (near boiling temperature)	10 gal

After immersion in the cleaning solution the parts should be rinsed in hot water and then in cold water. Following the rinse, the parts should be immersed for 5 to 10 min in a chromic phosphoric acid solution consisting of 3.5 pt of 75 percent phosphoric acid and 1.75 lb of chromic acid to 10 gal of water. The temperature of the solution should be 83 to 93°C when the parts are immersed. This process will remove corrosion, paint and anodic coating.

Finally, it is necessary to rinse the parts thoroughly with cold water followed by hot water. Corroded areas can be smoothed with No. 600 wet-or-dry paper and water. This should be followed by another hot-water rinse after which the parts are dried carefully. Internal passages and recesses should be checked to see that they are clear and that no moisture is retained.

The foregoing process is one of several which may be used for cleaning carburetor parts. Cleaning solutions suitable for aluminum and steel may be obtained from any chemical manufacturer who specializes in industrial chemicals and cleaning solutions. In every case, the manufacturer's directions for use should be carefully followed. It is particularly important that the operator use caution to avoid injury to himself because many cleaning chemicals will burn the skin and may cause blindness if splashed into the eyes. Protective clothing, gloves, and goggles should always be worn when dangerous chemicals are used.

Inspection of parts

Before assembly of the carburetor, all parts should be inspected for damage and wear. Inspections for a typical carburetor are as follows:

1. Check all parts for bends, breaks, cracks, or crossed threads.
2. Inspect the fuel strainer assembly for foreign matter or a broken screen.
3. Inspect the float needle and seat for excessive wear, dents, scratches, or pits.
4. Inspect the mixture-control plates for scoring or improper seating.
5. Inspect the float assembly for leaks by immersing in hot water. Bubbles will issue from a point of leakage.
6. Inspect the throttle shaft end clearance and the play in the shaft bushings.

In addition to the foregoing inspections, certain assemblies must be checked for fits and clearances. Among these are the fulcrum bushing in the float, the fulcrum pin, slot in the float needle, pin in the float assembly, bushing in the cover assembly, mixture-control stem, and the throttle shaft and bushings. The limits for these assemblies are given in the Table of Tolerance Values in the manufacturer's overhaul manual.

The foregoing inspections are those specified for the Bendix-Stromberg NA-S3A1 carburetor. Other carburetors, such as the Marvel-Schebler MA-3, MA-4, and MA-6 series, will have many additional inspections specified in the overhaul manual. In each case the manufacturer's instructions should be followed carefully.

Inspection of metering jets

The sizes of the metering jets in a carburetor are usually correct because these sizes are established by the manufacturer. Sometimes a jet may be changed or drilled to increase the size, so it is always well to check the sizes when the carburetor is overhauled. The correct sizes for the various jets are given in the specifications of the manufacturer in the overhaul manual, and the size numbers are usually stamped on the jet. The number on the jet corresponds to a numbered drill shank; hence it is possible to check the size of the jet by inserting the shank of a numbered drill into the jet as shown in Fig. 4·40. If the drill shank fits the jet without excessive play, the jet size is correct. The number of the jet should also be checked against the specifications in the overhaul manual to see that the correct jet is installed. Metering jets should also be examined closely to see that there are no scratches, burrs, or other obstructions in the jet passage because

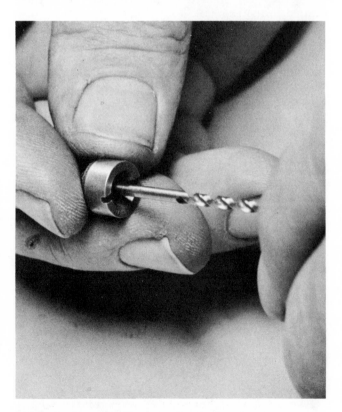

Figure 4·40   Checking metering jet for size.

these will cause local turbulence, which interferes with normal fuel flow. If a metering jet is defective in any way, it should be replaced by a new one of the correct size.

Repairs and replacement

The repair and replacement of parts for a carburetor depend upon the make and model being overhauled and should be performed in accordance with manufacturer's instructions. It is always proper to replace gaskets and fiber washers or any other part which shows substantial signs of wear or damage. When clearances and other dimensions are not within the specified limits, parts involved must be replaced or repaired.

A carburetor float is usually made of formed brass sheet and can be checked for leaks by immersing it in hot water. The heat will cause the air and any fuel fumes in the float to expand, thus making a stream of bubbles emerge from the leak.

If the float is found to have leaks, the leaks should be marked with a pencil or other means which will not cause damage. A small hole may then be drilled in the float to permit the removal of fuel which may have been trapped inside. After the hole is drilled, the fuel should be drained, and then the float should be immersed in boiling water until all fuel fumes are evaporated from the inside. This will permit soldering of the leaks without the danger of explosion. As a further precaution, the float should never be soldered with an open flame. The small leaks should be soldered before the drilled hole is sealed. Care must be taken that only a minimum of solder is applied to the float because the weight must not be increased more than necessary. An increase in the weight of the float will cause an increase in the fuel level which, in turn, will increase fuel consumption.

After the float is repaired, it should be immersed in hot water in order to determine that all leaks have been sealed.

Checking the float level

As explained previously, the fuel in the float chamber of a carburetor must be maintained at a level which will establish the correct fuel flow from the main discharge nozzle when the carburetor is in operation. The fuel level in the discharge nozzle is usually between $\frac{3}{16}$ and $\frac{1}{8}$ in. below the opening in the nozzle.

After the carburetor is partially assembled according to manufacturer's instructions, the float level may be checked. In a Bendix-Stromberg carburetor where the float and needle seat is in the lower part of the carburetor, the float level may be tested as follows:

1. Mount the assembled main body in a suitable fixture so that it is level when checked with a small spirit level.
2. Connect a fuel supply line to the fuel inlet in the main body, and regulate the fuel pressure to the value given on the applicable specification sheet. This pressure is $\frac{1}{2}$ psi for a NA-S3A1 carburetor used in a gravity-fed fuel system. When the fuel supply is turned on, the float chamber will

begin to fill with fuel and the flow will continue until it is stopped by the float needle on its seat.
3. Using a depth gage, measure the distance from the parting surface of the main body to the level of the fuel in the float chamber, approximately $\frac{1}{2}$ in. from the side wall of the chamber as shown in Fig. 4·41. The fuel level for the NA-S3A1 carburetor should be $\frac{13}{32} \pm \frac{1}{64}$ in. from the parting surface.
4. If the level of the float is not correct, remove the needle and seat and install a thicker washer under the seat to lower the level or a thinner washer to raise the level. A change in washer thickness of $\frac{1}{64}$ in. will change the level approximately $\frac{5}{64}$ in. for a NA-S3A1 carburetor.

Two different test procedures are used to establish the correct float level and the float-valve operation for the Marvel-Schebler MA series carburetors. The first of these is carried out during assembly after the float and lever assembly is installed. The throttle body is placed in an upside-down position as shown in Fig. 4·42. The height of the lower surface of each float above the gasket and screen assembly is then measured. For the MA-3 and MA-4 carburetors, this distance should be $\frac{7}{32}$ in. For the MA4-5 carburetor, the distance is $\frac{13}{64}$ in. When the throttle body is placed in the upside-down position, the float needle is bearing against the float valve and holding it in the closed position. This is the same position taken by the float when the carburetor is in the normal operating position and the float chamber is filled with fuel.

The method for testing the float-valve operation is illustrated in Fig. 4·43 and is performed after the carburetor is completely assembled. The procedure is as follows:

1. Connect the inlet fitting of the carburetor to a fuel pressure supply of 0.4 psi.

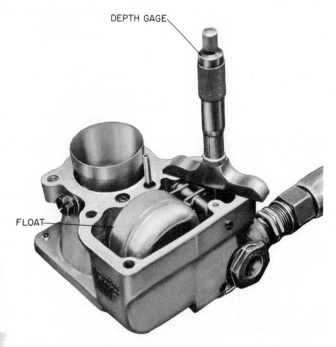

Figure 4·41 *Checking fuel level.*

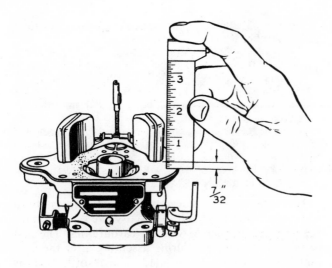

Figure 4·42 Measuring float distance on MA-3 carburetor. (Marvel-Schebler Div., Borg-Warner Corp.)

2. Remove the bowl drain plug, and connect a glass tube to the carburetor drain connection with a piece of rubber hose. The glass tubing should be positioned vertically beside the carburetor.

3. Allow the fuel pressure at 0.4 psi to remain for a period of at least 15 min, and then raise the fuel pressure to 6.0 psi. (There will be a slight rise in the fuel level as the pressure is increased.) Allow the 6.0 psi pressure to remain for at least 5 min after the fuel level has stabilized.

4. If the fuel does not rise to the level of the parting surface of the castings or run out of the nozzle, which can be observed through the throttle bore, the float valve and seat are satisfactory. If fuel is observed running out the nozzle, the bowl and throttle body must be separated and the float valve and seat cleaned or replaced.

In Fig. 4·43, the fuel level, shown as "Distance A," will automatically be correct if the float height is correct and the float valve does not leak.

The foregoing procedures are given as typical operations in the inspection and overhaul of float-type

TROUBLE-SHOOTING CHART

Trouble	Cause	Correction
Carburetor leaks when engine is stopped.	Float needle valve not seated properly because of dirt on seat.	Tap carburetor body with soft mallet while engine is running. Remove and clean carburetor. Check float level.
	Float needle valve worn.	Replace float needle valve.
Mixture too lean at idle.	Fuel pressure too low.	Adjust fuel pressure to correct level.
	Idle mixture control out of adjustment.	Adjust idle mixture control.
	Obstruction in idle metering jet.	Disassemble and clean carburetor.
	Air leak in the intake manifold.	Check intake manifold for tightness at all joints. Tighten assembly bolts.
Mixture too lean at cruising speed.	Air leak in the intake manifold.	Check intake manifold for tightness at all joints. Tighten assembly bolts.
	Automatic mixture control out of adjustment.	Adjust automatic mixture control.
	Float level too low.	Check and correct float level.
	Manual mixture control not set correctly.	Check setting of manual mixture control. Adjust linkage if necessary.
	Fuel strainer clogged.	Clean fuel strainer.
	Fuel pressure too low.	Adjust fuel pump relief valve.
	Obstruction in fuel line.	Check fuel flow and clear any obstructions.
Mixture too lean at full power setting.	Same causes as for lean cruise.	Make corrections as for lean cruise.
	Economizer not operating correctly.	Check economizer system for operation. Adjust or repair as required.
Mixture too rich at idle.	Fuel pressure too high.	Adjust fuel pressure to correct level.
	Idle mixture control out of adjustment.	Adjust idle mixture.
	Primer line open.	See that primer system is not feeding fuel to engine.
Mixture too rich at cruising speed.	Automatic mixture control out of adjustment.	Adjust automatic mixture control.
	Float level too high.	Adjust float level.
	Manual mixture control not set correctly.	Check setting of manual mixture control. Adjust linkage if necessary.
	Fuel pressure too high.	Adjust fuel pump relief for correct pressure.
	Economizer valve open.	Check economizer for correct operation. Quick acceleration may clear.
	Accelerating pump stuck open.	Quick acceleration of engine may remove foreign material from seat.
Poor acceleration. Engine backfires or misses when throttle is advanced.	Accelerating pump not operating properly.	Check accelerating pump linkage. Remove carburetor, disassemble and repair accelerating pump.

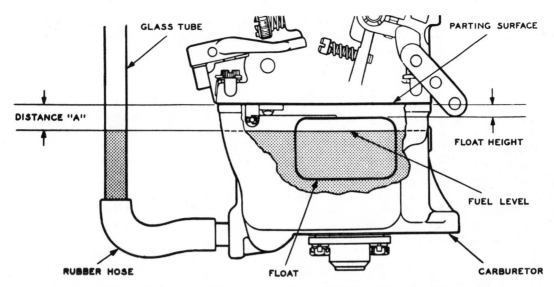

GLASS TUBE

PARTING SURFACE

DISTANCE "A"

FLOAT HEIGHT

FUEL LEVEL

RUBBER HOSE   FLOAT   CARBURETOR

Figure **4·43**   *Testing float valve operation. (Marvel-Schebler Div., Borg-Warner Corp.)*

carburetors; however, it is not possible in this text to give complete, detailed overhaul operations for specific float-type carburetors. When the technician is faced with the necessity of overhauling a particular carburetor, he should obtain the correct manufacturer's manual and all special bulletins pertaining to the carburetor. Furthermore, he should check the FAA Engine Specification for the particular engine upon which the carburetor is to be used to see if any parts changes or modifications are called for. The overhaul procedure should then be carried out according to the applicable instructions.

Trouble shooting

The trouble-shooting chart on page 84 provides some typical procedures for determining and correcting float-type carburetor malfunctions; however, it is not intended to cover all possible problems which may occur with a carburetor system. It must be understood that there are many types of carburetors and numerous variations exist in their operational characteristics.

REVIEW QUESTIONS

1. What is the function of a carburetor?
2. How does atmospheric pressure affect the operation of a carburetor?
3. What conditions of temperature and pressure have been established for a *standard atmosphere* at sea level?
4. Explain the operation of a venturi tube.
5. How is the venturi tube utilized in a carburetor?
6. What chemical action takes place when gasoline burns in an engine?
7. What fuel/air ratios are considered the *best power* range?
8. Express in decimals the approximate *lean best power* ratio for fuel and air.
9. Why does an engine "backfire" when the mixture is too lean?
10. Why is a rich mixture used during takeoff?
11. Explain the purpose of an air bleed in a carburetor.
12. What is the function of a metering jet?
13. How and why is the fuel/air mixture sometimes heated before it enters the engine?
14. Describe a throttle valve and its operation.
15. What are the essential parts of a float-type carburetor.
16. Discuss the effect of float level in a float-type carburetor.
17. How is the float level usually adjusted?
18. Describe the *main metering system.*
19. When an engine is operating at full power, what is the approximate amount of "suction" in the intake manifold above the throttle valve?
20. Describe the idling system of a typical float-type carburetor, including *idle air bleed* and *idle mixture.*
21. Why is the fuel/air ratio increased during idle operation?
22. What is the *idle cutoff?*
23. Describe the operation of the *accelerating well* in a Bendix NA-S3A1 carburetor.
24. What is the purpose of the *economizer valve* in a carburetor?
25. What would be the effect on engine operation if the economizer valve should stick in the open position?
26. What would happen if the economizer valve stuck closed?
27. Describe the operation of the *needle-type* economizer valve.
28. Explain the operation of the *piston-type* accelerating system.
29. What are the principal functions of the *mixture-control* system?
30. Explain the operation of the *back-suction* mixture control.
31. Why is it desirable to employ an *idle cutoff* for stopping the engine?
32. Describe the operation of the *automatic mixture control.*
33. What would be the effect on engine operation if the automatic mixture control should stick in the sea-level position?
34. Why is it necessary to have a fixed-pitch propeller setting when adjusting the carburetor mixture or fuel/air ratio?
35. Differentiate between *updraft* and *downdraft* carburetors.
36. What is the diameter of the carburetor barrel opening in an NA-R9B carburetor?

37. Describe the float and needle-valve assembly of the Marvel MA-3 carburetor.
38. What are the disadvantages of a float-type carburetor?
39. Describe the conditions under which carburetor icing may occur.
40. What temperature change occurs when water vaporizes?
41. Define *latent heat of vaporization.*
42. Give six laws of vaporization.
43. What are the symptoms of carburetor icing during the operation of an engine?
44. What precaution is taken to prevent carburetor icing?
45. Describe *fuel ice, impact ice, throttle ice.*
46. How is it possible for carburetor icing to take place when the free-air temperature is above the freezing point?
47. Describe methods for heating the carburetor intake air.
48. What are the effects of excessively high carburetor air temperature?
49. How is engine operation affected when there is an air leak at the carburetor mounting flange?

50. What items should be checked during the inspection of a carburetor when the engine is mounted in the airplane?
51. Describe the cleaning of carburetor parts.
52. What inspections should be made of the parts of a float-type carburetor?
53. How is the size of a metering jet checked?
54. Describe the repair of a leaking float.
55. Give the procedure for checking the float level of a Bendix NA-S3A1 carburetor.
56. How is the fuel level of a Marvel MA-3 carburetor checked?
57. If fuel drips from the carburetor when the airplane is not operating, what is the likely cause?
58. What is the effect on engine operation when the float level of the carburetor is too high?
59. What are the symptoms of an excessively rich mixture?
60. If the engine backfires or cuts out momentarily when the throttle is moved forward, what is the likely cause?

CHAPTER 5

Pressure-injection Carburetors

PRINCIPLES OF PRESSURE INJECTION

Introduction

The pressure-injection type of carburetor is a radical departure from float-type carburetor designs and presents an entirely different approach to the problem of aircraft-engine fuel feed. It employs the simple method of metering the fuel through fixed orifices according to air venturi suction combined with the new function of atomizing the fuel spray under positive pump pressure.

Advantages

Among the more important advantages obtained from the use of the pressure-injection type of carburetor are the following:

1. Ice does not form from the vaporization of fuel in the throttle body of the carburetor.
2. Since the system is entirely closed, it operates normally during all types of flight maneuvers. Gravity and inertia have very little effect.
3. The fuel is accurately and automatically metered at all engine speeds and loads regardless of changes in altitude, propeller pitch, or throttle position.
4. Atomizing the fuel under pressure results in smoothness, flexibility, and economy of powerplant operation.
5. The settings are simple and uniform.
6. Protection against fuel boiling and vapor lock is provided.

Principles of operation

The basic principle of the pressure-injection carburetor can be explained briefly by stating that airflow is utilized to regulate the pressure of fuel to a metering system which governs the flow of fuel according to the pressure applied. The carburetor therefore increases fuel flow in proportion to airflow and maintains a correct fuel/air ratio in accordance with the throttle and mixture settings of the carburetor.

The fundamental operation of a pressure-injection carburetor may be shown with the simplified diagram of Fig. 5·1. In this diagram are shown four of the main parts of a pressure carburetor system. These are (1) the **throttle unit,** (2) the **regulator unit,** (3) the **fuel-control unit,** and (4) the **discharge nozzle.**

When the carburetor is operating, the air flows through the throttle unit in an amount governed by the opening of the throttle. At the entrance to the air passage are impact tubes which develop a pressure proportional to the velocity of the incoming air. This pressure is applied to chamber A in the regulator unit. As the air flows through the venturi, a reduced pressure is developed in accordance with the velocity of the airflow. This reduced pressure is applied to chamber B in the regulator unit. It is readily seen that the comparatively high pressure in chamber A and the low pressure in chamber B will create a differential of pressure across the diaphragm between the two chambers. The force of this pressure differential is called the **air metering force,** and as it increases, it opens the poppet valve and allows fuel under pressure from the fuel pump to flow into chamber D. This unmetered fuel

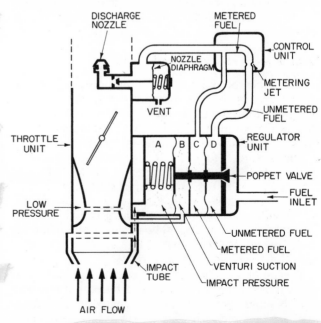

Figure 5·1 Simplified diagram of pressure-injection carburetor.

exerts force upon the diaphragm between chamber D and chamber C which tends to close the poppet valve. The fuel flows through one or more metering jets in the fuel-control unit and thence to the discharge nozzle. Chamber C of the regulator unit is connected to the output of the fuel-control unit to provide **metered fuel** pressure to act against the diaphragm between chambers C and D. Thus, unmetered fuel pressure acts against the D side of the diaphragm and metered fuel pressure acts against the C side. The fuel-pressure differential produces a force called the **fuel-metering force.**

When the throttle opening is increased, the airflow through the carburetor is increased and the pressure in the venturi is decreased. Thus the pressure in chamber B is lowered. At the same time, the impact pressure to chamber A is increased and the diaphragm between chambers A and B moves to the right because of the differential of pressure (air-metering force). This movement opens the poppet valve and allows more fuel to flow into chamber D. This increases the pressure in chamber D and tends to move the diaphragm and the poppet valve to the left against the air-metering force. This movement is modified by the pressure of metered fuel in chamber C. The pressure differential between chambers C and D (fuel-metering force) is balanced against the air-metering force at all times when the engine is operating at a given setting.

When the throttle opening is reduced, air-metering pressure decreases and the fuel-metering force starts to close the poppet valve. This causes a decrease in fuel-metering force until it is again balanced by the air-metering force.

Note particularly that an increase in airflow through the carburetor results in an increase in fuel-metering pressure across the metering jets in the fuel-control section, and this increase causes a greater flow of fuel to the discharge nozzle. A decrease in airflow has the converse effect.

Types of pressure-injection carburetors

A number of different types of pressure-injection carburetors have been manufactured, the majority being developed by the Bendix Products Division of the Bendix Corporation. Models have been manufactured for almost all sizes of reciprocating engines.

The carburetor for small engines has a single venturi in a single barrel and is designated by the letters PS meaning pressure-type single-barrel carburetor.

A pressure carburetor for larger engines has a double barrel with boost venturis and is designated by the letters PD (pressure-double). The triple-barrel carburetor is designated by the letters PT, and the rectangular barrel carburetor is designated by PR.

The numbers following the letter designation generally indicate the bore size of a carburetor or injection unit. Nominal bore sizes are designated in increments of ¼ in. beginning with No. 1 as a 1-in. nominal bore size. The actual bore diameter is ³⁄₁₆ in. larger than the nominal size. For example, the number 10 is 9 times

¼ in. larger than 1 in. in diameter, or 3.25 in. nominal diameter. The actual bore diameter is ³⁄₁₆ in. larger than the nominal diameter, or 3.4375 in.

Identification plates

Each new carburetor is identified with a **specification plate** or **production identification plate** attached to the main body. It identifies the manufacturer, unit serial number, model designation, and parts list and issue numbers to which the unit was manufactured.

Carburetors which are overhauled or modified are identified by means of a **service replacement identification plate.** A production identification plate and service replacement identification plate are shown in Fig. 5·2.

Operating units

The corresponding operating units comprising the various pressure-injection carburetors are similar in many respects. Each carburetor or injection system includes four to six principal units serving similar functions in the different carburetors.

The **throttle unit,** or **throttle body unit,** controls and measures the mass airflow through the carburetor to the engine. It contains the throttle and the venturi or venturis. By sensing the impact force and the velocity of the air, this unit provides the regulating forces used to influence fuel pressure and fuel/air mixture ratios.

The **regulator unit,** or **pressure-regulator unit,** automatically regulates the fuel pressure applied to the metering elements in the fuel-control unit. This regulation is accomplished by means of diaphragms responding to mass airflow and fuel flow as explained previously.

The **fuel-control unit** receives fuel under varying pressures from the regulator unit and meters it to the discharge nozzle. The fuel-control unit contains one or more metering jets and may also include the manual

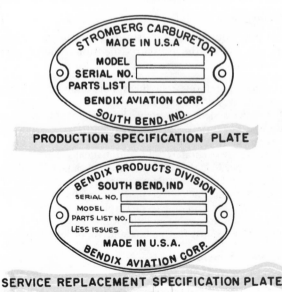

PRODUCTION SPECIFICATION PLATE

SERVICE REPLACEMENT SPECIFICATION PLATE

Figure 5·2 Identification plates.

mixture control. If a manual mixture control is included in the unit, the unit will usually contain jets (metering orifices) for "auto lean," "auto rich," and "full rich" operating conditions. It will also include a means whereby all fuel flow can be stopped to provide "idle cutoff" for stopping the engine.

The **discharge nozzle** for a pressure-injection carburetor may be somewhat complex, or it may be merely a fuel passage leading into the airstream on the engine side of the throttle with openings through which the fuel is sprayed into the airstream. Discharge nozzles are usually equipped with a valve to prevent fuel flow at very low pressures. Details of discharge nozzles will be explained for the specific carburetors described in this text.

An **accelerating pump** or similar device is usually required for a pressure-injection carburetor even as it is for a float-type carburetor. Some models of pressure carburetors employ diaphragm-type accelerating pumps, and others use throttle-operated piston pumps. A typical diaphragm pump consists of a diaphragm separating a fuel chamber and an air chamber. The air chamber is connected to the throttle bore on the engine side of the throttle. During low-power operation the air chamber has low pressure and fuel pressure moves the diaphragm in such a direction that a maximum volume of fuel is contained in the fuel chamber. When the throttle is opened rapidly, the pressure on the engine side of the throttle increases, and this pressure increase is transmitted to the air chamber of the accelerating pump. This increased pressure moves the diaphragm against the fuel chamber and forces the fuel out into the discharge nozzle, resulting in an extra supply of fuel for the acceleration period. Figure 5·3 is an illustration of a typical pressure discharge nozzle with a diaphragm-type accelerating pump.

An **enrichment valve,** commonly called a **power enrichment valve** or **fuel-head enrichment valve,** depending upon how it is actuated, takes the place of the economizer valve in the float-type carburetor. At high power settings it is necessary that the fuel/air ratio be

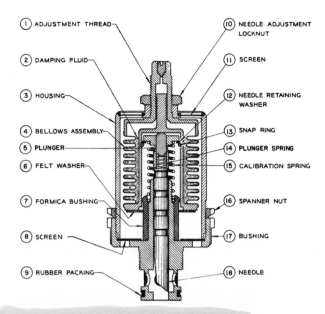

Figure **5·4** Automatic mixture-control unit.

① ADJUSTMENT THREAD	⑩ NEEDLE ADJUSTMENT LOCKNUT
② DAMPING FLUID	⑪ SCREEN
③ HOUSING	⑫ NEEDLE RETAINING WASHER
④ BELLOWS ASSEMBLY	⑬ SNAP RING
⑤ PLUNGER	⑭ PLUNGER SPRING
⑥ FELT WASHER	⑮ CALIBRATION SPRING
⑦ FORMICA BUSHING	⑯ SPANNER NUT
⑧ SCREEN	⑰ BUSHING
⑨ RUBBER PACKING	⑱ NEEDLE

increased to provide the extra cooling necessary. Pressure-injection carburetors are usually designed so the enrichment valve opens automatically when the throttle is moved to the higher power settings.

A number of pressure-injection carburetors make use of **automatic mixture-control (AMC) systems** which adjust the F/A mixture to compensate for changes in altitude. As previously explained, the pressure of the air decreases as altitude increases and this results in a decrease of available oxygen for a given volume of air. Thus the mixture will become richer as altitude increases unless the fuel flow is reduced in proportion to the decrease in air pressure. An automatic mixture-control unit is illustrated in Fig. 5·4. The bellows is filled with a measured amount of nitrogen and an inert oil to make it sensitive to temperature and pressure changes. As the bellows expands and contracts, it modifies the impact air pressure in chamber A of the regulator unit. This, in turn, affects the fuel pressure to the control unit and metering jets. It must be pointed out that the AMC cannot effectively modify chamber A pressure except in conjunction with the mixture-control bleeds located between chambers A and B. These bleeds tend to neutralize the pressure between A and B, however, the continuous flow of automatically controlled air to chamber A maintains the correct pressure differential.

Since the airflow at idling speeds is too small to provide good fuel regulation, it is necessary for pressure-injection carburetors to employ idling systems. An **idling system** is designed to provide a continued fuel flow at idling speeds because the main metering system cannot provide adequate fuel flow when the airflow through the carburetor is below a certain level. Usually, the idling system is effective during the first 10° of throttle travel.

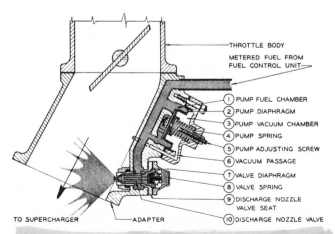

	THROTTLE BODY
	METERED FUEL FROM FUEL CONTROL UNIT
① PUMP FUEL CHAMBER	
② PUMP DIAPHRAGM	
③ PUMP VACUUM CHAMBER	
④ PUMP SPRING	
⑤ PUMP ADJUSTING SCREW	
⑥ VACUUM PASSAGE	
⑦ VALVE DIAPHRAGM	
⑧ VALVE SPRING	
⑨ DISCHARGE NOZZLE VALVE SEAT	
⑩ DISCHARGE NOZZLE VALVE	

TO SUPERCHARGER   ADAPTER

Figure **5·3** Discharge nozzle with diaphragm-type acceleration pump.

PRESSURE CARBURETOR FOR SMALL ENGINES

In order to provide the benefits of pressure-injection carburetion for small aircraft engines, the Bendix Products Division developed the PS series of carburetors. Figure 5·5 illustrates a PS-5C carburetor used on the Continental 0-470 series engines.

The PS-5C carburetor utilizes the principles explained previously in this chapter. It includes a throttle unit, regulator section, fuel-control unit, discharge nozzle, manual mixture control, acceleration pump, and idle system.

General description

The PS-5C injection carburetor is a single-barrel updraft unit that provides a closed fuel system from the engine fuel pump to the carburetor discharge nozzle. Its function is to meter fuel through a fixed jet to the engine in proportion to airflow. The discharge nozzle is located downstream of the throttle valve to prevent ice from forming in the carburetor. This carburetor provides positive fuel delivery regardless of aircraft altitude or attitude and maintains proper fuel/air ratios regardless of engine speed, propeller load, or throttle lever position.

Basic operation

The diagram of Fig. 5·6 should be studied to obtain visual concepts of the operating principles as they are described.

Air enters the carburetor throttle section through the air intake and passes through the venturi tube past the throttle valve and into the intake manifold of the engine. The flow of air is controlled by a conventional butterfly-type throttle valve. Intake air (impact pressure) also enters the annular space between the outside diameter of the venturi tube and the flange of the carburetor main body and flows through internal

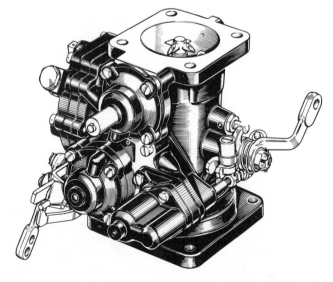

Figure 5·5 *A Bendix PS-5C pressure carburetor. (Bendix Products Div.)*

channels to chamber *A* of the regulator section and to the discharge-nozzle air bleed. It also flows to the high-pressure side of the manual mixture-control needle valve.

The velocity of the air flowing through the venturi creates a low-pressure area at the throat of the venturi tube. This low pressure is transmitted through internal channels to chamber *B* of the regulator and is known as **regulated venturi suction.** This pressure is also transmitted to the low-pressure side of the control diaphragm of the discharge nozzle and to the needle valve of the manual mixture control.

Since the **intake air pressure** in chamber *A* is greater than the regulated venturi suction in chamber *B*, a pressure differential is created. This pressure differential acts upon the air diaphragm which separates the two chambers. The differential force, acting on the air diaphragm, is termed **air-metering force** and increases or decreases with changes of airflow through the carburetor. Further control of the air-metering force is provided by the manual mixture control.

Movement of the air diaphragm in response to air-metering force is applied to the regulator poppet valve through a stem arrangement. The degree of opening of this poppet valve determines the pressure of unmetered fuel that is applied to the metering jet.

Fuel at engine pump pressure flows through the strainer into chamber *E* and past the poppet valve into chamber *D* of the regulator. The pressure of the fuel in chamber *D* is somewhat lower than the pressure in chamber *E* because of the pressure drop across the poppet valve. Fuel at this pressure is termed **unmetered fuel.** The pressure of this fuel is regulated by the degree of opening of the poppet valve. The poppet-valve movement is controlled by the forces acting on the air and fuel diaphragms. *A* chamber pressure minus *B* chamber pressure is a force acting on the air diaphragm, while *D* chamber pressure minus *B* chamber pressure is the force acting on the fuel diaphragm.

Fuel from chamber *D* flows through the **main metering jet** to chamber *C*. This jet meters fuel to the discharge nozzle during engine speeds above the idle range.

Metered fuel from chamber *C* flows through the **idle needle-valve seat** to the fuel side of the discharge-nozzle diaphragm. The opposite side of the diaphragm is exposed to regulated venturi suction and receives the force of an adjustable spring. When metered fuel pressure on the fuel side of the diaphragm overcomes the spring pressure, the needle valve will open and allow fuel to be discharged through the nozzle seat into the discharge-nozzle assembly. A fuel pressure drop is established as the fuel passes the discharge-nozzle needle valve. A supply of air from the impact pressure channel is directed to the discharge nozzle to help atomize the fuel as it is discharged. This serves the same purpose as the main air bleed in a float-type carburetor.

As the throttle is opened, airflow through the carburetor will increase, thus causing the air-metering force to increase. Since the air-metering force is

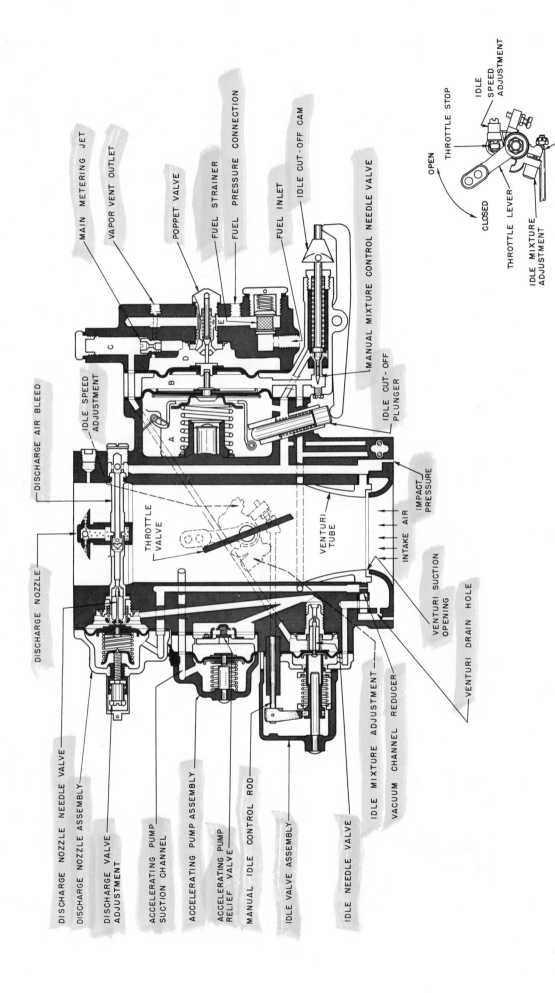

DISCHARGE AIR BLEED

MAIN METERING JET

VAPOR VENT OUTLET

POPPET VALVE

FUEL STRAINER

FUEL PRESSURE CONNECTION

FUEL INLET

IDLE CUT-OFF CAM

MANUAL MIXTURE CONTROL NEEDLE VALVE

THROTTLE STOP

IDLE SPEED ADJUSTMENT

OPEN

CLOSED

THROTTLE LEVER

IDLE MIXTURE ADJUSTMENT

IDLE CONTROL SHAFT (TO IDLE ASSEMBLY)

IDLE SPEED ADJUSTMENT

C

D

E

B

A

IDLE CUT-OFF PLUNGER

THROTTLE VALVE

IMPACT PRESSURE

VENTURI TUBE

INTAKE AIR

VENTURI SUCTION

DISCHARGE NOZZLE

VENTURI DRAIN HOLE

VENTURI OPENING

DISCHARGE NOZZLE NEEDLE VALVE

DISCHARGE NOZZLE ASSEMBLY

DISCHARGE VALVE ADJUSTMENT

ACCELERATING PUMP SUCTION CHANNEL

ACCELERATING PUMP ASSEMBLY

ACCELERATING PUMP RELIEF VALVE

MANUAL IDLE CONTROL ROD

IDLE VALVE ASSEMBLY

IDLE NEEDLE VALVE

IDLE MIXTURE ADJUSTMENT

VACUUM CHANNEL REDUCER

Figure 5·6   Schematic diagram of the PS-5C carburetor. (Bendix Products Div.)

91

stronger than the differential pressure across the fuel diaphragm (fuel-metering force), the regulator poppet valve will open farther. This will permit a greater volume of fuel to flow into chamber D, thus increasing the pressure of the unmetered fuel pressure applied to the main metering jet. When fuel pressure in chamber D is increased, the differential across the fuel diaphragm is increased and the poppet-valve movement is stopped. At this time the air-metering force is equal to the differential across the fuel diaphragm and the poppet valve will hold its position until the air-metering force increases or decreases. The fuel leaving chamber D is now metered by the main metering jet and not by the idle needle valve as it is during the idling range of engine speeds.

Idling system

In the idle range at low airflows, the differential pressure (unmetered fuel pressure minus regulated venturi suction) across the large fuel diaphragm plus the poppet-valve spring force will try to move the poppet valve to the closed position. However, this force is opposed by the regulator spring force in chamber A plus a small amount of air-metering force. These two opposing forces are balanced to hold the poppet valve open sufficiently to allow an ample amount of fuel to pass for idling purposes.

After passing through the main metering jet, the fuel is exposed to the idle needle valve and its diaphragm. The fuel pressure on the fuel side of the diaphragm is opposed by the unregulated venturi suction on the air side of the diaphragm. This establishes a differential pressure which tends to open the idle needle valve. The movement of the valve, however, is restricted and controlled by a fork on the throttle lever. At this point in the operating range, the actual metering of fuel is accomplished by the idle needle valve, because the orifice created by the needle valve and its seat is smaller than the main metering jet. As the throttle lever is opened, the fork on the idle lever will move out of contact with the idle pushrod and allow the differential pressure acting on the diaphragm to hold the idle needle valve open at or above high cruise throttle lever position.

The idle needle-valve assembly also serves as a power enrichment valve for high engine power settings. When the throttle reaches a position within 28° of wide open, an arm on the throttle shaft engages the manual idle control rod and releases the pressure of the discharge diaphragm spring, thus allowing the idle needle valve to move away from the needle-valve seat. This increases the orifice area to permit an increased fuel flow to the discharge nozzle.

Accelerating pump

A single-diaphragm vacuum-operated accelerating pump, which compensates for the lag in fuel flow that will occur when the throttle is opened rapidly, is incorporated in the Model PS-5C injection carburetor. The pump is composed of two chambers separated by a spring-loaded diaphragm. One side of the diaphragm is open to pressure above the throttle, while metered fuel pressure is applied to the other side of the diaphragm. This pressure differential causes the diaphragm to move in such a direction that it will compress the spring. When the throttle is opened rapidly, pressure above the throttle will increase, and this causes a corresponding increase in the pressure on the spring side of the diaphragm. This increase of pressure plus the force of the spring will move the diaphragm in a direction that will displace the fuel on the opposite side of the diaphragm. The displaced fuel temporarily increases the discharge-nozzle pressure and causes the nozzle to open farther, thus providing a momentary rich mixture for acceleration. The accelerating pump is shown in the diagram of Fig. 5·6.

Manual mixture control

A **manual mixture-control valve** provides a means of correcting for natural enrichment at altitude and for adjusting mixture at other times to obtain the most satisfactory operating conditions. The mixture control consists of a needle valve which is positioned in its seat by a pilot-controlled lever or knob. On one side of the seat is chamber B pressure, and on the other side is chamber A pressure. As the needle is moved out off its seat, chamber A pressure will bleed into chamber B, thus decreasing the pressure differential across the air diaphragm. This causes the poppet valve to close partially and reduce the fuel pressure in chamber D, which results in a leaner mixture. The reverse action takes place when the needle is moved back in its seat.

When the **manual mixture-control** lever is moved to the IDLE CUTOFF position, the **idle cutoff cam** on the linkage actuates a rocker arm which causes the plunger to move inward against the release lever in chamber A. The release lever compresses the regulator diaphragm spring and releases all spring tension on the diaphragm. While this is taking place, the manual mixture-control needle is being pulled out of its seat, thus reducing the air-metering force. With the air-metering force reduced, the differential pressure across the large fuel diaphragm, plus the spring force on the regulator poppet valve, closes the poppet valve, thus shutting off the fuel through the carburetor and to the engine.

PRESSURE CARBURETOR FOR LARGE ENGINES

A number of different models of pressure-injection carburetors have been designed for large engines; however, they all utilize the principles explained previously. These carburetors vary in size, type of mixture control, type of enrichment valves, shape of throttle body, and type of discharge nozzle. In this section we shall describe a typical model which illustrates the most important principles of operation.

Bendix-Stromberg PR-type carburetor

For the purpose of this discussion, the Bendix PR-58A1 carburetor is used inasmuch as it possesses

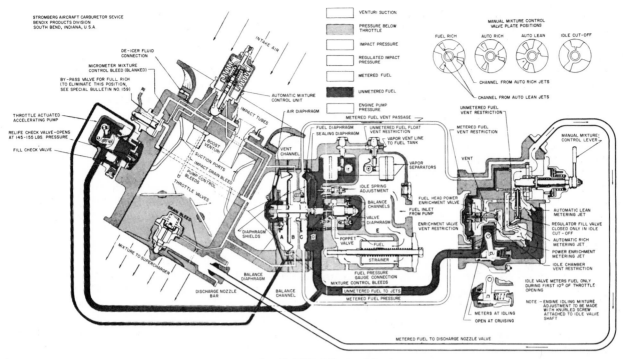

STROMBERG AIRCRAFT CARBURETOR SEVICE
BENDIX PRODUCTS DIVISION
SOUTH BEND, INDIANA, U.S.A.

CARBURETOR MODEL PR–58A1

Figure 5·7 Schematic diagram of Bendix PR-58A1 carburetor.

most of the characteristics of typical pressure-injection carburetors for large engines. A schematic diagram of this carburetor system is shown in Fig. 5 · 7.

Principal units

In order to understand the operation of the complete carburetor, it is necessary to be familiar with the construction and operation of each unit and its function in relation to the other units. There are four basic units of the carburetor: (1) the throttle unit, (2) the automatic mixture-control unit, (3) the pressure-regulator unit, (4) the fuel-control unit.

The throttle unit

The rectangular **throttle unit** is illustrated as part of the schematic diagram of Fig. 5 · 7. It is the foundation of the carburetor and contains the main venturi plates, boost venturi tubes, impact tubes, and butterfly throttle valves. Provisions are made on the throttle body for mounting the automatic mixture-control unit, the pressure-regulator unit, a mechanically operated accelerating pump, and the discharge nozzle and bar.

The principal function of the throttle unit is to control and provide a means of measuring the mass airflow to the engine. The discharge from the mechanically operated accelerating pump is transmitted to the balance chamber in the regulator unit front body where it momentarily unbalances the diaphragm assembly to deliver a greater volume of fuel to the discharge nozzle.

The automatic mixture control

The **automatic fuel-control unit** is shown in the schematic diagram mounted at the air inlet of the

throttle unit. It consists of a sealed metallic bellows operating a contoured needle valve. The sealed bellows is filled with a measured amount of nitrogen gas and an inert oil. The bellows senses air-pressure changes and imparts movement to the needle valve as pressure increases or decreases. The bellows movement positions the needle valve in accordance with air pressure, thereby regulating impact air pressure in chamber *A* of the regulator section. As the operation of the regulator section is studied, it will be seen that the automatic mixture control acts to reduce fuel pressure to compensate for natural enrichment at altitude.

The pressure-regulator unit

The **pressure-regulator unit** is mounted on the rear of the throttle body. It automatically regulates the fuel pressure applied to the metering elements in the fuel-control unit. This regulation is accomplished in response to variations in the mass airflow through the throttle body. The pressure regulator consists principally of a large air and fuel diaphragm mounted on a common stem supported by suitable guides. A poppet valve is attached to the stem so that any movement of the diaphragm is transmitted to the poppet valve, opening or closing the valve as the air flow through the throttle body increases or decreases. A fuel strainer and a vapor-separator system are also contained in the pressure-regulator unit.

The fuel-control unit

The **fuel-control unit** is attached to the regulator unit. It incorporates a series of fixed metering jets, a manual mixture-control valve and idle valve, a power-enrich-

93

ment valve, and a regulator-fill valve. The manual mixture-control valve has three different positions: (1) IDLE CUTOFF, (2) AUTO LEAN, and (3) AUTO RICH. During the first 10° of throttle opening, the idle valve meters the fuel, after which the idle valve is fully open and offers no restriction. The regulator-fill valve is closed only in the IDLE CUTOFF position and prevents fuel from being drawn from the metered fuel chamber C (Fig. 5·7) in the regulator, in order to stop all fuel flow to the engine.

All the Bendix-Stromberg injection carburetors do not have a three-position manual mixture control. Some units have a fourth position known as the EMERGENCY or FULL RICH position.

Operating principles

Air enters the carburetor at the air intake and passes downward through the main venturi plates and the boost venturi tubes past the throttle valves and into the supercharger. The flow of air is controlled in the usual manner by the throttle valves. Referring to Fig. 5·7, the boost venturi tubes, in conjunction with the main venturi plates, create a suction which is transmitted from the throat of the boost venturi tubes to a chamber in the regulator labeled B. A portion of the air flows into the impact tubes and flows through an internal channel past the automatic mixture-control needle where its flow is restricted. The flow, thus restricted, is termed **regulated impact pressure.** This regulated impact pressure is transmitted to the chamber in the regulator labeled A, and although it is lower than the original impact pressure, it is greater than the venturi suction in chamber B. This pressure differential between chambers A and B, acting on the air diaphragm between these two chambers, produces a force to the right tending to open the poppet valve. This force, termed the **air-metering force,** increases or decreases as the throttle valves are opened or closed to permit more or less air to flow through the throttle unit.

Fuel enters the regulator at the fuel inlet and passes through the fuel strainer into chamber E of the regulator. The pressure of the fuel in this chamber is the same as the pressure delivered by the engine-driven fuel pump and is the highest pressure in the carburetor. Fuel vapor or air is eliminated from chamber E by the action of the vapor separator. The valve of the separator opens when vapor or air accumulates in chamber E and allows the vapor or air to escape through a line to the fuselage fuel tank. An identical system is used to vent the unmetered fuel chamber D. These two venting systems are connected by an internal channel.

In reference again to Fig. 5·7, the liquid fuel then flows past the poppet valve into chamber D of the regulator. The pressure of the fuel in chamber D is lowered owing to the restriction of the poppet valve. The fuel at this reduced pressure is termed **unmetered fuel.**

The fuel then flows from chamber D of the regulator through an internal channel into the fuel-control unit

past the idle valve and then through the metering jets. After the fuel passes through the jets, the fuel pressure is further reduced. Fuel at this pressure is termed **metered fuel.** A portion of the metered fuel flows through another internal channel to the chamber in the regulator labeled C. This results in a pressure differential between chambers C and D acting on the fuel diaphragm to create a force to the left which tends to close the poppet valve. This force is termed the **fuel-metering force.**

The air-metering force (pressure in chamber A minus the pressure in chamber B) acting upon the large diaphragm creates a force which shifts the diaphragm to the right, thus opening the poppet valve. As the opening of the poppet valve increases, the pressure of the unmetered fuel in chamber D increases, thus permitting more fuel to flow through the jets of the fuel-control unit. This results in an increased dual-metering force (pressure in chamber D minus pressure in chamber C). The fuel-metering force is regulated by and equal to the air-metering force except in the idle range.

The **idle spring** in the regulator holds the poppet valve open in the idle range. This is necessary because the air-metering force is not great enough to open the poppet valve in this range. This situation causes the fuel-metering force to be slightly higher than the air-metering force which is assisted by the idle spring, thus furnishing the desired mixture enrichment in the idle range. The idle spring adjustment is used to vary the fuel-metering force at low air-metering forces and is to be adjusted only when the carburetor is tested on a flow bench.

The metered fuel then flows upward through the manual mixture-control plates through an external fuel-transfer line to the discharge nozzle in the bottom of the throttle body. The fuel presses against a spring-loaded discharge-nozzle diaphragm, and when this pressure is sufficient to overcome the force of the spring load, the nozzle valve opens and sprays fuel out into the rake-type discharge bar, where it is mixed with the air going to the supercharger.

When the airplane is cruising with the manual mixture control in the AUTO LEAN position, the fuel flow is limited by the size of the **auto-lean** jet. This jet is selected to give the maximum fuel economy. Additional fuel for best power when cruising is added by moving the manual mixture control to the AUTO RICH position, whereupon fuel also flows through the **auto-rich** jet.

For takeoff and emergency operation, a diaphragm-operated **power-enrichment valve** is incorporated in the fuel-control unit. When the force of the unmetered fuel pressure on the enrichment-valve diaphragm is sufficient to overcome the combined force of the metered fuel pressure and the enrichment-valve spring, the valve opens and allows additional fuel to flow through the open valve. Since the **power-enrichment** jet is larger than the **auto-rich** jet, a richer mixture will be obtained whenever the enrichment valve is open. When the power-enrichment valve is wide open, the metering of the fuel is accomplished by the **auto-lean** and **power-enrichment** jets.

From the facts given above it is apparent that this carburetor is fully automatic. The desired fuel/air ratio is maintained for any desired power or mixture selection, according to the engine manufacturer's requirements, without manual adjustment in flight.

Typical fuel/air ratio curve

Figure 5·8 is a typical fuel/air ratio curve obtained with the pressure-injection carburetor and the fuel-control unit. Notice that the cruise and takeoff values are maintained under altitude and temperature change, independently of propeller pitch, engine speed, or throttle position.

The idling range is from 0 to 1900 lb per hr of air, and the fuel flow is controlled in the same manner as the fuel flow of the fuel-control unit having an airflow economizer, described later in this chapter. The only difference is the position of the control-unit idle valve.

On the fuel/air ratio curve of Fig. 5·8, the **cruising** range is from 1900 to 5300 lb per hr of air. After about 10° of throttle movement, the idle needle valve is drawn out to its open position. The metering then shifts from the orifice formed between the idle needle valve and seat to the automatic-lean metering jet and the automatic-rich metering jet, providing that the manual selector valve is in the rich position.

If the selector valve is in the LEAN position, the automatic-rich metering jet is closed. Rich-automatic cruise is determined by the capacity of the automatic-lean and the automatic-rich metering jets. Lean-automatic cruise is obtained when the manual control is placed in such a position that the channel through the valve plates from the automatic-rich metering jet is closed, thus reducing the fuel flow.

The **power range,** as shown on the curve, is from the upper limit of cruising, 5300 to 9500 lb per hr of air. Gradually increasing fuel/air ratios are required from

either the RICH CRUISE or LEAN CRUISE positions up to 9500 lb per hr of air, or maximum air consumption.

Inspection and maintenance

The only inspections necessary for the PR-type carburetor are routine checks for security of mounting, attachment of linkages, leakage, and safetying. Operational checks are carried out at the preflight run-up and checkout.

Idle speed adjustments may be made according to the manufacturer's instructions. In general, the idle adjustment of the carburetor should be set to provide approximately a 20-rpm enrichment of the lean/best mixture at idling speed. This is accomplished by running the warmed-up engine at idle speed and then adjusting the idle mixture to provide the highest idle rpm. The mixture adjustment is then moved or turned toward the RICH direction until the rpm falls off about 20 rpm. The adjustment should then be checked by moving the mixture control toward IDLE CUTOFF to see if the 20 rpm is regained as the control is moved toward the leaner position. The idle enrichment is needed to provide for easier starting of the engine because of the poor vaporization of cold fuel, thus avoiding the backfiring which would otherwise occur. The idle mixture must not be too rich or the spark plugs will be fouled.

Since the PR-type carburetor is normally mounted on the upper part of the engine blower case, great care must be taken during removal and replacement. After all linkages and hose attachments and disconnected, all loose nuts, bolts, cotter pins, and other parts must be cleared away before the carburetor is lifted from its mounting. As soon as the carburetor is removed, a cover plate must be placed over the carburetor opening to prevent the entrance of any foreign material. This plate must remain in place until the carburetor is reinstalled.

Removal of carburetor from storage

When a new or overhauled carburetor is removed from extended storage, it should be prepared according to manufacturer's instructions before installation and operation. This preparation usually consists of removing drain plugs and caps from fittings to permit complete drainage of any preservative fluids from the inside. The fuel section of the carburetor should then be filled with gasoline and replugged. The gasoline should be allowed to remain in the carburetor for about 24 hr in order to soak the diaphragms. Care should be taken to see that gasoline is not permitted to enter the air sections of the regulator unit.

Malfunctions

Malfunctions of a pressure-type carburetor usually require that the carburetor be removed and checked on a flow bench. Minor adjustments of idling and control linkages can be made in the field, but such problems as plugged passages, ruptured diaphragms, and sticking valves cannot be corrected without at least partial disassembly. This can be done only in an approved carburetor overhaul shop.

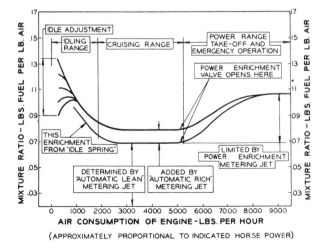

Figure 5·8 Fuel/air ratio curve.

REVIEW QUESTIONS

1. List the advantages of a pressure-injection carburetor.
2. How does the pressure-type carburetor measure airflow into the engine?
3. Explain how *air-metering force* is developed.
4. What pressures are used to develop the *fuel-metering force?*
5. Explain the purpose of the *fuel-control unit.*
6. Why is the discharge nozzle equipped with a valve?
7. Explain the operation of a diaphragm-type accelerating pump.
8. What is the purpose of an *enrichment valve?*
9. How is the *automatic mixture-control unit* constructed?
10. In a PS-type carburetor, what pressure is modified by the manual mixture control?
11. To what chamber of the regulator section is unmetered fuel pressure applied in the PS-type carburetor?
12. If the impact pressure openings were clogged in the PS carburetor, what would be the effect on engine operation?
13. Trace the fuel flow from unit to unit through the PS-type carburetor.
14. What is the effect of a pressure increase in the *D* chamber of the PS carburetor?
15. What arrangement is made in the PS carburetor to allow sufficient fuel flow for idling when the throttle is closed?
16. Explain the operation of the manual mixture control.
17. What are the four principal units of the PR-58 carburetor?
18. Explain the operation of the power enrichment valve in the PR-58 carburetor.
19. Under what conditions of operation does the PR carburetor provide the most economical fuel/air ratio?
20. What adjustments may be made on the pressure-type carburetor?

Fuel-injection Systems

DEFINITION

Fuel injection is the introduction of fuel or fuel/air mixture into the induction system of an engine or into the combustion chamber of each cylinder by means of a pressure source other than the pressure differential created by airflow through the venturi of a carburetor. The usual pressure source is an injection pump, which may be any one of several types. A **fuel-injection carburetor** discharges the fuel into the airstream at or near the carburetor. A **fuel-injection system** discharges the fuel near the supercharger impeller, in the intake port of each cylinder just ahead of the intake valve, or directly into the combustion chamber of each cylinder.

Fuel-injection systems have a number of advantages among which are the following:

1. Freedom from vaporization icing, thus making it unnecessary to use carburetor heat except under the most severe atmospheric conditions
2. More uniform delivery of fuel/air mixture to each cylinder
3. Improved control of fuel/air ratio
4. Reduction of maintenance problems
5. Instant acceleration of the engine after idling with no tendency to stall
6. Increased engine efficiency

Fuel-injection systems have been designed for all types of reciprocating aircraft engines from the four-cylinder opposed engines up to the 28-cylinder Pratt & Whitney R-4360 engine. They are presently used on a wide variety of light engine airplanes, large commercial aircraft, helicopters, and military aircraft.

CONTINENTAL CONTINUOUS-FLOW INJECTION SYSTEM

The Continental fuel-injection system is of the multi-nozzle, continuous-flow type which controls fuel flow to match engine airflow. The fuel is discharged into the intake port of each cylinder. Any change in air throttle position, engine speed, or a combination of both causes changes in fuel flow in the correct relation to engine airflow. A manual mixture control and a pressure gage, indicating metered fuel pressure, are provided for precise leaning at any combination of altitude and power setting. Since fuel flow is directly proportional to metered fuel pressure, settings can be predetermined and fuel consumption can be accurately predicted. The continuous-flow system permits the use of a typical rotary-vane fuel pump in place of a much more complex and expensive plunger-type pump. There is no need for a timing mechanism because each cylinder draws fuel from the discharge nozzle in the intake port as the intake valve opens.

The Continental fuel-injection system consists of four basic units. These are the **fuel-injection pump,** the **fuel/air control unit,** the **fuel manifold,** and the **discharge nozzles.** These units are shown in Fig. 6 · 1.

Fuel-injection pump

The fuel pump, Fig. 6 · 2, is a positive-displacement rotary-vane type with a splined shaft for connection to the accessory drive system of the engine. A spring-loaded diaphragm-type relief valve which also acts as a pressure regulator is provided in the body of the pump. Pump outlet fuel pressure passes through a calibrated orifice before entering the relief valve chamber, thus making the pump delivery pressure proportional to engine speed.

Fuel enters the pump assembly at the swirl well of the **vapor separator** as shown in the drawing. At this point, any vapor in the fuel is forced upward to the top of the chamber where it is drawn off by means of the **vapor ejector.** The vapor ejector is a small pressure jet of fuel which feeds the vapor into the vapor return line where it is carried back to the fuel tank. There are no moving parts in the vapor separator, and the only restrictive passage is used in connection with vapor removal; hence there is no restriction of main fuel flow.

Disregarding the effects of altitude or ambient-air conditions, the use of a positive-displacement engine-driven pump means that changes in engine speed affect total pump flow proportionally. The pump provides greater capacity than is required by the engine; hence a recirculation path is required. When the relief valve and orifice are placed in this path, fuel pressure proportional to engine speed is provided. These provisions assure proper pump pressure and delivery for all engine operating speeds.

A check valve, shown in the drawing, is provided so that boost pressure to the system from an auxiliary

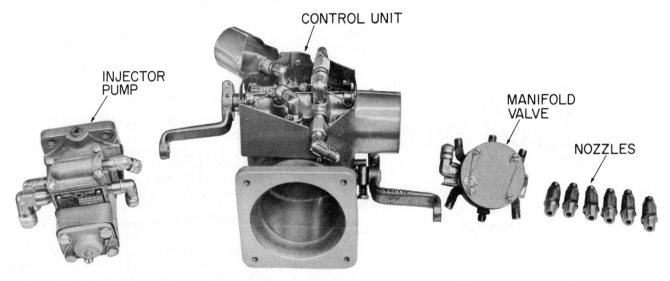

CONTROL UNIT

INJECTOR PUMP

MANIFOLD VALVE

NOZZLES

Figure **6·1**   Units of the Continental fuel-injection system. (Sky Store, Inc.)

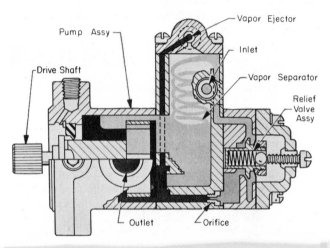

Pump Assy

Vapor Ejector

Drive Shaft

Inlet

Vapor Separator

Relief Valve Assy

Outlet

Orifice

Figure **6·2**   Fuel-injection pump. (Continental Motors Corp.)

pump can bypass the engine-driven pump when starting. This feature is also available to suppress vapor formation under high ambient temperatures of the fuel. Furthermore, this permits use of the auxiliary pump as a source of fuel pressure in the event of failure of the engine-driven pump.

Fuel-air control unit

The **fuel-air control unit** occupies the position ordinarily used for the carburetor at the intake manifold inlet. The unit includes three control elements, one for air in the **air throttle assembly** and two for fuel in the **fuel-control assembly** which is mounted on the side of the air throttle assembly.

The air throttle assembly is an aluminum casting which contains the shaft and butterfly valve. The casting bore size is tailored to the engine size and no venturi or other restriction is employed. Large shaft bosses provide adequate bearing area for the throttle

shaft so there is a minimum of wear at the shaft bearings. Wave washers are used to provide protection against vibration. A conventional idle speed-adjusting screw is mounted in the air throttle shaft lever and bears against a stop pin in the casting. The air throttle assembly is shown in Fig. 6·3.

The fuel-control unit, shown in Fig. 6·4, is made of bronze for best bearing action with the stainless-steel valves. The central bore contains a metering valve at one end and a mixture-control valve at the other end. These rotary valves are carried in oil-impregnated bushings and are sealed against leakage by O rings. Loading springs are installed in the center bore of the unit between the end bushings and the large end of each control shaft to force the valve ends against a fixed plug installed in the middle of the bore. This arrangement assures a close contact between the valve faces and the metering plug. The bronze metering plug has one passage that mates with the fuel return port and one through passage that connects the mixture-control

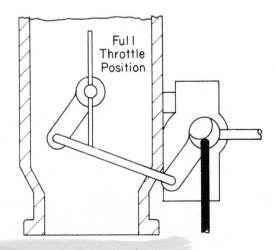

Full Throttle Position

Figure **6·3**   Fuel-air control unit.

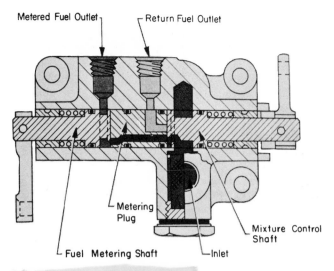

Figure 6·4 Fuel-control unit.

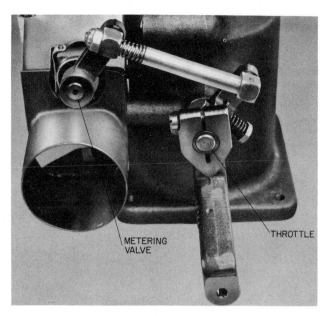

Figure 6·5 Linkage from throttle to fuel-metering valve assembly.

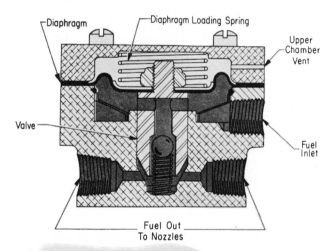

Figure 6·6 Fuel manifold valve.

valve chamber with the metering valve chamber. O rings are used to seal the metering plug in the body.

Each stainless-steel rotary valve includes a groove which forms a fuel chamber. A contoured end face of the mixture-control valve aligns with the passages in the metering plug to regulate the fuel flow from the fuel chamber to the metering valve or to the return fuel outlet. A control lever is mounted on the mixture-control valve shaft for connection to the cockpit mixture control. If the mixture control is moved toward the lean position, the mixture-control valve in the fuel-control unit causes additional fuel to flow through the return line to the fuel pump. This, of course, reduces the fuel flow through the metering plug to the metering valve. Rotation of the fuel-control valve toward the **rich** position causes more fuel to be delivered to the metering valve and less to the return fuel outlet.

On the metering valve a cam-shaped cut is made on one outer part of the end face which bears against the metering plug. As the valve is rotated, the passage from the metering plug is opened or closed in accordance with the movement of the throttle lever. As the throttle is opened, the fuel flow to the metered fuel outlet is increased. Thus, fuel is measured to provide the correct amount for the proper fuel/air ratio. The linkage from the throttle to the fuel-metering valve is shown in Fig. 6·5.

Fuel manifold valve

The **fuel manifold valve** is illustrated in the drawing of Fig. 6·6. The fuel manifold valve body contains a fuel inlet, a diaphragm chamber, a valve assembly, and outlet ports for the lines to the individual fuel nozzles. The spring-loaded diaphragm carries the valve plunger in the central bore of the body. The diaphragm is enclosed by a cover which retains the diaphragm loading spring. When the engine is not running, there is no pressure on the diaphragm to oppose the spring pressure; hence the valve will be closed to seal off the outlet ports. Furthermore, the ball in the center bore

of the valve plunger will be held on its seat to close the passage through the plunger. When fuel pressure is applied to the fuel inlet and into the chamber below the diaphragm, the diaphragm will be deflected and will raise the plunger from its seat. The pressure will also open the ball valve and allow fuel to pass through to the outlet ports.

A fine screen is installed in the diaphragm chamber so that all fuel entering the chamber must pass through the screen to filter out any foreign particles. During inspection or trouble shooting of the system, this screen should be cleaned.

Fuel discharge nozzle

The **fuel discharge nozzle,** shown in the drawing of Fig. 6·7, is mounted in the cylinder head of the engine with its outlet directed into the intake port. The nozzle

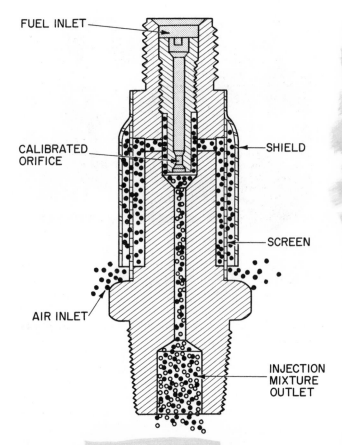

FUEL INLET

CALIBRATED ORIFICE

SHIELD

SCREEN

AIR INLET

INJECTION MIXTURE OUTLET

Figure 6·7 Fuel discharge nozzle.

body contains a drilled central passage with a counterbore at each end. The lower end of the nozzle is used for a fuel/air mixing chamber before the spray leaves the nozzle. The upper bore contains a removable orifice for calibrating the nozzles.

Near the top of the nozzle body radial holes connect the upper counterbore with the outside of the nozzle body to provide for air bleed. These holes enter the counterbore above the orifice and draw outside air through a cylindrical screen fitted over the nozzle body. The screen keeps dirt and other foreign material out of the interior of the nozzle. A press-fitted shield is mounted on the nozzle body and extends over the greater part of the filter screen, leaving an opening near the bottom. This provides both mechanical protection and an air path of abrupt change of direction as an aid to cleanliness. Nozzles are calibrated in several ranges, and all nozzles furnished for one engine are of the same range. The range is identified by a letter stamped on the hex of the nozzle body.

Complete system

The complete Continental fuel-injection system installed on an engine is shown in Fig. 6·8. This diagram shows the fuel- and air-control unit installed at the usual location of the carburetor, the pump installed on the accessory section, the fuel manifold valve installed on the top of the engine, and the nozzles in the cylinders at the intake ports. The simplicity of the system, which contributes to ease of maintenance and economy of operation, is clearly apparent.

Adjustments

The **idle speed adjustment** on the fuel-control unit is a conventional spring-loaded screw located in the air throttle lever. It should be set for the idling speed specified in the airplane manual.

The **idle mixture adjustment** is the locknut at the metering valve end of the linkage between the metering valve and air throttle levers. Tightening the nut to shorten the linkage provides a richer mixture. A leaner mixture is obtained by backing off the nut to lengthen

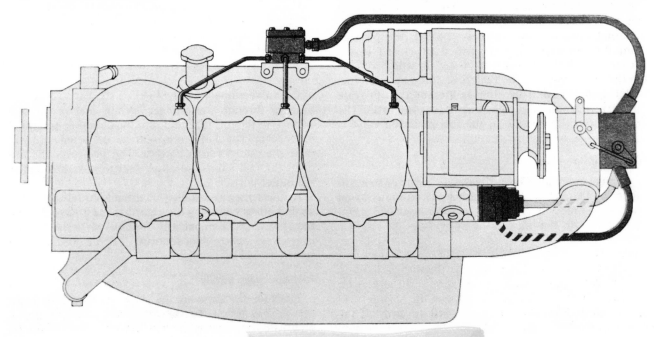

Figure 6·8 Continental fuel-injection system installed.

the linkage. The idle mixture should be adjusted to obtain a slight and momentary gain in idle speed as the mixture control is slowly moved toward the IDLE CUTOFF position.

The injection pump pressure is part of the basic calibration and requires the services of an authorized representative with the necessary equipment for testing and resetting.

Periodic inspection

In order to avoid any difficulty with the fuel-injection system it is well to perform certain inspections and checks, even though no operating discrepancies have been noted. The following inspections are recommended:

1. Check all attaching parts for tightness. Check safetying devices.
2. Check all fuel lines for leaks, evidence of damage such as sharp bends or flatted tubes, or chafing by metal-to-metal contact.
3. Check control connections, levers, and linkages for tight attaching parts, for safetying, and for lost motion owing to wear.
4. Inspect nozzles for cleanliness, with particular attention to air screens and orifices. Use a standard ½-in. spark-plug wrench (deep socket) to remove the nozzles. Do not remove the shields to clean the air screen in the nozzles. Do not use wire or other objects to clean the orifices. To clean the nozzles, remove them from the engine and immerse them in fresh cleaning solvent. Use compressed air to dry.
5. Unscrew the strainer plug from the fuel-injection control valve, and clean the screen in fresh cleaning solvent. Reinstall, safety, and check for leaks.
6. In periodic lubrication, apply a drop of engine oil on each end of the air throttle shaft and at each end of the linkage between the air throttle and fuel-metering valve. No other lubrication is required.
7. In the event that a line fitting in any part of the injection system must be replaced, only a fuel-soluble lubricant (such as engine oil) is authorized on the fitting threads as installation. Do not use any other form of thread compound.
8. If a nozzle is damaged and requires replacement, it is not necessary to replace the entire set. Each replacement nozzle must match the one removed as marked.

Operation

For the operation of an aircraft engine equipped with the Continental fuel-injection system, certain facts must be remembered by the technician or pilot.

1. When starting the engine, it is easy to flood the system if the timing of the starting events is not correct. When the mixture control is in any position other than IDLE CUTOFF, the throttle is open (even slightly), and the auxiliary fuel pump is operating, fuel will be flowing into the intake ports of the cylinders. Therefore the engine should be started within a few seconds after the auxiliary fuel pump is turned on.
2. The engine cannot be started without the auxiliary fuel pump because the engine-driven pump will not supply adequate pressure until the engine is running.
3. The auxiliary fuel pump should be turned off during flight. It may be left on during takeoff as a safety measure.
4. For takeoff, the throttle should be fully advanced and the mixture control should be set at FULL RICH.
5. For cruising, the engine rpm should be set according to

instructions in the operator's handbook. The mixture control may be set for best power or for an economy cruising condition, depending upon the desire of the operator. Care must be exercised to make sure that the mixture is not leaned too much.
6. Before reducing power for descent, the mixture should be set to best power. Upon entering the traffic pattern, the mixture control must be set to FULL RICH and kept in this position until after landing.
7. The engine is stopped by moving the mixture control to IDLE CUTOFF after the engine has been idled for a short time. All switches should be turned off immediately after the engine is stopped.

BENDIX FUEL-INJECTION SYSTEM

General description

The Bendix RS-type fuel-injection system utilizes the principle of measuring airflow and using the airflow signals to operate a servo valve. The servo valve governs the fuel pressure in accordance with engine requirements, and when the fuel pressure is applied across a metering jet, the fuel flow is proportional to airflow into the engine.

Fuel pressure regulation by means of a servo valve necessitates only a minimum fuel pressure drop through the entire metering system. This makes it possible to maintain metering pressures far above vapor-forming conditions and at the same time requires a fuel inlet pressure sufficiently low so that a diaphragm pump can be used. An inherent feature of the servo system is self-purging, which eliminates any possibility of vapor lock and the associated problem of difficult starting.

Airflow sensing system

The **airflow sensing system** for the Bendix fuel-injection system is similar to that previously described for pressure-injection carburetors. The schematic diagram of the system in Fig. 6·9 shows that inlet air passes through a **venturi** and is controlled by a **throttle valve**. **Impact tubes** sense the ram air pressure which is dependent upon air velocity and density. Air enters the **throttle body** through the air intake and passes through the venturi assembly, past the throttle valve, and into the intake manifold of the engine. The ram air pressure sensed by the impact tubes is conveyed to one side of the air diaphragm, and the other side of the diaphragm is exposed to the low pressure (suction) sensed at the venturi throat. It therefore becomes apparent that a differential pressure governed by airflow will exist across the air diaphragm. This pressure results in the **air-metering force** which acts through the **regulator lever** to move the **ball servo valve** toward a closed position as airflow increases.

The servo regulator

The section of the unit containing the air and fuel diaphragms is called the **servo regulator**. The two diaphragms are connected by means of the regulator lever so a force acting on one diaphragm will affect the other diaphragm. Fuel inlet pressure is applied to one

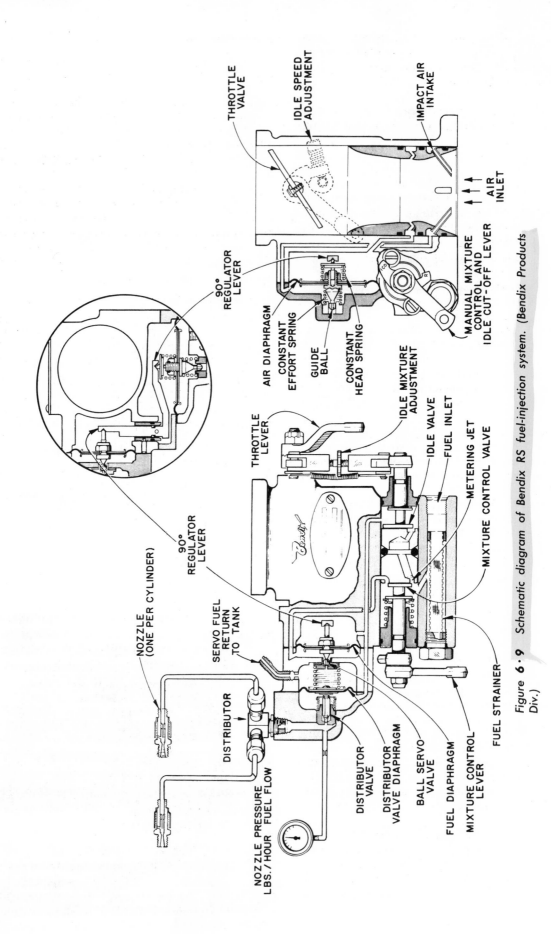

THROTTLE VALVE

IDLE SPEED ADJUSTMENT

IMPACT AIR INTAKE

AIR INLET

90° REGULATOR LEVER

AIR DIAPHRAGM

CONSTANT EFFORT SPRING

GUIDE BALL

CONSTANT HEAD SPRING

MANUAL MIXTURE CONTROL AND IDLE CUT-OFF LEVER

IDLE MIXTURE ADJUSTMENT

IDLE VALVE

FUEL INLET

METERING JET

MIXTURE CONTROL VALVE

THROTTLE LEVER

90° REGULATOR LEVER

FUEL STRAINER

NOZZLE (ONE PER CYLINDER)

SERVO FUEL RETURN TO TANK

DISTRIBUTOR

DISTRIBUTOR VALVE

DISTRIBUTOR VALVE DIAPHRAGM

BALL SERVO VALVE

FUEL DIAPHRAGM

MIXTURE CONTROL LEVER

NOZZLE PRESSURE LBS./HOUR FUEL FLOW

Figure 6·9 Schematic diagram of Bendix RS fuel-injection system. (Bendix Products Div.)

side of the fuel diaphragm, and the other side of the diaphragm is exposed to fuel which has passed through the metering jet. The differential pressure thus created across the fuel diaphragm is called **fuel-metering pressure.**

A careful study of the effects of fuel- and air-pressure differentials in the servo unit will reveal that the fuel differential pressure across the metering jet varies in accordance with airflow. Note that inlet fuel pressure is directed to one side of the fuel diaphragm, and the effect of this pressure is to open the ball servo valve. When the ball servo valve is open, the pressure on this side of the diaphragm decreases. This will cause a decrease in the differential pressure across the metering valve and a decrease in fuel flow to the **distributor valve.** If airflow increases, the air diaphragm will move in a direction to move the fuel diaphragm toward the ball servo valve. This will close the ball servo valve, and fuel differential pressure across the metering jet will increase, thus increasing fuel flow.

The fuel-metering force across the fuel diaphragm (metered fuel pressure against inlet fuel pressure) acts to oppose the action of the air-metering force, thus tending to open the ball servo valve. Whenever the air-metering force, fuel-metering force, and spring forces are balanced, the ball servo valve will maintain a fixed position.

The purpose of the regulator section is to provide regulated servo pressure to the distributor valve and discharge nozzles. When airflow is low, servo pressure will be high, and when airflow is high, servo pressure will be low.

The normally richer mixture required for engine idle is provided by the **constant head spring,** which is extended at low airflow. As airflow increases, the spring is collapsed and the retainer and air diaphragm stem become as a solid unit. The **constant effort spring** sets up a nominal load on the air diaphragm to assist the constant head spring.

Fuel-control system

The **fuel-control system** incorporated in the servo valve regulator control assembly is shown at the bottom of the left-hand drawing in Fig. 6·9. This section of the regulator includes a fine mesh fuel-inlet strainer, a rotary idle valve, and a rotary manual mixture-control valve. The idle valve is connected to the throttle valve by means of an adjustable link. A metering jet is incorporated in the passage between inlet fuel pressure and metered fuel pressure. On some models, an enrichment jet is also provided to supply extra fuel at high power settings. This is true of the Model RS-10B2 fuel-injection system designed for use with the Pratt & Whitney R-985 engine.

The manual mixture-control valve produces a full-rich condition when the lever is against the RICH stop and a progressively leaner mixture as the lever is moved toward the IDLE CUTOFF stop. Both idle speed (closed throttle position) and idle mixture can be readily adjusted externally on the unit to individual engine requirements.

Distributor valve

The **distributor valve** for the RS-5B1 fuel-injection system is mounted on the main servo regulator unit as shown in the drawing. The valve portion of the assembly incorporates a valve diaphragm and spring. Metered fuel pressure is applied to the left side of the diaphragm, tending to open the valve. Servo fuel pressure is applied to the right side of the diaphragm, tending to close the valve. The diaphragm and valve combination is acted upon by two springs, the heavier of which is located to the right of the diaphragm in the drawing. This spring closes the valve when the manual mixture control is placed in the IDLE CUTOFF position, thus shutting off the fuel supply. During normal operation of the system when the engine is running, the distributor valve will be opened by fuel pressure against servo and spring pressure.

Fuel pressure gage

A fuel pressure gage is incorporated in the system to provide the pilot with an indication of engine power output and fuel consumption. This gage is connected to or following the distributor valve to show the actual fuel pressure being applied to the discharge nozzles. Since fuel flow is proportional to pressure, the pressure shown on the gage will tell the pilot the percentage of maximum power being delivered by the engine. It also gives an indication of maximum power available at various altitudes. The fuel pressure gage is shown in Fig. 6·10.

Some installations utilize a fuel pressure gage calibrated in pounds-per-hour fuel flow, and in this case, the gage is called a **fuel-flow indicator.** The flow indicator must be vented to ambient air pressure, the same pressure sensed by the injection nozzles.

Fuel discharge nozzles

For unsupercharged engines, the **fuel discharge nozzles** are installed on each cylinder head so they will

Figure **6·10**   *Fuel pressure gage (flow indicator).*

inject the fuel spray directly into the intake port just ahead of the intake valve. During engine operation the fuel spray is continuous and a charge of fuel air mixture is drawn into the cylinder each time the intake valve opens. A diagram of a fuel discharge nozzle is shown in Fig. 6·11. It will be observed that the fuel is injected through a venturi-shaped chamber which is vented to the atmosphere. Air enters the nozzle through a screen which removes dirt or other foreign matter. The air entering the nozzle aids in the vaporization of the fuel.

It must be emphasized that fuel metering is provided by the servo regulator and not by the nozzles. The nozzles are calibrated to provide the correct fuel flow in accordance with the fuel pressure delivered by the servo regulator.

Typical installation

The servo regulator unit of the Bendix RS fuel-injection system can be mounted on the engine intake manifold inlet flange in a manner similar to that employed for a carburetor, taking into consideration that the throttle linkage and manual mixture-control linkage must be attached to the levers on the unit.

The fuel distributor will be mounted on the servo regulator unit for the RS-5B1 system or on a bracket below the cylinder center line for other configurations. The fuel distributor must be mounted with the nozzle line fittings in a horizontal plane.

The fuel discharge nozzles are installed in the ⅛-in.

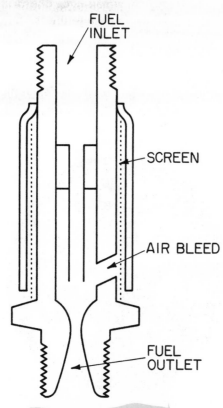

Figure 6·11   Fuel discharge nozzle.

pipe thread channel in the cylinder normally used for the primer fitting. A primer is not required with a fuel-injection system; hence the primer ports can be utilized for the nozzles. The nozzles have an identification number stamped on one of the hex flats on the nozzle body. This identification will be either a 12 or a 6. A nozzle identified with the number 12 indicates that it is a 12-lb nozzle and is used with a injection system having a 20-psi fuel inlet pressure. Nozzles identified with the number 6 indicate a 6-lb nozzle which is used with an injection system having a 12-psi fuel inlet pressure.

The identification number is also used to locate the air-bleed hole in the nozzle body. The number is located 180° from the air-bleed hole and must appear on the lower side when the nozzle is tightened into the cylinder port. This assures that the air-bleed hole is on top in order to eliminate a slight fuel bleeding from the opening just after the engine is shut down.

The nozzle-line length depends on the engine installation and the location of the fuel distributor unit. The nozzle lines are formed from ⅛-in.-OD stainless-steel tubing with suitable fittings to connect to the top of the nozzle at one end and to the fuel distributor plenum chamber fittings at the other end. The lines must be securely clamped to the engine at suitable locations to reduce line vibration.

The fuel inlet hose for the RS-5 injection system must be of an approved flexible type, No. 6 size. This hose connects from the fuel pump to the servo regulator unit.

If the distributor unit is mounted separate from the servo regulator, a No. 6 flexible hose is installed from the fuel outlet of the fuel-control section of the regulator to the fuel inlet fitting on the distributor unit.

A No. 4 flexible hose is installed from the servo valve fittings to the unrestricted side of the tee fitting in the fuel distributor unit. When the fuel distributor is mounted on the servo regulator, fuel is routed through drilled channels in the servo regulator to the distributor.

A No. 4 flexible hose or steel tubing is connected to the restricted side of the fuel distributor tee fitting and routed for a suitable connection to the vapor vent line for return to the fuel tank.

The fuel-flow indicator is connected to the plenum chamber of the distributor by means of a ⅛-in. copper tube. A No. 4 flexible hose connects the fuel inlet pressure gage line to the fuel pressure takeoff fitting on the servo regulator fuel-control section.

Throttle- and mixture-control adjustments

The throttle lever can be adjusted in 15° increments for the full 360° of the throttle shaft. The throttle linkage must be adjusted so the throttle lever will travel from stop to stop, and the throttle control on the pilot's panel will travel from full closed to full open with a slight cushion at both positions.

The mixture-control lever can be adjusted in 15° increments for the full 360° of the mixture-control shaft. The linkage must be adjusted so that both the pilot's control and the mixture-control lever travels from the IDLE CUTOFF position to the FULL-RICH position. The pilot's mixture control should have a slight cushion at both extreme positions.

Preparation for service

The RS injection system should be purged of any preservative oil in the fuel section of the unit before it is placed in operation. After the injection system has been installed on the engine, the fuel boost pump should be turned on and the mixture control placed in FULL RICH position to fill the system with fuel and eliminate the air from the fuel distributor and nozzle lines. The air being purged from the system can be heard as it escapes from the bleed holes in the nozzles. When the hissing of the air from the nozzles stops, the mixture control should be placed in the IDLE CUTOFF position. The system is then ready for engine start.

Idle speed and mixture adjustment

Adjustment of the idle speed and mixture must be made with the engine running. The engine should be started in accordance with instructions in the operator's manual and then warmed up until the oil temperature and cylinder-head temperature are normal. The magnetos should be checked in the approved manner to make sure that engine operation is satisfactory.

Idle speed is checked by placing the throttle in the fully closed position. The engine speed should be approximately 650 rpm. If the speed is not correct, it may be adjusted by turning the screw on the throttle stop arm. Turning the screw to the right will increase rpm, and turning it to the left will decrease rpm. The idle speed will have to be readjusted if it changes appreciably after the mixture-control adjustment has been made.

If the airplane has a variable-pitch propeller, the idle mixture should be adjusted with the propeller in the full low fixed pitch. In aircraft employing fuel boost pump pressure for ground, takeoff, and landing operations, the idle mixture must be adjusted with the fuel boost pump turned on.

The idle mixture should be adjusted so the fuel/air ratio is slightly on the rich side of **best power** setting. This is checked by moving the mixture control with a smooth, steady pull into the IDLE CUTOFF position. Before the engine rpm begins to decrease, a slight increase in rpm should occur. The mixture control should then be returned to FULL RICH before the engine cuts out. If the engine rpm starts to drop off immediately when the mixture control is placed in the IDLE CUTOFF position, the mixture is at or on the lean side of best power and must be adjusted.

The manifold pressure gage may also be used with an engine to check idle mixture. If the manifold pressure gage holds steady momentarily, then rises as engine speed decreases, the idle mixture is at or on the lean side of the best power setting.

Idle mixture can be adjusted by rotating the idle mixture adjustment in the linkage between the idle valve lever and the throttle arm. The adjustment should

be moved one or two notches at a time and then rechecked as explained above. Each time an adjustment is changed, the engine should be cleared by running it at approximately 2000 rpm for a few seconds before the mixture is checked.

Maintenance

Normally a fuel-injector system requires very little maintenance. Routine inspection should be made during regular inspections of the airplane and powerplant. These include inspection for leaks, safetying, security of mounting, and security of throttle- and mixture-control rods and linkages. The fuel-injector inlet strainer should be cleaned after the first 25 hr of operation and every 50 hr thereafter.

If an airplane is going to be taken out of service for an extended period of time, it is recommended that the fuel section of the injector be completely drained of all fuel. The drain plugs should be reinstalled, and the fuel inlet connected to an oil-supply line to inject oil into the fuel section at 5 psi. The oil must be grade 1010 conforming to MIL-0-6081. The oil pressure should be maintained until oil flows from the nozzles, thus assuring that the entire system is filled with oil.

Extreme caution should be exercised when handling or working around the injector to prevent oil or fuel from entering the air sections of the injector. Fluids can easily enter the air section of the injector through the annular groove around the venturi or the impact tubes. For this reason, some type of protection plate should be installed on the scoop mounting flange when routine maintenance is performed on the engine, such as washing down the engine and air scoop, servicing the air filter, or injecting preservative into the engine prior to storing.

THE RS-10B2 FUEL-INJECTION SYSTEM

The Bendix RS-10B2 fuel-injection system is used on the Pratt & Whitney R-985 engine and takes the place of the NAR-9B carburetor. The principal units of this system are shown in Fig. 6·12.

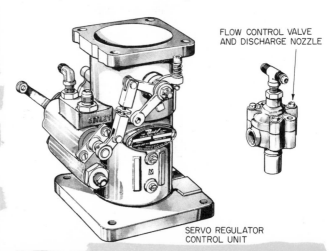

FLOW CONTROL VALVE
AND DISCHARGE NOZZLE

SERVO REGULATOR
CONTROL UNIT

Figure 6·12 Principal units of the Bendix RS-10B2 injection system.

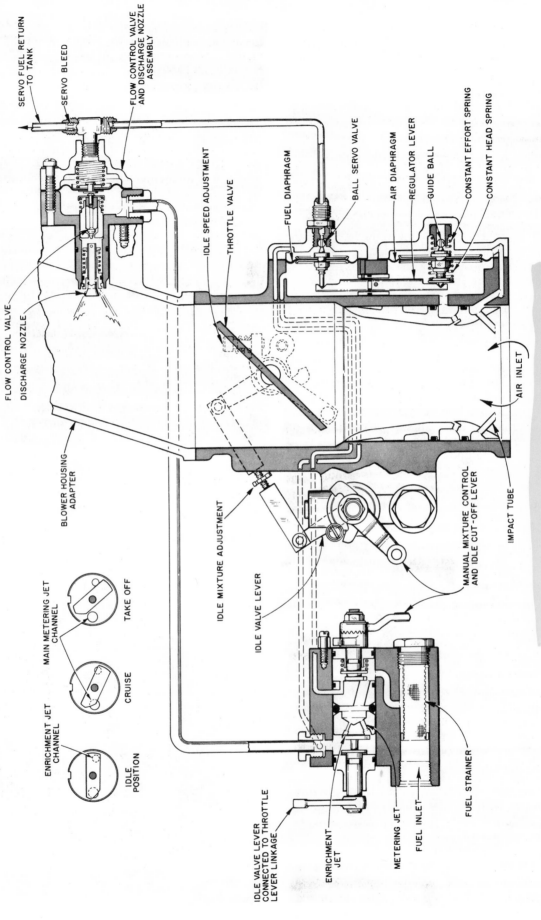

SERVO FUEL RETURN TO TANK

SERVO BLEED

FLOW CONTROL VALVE AND DISCHARGE NOZZLE ASSEMBLY

IDLE SPEED ADJUSTMENT

THROTTLE VALVE

FUEL DIAPHRAGM

BALL SERVO VALVE

AIR DIAPHRAGM

REGULATOR LEVER

GUIDE BALL

CONSTANT EFFORT SPRING

CONSTANT HEAD SPRING

FLOW CONTROL VALVE DISCHARGE NOZZLE

BLOWER HOUSING ADAPTER

AIR INLET

IDLE MIXTURE ADJUSTMENT

IDLE VALVE LEVER

MANUAL MIXTURE CONTROL AND IDLE CUT-OFF LEVER

IMPACT TUBE

MAIN METERING JET CHANNEL

TAKE OFF

ENRICHMENT JET CHANNEL

CRUISE

IDLE POSITION

IDLE VALVE LEVER CONNECTED TO THROTTLE LEVER LINKAGE

ENRICHMENT JET

METERING JET

FUEL INLET

FUEL STRAINER

Figure 6·13   Schematic diagram of the RS-10B2 injection system.

106

Operation

The operation of the RS-10B2 injection system is identical with that of the RS-5B1 and the RS-10B1 systems described in the foregoing sections of this chapter, with the exception of the discharge-nozzle arrangement. An examination of the diagram in Fig. 6·13 will show the air chamber and diaphragm linked with the fuel chamber and diaphragm by means of the regulator lever. Since the RS-10B2 system is designed for an engine with an internal blower, the fuel discharge nozzle is installed in a position to inject the fuel into the airstream ahead of the blower. For this reason, only one discharge nozzle is required.

In the diagram of the fuel-control unit it will be observed that an enrichment jet is included in the metering system. This jet is included to enrich the mixture for high-power settings in order to reduce the danger of overheating and detonation.

The distributor valve and discharge nozzle assembly are separately mounted on the engine blower housing adapter, as shown in the diagram. Metered fuel and servo fuel are supplied to this unit through external fuel lines.

The **flow-control-valve** portion of the assembly incorporates a valve diaphragm and spring. Metered fuel pressure is applied to the left side of the diaphragm tending to open the flow-control valve. Servo fuel pressure is applied to the right side of the diaphragm tending to close the valve. The diaphragm and valve arrangement is acted upon by two springs, the heavier of which is located to the right of the diaphragm and is used to close the valve when the manual mixture control is placed in the IDLE CUTOFF position, thus shutting off the supply of fuel.

As explained in the previous section for the RS-5 injection system, an increase in airflow through the venturi will cause the air diaphragm to move in a direction to close the servo valve. This reduces the servo pressure to the flow-control valve and permits fuel flow to increase.

The discharge nozzle incorporates a light spring which tends to hold the nozzle valve closed. The primary purpose of the discharge nozzle is to break up and atomize the fuel as it is injected into the engine blower housing adapter.

During steady-state operation, fuel flow is proportional to airflow through the servo valve regulator assembly, except as varied by the position of the manual mixture-control valve in the fuel-control system. During an acceleration, servo pressure is reduced as a result of air-metering force moving the ball servo valve in its closing direction. The differential fuel pressure across the diaphragm in the flow-control valve is therefore increased, and the flow-control valve is opened farther, thereby increasing discharge nozzle flow. The opposite occurs when the engine decelerates.

Overhaul and test

Pressure-injection units should be overhauled in properly certificated repair stations where suitable con-

ditions exist and equipment is available to perform the various operations in accordance with the manufacturer's overhaul manual. The testing of an overhauled unit must be done on an approved flow bench designed to operate with the units being tested.

FUEL INJECTION FOR LARGE ENGINES

Direct fuel-injection systems for large engines differ from the systems previously described in that the fuel is injected directly into the combustion chamber of the large engine. The fuel is injected by means of a piston pump which is regulated to deliver accurately measured quantities of fuel according to the quantity of air entering the cylinders through the intake valves from the intake manifold.

The master control

The **master control** unit of a direct fuel-injection system is identical in most respects with the pressure-injection carburetors previously described in this chapter. Figure 6·14 is an illustration of a fuel-control unit manufactured by the Bendix Products Division of Bendix Corporation. Figure 6·15 is a schematic diagram of the complete fuel system showing how the various units are arranged. The upper center drawing in Fig. 6·15 illustrates the principal operating parts of the fuel-control unit.

The function of the fuel-control unit is to meter fuel to the injection pump. The quantity of fuel is automatically controlled in proportion to the air entering the engine to produce the most efficient fuel/air ratios for various engine-operating conditions of load, speed, altitude, and temperature.

The air flowing through the compound venturi of the

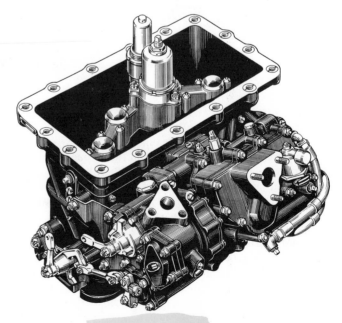

Figure 6·14 Master control unit.

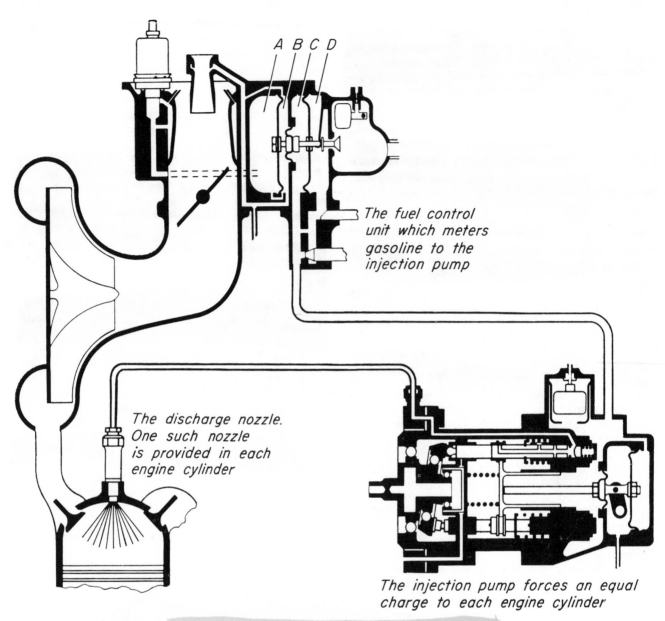

A B C D

The fuel control
unit which meters
gasoline to the
injection pump

The discharge nozzle.
One such nozzle
is provided in each
engine cylinder

The injection pump forces an equal
charge to each engine cylinder

Figure 6·15   Schematic diagram of direct fuel-injection system.

control unit creates a partial vacuum, or suction. This low pressure is transmitted to one side of an air-metering-force diaphragm, chamber *B*. Air-scoop impact pressure is transmitted from the impact tubes to the opposite side of this diaphragm, chamber *A*.

The **automatic-mixture-control** unit corrects the air-metering pressures to compensate for variations in atmospheric pressure and temperature. Thus the resultant air-metering force is a measure of the mass, or weight, of the air entering the engine.

The diaphragm shown between chambers *C* and *D* in Fig. 6·15 is balanced between unmetered fuel on one side and metered fuel on the opposite side. When these two pressures are equal, no fuel flows through the metering jet. The air-metering force, which is the difference of pressure between chambers *A* and *B*, acts upon the air diaphragm and tends to upset the fuel-pressure

balance by opening the poppet valve and allowing fuel to flow into chamber *D*. This causes a pressure differential across the metering jet which is exactly proportional to the mass airflow through the venturi, since the air and fuel diaphragms are connected. The metered fuel flows from the control unit to the injection pump as shown in the diagram.

BENDIX PR-58S2 INJECTION SYSTEM

Master control

The **master control** for the Bendix PR-58S2 injection system designed for the Wright R-3350 engine is illustrated in the schematic diagram shown in Fig. 6·16. It

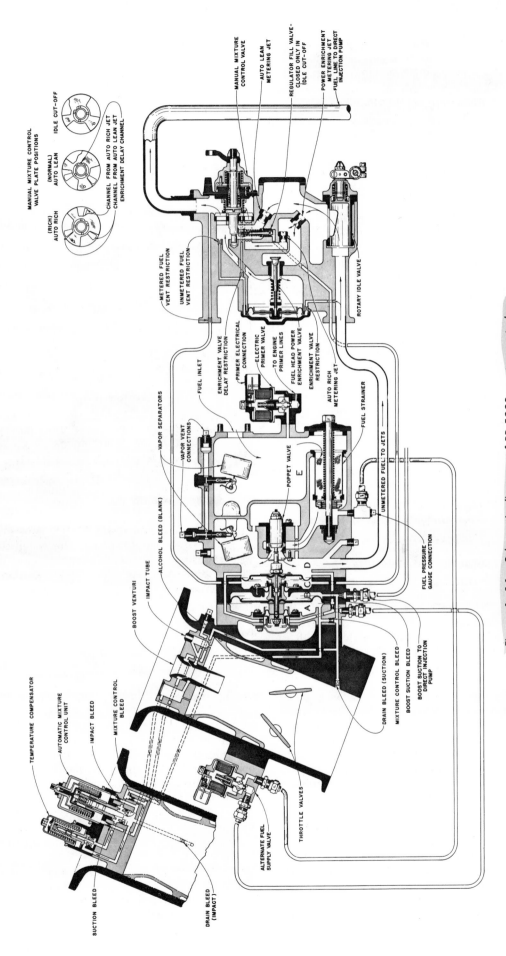

MANUAL MIXTURE CONTROL
VALVE PLATE POSITIONS

IDLE CUT-OFF

(NORMAL)
AUTO LEAN

(RICH)
AUTO RICH

CHANNEL FROM AUTO RICH JET
CHANNEL FROM AUTO LEAN JET
ENRICHMENT DELAY CHANNEL

MANUAL MIXTURE
CONTROL VALVE

AUTO LEAN
METERING JET

REGULATOR FILL VALVE-
CLOSED ONLY IN
IDLE CUT-OFF

POWER ENRICHMENT
FUEL LINE TO DIRECT
INJECTION PUMP

METERED FUEL
VENT RESTRICTION

UNMETERED FUEL
VENT RESTRICTION

ROTARY IDLE VALVE

ENRICHMENT VALVE
DELAY RESTRICTION

PRIMER ELECTRICAL
CONNECTION

ELECTRIC
PRIMER VALVE

TO ENGINE
PRIMER LINES

FUEL HEAD POWER
ENRICHMENT VALVE

ENRICHMENT VALVE
RESTRICTION

AUTO RICH
METERING JET

FUEL STRAINER

FUEL INLET

VAPOR SEPARATORS

VAPOR VENT
CONNECTIONS

ALCOHOL BLEED (BLANK)

POPPET VALVE

E

UNMETERED FUEL TO JETS

FUEL PRESSURE
GAUGE CONNECTION

A B C D

TEMPERATURE COMPENSATOR

AUTOMATIC MIXTURE
CONTROL UNIT

IMPACT BLEED

MIXTURE CONTROL
BLEED

BOOST VENTURI

IMPACT TUBE

DRAIN BLEED (SUCTION)

MIXTURE CONTROL BLEED

BOOST SUCTION BLEED

BOOST SUCTION TO
DIRECT INJECTION
PUMP

SUCTION BLEED

DRAIN BLEED
(IMPACT)

ALTERNATE FUEL
SUPPLY VALVE

THROTTLE VALVES

Figure 6·16 Schematic diagram of PR-58S2 master control.

will be recognized that this control system is similar to the pressure-injection carburetor for large engines. The *A* and *B* chambers in the regulator unit provide the **air-metering force** across the air diaphragm, and the *C* and *D* chambers provide the **fuel-metering head** or force. The main poppet-valve opening is controlled by the balance between these two forces.

The metered fuel, instead of being routed to a discharge nozzle, is directed to the fuel-injection pump. The output of the pump is controlled by a diaphragm balanced between boost venturi suction and metered fuel pressure.

Chamber *E* of the regulator unit contains a fuel strainer, vapor separator, and fuel at engine pump pressure. The poppet valve is located between chambers *D* and *E*. When chamber *D* fills with fuel, the vapor separator in *D* chamber eliminates any vapor not discharged from the vapor separator in chamber *E*. Fuel flow from chamber *D* (unmetered fuel pressure) through the metering jets in the fuel-control unit is accompanied by a pressure drop in chamber *C* (metered fuel pressure). The direct fuel-injection pump provides *C* chamber with a constant back pressure (about 6 or 7 psi). This metered fuel pressure will not vary any appreciable amount during engine operation, although fuel flow increases proportionally to engine demand. During operation, *B* chamber pressure (boost venturi suction) will be approximately one-third of the pressure in chamber *A*.

Electric primer valves

The PR-58S2 master control uses two electric primer valve assemblies. One primer supplies unmetered fuel to the engine priming nozzles, and the other provides an alternate fuel-supply system. The electric primer valve position is normally closed by spring action. The coil, when energized, overcomes spring force and opens the valve. Coil design permits continuous operation without an excessive temperature rise. Installation of the primer to the master control does not provide a positive ground. For this reason, a shielded cable or similar means must be used for direct connections to the airframe to provide satisfactory grounding for the solenoid coil.

The alternate fuel-supply system was designed to provide a source of fuel when icing occurs in the induction system. This condition will cause a drop in metering suction, resulting in an undesirable drop in fuel flow. The alternate fuel-supply system, by using an electric primer, supplies fuel at engine pump pressure to the balance diaphragm located in chamber *A* of the regulator unit. This pressure compensates for the loss of metering suction caused by ice and again establishes a metering head that provides an adequate fuel flow. Throttle position must be adjusted to provide the required fuel/air ratio until such time as the ice condition has been corrected. Extreme altitude may cause ice crystals to form in the inlet fuel filter. However, the bypass-valve-type strainer will supply adequate fuel in the event the screen becomes clogged.

Operating characteristics

The fuel/air ratio curve in Fig. 6·17 illustrates graphically a fuel-airflow schedule for the average PR-58S2 master control. Following the curve from the idle range through takeoff the regulator unit maintains the correct metering pressure and supplies fuel ready for metering to the fuel control at all times. The cruise and takeoff fuel/air ratios are maintained with respect to altitude change, independently of propeller pitch, engine speed, or throttle position; however, the volume of fuel delivered will vary in proportion to airflow.

Variations of the curve in the idle range indicate different idle adjustments, and as the airflow increases, the fuel/air ratio becomes leaner. At about 4000 lb per hr airflow, metering suction has overtaken constant head idle spring tension and the poppet-valve stem is functioning as an integral unit; hence the fuel/air ratio curve follows a single line. The rotary idle valve, past its metering phase, supplies fuel to the metering jets. Fuel metering through the cruise range is across the auto lean metering jet. With the manual mixture control in AUTO LEAN position the fuel supplied across the auto rich jet is blanked off, otherwise fuel flows are the same as in AUTO RICH. From the fuel curves illustrated, fuel/air ratio through the cruise range in AUTO RICH is about 1 part fuel to 12 parts air. In AUTO LEAN the ratio is about 1 part fuel to 16 parts air. During late cruise, the power-enrichment valve opens and increasing fuel flow is indicated by the upswing on the curve. The power-enrichment valve meters fuel in conjunction with the auto-lean and auto-rich metering jets until the combined metering area of the power-enrichment valve and the auto-rich metering jet is greater than the area of the power-enrichment metering jet. At this time the auto-lean and power-enrichment jets assume the metering and the curve tends to level off, adequately supplying the engine with the proper fuel/air mixture to perform safely through the power range.

Fuel injection pump

The **fuel-injection pump,** illustrated in Fig. 6·18, directs the fuel under a relatively high pressure to the discharge nozzles in the cylinders. The pump illustrated provides for nine cylinders. Two such pumps are used for 18-cylinder engines and are synchronized by means of an interconnecting control rod.

The injection pump automatically divides the metered fuel into exactly equal charges for each engine cylinder and forces one such measured charge of fuel directly into each cylinder, timed for injection during the intake stroke.

A **wobble plate** within the pump housing is driven from the engine at one-half engine speed. This imparts a continuous reciprocating motion to the pump pistons or plungers. The effective stroke of the pistons or plungers is controlled by the position of the bypass sleeves which surround the plungers.

The diaphragm shown at the extreme right of the pump drawing serves to control the axial position of

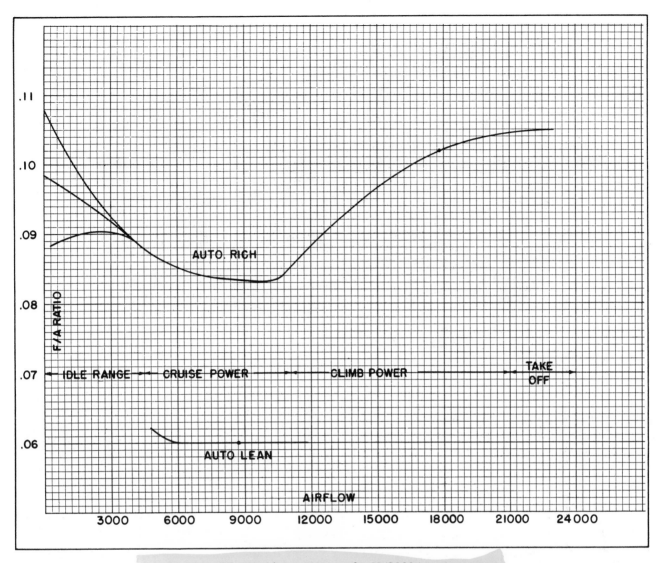

Figure 6·17   Fuel/air ratio curve for PR-58S2 injection system.

the bypass sleeves. The pressure of the fuel from the control unit acts upon this spring-loaded diaphragm, causing it to move inward as the pressure increases. The air chamber at the inner side of the diaphragm is connected to the low-pressure air from the boost venturi of the control unit. The velocity of the air through the control unit determines the amount of "suction" to the air side of the fuel-pump control diaphragm. As the velocity increases, the suction increases, thus tending to aid the fuel pressure in moving the diaphragm inward to increase the effective stroke of the plungers. The air and fuel forces applied to the pump diaphragm are opposed by a heavy spring in the center of the pump. This spring moves the diaphragm outward as fuel pressure and air suction decrease.

The operation of the direct fuel-injection system is such that, as the throttle is opened, the airflow through the control unit increases. The quantity of air acting through the control unit and pump diaphragm deter-

mines the quantity of fuel delivered by the pump, thus maintaining the correct ratio of fuel and air to the engine.

Discharge nozzle

The **discharge nozzle** used with the direct fuel-injection system is a very important unit of the system. Essentially, it is a spring-loaded control valve designed to keep the fuel inlet closed until a pressure of approximately 500 psi is applied. The valve opens instantly, giving a sharp start to the fuel injection, and closes instantly when the pressure is released. The fuel is injected into the cylinder in a fine spray at a high velocity, which causes it to become completely vaporized and well mixed with the air in the cylinder.

Synchronization

The two injection pumps mounted on the 18-cylinder R-3350 engine must be accurately synchronized. Since

111

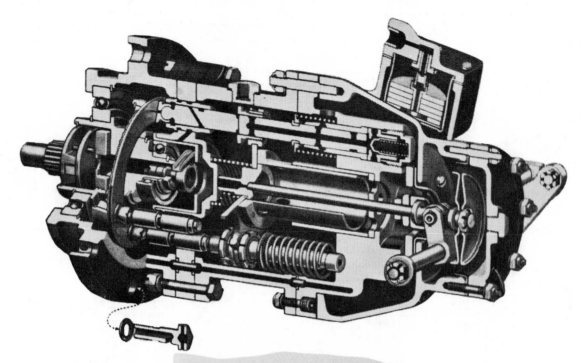

Figure 6·18   Direct fuel-injection pump.

each pump supplies fuel for a separate group of nine cylinders, lack of synchronization will cause one group of nine cylinders to receive a greater quantity of fuel than the other group. This will result in rough engine operation.

Synchronization of the injection pumps is assured by means of the synchronization bar which connects the synchronizing arms of the pumps together. Thus the movement of the control mechanism (bypass control plate) of one pump must coincide with identical

Figure 6·19   Injection pumps showing use of synchronization bar.

movement of the control mechanism of the other pump. The bypass sleeves in both pumps will be in the same position relative to the pump plungers, and the plungers in both pumps will have the same effective stroke. At inspections, the synchronization bar should be checked for looseness, and if necessary, it should be adjusted. The arrangement of the synchronization bar is shown in Fig. 6 · 19.

WATER INJECTION

Water injection, also called **antidetonation injection** (ADI), is the use of water with the fuel/air mixture to provide additional cooling for the mixture and the cylinders so that additional power can be drawn from the engine without the danger of detonation.

It is often necessary to use the maximum power which an engine can produce in order to take off from short fields, for military emergencies, and when it is necessary to "go around" after making a landing approach. A "dry" engine—that is, without water injection—is limited in its power output by the detonation which results when operating limits are exceeded. The injection of water into the fuel/air mixture has the same effect as the addition of antiknock compounds in that it permits the engine to deliver greater power without the danger of detonation.

The average engine operating without water injection requires a rich mixture with a ratio of approximately 10 parts air to 1 part fuel by weight. With this mixture a portion of the fuel is unburned and acts as a cooling agent. The additional unburned fuel subtracts from the power of the engine. When water is added to the fuel/air mixture in proper quantities, the power of the engine may be increased. The water cools the fuel/air mixture, thus permitting a higher manifold pressure to be used. The fuel/air ratio may be reduced to the rich best power mixture, thus deriving greater power from the fuel consumed. When water injection is employed, the air/fuel ratio may be reduced to approximately 12½:1, which is a much more efficient mixture than the 10:1 ratio required otherwise.

The use of water injection permits an increase of 8 to 15 percent in takeoff horsepower. During World War II this extra power contributed greatly to the superiority of the United States air forces. Today, this same advantage is gained by our airlines in commercial operations.

The equipment required for water injection includes a storage tank, a pump, a water regulator, a derichment valve, and necessary controls. The water regulator is controlled by the unmetered fuel from the carburetor balanced against the water pressure delivered by the water pump. The two forces acting on the opposite side of a diaphragm control the water valve.

The derichment valve in the carburetor is controlled by the water pressure. The pressure acts upon a diaphragm and closes the passage which provides fuel for power enrichment. This reduces the amount of fuel delivered to the discharge nozzle and produces a fuel ratio for best power. If the water pressure should fail, the fuel is instantly increased so that excess fuel is available for cooling.

In order to prevent freezing of the water for an ADI system, the water is usually mixed with a certain quantity of alcohol. The alcohol does not appreciably change the cooling effects of the water.

Water injection is commonly employed with jet engines during takeoff. The water increases the mass flow through engine and prevents overheating of the turbine, thus making it possible to operate the engine at a higher thrust than would otherwise be possible.

REVIEW QUESTIONS

1. What is meant by *fuel injection?*
2. List the advantages of a fuel-injection system.
3. What are the four basic units of the Continental continuous-flow fuel-injection system?
4. What factor governs the fuel pump pressure?
5. Describe the operation of the *vapor separator* and the *vapor ejector.*
6. What is the function of the *air throttle* assembly?
7. How many fuel-control elements are included in the *fuel-control assembly?* What are they?
8. Describe the operation of the *fuel manifold valve* for the Continental fuel-injection system.
9. At what point on the engine are the fuel discharge nozzles installed?
10. Describe the construction of a fuel discharge nozzle for the Continental system.
11. What adjustments may be made for the operation of the Continental fuel-injection system?
12. What precaution must be taken in the operation of the Continental system before starting the engine?
13. At what times is the auxiliary fuel pump turned on?
14. Describe the *airflow sensing system* in the Bendix RS fuel-injection unit.
15. Describe the operation of the servo valve in the Bendix RS fuel-injection unit.
16. What would be the effect on engine operation if the air diaphragm became ruptured?
17. Describe the distributor valve for the Bendix RS system.
18. How would you proceed in adjusting the idle mixture for the Bendix RS system?
19. Compare the Bendix RS-10 system with the RS-5 system.
20. Why does the RS-10B2 system designed for the Pratt & Whitney R-985 engine require only one discharge nozzle?
21. Compare the *master control unit* of the direct fuel-injection system for large engines with the pressure carburetor for similar engines.
22. What two forces are used to control the output of the direct fuel-injection pump?
23. What is the purpose of the alternate fuel-supply system in the PR-58S2 master control unit?
24. What is the function of the wobble plate in the injection pump?

25. What fuel pressure is required to open the discharge nozzles?
26. What is the specific function of the synchronization bars?
27. What is the effect on engine operation when the synchronization bar is out of adjustment? Why?
28. What is meant by *water injection* or ADI?
29. Compare the fuel/air ratios for full power operation with and without water injection.
30. What increase in engine power may be obtained through the use of water injection?
31. What is the purpose of the *derichment valve* in the carburetor or master control?
32. What means is used to prevent the freezing of the water or ADI liquid?
33. What is the value of water injection with a turbojet engine?

CHAPTER 7

Induction Systems and Supercharging

GENERAL DESCRIPTION

The complete induction system for an aircraft engine includes three principal sections: (1) the **air scoop** and **ducting** leading to the carburetor, (2) the **carburetor** or **air-control section** of an injection system, and (3) the **intake manifold and pipes.** These sections comprise passages and controlling elements for all the air which must be supplied to the engine.

Air scoop and ducting

A typical air scoop is simply an opening facing into the airstream. This scoop receives ram air, usually augmented by the propeller slipstream. The effect of the air velocity is to "supercharge" the air a small amount, thus adding to the total weight of air received by the engine. The power increase thus afforded may be as much as 5 percent. The design of the air scoop has a substantial effect on the amount of increased power provided by ram air pressure.

The ducting system for a nonsupercharged engine comprises four principal parts, namely: (1) the **air scoop,** (2) **air filter,** (3) **alternate air valve,** and (4) the **carburetor air heater** or **muff.** The air filter is installed at or near the air scoop to remove dust, sand, and larger foreign particles from the air before it is carried to the engine. The filter usually consists of a mat of metal filaments encased in a frame and dipped in oil. The oil film on the metal filaments catches and holds dust and sand particles. Normally the air filter should be removed, cleaned, and reoiled every 25 hr of engine operation. If the airplane is operating in a particularly dusty or sandy area, the filter should be serviced at more frequent intervals. An induction system is shown in Fig. 7·1.

The alternate air valve is operated by means of the carburetor heat control in the cockpit. The valve is

simply a gate which closes the main air duct and opens the duct to the heater muff when the control is **on.** During normal operation, the gate closes the passage to the heater muff and opens the main air duct. The gate is often provided with a spring which tends to keep it in the normal position.

The heater muff is a shroud placed around a section of the exhaust pipe. The shroud is open at the ends to permit air to flow into the space between the exhaust pipe and the wall of the shroud. A duct is connected from the muff to the main air duct. During operation of the carburetor air heater system, **protected air** within the engine compartment flows into the space around the exhaust pipe where it is heated before being carried to the main air duct.

Some induction systems are designed to permit direct ram air to enter the carburetor without first passing through an air filter. In such a case the air filter is installed in an alternate duct. When the airplane is operating on the ground in sandy or dusty conditions, the direct air duct is closed by means of a gate valve and air is drawn into the carburetor through the air filter. After takeoff, when the airplane is flying in clear air, the air intake is shifted back to the direct duct. It must be remembered that the air filter reduces air pressure to the carburetor to some extent, thus reducing the power output.

Intake manifolds

The typical **opposed-type** or **flat-type aircraft engine** has an induction system with an individual pipe leading to each cylinder. On some models of this type, one end of each pipe is bolted to the cylinder by means of a flange and the other end fits into a slip joint in the manifold. On other models of this type, the pipes are connected to the manifold by short sections of rubber (or synthetic-rubber) hose held by clamps. In still other

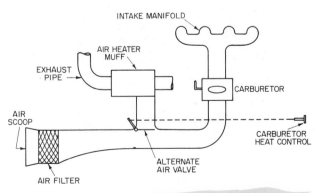

Figure 7·1   Diagram to illustrate a simple air induction system.

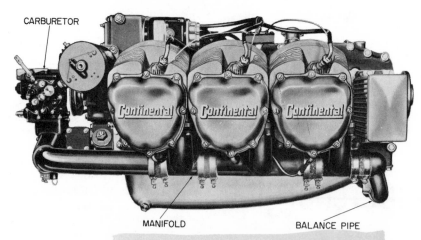

CARBURETOR

MANIFOLD   BALANCE PIPE

Figure 7·2   Intake pipes and manifold for an opposed engine.

models of this type, the carburetor is mounted on the oil sump and the fuel/air mixture flows from the carburetor through passages in the oil sump and then out through each of the individual pipes leading to the engine cylinders. As the mixture of fuel and air flows through the passages in the oil sump, heat is transferred from the oil to the fuel/air mixture. This arrangement accomplishes two purposes to a certain extent: (1) It cools the oil slightly, and (2) it increases the temperature of the fuel/air mixture slightly for a better vaporization of the fuel. The intake manifold and pipes for opposed engines are shown in Fig. 7·2.

Figure 7·3 Supercharger section and intake pipes for a radial engine.

The type of induction system used on a radial-type engine principally depends upon the horsepower output desired from the engine. On a small radial engine of low output, the air is drawn through the carburetor, mixed with fuel in the carburetor, and then carried to the cylinders through individual intake pipes. In some engines, an intake manifold section is made a part of the main engine structure. The fuel/air mixture is carried from the outer edge of the manifold section to the separate engine cylinders by individual pipes which are connected to the engine by means of a slip joint. The purpose of the slip joint is to prevent the damage which would otherwise occur from the expansion and contraction caused by changes in temperature.

In a typical **high-output radial engine,** an internal blower or a supercharger is located in the rear section of the engine. The fuel/air mixture passes from the carburetor through the supercharger or blower and then flows out through individual intake pipes to the engine cylinders. An arrangement of this type is shown in Fig. 7·3.

Importance of gastight seal

The portion of the intake system of an engine between the carburetor and the cylinders must be installed gastight to provide proper engine operation. When the manifold pressure is below atmospheric pressure, which is always the case with unsupercharged (naturally aspirated) engines, an air leak in the manifold system will allow air to enter and lean out the fuel/air mixture. This can cause overheating of the engine, detonation, backfiring, or complete stoppage.

In a supercharged engine, a portion of the fuel/air mixture will be lost if leakage occurs in the intake manifold or pipes. This, of course, will cause a reduction in power and a waste of fuel.

One method of forming a gastight connection for intake pipes is to provide a synthetic-rubber packing ring and a packing-retaining nut to form a slip-joint seal at the distribution chamber, thus allowing the intake pipes to slide in and out of the distribution-chamber opening while the metal of the engine cylinder is expanding and contracting from changes of temperature. Obviously, it is necessary to place a gasket at the cylinder intake port between the pipe flange and the cylinder port and secure the flange rigidly by bolts and nuts.

Another method of forming a gastight connection for intake pipes is to use a packing ring and packing-retaining nut which screws into or over the intake-port opening. Still another method is to have short stacks protruding from the intake ports, using rubber couplings to connect the pipes to these protruding stacks.

Induction system for six-cylinder opposed engine

The principal assemblies of an induction system for the Cessna 310 airplane equipped with a Continental I0-470-D engine are shown in Fig. 7·4. With this system, ram air enters the air box at the left rear engine

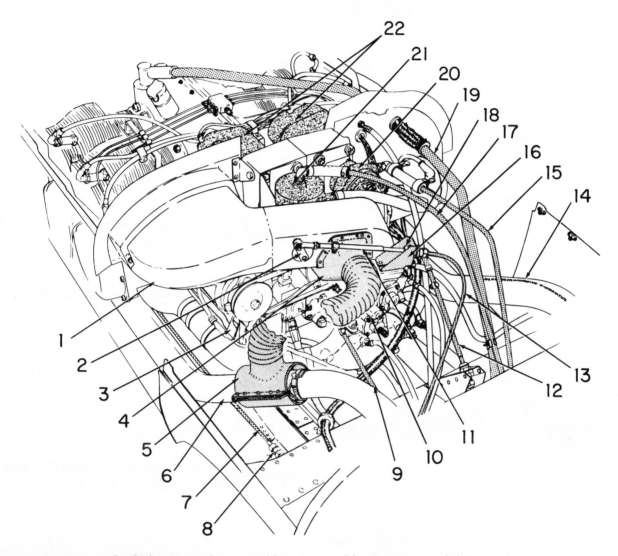

1. Carburetor air box assembly
2. Alternate air actuating arm
3. Engine mount
4. Carburetor heat adapter
5. Carburetor heat shroud
6. Left exhaust stack
7. Propeller control conduit
8. Conduit connector
9. Throttle control sliding end
10. Carburetor
11. Alternate air control sliding end
12. Mixture control sliding end
13. Alternate air control conduit
14. Right exhaust stack
15. Vacuum line
16. Control mounting bracket
17. Air-oil separator line
18. Alternate air connector
19. Crankcase breather line
20. Vacuum pump
21. Air-oil separator
22. Magnetos

Figure 7·4   Induction system for six-cylinder opposed engine. (Cessna Aircraft Co.)

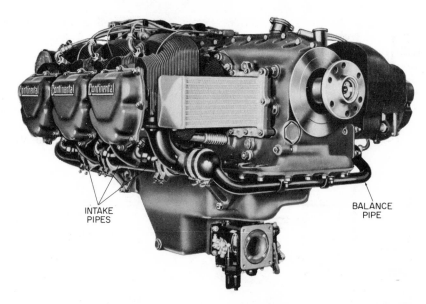

Figure **7·5** *Intake pipes.*

baffle and is ducted to the rear where it passes through an air filter before entering the fuel/air control unit. Between the filter and the fuel/air control unit is an induction air door which serves as a gate to close the heater duct or the main air duct, depending upon the position of the control. In case the air filter becomes clogged, the door will open automatically to allow air to enter from the heater duct.

From the fuel/air control unit air is supplied to the cylinders through intake manifold piping. This piping is arranged in jointed sections along the lower side of the cylinders on each side of the engine to form two manifolds leading from the Y fitting at the fuel/air control unit. This arrangement is shown in Fig. 7·5. A balance pipe is connected between the two manifolds at the front end. This pipe equalizes the pressure in the manifolds, thus providing for a more uniform airflow to the cylinders. Short sections of individual piping lead from the manifold to each cylinder intake port. Fuel is injected continuously into the intake ports of each cylinder while the engine is operating.

It must be emphasized that induction systems are designed in many ways to suit the operation of various engine and aircraft combinations. Most systems, however, include the elements described in this section, and each is designed to provide the engine with adequate air for the most efficient operation. The characteristics of induction systems utilized with superchargers are described in the following sections.

PRINCIPLES OF SUPERCHARGING

The value of supercharging for reciprocating aircraft engines was clearly demonstrated during World War II. The turbosupercharger (turbine-driven supercharger) was of particular importance because it permitted our bombers to operate at extreme altitudes from which vantage point they could bomb enemy targets with much less danger of attack than at lower altitudes. After the war, engine-driven and turbine-driven superchargers were used on commercial airliners to permit high-altitude flight.

The properties of gases as related to supercharging

To understand the principles of supercharging requires a knowledge of **mass, volume,** and **density** as applied to the properties of gases. All matter can be classified as solids and fluids. In turn, fluids include both liquids and gases. Solids, liquids, and gases all have weight, but the weight of gases is by no means a constant value under all conditions. For example, at sea-level pressure about 13 cu ft of air weighs 1 lb, but at greater pressures the same volume would weigh more, and at lower pressures it would weigh less.

Mass is not the same as **weight,** but for an ordinary layman's discussion it is often loosely used as if it were the same as weight. Mass should not be confused with volume, because **volume** designates merely the space occupied by an object and does not take into consideration density or pressure. The relation among these various factors is explained by the various laws pertaining to the behavior of gases.

From experience it is known that any gas can be compressed to some extent, and this compression is accomplished by exerting some force on the gas, that is, increasing its pressure. Boyle's law expresses the relationship between pressure and volume as follows: **In any sample of gas, the volume is inversely proportional to the absolute pressure if the temperature is kept constant.**

With reference to the quantity of air in a closed cylinder fitted with a movable piston, shown in Fig. 7·6, if it is assumed that the temperature is constant and that there is no leakage past the piston, then the volume and pressure are inversely related in accordance with Boyle's law.

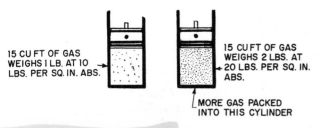

15 CU FT OF GAS WEIGHS 1 LB. AT 10 LBS. PER SQ. IN. ABS.

15 CU FT OF GAS WEIGHS 2 LBS. AT 20 LBS. PER SQ. IN. ABS.

MORE GAS PACKED INTO THIS CYLINDER

Figure 7·6   Quantity of charge.

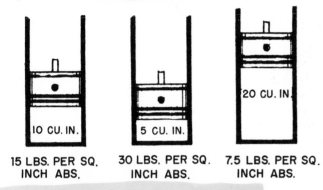

10 CU. IN.

5 CU. IN.

20 CU. IN.

15 LBS. PER SQ. INCH ABS.

30 LBS. PER SQ. INCH ABS.

7.5 LBS. PER SQ. INCH ABS.

Figure 7·7   Relative volumes and pressures.

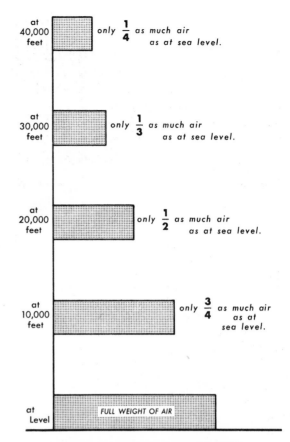

at 40,000 feet — only $\frac{1}{4}$ as much air as at sea level.

at 30,000 feet — only $\frac{1}{3}$ as much air as at sea level.

at 20,000 feet — only $\frac{1}{2}$ as much air as at sea level.

at 10,000 feet — only $\frac{3}{4}$ as much air as at sea level.

at Level — FULL WEIGHT OF AIR

Figures are APPROXIMATE and mean WEIGHT of air.

Figure 7·8   Effect of altitude on density of air.

In the picture at the left in Fig. 7·6, 15 cu ft of gas weighs 1 lb at 10 psia pressure. In the picture at the right, 15 cu ft of gas weighs 2 lb at a pressure of 20 psia because more gas is packed into the cylinders. The volume is the same in both pictures, but the pressure is changed, and hence the mass or quantity of air below the piston is changed.

In Fig. 7·7, cylinders are shown with their pistons. The one at the left has a volume of 10 cu in. under the piston, the one in the middle has a volume of 5 cu in. under the piston, and the one at the right has a volume of 20 cu in. under the piston.

If the density of the air in the cylinder at the left is accepted as standard, the air in the middle cylinder has a density of 2 and the air in the cylinder at the right has a density of only ½.

The weight of the air surrounding the earth is sufficient to exert considerable pressure on objects at sea level. At altitudes above sea level the pressures, density, and temperatures of the air are lower. At an altitude of 20,000 ft the pressure and density of the atmosphere are only about one-half their value at sea level.

Unless something is done to offset the decreasing density, at sea level the engine would receive the full weight of air, at 10,000 ft it would receive only three-fourth's as much air by weight as at sea level, at 20,000 ft it would get only one-half as much air by weight as at sea level, at 30,000 ft it would obtain only one-third as much air by weight as at sea level, and at 40,000 ft it would receive only one-fourth as much air by weight as at sea level. These relations are illustrated in Fig. 7·8.

These relations are important in any discussion of an internal-combustion engine because the power developed by the engine depends principally upon the mass of the induced charge. An engine that is not super-charged can induce only a definite value according to its volumetric efficiency and piston displacement. In order to increase the mass of the charge, it is necessary to increase the pressure and the density of the incoming charge by means of a supercharger. Therefore, it is possible to say that the function of a supercharger is to increase the quantity of air (or fuel/air mixture) entering the engine cylinders.

Superchargers were developed originally for the sole purpose of increasing the density of the air taken into the engine cylinders at high altitudes to obtain the maximum power output. However, with improvements in the production of fuels and in the design of engines, it became possible to operate a supercharger at low altitudes to increase the induction-system pressure, thus increasing the charge density, above the normal value of atmospheric pressure.

Figure 7·9 illustrates the effect of temperature on gas volume. The elastic property of gases is demonstrated when any change occurs in the temperature. If the temperature of a given quantity of any gas is raised and the pressure is held constant, the gas will expand in proportion to absolute temperature. This is expressed in the following equation:

$$\frac{V_1}{V_2} = \frac{T_1}{T_2} \qquad \text{constant pressure}$$

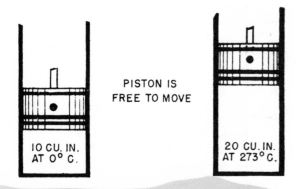

PISTON IS FREE TO MOVE

10 CU. IN. AT 0° C.

20 CU. IN. AT 273° C.

Figure 7·9   Effect of temperature on gas volumes.

The foregoing equation is known as Charles's law, attributed to the French mathematician and physicist Jacques A. C. Charles (1746–1823).

In Fig. 7·9 the temperature of the gas in the first cylinder is at 0°C or 273°K (absolute). When the gas temperature is raised to 273°C, the absolute temperature is doubled; hence the volume is doubled. To illustrate further, if a quantity of gas has a volume of 10 cu ft at 10°C and we wish to find the volume at 100°C, we must convert the temperature indications to absolute (Kelvin) values. To do this we merely add 273 to the centigrade value. Then, 10°C becomes 283°K and 100° becomes 373°K. Applying the formula,

$$\frac{10}{V_2} = \frac{283}{373}$$

$$283 V_2 = 3730$$

$$V_2 = \frac{3730}{283} = 13.18 \text{ cu ft}$$

Thus we see that the increase in temperature has increased the volume of the gas from 10 to 13.18 cu ft, the pressure remaining constant.

The pressure of a gas varies in proportion to the absolute temperature if the volume is held constant. This is expressed by the equation

$$\frac{P_1}{P_2} = \frac{T_1}{T_2} \qquad \text{volume constant}$$

This principle is illustrated in Fig. 7·10 where the gas

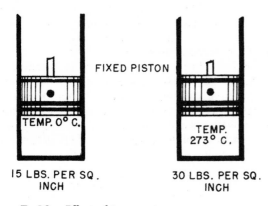

FIXED PISTON

TEMP. 0° C.

TEMP. 273° C.

15 LBS. PER SQ. INCH

30 LBS. PER SQ. INCH

Figure 7·10   Effect of temperature on gas pressures.

temperature has been doubled; that is, it has been raised from 0°C (273°K) to 273°C (546°K). Since the absolute temperature has been doubled with the volume held constant, the pressure has doubled.

Manifold pressure

Manifold pressure is the pressure in the intake manifold of the engine. The weight of the fuel/air mixture entering the engine cylinders is measured by the manifold pressure and the temperature of the mixture. In an ordinary automobile engine the manifold pressure is less than outside atmospheric pressure because of the air-friction losses in the air-induction system. In a supercharged engine, however, the manifold pressure may be higher than the pressure of the atmosphere. When the supercharger is operating, the manifold pressure may be greater or less than the atmospheric pressure, depending upon the settings of the supercharger control and throttle.

It must be pointed out that manifold pressure is of prime importance on high-performance engines equipped with constant-speed propellers. If the manifold pressure is too high, detonation and overheating will occur. These conditions will damage the engine and cause engine failure if permitted to exist for an appreciable length of time. During the operation of a supercharged engine, it is particularly important that the pilot or flight engineer pay strict attention to the power settings (rpm and manifold pressure) of the engines.

If an engine has a particularly high compression ratio, it is quite likely that the supercharger cannot be used at all until an altitude of 5000 ft or more is reached. If the supercharger on such an engine is operated at low altitudes, the pressures and temperatures in the combustion chambers will cause detonation and preignition.

Another factor governing the manifold pressure to be used with an engine is the octane rating or performance number of the fuel. If a fuel has very high antidetonation characteristics, the maximum manifold pressure may be higher than it would be with a fuel having a lower antiknock rating. For this reason, it is essential that the person servicing an airplane note the fuel rating marked on the fuel tank cover. If, in an emergency, it becomes necessary to use a fuel with a rating lower than that specified for the airplane, the pilot can avoid trouble by operating the engine at lower manifold pressures than he would normally.

Purposes of supercharging

The main purpose of supercharging an aircraft engine is to increase the manifold pressure above the pressure of the atmosphere in order to provide high power output for takeoff and to sustain the maximum power at high altitudes.

Increased manifold pressure increases the power output in two ways:

1. **It increases the weight of the fuel/air mixture (charge) delivered to the cylinders of the engine.** At a constant temperature the weight of the fuel/air mixture that can be contained in a given volume of space is dependent upon the

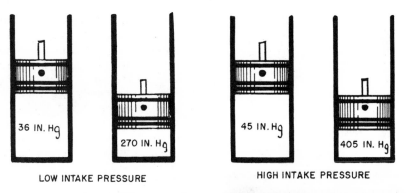

LOW INTAKE PRESSURE   HIGH INTAKE PRESSURE

Figure 7·11   Effect of manifold pressure.

pressure of the mixture. If the pressure on any given volume of gas is increased, the weight of that gas is increased because the density is increased.

2. **It increases the compression pressure.** The compression ratio for any given engine is constant; hence the greater the pressure of the fuel/air mixture at the beginning of the compression stroke, the greater will be the **compression pressure,** the latter being the pressure of the mixture at the end of the compression stroke. Higher compression pressure causes a higher mean effective pressure and consequently a higher engine output.

Figure 7·11 illustrates the increase of the compression pressure. In the cylinder at the extreme left, the pressure is only 36 in. Hg at the beginning of the compression stroke. At the end of the compression stroke the compression pressure in the second cylinder from the left is 270 in. Hg. In this case, the intake pressure is comparatively low.

The pressure is 45 in. Hg in the third cylinder from the left in Fig. 7·11, and the compression pressure in the cylinder at the extreme right is 405 in. Hg. Since the pressure is relatively high at the beginning of the compression stroke, it is still higher at the end. In this case the intake pressure is high in comparison with that represented by the two drawings to the left. Increased temperature as a result of the compression also adds to the pressure.

Relation between horsepower and manifold pressure

The relation between the manifold pressure and the engine power output for a certain engine at maximum rpm is shown on the chart in Fig. 7·12, where the manifold pressure in inches of mercury is plotted horizontally and the horsepower is plotted vertically. By referring to a manifold pressure of 30 and then following the vertical line upward until it intersects the curve, it is found that the curve intersects the 30 in. Hg line at a horsepower of about 550. This means that, when the engine is not supercharged, the theoretical maximum pressure in the intake manifold is assumed to be almost 30 in. Hg, which is the atmospheric pressure at sea level, and the power developed by the engine is about 550 hp. However, in actual practice, it is impossible to obtain an intake manifold pressure of 30 in. in an unsupercharged engine because of friction losses in the manifold.

Refer to a manifold-pressure reading of 45, and

follow the vertical line upward until it intersects the curve. This shows that, if the manifold pressure is increased to 45 in. by supercharging, the engine output is then about 1050 hp.

It may occur to a student that the manifold pressure could be increased indefinitely to obtain more power, but it must be strongly emphasized that this is not true. Excessive manifold pressure always adversely affects the operation of the engine and ultimately damages it permanently.

The sea-level supercharger and the sea-level engine

The **sea-level supercharger,** illustrated in Fig. 7·13, is sometimes called a **ground boost blower.** It consists of a centrifugal compressor connected to the air intake together with the necessary mechanism for driving it from the engine crankshaft through a gear train. The pumping capacity depends upon the size of the impeller and the speed at which it is rotated.

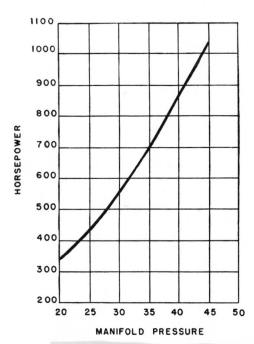

Figure 7·12   Relation between horsepower and manifold pressure.

121

Figure 7·13 Sea-level supercharger.

If other factors remained the same, the gain in power output from the engine would be in proportion to the increase of pressure. However, the other factors do not remain constant, and there are limits beyond which safe operation is not possible. One of these factors is temperature. When the air is compressed, its temperature is raised. This reduces the efficiency of the supercharger because heated air expands and increases the amount of power required to compress it and push it into the cylinders. It also reduces the efficiency of the engine because any gas engine operates better if the intake mixture of fuel and air is kept cool. When the fuel/air mixture reaches an excessively high temperature, preignition and detonation may take place, there is a loss of power and often a complete mechanical failure of the powerplant.

The rise in temperature resulting from the supercharging is in addition to the heat generated by the compression within the engine cylinders. For this reason, the combined compression of the supercharger and the cylinders must be kept within the correct limits determined by the antiknock qualities or octane ratings of the fuel used in the engine.

If a sea-level supercharger is designed with enough capacity to raise the pressure of air at sea level from 14.7 to about 20 psi, it is possible to obtain about 40 percent more power than would be generated if there were no supercharging to increase the air pressure. If this sea-level supercharger were installed with a 1000-hp engine, the piston displacement of the 1000-hp engine need not be any greater than the piston displacement of a 710-hp engine that is not supercharged.

However, it must be understood that an engine which is to be provided with a supercharger must be designed to withstand the higher stresses which are developed by the increased power. It is not simply a matter of adding a supercharger to a 710-hp engine in order to obtain a 1000-hp output.

The difference between 710 and 1000 hp is obviously 290 hp, but it requires about 70 hp to operate the supercharger for this imaginary engine; hence, not merely 290 hp but 290 plus 70, or 360 hp, must be developed within the engine in order to obtain the 1000-hp output. This means that the supercharger must account for the development of an additional 360 hp when added to the 710-hp engine in order actually to obtain the 1000 hp we want.

Internal and external superchargers

Most superchargers used on conventional airplanes are alike in that an impeller or "blower" (rotating at high speed) is used to compress either the air before it is mixed with the fuel in the carburetor or the fuel/air

mixture which leaves the carburetor. It is therefore possible to classify superchargers according to their **location** in the induction system of the airplane as either an **internal type** or an **external type.**

When the supercharger is located between the carburetor and the cylinder-intake parts, it is an internal type as shown in Fig. 7·14. Air enters the carburetor at atmospheric pressure and is mixed in the carburetor with the fuel. The fuel/air mixture leaves the carburetor at near-atmospheric pressure, is compressed in the supercharger to a pressure greater than atmospheric, and then enters the engine cylinders. The power required to drive the supercharger impeller is transmitted from the engine crankshaft by means of a gear train. Because of the high gear ratio, the impeller rotates much faster than the crankshaft. If the gear ratio is adjustable for two different speeds, the supercharger is described as a two-speed supercharger. In general, the internal-type supercharger may be used with an engine which is not expected to operate at very high altitudes or, in any event, where it is not necessary for air to be delivered under pressure to the carburetor intake.

An **external-type** supercharger delivers compressed air to the carburetor intake, as shown in Fig. 7·15. The air is compressed in the supercharger and then delivered through an air cooler to the carburetor where it is mixed with the fuel. Since the power required to drive the ordinary type of external supercharger is obtained from the action of the engine exhaust gases

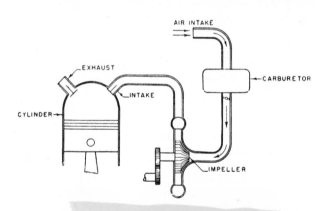

Figure 7·14 Internal supercharger arrangement.

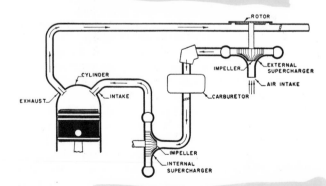

Figure 7·15 System showing location of external supercharger.

against a bucket wheel or turbine, the external type is also called a **turbosupercharger** or **turbocharger.** The speed of the impeller depends only on the quantity and pressure of the exhaust gases directed against the bucket wheel; hence the turbosupercharger is also a **multispeed** supercharger.

Stages

A **stage** is an increase in pressure. Superchargers can be classified as single-stage, two-stage, or multiple-stage, according to the number of times an increase of pressure is accomplished. The single-stage supercharging system may include either a single-speed or a two-speed internal supercharger. Even though the two-speed internal supercharger has two definite speeds at which the impeller can rotate, only one "boost" in pressure can be accomplished at any time; hence it is still a single-stage system. A single-stage supercharger system is shown in Fig. 7·14.

The effect of altitude on engine power output

When an airplane climbs above the surface of the earth, the pressure of the atmosphere decreases and the density of the air also decreases. The less dense air, described as "thin air" by laymen, offers less resistance to the flight of the airplane than the denser air near the earth's surface for the same reason that it is easier to swim in water than it would be to swim in lubricating oil, molasses, or some other fluid having a density greater than water. In addition, the back pressure on the engine exhaust gases is reduced. The air at the higher altitudes is colder than that near the surface of the earth. All these factors tend to increase the effectiveness of an engine.

Associated with the above advantages, there are several disadvantages to increased altitude. The air at higher altitudes weighs less per cubic foot and there is less air pressure available for pushing it into the cylinders of the engine; hence, the power output of an engine decreases as the altitude increases. This can be compared with driving an automobile up a mountain road. The motorist finds that there is a loss of engine power output as he climbs toward the top of the mountain. The automobile engine receives the same **volume** of air, but the **weight** of the air is less; hence there is not enough oxygen delivered to the engine cylinders to provide efficient combustion for the fuel/air mixture.

There are certain minor problems associated with engine operation at increased altitude, whether the engine is in an automobile or in an airplane. For example, the reduced atmospheric pressure lowers the boiling point of gasoline so that the fuel system is in danger of vapor lock unless it has been especially designed to avoid this problem. Also, the reduced density of the atmosphere at higher altitudes causes the air to have less resistance to the passage of electricity. This tends to allow the electric current to "leak out" of the ignition system before it produces the sparks in the spark plugs.

Returning to the major problems of engine power output at increased altitudes, we find that an automobile engine which delivers 100 hp at sea level can deliver only about 60 hp at the top of Pikes Peak, which is about 14,000 ft above sea level. Since comparatively few automobiles are driven to the top of Pikes Peak, this loss of power with increased altitude does not have much effect on the work of the automobile engineers who design engines, but it is a very real problem to the designers of powerplants for airplanes.

Many airplanes are required to climb to an altitude of at least 20,000 ft. At that altitude, a cubic foot of air weighs only about one-half of what it weighs at sea level. In order to have the same **weight** of air at 20,000 ft as at sea level, there must be twice as much **volume** of the thinner air. Likewise, at 40,000 ft, the volume of the thinner air must be four times as great because 1 cu ft of air at that altitude weighs only about one-fourth of what it weighs as sea level.

The actual air pressure at 20,000 ft altitude is less than one-half the air pressure at sea level, being about 13.75 in. Hg at 20,000 ft and 29.92 in. Hg at sea level. The density of the air, however, does not decrease as much as the pressure decreases because of the decrease in temperature. The standard temperature at sea level is 59°F, and at 20,000 ft it is −12.3°F; hence the actual weight of a given volume of air is slightly more than one-half the weight the same volume of air would have at standard sea-level conditions. At 40,000 ft the **pressure** of the air is less than one-fifth the sea-level pressure, but because of the temperature decrease, the **weight** of a given volume of air is about one-fourth the weight of the same volume at sea level.

A sea-level supercharger provides an effective means for increasing the **pumping capacity** of the engine with a minimum increase in weight, but a powerplant equipped with the sea-level supercharger is affected by changes in altitude in the same manner as an unsupercharged engine, as shown in Fig. 7·16.

The human body has a supercharging system of its own. When a person climbs a mountain or rides in an airplane to higher altitudes, his lungs attempt to compensate for the thinness of the air by pumping in more air, thereby trying to obtain the quantity of oxygen needed for the combustion process of the body. In itself, the gasoline engine has no provision for such a

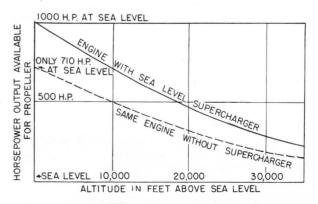

Figure 7·16   Effect of altitude with sea-level supercharger.

process. If it is to provide adequate power at higher altitudes, the engine must be provided with special supercharging equipment to compensate for the thinness of the atmosphere.

It may appear at this point that the solution to the problem is simply to install a blower of enough capacity to take care of the highest altitudes at which the airplane is expected to fly. Unfortunately, it is necessary to provide enough power at increased altitudes and also **avoid excessive power at the lower altitudes.** If the dense air at or near sea level were compressed as much as it is necessary to compress the thin air at high altitudes, there would be several unsatisfactory conditions. First, the engine would be overloaded and would soon fail because of the excessively high temperatures and pressures of the air delivered to the cylinders. Second, the extra power required to drive such a supercharger at or near sea level would be a waste of energy.

It is obvious that the greater the capacity of the supercharging equipment, the more efficient will be the performance at high altitudes, but it is also apparent that the airplane has to take off from the surface of the earth and climb through low altitudes, where the air is dense, in order to reach the higher altitudes where the supercharging equipment is needed. Therefore, some provision must be made for slowing down the supercharging process or otherwise reducing its effect while it is operating at or near sea level.

The foregoing facts account for the basic difference between a sea-level supercharger and an altitude supercharger. The capacity of the sea-level supercharger is determined by the operating conditions which the engine can safely experience at or near sea level and the supercharging required at higher altitudes. It has no special controls or regulating devices, but there must be some provision for protecting it against the adverse effects of excessive temperatures and pressures at the lower levels.

In theory, the ideal altitude supercharger would provide the engine with the same weight of air, thus enabling it to deliver full power regardless of the altitude. Some superchargers have been designed and constructed according to this theory, but in practice a compromise is required, taking into consideration not only the engine efficiency but the overall efficiency of the airplane and its effectiveness in performing the task for which it was designed.

Factors considered in designing altitude superchargers

If the power to run the supercharger is taken from the engine crankshaft, the net gain in horsepower obtained by supercharging is reduced.

The net gain in horsepower obtained from supercharging is not fully reflected in overall airplane performance because the supercharging equipment requires additional space and adds to the weight of the airplane.

The speed-changing devices or multiple-stage compressors or both required to make a supercharger effective at different altitudes need additional space, add to the weight of the airplane, and complicate the operation, inspection, and maintenance procedures.

The degree of supercharging must be restricted within definite limits to avoid the dangers of pre-ignition and detonation which result from excessive temperatures and pressures.

A special cooling apparatus must be used to reduce the temperature of the fuel/air mixture because of the excessive heat resulting from the extra compression required at extreme altitudes. This apparatus requires space, adds to the weight of the airplane, and complicates operation, inspection, and maintenance. The special radiators used for this cooling are called **intercoolers** or **aftercoolers,** depending upon their location with reference to the carburetor.

INTERNAL SINGLE-SPEED SUPERCHARGER

System for six-cylinder opposed engine

An internal single-speed supercharger consists of a gear-driven impeller placed between the carburetor and the intake ports of the cylinders. Figure 7·17 shows the supercharger installation for a Lycoming GSO-480 series engine. The supercharger is mounted on the rear end of the engine and is driven at 11.27 times crankshaft speed. At this speed the supercharger is capable of delivering a maximum manifold pressure of 48 in. Hg.

Figure 7·17 Supercharger installation for light airplane engine. (Lycoming Div., Avco Corp.)

124

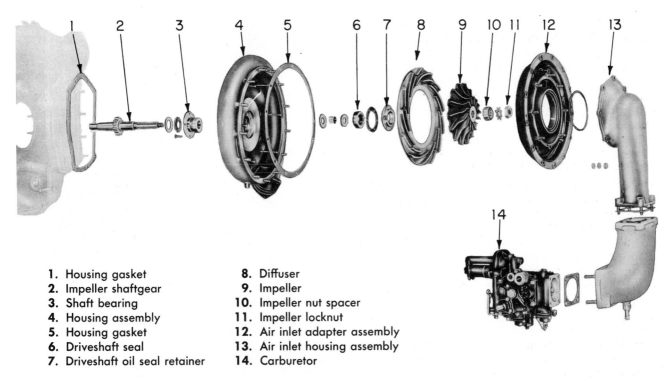

1. Housing gasket
2. Impeller shaftgear
3. Shaft bearing
4. Housing assembly
5. Housing gasket
6. Driveshaft seal
7. Driveshaft oil seal retainer
8. Diffuser
9. Impeller
10. Impeller nut spacer
11. Impeller locknut
12. Air inlet adapter assembly
13. Air inlet housing assembly
14. Carburetor

Figure 7·18   Exploded view of supercharger.

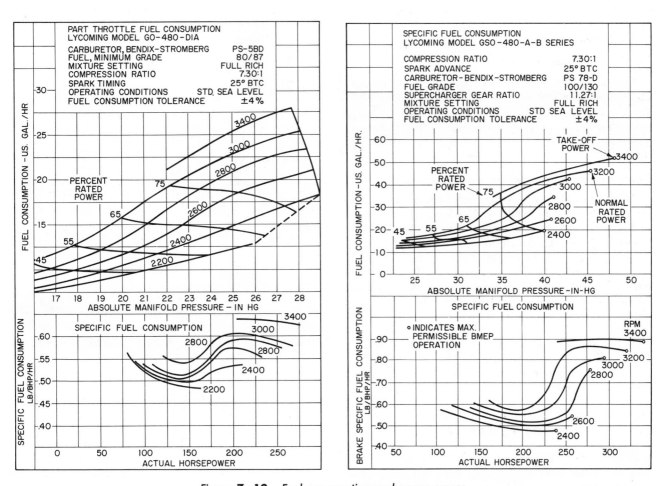

Figure 7·19   Fuel consumption and power curves.

An exploded view of the supercharger components is shown in Fig. 7·18. From the arrangement and design of the parts it is seen that the fuel/air mixture from the carburetor is drawn into the center of the impeller whence it is thrown outward by centrifugal force, through the diffuser, and into the supercharger housing. From here it flows into the portion of the induction system surrounded by the oil sump and then into the individual intake pipes to each cylinder.

Engine performance with supercharger

The effects of supercharging on the performance of a particular engine can be seen by examination of the fuel consumption and power curves in Fig. 7·19. The chart on the left shows the performance of the GO-480-D series Lycoming engine, and the chart on the right shows the performance of the GSO-480 series engines. Note that both engines have a maximum rpm of 3400 rpm and the compression of both engines is 7.30:1. The maximum power available from the GO-480-D engine is 275 hp, whereas the maximum power available from the GSO-480 engine is 340 hp.

Because of the higher manifold pressures used with the supercharged engine, it is necessary to employ fuel with a comparatively high performance number. On the chart for this engine, the performance rating of the fuel is shown to be 100/130. The technician who services an airplane having a supercharged engine must make certain that he fills the fuel tanks with the correct grade of fuel.

Service and maintenance

No service or maintenance is required with the supercharger described above other than normal inspections. At the time of engine overhaul the supercharger is inspected and overhauled in accordance with the instructions given in the manufacturer's engine overhaul manual.

Single-speed supercharger for a radial engine

The principal components of the supercharger section for the Pratt & Whitney R-985 engine are shown in Fig. 7·20. It will be observed that the supercharger consists of an impeller mounted in the supercharger (blower) case of the engine, immediately forward of the rear case. The rear case contains the diffuser vanes which distribute the fuel/air mixture evenly to the nine intake pipes which are attached by means of seals and packing nuts to the openings around the outside of the case.

The impeller is driven by the engine at a speed of ten times the crankshaft speed. This provides for a maximum manifold pressure of 37.5 in. Hg and a power output of 450 hp.

TWO-SPEED INTERNAL SUPERCHARGER

A two-speed internal supercharger is designed to permit a certain degree of supercharging at sea level and additional supercharging for altitude operation.

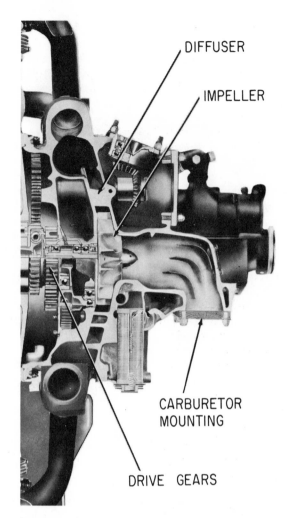

Figure 7·20 Supercharger for radial engine.

Typical of a two-speed system is that installed on the Pratt & Whitney R-2800 Double Wasp CB series engines. The impeller for this supercharger is driven at a ratio of 7.29:1 by the low-ratio clutch and at 8.5:1 by the high-ratio clutch. In some models of the engine the high gear ratio may be as much as 9.45:1.

Supercharger case

The supercharger case for the R-2800 engine is a magnesium-alloy casting which is attached to the crankcase rear section. To the rear of the supercharger case is the intermediate rear case. The impeller of the supercharger is housed between the two sections. The front face of the case incorporates a steel liner to accommodate the impeller shaft front oil seal rings and a bushing to support the rear end of the rear counterweight intermediate-drive gear shaft. A vaned diffuser is secured to the rear face of the case. Located around the periphery of the case are nine fuel/air mixture outlet ports. Attached to each port is a V-shaped intake pipe through which the fuel/air mixture is carried to one front and one rear cylinder.

Intermediate rear case

The intermediate rear case, which is attached to the rear of the supercharger case, houses the impeller and accessory drive shafts and provides support for the front end of the shafts in the various accessory gear trains. A supercharger intake insert, which forms a throat for the impeller, is located in the front face of the case. The web of the insert incorporates a steel liner which serves the dual purpose of accommodating the impeller shaft center oil seal rings and providing a fuel distributor for the fuel slinger.

The rear face of the case incorporates a steel liner to accommodate the impeller shaft rear oil seal rings and bushings to support the front ends of two clutch shafts or two impeller intermediate-drive gear shafts, a generator drive gear shaft, and a vacuum-pump shaft.

Impeller and impeller shaft

The impeller is splined to the impeller shaft, and the assembly is supported on the accessory drive shaft on bronze bearings which are installed in the inside diameter of the impeller shaft. The impeller is driven by a train of gears starting with the accessory drive-shaft adapter which is splined to the front end of the accessory drive shaft and the rear of the crankshaft. The drive continues through the accessory spring drive gear which is splined to the rear end of the accessory drive shaft, to the clutch shaft drive pinion, to the clutch gears, and to the integral spur gears on the rear of the impeller shaft.

Clutches

A desludger-type dual clutch is mounted on each side of and parallel to the impeller shaft. Each clutch shaft is supported at its front end by a bushing in the rear of the intermediate rear case and at the rear end by a bushing in the rear case. The **cones** of the clutches are splined to the clutch shaft and engage the clutch gears from the inside through a cone-shaped facing (lining). This arrangement can be seen in the diagrams of Fig. 7·21. Observe that the high-ratio gear is larger in diameter than the low-ratio gear. This accounts for the difference in drive ratio.

A narrow ring gear with a drilled vent hole rides on each clutch gear support. These ring gears turn at a different rate from their adjacent clutch gears, so that the single vent holes will line up at intervals with one of several corresponding holes drilled in the clutch gear supports. As these holes line up, a spurt of oil is allowed to escape from behind the cones, thus preventing the accumulation of sludge.

A study of Fig. 7·21 will show how the clutch mechanism is operated. In the diagram on the right, the high-ratio clutch is engaged because of the oil pressure applied to the space between the **support assembly** and the high-ratio cone. The force presses the cone facing against the inside of the gear, thus causing the gear to turn with the shaft and cone. In the diagram at the left, the pressure oil is directed to the space between the support for the low-ratio gear and the low-ratio cone, thus engaging the low-ratio clutch. An exploded view of the clutch and gear assembly is shown in Fig. 7·22.

An understanding of the basic arrangement for the two-speed gear drive can be obtained by studying the simplified drawing of Fig. 7·23. In this drawing gear 5 is the spur gear driven by the accessory drive gear. Gear 2 is the low-ratio drive gear, and gear 1 is the high-ratio drive gear. If the clutch inside gear 2 is engaged, gear 2 will be turning with the shaft and will be driving gear 4, which is integral with the impeller shaft. It is apparent that the impeller shaft will be turning about 1½ times the speed of the clutch drive shaft. This is the low-ratio drive. Remember that the clutch in gear 1 is not engaged and gear 1 is idling.

If the clutch in gear 1 is engaged, then gear 1 will turn at the same rate as the clutch drive shaft and will drive gear 3 at about 2½ times the speed of the clutch drive shaft. This is the high-ratio drive. At this time, gear 2 will be idling. The clutches for both gears cannot be engaged at the same time.

Selector valve

A manually operated two-position impeller ratio selector valve is mounted on the top of the engine rear case. If the valve is moved into **high** position, pressure will be directed to the chamber between the cone and the high-ratio clutch gear support. If the valve is moved to the **low** position, pressure oil will be similarly directed to each low-ratio clutch. The oil pressure causes the cones to engage the gears which operate in parallel to drive the impeller. The selector valve is shown in each of the diagrams of Fig. 7·21.

THE TURBOSUPERCHARGER

A **turbosupercharger** is an external supercharger designed to be driven by means of a turbine wheel which receives its power from the engine exhaust. Ram air pressure or alternate air pressure is applied to the inlet side of the turbocompressor (blower), and the output is supplied to the inlet side of the carburetor or fuel injector. If a high degree of air compression is done by the compressor, it may be necessary to pass the compressed air through an intercooler to reduce the air temperature. As mentioned previously, if the carburetor air temperature is too high, detonation will occur.

The exhaust gases are usually diverted from the main exhaust stack by means of a **waste gate.** On large engines, the position of the waste gate is automatically controlled by reference to selected manifold pressure. The waste gate is closed to direct the exhaust gases through the turbine. The degree of closing determines the amount of air-pressure boost obtained from the supercharger.

The general arrangement of a turbosupercharger system is shown in the schematic diagram of Fig. 7·24.

A turbosupercharger system can be used to maintain a given manifold pressure to the design altitude of the system. Above this altitude, which is called the **critical**

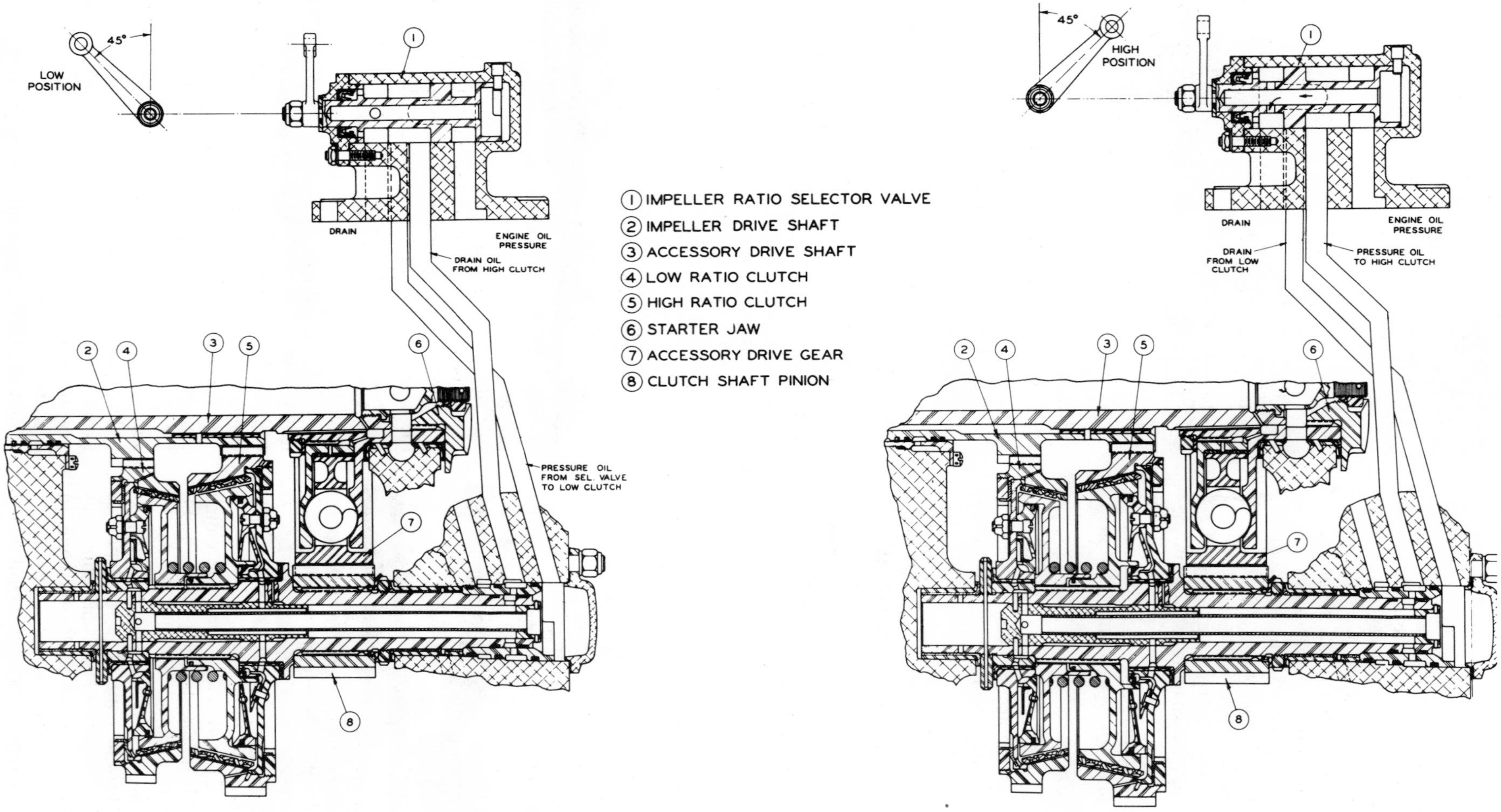

SELECTOR VALVE IN HIGH POSITION WITH HIGH CLUTCH ENGAGED

SELECTOR VALVE IN LOW POSITION WITH LOW CLUTCH ENGAGED

① IMPELLER RATIO SELECTOR VALVE
② IMPELLER DRIVE SHAFT
③ ACCESSORY DRIVE SHAFT
④ LOW RATIO CLUTCH
⑤ HIGH RATIO CLUTCH
⑥ STARTER JAW
⑦ ACCESSORY DRIVE GEAR
⑧ CLUTCH SHAFT PINION

Figure *7·21* Operation of clutch mechanism.

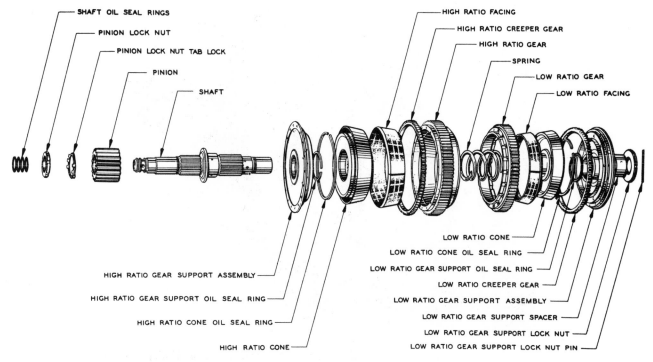

Figure **7·22** *Exploded view of clutch and gear assembly.*

SHAFT OIL SEAL RINGS
PINION LOCK NUT
PINION LOCK NUT TAB LOCK
PINION
SHAFT

HIGH RATIO FACING
HIGH RATIO CREEPER GEAR
HIGH RATIO GEAR
SPRING
LOW RATIO GEAR
LOW RATIO FACING

HIGH RATIO GEAR SUPPORT ASSEMBLY
HIGH RATIO GEAR SUPPORT OIL SEAL RING
HIGH RATIO CONE OIL SEAL RING
HIGH RATIO CONE

LOW RATIO CONE
LOW RATIO CONE OIL SEAL RING
LOW RATIO GEAR SUPPORT OIL SEAL RING
LOW RATIO CREEPER GEAR
LOW RATIO GEAR SUPPORT ASSEMBLY
LOW RATIO GEAR SUPPORT SPACER
LOW RATIO GEAR SUPPORT LOCK NUT
LOW RATIO GEAR SUPPORT LOCK NUT PIN

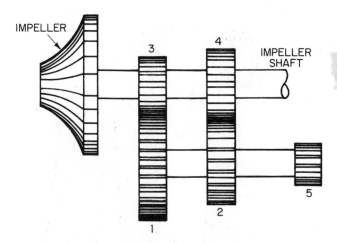

IMPELLER
IMPELLER SHAFT
3
4
1
2
5

Figure **7·23** *Simplified diagram to illustrate gear operation.*

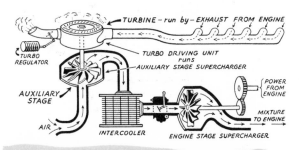

TURBINE – run by – EXHAUST FROM ENGINE
TURBO REGULATOR
TURBO DRIVING UNIT runs AUXILIARY STAGE SUPERCHARGER
POWER FROM ENGINE
AUXILIARY STAGE
AIR
MIXTURE TO ENGINE
INTERCOOLER
ENGINE STAGE SUPERCHARGER

Figure **7·24** *Turbosupercharger system diagram.*

altitude, the manifold pressure will begin to fall off as altitude is increased. We may therefore define critical altitude as the altitude above which a particular engine-supercharger combination will no longer deliver full power.

TURBOSUPERCHARGER FOR LIGHT-AIRCRAFT ENGINE

A turbosupercharger installation for a light airplane engine is shown in Fig. 7·25. This is the Rajay Turbo 200, also called a **turbocharger,** manufactured by the Rajay Corporation of Long Beach, California, for installation on the Piper PA-23 150 and 160 airplanes.

It will be observed from the photograph that the exhaust pipes from each cylinder are all connected into one main exhaust stack. A **waste gate** is placed near the outlet of the stack to block the exit of the exhaust gases and direct them through a duct into the turbine. The turbine drives the compressor, which increases the air pressure to the carburetor inlet.

This particular turbocharger is designed for use at altitudes above 5000 ft because maximum engine power is available without supercharging below that altitude.

Description

The Rajay 200 turbocharger is a 12.5-lb unit of high-speed turbine equipment designed by the Thompson Ramo Wooldridge Corporation primarily for use on small high-performance diesel engines. The basic design has been modified to be compatible with the aircraft powerplant application.

129

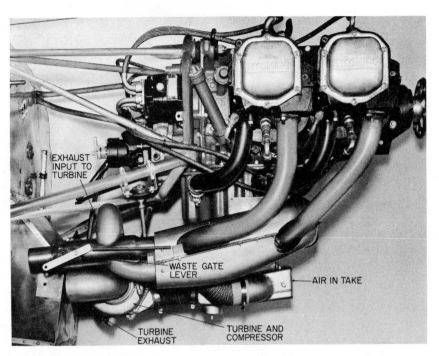

Figure **7·25** *Turbosupercharger installation for light airplane engine. (Rajay Corporation, Long Beach, Calif.)*

The unit consists of a precision-balanced rotating shaft with a radial inflow turbine wheel on one end and a centrifugal compressor impeller on the other end, each with its own housing. The turbine, driven by engine exhaust gases, powers the impeller which supplies air under pressure to the carburetor inlet. This higher pressure supplies more air by weight to the engine with the advantage of a proportionally higher power output and a minimum increase in weight.

A photograph of the turbosupercharger and its ducting to the carburetor air box is shown in Fig. 7·26. This photograph may be compared with the diagram of Fig. 7·27 to gain a clear understanding of the operating principles.

In the carburetor air box is a **swing check valve** which is open during **naturally aspirated** operation, that is, when the supercharger is not in operation. The check-valve operation is automatic, and the valve will close when turbo boost pressure is greater than ram air pressure. When the waste gate in the exhaust stack outlet is closed or partially closed, exhaust gases are directed to the turbine. The rotation of the turbine causes the compressor to draw air from the air box and deliver it under pressure through the duct forward of the carburetor.

It will be observed in the diagram that carburetor heat may be obtained through the alternate air duct, regardless of whether the supercharger is operating or not. If carburetor heat is desired, the alternate air valve is closed, shutting off ram air allowing air to be drawn through the heat muff. With this installation, carburetor heat should not be used when turbo boost is more than 5 in. Hg.

The bearings of the turbosupercharger are of the sleeve-journal type and utilize pressure lubrication

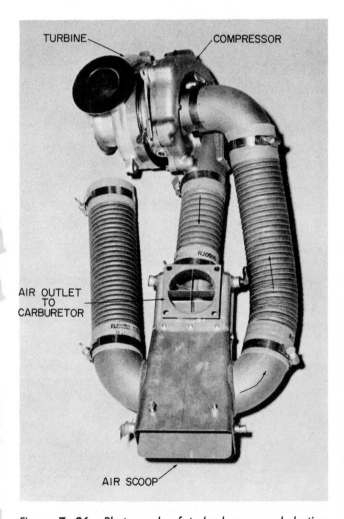

Figure **7·26** *Photograph of turbocharger and ducting.*

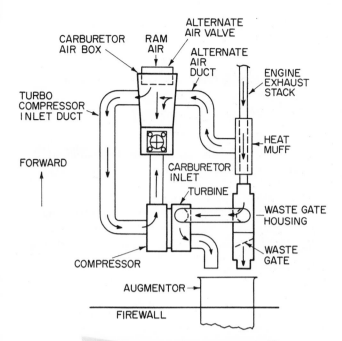

Figure 7·27 Diagram of turbocharger system.

from the engine. This type of bearing is low in cost and has a high degree of reliability.

The turbine and turbine housing are cast of high-temperature alloys, with the central main housing, compressor housing, and impeller cast of aluminum alloy for light weight and good thermal characteristics. The design and construction result in a unit which is completely air cooled.

Lubrication system

Lubricant for the turbosupercharger is supplied by a line connected to a fitting on the engine governor fuel pump dual drive pad. A fitting included in this lubricant supply line incorporates a pressure-regulator poppet valve to reduce engine gallery oil pressure from the normal 60- to 80-psi range to a pressure of 30 to 50 psi, which is required for the supercharger. At this pressure range, between 1 and 2 qt per min of lubricating oil will be supplied to the unit. This quantity of oil is but a small percentage of the total oil-pump capacity. The oil which is supplied to the turbosupercharger is normally returned to the engine sump by way of the bypass pressure-relief valve.

Incorporated in the turbo lubricant supply line is a pressure switch which will activate a red warning light in the event that turbocharger oil pressure is below 27 to 30 psi. If the oil pressure is lost, the pilot simply removes the turbocharger from service by opening the waste gate and returns the engine to naturally aspirated operation to save the turbocharger bearings. The turbocharger lubricating-oil sump is scavenged by means of the fuel-pump drive gears contained in the duel drive unit for the pump.

Controls

As previously explained, the principal factor in turbocharger operation is the degree of waste gate closure. This determines the amount of the total engine exhaust gas flow through the turbine and the resulting level of boost. A separate Ahrens push-pull control with a precise vernier adjustment is installed for actuation of the waste gate. This permits convenient, exact matching of manifold pressures for both engines on the airplane.

Operation

Since the Rajay 200 supercharger is designed for operation at altitudes above 4000 to 6000 ft, the ground operation of the engine is the same as required for an unsupercharged engine. During climb, when the airplane reaches an altitude where power begins to fall off, the pilot places the throttle in wide-open position and begins to close the waste gate with the separate control located on the fuel valve selector console. The operation of the supercharger makes it possible to maintain sea-level manifold pressure of 28 in. Hg absolute during the climb of the aircraft to an altitude of 20,000 ft.

Typical engine operating conditions for climb are as follows:

1. 2400 rpm maximum and 2200 rpm minimum with turbo operative.
2. 25 to 28 in. Hg maximum manifold pressure.
3. 400 to 475°F maximum cylinder-head temperature with turbo operating. A cylinder-head temperature gage is required.
4. Carburetor inlet air temperature 100 to 160°F, depending upon power setting and temperature of outside air. A performance number for the fuel will have been specified to preclude any possibility of detonation.

After the airplane has attained the desired cruising altitude, power should be reduced to 23 to 25 in. Hg MP and the rpm to the 2200 to 2300 cruising range. The aircraft is then trimmed for cruising speed, and the fuel-air mixture adjusted for best economy. When the engine is operating below 75 percent power, leaning can be accomplished by pulling the mixture control back slowly until there is a slight drop in MP. The mixture control is then moved forward until smooth, steady engine operation is attained.

When it is desired to let down and prepare for landing, the turbosupercharger should be shut off by opening the waste gate and carburetor heat should be turned on. The throttle should not be closed suddenly because rapid cooling of the cylinder heads may cause cracking or other damage. During letdown the throttle should not be entirely closed and should occasionally be opened sufficiently to "clear" the engine.

TURBOSUPERCHARGER FOR LARGE ENGINES

Although there are but few turbosuperchargers still being employed on large aircraft, there is a sufficient number to warrant an examination of such systems. Furthermore, a study of the turbosupercharger is of value in providing an overall understanding of engine operation.

Complete system

A schematic diagram of a complete turbosupercharger system is shown in Fig. 7·28. The exhaust gases from the engine are collected in an exhaust manifold and sent to a **nozzle box** through an **exhaust stack.** Since the exhaust gases are extremely hot, this system must be made of materials which resist heat to a high degree. To provide a safety factor in case of exhaust-stack failure, an exhaust shroud, which is a pipe concentric around the exhaust stack, is installed. The shroud has two functions as follows: (1) It forms a fire wall around the exhaust stack, and (2) it permits the cooling of the hot exhaust gases before they enter the nozzle box. A cooling blast of air from a ram air intake flows between the shroud and the exhaust stack.

In one type of supercharger installation, the nozzle box has a single inlet and a single outlet. A butterfly-type valve, called a **waste gate,** is in the outlet. If the waste gate is open, the exhaust gases flow through the nozzle box to the outside air. If the waste gate is closed, the exhaust gases are directed, by means of diaphragms in the nozzle box, against the **buckets** of a **rotor** or **bucket wheel** which is mounted on a shaft. These buckets are placed radially around the circumference of the rotor and are shaped so that the pressure of the

gases against them causes the rotor to rotate. After the gases pass through the buckets, they reach the outside air.

In another type of installation, there is **no waste gate on the nozzle box.** The waste gate is located in a short branch pipe attached to the exhaust stack. In this type of installation, an open waste gate bypasses all the exhaust gases around the nozzle box and rotor.

Since the compression of the air by the impeller generates a large amount of heat, the temperature of the air leaving the compressor casing is higher than that desired for proper operation. For this reason, an **intercooler,** shown in Fig. 7·28, is installed between the compressor discharge and the carburetor, thereby avoiding the dangers of detonation and preignition and the reduction of volumetric efficiency that would accompany the entrance of too hot a charge into the engine cylinders.

Intercoolers have been discussed previously in this text, but a few more comments on their construction and function will maintain the logical flow of thought in our explanation of supercharging principles. The intercooler may consist of a radiator element that resembles a radiator for either liquid or oil cooling. Compressed air passes through tubes in the core, and cooling air surrounds the tubes. Shutters located at the

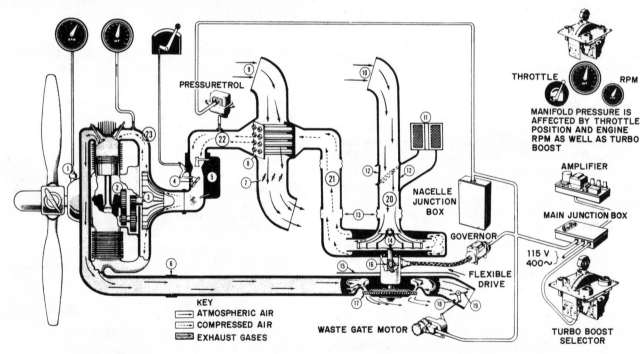

KEY
▭ ATMOSPHERIC AIR
▭ COMPRESSED AIR
▭ EXHAUST GASES

1. Propeller governor	9. Intercooler air scoop	17. Turbine wheel
2. Gear drive for internal blower	10. Carburetor air scoop	18. Waste gate stop
3. Internal blower	11. Air filter	19. Waste gate
4. Throttle	12. Filter control gates	20. Incoming air pressure
5. Carburetor	13. Flexible couplings	21. Turbo output pressure
6. Expansion joint	14. Turbo compressor	22. Carburetor inlet pressure
7. Intercooler shutters	15. Heat baffle	23. Manifold pressure
8. Intercooler	16. Worm-gear drive	

Fig. **7·28**   Complete turbosupercharger system.

rear of the intercooler are opened and closed from the pilot's compartment to regulate the degree of cooling. When the shutters are fully opened, they provide the maximum degree of cooling. When they are closed, they not only reduce the cooling but also can be used for heating to eliminate the tendency of ice to form in certain types of carburetors.

Flexible joints are generally located between the ram air intake and the supercharger compressor, between the compressor and the intercooler, and between the intercooler and the carburetor. They are connected tightly enough to prevent the leakage of the compressed air and constructed well enough to avoid a mechanical failure which would result in a warping of the duct if the attachment were too rigid or tight. These joints are sleevelike tubes, usually made of some synthetic-rubber material like neoprene and clamped to the adjoining edges of a ducting section. They reduce the vibration which would otherwise occur between any rigidly mounted unit or part and a nonrigidly mounted unit or part, an example being the ducting passage between the intercooler and the carburetor.

The General Electric type BH-4 turbosupercharger

A cutaway view of the General Electric type BH-4 turbosupercharger is shown in Fig. 7·29. This supercharger was standard equipment on the Boeing Stratocruiser airliner.

During World War II turbosuperchargers such as the type B-2 were used on many military aircraft to provide high performance for takeoff and high-altitude flight. The extra power made possible by the use of the turbosupercharger was an important factor in the success of both bombers and fighter aircraft.

The type BH-4 turbosupercharger was designed especially to permit the airliner to fly at high altitudes, above storms and surface disturbances, thus providing greater safety and passenger comfort. It is not used for takeoff, since maximum power can be developed at low altitudes without applying additional boost to the intake air.

On the Boeing Stratocruiser the BH-4 supercharger was also utilized for cabin pressurization. Adequate air pressure and volume are delivered by the supercharger both for manifold pressure boost for the engine and for cabin pressurization.

A study of Fig. 7·29 will aid in understanding the construction and operation of the BH-4 turbosupercharger.

ELECTRONIC TURBO CONTROL SYSTEM

The most satisfactory type of control system for the turbosupercharger consists of various sensing devices whose signals are integrated and the results applied through an electronic amplifier to the waste gate. This type of system consists of four principal operating units: (1) the turbo boost selector, (2) the Pressuretrol, (3) the governor, and (4) the waste-gate motor. In connection with these units are the necessary junction

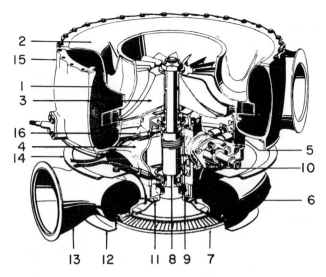

1. Diffuser
2. Compressor casing (rear)
3. Impeller
4. Bearing-and-pump casing
5. Oil lines
6. Nozzlebox diaphragm
7. Bucket wheel
8. Pump drive sleeve
9. Oil jet
10. Oil pump
11. Sealing plate assembly
12. Nozzlebox mounting ring
13. Nozzlebox
14. Baffle ring
15. Compressor casing (front)
16. Bearing temperature indicator

Figure **7·29** Cutaway view of type BH-4 turbosupercharger.

boxes, wiring, and power supply. A schematic diagram of the electronic system is shown in Fig. 7·30.

In operating the turbo control, the pilot selects the desired manifold pressure with the turbo boost selector. This unit transmits a signal to the Pressuretrol and thence to the amplifier. The amplifier receives the signal for either opening the waste gate or closing it and through the discriminators sends the proper current to the waste-gate motor to obtain the desired result.

Turbo boost selector

The turbo boost selector is the pilot's control unit through which he regulates the operation of the turbo control system. The boost selector contains a transformer, a main potentiometer which is operated by the quadrant lever, and four calibrating potentiometers through which the signals are sent to each of the four engines.

The voltage across the main potentiometer is supplied by the transformer. The primary of the transformer is connected to the 115-volt 400-cycle alternating current from the airplane a-c supply. The pilot adjusts the wiper of the main potentiometer with the quadrant control, thus producing the signal for the desired manifold pressure. The signal from the main potentiometer is directed to each of the four calibrating

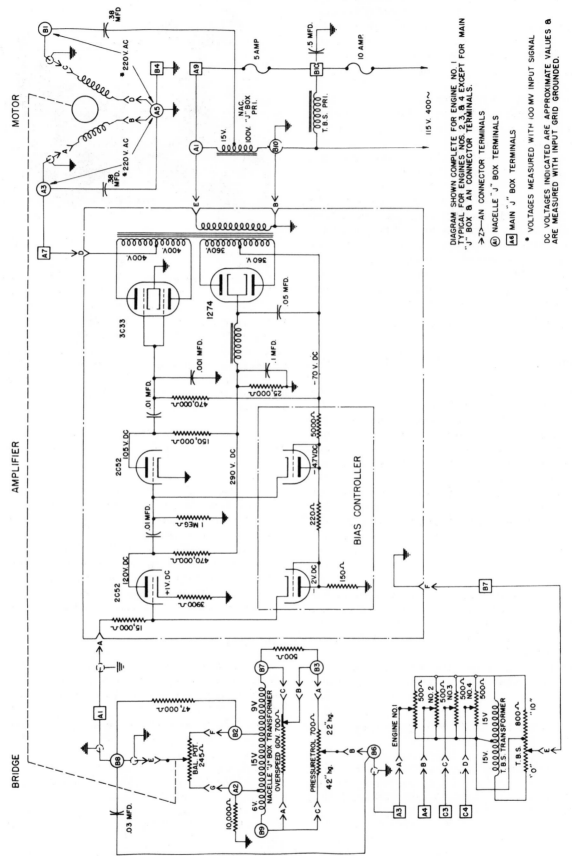

Figure 7·30 Electronic control system for supercharger.

134

potentiometers and thence to the individual engine systems. The calibrating potentiometers are adjusted with knobs which are arranged adjacent to the boost-selector lever. Thus the manifold pressure for each engine can be adjusted to agree with the others.

The Pressuretrol

The **Pressuretrol** is the primary sensing unit of the turbo control system. It consists of a sealed bellows installed within a chamber to which is connected a line from the intercooler header duct. Thus the pressure in the intercooler duct is transmitted to the chamber of the Pressuretrol surrounding the bellows.

The Pressuretrol contains a potentiometer which is actuated by the bellows. As the pressure in the area surrounding the bellows increases, the bellows contracts, moving the wiper of the potentiometer in a direction which sends a signal through the system calling for "waste gate open." As the waste gate opens, the turbosupercharger slows down and the pressure in the intake system decreases. The reverse action takes place if the pressure in the intercooler duct decreases below the required level.

The overspeed governor

The **overspeed governor** is designed to prevent the bucket wheel of the supercharger from rotating at a speed beyond the safe limit. It is driven by a flexible shaft from the supercharger tachometer drive.

The principal operating parts of the governor are a clutch, a gear train, a flyball governor, and a driving mechanism which moves the potentiometer wipers. When an overspeed condition develops, the flyweights of the governor move outward and cause the potentiometer wipers to move in a direction which produces a "waste-gate-open" signal. The waste gate will open and reduce the speed of the turbo even though the manifold pressure of the system is lower than that selected by the pilot.

In some installations the overspeed governor has been removed and overspeed warning lights are used to notify the pilot that an overspeed condition exists. The pilot or flight engineer then can reduce the turbo speed with the boost selector.

The waste-gate motor

The **waste-gate motor** is a two-phase reversible type. It operates through a gear train to adjust the position of the waste gate. A potentiometer is used as a follow-up with the motor so that the incoming signal will be neutralized when the motor has moved the waste gate to the proper position.

The direction in which the waste-gate motor will rotate is determined by the signals. Since the motor is a two-phase type, it has two sets of field poles. The current for one field is approximately 90° out of phase with the current in the other field. The current supplied by the amplifier will either lead or lag the current in the other field of the motor by approximately 90°. This lead or lag determines the direction of rotation.

The amplifier

The function of the turbo control **amplifier** is to receive the signals from the Pressuretrol and boost-selector bridge circuits and from these signals to cause the waste-gate motor either to open or to close the waste gate. The "waste-gate-open" signal is 180° out of phase with the "waste-gate-closed" signal.

The amplifier amplifies the signal and then, through the discriminator circuits, sends a current to the waste-gate motor which causes it to rotate in a direction which will move the waste gate in the required direction.

REVIEW QUESTION

1. Name the principal sections of an induction system.
2. What is the function of the alternate air valve?
3. What detrimental effect does the air filter have on engine operation?
4. Explain how engine oil is sometimes used to warm the fuel/air mixture.
5. What is the effect of an air leak in the manifold between the carburetor and the cylinder for an unsupercharged engine?
6. What is the function of the *balance pipe* connected between the forward ends of the intake manifolds on some opposed engines?
7. Give the advantages of supercharging.
8. Compare the density of the atmosphere at sea level and at 20,000 ft.
9. Explain the significance of *manifold pressure* in the operation of an aircraft engine.
10. What is the effect of excessive manifold pressure?
11. What is an *internal* supercharger?
12. What engine instruments are particularly important in the operation of a supercharged engine?
13. When an engine is equipped with a direct-drive sea-level supercharger, what effect does altitude have on the power output?
14. What means is used to prevent excessive intake air temperatures when a supercharger is used?
15. Explain the operation of a two-speed internal supercharger.
16. What device is used to change the speed of a two-speed supercharger?
17. Describe the function of the *waste gate* in a turbosupercharger system.
18. What is meant by *critical altitude?*
19. Describe a turbosupercharger system for a light airplane.
20. What is the function of the *overspeed governor* in an electronically controlled supercharger system?

CHAPTER 8

Aircraft Fuels and Fuel Systems

PRODUCTION AND CHARACTERISTICS OF AIRCRAFT FUELS

Chemistry of combustion

From a chemical point of view, the burning of a substance, whether liquid, solid, or gas, consists of the uniting of one or more of the elements in the substance with the oxygen which is present in the atmosphere. This results in the formation of oxides of the elements which have reacted with the oxygen. This is called oxidation. The rusting of iron, too, is oxidation, the rust being the red iron oxide formed.

Oxygen, which is indispensable to combustion, is present in the atmosphere by volume to an extent of about 21 percent. It combines with a great number of the elements. In each instance, the amount of heat liberated is greatly dependent upon the makeup of the burning substance. Nitrogen and other gases constitute the remaining 79 percent of the atmosphere by volume. These gases, in general, do not enter into the process of combustion.

The chemical actions which take place during the burning of an aircraft fuel are relatively simple. As described in the section explaining carburetion, gasoline consists of carbon (C) and hydrogen (H) in combinations to form hydrocarbon molecules. For example, heptane molecules are represented by the chemical symbol C_7H_{16}, meaning that 1 molecule of heptane contains 7 atoms of carbon and 16 atoms of hydrogen. When heptane is burned with oxygen, the following action takes place:

$$C_7H_{16} + 11O_2 = 7CO_2 + 8H_2O$$

Thus we see that, when 1 molecule of heptane is burned with 11 molecules of oxygen (22 atoms), the products of combustion are 7 molecules of carbon dioxide and 8 molecules of water. This action represents perfect combustion.

Classification of fuels

Fuels may be classified as solids, gases, and liquids. **Solid fuels,** such as coal and wood, are widely used for producing heat energy for external-combustion engines, for example, the steam engine. Such fuels have slow burning rates and low heat value but are satisfactory for use in steam engines because the heat of burning is transferred to water, which in turn becomes steam under pressure and supplies the actual driving force to the piston.

On the other hand, the internal-combustion piston-type engines which are used in airplanes require a fuel which burns readily and which produces heat rapidly enough to force the piston down by a rapid expansion of gases.

Solid fuels (propellants) for rocket engines usually consists of an inorganic oxydizer dispersed in a mixture of organic plastic or a double-base propellant consisting of the colloid of nitroglycerin-nitrocellulose. In addition to the chemicals which make up the major ingredients, a small percentage of additives is used to modify the burning rate.

Gaseous fuels, such as natural petroleum and illuminating gas, are used to some extent in internal-combustion engines of the stationary type. However, they are of low heat value, and the large space necessary to store an adequate supply makes them unsuitable for aircraft-engine use.

Liquid fuels commonly used in airplane engines are the paraffins, the naphthenes, and some aromatic hydrocarbons. Gasolines are blends of some of these products. Gasoline is the most suitable fuel for piston engines because it meets the fundamental requirements for such engines better than any other fuel known today.

Fundamental requirements for a good aircraft fuel

The fundamental requirements for a good aircraft fuel to be used in modern internal-combustion reciprocating aircraft engines are as follows: (1) It must vaporize easily enough at low temperatures to ensure starting of the engine but not so easily that it will cause vapor lock, (2) it must have a high energy content per unit weight and a sufficiently high octane rating to permit high compression without detonation, (3) it must be reasonably free of gum-forming compounds, and (4) it must have a low sulfur content to reduce corrosive action.

136

The story of gasoline

Since the bulk of aviation fuel except for turbojet and turboprop engines is gasoline, the story of its development should be of value. Gasoline is a hydrocarbon compound which is usually obtained from petroleum. It has a relatively high heat value of about 19,000 Btu **(British thermal units, the quantity of heat required to raise one pound of water one degree Fahrenheit)** as compared with about 12,000 Btu per lb for alcohol.

Hydrocarbon compounds are defined by chemists as those compounds which contain two elements, hydrogen and carbon. The chief sources of hydrocarbon compounds are petroleum, natural gas, coal, and some varieties of plants.

Petroleum deposits are found in most regions throughout the world. It is of passing interest to note that the origin of these deposits is not definitely known. One theory has it that petroleum is the result of the decaying of prehistoric animals. Another theory states that petroleum was formed by the reaction between underground water deposits and iron carbides.

In its crude, unrefined state, petroleum is a dark, greenish-brown viscous oil solution which contains many hydrocarbons. Dissolved in this solution are a large number of solids and gaseous hydrocarbons. Petroleum in its natural form varies in composition from one region to another. The crude oil, or petroleum, deposits of Pennsylvania are composed mainly of paraffin-base hydrocarbon. California crudes have an asphalt base, while those crudes from Oklahoma and Texas have a variety of bases. Some of them are similar to Pennsylvania crudes, and others resemble western crudes.

Producing gasoline from petroleum

There are many methods of producing gasoline from crude oil, but the principal processes are termed **fractional distillation, cracking, polymerization, hydrogenation, and alkylation.**

The **fractional-distillation** process was first developed and is still widely used to produce what is known as "straight-run" gasoline. In this method, the crude oil is heated at atmospheric pressure in a heating unit (see Fig. 8 · 1). The various hydrocarbon liquids in the crude oil vaporize first, followed by those of higher boiling points. These vapors are then passed through a condenser, where they are returned to liquids. Proper temperature-regulation processes produce various grades of gasoline, kerosene, diesel fuel, fuel oil, and lubricating-oil stocks. The fractional-distillation process does not change the chemical composition of any of the parts of the original crude petroleum.

The **cracking process** increases the amount of gasoline obtained from the crude petroleum, and it is through this method that gasoline is produced in quantity and at low cost. In the cracking process, the parts of the crude oil remaining from the fractional-distillation process, which are suitable for neither gasoline nor lubricating oil, are placed in a sealed heating

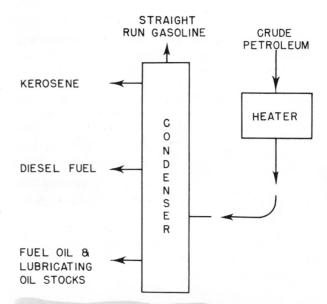

Figure **8 · 1**   *Fractional-distillation process.*

chamber and subjected to high temperatures and pressures. Under this treatment, the heavier carbon liquids are chemically changed and a part of them converted into "cracked" gasoline. **This is known as thermal cracking.** Another cracking process uses temperature, pressure, and a catalyst. **A catalyst is a substance which speeds the rate of a chemical reaction without becoming a part of the reaction.**

A **hydrocarbon** is a compound containing hydrogen and carbon only. The chief natural sources of hydrocarbons are petroleum, natural gas, coal, and varieties of plants that yield such hydrocarbons as rubber, turpentine, etc.

Figure 8 · 2 shows how the cracking process separates the heavier hydrocarbons into lighter fractions.

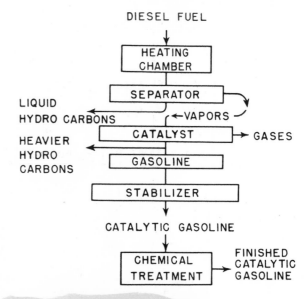

Figure **8 · 2**   *The cracking process.*

Cracked gasoline is thoroughly refined to eliminate gum-producing qualities which develop in the cracking process. To this end also, an antigum agent is sometimes added to the gasoline before storage.

The process known as **polymerization and hydrogenation** was originally used to produce isooctane, a hydrocarbon of high antiknock qualities. The process consists of two stages. The first, polymerization, uses selected refinery gases, such as the butanes, which are acquired from the cracking units. These gaseous hydrocarbons are united in the polymerization unit to make the heavier, less volatile hydrocarbons. **Polymerization means the making of heavier hydrocarbons from lighter hydrocarbons.**

The second step in the process, **hydrogenation,** combines hydrogen with polymer gasoline. Isooctane of good stability and a 100 octane number is the final product (see Fig. 8·3).

The **alkylation process** reduces the production of isooctane to one step. Alkylation makes use of gaseous hydrocarbons from the cracking units and natural gas to make liquid hydrocarbons. The gaseous hydrocarbons are run through an alkylation unit in which a catalyst is used. This produces a total alkylate which is stabilized and fractionated to make two products, aviation fuel and safety fuel.

Characteristics of gasoline

It has been mentioned that gasoline possesses desirable characteristics which make it more suitable for use as aviation fuel. These characteristics, as compared with other fuels, are high heat value and the ability to evaporate when exposed to the air at ordinary temperatures. A fuel such as gasoline evaporates readily at low temperatures and is said to have high volatility. For engine starting purposes, high volatility is a desirable characteristic. However, a gasoline which evaporates too readily is apt to "boil" and form air bubbles in the

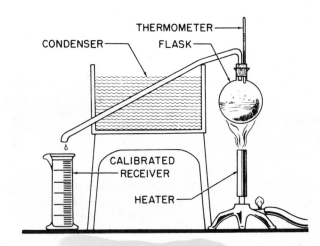

Figure **8·4** Fractional-distillation test.

fuel lines, resulting in **vapor locks. A good aircraft fuel must have high volatility to start an engine easily but not so high as readily to form excessive vapors within the fuel systems.**

Testing fuels

To determine the volatility of an aircraft fuel, a fractional-distillation test is made. Figure 8·4 illustrates this test and shows the type of apparatus used. In the test, a measured quantity of gasoline to be tested is placed in a glass flask and glass tubing is then connected from the flask through a condenser unit to a calibrated receiver. Heat is applied under the flask, and the amount of fuel condensed in the receiver at various temperatures is observed. This action can be plotted on a graph, as shown in Fig. 8·5, and a temperature range found where condensation of 10, 50, and 90 percent of the fuel takes place.

The temperature at which 10 percent of a fuel being

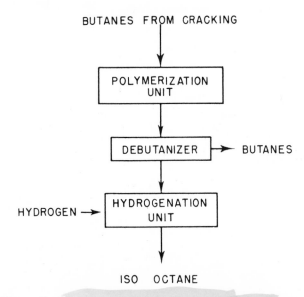

Figure **8·3** Polymerization to produce isooctane.

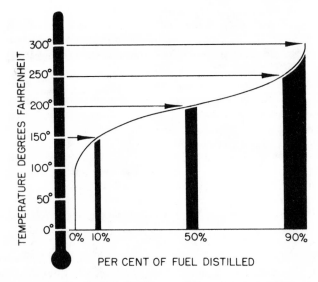

Figure **8·5** Fuel distillation at different temperatures.

tested is boiled off is indicative of the lowest atmospheric temperature at which an engine will start when primed with this fuel. The temperature at which 50 percent of the fuel condenses determines engine acceleration ability; 90 percent determines overall engine performance.

The volatility of a gasoline is also important because of its effect on carburetor icing. Fuel engineers speak of the **latent heat of vaporization,** which means simply the amount of heat necessary to vaporize a given amount of fuel. Vaporization cannot take place without heat. In a carburetor this heat for vaporizing the fuel is taken from the air and from metal. If too much heat is taken for vaporization, there is danger of ice forming. A highly volatile fuel extracts heat from its surroundings more rapidly than a less volatile fuel. Carburetor icing has been practically eliminated from all aircraft except the small types equipped with float-type carburetors. This has been accomplished by the use of pressure-injection and direct fuel-injection systems, with the fuel injection occurring in locations not conducive to ice formation.

Explanation of vapor lock

One of the most dangerous troubles which may be encountered in a fuel system is known as **vapor locking.** This trouble may develop if the liquid fuel vaporizes before reaching the carburetor. When this happens, there is likelihood of bubbles forming in the line, thus blocking passage of the liquid fuel to the carburetor or resulting in an improper mixture. If a mixture of

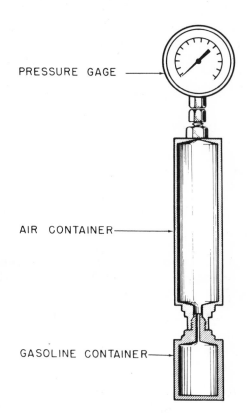

PRESSURE GAGE

AIR CONTAINER

GASOLINE CONTAINER

Figure 8·6 The Reid vapor-pressure bomb.

liquid fuel and considerable fuel vapor is delivered to the carburetor, the total weight of available fuel is seriously reduced and it may be insufficient to run the engine at full power.

For this reason, aviation fuels, which in general are blended of a number of different gasolines, are checked carefully for vaporizing properties. An instrument known as the **Reid vapor-pressure bomb** is used. In this apparatus, shown in Fig. 8·6, a pressure gage, attached to one end of a sealed container, registers the amount of vapor pressure a given fuel creates at various temperatures.

Causes of fuel knocks

Various liquid fuels when mixed with air may be compressed to certain limits, and since the power developed by an internal-combustion engine is largely dependent on the extent of the compressed charge, this factor is taken into consideration in the design of an aircraft engine and in the selection of the engine fuel. If the correct fuel is used, smooth, efficient engine performance is assured. However, if the fuel selected is unsuitable, it will "crack up" and give evidence of abnormal burning once the compression limit of the particular fuel/air mixture is reached.

Every motorist at some time or another has been annoyed by the "pinging" noise in his engine, usually upon acceleration, which is the result of this abnormal and uncontrolled burning of the charge in the cylinders. The noise is called a **fuel knock,** and what happens is that the charge, when ignited by the spark plug, burns normally and smoothly part of the way across the combustion chamber. Then if either the fuel or the engine operating condition is unsatisfactory, the charge burns almost instantaneously; there is a power lag and a noticeable clatter.

Unfortunately, in an aircraft engine fuel knocks cannot be heard, either in flight or on the ground. The fuel knock can be detected only by increased cylinder temperatures, loss of power, or other evidence of faulty engine operation.

The preignition knock

A knock similar to the one just described may occur in an aircraft engine when the compressed charge is, in some way, ignited before the spark jumps the gap between the spark-plug electrodes, or points. This is called a **preignition knock.** Of fuel knocks, this one is probably the most destructive. If the condition which causes it is not immediately corrected, backfire pressure in the induction system may damage the supercharger and the untimed combustion may melt pistons and crack cylinder heads through excessive overheating.

Preignition, also called surface ignition because it is caused by surface conditions within the combustion chamber, is the ignition of the compressed charge before the action of the spark plug. It may be caused by valves which have been ground, or lapped, to feather-edges during an overhaul and which consequently become red hot in operation owing to their thinness, by excessive carbon in cylinder heads, and by spark plugs thickly coated with carbon. The normal heat of the engine may cause the carbon formation in the combustion chambers, the thin valves, or the faulty spark plugs to glow incandescently, thus firing the charge prior to regular spark-plug action.

Aside from the fact that preignition and the use of unsuitable fuel can do great damage to the aircraft engine, the possibility of its causing engine failure while in flight should be of sufficient importance to guarantee every measure being taken to correct this faulty condition once its existence is known.

Detonation

The word **detonation** is generally used by automotive and aircraft engine specialists to describe severe fuel knock. Actually, in plain English, detonation means an explosion, but when the word is used by internal-combustion-engine men, it is not employed in its normal, everyday sense. Fuel knock is merely the result of abnormal burning or uncontrolled combustion.

The availability of improved metal alloys has made it possible to construct engines of high power output, with higher compression ratios and higher manifold pressures than before. However, the improvement of engines has been limited by the fact that detonation will occur when any vaporized fuel in an engine cylinder is compressed to a critical pressure which is characteristic of that particular fuel.

Detonation means that, after the fuel is ignited, the fuel/air mixture burns at a normal rate until a substantial portion of the mixture is consumed and then the remainder burns with explosive rapidity. There is an unusual rise in pressure, accompanied by a distinct metallic knock. The gases of combustion, the engine valves, and various parts of the engine are heated to excessive temperatures. Overheating of the engine causes expansion of the fuel/air mixture; less fuel is burned; hence the engine power output is decreased. A large part of the power loss resulting from detonation is due to the fact that the piston cannot accelerate rapidly enough to convert the abnormally high transient pressures into useful power. Cylinder walls and other metal parts vibrate and chatter owing to the sudden pressure increase of "explosion." Detonation may cause the engine to stop; may cause cracked pistons, burned valves, and other mechanical damage in the engine; and may also lead to preignition.

Preignition always occurs before the normal period of ignition. Detonation, on the other hand, occurs after the fuel has been ignited. Since preignition occurs when metal parts within the combustion chamber are overheated from any cause, thus igniting the fuel/air mixture before the ignition spark jumps the gap, it is apparent that the excessive temperatures which exist in a condition of detonation can lead to preignition, as mentioned above.

Preignition advances the ignition period abnormally and further reduces the engine efficiency. If the ignition switch of an overheated engine is opened, the engine may continue to run for several minutes because of this unintentional ignition of the fuel.

Causes of detonation

Some of the various factors which contribute to cause detonation are the cylinder temperature, the amount of the induced charge, the temperature of the fuel/air mixture, the mixture ratio of gasoline and air, the intake manifold pressure, the positions of the spark plugs, and the shape of the combustion chamber. All these factors pertain to the design or adjustment of the carburetor, the supercharger, or the engine itself. In addition to these factors, one of the most important factors contributing to detonation is the antiknock or octane value of the fuel. Since this topic pertains directly to the subject of this chapter, it is discussed at this point.

Octane number

Gasoline is rated for engine-fuel purposes according to its antiknock value. This value is expressed in terms of an octane number. Chemically, gasolines are classified as mixtures or hydrocarbons. Two of these hydrocarbons are isooctane and normal heptane. Isooctane possesses high antiknock qualities, while normal heptane is of low antiknock value. This quality, or value, is expressed in the percentage of isooctane in the mixture. **For example, a reference fuel of 70 octane means a mixture of 70 percent isooctane in normal heptane.**

The octane rating of a fuel is tested in a special engine which compares the performance of the fuel being tested with the performance of a reference fuel, usually a mixture of isooctane and normal heptane. The test engine is coupled to a generator which provides a constant load factor. Two valves, two fuel chambers, and two carburetors are used. The engine is first run on the fuel being tested, and its knocking qualities are noted. The engine is then switched over to the test-fuel mixture. The mixture is varied until it has the same knock qualities as the fuel being tested. The tested fuel is given a number which is determined by the percentage of isooctane in the reference-fuel mixture.

Performance number

Aviation fuels have been developed which possess greater antiknock qualities than 100 octane, or pure isooctane. To classify these fuels, a special **performance number** is used. This scale, or rating, is based on isooctane to which measured quantities of tetraethyl lead are added. For example, isooctane has an octane number of 100. Likewise, it has a performance number of 100. If tetraethyl lead is added to it, a performance number above 100 is obtained. The performance numbers obtained by mixing various amounts of tetraethyl lead with octane are shown in the chart of Fig. 8·7.

When ordinary gasoline is rated, the octane number is generally used, but since, with the addition of lead, the rating may run over the fixed 100 rating of iso-

140   *12,500 lbs or under gross take off weight*

light aircraft.

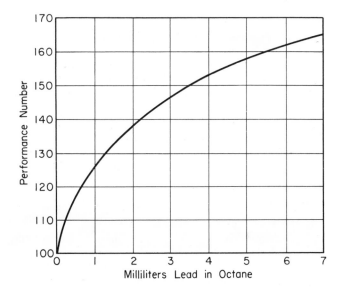

Figure 8·7 Chart to show performance number.

octane, it is preferable to rate aviation gasoline by giving it a performance number.

Since the antiknock qualities of a fuel will vary according to the fuel/air ratio, the performance numbers are expressed with two numbers, one rating for a lean mixture and one for a rich mixture. The performance numbers are expressed as follows: 100/130, 115/145. The first number in each set is the lean performance number; the second number is the rich performance number.

Use of lead in aviation fuels

Lead, in a form called tetraethyl lead, is used in relatively small quantities in aviation gasoline to improve antiknock qualities. The standard method in this country for expressing lead quantity is in terms of milliliters per gallon. The maximum lead concentration used is 630 volumes of gasoline to 1 volume of tetraethyl lead. This corresponds to 6 ml of tetraethyl lead to 1 gal of gasoline.

Lead, if added alone to gasoline, would burn to lead oxide, which is a solid with a very high boiling point. For this reason the lead would remain as a residue in the cylinders to a large extent. To prevent this, a gasoline-soluble bromine compound is added to the lead. The mixture forms lead bromide, which has a much lower boiling point than lead oxide, and therefore a large proportion will be expelled from the cylinders with the exhaust gases.

Dye is added to the lead and gasoline-soluble bromine compound to indicate that the gasoline contains lead and should not be used for washing engine parts or in cookstoves or lamps. The dye is a solid and is left as a residue when the gasoline evaporates. The mixture of lead, bromine compound, and dye is known as lead antiknock compound. The effects of various fuel mixtures with tetraethyl lead are shown in Fig. 8·8.

Engine design and fuel performance

Aircraft engines are specifically designed to operate with fuels having certain octane ratings or performance numbers. The minimum octane rating or performance number is usually more critical than the maximum, although the use of a grade of fuel of either too high or too low a rating may cause engine failure. FAA Specifications for Aircraft specify the minimum octane rating of fuel to be used with each engine installation. The use of a fuel with too low a rating will usually lead to detonation with its accompanying damage to the pistons and cylinders and eventual engine failure.

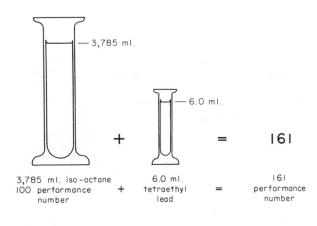

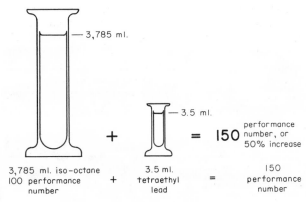

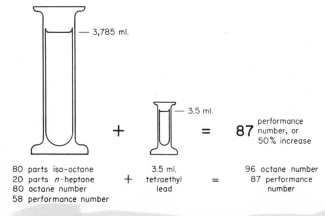

Figure 8·8 Effects of tetraethyl lead in various fuel mixtures.

80/87 - Red   100/130 - Green
91/96 - Blue   115/145 - Purple

141

The principal factors governing the grade of fuel required for an engine are the compression ratio and the manifold pressure. Supercharged engines require a higher grade of fuel than unsupercharged engines having the same compression ratio. As compression ratio and manifold pressure increase, the pressure of the fuel/air mixture in the cylinder also increases. Higher pressures lead to higher temperatures, which, in turn, increase the possibility of detonation.

Present engines designed for use with grade 100/130 fuel have compression ratios varying between 7:1 and 9:1. For a fixed manifold pressure in any given engine, increase of compression ratio increases power only slightly but has a noticeable effect on fuel economy.

When a supercharger is used with an engine, it is likely that fuel with a performance number of 115/145 will be required.

High compression ratios make economical long-range operation possible and help in connection with cylinder cooling. The cooling effect is due to the fact that more of the heat in the fuel is converted to useful work at the crankshaft and less goes into the cylinder walls. High compression is also advantageous in that a reduced weight of air is required for a given horsepower; this is of particular advantage at high altitude.

Increase of compression ratio improves fuel economy at the expense of reducing the power for takeoff and emergency. Thus attempts to increase range by higher compression ratio may defeat their purpose by so reducing takeoff power that the airplane cannot take off with full fuel tanks, since high compression ratios increase the possibility of detonation. The ideal situation exists when a maximum compression ratio compatible with the fuel being used is designed into the engine. Any increase of compression ratio above that with which the fuel will burn satisfactorily under full power conditions will bring about detonation and loss of power.

It is apparent, then, that there is a limit beyond which compression ratios cannot be increased. The use of water injection has extended the limit; it permits an engine to operate under higher cylinder pressures for takeoff without the danger of detonation.

Corrosive effects of leaded fuels

As previously stated in this chapter, tetraethyl lead is used with aviation fuels to improve the antiknock quality. It was also noted that the use of tetraethyl lead requires the addition of a bromine compound to prevent lead residue from remaining in the cylinders. The bromine compound commonly used in ethylene dibromide.

The burning of tetraethyl lead and ethylene dibromide produces the compound lead bromide, most of which is carried out of the cylinder with the exhaust gases. However, a certain amount will remain even under the best conditions. Lead bromide in the presence of water and metals, particularly aluminum, produces corrosive liquids which cause rusting of steel and cast iron. Water, without which rust will not form, may be trapped in the cylinder with the exhaust gases (which contain water vapor) after the engine has been shut down. One gallon of water is produced for each gallon of gasoline burned.

Great damage has been caused to engines by the corrosive action of lead bromide residue. This occurs especially when an engine is allowed to stand without attention for several weeks. If an engine is not to be operated for an extensive period, it must be properly preserved. The engine should be run for at least 15 min on unleaded fuel; then the interior of the cylinders should be coated well with a rust-inhibiting oil.

Fuel for gas-turbine engines

Basically a gas-turbine engine can be designed to operate on almost any fuel—liquid, gas, or solid—which has sufficient heat energy and which can be delivered to the combustors in a combustible form. Actually, there are many conditions which determine what type of fuel is most desirable, and these conditions reduce the number of fuel types used for jet engines or gas turbines.

Among the factors which determine the type of fuel used for jet engines are cost of production, availability, ease in handling, suitability for use at high altitudes, safety in use, amount of energy available from a given weight of the fuel, type of residue after combustion, and viscosity. The fuels which have been most satisfactory up to the present are those distilled from crude oils. These are kerosene, gasoline, and combinations of kerosene and gasoline.

Kerosene, or JP-1 fuel, is a very satisfactory fuel and has a number of advantages. Because of its low volatility it largely eliminates vapor lock and loss of range due to evaporation and related causes. It has good lubricating qualities because of its viscosity and therefore reduces wear of the fuel pumps. Kerosene has about 10 percent more heat energy per unit volume than gasoline.

Among the disadvantages of kerosene compared with gasoline as a jet-engine fuel are lower heat energy per unit weight than gasoline, more difficult starting both on the ground and in flight, more likelihood of blowout at high altitude, more solid matter carried in suspension, greater time required for refueling, and more likelihood of fuel-tank explosions in combat.

Although gasoline has a number of advantages as a jet-engine fuel, such as easier starting and less likelihood of fuel-tank explosion in combat, it has certain disadvantages. The principal disadvantages are vapor lock and loss of fuel in flight due to evaporation and escape of fine particles of liquid gasoline with escaping vapors. Gasoline is a poor lubricant; hence there is more difficulty with fuel-metering pumps when it is used as fuel.

Fuel which may be termed as compromises between gasoline and kerosene have been developed in order to eliminate some of the disadvantages and retain some of the advantages of both kerosene and gasoline. JP-3 and JP-4 are such compromise fuels.

JP-3 has all the operating disadvantages of gasoline plus some that do not exist with gasoline. Owing to the fact that it has a much higher end point than either aviation or motor gasoline, it can and does contain high-boiling materials with undesirable combustion characteristics. Its only major operating advantage over gasoline is a higher energy content per unit volume. In comparison with JP-1 kerosene, JP-3 fuel has combustion advantages in regard to cold starting, relighting at altitude, and altitude blowout.

JP-4 fuel has a few advantages, chiefly in the elimination of vapor lock, slugging (boiling off), etc. Because the light ends (butanes, pentanes, and hexanes) have been eliminated, the combustion performance is inferior to either JP-3 or gasoline, but it is still superior to kerosene in this respect.

During the several years that commercial jet aircraft have been in operation, engine manufacturers and aircraft operators have generally agreed to the use of kerosene as a fuel for commercial gas-turbine engines. The advantages of heat content, low vapor pressure, high flash point (for safety in handling), and other factors outweigh the disadvantages.

Aromatic and alcohol aviation fuels

Gasoline, the aromatics, and alcohol are the ideal fuels for internal-combustion engines. The following discussion will point out the relative merits of aromatics and alcohol as aviation fuels.

The so-called **aromatics** are hydrocarbon compounds which are acquired either from coal as a byproduct during the manufacture of coke or from oil. They are also present in straight-run gasoline as a natural product of the fractional-distillation process to an extent of about 7 percent or less. Aromatic fuel is so named because the atomic arrangement of its molecular structure is identical with that in perfumes. **A molecule is the smallest part of a substance that is capable of independent existence while still retaining its chemical properties.** Atoms are the smallest existing particles of an element.

Prior to the entry of the United States into World War II, aviation fuels containing up to 40 percent aromatics were used in Great Britain and Germany. During the same period, the use of aromatics in the United States was confined to a small percentage of the total aviation fuels produced. However, World War II brought about the development of aircraft engines in the United States which required a fuel of a performance number above 100. This, in turn, created an enormous demand for aromatics. Fuel containing 20 to 30 percent aromatics was produced by the use of catalytic cracking. This supply proved to be very advantageous to the military. The quantity of aviation fuel available was increased, and greater engine performance was achieved.

In the case of two fuels having equal performance numbers, both lean and rich, one not containing aromatics is somewhat preferable to another containing 15 percent aromatics. Also, aromatic fuel blends cause trouble with rubber parts and require the use of synthetic rubber for fuel hose, pump packings, carburetor diaphragms, etc. The use of aromatics in World War II was partly an expedient measure, because paraffinic blending agents could not be produced fast enough and also because the expansion of facilities for making paraffinic agents would have taken steel needed for other purposes.

Benzol is the best known of the aromatic group. It has a high compression point at rich mixtures, and tests show that it will withstand a compression pressure of 175 psi within the combustion chamber of an engine before knocking. Benzol, however, has certain undesirable characteristics, among them a slow burning rate. It is also a powerful solvent of rubber. This objection to it was, to some extent, overcome by the development of synthetic-rubber fuel lines. However, for various reasons, the amount of benzol in aviation fuel is, at present, limited to 5 percent by volume.

Three other important aromatics are called **toluene, xylene, and cumene.** Some of the characteristics of toluene, such as low freezing point, good volatility, and rubber solvent properties less powerful than benzol, make it suitable for blending in aviation fuel up to 15 percent by volume. Before World War II, it was made with benzol from coal and during the war from oil.

Xylene also has desirable qualities for blending in aviation fuels. However, it can be used only in limited quantities owing to its relatively high boiling point.

Cumene is made from benzol. This limits the amount which can be used for blending purposes. It has an extremely high boiling point, which tends to cause uneven distribution of the fuel/air charge to the various cylinders of the aircraft engine.

Since all aromatics are rubber solvents to some extent, the use of aviation fuels containing large amounts of aromatics requires aromatic-resistant materials in the fuel system. Parts such as flexible hoses, pump packings, and carburetor diaphragms must be made of special synthetic rubber.

Purity of aviation fuel

It is important that aviation fuel be free of any such impurities as water, dirt, acid, or alkali. It must also be low in sulfur and gum content. Sulfur has a corrosive effect on the various metal parts of the fuel system and engine. Gum may cause valves to stick, and it will clog fuel-metering jets and restrictions. A simple test which will detect the presence of any corrosive impurities is made by placing a small quantity of a fuel in a spun-copper dish and evaporating it in a steam bath. An appreciable amount of gum content will discolor and blacken the copper.

Excessive water in the fuel system of an engine constitutes a serious problem. A small amount of water will pass through the system and carburetor jets without radically affecting engine performance, but any appreciable amount of water in the system will stop the flow of fuel through the metering jets and result in engine failure.

Effective water removers are used in airplane servicing equipment to eliminate the danger of water being pumped into the tanks during the refueling operation. However, condensation will form within fuel tanks during periods of variable atmospheric temperatures, the amount of this condensation being proportionate to the extent of air space in the tank above the fuel line. To eliminate the possibility of this trouble, the tanks should be kept filled, especially at night or at such times when extreme changes in temperature are apt to occur.

When the presence of water in the fuel tank is expected, a simple test to determine this can be made. The test consists of draining a small quantity of fuel from the lowest point in the system and in checking the sample with a strip of especially prepared paper, which is coated with a chemical, soluble in water. If water is present in the liquid to a dangerous extent, the coating on the testing paper will be removed.

TYPES OF FUEL SYSTEMS AND COMPONENTS

General considerations

The purpose of a fuel system is to deliver a uniform flow of clean fuel under constant pressure to the carburetor or other fuel-control unit. The supply must be adequate to meet all engine demands at various altitudes and attitudes of flight. Recommended installations employ gravity-feed or mechanical pumping systems.

The location of the various units in the fuel system must be such that the entire fuel supply is available for use when the airplane is in the steepest climb or in its best angle of glide, and the arrangement should prevent the feed ports from being uncovered during reasonable maneuvers. Tanks and units in multiple-tank installations should make positive and immediate feed from one tank to another possible in the event one runs dry, but the fuel pump should not normally draw fuel from more than one tank at a time. However, in the case of transport category airplanes, this is permissible if provision is made to prevent the introduction of air into the system.

A gravity-feed system should not supply fuel to any one engine from more than one tank unless the tank air spaces are interconnected in such a manner as to assure equal feed.

In multiengine airplanes the system should be such that each engine is supplied from its own tank, lines, and fuel pumps, although means may be provided to transfer fuel from one tank to another or to run two engines from the same tank in an emergency.

In the case of systems whose outlets are interconnected, it should not be possible for fuel to flow between tanks in quantities sufficient to cause an overflow from the tank vent when the airplane is operated in the condition most apt to cause such overflow and when the tanks are full.

The fuel-flow rate for the auxiliary and the fuel-transfer system is established in the same manner as that for the main system, with the exception that it is based on the maximum continuous power and speed of the engine instead of the takeoff horsepower.

In all fuel systems, a positive means of shutting off the fuel to all engines must be available to the pilot in the cockpit or on the flight engineer's panel.

Fuel systems vary in design and simplicity and consequently vary in the number of units involved, from the small single-engine plane to the large jet transport. In this section, several representative types of fuel systems are considered.

The gravity fuel system

The gravity fuel system is the simplest type used. Such a system is suitable for small planes with engines of low horsepower. Figure 8·9 shows a gravity system consisting of a fuel-storage tank and lines which run to a shutoff cock, a strainer, and the carburetor. (The fuel-quantity gage is not shown.) This type of system must supply a head pressure adequate for proper engine functioning under all normal conditions of operation including approved maneuvers and acrobatics.

Head pressure is the pressure built up by the weight of the fuel flowing from a high to a low level. It varies with the difference between the two levels. When the gravity

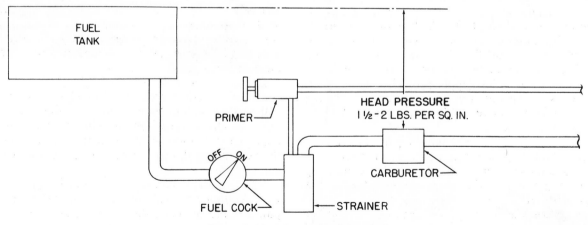

Figure 8·9 Gravity fuel system.

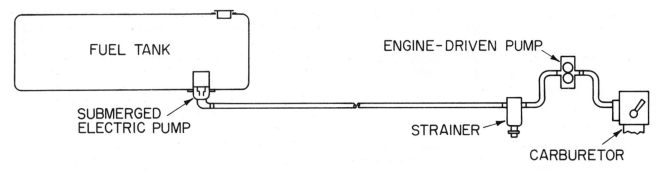

Figure **8·10**   Fuel system with pumps in series.

system is used on an airplane, the tank must, of course, be located above the carburetor inlet level and the fuel-flow rate must be 150 percent of the actual takeoff fuel consumption of the engines. A fuel head of 39 in. is necessary to produce a pressure of 1 lb.

Pump systems

Figure 8·10 shows a series pump system. In this system, the fuel is drawn from the tank and forced to the carburetor by an engine-driven pump. An electric boost pump, installed in the tank for emergency use and starting, and the engine-driven pump are connected in series. Hand-operated pumps are not usually installed on modern aircraft because of the availability of the more convenient electric boost pumps and the fact that most airplanes are equipped with electrical systems.

The fuel flow rate for pump systems must be 0.9 lb per hr for each takeoff horsepower or 125 percent of the actual takeoff fuel consumption of the engine, whichever is greater. This flow rate is applicable to both the primary engine-driven pump and the boost pump and must be available when the pump is running at the speed at which it would normally be operating during takeoff.

Types of fuel pumps

One of the most satisfactory pumps for positive delivery of fuel is the **vane pump.** A schematic diagram of such a pump is shown in Fig. 8·11. The rotor holds the sliding vanes and is installed in the liner with its axis of rotation eccentric to the axis of the liner. When the rotor is turning, the vanes maintain a constant contact with the surface of the liner. Fuel enters the inlet port and is forced by sliding vanes through the outlet port. The floating pin aligns the sliding vanes against the surface of the liner. In one position the two lower vanes extend from the rotor, while the two upper vanes are forced into the rotor by the surface of the liner.

Variable-volume pumps

The pump shown in Fig. 8·12 is known as a **variable-volume vane-type pump.** This pump delivers varying amounts of fuel under constant pressure to the carburetor. The amount of fuel is regulated to meet the demands of the carburetor.

This type of pump is designed to deliver much more fuel than the amount normally needed by the engine. Fuel enters the pump at the inlet side and is forced around the housing to the outlet side by the action of the sliding vanes. The spring-loaded relief valve is adjusted so that it releases at a specific pressure. When the pump pressure is above the predetermined setting, the relief valve is forced up from its seat and the excess fuel is relieved to the inlet side of the pump.

This relief valve has a diaphragm which has two functions: (1) It provides venting to the atmosphere or to supercharger pressure, and (2) by means of a balancing action, it helps to maintain a constant dis-

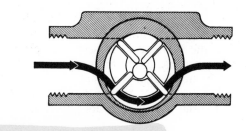

Figure **8·11**   Vane-type fuel pump.

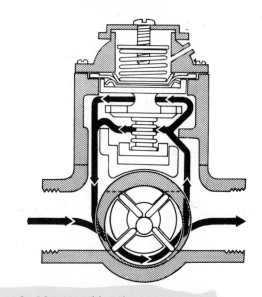

Figure **8·12**   Variable-volume vane pump.

145

charge pressure no matter how much the pressure on the suction side of the pump may vary.

When the diaphragm-type relief valve is used in a pressure-type fuel system, the pilot may complain that the fuel pressure is normal on the ground but increases with altitude. This may occur when the air vent on the fuel pump is partly clogged.

Operation of bypass valve

The bypass valve, shown in the pump diagram of Fig. 8·13, provides a means for the boost pump to force fuel around the vanes and rotor of the main pump for starting the engine or for emergency operation if the main pump fails. The bypass valve is held in the closed position by a spring when the pump rotor is turning.

The relief-valve spring in some pumps is located within a metal bellows to compensate for variations in atmospheric pressure. Other types use a fuel-resistant synthetic-rubber diaphragm instead of bellows. When relief valves are designed to compensate for atmospheric pressure variations, they are known as balanced relief valves.

Fuel-pump operation

The chamber housing the diaphragm of the fuel pump incorporates a tapped hole to which a vent line is attached. As the airplane climbs to higher altitudes, the atmospheric pressure on the fuel in the tank decreases, resulting in a lowered fuel-pump inlet pressure. To compensate for this lower pressure, the relief-valve diaphragm is vented to the atmosphere or to the fuel tanks. Thus, the decrease in atmospheric pressure in the tanks is compensated by the pressure-relief valve. Sometimes the diaphragm is vented to the carburetor deck or to the carburetor air scoop. This subjects the diaphragm to atmospheric pressure plus ram pressure.

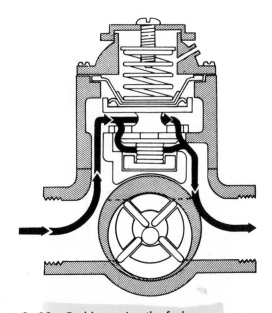

Figure 8·13   Fuel bypassing the fuel pump.

Ram pressure is that which is developed in the carburetor air scoop by the forward speed of the airplane. The vent has a restrictor fitting in the line. If a diaphragm is ruptured, the restrictor limits the loss of fuel through the vent when the pump inlet pressure is greater than atmospheric pressure or restricts the amount of air entering the pump inlet when the pump inlet pressure is less than that of the atmosphere.

Setting fuel-pump pressure

To adjust the pressure setting on a fuel pump, the adjusting-screw locknut is loosened and the adjusting screw is turned clockwise to increase pressure or counterclockwise to decrease pressure. Usually, markings on the pump body show the correct direction to turn the adjusting screw to increase or decrease pressure. If no markings are visible, turn the screw very slightly in one direction while noting the effect on the pressure gage.

When the pressure has been set, the locknut should be tightened and safetied with the proper-gage safety wire.

Fuel pumps vary in general design. There may be from two to six sliding vanes, and sometimes the aligning pin, which holds the vanes against the liner surface, is omitted and other means used to accomplish the same result. Some pumps use the sylphon (metal bellows) type of balanced relief valve, while others use the diaphragm type. Regardless of the variations in design, the operating principle of all vane-type engine-driven fuel pumps remains the same.

Fuel boost pumps

In pressure-type fuel systems, since the fuel pump depends upon the engine for its operation, fuel is not delivered by it until the engine is running. Consequently, a manually operated or an electrically driven fuel boost pump is used for starting, in takeoff and in climb, and in the event the engine-driven pump fails.

Government regulations make it mandatory that emergency fuel pumps be provided.

Emergency pumps should be capable of delivering the same amount of fuel as engine-driven pumps. If they are of the manually operated type, they should not require excessive effort for their continued operation at the rate of 60 cycles (120 single strokes) per min.

Manually operated or electrically driven pumps are also used to pump fuel from an auxiliary tank to a main fuel tank. Modern airplanes use electrically driven pumps. The electrically driven boost pumps are often built into fuel supply tanks. An electrically driven boost pump is shown in Fig. 8·14.

Boost-pump design

The boost pump may be similar in internal construction to the engine-driven pump, although the rotor is usually of conventional centrifugal design. The most noticeable difference between the two pumps is that the engine-driven pump has an eccentric vane-type rotor with a self-contained valve unit. The auxiliary

Figure 8·14   An electrically driven boost pump. (Pesco Products Div.)

pump is designed primarily to supplement or replace the work of the engine-driven pump through the valve system of the latter. Centrifugal-type pumps for multi-engine aircraft often permit two speeds of the electric motor with corresponding high- and low-pressure outputs.

An auxiliary pump which is located in the bottom of a fuel tank is said to be of the submerged type. Powered by an explosionproof electric motor, it is used for starting purposes and to transfer fuel from one tank to another. When the pump is not in use, the fuel flows by gravity and the suction of the engine-driven pump. The boost pump is so designed that there is very little loss in pressure under these conditions.

Fuel boost pump for jet transport aircraft

Because of the great volume of fuel required by the engines of a jet transport airplane, large-capacity boost pumps are installed in the bottoms of the fuel tanks. These pumps remove fuel from the main tanks and deliver it under pressure via fuel feed lines to the engines. The fuel may be fed from a particular tank to a particular engine, or it may be fed through a fuel manifold to other engines.

Each pump for the Boeing 720 jet airliner is a centrifugal type driven by a three-phase a-c electrical motor. The motor is supplied by the 115/220-volt power supply. The pumps are explosionproof and are located in doghouse-type covers at the lowest points in the main tanks. They are bolted to the lower wing surface and project up into the pump housings as shown in Fig. 8·15.

Fuel enters each pump through a manually operated flapper valve and a wire mesh screen at the inlet port.

The flapper valve, designated the **pump-removal valve,** is designed to permit the removal of the pump without draining the fuel tank. During normal operation the valve is in the open position, but when it is desired to remove the pump, the valve may be closed manually by means of two screws which operated the hinge fittings of the flappers.

A part of the fuel being pumped is recirculated through the boost pump to cool the motor and lubricate the bearings. Since there are no electrical contacts within the motor, the fuel in the motor is not detrimental. The cooling fuel discharges through holes in the top of the motor case and mixes with incoming fuel in the pump housing. A vapor discharge line vents the pump housing to the tank.

It is important to note that there are many differences, both minor and major, among the various makes and models of aircraft, and it is essential that the technician use the correct manufacturer's instruction when servicing or performing maintenance on any particular aircraft installation. The fundamental skills and technical know-how are the same in any case, but the procedures may vary widely.

Fuel strainers

Because of the ever-present possibility of fuel contamination by various types of foreign matter, aircraft fuel systems are required to include fuel strainers and filters. The fuel is usually strained at three points in the system: first, through a finger strainer or boost-pump strainer in the bottom of the fuel tank; second, through a master strainer which is usually located at the lowest point in the fuel system; and third, through a strainer in the carburetor or near the fuel-control unit.

Good fuel-system practice provides for one or more strainers installed between the fuel tank and the carburetor or between the fuel tank and the engine-driven fuel pump. The strainer must be of the proper size and design for the capacity of the fuel system in which it is installed. It must have a sediment space and drain and an easily removable screen for cleaning purposes and be installed in an accessible place.

A fuel strainer assembly must not be mounted in such a manner that its weight is supported by the connecting lines or by the inlet or outlet connections of the assembly. This means that the strainer or filter assembly must be mounted independently on the aircraft or nacelle structure or upon the engine.

The screen in the fuel tank outlet must have 8 to 16 meshes per inch and a clear area of five times the fuel outlet area, and if the strainer is of the finger type, the diameter must not be less than the diameter of the outlet.

The tank strainer keeps larger particles of foreign matter in the tank from entering the system lines. The main strainer, located at the lowest point in the system, collects foreign matter from the line between the tank and the strainer and also serves as a water trap. The filter or screen in the carburetor or near the fuel control in a jet-engine system removes the extremely fine

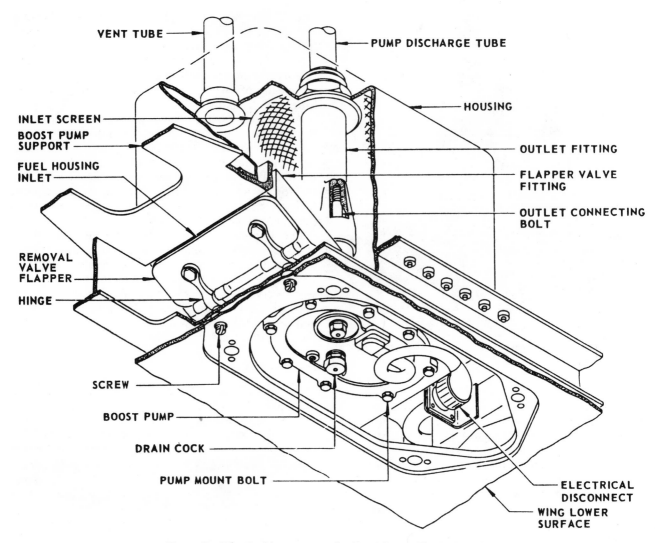

VENT TUBE

PUMP DISCHARGE TUBE

INLET SCREEN

BOOST PUMP
SUPPORT

FUEL HOUSING
INLET

HOUSING

OUTLET FITTING

FLAPPER VALVE
FITTING

OUTLET CONNECTING
BOLT

REMOVAL
VALVE
FLAPPER

HINGE

SCREW

BOOST PUMP

DRAIN COCK

PUMP MOUNT BOLT

ELECTRICAL
DISCONNECT

WING LOWER
SURFACE

Figure 8 · 15   Fuel boost pump for jet airliner. (The Boeing Co.)

particles which may interfere with the operation of the sensitive valves and other operating mechanisms. Some filters are so fine that they remove all particles larger than 40 microns in diameter. A **micron** is one-thousandth of a millimeter.

A main fuel screen for a light airplane is shown in Fig. 8·16. This unit includes a glass sediment bowl and a screen and is called a **gascolator.** It consists of a cast-metal top or cover, the screen, and the glass bowl together with the necessary assembling parts. The bowl is attached to the cover by a clamp and thumb nut. Fuel enters the unit through the inlet on the top, filters through the screen, and exits through a connection to the carburetor inlet.

At designated periods the glass bowl is drained and the screen is removed for inspection and cleaning. The tank and carburetor screens are also cleaned periodically, depending upon the installation, type of strainer, and the inspection procedure established for the system.

An exploded view of one of the fuel strainer assem-

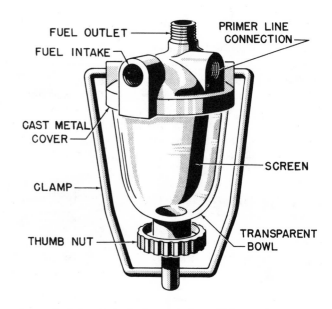

FUEL OUTLET

PRIMER LINE
CONNECTION

FUEL INTAKE

CAST METAL
COVER

SCREEN

CLAMP

THUMB NUT

TRANSPARENT
BOWL

Figure 8 · 16   Main fuel screen for a light airplane.

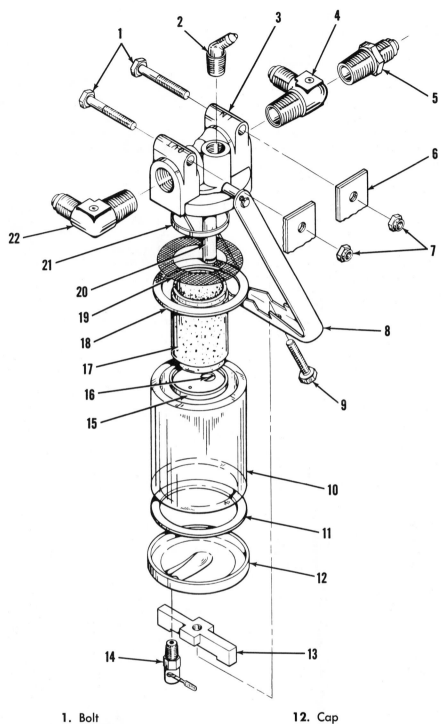

1. Bolt
2. Elbow
3. Body assembly
4. Fitting for left engine installation
5. Fitting for right engine installation
6. Mounting bracket
7. Nut
8. Arm assembly
9. Bolt
10. Glass bowl
11. Lower gasket

12. Cap
13. Stiffener
14. Drain valve
15. Lid assembly
16. Retainer spring
17. Filter
18. Upper gasket
19. Flat screen
20. Standpipe
21. Filter ring
22. Elbow

Figure 8·17   Fuel strainer assembly for Cessna Model 310 airplane. (Cessna Aircraft Co.)

blies for the Cessna Model 310 airplane is shown in Fig. 8 · 17. This fuel strainer is located in the nacelle of each engine and is attached to the lower center part of the fire wall. A quick drain valve is incorporated at the bottom of the unit to permit the drainage of a small amount of fuel during the preflight inspection. This is to assure that no water will reach the carburetor.

A drawing of the fuel filter used with the General Electric CJ-805 jet engine is shown in Fig. 8 · 18. The principal elements of this filter unit are the case, filter, and bypass or pressure-relief valve.

Fuel enters the filter and surrounds the filter screen, passes through the screen into an inner chamber, then flows out the discharge port. If the filter becomes clogged, the fuel is bypassed through the relief valve, which opens when the pressure differential across the filter is 20 to 24 psi. The pressure drop across a clean filter is 10 psi maximum with fuel in at 32 to 38°C and at a flow rate of 57.5 gpm. If the filter becomes clogged, the pressure drop across the filter is 32 psi maximum with maximum flow through the relief valve.

The filter screen is constructed of sinter-bonded stainless-steel wire cloth. The screen filters out all particles larger than 40 microns.

Drains

One or more accessible drains must be provided at the lowest point on the fuel system to drain all parts of each system completely when the airplane is in its normal position on level ground. Such drains must discharge clear of all parts of the airplane and be equipped with suitable safety locks to prevent accidental opening.

Fuel selector valves

Fuel selector valves, sometimes called **fuel cocks,** provide a means of shutting off the fuel flow, of selecting the tank in a multipletank installation, of transferring fuel from one tank to another, and of directing the fuel to one or more engines in a multi-engine airplane.

One or more of these valves is used to shut off all fuel to each engine. Such a valve must be positive and quick acting, and the valve controls should be located

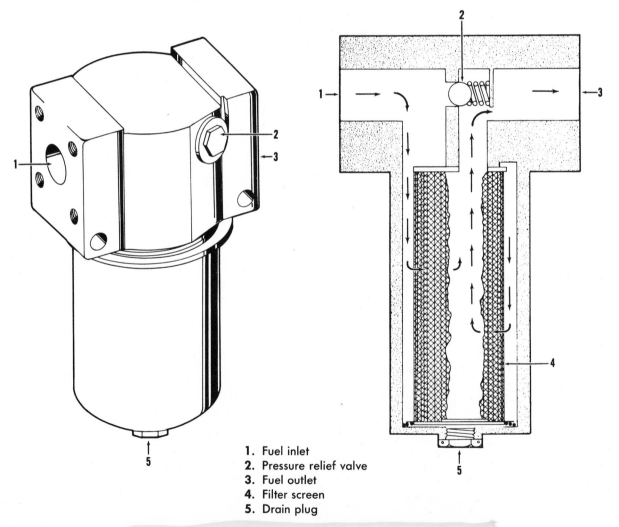

1. Fuel inlet
2. Pressure relief valve
3. Fuel outlet
4. Filter screen
5. Drain plug

Figure 8 · 18   Fuel filter for GE CJ-805 jet engine. (General Electric Co.)

150

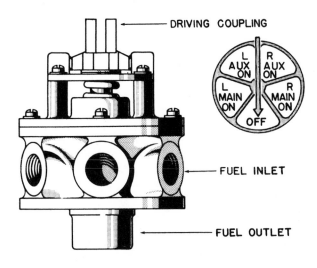

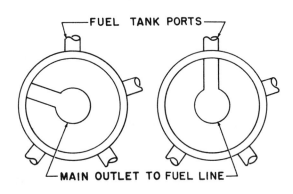

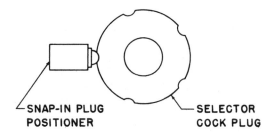

Figure 8 · 19   Fuel selector valve for a light airplane.

nections around the circumference of the selector casing.

A schematic diagram of a cam-operated ball-type valve for light aircraft is shown in Fig. 8 · 20. As the cam is rotated, it is possible to turn on one or both of the tanks to which the valve is connected. This type of valve is usually employed where a main tank and an auxiliary tank are connected to the system.

Fuel-control valves in large transport aircraft are usually operated by electric motors. Switches to control the motors are located on the flight engineer's fuel-control panel in the aircraft immediately aft of the pilot's compartment. An electrically operated valve assembly of this type includes a reversible electric motor linked to a sliding valve assembly. The motor moves the valve **gate** in and out of the passage through which the fuel flows, thus shutting the fuel off or turning it on. The valves are usually placed near the tanks with which they are associated.

Certain specific requirements for fuel valves must be understood by the technician. These requirements are as follows:

1. Fuel valve controls must be so arranged that flight personnel can shut off rapidly the flow of fuel to any individual engine.
2. Fuel shutoff valves must be located on the side of the fire wall most remote from the engine. In many cases the valves are located in the wings at some distance from the engines.
3. Valve controls must be so arranged that there is little danger of their being shut off inadvertently and that they can be turned on quickly if they are accidently shut off.
4. Valves must be provided with either positive stops or "feel" devices in the ON and OFF positions. This requirement is to make sure that the person operating the control will know that he has turned the valve completely on or off.
5. Fuel-control valves must be supported in such a manner that loads resulting from their operation or from accelerated flight conditions are not transmitted to the fuel lines connected to the valves.
6. Valves must be so installed that the effects of gravity and vibration will tend to turn their handles to the OPEN rather than to the CLOSED position.
7. Fuel valve handles and their connections to the valve mechanism must incorporate design features to minimize the possibility of incorrect installation.

Combination fuel unit

A fuel unit which combines the functions of the fuel valve, fuel strainer, and booster pump is shown in the exploded view of Fig. 8 · 21. This unit is employed on certain models of the Beechcraft Bonanza and Debonair airplanes. An examination of this illustration will reveal the conical valve (2) which is operated by the handle (14). The spring (15) exerts pressure on the valve to hold it snugly in the valve seat, thus preventing leakage. Two pump check valves (7) are required at each end of the pump cylinder in order to provide opening and closing of the fuel passages as the pump is operated. One valve at each end is in the inlet passage, and the other valve is in the outlet. The pressure-relief valve is shown at (16). The pump handle (17) is

within easy reach of the pilot or pilots or the flight mechanic. In multiple-tank installation, the valve arrangement should be so arranged that each tank can be used separately.

Fuel selector valves for light airplanes are usually simple in design, construction, and operation. The selector valve shown in Fig. 8 · 19 consists of a cylindrical aluminum housing with several fuel inlet ports around its circumference. The outlet port is located on the end. A center shaft, or plug, directs fuel from one of the inlet ports to the outlet connection. This center shaft is connected by linkage to the cockpit control. When the control is in the OFF position, the center shaft in the valve does not line up with any fuel con-

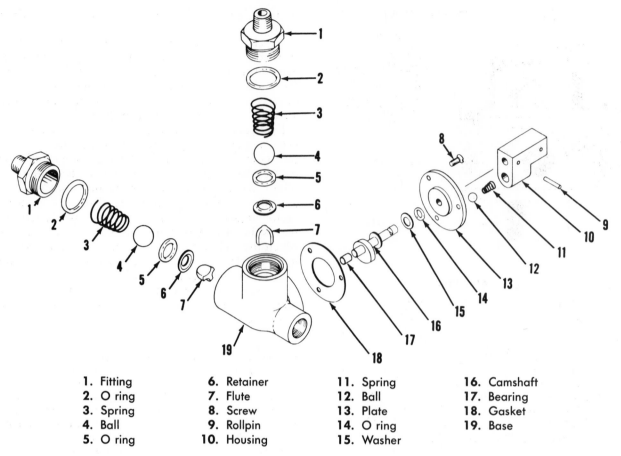

1. Fitting	6. Retainer	11. Spring	16. Camshaft
2. O ring	7. Flute	12. Ball	17. Bearing
3. Spring	8. Screw	13. Plate	18. Gasket
4. Ball	9. Rollpin	14. O ring	19. Base
5. O ring	10. Housing	15. Washer	

Figure 8·20 Cam-operated ball-type fuel valve. (Cessna Aircraft Co.)

hinged to the bracket (18) and linked to the piston (19).

The fuel strainer (20) fits into a chamber adjacent to the pump cylinder. When the unit is assembled, the drain valve (21) is at the bottom of the strainer chamber.

Primers and priming systems

Unlike an automobile engine, an aircraft engine must be primed before starting, as the carburetor does not function properly until the engine is running. For this reason, it is necessary to have a separate system to charge, or prime, the cylinders with raw fuel for starting. This is accomplished by the priming system. The usual arrangement is to have the primer draw fuel from the carburetor inlet bowl or the fuel strainer and direct it to a distributor valve which, in turn, distributes the fuel to the various cylinders. Figure 8·22 illustrates the action of a typical priming system used on a small aircraft engine.

Other priming systems, used on internally geared supercharged engines, discharge the fuel into the super-charger diffuser section through a jet located on the carburetor or in the diffuser section.

The priming system shown in Fig. 8·22 has an undesirable feature in that the pump-body assembly is located in the pilot's cockpit. This causes the addition of fuel lines in the pilot's compartment and presents a fire hazard. For this reason, remote-control electric-solenoid primer valves have been developed. The solenoid valve is usually located on or near the carburetor and is wired to a control switch in the cockpit. When the switch is engaged, the solenoid-actuated valve opens and allows fuel, under booster-pump pressure, to enter the priming system. The valve is returned to the closed position by means of a spring.

Engines equipped with direct fuel-injection systems do not require separate priming systems because the injection system pumps fuel directly into the intake ports of the engine.

Oil-dilution systems

It is a well-known fact that oil congeals in cold weather, and such oil in the working parts of an engine makes the engine difficult to turn and, therefore, hard to start. To end this trouble, motorists in cold climates sometimes dilute the crankcase oil of their automobile engines with kerosene.

Similarly, a rather ingenious method, known as **oil dilution,** is employed to facilitate starting aircraft engines when the temperature is very low. With this method, a length of tubing connects the carburetor or other fuel pressure source through a solenoid valve to the oil Y drain or elsewhere to the oil system.

The oil is diluted after the engine has been operated

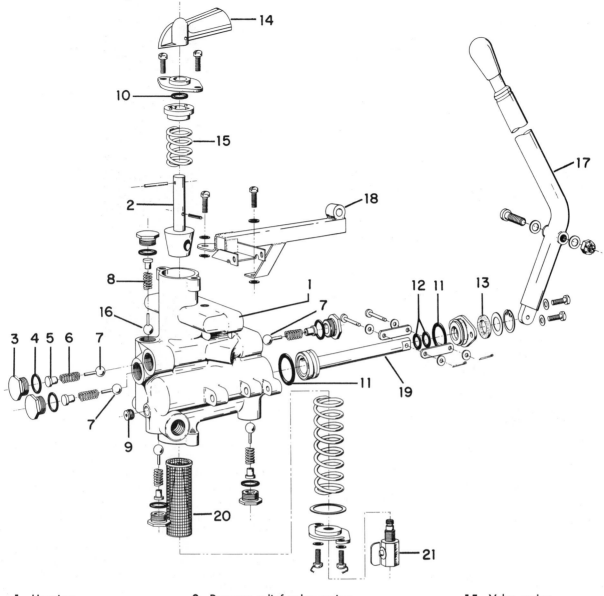

1. Housing
2. Fuel selector valve
3. Plug
4. O ring
5. Guide
6. Check valve spring
7. Valve

8. Pressure relief valve spring
9. Plug (AN932-2)
10. Selector valve O ring
11. Piston head and cylinder head O ring
12. Piston rod O ring
13. Felt washer
14. Valve handle

15. Valve spring
16. Pressure relief valve
17. Pump handle
18. Bracket
19. Pump piston
20. Fuel strainer
21. Drain valve

Figure 8·21   Combination fuel unit. (Beech Aircraft Co.)

and is fully warmed up, for example, at the end of a flight before shutting down the engine. With the engine running at a fast idle, the oil-dilution valve switch is turned on and held in the ON position for the time specified in the operator's manual. After dilution the engine is immediately shut down with the dilution valve open so the fuel will remain in the oil. The next time the engine is started, the diluted oil flows freely to all bearing surfaces and the engine turns easily.

Figure 8·23 is a simplified schematic diagram showing the arrangement of an oil-dilution system. When the oil-dilution switch in the cockpit is closed, the valve is lifted from its seat by the solenoid. Fuel then flows through the inlet port and valve. It exits through the outlet port and is directed to the oil-system connection. A cutaway of the solenoid valve is shown in Fig. 8·24.

Students usually raise the question of the disposal of

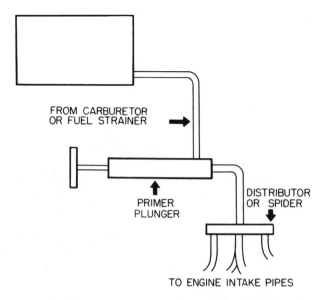

Figure **8·22**   Priming system for a light aircraft engine.

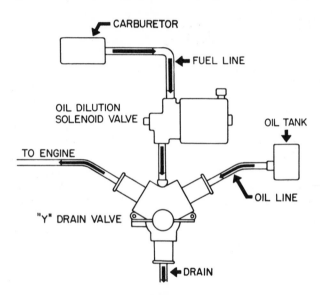

Figure **8·23**   Schematic diagram of an oil-dilution system.

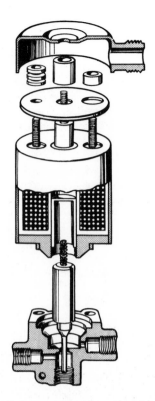

Figure **8·24**   Cutaway view of a solenoid valve.

the fuel in the oil when the engine is running. The explanation is simple. Gasoline has a lower vaporization point than oil. The heat of the engine, after a few minutes of operation, vaporizes the fuel, and the fuel vapors pass out through the oil-system breathers.

A fuel system which has an oil-dilution system must be checked regularly to ascertain that the valve is operating properly. On occasions, oil-dilution valves have become inoperative through sticking or through some mechanical failure, with consequent damage resulting from excessive gasoline in the fuel supply. A sticking oil-dilution valve may, in some systems, be detected by checking the fuel pressure. A drop in fuel pressure can indicate a sticking valve. Excessive vapors coming from the engine breathers may also indicate this condition, and since it constitutes a fire hazard, it must be corrected immediately.

A hopper-type oil tank is important for large aircraft which utilize dry sump engines and carry a substantial supply of oil in the oil tank. The hopper in the tank segregates the oil which has been diluted from the large supply in the tank. This separation is not complete, but it is sufficient to reduce substantially the amount of fuel required for dilution.

It must be noted that aircraft powered by piston engines and designed for long-distance flight actually carry oil considerably in excess of what is required for the flight. The extra oil provides for good temperature control of the engine, and it also makes available a reserve in case of leakage or excessive oil consumption by the engine.

Fuel pressure gages

In fuel systems which employ an engine-driven pump or electrically operated boost pumps, it is necessary that the system be provided with a suitable pressure gage. This gage is essential because the fuel pressure entering the carburetor or fuel-injection unit must be known by the pilot or flight engineer to determine that the system is operated properly and often to determine engine power output.

The fuel pressure reading is especially important during takeoff and serves as a check on the pump and relief valve. In addition, during flight, the pressure gage gives the pilot a check on fuel flow while changing from one tank to another.

An electrically operated fuel-pressure warning device is sometimes employed to warn the pilot of fuel pressure drop. This device is usually connected to the proper carburetor fitting and is so adjusted that, when the fuel pressure drops a small amount below the minimum allowable pressure, a signal light in the cockpit is turned on.

Fuel pressure gages are usually of the diaphragm or bellows type. That is, the fuel pressure is fed into an expandable bellows or diaphragm and the expansion of the unit is transmitted through various linkages to the indicating needle. The fuel pressure gage may be included as a separate indicator in an **engine gage unit.** The face of an engine gage unit is shown in Fig. 8·25. It will be observed that the unit gives indications of oil temperature, oil pressure, and fuel pressure. Thus the pilot can observe the one composite instrument and obtain a quick indication of the engine operation.

A fuel pressure gage often used with fuel-injection systems on light aircraft engines is shown in Fig. 8·26.

The fuel pressure reading is a direct indication of engine power output when in a fuel-injection system for light aircraft engines; hence the gage is marked to indicate **percent of power.**

Fuel flowmeter

Fuel flowmeters are used with many fuel systems to show the amount of fuel consumed per hour. These indicators are usually calibrated to read in pounds per hour. The face of a typical fuel-flow indicator is shown in Fig. 8·27.

A fuel-flow indicator system consists of a fuel-flow transmitter located in the fuel line leading from the tank to the engine and an indicator located on the instrument panel or on the flight engineer's panel. The transmitter signal may be developed by a single movable vane mounted in the fuel-flow path in such a manner that its movement will be proportional to fuel flow. As fuel flow increases, the vane must move to allow more fuel to pass, and this movement is linked to a synchro unit which develops the electrical signal to be sent to the indicator. A schematic diagram of such a system is shown in Fig. 8·28.

The fuel-flow transmitter used in a modern jet airliner fuel system to handle the large volume of fuel required for jet engine operation is somewhat more complex than the vane type just described. In one such system the transmitter consists of an impeller and a turbine mounted in the main fuel line leading from the tank to the engine. The impeller is driven by a specially designed motor which utilizes simulated three-phase 4-cycle current to drive the motor at 240 rpm. The motor drives the impeller through a 4:1 reduction gear; hence the impeller rotates at 60 rpm. Electrical power for the motor is provided by a special **fuel-flow power-supply unit** which consists of a permanent-magnet d-c motor driving a commutator to chop the d-c power into pulses which are fed to the three-phase impeller motor.

Figure 8·25   An engine gage unit.

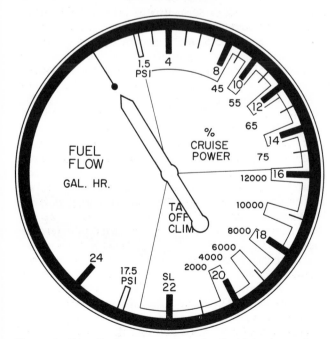

Figure 8·26   Fuel pressure gage for fuel-injection system.

Figure 8·27   Fuel-flow indicator.

155

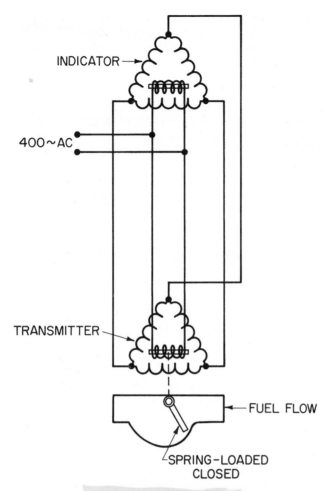

INDICATOR →

400 ~ AC

TRANSMITTER →

← FUEL FLOW

SPRING-LOADED CLOSED

Figure 8 · 28 System for fuel-flow indicator.

During operation, fuel flows through the passages in the impeller and then continues on through passages in the turbine. The fuel, in passing through the impeller, is given a velocity at right angles to the direction of flow because the impeller is rotated at a constant angular velocity of 60 rpm by the impeller motor. This angular velocity constitutes a change in momentum of the fuel which is directly proportional to the mass of fuel flowing. The angular momentum of the fuel is removed while passing through the turbine, and the energy required for this change is converted to torque on the turbine. This torque is directly proportional to the mass rate of flow. Restraining springs on the turbine oppose the torque and produce a deflection of the turbine proportional to the flow rate. This deflection is transmitted to the fuel-flow indicator on the flight engineer's panel. In the indicator a second-harmonic voltage causes second-harmonic currents to flow and in conjunction with the fundamental-frequency exciting current of the indicator creates a d-c magnetic flux across the diameter of the indicator stator. It will be observed in the drawing of Fig. 8 · 29 that the stators of both the transmitter and the indicator receive power from the same 115-volt a-c source. The angular position of the cross flux in the indicator follows the position of

the transmitter magnet. The permanent-magnet rotor of the indicator lines up with the cross flux to provide the indication of fuel flow.

Fuel-tank construction and requirements

Fuel tanks for aircraft may be constructed of aluminum alloy, terneplate, fuel-resistant synthetic rubber, plastics, and stainless steel. Tanks which are an integral part of the wing are of the same material as the wing and have the seams sealed with fuelproof sealing compound.

The material selected for the construction of a particular fuel tank depends upon the type of airplane in which the tank will be installed and the service for which the airplane is designed. Fuel tanks and the fuel system in general must be made of materials which will not react chemically with any fuels which may be used. Aluminum alloy, because of its light weight, strength, and the ease with which it can be shaped and welded, is widely used in fuel-tank construction.

Many aircraft now use synthetic-rubber bladders for fuel cells. These cells are light in weight and give excellent service if maintained according to the manufacturer's instructions.

Metal fuel tanks generally are required to withstand an internal test pressure of 3½ psi without failure or leakage. Furthermore, they must withstand without failure any vibration, inertia loads, and fluid and structural loads to which they may be subjected during operation of the aircraft.

Integral fuel tanks, such as those in the wings of jet airliners, must be provided with facilities for the inspection and repair of the tank interiors. This requirement is met by installing access panels in the skin on the bottom side of the wings.

Fuel tanks located within the fuselage of a transport aircraft must be capable of withstanding rupture and retaining the fuel underneath the inertia forces which may be encountered in an emergency landing. These forces are specified as 4.5 *g* downward, 2.0 *g* upward, 9.0 *g* forward, and 1.5 *g* sideward. Such tanks must be located in a protected position so that exposure to scraping action with the ground will be unlikely.

Fuel tanks must be equipped with sumps to collect sediment and water. On transport-type aircraft the sump capacity must be at least 0.10 percent of the total tank capacity or ¹⁄₁₆ gal, whichever is greater, and on other types of aircraft the sump capacity must be 0.25 percent of the tank capacity or ¹⁄₁₆ gal, whichever is greater. The construction of the tank must be such that any hazardous quantity of water in the tank will drain to the sump when the airplane is in the ground attitude. If the fuel system for small aircraft is supplied with a sediment bowl which permits ground inspection, the sump in the tank is not required. Fuel sumps and sediment bowls must be equipped with an accessible drain to permit complete drainage of all the sump or sediment bowl. The drain must discharge clear of all portions of the airplane and must be provided with means for positive locking of the drain in the closed position, either manually or automatically.

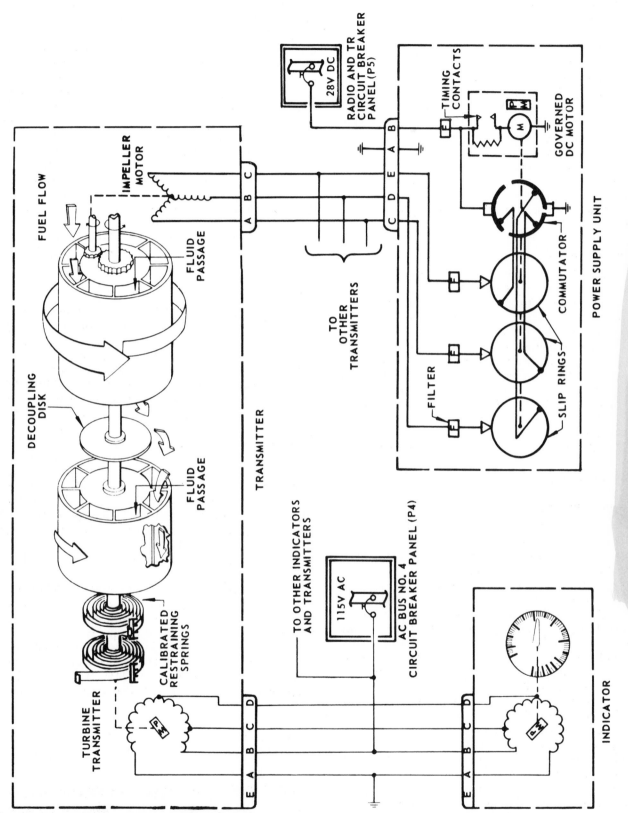

Figure 8·29 Fuel-flow indicating system for a jet airliner. (The Boeing Co.)

Usually fuel tanks are required to have an expansion space of not less than 2 percent of the tank capacity. In the case of nontransport aircraft, if the tank vent discharges clear of the aircraft, no expansion space is required. The construction of the tank must be such that it is not possible to fill the tank expansion space when the airplane is on the ground. Fuel tanks which may be filled through a pressure fitting under the wing are equipped with automatic shutoff devices to prevent overfilling the tank.

The fuel-tank filler connection must be designed in such a manner that any spilled fuel will drain clear of the airplane and will not enter the wing or any portion of the fuselage. The filler cap must provide a tight seal and be designed so it cannot come off in flight. The filler connection must be marked with the word "Fuel," the minimum grade of fuel, and the capacity of the tank.

Fuel-tank capacity

The total usable capacity of the fuel tanks must be sufficient for not less than ½-hr operation at rated maximum continuous power. Fuel tanks having a capacity of 0.15 gal for each maximum (except takeoff) horsepower are considered suitable. Fuel quantity indicators must be calibrated to show zero gallons when the usable fuel supply is exhausted. If the unusable fuel supply exceeds 5 percent of the tank capacity or 1 gal, whichever is greater, a placard and a suitable notation in the "Airplane Flight Manual" must be provided to indicate to the flight personnel that the fuel remaining in the tank when the quantity indicator reads zero cannot be used for flight. The weight of the unusable fuel supply must be included in the empty weight of the airplane.

Fuel-tank installation

A number of special requirements are provided for the installation of fuel tanks in aircraft. These requirements are established principally to provide for safety, reliability, and durability of the fuel tank.

The method for supporting tanks must be such that the fuel loads are not concentrated at any particular point of the tank. Nonabsorbent padding must be provided to prevent chafing and wear between the tank and its supports. Synthetic-rubber bladders or flexible fuel-tank liners must be supported by the structure so they are not required to withstand the fuel load. The interior surface of the tank compartment must be smooth and free of any projections which might damage the liner unless the liner is provided with suitable protection at possible points of wear. A positive pressure must be maintained within the vapor space of all bladder cells under all conditions of operation including the critical condition of low airspeed and rate of descent likely to be encountered in normal operation. Pressure is maintained by means of a tank vent tube, the open end of which is faced into the wind to provide continuous ram air pressure.

Fuel-tank compartments must be ventilated and drained to prevent the accumulation of flammable fluids or vapors. The compartments adjacent to tanks which are an integral part of the airplane structure must also be ventilated and drained.

Fuel tanks must not be installed on the engine side of the fire wall. Not less than ½ in. of clear air space must be provided between the fuel tank and the fire wall. No portion of the engine nacelle skin which lies immediately behind a major air egress opening from the engine compartment shall act as the wall of an integral tank. This requirement is to prevent the spread of fire from the engine compartment to the fuel tanks.

Fuel tanks must not be installed in compartments which are occupied by passengers or crew except in the case of single-engine airplanes. In this case a fuel tank which does not have a capacity of more than 25 gal may be located in personnel compartments if adequate drainage and ventilation are provided. In all other cases, the fuel tank must be isolated from personnel compartments by means of fumeproof and fuelproof enclosures.

Fuel jettisoning requirements

For transport-type aircraft, if the maximum takeoff weight for which the aircraft is certificated is greater than 105 percent of the certificated landing weight, provision must be made to jettison enough fuel to bring the weight of the airplane down to the certificated landing weight. The average rate of fuel jettisoning must be 1 percent of the maximum takeoff weight per minute, except that the time required to jettison the fuel need not be less than 10 min.

The fuel jettisoning system and its operation must be free of fire hazards, and the fuel must discharge clear of any part of the airplane. Fuel fumes must not enter the airplane during operation of the jettisoning system. During operation of the system, the controllability of the airplane must not be adversely affected. The further detailed requirements of the jettisoning system are specified in Federal Air Regulations.

Fuel lines and fittings

In an aircraft fuel system, the various components are connected by means of aluminum-alloy tubing and flexible hose assemblies with approved connecting fittings. A typical fuel hose assembly is shown in Fig. 8·30. This hose is made of synthetic rubber and is reinforced with fiber braid embedded in bonding material. The hose conforms to MIL-H-5593A and is connected with an AN-773 hose end assembly. Another

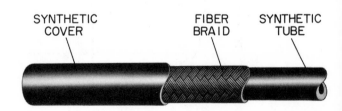

SYNTHETIC COVER FIBER BRAID SYNTHETIC TUBE

Figure **8·30**   *Fuel hose assembly. (The Weatherhead Co.)*

Figure 8·31 Hose assembly with reusable fittings.

hose assembly suitable for fuel systems is shown in Fig. 8·31. This is the Weatherhead 3H-241 hose assembly equipped with reusable type end fittings. This hose has a working temperature range of −40 to +300°F when used with fuel. The hose is covered with stainless-steel braid.

Fuel lines must be of a size which will provide the required fuel-flow rate under all conditions of operation. For gravity systems this rate is not less than 150 percent of the takeoff fuel consumption, and for pump systems the fuel-flow rate must be not less than 0.9 lb per hr for each takeoff horsepower or 125 percent of the actual takeoff fuel consumption of the engine. For transport aircraft, the fuel-flow rate must be not less than 100 percent of the maximum fuel flow required by the engine or engines under all intended operating conditions and maneuvers.

The installation of the fuel lines must be such that there are no sharp bends, that is, bends with a radius of less than three diameters. Fuel lines must be routed

so there are no vertical bends where water or vapor can collect. A bend downward and then upward will permit water to collect, and a bend upward and then downward will permit vapor to collect.

If a copper line is used in a fuel system, it should be annealed after bending and at overhaul periods; however, aluminum lines should not be annealed.

Parts of the fuel system attached to the engine and to the primary structure of the airplane must be connected by means of flexible hose assemblies. Flexible hose assemblies should also be used to connect a stationary unit with a unit under vibration.

Fuel lines must be securely anchored to prevent vibration during operation of the engine. Usually the mountings and clamps installed by the manufacturer will be adequate. Metal lines should be bonded to prevent radio interference.

All fuel lines and fittings must be of an approved type. If replacements are furnished by the manufacturer, they will usually be satisfactory for a particular installation.

FUEL SYSTEMS

Systems for light two-place airplane

The simple fuel system for a light single-engine airplane is shown in Fig. 8·32. The fuel tanks for this system are mounted in the wing roots and are con-

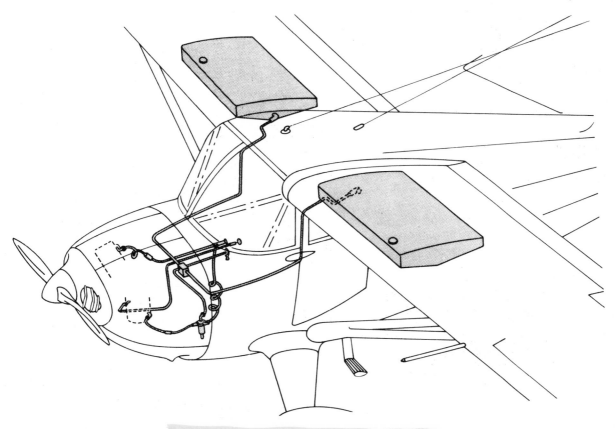

Figure 8·32 Fuel system for single-engine airplane.

structed of welded aluminum alloy. The fuel tanks are held securely in place by means of padded steel straps attached to the wing spars. The padding is treated to make it nonabsorbent. The fuel filler caps are on the top of the wing, and the fuel outlets for the tanks are at the lowest point in the inboard end of the tanks. Fuel flow is by gravity to the fuel valve located forward of the fire wall. From the valve the fuel flows to the "gascolator" (sump and screen assembly) in the lowest point of the system. From the sump the fuel lines lead to the carburetor and to the primer pump which is located on the instrument panel.

Fuel system for single-engine four-place airplane

The fuel system for typical models of the Beechcraft Model 35 four-place airplane is shown in Fig. 8·33. This fuel system normally utilizes two 25-gal fuel cells made of fuel-resistant synthetic rubber. The cells are held in place in the wing compartments by means of snap fasteners. Metal fuel lines are inserted into nipples on the cells and are secured by means of clamps around the nipples. The main fuel lines lead from the cells to the fuel unit in the fuselage. The fuel unit includes the fuel selector valve, the main strainer, and, in some units, a hand booster pump. From the fuel unit the fuel passes through metal tubing and flexible tubing to the engine-driven fuel pump. From this pump the fuel goes to the carburetor or the fuel-injection unit, depending upon the engine fuel-control configuration. The system is provided with a fuel pressure gage mounted in the cockpit. This gage is connected to the pressure side of the fuel-injection unit or pressure carburetor to indicate the actual pressure applied to the fuel-control section. Excess pressure is bypassed back to the inlet side of the pump.

The fuel cells are furnished with vent lines to provide

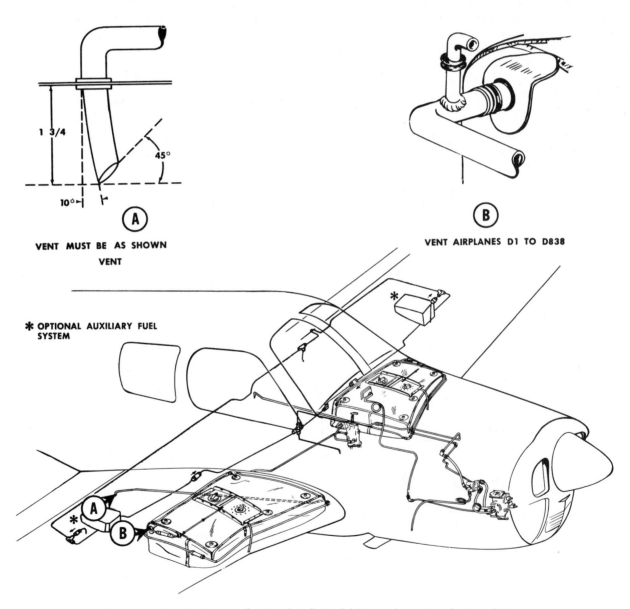

Figure **8·33**   *Fuel system for Beechcraft Model 35 airplane. (Beech Aircraft Co.)*

a positive pressure on the fuel in the cells at all times during flight. As shown in the drawing of Fig. 8 · 33, the fuel vent lines are arranged to pick up ram air pressure during flight. The vents also serve to prevent excessive pressure from developing in the tanks. This is particularly important when the airplane is parked in the hot sun.

The drawing of Fig. 8 · 33 also includes an auxiliary system which may be installed on some models of the airplane. The auxiliary system consists of two 10-gal tanks, one installed in each wing outboard of the main tanks.

Fuel system for light twin airplane

A schematic diagram of the fuel system for a modern light twin airplane, the Cessna Model 310, is shown in Fig. 8 · 34. The fuel system shown is employed with models of the airplane which utilize direct fuel injection for the engines.

The fuel supply is contained in two fuel bladders, one located in each wing-tip tank. The bladders are made of fuel-resistant synthetic rubber with fabric reinforcement. The total fuel capacity of each bladder is 51 gal, of which 50.5 gal is usable. The wing-tip tanks are streamlined aluminum-alloy shells designed to give adequate structural support to the fuel bladders. The tanks are easily removed from the wing tips to which they are secured by means of bolts through the attaching fittings. An electrically operated boost pump is incorporated in each fuel tank to furnish fuel pressure for priming, starting, and emergency use in case the engine-driven pump should fail. From the boost pumps, fuel is fed to the selector valves located in the wings, then through the fuel strainers and engine-driven pumps to the fuel-injection unit. The engine-driven fuel-injection pump assembly includes a vapor separator and a pressure-regulating valve. A detailed description of the fuel-injection system is given in Chap. 6 of this text.

A vapor return line is provided between the fuel-injection pumps and the fuel tanks. This eliminates the collection of vapor and resulting vapor lock in the

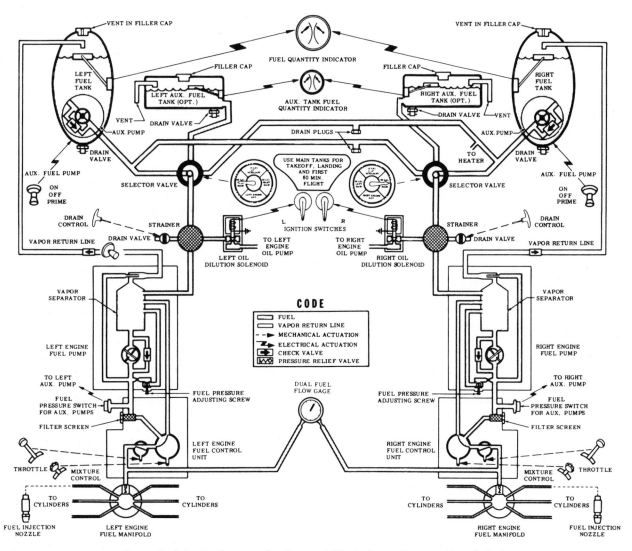

Figure 8 · 34 *Fuel system for Cessna 310 airplane. (Cessna Aircraft Co.)*

pump or fuel-injection unit. The vapor return lines carry some fuel in addition to the vapor back to the fuel tanks. Quick drain valves are provided in each wing-tip tank and in each fuel strainer to facilitate draining of water or sediment. These are used to drain a small amount of fuel during each preflight inspection to assure that all water and sediment are removed before the airplane is flown.

The fuel-system diagram of Fig. 8·34 should be studied carefully to observe the relative positions of all the units of the system. The fuel-quantity gage units can be seen in each tank, and these are electrically connected to the fuel-quantity indicators located on the instrument panel of the airplane. It can be noted also that the fuel booster pumps in the tanks are electrically operated through switches which are located in the cockpit. The booster pumps are provided with bypass arrangements so there will be a free flow of fuel when the pumps are not operating. The oil-dilution solenoid valves receive fuel from the main fuel strainer cases. These valves are also operated by switches in the cockpit.

Since this system is designed for operation with direct fuel-injection units, the fuel pressure gages are connected between the fuel controls and the fuel manifolds. This is to give an indication of the pressure actually applied to the injection nozzles, thus providing the pilot with an accurate measure of engine power.

Fuel system for a jet airliner

Although it is not possible in a standard textbook to provide a detailed description of the fuel system for a modern jet airliner, we shall give a brief description of such a system so the student will have a reasonably complete concept of the size and complexity of such a system.

Figure 8·35 is a schematic diagram of the fuel system in one wing of a Boeing 720 jet transport aircraft. The fuel system is an arrangement of fuel tanks and component systems which ensure that the engines are supplied with fuel in the proper amount at all times. The fuel is distributed in four main tanks, two reserve tanks, and a center wing tank. The fuel tanks and all system components are suitable for use with any acceptable fuel which conforms to the engine manufacturer's specifications. The fuel capacity for each tank is given in Fig. 8·36, which shows the complete arrangement of fuel tanks for the airplane.

All the fuel tanks are located in the interspar area of the wing structure between the front and rear spars. The wing skin and ribs form the walls of the tanks, and the intermediate ribs serve as baffle plates to prevent excessive sloshing and rapid weight shifting of the fuel. The four main tanks and the two reserve tanks are completely integral with the wing structure. The center wing tank consists of two integral sections at the wing roots and a center wing cavity containing bladder-type fuel cells. All fuel tanks are made fuel-tight by the use of sealing compound and sealed fasteners.

A **fuel vent system** provides positive venting to the atmosphere of all fuel tanks, fuel cells, and cavities, thereby preventing excessive internal or external pressures across the tank walls during all flight maneuvers. Venting of the four main tanks, two reserve tanks, and integral sections of the center wing tank is accomplished with sealed spanwise upper wing skin stiffener ducts, interconnected with appropriate drains and vent tubing which connect to vent ports located in critical areas of the tanks. The vent system is connected to a surge tank at the wing tip which is vented overboard through a vent scoop. The center wing cavity is vented overboard through a separate vent and drain system. The cavity vent system maintains atmospheric pressure on the outside of the bladder-type fuel cells. The fuel cells are vented into the integral sections of the center wing fuel tank.

The **engine fuel feed system** consists of fuel lines, pumps, and valves which distribute the fuel to the engines. This system includes four tank-to-engine fuel feed systems which are interconnected by a fuel manifold such that fuel may be delivered from any main tank or the center-wing tank to any or all engines. The two reserve tanks store fuel and supply the fuel by gravity flow to main tanks Nos. 1 and 4 through electrically operated transfer valves. The fuel feed line from each main tank is pressurized by two boost pumps which are controlled by separate switches and independent circuits so that engine operation will not be affected by power failure to any single boost pump. The center-wing-tank boost pumps, known as the **fuel boost override** pumps, will override the main-tank boost pumps to supply fuel through the manifold to the engines. The distribution of fuel to the engines is controlled by electric-motor-driven slide valves in the fuel lines. The valves are classified into three groups: (1) the **engine fuel shutoff valves,** which shut off fuel to the engines; (2) the **fuel manifold valves,** which control manifold distribution; and (3) the **reserve tank transfer valves,** which control fuel from the reserve tanks to main tanks Nos. 1 and 4. All these valves are controlled by manually operated switches located on the flight engineer's lower panel in the control cabin.

Pressure fueling is accomplished on the Boeing 720 airplane from a station located on the lower surface of each wing between the inboard and outboard engine nacelles. Each pressure fueling station consists of two fueling nozzle ground connectors, two fueling receptacles, and a fueling manifold. Four fueling manual shutoff valves at each fueling station permit the fuel tanks to be serviced individually. Each station services the main and reserve tanks on its respective side of the airplane. The center wing tank is serviced from either wing station. The maximum fuel-delivery pressure is 50 psi. A **restricting orifice plate** at each fueling manual shutoff valve limits the flow rate for the tank serviced. The approximate flow rates for the various tanks are as follows: main tanks Nos. 1 and 4, 234 gpm; main tanks Nos. 2 and 3, 227 gpm; and reserve tanks Nos. 1 and 4, 65 gpm. The center-wing-tank rate is 250 gpm per side except on certain airplanes.

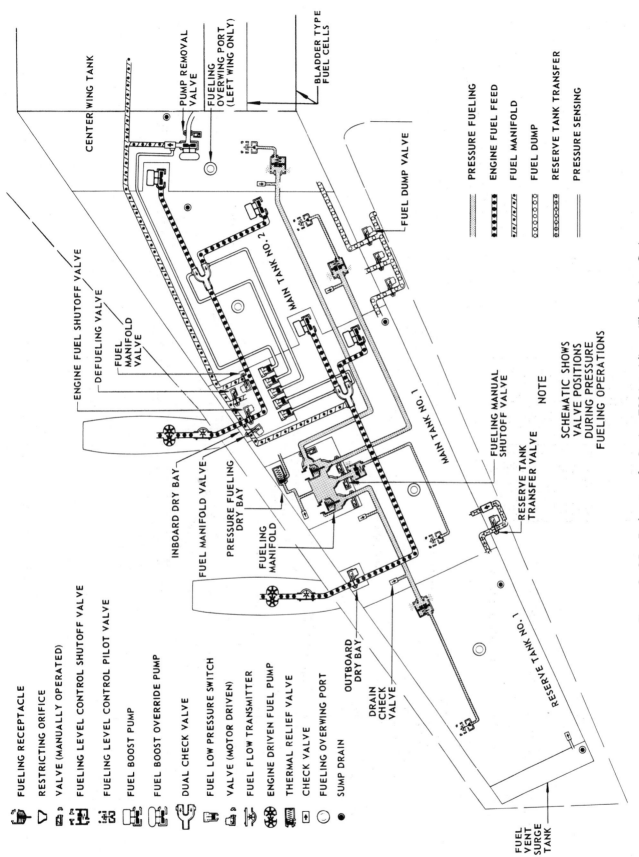

FUELING RECEPTACLE

RESTRICTING ORIFICE

VALVE (MANUALLY OPERATED)

FUELING LEVEL CONTROL SHUTOFF VALVE

FUELING LEVEL CONTROL PILOT VALVE

FUEL BOOST PUMP

FUEL BOOST OVERRIDE PUMP

DUAL CHECK VALVE

FUEL LOW PRESSURE SWITCH

VALVE (MOTOR DRIVEN)

FUEL FLOW TRANSMITTER

ENGINE DRIVEN FUEL PUMP

THERMAL RELIEF VALVE

CHECK VALVE

FUELING OVERWING PORT

SUMP DRAIN

CENTER WING TANK

PUMP REMOVAL VALVE

FUELING OVERWING PORT (LEFT WING ONLY)

BLADDER TYPE FUEL CELLS

ENGINE FUEL SHUTOFF VALVE

DEFUELING VALVE

FUEL MANIFOLD VALVE

MAIN TANK NO. 2

FUEL DUMP VALVE

INBOARD DRY BAY

FUEL MANIFOLD VALVE

PRESSURE FUELING DRY BAY

FUELING MANIFOLD

MAIN TANK NO. 1

FUELING MANUAL SHUTOFF VALVE

RESERVE TANK TRANSFER VALVE

OUTBOARD DRY BAY

DRAIN CHECK VALVE

RESERVE TANK NO. 1

FUEL VENT SURGE TANK

PRESSURE FUELING

ENGINE FUEL FEED

FUEL MANIFOLD

FUEL DUMP

RESERVE TANK TRANSFER

PRESSURE SENSING

NOTE

SCHEMATIC SHOWS VALVE POSITIONS DURING PRESSURE FUELING OPERATIONS

Figure 8 · 35   Fuel system for Boeing 720 jet airliner. (The Boeing Co.)

163

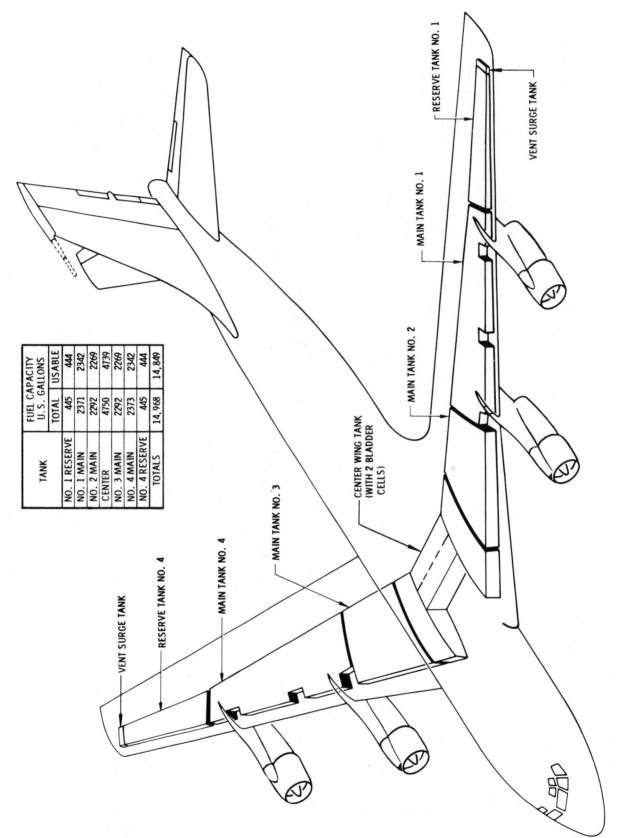

TANK	FUEL CAPACITY U.S. GALLONS	
	TOTAL	USABLE
NO. 1 RESERVE	445	444
NO. 1 MAIN	2371	2342
NO. 2 MAIN	2292	2269
CENTER	4750	4739
NO. 3 MAIN	2292	2269
NO. 4 MAIN	2373	2342
NO. 4 RESERVE	445	444
TOTALS	14,968	14,849

RESERVE TANK NO. 1

VENT SURGE TANK

MAIN TANK NO. 1

MAIN TANK NO. 2

CENTER WING TANK (WITH 2 BLADDER CELLS)

MAIN TANK NO. 3

MAIN TANK NO. 4

RESERVE TANK NO. 4

VENT SURGE TANK

Figure 8·36 Fuel-tank installation for jet airliner.

Each tank has a **fueling level-control pilot valve** (see Fig. 8·37) which actuates a **fueling level-control shutoff valve** to shut off the fuel flow automatically when the maximum tank capacity has been reached. A **fueling preset system** permits the tanks to be fueled to a predetermined level without constant observation of the fuel-quantity indicators. The fueling preset system controls are located on the flight engineer's panel. Preset switches and potentiometers are actuated in conjunction with fuel-quantity indicators. The preset system incorporates signal lights at the fueling station to inform the refueling operator that the desired quantity of fuel has been pumped into the various tanks.

The **fuel dump system,** consisting of lines, valves, dump chutes, and chute-operating mechanism, provides the means whereby fuel can be dumped in flight. Each wing contains an extendable dump chute which must be fully extended before fuel can be dumped. Each chute is fed fuel by dump lines from the main and center wing tanks on their respective sides of the airplane. The reserve tank fuel is transferred to and dumped with the main outboard tank fuel. The controls are located on the flight engineer's auxiliary panel. When all dump valves are open, the system will dump all fuel in excess of 10,848 lb at an average rate of approximately 2500 lb per min. The 10,848 lb of fuel remaining in the fuel tanks is required as a safety measure to allow the airplane adequate flight time to reach a suitable airport and make a safe landing. The

principal reason for dumping fuel is to reduce the landing weight of the airplane prior to making an emergency landing.

The **fuel-quantity indicating system** incorporates electric capacitance tank probes mounted internally in each fuel tank. The probes have a compensator for fuel density variations. The probes feed signals to the fuel-quantity indicators on the flight engineer's lower panel. These indicators are calibrated to show the weight of fuel remaining in each tank.

The **fuel-flow indicating system** utilizes a **fuel-flow transmitter** (described previously) to send electrical signals to the fuel-flow indicators at the pilot's station. The fuel-flow indication makes it possible for the pilot to determine individual engine power output and also the flight time remaining before the airplane must land and refuel.

The **fuel-temperature-indicating system** is required to tell when there may be danger of ice crystals forming in the fuel. It must be remembered that jet airliners fly regularly at altitudes of over 30,000 ft and the fuel therefore reaches temperatures well below the freezing point of water. After such an airplane has landed, frost will often be found on the lower surface of the wings. The fuel-temperature-indicating system provides a means for checking the temperature of fuel in main tank No. 1 and in the fuel line at each engine. The system consists of an **indicator** and a **five-position selector switch** on the flight engineer's lower panel.

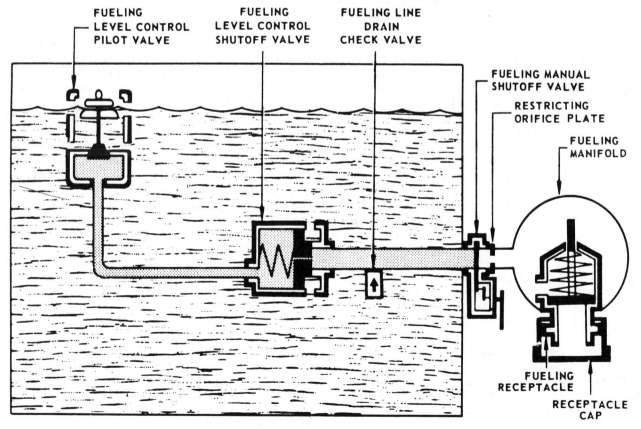

Figure 8·37   Fuel level-control pilot valve.

A temperature bulb is located in main tank No. 1 and in the outlet side of the fuel filter at each engine.

Each engine has a manually controlled engine fuel deicing system which removes any ice formed in the fuel before it reaches the fuel-control unit. The principal components of each deicing system are a **fuel filter,** an **air-control valve,** and **fuel deicing heater.** The control switches and icing indicator lights are located on the flight engineer's lower panel.

The **fuel filter** is fitted with a pressure warning switch which detects filter icing and then turns on the fuel icing indicator light on the flight engineer's lower panel. The **air-control valve** controls the flow of high-pressure discharge air from the engine compressor to the heater through which all the fuel passes. A fuel-temperature bulb is located on the outlet side of the filter to monitor the fuelout temperature.

All fuel tanks in the Boeing 720 airliner have an exterior filler cap for individual tank servicing. The caps are located on the top of the wings, as shown in Fig. 8 · 35, thus making it possible to fill the tanks when pressure fueling is not available. The main tanks have baffle check valves installed in the bottom of the inboard ribs to allow fuel to flow inboard toward the boost pumps during normal flight attitude and to prevent fuel flow away from the pump area during turbulence or airplane maneuvers. This provision assures that engine stoppage will not be caused by a momentary cutoff of fuel flow.

Pressure defueling of the main tanks or center wing tank is accomplished through a defueling valve located in the inboard dry bay of each wing. The fuel boost pumps in the main tanks or the override pumps in the center wing tank deliver fuel to the defueling valves through their respective fuel manifold valves. The defueling rate is approximately 50 gpm for each tank. Alternatively, fuel can be drawn from the tanks through the defueling valve by means of the truck defueling pump. The reserve tanks are defueled through the reserve tank transfer valve to the adjacent main tanks. Residual fuel in each tank can be drained through fuel sump drain cocks located in the bottom of each tank.

In addition to the fuel-quantity indicating system, provisions are made to determine the quantity of fuel in each tank with the airplane in the taxi attitude by calibrated **drip sticks** located in the wing lower surface. When the cap and hollow drip-stick assembly is drawn out from the wing lower surface, fuel enters the open top of the stick when it reaches the fuel level and can be observed at a small drip hole near the cap base. The drip-stick reading in inches when fuel first appears at the drip hole is compared with a special chart to give a reading of fuel quantity in gallons or kilograms.

The following components of the Boeing 720 fuel system should be located in the drawing of Fig. 8 · 35 and the purpose of each unit determined:

Fueling receptacle. The attachment for the pressure fueling hose. The receptacle is fitted with a valve which is automatically closed when the fueling hose is disconnected.

Restricting orifice. A flow-limiting device to prevent excessive fuel flow during pressure fueling.

Manually operated shutoff valves. These valves are provided at the pressure fueling station to permit a positive closing of fuel lines.

Fueling level-control shutoff valve. This valve automatically closes the fueling line to a tank when that tank is filled to its maximum level.

Fueling level-control pilot valve. During pressure fueling, this valve closes when the full fuel level is reached. The closing of this valve causes pressure to be applied to the fueling level-control shutoff valve, thus causing it to close (see Fig. 8 · 37).

Motor-driven valve. These are slide valves operated by electric motors. They are used for fuel control throughout the system.

Fuel-flow transmitter. The electrically operated unit which senses the rate of fuel flow to each engine. Details of the operation have been given earlier in this chapter.

INSPECTION, MAINTENANCE, AND REPAIR OF FUEL SYSTEMS

General inspections

Inspections for a fuel system may follow a regular pattern established by a particular organization for the inspection of operating aircraft, or they may be specified by the manufacturer of the aircraft. Inspections are often classified as **preflight, 20** or **25-hr, 50-hr, 100-hr,** and **periodic.**

Preflight inspection

The preflight inspection of a fuel system includes checking the fuel tanks visually for quantity of fuel. This requires the removal of tank filler caps and looking into fuel tanks. Sometimes a dipstick must be used in order to determine that the proper quantity of fuel is in the tanks. Another most important preflight inspection of the fuel system is the opening of fuel drains. All fuel drains should be opened for a few seconds to allow any accumulated water or sediment to drain out of the system.

Other preflight inspections may be established by the owner or operator of the aircraft under particular circumstances, and in each case, the required inspection should be carried out before the airplane is flown.

During engine runup, the fuel pressure and the proper operation of booster pumps should be checked. If any malfunction is found in the fuel system, the airplane should not be flown until the malfunction is corrected.

25-hr inspections

A 25-hr routine inspection of the fuel system probably will not require more than a visual inspection for signs of fuel leakage and draining of the main fuel strainer. During the visual inspection the security of all lines and fittings should be checked. Special inspections may be required after 25 hr of operation for a new engine or a new airplane. These inspections are recommended because of metal particles and other foreign matter which may have accumulated during the first 25 hr of flight. In such instances it is advisable to clean all fuel strainers, drains, and vent lines. All fittings, mountings, and attachments should be checked for security.

100-hr or periodic inspections

The 100-hr or periodic inspection requires a complete examination of the fuel system. All fuel strainers should be removed and cleaned, all drains should be opened, and sumps should be drained to make sure that all sediment and water is removed from the system. The carburetor float chamber should be drained to remove water and sediment, and the carburetor fuel filter should be cleaned. All fuel lines and hoses should be examined carefully for condition, security, and wear due to rubbing on any portion of the structure. Any unsatisfactory condition must be corrected. The primer system and oil-dilution system should be checked for satisfactory operation.

Required inspections are usually listed in the manufacturer's service manual, and all special inspections should be accomplished as specified.

Repair of metal fuel tanks

Before actual repair procedures are described, it is important to consider certain safety precautions. The fuel vapor present in all empty fuel tanks which have been in service is explosive; therefore caution should be observed in their repair. The following steps are recommended to eliminate fire and explosion hazards: The tank drain plug is removed, and live steam is circulated through the tank by placing the steam line in the filler neck opening. This steaming should continue for at least ½ hr.

In another approved procedure, hot water (150°F) is allowed to flow through the tank from the bottom and out the top for 1 hr. **Never apply heat to a tank when it is installed in an airplane.** This safety procedure applies only to welded or soldered metal tanks, not to riveted ones. The use of hot water in a riveted tank may loosen the sealing compound between joints and cause leaks. Heat is not required for rivet repairs, thus it is not necessary to flush the tank with hot water.

Metal fuel tanks are repaired by welding, soldering, or riveting. The repair method used, of course, depends on the construction of the tank. Tanks constructed of commercially pure aluminum 3003S, 5052SO, or similar metals may be repaired by welding. Heat-treated aluminum-alloy tanks are generally put together by riveting.

When it is necessary to repair a riveted tank with a riveted patch, a sealing compound which is insoluble in gasoline should be used to seal the patch. If the tank is to be used with aromatic fuels, the sealing compound must be of a type which is insoluble in aromatic fuel.

Leaks in tanks may be located by plugging all the outlets except one and admitting air pressure of about 2½ psi. The application of soapy water on the seams of the tank will cause bubbles to form wherever a leak exists. The areas of leakage should then be marked with a red pencil, and the repair made by using the proper method.

One type of solder repair used on stainless-steel tanks is accomplished by applying a cover patch of 0.018 terneplate over the crack and soldering it in place with soft solder. The patch is cut and formed so that it overlaps the damaged area by approximately ½ in. Figure 8·38 illustrates this method.

After a soldering repair is made, the tank must be flushed with warm water to remove all traces of the soldering flux and any solder beads which may have fallen into it.

Similarly, after welding a fuel tank, it is necessary to remove all the welding flux to prevent corrosion. This is accomplished by immediately washing the inside and outside surfaces of the tank with hot water. After the water bath, the tank is drained and then filled with a 5 percent nitric or sulfuric acid solution. This solution should be allowed to remain in the tank for 1 hr, after which the tank should be rinsed with clean fresh water. The outside weld also should be washed with the acid solution.

To ensure that the water has removed all the corrosive elements, a small quantity of 5 percent silver nitrate is placed in a sample of the rinse water. If a heavy white precipitate results, the rinsing operation should be repeated.

Minor seepage in a riveted tank can be repaired with a sealing compound, such as Thiokol B-18, applied externally. To do this, first clean the surface of all dirt, grease, and corrosion. Steel wool may be used for this purpose. After the surface is thoroughly cleaned, apply two coats of the compound, using a small brush.

The first coat should be fairly thick, and after it has been allowed to dry for approximately 30 min, a second light coat should be applied and allowed to dry for 48 hr.

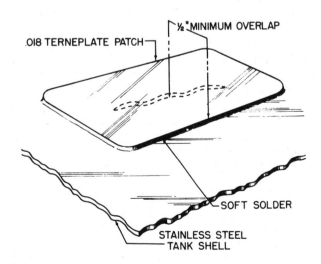

Figure 8·38 Solder patch for fuel tank.

Dripping or running leaks in a riveted tank must be repaired by tightening the metal seam. This is done by drilling out all worn and damaged rivets near the leak and replacing them with new rivets. The new rivets should be headed by using a pneumatic squeeze riveter if such a tool is available and can be used. It is good practice to dip the new rivets in Thiokol or a similar compound before installation. This compound should also be applied to the seam in the same manner as for stopping seepage. If it is necessary to rivet a patch in place, a sealing compound which is insoluble in gasoline should be used. Bakelite varnish, Thiokol, neoprene, and zinc chromate compound are acceptable sealing cements for this purpose.

Repair of synthetic-rubber fuel cells

The repair of synthetic-rubber fuel bladders or cells is usually described in the manufacturer's overhaul manual. Typical of such instructions for an outside patch are the following provided for the fuel cells of the Model 35 Beechcraft airplane:

1. Use a piece of synthetic-rubber-coated outside repair material (U.S. Rubber Company 5136) large enough to cover the damage at least 2 in. from the cut in any direction. Buff this material lightly and thoroughly with fine sandpaper, and wash with methyl ethyl ketone (U.S. Rubber Company 3339 solution) to remove buffing dust.
2. Cement the buffed side of the patch with two coats of black rubber cement (3M Company EC678). Allow each coat to dry 10 to 15 min.
3. Buff the cell area to be patched lightly and thoroughly with fine sandpaper, and wash with methyl ethyl ketone to remove buffing dust.
4. Cement the buffed area with two coats of 3M Company EC678 cement. Allow each coat to dry 10 to 15 min.
5. Freshen the cemented area of the patch and the cemented area of the cell with methyl ethyl ketone.
6. While still tacky, apply the edge of the patch to the edge of the cemented area and roll or press it down ½ to 1 in. at a time to prevent air from being trapped between the patch and the cell.
7. Seal the patch and a ½-in. strip of the cell around the patch with one coat of black rubber cement, and allow the patch to remain undisturbed for 6 hr.

A damaged fuel cell must be patched inside as well as outside when the damage goes entirely through the cell wall. Instructions for the inside patching process are as follows:

1. After the damaged area has been patched on the outside of the cell and the repair allowed to stand a minimum of 6 hr, the cell is ready to have the patch applied on the inside of the cell. The damaged area to which this patch is to be applied may be pulled through the filler neck opening to make the repair simpler.
2. Lightly and thoroughly buff a piece of Buna nylon sandwich material (U.S. Rubber Company 5063).
3. Cement the patch opposite the red fabric side with two coats of the same cement used for the outside patch, allowing each coat to dry 10 to 15 min.
4. Buff the cell area to be patched lightly and thoroughly with fine sandpaper, then wash off the dust with methyl ethyl ketone.

5. Coat the buffed area of the cell with two coats of cement, allowing each coat to dry 10 to 15 min.
6. Freshen the cemented areas of the patch and cell with methyl ethyl ketone.
7. While the cemented areas are still tacky, apply the edge of the patch to the edge of the cemented area, centering the patch over the cut in the fuel cell. Hold part of the patch off the cemented area, and roll or press it down ½ in. across at a time to avoid trapping air between the patch and the cell.
8. Remove the red fabric from the patch by moistening it with methyl ethyl ketone.
9. Seal-coat the patch and a ½-in. strip of the cell around the patch with two coats of the black cement. Allow the first coat to dry 15 min and the second coat to dry 12 hr or more, so that, when the cell is in its original position, the patching area will not stick to other areas of the cell.

Thick-walled fuel cells such as those installed in transport aircraft can be repaired using methods and materials similar to those described above. In every case, however, the repair should be accomplished in accordance with manufacturer's instructions and by a person trained in the procedures.

Reinstallation of fuel tanks or cells

In general, the reinstallation of fuel tanks or cells is accomplished by reversing the process of removal. When metal tanks are reinstalled, the felt padding should be examined for condition. If new felt is installed, it should be treated to make it nonabsorbent. Rawhide leather, which contains free alkalies, is unsuitable for padding an aluminum tank because excessive corrosion will take place where the pad comes in contact with the metal. The tanks must be anchored securely, and vibration held to a minimum, especially where aluminum-alloy tanks are used, since such tanks are subject to cracking.

Metal tanks are subject to both internal and external corrosion, and steps should be taken to prevent this. Zinc chromate primer is a satisfactory external corrosion resistant, and internal corrosion may be prevented by the use of dichromate crystals in a separate container located in the tank sump. This latter practice is not commonly employed in modern aircraft because fuel tanks are designed so it is possible to drain all water out of the tanks by means of the sump drains.

Synthetic-rubber bladders and cells are held in place by lacing cord, snaps, or both. The reinstallation procedure must follow the manufacturer's instructions to assure that the cells are properly supported in the tank compartment. The area in which the cell is installed must be inspected to make sure that there are no sharp edges or protrusions which may cause wear or other damage to the cells. Any portion of the structure which may cause damage must be covered with padding.

Testing fuel tanks

Fuel tanks must be capable of withstanding certain pressure tests without failure or leakage. These pressures may be applied in a manner simulating the actual pressure distribution in service.

Conventional metal tanks whose walls are not supported by the aircraft structure must withstand a pressure of 3.5 psi. If there is any doubt regarding the airworthiness of a particular fuel tank, it may be tested by applying air pressure through a pressure regulator set to 3.5 psi. If this is done, great care must be taken to avoid excessive pressure.

The maintenance technician is not usually required to carry out all the tests for tanks required by Federal Air Regulations for original testing of tanks. Tests required at overhaul periods will be described in the manufacturer's overhaul manual.

Servicing fuel tubing

In servicing the fuel system it is sometimes necessary to make flares on the ends of tubing. This work is not difficult if the proper tools are used according to standard plumbing practice.

Figure 8·39 shows a conventional flaring tool which consists of a split metal block in which various size holes, to fit standard tubing diameters, have been drilled. The halves of the block bisect the holes. The block is hinged at one end so that it can be separated. The tubing to be flared is placed in the proper hole with one end extending to the top of the taper. The handle clamps the two blocks firmly against the tubing. The sharp edges of the tubing are smoothed with a scraper or small file to reduce the tendency to crack when the flare is made. The top pin is located over the tubing end and is then struck several reasonable blows with a mallet. This will flare out the tubing end so that it will conform to the taper in the block. Approved shop practice is to strike the pin a few reasonably firm blows rather than many light ones, as a better flare will result with less chance of cracking.

A number of suitable flaring tools other than the one shown in Fig. 8·39 are available. Some models utilize a screw arrangement to force the cone into the end of the tubing to form the flare. Any tool which does not

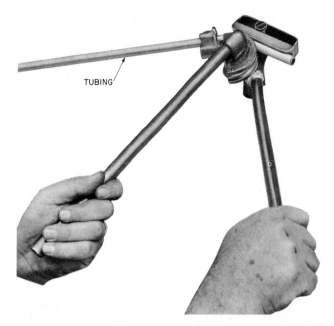

Figure 8·40   Hand-operated tube bender.

leave scratches or other damage on the tubing is satisfactory for making flares.

Bending tubes

A hand tool called a **tube bender** is sometimes used to make bends in tubing. If the tube is bent rather sharply, the bending operation is done in steps to prevent collapsing or fracture of the tube. A hand-operated tube bender is shown in Fig. 8·40. A bender of this type will produce excellent bends when used according to instructions.

Production tube benders are used when it is necessary to bend a large number of similar tubing assemblies. Benders of this type are usually found in factories where tubing is made up in standard sizes and shapes to fit systems of an aircraft or missile in production.

Installation of hoses, lines, and fittings

Before fuel lines and hoses are installed, they should be carefully inspected. Aluminum or aluminum-alloy lines should not be annealed after forming because such materials are very sensitive to high temperatures and it is not possible to obtain a proper annealing of the material except under carefully controlled conditions. On the other hand, copper tubing can be satisfactorily annealed merely by heating it to a cherry red and then quenching it in cold water. Fuel lines should be inspected for scratches, abrasion, corrosion, kinks, dents, cuts, or any other damage which may cause them to be unairworthy. The end fittings should be examined for cracks, cross threads, flattening, and other damage. The lines should be checked for cleanliness inside so there will be no danger of putting foreign material in the system.

Fuel hoses should be inspected, especially at the ends where the fittings are installed. Damaged fittings should be replaced. Hose assemblies which have worn

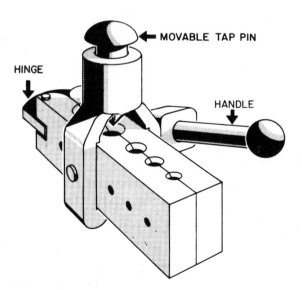

Figure 8·39   Tube flaring tool.

surfaces, swelling, or leaks of any kind should be replaced. Many hose assemblies are equipped with reusable end fittings. When such fittings are damaged, they may be replaced as shown in Fig. 8·41. Undamaged fittings may also be removed from damaged tubing and used on new tubing. The steps for installation of the fittings are as follows:

1. Mount the end socket in a vise or other holding fixture, and screw the square end of the hose into the socket by turning the hose counterclockwise into the left-hand thread. The cover should not be removed from the hose.
2. Assemble the hose insert, tube nut, tube connector, and mandrel. Tighten the tube nut until the assembly is rigid. (Tube sizes 16 and over do not require a mandrel.)

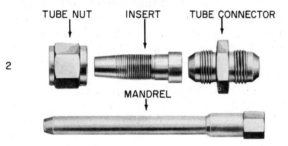

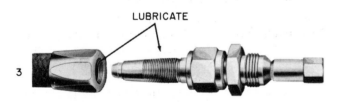

Figure 8·41   Installation of hose fittings.

170

3. Lubricate the hose ID and the insert of the subassembly with lubricating oil or light grease.
4. Screw the subassembly into the hose and socket. Leave 1/16-in. clearance so the nut is free to swivel.

During the assembly of fuel lines and hoses, it is important that certain standard practices be followed. These are as follows:

1. Tube and hose fittings should never be forced into place.
2. Fittings should be in accurate alignment before assembling. Alignment should be such that the fittings can be assembled and screwed together by hand.
3. No tube or hose should be under tension or other stress after fittings are tightened.
4. All fittings should be carefully checked for cleanliness before assembly.
5. Fittings should be tightened with the proper torque (see Table 8·1).

Table 8·1   Torque values for tube fittings

| Tube OD, in. | Wrench torque range for tightening tube nuts, in.–lb | |
	Aluminum alloy 1100-H14 or 5052-0	Stainless steel
3/16		30–70
1/4	40–65	50–90
5/16	60–80	70–120
3/8	75–125	90–150
1/2	150–250	155–250
5/8	200–350	300–400
3/4	300–500	430–575
1	500–700	550–750
1 1/4	600–900	
1 1/2	600–900	

When tube fittings are assembled, no lubrication or joint compound should be used except for petroleum-type lubricating oil or petroleum jelly. In certain instances an approved-type thread compound may be used with pipe fittings, but the compound must not be of the hardening type. A small amount of the compound may be applied to the male threads of the assembly.

TROUBLESHOOTING

Fundamentals

Accurate and rapid troubleshooting on a fuel system necessitates a complete understanding of the operation and purpose of the entire system and its various units.

Most maintenance technicians are able to make quick and satisfactory repairs after a trouble has been located but may have problems when trying to trace the source of the difficulty. As in all troubleshooting, if the technician will follow a definite plan or procedure in locating a defective unit, time will be saved and the long process of haphazardly removing unit after unit with the hope that eventually the trouble will be found is eliminated.

The first step in locating a fuel-system defect is to analyze the symptoms. This gives a clue as to the identity of the units or parts of the system which are defective or inoperative. In this way, by logical reasoning, the faulty unit can be ascertained and checked and the necessary servicing steps taken.

In checking for fuel-system troubles, a close observance of the action of the gages, indicators, and various units of the system is important.

Several typical examples of fuel-system troubleshooting procedures are as follows:

The daily line inspection shows an adequate fuel supply, and the check of the strainer indicates a normal flow of fuel through the strainer drain, but when the boost pump is turned on, the fuel-pressure-indicator needle fluctuates slightly and does not register the correct pressure.

Since the flow of fuel to the strainer was normal, the trouble could not be in the tank screen, the selector valve, or in the lines to the strainer. The trouble must exist between the strainer and the carburetor.

As the fuel-pressure connection is taken from the float-chamber side of the carburetor screen, improper fuel pressure at the gage would indicate that the fuel is restricted at some point between the carburetor bowl and the strainer. This would call for the removal of the carburetor screen. If it is clear, hose fittings between the carburetor and the strainer are loosened and the hoses disconnected in succession. After each hose is disconnected, the boost pump is operated to check for a free flow of fuel at this point. The restriction in the line is thus located systematically.

Another example: An engine is started on the primer charge but does not continue to run unless the boost pump is left turned on. The fuel-pressure indicator shows normal pressure as long as the pump is operated, but it becomes erratic and the reading drops when the boost pump is turned off.

The trouble should be approached logically. From the discussion earlier in the text, it was shown that the boost pump uses the same line as the engine-driven pump to force fuel to the carburetor. It was also shown that a bypass valve is incorporated in the engine-driven fuel pump to allow fuel under boost pump pressure to flow around the engine-driven pump rotor and vanes. The lines and units of the system are not blocked, since the engine will operate under boost-pump pressure. So it is obvious that the trouble is in the engine-driven pump.

In general, when a normally operating fuel pump suddenly ceases to function, it should be removed for dismantling and inspection. However, before doing this, the pressure-relief-valve setting should be readjusted while the boost pump is being operated. If this does not correct the trouble, the procedure for removing the pump should be followed.

Another example involves an airplane which is equipped with a gravity-feed fuel system and a float-type carburetor. The engine is started and runs normally for a few minutes, then stops. After a short period of time, the engine is restarted. It runs for a few minutes and again stops.

Judging from the symptoms, it is apparent that for one reason or another the supply of fuel is restricted. When the engine is not running, the carburetor float chamber fills with fuel, but when the engine is started, the supply drops off sharply.

An experienced technician would probably know immediately the cause of this trouble. The beginner, however, would get along better by adopting a fixed procedure. The first step in such a procedure in this particular case would be to isolate the part of the fuel system causing the trouble. The gascolator, or strainer drain, is opened and shows a restricted fuel supply. Thus, it is determined that the fault is located somewhere in the system between the tank and the strainer. The next step would be to isolate the trouble still further by disconnecting a line at the shutoff cock. If this is done and it is seen that the flow of fuel is still restricted, the elimination procedure is continued, but before the tank screen is removed, the tank vent is checked. In this case it was found to be clogged.

Other units, such as the carburetor, can cause the same symptoms to appear. Hence it is better to follow a definite procedure which isolates the trouble rather than to start checking the first unit that comes to mind.

Yet another example of troubles which may be encountered in the fuel system: A pilot reports that the fuel pressure was normal on the ground but that it increased with altitude. Such a condition is obviously caused by the fuel-pump pressure-relief valve.

The relief-valve pressure setting itself cannot be at fault, since the pressure was normal on the ground. Hence the fault must be due to the altitude-compensating part of the valve. An increase in fuel pressure with altitude is the result of improper balance on the diaphragm between carburetor-scoop pressure and atmospheric pressure on the fuel in the tanks. In other words, ground atmospheric pressure is trapped on the top of the fuel-pressure-relief-valve diaphragm. Therefore there must be a restriction in the fuel-pressure-relief-valve vent. The vent line, from the fuel-pump relief valve to the carburetor scoop, is disconnected, and the restrictor fitting is cleaned with the shank end of a twist drill of the proper size.

An engine is started and "gallops" at idling speed. The tachometer shows the rpm at idling to be excessively low. As the throttle is opened, the fuel mixture becomes richer, a condition which is indicated by black smoke coming from the exhaust pipe.

This trouble may be due to the carburetor, but it is assumed that the carburetor is functioning normally.

Some unit in the fuel system other than the carburetor is allowing fuel to enter the engine cylinders. The only unit which can do this is the primer. If a hand primer is used and the handle is not locked in the closed position, the engine will siphon fuel from the strainer through the primer and into the cylinders through the intake valves, or if a solenoid-operated primer valve sticks, the same trouble will result. Hence, when such indications appear the priming system should first be checked.

Any malfunctioning of the fuel system which causes violent backfiring through the carburetor and induction system should be investigated immediately. If this malfunctioning is allowed to continue, serious engine damage may result with the possible loss of the airplane. Backfiring can be caused by sticking intake valves, intake valve clearances too close, and fuel-system units which, through their failure, cause excessively lean mixtures. Lean mixtures are generally caused by a faulty carburetor, low fuel pressure, or allowing one fuel tank to run dry before switching to another.

Operating data helpful in troubleshooting

In troubleshooting the fuel system, it is most helpful to have a good overall knowledge of the particular airplane in which the trouble is encountered. Just as the physician in diagnosing the illness of a patient tries to get a good knowledge of the patient's general health before prescribing a remedy for a particular ailment, so should the technician learn to know the various operating weaknesses (if any) of the airplanes he customarily repairs. This information he obtains by observation, from his conversations with the pilots, or from the flight record forms. Generally, the engine operation temperatures and pressures are the most reliable clues to any fuel-system trouble which may be encountered.

Fuel-system troubles are rather elementary, but usually they occur more frequently than troubles encountered in the carburetor, and since they so greatly affect the operation of the airplane, they should be corrected as quickly as possible. In their effect on the engine they can be said to be general in nature. An ignition-system trouble, such as a faulty spark plug, will affect only one cylinder of an engine in the first instance; fuel-system troubles may affect all cylinders and result in complete engine failure. For this reason, the fuel system requires the close attention of an expert and capable technician.

REFUELING THE AIRPLANE

Fundamentals

One of the little thought of, yet important, duties of the maintenance technician is servicing the airplane with fuel. In doing this work, care must always be exercised to avoid overlooking some detail of the task which might result in great damage being done to the airplane, not to mention the serious injury which may befall the pilot through some negligence.

Fire, or rather uncontrolled fire, is a hazard in any occupation, but it is particularly a great danger with regard to refueling the airplane.

A maintenance technician needs to "keep his head about him" in doing any of the maintenance required for an airplane, but in serving it with fuel or in checking

its fuel system, he **must keep his mind on his work** or great damage may result.

Not only must the technician be conscious of every operation during the refueling task, but all personnel must be aware of the seriousness of his job and be properly warned when it is in progress. To this end, rules and restrictions have been set up by airlines to prevent any mistakes being made.

In general, if cleanliness, carefulness, good judgment, exactness, and thoroughness are stressed in doing the job, it will be done efficiently and with little danger.

It must be noted that the refueling of a small, privately owned airplane will be a vastly different operation from the refueling of a modern jet transport airplane. Between these two extremes there is a wide variety of airplane characteristics to be considered.

There is much more to the refueling operation than meets the eye. The procedure is considerably more complex than merely unfastening a tank cap and putting in fuel the same as you would in an automobile. In the first place it is desirable to fill the tanks at the end of a flight rather than at the beginning. In this way the possibility of moisture collecting in the tank is greatly lessened. If the airplane has been flying at high altitudes, the remaining fuel in the tank will be cold, and at the warmer ground temperatures condensation from moisture in the air might form on the inner tank walls.

Other workers in the area should be cautioned against doing any work on the airplane while it is being refueled.

Condensation occurs under extreme changes in temperature, but it may also occur from the difference in day and night temperatures. When the tank is filled at the end of the flight, there is very little air space within it for condensation to take place.

It is also important to refuel at the end of a flight so as to reduce the possibility of excessive vapors collecting in the tank. If the air space in the tank is reduced by filling it, there is less danger of fire.

A full tank also assures an ample supply of fuel for the next takeoff, and since the refueling operation is, of necessity, a painstaking and time-consuming task, the advantage of doing the job at the end of a flight is obvious.

Refueling procedure

Assuming that the refueling job is about to begin, the following procedure is recommended:

1. The person assigned to the task should first see to it that the airplane is in a safe place, the wheels carefully chocked, or the brakes set. If fuel is to be taken from a truck, it should be driven up carefully and positioned parallel to the wings of the airplane at a reasonable distance from it.
2. Fire extinguishers should be placed within easy reach in case of fire.
3. Every piece of equipment used in doing the work should be absolutely clean. The refueling hose nozzle should be wiped clean with a cloth free of lint and dirt. The hose nozzle should never be dragged over any part of the airplane or the ground.
4. The amount of fuel needed and the grade should be ascer-

tained. It is very important that the airplane be refueled with gasoline of the correct octane or performance number. Efficient performance of the engine depends upon this. Every aircraft engine requires fuel of a specific grade, and this information will be found marked on or near the fuel filler cap. If the airplane is equipped with turbojet or turbo-prop engines, the proper grade of gas-turbine engine fuel will be indicated. Substitution of fuel may cause trouble which may very well prove serious.

5. If the person refueling the aircraft is required to stand or walk on any unprotected part of the airplane during the refueling operation, the part or parts of the airplane involved should be protected with canvas covers, and the ground should be free of loose tools or parts so that there is no danger of stumbling over them.

6. It should be understood that gasoline flowing through a hose may build up a charge of static electricity. When the refueling hose nozzle is withdrawn from the tank, the charge of static will ignite the fuel. For this reason, before starting the refueling operation, the nozzle of the hose must be grounded.

Usually refueling hoses have ground wires attached, in which case all that needs to be done is to connect the wire (by means of the clip provided) to some metal part of the airplane. If a ground wire is not available, a short length of wire to which suitable clips have been soldered, will serve the purpose. Two of these wires are needed. One end of one of the wires should be attached to the metal part of the nozzle; the other end should be clipped to the fuel tank. The remaining wire is used similarly to "ground" the airplane in much the same manner that a fuel delivery truck is grounded by a length of chain. However, the airplane grounding wire should be attached to some metal part permanently embedded in the earth. It is recognized that grounding devices are not always available, especially at small rural airports. In any such case, however, the fuel nozzle should be connected to a metal structure of the airplane by means of a grounding cable. This will prevent a spark from jumping between the nozzle and the fuel tank inlet when the nozzle is removed.

Where fuel is drawn from a fuel pit, the same procedure of grounding the airplane is followed. In this case there should be an electrical connection between the fuel nozzle and the underground tank and the airplane also should be grounded.

7. Care must be exercised to avoid damaging the filler neck of the airplane fuel tank when the tank is being filled with gasoline. The fuel hose nozzle should be carefully supported, and the fuel introduced slowly so that there is no danger of splashing or overfilling the tank.

Refueling large jet aircraft

Modern jet or turboprop aircraft are usually equipped with single-point, underwing refueling systems. This means that a fuel hose can be connected at one point under the wing of the aircraft to refuel the entire system or that a fueling station is provided under each wing so that all the tanks in one wing can be fueled from one station.

The fueling operation of such a system consists essentially of coupling the fuel hose nozzles to the receptacles, opening the fueling manual shutoff valves, and pumping fuel to the tanks. The fuel tanks may be filled completely by opening the fueling manual shutoff valves and allowing the fueling level-control valves to shut off the fuel flow. If it is desired to fill the tanks partially, the preset indicators may be employed to show when the desired quantity of fuel has entered a particular tank. At this time an indicator light will turn on and the fuel to the tank can be shut off by means of the manual valve.

The fueling of jet transport aircraft is usually accomplished by trained refueling crews, and it is not necessary that the maintenance technician be concerned with the operation. It is well, however, for the technician to be familiar with the procedure and the mechanisms involved, because malfunctions of the system must be corrected, and it is the maintenance technician who must correct them.

The procedures for refueling a jet transport airplane are established by the airline involved, and instructions are published for the guidance of those concerned with refueling. These instructions must be followed carefully.

REVIEW QUESTIONS

1. Name the three main classes of fuels.
2. What are the requirements of a good fuel for piston-type engines?
3. What is a *hydrocarbon?*
4. Briefly explain each of the following: *fractional distillation, cracking, polymerization, hydrogenation, alkylation.*
5. What is a *catalyst?*
6. What causes *vapor lock?*
7. Explain *preignition knock, detonation.*
8. How is the *octane number* of a fuel determined?
9. How does a high-octane fuel cause an engine to produce more power?
10. How is the performance number of a fuel determined?
11. Explain why performance numbers are given in pairs.
12. Why is it necessary to add materials other than tetraethyl lead to a fuel when treating it to increase knock resistance?
13. What factors in engine design determine the rating of the fuel which must be used in the engine?
14. Give the advantages of a high compression ratio.
15. What detrimental effect to the engine is caused by fuel additives?
16. What type of fuel is most commonly employed for gas-turbine engines?
17. How can the formation of water in a fuel tank be reduced?
18. What fuel-flow rate is required for pump fuel systems?
19. Describe the operation of a vane-type fuel pump.
20. Describe the valve arrangement which must be included with a fuel pump.
21. What provision is made in a fuel-pump relief valve to compensate for changes in atmospheric pressure?
22. Explain the purpose of a fuel boost pump.
23. A fuel boost pump is usually of what type?
24. Describe the fuel boost pump installation for a Boeing 720 jet airliner.
25. Explain the importance of adequate fuel strainers in a fuel system for aircraft.

26. Give the requirements for drains in a fuel system.
27. At what point in the aircraft must the fuel valve controls be located?
28. List the general requirements for fuel valves and controls for the valves.
29. What type of engine equipment renders a priming system unnecessary?
30. Explain the need for an oil-dilution system, and describe the operation of such a system.
31. Why is it required that an engine oil system have a capacity much greater than that required for lubrication?
32. Discuss the need for a fuel pressure gage.
33. In what circumstances does a fuel pressure gage act as an indicator of engine power output?
34. In what units is a fuel flowmeter usually calibrated?
35. Of what materials are fuel tanks constructed?
36. What internal pressure is a metal fuel tank required to withstand?
37. What inertia forces must the fuel tanks in a transport aircraft be required to withstand?
38. What is the required capacity of the fuel-tank sump?
39. What markings are required at the fuel filler cap location?
40. What is the general requirement for fuel-tank capacity?
41. Why is positive pressure required within the vapor space of bladder fuel cells, and how is this pressure maintained?
42. Give the requirements for fuel cell compartments including location in the aircraft.
43. What are the two principal safety requirements for a fuel jettisoning system?
44. What is the required capacity of a main fuel-supply line in a gravity fuel system? In a pump system?
45. Explain what precautions should be observed in routing fuel lines.
46. At what point in a fuel system are flexible hoses or lines required?

47. How are the fuel lines attached to the outlets of a fuel bladder in a light airplane?
48. What is the purpose of the vapor return line?
49. Briefly describe the fuel system for a typical jet airliner.
50. When the pressure refueling system is used for a jet airliner, what prevents overfilling the tanks?
51. Why is a fuel-temperature indicating system required for a jet airliner?
52. Describe a fuel deicing system.
53. What inspections should be made of a fuel system immediately before every flight?
54. Describe a periodic or 100-hr inspection for a fuel system.
55. What precaution must be observed before repairing a metal fuel tank by soldering or welding?
56. How can leaks in a fuel tank be located?
57. What process must be followed after repairing a metal fuel tank by soldering or welding? How is this done?
58. How can a seam in a riveted metal tank be sealed?
59. Briefly describe the repair of a synthetic-rubber fuel cell by patching.
60. How are synthetic-rubber fuel cells held in place?
61. How can a repaired metal fuel tank be tested?
62. What precautions should be observed when installing fuel lines and fittings?
63. What procedure should be followed when an airplane engine will not start as a result of fuel stoppage?
64. In the operation of a light airplane engine, the engine starts satisfactorily and then stops in a few minutes. It starts again a little later and then stops again. What is the likely cause of the trouble?
65. What symptoms are observed when the priming system is leaking into the engine?
66. Discuss the precautions required in refueling an airplane.
67. How is the danger of static electricity eliminated when an airplane is being refueled?

CHAPTER 9

Aviation
Lubricants and
Lubricating Systems

CLASSIFICATION OF LUBRICANTS

Definition

A **lubricant** is any natural or artificial substance having greasy or oily properties which can be used to reduce friction between moving parts or to prevent rust and corrosion on metallic surfaces. Lubricants may be classified according to their origins as animal, vegetable, mineral, or synthetic.

Animal lubricants

Examples of lubricants having an animal origin are tallow, tallow oil, lard oil, neat's-foot oil, sperm oil, and porpoise-jaw oil. These are highly stable at normal temperatures, and hence they can be used to lubricate firearms, sewing machines, clocks, and other light machinery and devices. Porpoise-jaw oil, for example, is used to lubricate expensive watches and very delicate instruments. However, none of the lubricants of animal origin are suitable for lubricating aircraft internal-combustion engines because they produce fatty acids at high temperatures.

Vegetable lubricants

Examples of vegetable lubricants are castor oil, olive oil, rape oil, and cottonseed oil. These oils tend to oxidize when exposed to the atmosphere. Both vegetable and animal oils have a lower coefficient of friction than most mineral oils, but they wear steel away rapidly because of their ability to loosen the bonds of iron on the surface. For this reason, cottonseed oil is often used as a cutting oil for hard steels.

Castor oil, like other vegetable oils, will not dissolve

in gasoline. Since the crankcase was part of the induction system in many of the early rotary-type internal-combustion engines, castor oil proved to be an excellent lubricant from this view-point. Unfortunately, castor oil oxidizes easily, and it also creates a gummy condition, causing piston rings to stick and restricting the flow of any fluid through a small orifice. In spite of these disadvantages, it has been used successfully in high-power racing-automobile engines because they are operated for only short periods of time between overhauls.

Of all the lubricants, castor oil has the most **oiliness.** If some means could be found for overcoming its several disadvantages, it might some day be used more generally as an engine oil, but meanwhile it cannot be used as an aircraft-engine oil.

Mineral lubricants

Mineral lubricants are used to a large extent in the lubrication of aircraft internal-combustion engines. They may be classified as solids, semisolids, and fluids.

Solid lubricants, such as mica, soapstone, and graphite, are fairly satisfactory in a finely powdered form on slow-speed machines, but they do not dissipate heat rapidly enough for high-speed machines. They fill the low spots in the metal on a typical bearing surface to form a perfectly smooth surface, and at the same time they provide a slippery film that reduces friction. When a solid lubricant is finely powdered and is not too hard, it may be used as a mild abrasive to smooth the surface previously roughened by excessive wear or by machine operations in a factory. Some solid lubricants can carry heavy loads, and hence they are mixed with certain fluid lubricants to reduce the wear between adjacent surfaces subjected to high unit pressures.

Powdered graphite is used to lubricate firearms in extremely cold climates, instead of using oils and greases which become gummy and render the arms inoperative.

Synthetic lubricants

Because of the high temperature required in the operation of gas-turbine engines, it became necessary for the industry to develop lubricants which would retain their characteristics at temperatures which will cause petroleum lubricants to evaporate and break down into heavy hydrocarbons. These new lubricants are called synthetics because they are not made from natural materials. Typical of such synthetic lubricants is MIL-L-7808E.

Semisolid lubricants

Extremely heavy oils and greases are examples of semisolid lubricants. Grease is a mixture of oil and

175

soap. It gives good service when applied periodically to certain units, but its consistency is such that it is not suitable for circulating or continuous-operating lubrication systems. In general, sodium soap is mixed with oil to make grease for gears and hot-running equipment, calcium soap is mixed with oil to make cup grease, and aluminum soap is mixed with oil to make grease for ball-bearing and high-pressure applications.

Fluid lubricants (oils)

Fluid lubricants (oils) are used as the principal lubricant in all types of internal-combustion engines because they can be pumped easily and sprayed readily and because they absorb and dissipate heat quickly and provide a good cushioning effect.

Summary of advantages of mineral-base lubricants

In general, lubricants of animal and vegetable origin are chemically unstable at high temperatures, often perform poorly at low temperatures, and are unsuited for aircraft-engine lubrication. On the other hand, lubricants having a mineral base are chemically stable at high temperatures, perform well at low temperatures, and are widely used for aircraft-engine lubrication.

The source of engine-lubricating oils

Petroleum, which is the source of volatile fuel gasoline, is also the source of engine-lubricating oil. Crude petroleum is refined by the processes of distillation, dewaxing, chemical refining, and filtration.

In the process of distillation, crude petroleum is separated into a series of products varying from gasoline to the heaviest lubricating oils according to the boiling point of each. The dewaxing process essentially consists in chilling the waxy oil to low temperatures and allowing the waxy constituents to crystallize, after which the solid wax can be separated from the oil by filtration. After the removal of the wax, resinous and asphaltic materials are removed from the lubricating oil by chemical refining. The oil is then treated with an absorbent which removes the last traces of the chemical refining agents previously used, improves the color, and generally prepares it for shipment and use.

Base crudes and lubricating-oil production

There are two base **crudes: naphthenic** and **paraffinic.** In the United States, the true **paraffinic-base crudes** are found in the Pennsylvania or Allegheny region. These are regarded as the oldest crudes ever discovered and are believed to have originated about 100,000,000 years ago. The **naphthenic-base crudes** are found principally in southern Texas and California. These crudes are probably about 60,000,000 years old. Lubricants made from naphthenic-base crudes are sometimes called **coastal** or **asphaltic-base** oils.

The mid-continent field is another source of supply for the manufacture of lubricating oils. The crude base found in the mid-continent area is equivalent to a natural blend of paraffinic- and naphthenic-base crudes and is obtained principally in east Texas, Oklahoma,

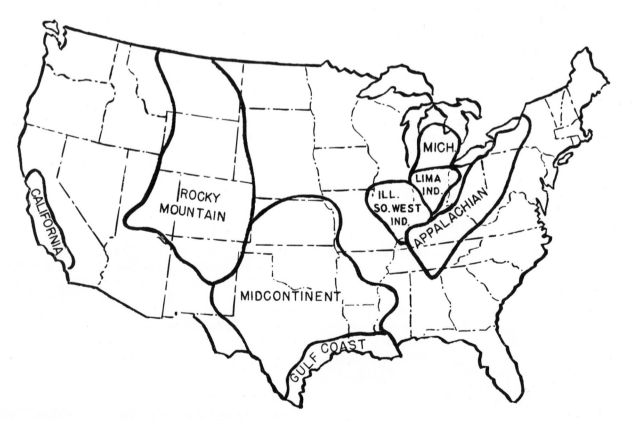

Figure 9·1   Map showing the principal crude-oil areas in the United States.

	Pennsylvania crude	Mid-continent crude	Coastal crude
API gravity	High: Light oils 27–32° Heavy oils 25–27°	Intermediate: Light oils 24–27° Heavy oils 22–24°	Low: Light oils 19–24° Heavy oils 17–22°
Flash point	High: Light oils 390–450°F Heavy oils 450–550°F.	Intermediate: Light oils 330–420°F Heavy oils 410–525°F	Low: Light oils 300–385°F Heavy oils 370–480°F
Fire point	High: Light oils 450–510°F Heavy oils 510–620°F	Intermediate: Light oils 375–480°F Heavy oils 450–600°F	Low: Light oils 350–425°F Heavy oils 425–535°F
Viscosity	For any common viscosity at a specific high temperature, oils in this group will be lighter than mid-continent or coastal at a corresponding low temperature	For any common viscosity at a specific high temperature, oils in this group will be lighter than coastal and heavier than Pennsylvania at a corresponding low temperature	For any common viscosity at a specific high temperature, oils in this group will be heavier than Pennsylvania or mid-continent at a corresponding low temperature.
SAE 50 or aviation grade 100	Example: Viscosity: At 210°F, 100 sec At 100°F, 1,200 sec At 0°F, 110,000 sec Viscosity index 99.3	Example: Viscosity: At 210°F, 100 sec At 100°F, 1,600 sec At 0°F, 600,000 sec Viscosity index 71.8	Example: Viscosity: At 210°F, 100 sec At 100°F, 2200 sec At 0°F, 2,000,000+ sec Viscosity index 30.6
Pour point	High due to paraffinicity	Intermediate	Low but extremely viscous
Carbon (amount)	High but stable	Medium	Low
Carbon (character)	Hard	Medium	Soft

Kansas, and Illinois. This crude is believed to be about 80,000,000 years old.

Figure 9·1 is a map prepared by the Sinclair Refining Company showing the principal crude areas in the United States. Notice that the paraffin-base crudes are found not only in western Pennsylvania but also in several other states which can be regarded as located in the Appalachian Mountain area. The coastal or naphthenic-base crudes are shown as found along the Gulf Coast and in California. In addition to the mid-continent region already mentioned, the maps show that mixed-base crudes are found in the Rocky Mountain area and also in several states to the west of the Appalachian area, such as Michigan, Indiana, and Illinois.

Table 9·1 shows the natural characteristics of oils made from the three crudes without special refining or treating. The terms such as API gravity, flash point, etc., given in the vertical column at the left of the table are all explained in this chapter. In studying this table, it should be understood that special refining processes make it possible for the refiner to alter the natural characteristics. For example, it is possible to make oils having the same specifications as Pennsylvania oils from other crudes, such as those found in the mid-continent area.

LUBRICATING-OIL PROPERTIES

The most important properties of an aircraft-engine oil are its flash point, viscosity, pour point, and chemical stability. There are various tests for these properties which can be made at the refinery and in the field. In addition, there are tests which are of interest principally to the petroleum engineers at the refinery, although all personnel interested in aircraft-engine lubrication should have some familiarity with such tests in order that they can intelligently read reports and specifications pertaining to petroleum products.

Some of the properties tested at the refinery are the gravity, color, cloud point, carbon residue, ash residue, oxidation, precipitation, corrosion, neutralization, and oiliness.

Gravity

The **gravity** of a petroleum oil is a numerical value which serves as an index of the weight of a measured volume of the product. There are two scales generally used by petroleum engineers. One is the specific-gravity scale, and the other is the American Petroleum Institute gravity scale, abbreviated API. **Gravity is not an index to quality.** It is a **property** of importance only to those operating the refinery, but it is a convenient **term** for use in figuring the weights and measures and also in the distribution of lubricants.

Specific gravity is the weight of any substance compared with the weight of an equal volume of a standard substance. When water is used as a standard, the specific gravity is the weight of a substance compared with the weight of an equal volume of water.

A hydrometer is used to measure specific gravity, and it is also used in conducting the API gravity test.

Formerly, the petroleum industry used the Baumé scale, but it has been superseded by the API gravity scale which magnifies that portion of the specific-gravity scale which is of greatest interest for testing petroleum products. The test is usually performed with a hydrometer, using a thermometer and conversion scale for temperature correction to the standard temperature of 60°F, as shown in Fig. 9·2.

Water has a specific gravity of 1.000, weighs 8.328 lb per gal, and has an API gravity reading of 10 under standard conditions for the test. An aircraft lubricating oil, which has a specific gravity of 0.9340 and weighs 7.778 lb per gal, has an API gravity reading of 20 under standard conditions. If an aircraft lubricating oil has a specific gravity of 0.9042 and weighs 7.529 lb per gal, its API gravity reading is 24. These are merely examples of the relationship between specific-gravity figures and API gravity readings. In actual practice, when the specific gravity and the weight in pounds per gallon at standard temperature are known, the API reading can be obtained from a table prepared for this purpose.

Flash point

The **flash point** of an oil is the temperature to which the oil must be heated in order to give off enough vapor to form a combustible mixture above the surface that will momentarily flash or burn when the vapor is

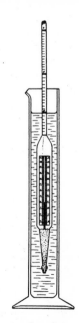

Figure **9·2** *Hydrometer for determining API gravity.*

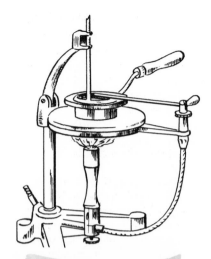

Figure **9·3** *Cleveland open cup tester.*

brought into contact with a very small flame. The rate at which oil vaporizes in an engine depends on the temperature of the engine and the grade of the oil. If the vaporized oil burns, the engine is not properly lubricated. The operating temperature of any particular engine determines the grade of oil which should be used.

The **fire point** is the temperature to which any substance must be heated in order to give off enough vapor to burn continuously when the flammable air-vapor mixture is ignited by a small flame. The fire-point test is mentioned occasionally in reports on lubricants, but it is not used so much as the flash-point test and should not be confused with it.

Lubricating oils are tested in the United States by means of the **Cleveland open cup** in accordance with the recommendations of the American Society for Testing and Materials (ASTM). This apparatus, shown in Fig. 9·3, is simple and adaptable to a wide range of products. It can be used for both flash-point and fire-point tests. When a test is made, the amount of oil, the rate of heating, the size of the igniting flame, and the time of exposure are all specified and must be carefully controlled to obtain accurate results from the test.

In a test of stable lubricating oils, the fire point is usually about 50 or 60°F higher than the flash point. It should be understood that the determination of the fire point does not add much to a test, but the flash point of oil gives a rough indication of its tendency to vaporize or to contain light volatile material.

If there is any foaming during the flash-point test, it indicates the presence of moisture in the sample of oil being tested. If there are a few popping noises during the test, these indicate the presence of a very small quantity of moisture, that is, what the scientists refer to as a **trace** of moisture.

In a comparison of oils, if one has a higher or lower flash or fire point, this does not necessarily reflect on the quality of the oil unless the fire point or flash point is exceptionally low in comparison with the fire or flash point of similar conventional oils.

If oil which has been used in an aircraft engine is tested and found to have a very low flash point, this indicates that the oil has been diluted by engine fuel. If the oil has been diluted only slightly with aviation-grade gasoline, the fire point is not lowered much because the gasoline in the oil ordinarily evaporates before the temperature of the fire point is reached. If the oil has been greatly diluted by gasoline, the fire point will be very low.

In testing oil which has been used in an engine, it is possible to obtain more accurate results from the flash-point and fire-point tests if the sample of oil is obtained from the engine while both the engine and the oil are still hot.

Viscosity

Viscosity is technically defined as the fluid friction or the body of an oil. In simple terms, viscosity may be regarded as the resistance an oil offers to flowing. A heavy-bodied oil is high in viscosity and pours or flows slowly; it may be described as a **viscous** oil. The lower the viscosity, the more freely an oil pours or flows at temperatures above the pour point. Oil that flows readily is described as having a low viscosity. The amount of fluid friction exhibited by the oil in motion is a measure of its viscosity.

The **Saybolt Universal viscosimeter,** illustrated in Fig. 9·4, is the standard American instrument for testing petroleum products and lubricants. The tests are usually made at temperatures of 100, 130, and 210°F.

This instrument has a tube in which a specific quantity of oil is brought to the desired temperature by a surrounding liquid bath. The time in seconds required for exactly 60 cu cm of the oil to flow through an accurately calibrated outlet orifice is recorded as **seconds Saybolt Universal viscosity.**

Commercial aviation oils are generally classified by

symbols such as 80, 100, 120, and 140, which approximate the seconds Saybolt Universal viscosity at 210°F. Their relationship to Society of Automotive Engineers (SAE) numbers are given in Table 9·2.

Table 9·2 Grade designations for aviation oils

Commercial aviation no.	Commercial SAE No.	AN Specification No.
65	30	1065
80	40	1080
100	50	1100
120	60	1120
140	70	

Engineers use viscosity-temperature charts, published by the ASTM, in order to find quickly the variation of viscosity with the temperature of petroleum oils when the viscosities and any two temperatures are known. The two known temperatures are plotted on a chart, and a straight line is drawn between these points. When the straight line is extended beyond the two known points, the viscosities at other temperatures can be read on the chart from that line.

The **viscosity index,** abbreviated VI, is an arbitrary method of stating the rate of change in viscosity of an oil with changes of temperature. The viscosity index of any specific oil is based on a comparative evaluation with two series of standardized oils: one having an assigned viscosity-index value of 100, which is somewhat typical of a conventionally refined Pennsylvania oil, and the other series having an assigned viscosity-index rating of 0, which is typical of certain conventionally refined naphthenic-base oils. The viscosity characteristics of these two series of standardized oils have been arbitrarily chosen and adopted by the ASTM.

The average viscosity-index values of some of the better known lubricating oils, depending upon their geographical source, are as follows: (1) Pennsylvania, 95 to 100; (2) mid-continent, 62 to 75; (3) east Texas, 50 to 60; (4) California, 0 to 35; Gulf Coast, 10 to 30; Republic of Colombia, 30 to 40; Peru, 15 to 25. These values are for the regular, conventional refining processes.

When a method of refining known as **solvent-treat** is used, the average viscosity-index values may be raised, depending upon the geographical source, as follows: (1) Pennsylvania, 100 to 110; (2) mid-continent, 80 to 100; (3) east Texas, 80 to 95; and (4) California, 40 to 65. It should be understood that an assigned viscosity-index value of 100 is typical of the conventionally refined Pennsylvania oil; hence, the use of a refining process for raising the viscosity-index value can increase the value above 100. However, when the **solvent-treat** process of refining is used, close control must be exercised during the refining or the oil will lack some of its natural lubricating and corrosion-inhibiting properties.

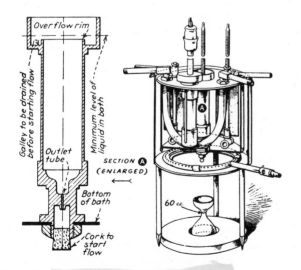

Figure 9·4 Saybolt Universal viscosimeter.

Certain compounds can be added to the oil at the plant to raise the viscosity-index value above what it would be by any normal refining process, but this should not be interpreted by the reader to mean that it is safe to purchase compounds and dump them into the oil after it is received from the refinery or one of its agents.

The viscosity-index value is not fixed for all time when the oil is sold by the refinery or its distributors. If a lubricating oil is subjected to high pressure without any change in the temperature, the viscosity increases. Naphthenic oils of high viscosity vary more with pressure than paraffinic oils. Those oils known as **fixed oils** vary less in viscosity than either the naphthenic or the paraffinic oils.

The general rule is that oils of lower viscosity are used in colder weather and oils of higher viscosity are used in warmer weather, but it is also important to choose an oil which has the lowest possible viscosity for providing an unbroken film of oil while the engine is operating at its maximum temperature, thus reducing friction to the minimum when the engine is cold.

No table of recommended operating ranges for various grades of lubricating oil can have more than a broad, general application because the oil must be especially selected for each particular make, model, type, and installation of engine, not forgetting the operating conditions of both the engine and the airplane in which it is installed. However, a few recommendations may provide a starting point from which those selecting oil can proceed.

Commercial aviation grade No. 65 (SAE 30 or AN 1065) may be used at ground air temperatures of 4°C (40°F) and below. The **oil-in** temperature is the temperature of the oil before it enters the engine, as indicated by a thermometer bulb or other temperature-measuring device located in the oil system near the engine-oil pump. The safe oil-in temperature for this grade is from 20°C (68°F) to 95°C (203°F).

Commercial grade No. 100 (SAE 50 or AN 1100) may be used in some engines for all temperatures as directed by the manufacturer's instructions. For example, the Beechcraft G-18S airplane manual specifies MIL-L-6082, grade 1100 (SAE 50) for both summer and winter operation.

Some manufacturers specify different grades of oil, depending upon outside-air temperatures. For the Continental IO-470D engines installed on the Cessna 310 airplane, grade 1100 oil is recommended when temperatures are generally above 40°F and grade 1065 oil when the temperatures are below 40°F.

When servicing the oil tank for an engine installed in an airplane, the operator can find the proper grade of oil marked on or near the filler cap. If this marking should become obliterated, the operator's manual for the airplane will contain the information.

Viscosity and cold-weather starting

The **pour point** of an oil indicates how fluid it is at low temperatures under laboratory conditions, but it does not necessarily measure how pumpable it is under field conditions. The **viscosity** is a far better indication of whether or not the oil will make it possible to start at low temperatures and how well the oil can be pumped. At low temperatures it is desirable to have a combination of a low pour point and low viscosity if the proper viscosity for operating temperatures is still retained.

In order to thin the lubricating oil for starting engines in cold weather, engine gasoline may be added directly to the oil if provisions are made for this in the powerplant of the airplane. The cold oil, diluted with gasoline, circulates easily and provides the necessary lubrication. Then when the engine reaches its normal operating temperature, the gasoline evaporates and leaves the oil as it was before it was diluted.

When **oil dilution** is practiced, less power is needed for starting and the starting process is completed more quickly. The only important disadvantage is that the presence of ethyl gasoline in the oil may cause a slight corrosion of the engine parts, but this objection is outweighed by the advantages.

The grade of oil to be used for oil dilution in starting depends upon various factors, but two general rules may prove useful in the absence of specific instructions for the particular powerplant installed on the airplane under operation. These broad rules, subject to exceptions, of course, are as follows:

1. Never use an oil lighter than commercial aviation 100 (SAE 50 or AN 1100) for dilution.
2. Select the oil to be used for diluting with engine fuel according to the ground temperature, as previously explained.

Color

The **color** of a lubricating oil is obtained by reference to transmitted light; that is, the oil is placed in a glass vessel and held in front of a source of light. The intensity of the transmitted light must be known in conducting a test because it may cause the color to vary.

The apparatus used for a color test is that approved by the American Society for Testing and Materials and is called an **ASTM Union Colorimeter.** Colors are assigned numbers which range from 1 (lily white) to 8 (darker than claret red). Oils darker than No. 8 color value are diluted with kerosene (85 percent kerosene by volume and 15 percent lubricating oil by volume) and then observed in the same manner as oils having color values from 1 to 8.

When reflected light, as distinguished from direct light, is used in a color test, the color is called the **bloom** and is used, among other things, to indicate the origin and refining method of the oil.

Cloud point

The **cloud point** is that temperature at which the separation of wax becomes visible in certain oils under prescribed testing conditions. When such oils are tested, the cloud point is a temperature slightly above the solidification point. If the wax does not separate before solidification, or if the separation is not visible, the cloud point cannot be determined.

The pour point

The **pour point** of an oil is that temperature at which the oil will just flow without disturbance when chilled. In practice, the pour point is the lowest temperature at which an oil will flow (without any disturbing force) to the pump intake. The fluidity of the oil is a factor of both pour test and viscosity. If the fluidity is good, the oil will immediately circulate when engines are started in cold weather. Petroleum oils, when cooled sufficiently, may become plastic solids as a result either of the partial separation of the wax or of the congealing of the hydrocarbons composing the oil. To lower the pour point, **pour-point depressants** are sometimes added to oils which contain substantial quantities of wax.

Figure 9·5 shows the apparatus used for conducting the pour-point and cloud-point tests. The parts to be especially observed are the thermometers, the glass test jar, the jacket, the ring gasket, the cooling bath, and the cork or felt disk.

The general statement is sometimes made that the pour point should be within 5°F of the average starting temperature of the engine, but this should be considered in connection with the viscosity of the oil, since the oil must be viscous enough to provide an adequate oil film at engine-operating temperatures. Therefore, for cold-weather starting, the oil should be selected in accordance with the operating instructions for the particular engine, considering both the pour point and the viscosity.

Carbon-residue test

The purpose of the **carbon-residue test** is to study the carbon-forming properties of a lubricating oil. There are two methods: (1) the Ramsbottom carbon-residue test and (2) the Conradson test. The Ramsbottom test is widely used in Great Britain and is now preferred by many American petroleum engineers be-

cause it seems to yield more practical results than the Conradson test, which was formerly more popular in the United States.

The apparatus for the **Ramsbottom test** is illustrated in Fig. 9·6. A specific amount of oil is placed either in a heat-treated glass bulb well or in a stainless-steel bulb used for the same purpose. The oil is then heated at a high temperature by a surrounding molten-metal bath for a prescribed time. The bulb is weighed before and after the test. The difference in weight is divided by the weight of the oil sample and multiplied by 100 to obtain the percentage of carbon residue in the sample.

The apparatus for the Conradson test is illustrated in Fig. 9·7. Oil is evaporated under specified conditions for conducting the test. The parts to be observed in the illustration are the burner, the porcelain crucible, the wire gauze, the spun sheet-iron crucible, the Skidmore iron crucible, the asbestos block, the hood, and the flame gage. The carbon residue from the Conradson test should not be compared directly with the carbon residue from the Ramsbottom test, since the residues are obtained under different test conditions, but tables have been prepared by engineers which give the average relation between the results of tests performed

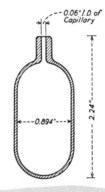

Figure **9·6**   Bulb for Ramsbottom carbon-residue test.

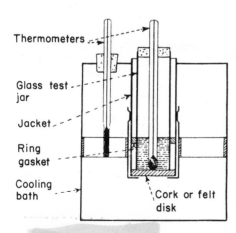

Figure **9·5**   Cloud and pour test.

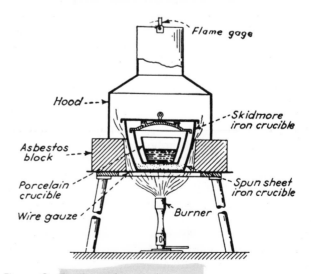

Figure **9·7**   Conradson carbon test.

by the two methods. Such tables are obviously of little interest to the majority of aviation personnel, but they are mentioned for the guidance of those who specialize in this field.

Petroleum engineers advise those who are not in their field to be cautious in evaluating carbon-residue tests, since the carbon deposits from oil vary with the type and mechanical condition of the engine, the service conditions, the cycle of operation, the other characteristics of the oil, and the method of carbureting the fuel. In the early days of internal-combustion engines, carbon-residue tests were more important as an indication of the carbon-forming properties of lubricating oil than they are today. The methods now used to refine petroleum products tend to make the carbon-residue tests less useful than they were originally.

The ash test

The **ash test** is an extension of the carbon-residue test. If an unused (new) oil leaves almost no ash, it is regarded as pure. The **ash content** is a percentage (by weight) of the residue after all carbon and carbonaceous matter have been evaporated and burned.

In a test of used lubricating oil, the ash is analyzed chemically to determine the content of iron, which shows the rate of wear; sand or grit, which comes from the atmosphere; lead compounds, which come from leaded gasoline; and other metals and nonvolatile materials. The ash analysis tells something about the performance of the engine-lubricating oil, but it is only one of many tests which are used to promote efficiency.

Oxidation tests

Aircraft-engine lubricating oils may be subjected to relatively high temperatures in the presence of both air and what the engineers call catalytically active metals or metallic compounds. This causes the oil to oxidize. It increases the viscosity, and it also forms sludge, carbon residues, lacquers or varnishes (asphaltines), and sometimes inorganic acids.

There are several methods of testing for oxidation, the details of which do not interest most people outside the research laboratories, although the conclusions are important to aircraft-engine personnel in general. The U.S. Air Force has its own oxidation test, the U.S. Navy has its work factor test, and both Pratt & Whitney and Wright Aeronautical Corporation have their own tests.

It has been found that, when the carbon residue of engine oils is lowered below certain limits, the products of oxidation are soluble in hot oil. Deposits of lacquer form on the metallic surfaces, such as on the pistons, in the ring grooves, and on valve guides and stems, and anywhere that the oil flows comparatively slowly in the engine. In addition, a sludge of carbonlike substance forms in various places. To overcome this situation, certain compounds, which are known as **antioxidant** and **anticorrosion** agents, have been used to treat lubricating oils before they are sold to the public.

Precipitation number

The **precipitation number** recommended by the ASTM is the number of milliliters of precipitate formed when 10 ml of lubricating oil are mixed with 90 ml of petroleum naphtha under specified conditions and then centrifuged (subjected to centrifugal force) under prescribed conditions. The volume of sediment at the bottom of the centrifuge tube (container) is then taken as the ASTM precipitation number.

Corrosion and neutralization number

Lubricating oils may contain acids. The **neutralization number** recommended by the ASTM is the weight in milligrams of potassium hydroxide required to neutralize 1 g of oil. A full explanation of this topic belongs in the field of elementary chemistry and is beyond the scope of this text.

The neutralization number does **not** indicate the corrosive action of the used oil in service. For example, it has been found that in certain cases an oil having a neutralization number of 0.2 might have high corrosive tendencies in a short operating period while another oil having a neutralization number of 1.0 might have no corrosive action on bearing metals.

Oiliness

Oiliness is the property that makes a difference in reducing the friction when lubricants of the same viscosity but with different oiliness characteristics are compared under the same conditions of temperature and film pressure. Oiliness, contrary to what might be expected, depends not only upon the lubricant but also upon the surface to which it is applied. Oiliness has been compared with metal wetting, but oiliness is a wetting effect that reduces friction, drag, and wear. It is especially important when the film of oil separating rubbing surfaces is very thin, when the lubricated parts are very hot, or when the texture (grain) and finish of the metal are exceedingly fine. When some oil films are formed, there may be almost no viscosity effects, and then the property of oiliness is the chief source of lubrication.

Extreme-pressure or hypoid lubricants

When certain types of gearing are used, such as spur-type gearing and hypoid-type gearing, there are high tooth pressures and high rubbing velocities that require the use of a class of lubricants called **extreme-pressure or hypoid lubricants** (abbreviated EP lubricants). Most of these special lubricants are mineral oils containing loosely held sulfur or chlorine or some highly reactive material. If ordinary mineral oils were used by themselves, any metal-to-metal contact in the gearing would usually cause scoring, galling, and the local seizure of mating surfaces.

The characteristics of these EP lubricants are as follows:

1. They prevent the galling or scoring of mating surfaces.
2. They reduce wear by conditioning the mating surfaces.
3. They make possible a low degree of friction.

Chemical and physical stability

An aircraft-engine oil must have **chemical stability** against oxidation, thermal cracking, and coking. It must have physical stability with regard to pressure and temperature.

Some of the properties discussed under other topic headings in this chapter are closely related to both chemical and physical stability. The oil must have resistance to emulsion. It should be nonvolatile. There should be no objectionable compounds of decomposition with fuel byproducts. The viscosity characteristics should be correct, as we have explained in detail. If anything is added during the refining process, the resultant should be uniform in quality and pure.

When all the other factors are favorable, the oil should have a minimum coefficient of friction, maximum adhesion to the surfaces to be lubricated, oiliness characteristics, and adequate film strength.

LUBRICANT REQUIREMENTS AND FUNCTIONS

Characteristics of aircraft lubricating oil

The proper lubrication of aircraft engines requires the use of a lubricating oil which has the following characteristics:

1. It should have the proper **body (viscosity)** at the engine-operating temperatures usually encountered by the airplane in which it is used, it should be distributed readily to the lubricated parts, and it must resist the pressures between the various lubricated surfaces.
2. It should have **high antifriction characteristics** to reduce the frictional resistance of the moving parts when separated only by boundary films. An ideal fluid lubricant provides a strong oil film to prevent metallic friction and to create a minimum amount of oil friction or oil drag.
3. It should have **maximum fluidity at low temperatures** to ensure a ready flow and distribution when starting at low temperatures. Some grades of oil become practically solid in cold weather, causing high oil drag and impaired circulation.
4. It should have **minimum changes in viscosity with changes in temperature** to provide uniform protection where atmospheric temperatures vary widely. The viscosity of oils is greatly affected by temperature changes. For example, at high operating temperatures, the oil may be so thin that the oil film is broken and the moving parts wear rapidly.
5. It should have **high antiwear properties** to resist the wiping action that occurs wherever microscopic boundary films are used to prevent metallic contact. The theory of fluid lubrication is based on the actual separation of the metallic surfaces by means of an oil film. As long as the oil film is not broken, the internal friction (fluid friction) of the lubricant takes the place of the metallic sliding friction which otherwise would exist.
6. It should have **maximum cooling ability** to absorb as much heat as possible from all lubricated surfaces and especially from the piston head and skirt. One of the reasons for using liquid lubricants is that they are effective in absorbing and dissipating heat. Another reason is that liquid lubricants can be readily pumped or sprayed. Many engine parts, especially those carrying heavy loads at high rubbing velocities, are lubricated by oil under direct pressure. Where direct-pressure lubrication is not practical, a spray or mist of oil provides the required protection. Regardless of the method of application, the oil absorbs the heat and later dissipates it through coolers or heat exchangers.
7. It should offer the **maximum resistance to oxidation,** thus minimizing harmful deposits on the metal parts.
8. It should be **noncorrosive** to the metals in the lubricated parts.

The functions of engine oil

Engine oil performs four functions as follows:

1. It **lubricates,** thus reducing the friction between moving parts.
2. It **cools** the various parts of the engine.
3. It tends to **seal** the combustion chamber by filling the walls, thus preventing the loss of compression past the piston rings.
4. It tends to **clean** the engine by carrying sludge and residues away from the moving engine parts and depositing them in the oil filter.

AVIATION GREASES

Oil and grease compared for aviation purposes

Oil is the ideal lubricant under many conditions, especially when the design and operation of the equipment make it possible to apply the lubricant as a fluid. However, in many aircraft-engine accessories, airplane control mechanisms, linkage bearings, and landing wheels, fluid oil cannot be used. There are several reasons why this is true as follows: (1) The inaccessibility of the parts or the physical difficulty of servicing the parts may make it impractical to lubricate regularly with oil; (2) the oil may reach sensitive parts where it will cause damage, such as the electric fields of instruments, motors, generators, magnetos, etc.; and (3) under many conditions, oil leaks too rapidly to maintain good lubrication.

Factors considered in selecting greases

The many different applications or uses of grease lubricants have made it necessary to develop greases to serve a wide variety of purposes. In selection of a grease, the **type of friction** encountered must be considered. We must consider **rolling friction, sliding friction,** and **wiping friction.** Another most important factor is the **temperature** under which the grease must work. If the temperature is high, a high-temperature grease must be employed to avoid losing the grease by its melting and flowing out of the bearing. A third principal factor to be considered is the **speed of relative motion between the bearing surfaces.** The characteristics of a grease used for high-speed bearings must be different from those of a grease used in low-speed applications. **Bearing load** is important. If the grease is too light and not sufficiently cohesive, it may be pressed out to the extent that metal surfaces come in contact.

Grease may be either semifluid or nonfluid. It is usually made by combining oil with one or more types of soap. It is apparent that the quality and the grade of the oil combined with the soap affect the quality of the product. In addition, the quantity and type of soap base, the actual composition of the product, the manufacturing processes, and the uniformity of production are factors which determine the character and quality of a grease lubricant.

Consistency or penetration

The **consistency** or **penetration** is the most important characteristic of a grease. It is measured by an apparatus called a **penetrometer**, illustrated in Fig. 9·8. A container full of grease to be tested is placed on a table. A cone is lowered until the tip barely touches the top surface of the grease sample. An actuating plunger is released to permit the cone to rest free on the grease for 5 sec. The depth to which the cone sinks into the grease is indicated on a scale calibrated to measure the depth of penetration in tenths of a millimeter.

If the grease is soft, the cone will penetrate deeper and give a higher reading than it will if the grease is hard. The standard temperature for this test is 77°F. Other variables, such as the presence of air pockets in the grease, are rigidly controlled to make all tests as uniform as possible. "Unworked" samples are sometimes tested in their original containers. Some types of greases are "worked" before the test to give them uniform consistency. In the report on the test it is stated whether or not the grease was worked before the test.

Gear lubricants and certain other greases, especially semifluid greases, are too soft to obtain accurate readings with a penetrometer. Various tests, are used, but they are still in the experimental stage and are not yet standardized enough for publication.

Grease numbers

It was once thought sufficient to describe greases as "soft," "medium," or "hard," but the modern method is to follow a procedure recommended by the National Lubricating Grease Institute (abbreviated NLGI). This organization assigns what it calls NLGI numbers that represent worked penetration limits. For example, a grease commonly described as soft is given an NLGI

number of 0 if the penetration reading from the penetrometer test is from 355 to 385; if it is from 310 to 340, the NLGI number is 1. Likewise, if the grease is commonly described as medium, it is given an NLGI of 2 or 3, depending upon the penetrometer test. In a similar manner, if the grease is commonly described as hard, it receives an NLGI number of 4 or 5, again depending upon the penetrometer test.

NLGI numbers may be compared with the SAE numbers for oils. They designate the grade but not the quality. They are important to anyone who wishes to know for sure exactly what grade of grease he is obtaining. Before these numbers were established, each manufacturer described his products according to his own whims.

Dropping point

The **dropping point** of a grease is the temperature at which a sample of the grease passes from a semisolid to a fluid state under conditions of rest. It is sometimes erroneously called the **melting point,** but this term should be avoided.

Figure 9·9 illustrates the apparatus for making the dropping-point test. A small sample is placed in a small metal cup which has an orifice in the bottom. The cup is placed in a special test tube. A thermometer is adjusted to read the temperature accurately. The equipment is then placed in an oil bath and heated at a specified rate. Grease gradually protrudes through the orifice as the temperature increases. When a drop falls or reaches the bottom of the test tube, the temperature indicated by the thermometer at that instant is recorded as the dropping point of the grease.

The ASTM reports that the dropping point does not relate **directly** to the performance of a grease in an airplane under field conditions. The design of a lubricated bearing, rotational speeds, and other factors are more important than the dropping-point characteristic.

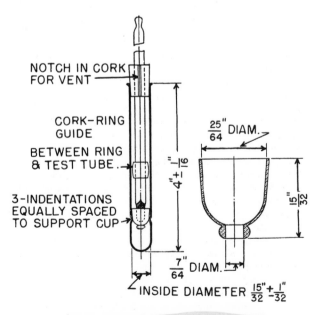

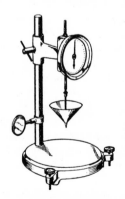

Figure **9·8** Penetrometer for testing grease consistency.

Figure **9·9** Apparatus for dropping-point test.

Special tests

There are many tests for greases which are beyond the scope of this text. Greases are tested for cohesion, bleeding, congealing, film strength, water resistance, storage ability, pumpability, adhesion, low-temperature torque, and high-temperature oxidation. The procedures for performing these tests vary widely according to the special requirements or specifications for which the test is made.

Requirements for aircraft lubricating greases

The characteristics required of aircraft-engine lubricants apply in general to aircraft lubricating greases, but those which are especially important in judging greases are presented as follows:

1. The grease should have the **proper consistency** for the method of application employed and for complete distribution to the surfaces to be lubricated.
2. The grease should have **high antiwear properties** to prevent metallic contact where pressures are applied suddenly and especially where boundary films are expected to protect the surfaces.
3. The grease should have **adequate plasticity at low temperatures** to prevent sluggish action and the sticking of moving parts. **Plasticity** is a state or condition of being easily subjected to molding into any form under pressure. In this case, it merely means that the grease should not become gummy or hard at low temperatures but should flow easily.
4. The grease should have **high antifriction characteristics** to reduce the frictional resistance of the moving parts.
5. The grease should offer **resistance to separation** at high temperatures or when subjected to heavy pressures. This means that it should not break down into its chemical components, thus losing its lubricating properties. In other words, it should be chemically stable.

Types of greases

Most grease lubricants can be divided into groups as follows: (1) calcium-soap greases, (2) sodium-soap greases, (3) aluminum-soap greases, (4) lithium-soap greases, (5) special greases, and (6) mixed-base greases.

Calcium-base greases are a combination of light to medium weights or grades of oil with calcium soaps, examples being cup greases and pressure-system greases. The texture is smooth, and there is no "tackiness" at normal temperatures. These lubricants are rarely used at operating temperatures above 175°F, where high centrifugal speeds may throw out the lubricant, or where the lubricated part is subjected to shock loading. These greases are more suitable at low temperatures. Also, they are very water repellent.

Sodium-base greases are a combination of medium to heavy weights or grades of oil with sodium soaps. They are generally used to lubricate antifriction ball, roller, and needle-type bearings that are subjected to shock loads or high temperatures and when there is need to retain the lubricant under conditions of high rotation or centrifugal motion. They are very susceptible to moisture and are very adhesive and cohesive. The texture may be either smooth or fibrous, depending upon the amount of milling or working they receive during the manufacturing process. They have a

wide range of adaptability to temperature and rotating-speed changes. Common aircraft applications are the lubrication of engine accessories and wheel bearings, but it should be understood that sodium-base greases can be manufactured to meet a very great variety of aircraft-engine and general aircraft requirements.

Aluminum-base greases are suitable for plain bearings where the speed of rotation is slow, the part is subjected to shock loads, and the part or unit is exposed to water frequently. They are water repellent, resist thinning at high temperatures, and resist shock loading. Under certain conditions, these greases may be tacky, stringy, or very adhesive and cohesive. They are widely used on airplanes to lubricate Lord mountings, landing-gear joints, and similar parts or units.

Lithium-base grease is used for extremely low-temperature applications. One such grease conforms to specification MIL-G-7421B. This is a smooth, brown, buttery grease consisting of a synthetic-oil base and a lithium-soap thickener. Additional materials are added to provide resistance to oxidation and corrosion. This grease is designed to operate over the temperature range of −100 to 250°F. It is intended for use in antifriction bearings, gears, rolling and sliding surfaces requiring small breakaway torques, electrical equipment, small actuators, and other applications where low temperatures are likely to be encountered.

Since this grease is made with a synthetic-oil base, it is likely to soften natural rubber and some paints. For this reason it must be used only where the associated materials will not be affected.

Special greases usually are made of soap bases other than calcium, sodium, or aluminum, examples of the soaps used being barium, lithium, and lead. Greases made from barium soap are used for the same purposes as aluminum-soap lubricants. Greases made from lead soaps are used where the rubbing conditions or the high loading make it necessary to obtain a very tough lubricating film. Lithium soap is used to make greases that are highly water repellent, and for purposes where there must be a minimum drag at very low temperatures. In this connection, it should be understood that, when low-temperature greases are desired, the oil mixed with the soap is usually very light, with a low pour-test rating and a high viscosity index.

Additives

Graphite is usually added to the conventionally made calcium- or sodium-soap-base greases according to the application for which the grease is intended, especially for sliding surfaces that are not easily reached for frequent lubrication. Graphite is especially valuable in a grease used as an **antiseize thread** lubricant.

Talc is sometimes used instead of graphite for inaccessible sliding surfaces.

Mica may be added where high temperatures are frequently encountered. It is also valuable when added to grease prepared as an antiseize lubricant. Spark-plug thread lubricants usually contain some mica.

Zinc, lead, and other metal oxides are used either as

general lubricants or added to grease for antiseize purposes. They produce greases that are approximately white in color.

A **mixed-base grease** is a combination of several soap bases. Usually, if one soap base predominates in the combination, the grease is classified under the heading of that base.

Special engine lubricants

Oil is the principal aircraft-engine lubricant, but **special lubricants,** most of which are greases, are used for special purposes and given names which usually indicate their use. Examples are thread lubricant, spark-plug lubricant, high-melting-point grease, petrolatum, and rust-preventive compound.

Petrolatum is a pure, refined mineral oil which can be used as a light petroleum grease or as a combined rust preventive and lubricant. It is commonly used on aircraft battery terminals.

Thread lubricant is composed of about 75 percent heavy mineral oil and about 25 percent lead soap. It is a semifluid composition used on the threaded parts of aircraft engines to prevent oxidation or corrosion.

Spark-plug lubricant is about 60 percent heavy mineral oil and about 40 percent finely ground mica. It is used on the threads of spark plugs to make it easier to remove and replace them from the engine cylinders.

High-melting-point grease, also called **fiber grease,** is composed of sodium soap and mineral oil. It may vary in consistency from soft to hard. It is used to lubricate "hot-running" equipment, particularly electrical units.

Rust-preventive compounds are used to prevent the corrosion of the unpainted surfaces of aircraft engines while they are in storage. They are available in two grades. The light grade is composed of 90 percent vegetable oil, 7 percent alcohol, and 3 percent triethanolamine and is especially effective in preventing the corrosion of engine cylinder barrels, valves, and valve mechanisms exposed to the action of ethyl fuels. This light grade is used on the internal surfaces of engines because it is not necessary to remove it when the engine is prepared for operation after being in storage. The heavier grade is applied to the external parts of engines and can be removed by using kerosene as a solvent.

A suitable corrosion-preventive oil complies with the specification MIL-C-6529C. This preservative oil is made up of aircraft lubricating oil, grade 1100, and corrosion-preventive additives. The material may be used full strength, or it may be mixed with 75 percent lubricating oil, and in this diluted condition it can be used for regular engine operation.

THE NEED FOR LUBRICATION

There are many moving parts in an aircraft engine. Some reciprocate and some rotate, but regardless of the motion, each moving part must be guided in its motion or held in a given position during motion. The contact between surfaces moving in relation to each other produces friction which consumes energy. This energy is transformed into heat at comparatively low temperatures and therefore reduces the power output of the engine. Furthermore, the friction between moving metallic parts causes wear. If lubricants are used, a film of lubricant is applied between the moving surfaces to reduce wear and to lower the power loss.

Sliding friction

When one surface slides over the other, the interlocking particles of metal on each surface offer a resistance to motion known as **sliding friction.** If any supposedly smooth surface is examined under the microscope, it will be seen that it has hills and valleys. The smoothest possible surface is only relatively smooth. No matter how smooth the surfaces of two objects may appear to be, when they slide over each other, the hills in one catch in the valleys of the other.

Rolling friction

When a cylinder or sphere rolls over the surface of a plane object, the resistance to motion offered by the surfaces to each other is known as **rolling friction.** In addition to the interlocking of the surface particles which occurs when two plane objects slide over each other, there is a certain amount of deformation of both the cylinder or sphere and the plane surface over which it rolls. There is less rolling friction when ball bearings are used than there is when roller bearings are employed. At first thought, this may not seem reasonable, but actually rolling friction is less than sliding friction and is always preferred by mechanical designers when the surface permits what they call **line** or **point contact.** A simple explanation of the reduction of friction obtained with a rolling contact is that the interlocking of surface particles is considerably less than in the case of sliding friction. Therefore, even when the deformation is added, the total friction by rolling contact is less than it is by sliding contact.

Wiping friction

Wiping friction occurs particularly between gear teeth. Some gear designs, such as the hypoid gears and worm gears, have greater friction of the wiping type than other designs such as the simple spur gear. Wiping friction involves a continuously changing load on the contacting surfaces, both in intensity and in direction of movement, and it usually results in extreme pressure for which special lubricants are required. Lubricants for this purpose are called extreme-pressure (EP) lubricants.

Factors determining the amount of friction

The **amount of friction between two solid surfaces** depends largely upon the rubbing of one surface against the other, the condition and material of which the surfaces are made, the nature of contact movement, and the load carried by the surfaces. The friction is usually less at high speeds. When a soft bearing material is used in conjunction with hard metals, the softer metal can mold itself to the form of the harder metal, thus reducing friction. Increasing the load increases the friction.

The introduction of lubricant between two moving metallic surfaces produces a film which adheres to both surfaces. The movement of the surfaces causes a shearing action in the lubricant. In this manner the metallic friction between surfaces in contact is replaced by the smaller internal friction within the lubricant. Only fluid lubricants with a great tendency to adhere to metal are able to accomplish this purpose, since they enter where the contact between the surfaces is closest and where the friction would be the greatest if there were no lubrication. The adhesive quality of the lubricant tends to prevent actual metallic contact. The viscosity tends to keep the lubricant from being squeezed out by the pressure on the bearing surfaces.

Although the amount of friction between two solid surfaces depends upon the load carried, the rubbing speed, and the condition and material of which the surfaces are made, the fluid friction of a lubricant is not affected in the same manner. The **internal friction of the lubricant** that replaces the metallic friction between moving parts is determined by the rubbing speed, the area of the surfaces in contact, and the viscosity of the lubricant. It is not determined by the load or the condition and material of which the surfaces are made.

Lubrication-system components

The purpose of a lubrication system is to supply oil to the engine at the correct pressure and volume to provide adequate lubrication and cooling for all parts of the engine which are subject to the effects of friction. The oil tank must have ample capacity, the oil-pump volume and pressure must be adequate, and the cooling facilities for the oil must be such that the oil temperature is maintained at the proper level to keep the engine cool. Several typical systems are described in this section.

The lubrication is distributed to the various moving parts of a typical internal-combustion engine by one of the three following methods: (1) pressure, (2) splash, or (3) a combination of pressure and splash.

Pressure lubrication

In a typical pressure-lubrication system, a mechanical pump supplies oil under pressure to the bearings. The oil flows into the inlet or suction side of the pump, usually located higher than the bottom of the oil sump so that sediment which falls into the sump will not be drawn into the pump. The pump may be either the eccentric-vane type or the gear type, but the gear type is more commonly used. It forces oil into an oil manifold, which distributes the oil to the crankshaft bearings.

Oil flows from the main bearings through holes drilled in the crankshaft to the lower connecting-rod bearings. Each of these holes through which the oil is fed is located so that the bearing pressure at that point will be as low as possible.

Oil reaches a hollow camshaft through a connection with the end bearing or the main oil manifold and then flows out of the hollow camshaft to the various camshaft bearings and cams.

The engine cylinder surfaces receive oil sprayed from the crankshaft and also from the crankpin bearings. Since oil seeps slowly through the small crankpin clearances before it is sprayed on the cylinder walls, considerable time is required for enough oil to reach the cylinder walls, especially on a cold day when the oil flow is more sluggish. This situation is one of the chief reasons for diluting the engine oil with engine fuel for cold starting.

Splash lubrication and combination systems

Pressure lubrication is the principal method of lubrication used on all aircraft engines. Splash lubrication may be used in addition to pressure lubrication on aircraft engines, but it is never used by itself. Hence, aircraft-engine lubrication systems are always of either the pressure type or the combination pressure-and-splash type, usually the latter. For this reason, this text discusses the pressure type of lubrication system but calls attention to those units or parts which are splash lubricated.

Principal components of a lubrication system

An aircraft-engine lubrication system includes a pressure oil pump, an oil pressure-relief valve, an oil reservoir (either as a part of the engine or separate from the engine), an oil pressure gage, an oil temperature gage, and the necessary piping and connections. In addition, many lubrication systems include oil coolers and/or temperature-regulating devices. Oil-dilution systems are included where they are deemed necessary for cold-weather starting.

Oil capacity

The capacity of the lubrication system must be sufficient to supply the engine with an adequate amount of oil at a temperature not in excess of the maximum which has been established as safe for the engine. On a multiengine airplane, the lubrication system for each engine must be independent of the systems for the other engines.

The usable tank capacity must not be less than the product of the endurance of the airplane under critical operating conditions and the maximum oil consumption of the engine under the same conditions, plus an adequate margin to assure satisfactory circulation, lubrication, and cooling. In lieu of a rational analysis of airplane range, a fuel-oil ratio of 30:1 by volume is acceptable for airplanes not provided with a reserve or transfer system. If a transfer system is provided, a fuel-oil ratio of 40:1 is considered satisfactory.

Oil tanks

Dry sump engine-lubrication systems require a separate oil tank for each engine system. These tanks are constructed of welded sheet aluminum, riveted aluminum, or stainless steel. Some aircraft are equipped with synthetic-rubber tanks similar to fuel cells.

An outlet for the tank is normally located at the lowest section of the tank to permit complete drainage, either in the ground position or in a normal flight attitude. If the airplane is equipped with a propeller feathering system, a reserve of oil must be provided for feathering, either in the main tank or in a separate reservoir. If the reserve oil supply is in the main tank, the normal outlet must be arranged so the reserve oil supply cannot be drawn out of the tank except when it is necessary to feather the propeller.

Provision must be made to prevent entrance into the tank itself or into the tank outlet of any foreign object or material which might obstruct the flow of oil through the system. The oil-tank outlet must not be enclosed by any screen or guard which would reduce the flow of oil below a safe value at any operating temperature condition. The diameter of the oil outlet must not be less than the diameter of the inlet to the oil pump. That is, the pump must not have greater capacity than the outlet of the tank.

Oil tanks must be constructed with an expansion space of 10 percent of the tank capacity or ½ gal, whichever is greater. It must not be possible to fill the expansion space when refilling the tank. This provision is accomplished by locating the filler neck or opening in such a position that it is below the expansion space in the tank. Reserve oil tanks which have no direct connection to any engine must have an expansion space which is not less than 2 percent of the tank capacity.

Oil tanks designed for use with reciprocating engines must be vented from the top of the expansion space to the crankcase of the engine. The vent opening in the tank must be so located that it cannot be covered by oil under any normal flight condition. The vent must be so designed that condensed water vapor which might freeze and obstruct the line cannot accumulate at any point. Oil tanks for acrobatic aircraft must be designed to prevent hazardous loss of oil during acrobatic maneuvers including short periods of inverted flight.

If the filler opening for an oil tank is recessed in such a manner that oil may be retained in the recessed area, a drain line must be provided which will drain such retained oil to a point clear of the airplane. The filler cap must provide a tight seal and must be marked with the word "oil" and the capacity of the tank.

The strength of the oil tank must be such that it can withstand a test pressure of 5 psi and can support without failure all vibration, inertia, and fluid loads which will be imposed during operation.

The quantity of oil in the oil tank or in the wet sump of an engine can usually be determined by means of a dipstick. In some cases the dipstick is attached to the filler neck cap. Before any flight, it is standard practice to check visually the quantity of oil.

Plumbing for the lubrication system

The plumbing for the oil system is essentially the same as that required for fuel systems or hydraulic systems. Where lines are not subject to vibration, they are constructed of aluminum-alloy tubing and connections are made with approved tubing fittings, AN or MS type. In areas near the engine or between the engine and the fire wall where the lines are subject to vibration, synthetic hose of an approved type is used. The hose connections are made with approved hose fittings which are securely attached to the hose ends. Fittings of this type are described in Chap. 8 of this text.

Hose employed in the engine compartment of an airplane should be of a fire-resistant type to minimize the possibility of hot oil being discharged into the engine area if a fire occurs.

The size of oil lines must be such that they will permit flow of the lubricant in the volume required without restriction. The size for any particular installation is specified by the manufacturer of the engine.

The oil-temperature regulator

The purpose of the **oil-temperature regulator,** illustrated in Fig. 9 · 10, is to cool the oil from the engine and thereby prevent excessively high oil temperatures. The outer cylinder is about 1 in. larger in diameter than the inner cylinder. This provides an oil passage between the cylinders and enables the oil to bypass the core either when the oil is at the correct operating temperature or when the oil is too cold. When the oil from the engine is too hot for proper engine operation, the oil is routed through the cooling tubes by the viscosity valve. Note that the oil which passes through the core is guided by baffles which force it to flow

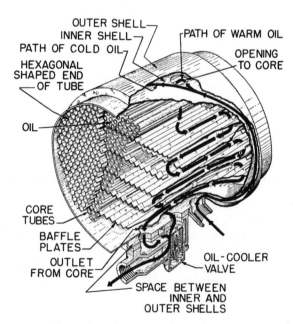

Figure 9 · 10 Oil cooler assembly.

around these tubes and thus flow through the length of the core several times. The ends of the tubes are hexagonal in shape and form "honeycombs" at both ends of the unit.

The installation of this unit is simple. It is placed in position, mounting straps are installed, and then the inlet and outlet fittings are attached. Its removal is accomplished in the reverse order.

The oil viscosity valve

The **oil viscosity valve,** illustrated in Fig. 9·11, is generally considered part of the oil-temperature-regulator unit, and the part illustrated in Fig. 9·10 is then called an **oil cooler.** The viscosity valve consists essentially of an aluminum-alloy housing and a thermostatic control element. The valve is attached to the oil-temperature cooler. Together, the **oil cooler** and the **oil viscosity valve,** which form the **oil-temperature-regulator unit,** have the twofold duty of maintaining a desired temperature and also keeping the viscosity within required limits by controlling the passage of the oil through the unit.

Through its thermostatic control, the viscosity valve routes the oil through the cooling core of the oil cooler when the oil is hot and causes the oil to bypass the core when the oil is not warm enough for correct engine lubrication.

In the drawing of Fig. 9·11, when the oil is cold, the valve will be off its seat and can flow through the opening on the left. This passage permits the oil to flow from the area around the outside of the cooler; hence it does not become cooled. As the oil becomes heated, the valve closes, thus forcing the oil to flow through the opening on the right which leads from the radiator section of the cooler. This, of course, exposes the oil to the cooling action of the radiator section.

Oil pressure-relief valves

The pressure of the oil must be great enough to lubricate the engine and its accessories adequately under all operating conditions. If the pressure becomes excessive, the oil system may be damaged and there may be leakage.

The purpose of an **oil pressure-relief valve** is to control and limit the lubricating-oil pressure, to prevent damage to the lubrication system itself, and to ensure that the engine parts are not deprived of adequate lubrication because of a system failure. There are several types of oil pressure-relief valves, a few of which are described below.

The single pressure-relief valve

The typical single pressure-relief valve, illustrated in Fig. 9·12, has a spring-loaded plunger, which has a tapered valve at one end, an adjusting screw for varying the spring tension, a locknut to keep the adjusting screw tight, a passage from the pump, a passage to the engine, and a passage to the inlet side of the pump. Normally, the valve is held against its seat by spring tension, but when the pressure from the pump to the engine becomes excessive, the increased pressure pushes the valve off its seat. The oil then flows past the valve and its spring mechanism and is thus by passed to the inlet side of the oil pump.

The compensating oil pressure valve and its thermostatic control valve

The **compensating oil pressure-relief valve,** working with its **thermostatic control valve,** automatically regulates the pressure of the oil in the lubrication system. These units are illustrated in Fig. 9·13, which shows the passage A for high-pressure oil arriving from the pump, passage B to the engine, the low-pressure oil passage C, the route for the return of oil to the pump, the metered or low-pressure oil chamber, and the two units already mentioned.

The oil pump sends oil under pressure through the strainer to passage A. From passage A, most of the oil flows through passage B to the engine. Referring to the illustration, some of the oil flows through a restriction that reduces its pressure and then circulates over and around the thermostatic control valve. From this valve, low-pressure oil flows through a hollow shaft to lubricate units other than those lubricated by the major portion of the oil which leaves through passage B to the engine.

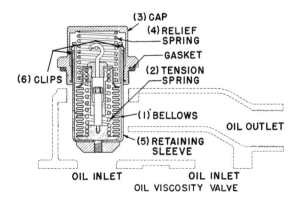

Figure **9·11** Oil viscosity valve.

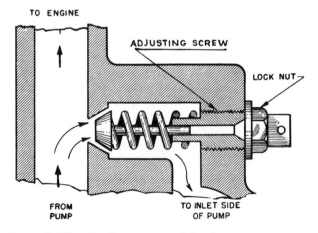

Figure **9·12** Single pressure-relief valve.

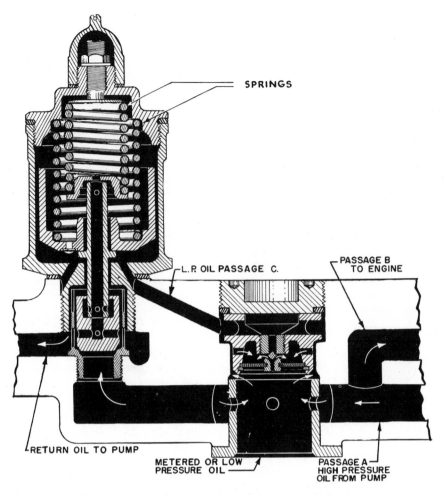

Figure 9·13 Compensating oil pressure-relief valve.

The thermostatic control valve is designed and adjusted to open at a prescribed critical temperature, usually 40°C (104°F). When the temperature is below 40°C, the thermostatic control valve is closed and the oil in passage C, which leads to the main relief valve, is not under pressure. When the temperature of the oil reaches 40°C, the valve opens and allows low-pressure oil to flow through passage C to the main relief valve, where it acts on the compensating piston and overcomes the force of the outer spring in that unit.

When the thermostatic control valve is closed, the pressure of the oil in passage A must be great enough to overcome the tension of two springs before the main relief valve can be forced off its seat, thus permitting excess oil to return to the inlet side of the oil pump. When this happens, the oil in both passage A and passage B must be under very high pressure.

When the thermostatic control valve is open, the pressure in passage A need not be so great as it must be if the thermostatic control valve is closed in order to allow excess oil to return to the inlet side of the pump. The reason is that the pressure in passage A needs to overcome the tension of only one spring in order that the oil pressure may be restored to its normal operating value.

The usual relief valve of this type can be adjusted for the pressure setting or "kick-out" pressure by removing a cap, loosening a locknut, and turning a screw. Generally, turning the pressure-adjusting screw to the right, in a clockwise direction, raises the pressure setting required to kick out, and turning the screw to the left, that is, in a counterclockwise direction, lowers the kick-out pressure.

General design of relief valves

Oil pressure-relief valves utilized in modern light airplane engines are comparatively simple in design and construction and usually operated according to the principle illustrated in Fig. 9·14. The relief-valve assembly consists of a plunger and a spring mounted in a passage of the oil-pump housing. When oil pressure becomes too high, the pressure moves the plunger against the force of the spring to open a passage, allowing oil to return to the inlet side of the pump.

Oil pressure-relief valves for large reciprocating engines are usually of the compensating type previously described. This type of relief valve assures adequate lubrication to the engine when the engine is first started by maintaining a high pressure until the oil has warmed sufficiently to flow freely at a lower

190

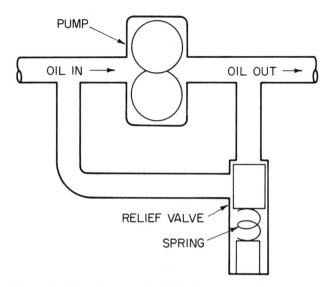

Figure **9·14** Engine oil relief valve.

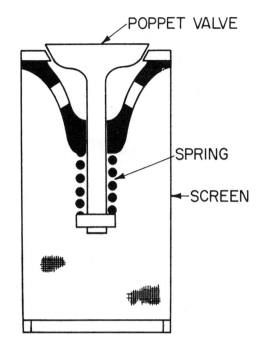

Figure **9·15** Oil screen with relief valve.

pressure. The relief-valve setting can usually be adjusted by means of a screw which changes the pressure on the spring or springs controlling the valve. Some of the simpler types of relief valves do not have an adjusting screw, and in these cases, if the relief-valve pressure setting is not correct, it is necessary to change the spring or insert one or more washers behind the spring.

Strainer-type filters

The purpose of any filter is to remove solid particles of foreign matter from the oil before it enters the engine. The **strainer-type oil filter** is simply a tubular screen. Some of these filters are designed so they will collapse if they become clogged, thus permitting continuation of oil flow. Other screens or filters are designed with relief valves which open if they become clogged. An oil screen of this type is shown in Fig. 9·15.

Cuno oil filter

The Cuno oil filter has a series of laminated plates or disks, with one set of disks rotating in the spaces between the other disks. The oil is forced through the spaces between the disks, flowing from the outside of the disks, between the disks and spacers to the inside passage, and thence to the engine. Foreign-matter particles are stopped at the outer diameter of the disks, and this accumulation of matter is removed by rotating the movable disks. This is accomplished by means of a handle outside the filter case. After long periods of time, the filter case is opened and the sludge removed. At this time, also, the entire filter assembly can be thoroughly inspected and cleaned.

Inspection of oil filter

The oil filter provides an excellent method for discovering internal engine damage. During the inspection of the engine oil filter, the residue on the screens or disks and the residue in the filter housing are carefully examined for metal particles. A new engine or a newly overhauled engine will often have a small amount of fine metal particles in the screen, but this is not considered abnormal. Aften the engine has been operated for a time and the oil has been changed one or more times, there should not be an appreciable amount of metal particles in the oil screen. If an unusual residue of metal particles is found in the oil screen, the engine should be taken out of service and disassembled to determine the source of the particles. This precaution will often result in preventing a disastrous engine failure in flight.

Oil filter for turbojet engine

The main oil filter for the General Electric CJ-805 engine is illustrated in Fig. 9·16. The oil enters the inlet port, surrounds the filter cartridge, flows through the cartridge to the inner oil chamber and out to the engine. If the filter becomes clogged, the oil is bypassed through the pressure-relief valve to the discharge port. A differential pressure of 14 to 16 psi is required to unseat the relief valve.

The filter cartridge is composed of a stack of pancake elements capable of filtering out particles larger than 46 microns in size. With the oil temperature at 150°F and a flow of approximately 15 gpm, the pressure drop across a clean filter is about 6 psi. The estimated maximum pressure drop across a clogged filter is 23 psi.

A magnetic detector is installed in the side of the filter case to indicate the presence of metal contamination without opening the filter. When the magnetic detector picks up ferrous-metal particles, the center plug will become grounded to the case. If a "hot" test

191

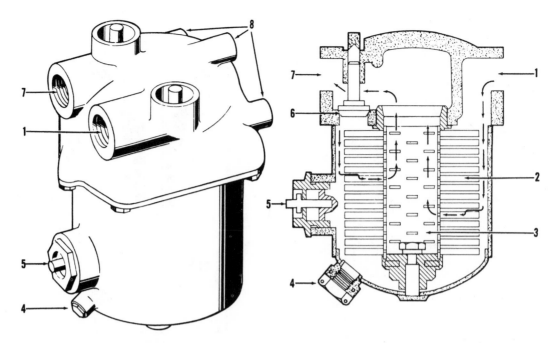

Figure 9·16   Oil filter for turbojet engine: (1) inlet port, (2) filter disc, (3) inner oil chamber, (4) drain plug, (5) magnetic chip detector, (6) pressure-relief valve, (7) discharge port, (8) mounting bosses. (General Electric)

light is connected between the center terminal of the detector and ground, the light will burn and indicate metal particles on the detector.

Oil separator

In any air system where the presence of oil or oil mist may exist, it is often necessary to utilize a device called an oil separator. This device is usually placed in the discharge line from a vacuum pump or air pump, and its function is to remove the oil from the discharge air. The oil separator contains baffle plates which cause the air to swirl around and deposit any oil on the baffles and on the sides of the separator. The oil then drains back to the engine through the oil outlet. The separator must be mounted at an angle of about 20° to the horizontal with the oil drain outlet at the lowest point. By eliminating oil from the air, the oil separator prevents the deterioration of rubber components in the system. This is particularly important in the case of deicer systems where rubber boots on the wing leading edges are inflated with air from the vacuum pump.

Oil pressure gage

An **oil pressure gage** is an essential component of any engine oil system. These gages are usually of the bourdon-tube type and are designed to measure a wide range of pressures, from no pressure up to above the maximum pressure which may be produced in the system. The oil-gage line, which is connected to the system near the outlet of the engine pressure pump, is filled with low-viscosity oil in cold weather to obtain a true indication of the oil pressure during the warmup

of the engine. If high-viscosity oil is used in cold weather, the oil pressure reading will lag the actual pressure developed in the system.

Oil pressure pumps

Oil pressure pumps may be of either the gear type or the vane type. A gear-type pump usually consists of two specially designed, close-fitting gears rotating in a case which is accurately machined to provide minimum space between the gear teeth and the case walls. The operation of a typical gear pump is shown in Fig. 9·17. The gear-type pump is utilized in the majority of reciprocating engines.

Scavenger pump

The scavenger pump or pumps for a lubrication system are usually designed with a greater capacity than

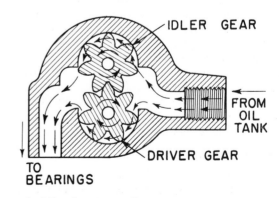

Figure 9·17   Gear-type oil pump.

the pressure pump. In a typical engine, the gear-type scavenger pump is driven by the same shaft as the pressure pump but the depth of the scavenger-pump gears is twice that of the pressure-pump gears. This gives the scavenger pump twice the capacity of the pressure pump. The reason for a higher capacity scavenger pump is that the oil which flows to the sump in the engine is somewhat foamy and therefore has a much greater volume than the air-free oil which enters the engine via the pressure pump. In order to keep the oil sump drained, the scavenger pump must handle a much greater volume of oil than the pressure pump.

Oil-dilution system

Since the **oil-dilution** system combines the services of both the fuel system and the oil system, it was described in the chapter on fuel systems. For a brief review, however, we present a schematic diagram (Fig. 9·18) showing how the oil-dilution system is connected between the fuel system and the oil system. In the

diagram it will be observed that a line is connected to the fuel system on the pressure side of the fuel pump. This line leads to the oil-dilution solenoid valve, and from the solenoid valve the line leads to the Y drain which is in the engine inlet line of the oil system. If the system does not include a Y drain, the oil-dilution line may be connected at some other point in the engine inlet line. The oil-dilution solenoid valve is connected to a switch in the cockpit so the pilot can dilute the oil after flight and before shutting down the engine. A cutaway drawing of the solenoid valve is shown in Fig. 9·19.

TYPICAL LUBRICATION SYSTEMS

System for wet sump engine

A schematic drawing of the lubrication system for the Continental IO-470-D engine installed on the Cessna 310 aircraft is shown in Fig. 9·20. Lubricating oil for the engine is stored in the sump, which is attached to the lower side of the engine. Oil is drawn from the sump through the suction oil screen, which is positioned in the bottom of the sump. After passing through the gear-type oil pump, the oil is directed through the oil filter screen and thence along an internal gallery to the forward part of the engine where the oil cooler is located. A bypass check valve is placed in the bypass line around the filter screen to provide for oil flow in case the screen becomes clogged. A nonadjustable pressure-relief valve permits excess pressure to return to the inlet side of the pump.

Oil temperature is controlled by a thermally operated valve which either bypasses the oil around the externally mounted cooler or routes it through the cooler passages. Drilled and cored passages carry the oil from the oil cooler to all parts of the engine which

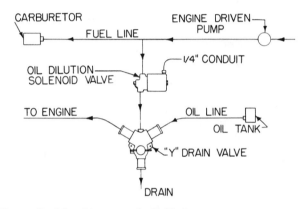

Figure 9·18 Diagram of oil-dilution system.

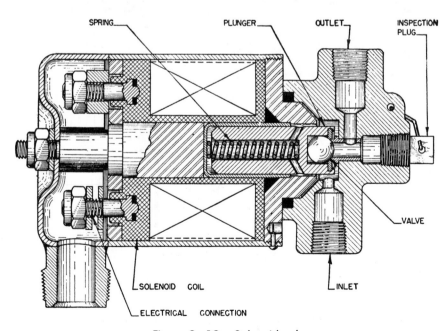

Figure 9·19 Solenoid valve.

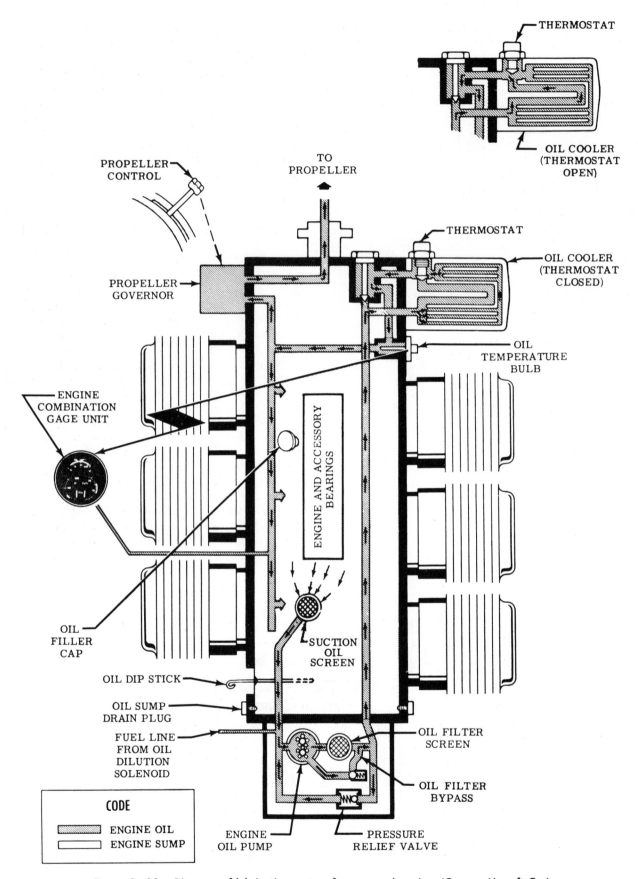

THERMOSTAT

OIL COOLER
(THERMOSTAT
OPEN)

PROPELLER
CONTROL

TO
PROPELLER

THERMOSTAT

OIL COOLER
(THERMOSTAT
CLOSED)

PROPELLER
GOVERNOR

OIL
TEMPERATURE
BULB

ENGINE
COMBINATION
GAGE UNIT

ENGINE AND ACCESSORY BEARINGS

OIL
FILLER
CAP

SUCTION
OIL
SCREEN

OIL DIP STICK

OIL SUMP
DRAIN PLUG

OIL FILTER
SCREEN

FUEL LINE
FROM OIL
DILUTION
SOLENOID

OIL FILTER
BYPASS

CODE

ENGINE OIL
ENGINE SUMP

ENGINE
OIL PUMP

PRESSURE
RELIEF VALVE

Figure 9·20   Diagram of lubricating system for opposed engine. (Cessna Aircraft Co.)

194

require lubrication. Oil from the system is also routed through the propeller governor to the crankshaft and thence to the propeller for control of pitch and engine rpm.

The oil-temperature bulb is located at a point in the system where it senses oil temperature after the oil has passed through the cooler. Thus the temperature gage indicates the temperature of the oil **before** it passes through the hot sections of the engine.

The oil pressure-indicating system consists of plumbing that attaches to a fitting on the lower left portion of the crankcase between Nos. 2 and 4 cylinders. The plumbing is routed through the wings, into the cabin, and to the forward side of the instrument panel. Here it connects to a separate engine gage unit for each engine. A restrictor is incorporated in the elbow of the engine fitting to protect the gage from pressure surges and to limit the loss of engine oil in case of a plumbing failure. This restriction also aids in retaining the light oil which may be placed in the gage line for cold-weather operation.

This lubrication system may be equipped with provision for oil dilution. A fuel line is connected from the main fuel strainer case to an oil-dilution solenoid valve mounted on the engine fire wall. From the solenoid valve a fuel line is routed to a fitting on the engine which connects with the suction side of the engine oil pump. When the oil-dilution switch is closed, fuel flows from the fuel strainer to the inlet side of the oil pump. A total of 4 qt of fuel is required for dilution in this particular engine.

Oil system for dry sump engine

Typical of lubrication systems for large aircraft equipped with dry sump reciprocating engines is the system illustrated in Fig. 9·21. This system is installed in the Convair 340 airliner which is equipped with Pratt & Whitney R-2800 engines. The oil for this system is stored in the tank shown in the upper rear portion of the nacelle. Oil is drawn from the tank through a fire-wall shutoff valve to the engine inlet, where it enters the engine-driven oil pump which circulates the oil under pressure through the engine. The oil is then picked up by the scavenger pump and forced through the engine outlet to the cooler and back to the supply tank where it started.

The oil system includes, in the oil return line, a thermostat which controls the cooler flap mechanism,

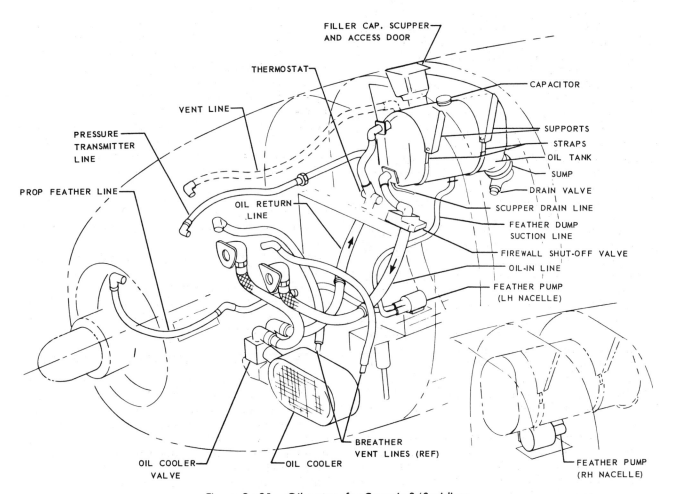

Figure 9·21 Oil system for Convair 340 airliner.

195

thus maintaining the oil temperature within the required limits. If the oil is cool, the cooler flap is closed, but as the oil temperature increases, the flap opens and allows cooling air to flow through the cooler in sufficient quantity to maintain the desired temperature.

Lubrication system for a turbojet engine

A discussion of lubrication systems for aircraft powerplants would not be complete without a discussion of the system for a modern turbojet engine. For this we have chosen the system of the General Electric CJ-805 engine which is currently installed in the Convair 880 and 990 jet airliners. This system is illustrated in Fig. 9·22.

The CJ-805 turbojet engine has a pressurized, recirculating oil system. The oil (synthetic, MIL-L-7808) is contained in an engine-furnished and mounted tank. Engine oil is used for lubrication and cooling of the engine bearings and gears. A special compartment is provided in the oil tank to store oil for the generator constant-speed drive (CSD). The CSD is referred to as "customer furnished" because it is not supplied by the engine manufacturer.

Oil flows from the engine compartment of the oil tank to the vane-type supply pump. This pump increases the supply oil pressure 20 to 65 psig, depending on engine speed, and discharges oil through an antileak check valve to the supply oil filter. Filtered oil is directed to a tee which divides the flow to supply (forward of the tee) the front gearbox and the No. 1 bearing, transfer gearbox, and the horizontal drive shaft damper bearing. Oil is piped to the five oil jets in the front gearbox and No. 1 bearing area through the No. 5 compressor front frame strut. Seven oil jets distribute the oil in the transfer gearbox, and one oil jet supplies the horizontal drive shaft damper bearing.

Aft of the tee in the supply line, oil is piped to the rear gearbox where four jets distribute the oil. A line through the No. 5 strut of the compressor rear frame carries oil to the No. 2 bearing area where four jets distribute the oil. Oil to lubricate the No. 3 bearing is piped through the No. 3 strut of the turbine frame. Three jets distribute the oil over the No. 3 bearing.

Immediately following engine starts, after prolonged periods in cold weather, supply pressure can range as high as 500 psig before the oil begins to warm up. A pressure-relief circuit protects the airframe instrumentation from pressures above 200 psig. A calibrated orifice, or pressure damper, and an oil pressure tap are in a fitting downstream of the supply oil filter. A pressure-relief valve downstream of the pressure tap bypasses sufficient oil to maintain the pressure at 200 psig. Bypassed oil is returned to the inlet of the supply pump.

Lubricating oil in the bearing sumps, the damper bearing, and the gearboxes is filtered, cooled, and returned to the engine section of the oil tank via the scavenge subsystem. The capacity of the scavenge subsystem is approximately 2.5 times the actual amount supplied in any one area. The difference in capacity is made up of sump pressurizing air.

During all flight attitudes scavenge oil from the No. 1 bearing sump and the front gearbox drains through the No. 5 strut of the compressor front frame to the transfer gearbox. This oil, plus the oil in the transfer gearbox, is returned by one element of the transfer gearbox scavenge pump. The scavenge flow from the damper bearing is piped to the second element of the transfer gearbox scavenge pump. Discharge flow from both elements of the scavenge pump is routed to the scavenge filter.

The rear gearbox scavenge pump consists of three independent elements. One element scavenges oil from the bearings and gears in the rear gearbox. The second element scavenges oil that flows through the No. 6 strut of the compressor rear frame from the dive sump of the No. 2 bearing. Oil from the climb sump of the No. 2 bearing flows through the No. 5 strut of the compressor rear frame and into the third element of the pump. Discharge flow from all three elements is manifolded and routed to the scavenge filter.

A two-element pump scavenges the climb and dive sumps of the No. 3 bearing. Oil scavenged by the pump elements is discharged through strut 5 of the turbine frame and piped to the scavenge filter.

Filtered scavenge oil flows to the engine fuel-oil cooler where it is cooled by engine fuel flowing through the cooler core. However, at oil inlet temperatures below 100°F a pressure-relief valve opens and bypasses oil around the cooler core. A fuel-temperature sensor opens the oil bypass valve when fuel temperature reaches 241°F because the fuel cannot safely absorb additional heat from the scavenge oil. Scavenge oil is returned from the cooler to the engine compartment of the oil tank where entrained air is separated from the oil. The oil is ready for reuse in the supply oil subsystem.

Return oil from the airframe CSD is routed to the CSD fuel-oil cooler. The CSD cooler is similar in operation to the engine fuel-oil cooler and will bypass the CSD oil when fuel temperature reaches 241°F. Some flight conditions may require additional cooling capacity for the CSD circuit in which case an airframe-supplied cooler and controller device is required. The CSD oil is returned to the CSD section of the oil tank. Here the entrained air is separated from the oil, and the oil is ready for reuse in the CSD system.

INSPECTION AND MAINTENANCE

Many of the important points to be observed in the inspection and maintenance of an aircraft-engine lubrication system have been explained in the preceding pages. It is also obvious that, before an airplane is serviced, the handbooks and manuals issued by the manufacturers of the equipment for that particular make, model, and type of airplane should be consulted. The following general instructions apply broadly to all airplane-lubrication systems.

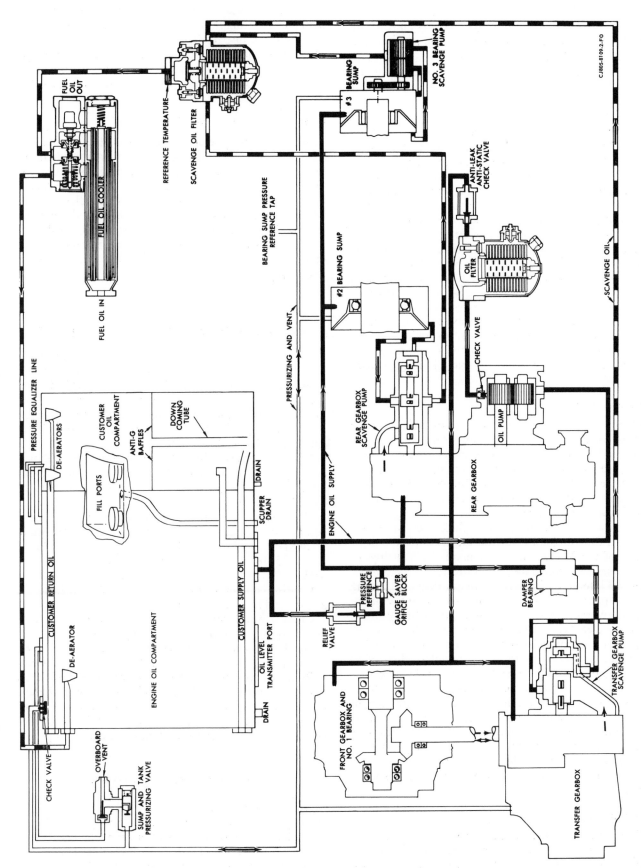

Figure. 9·22 Oil system for CJ-805 turbojet engine. (General Electric)

FUEL OIL OUT
FUEL OIL IN
FUEL OIL COOLER
REFERENCE TEMPERATURE
SCAVENGE OIL FILTER
#3 BEARING SUMP
NO. 3 BEARING SCAVENGE PUMP
BEARING SUMP PRESSURE REFERENCE TAP
#2 BEARING SUMP
ANTI-LEAK ANTI-STATIC CHECK VALVE
OIL FILTER
CHECK VALVE
SCAVENGE OIL
PRESSURIZING AND VENT
REAR GEARBOX SCAVENGE PUMP
OIL PUMP
ENGINE OIL SUPPLY
REAR GEARBOX
PRESSURE EQUALIZER LINE
CUSTOMER OIL COMPARTMENT
DE-AERATORS
ANTI-G BAFFLES
DOWN COMING TUBE
FILL PORTS
DRAIN
SCUPPER DRAIN
ENGINE OIL SUPPLY
PRESSURE REFERENCE
GAUGE SAVER ORIFICE BLOCK
DAMPER BEARING
CUSTOMER RETURN OIL
DE-AERATOR
ENGINE OIL COMPARTMENT
OIL LEVEL TRANSMITTER PORT
CUSTOMER SUPPLY OIL
DRAIN
RELIEF VALVE
FRONT GEARBOX AND NO. 1 BEARING
TRANSFER GEARBOX SCAVENGE PUMP
CHECK VALVE
OVERBOARD VENT
SUMP AND TANK PRESSURIZING VALVE
TRANSFER GEARBOX

CJ-805-8109-2-FO

Filling the oil tank

Do not try to fill the oil supply tank to the top. There must be an air space left for the expansion of oil, and the tank is usually constructed so the expansion space cannot be filled. Make sure that the correct type and grade of oil is placed in the tank.

Engine warm-up

During the engine warm-up on the ground, operate at low speed until the oil temperature rises enough to show that the oil is circulating properly. At the, beginning, the oil is cold and its viscosity is high; hence, its rate of flow is usually low even when the pressure is high. If the engine is operated at excessively high speeds in the beginning, the lack of adequate lubrication may cause damage. At the same time, the engine should not be operated for too long a period on the ground or this will cause damage. Normally, when the oil pressure is within the required range and remains steady for a few minutes, the engine should be ready for takeoff.

The foregoing instructions apply only to reciprocating engines. A turbojet or turboprop engine requires but a few seconds to reach satisfactory operating temperatures, and a warm-up period is not specified or required.

Inspection of tanks

The oil supply tank is inspected periodically for the general condition of the attaching straps or other devices used to secure the tank in place, the condition of the seams and walls of the tank, signs of leakage, and the security of the attached plumbing. Self-sealing oil tanks are inspected and repaired in the same manner as self-sealing fuel tanks.

To remove an oil tank for replacement or repair, the oil is first drained from the lubrication system by means of the Y drain or other main drain fitting. In some cases a special drain plug is located in the bottom of the oil tank to drain oil from the propeller feathering reserve space. The vent lines, oil inlet and outlet lines, scupper overflow tube, and all other attached plumbing must be removed. The attachment bolts, clamps, straps, and any other attaching fittings are removed or disconnected. When the tank is completely clear of all attachments, it is lifted from the airplane. The installation of an oil tank can be considered the reverse of removal. After all checks have been made and the oil tank mounting has been inspected, the oil tank is lifted into place and secured with the tank straps or other means of attachment. Lines and fittings are then connected as in the original installation. Fittings are torqued to the correct values by means of a special torque wrench.

Inspection of plumbing

The inspection of the plumbing for an oil system is similar to the inspection of any other plumbing. The tubing, hose, tubing fittings, hose fittings, hose clamps, and all other components of the system are inspected for cracks, holes, dents, bulges, and other signs of damage that might restrict the flow or cause a leak. All lines are inspected to see that they are properly supported and are not rubbing against a structure. Fittings should be checked for signs of improper installation, overtorquing, excessive tension, or other conditions which may lead to failure.

Inspection of screens and filters

When screen-type filters are used, they should be removed, cleaned, and inspected for breaks whenever the lubrication system is given a major inspection. At this time, the residue in the screen and in the screen housing should be checked for metal particles or chips which would indicate internal failure in the engine.

Special types of filters such as the stacked-disk type should be serviced according to the manufacturer's instructions. The construction of such filters is such that improper treatment may render the filter unserviceable.

LUBRICATION OF THE AIRPLANE

Every airplane has many bearings and other moving parts which must be lubricated to prevent wear and assure proper operation. The correct methods and materials are specified in the manufacturer's service or maintenance manual. Some typical lubrication instructions for a Cessna 182 airplane are given here to emphasize the need for such service.

Wheel bearings. Wheel bearings should be cleaned and repacked at the first 100-hr inspection and thereafter, every 500 hr. The grease should conform to MIL-G-7711 or equivalent.

Nose gear and main gear. When bearings are equipped with standard grease fittings, the appropriate grease gun may be used. These points should be greased every 25 to 100 hr, according to instructions. Use MIL-G-7711.

Control column bearings. Use the grease mentioned above, and lubricate by hand as required.

Control wheel shaft universals. Lubricate with general-purpose oil, MIL-L-7870, using an oilcan.

Needle bearings in control bell cranks and levers. Lubricate by hand, using MIL-G-7711 or equivalent.

Piano hinges on control surfaces. Use powdered graphite. Lubricate unsealed pulley bearing, rod ends, Oilite bearings, pivot and hinge points, and any other friction point obviously needing lubrication with general-purpose oil every 1000 hr or oftener if required.

REVIEW QUESTIONS

1. Describe a lubricant.
2. Why is a mineral lubricant more satisfactory for aircraft engines than either a vegetable or animal lubricant?
3. Why are fluid lubricants used in aircraft engines?
4. What are the sources of mineral lubricants?
5. What are the principal properties of a lubricant?

6. What is the significance of *flash point?*
7. Why is the *viscosity* of an engine oil important?
8. Under what conditions would you wish to select a lubricant with a very low *pour point?*
9. Name characteristics which should be possessed by a good engine lubricating oil.
10. What are the functions of the lubricating oil in an engine?
11. Of what materials are greases made?
12. What factors are considered in selecting a grease for a particular application?
13. What are the principal requirements for aircraft lubricating greases?
14. When would you use a corrosion-preventative oil?
15. Describe three types of friction.
16. What is meant by pressure lubrication?
17. Name the principal components of an aircraft engine lubricating system.
18. What is the required capacity of an engine oil system?
19. Describe the principal features of an aircraft oil tank.
20. Compare the plumbing for a lubricating system with that of a fuel system.
21. Explain the size requirement for the oil line leading from oil tank to the pump.
22. Describe the operation of an oil-temperature regulator.
23. What are the functions of the system relief valve?
24. Describe the operation of a relief valve.
25. What is the purpose of a thermostatic control valve?
26. How is an oil-pressure relief valve usually adjusted?
27. Describe an oil filter.
28. What inspection should be made with respect to engine operation at the time that an oil filter is being cleaned?
29. What design features may be incorporated to prevent a clogged oil filter from reducing oil flow?
30. Describe the oil filter for the General Electric CJ-805 turbojet engine.
31. Explain the operation of an oil-dilution system.
32. At what point in an engine lubrication system should the oil-temperature bulb (sensor) be located?
33. Describe the principal features of the oil system for the Continental IO-470-D engine.
34. Why does a scavenge oil pump have greater capacity than a pressure pump?
35. Name the principal components of the dry-sump oil system used for the Convair 340 airliner.
36. How many pressure pumps are used in the lubrication system for the General Electric CJ-805 jet engine system? Scavenger pumps?
37. What are the important points to remember when filling an engine oil tank?
38. Why is it necessary to *warm up* an airplane engine before flying the airplane?
39. Describe the inspection of an oil system.
40. Explain the lubrication requirements of parts not lubricated by the engine oil system.

Principles of Electricity

CHAPTER 10

In order to become proficient in the maintenance, adjustment, and troubleshooting of the ignition system and the other electrical systems and accessories associated with a powerplant, it is essential that the aviation maintenance technician have a good understanding of the basic principles of electricity. It is not the purpose of this chapter to provide a complete course in electrical theory and practice; however, the basic principles will be examined to the extent necessary for the powerplant technician to carry out his duties with respect to ignition systems and the other electrical systems related to the powerplant.

THE ELECTRIC CURRENT

Principles

Many persons believe that the electric current is a mysterious force which cannot be comprehended by the ordinary individual and that anyone who does understand the nature of electricity and the operation of electrical equipment must be a special type of genius. This idea, of course, has no foundation in fact, and anyone of reasonable intelligence who applies himself diligently can learn to understand electricity in a comparatively short time.

The first requirement for an understanding of electricity is to know what electricity consists of and where it originates. We therefore must consider the nature of matter itself. **Matter,** from the point of view presented here, is anything which has substance and occupies space. Air, liquids, metals, wood, plastics, and gases all represent various forms of matter.

At the present time, matter in its many forms is known to consist of more than 100 elements. An element is a basic substance, unique in its nature and character and unlike any other element. The element is composed of **atoms,** which are the smallest particles of a substance which can exist without changing the nature of the substance.

Some substances are **compounds,** and these are made up of a chemical combination of elements. Compounds are composed of **molecules,** the molecule being a chemical combination of two or more atoms. Water is a compound because it is a chemical combination of the elements hydrogen and oxygen. Other compounds are sugar, salt, sulfuric acid, cellulose, etc. Many of the common substances with which we are familiar are composed of mixtures of elements or mixtures of compounds.

The basic component of electricity is the **electron,** which is found in the atom. Every atom consists of a **nucleus** with one or more orbiting electrons. The atom of hydrogen has a single particle as a nucleus and a single electron orbiting this particle. This is the simplest atom and may be represented by the diagram of Fig. 10·1. The nucleus of the hydrogen atom, called a **proton,** carries a **positive** electrical charge, and the electron carries a **negative** electrical charge. The positive charge of the proton is equal and opposite to the negative charge of the electron. Most of the elements have a comparatively large number of protons and electrons, and some have electrons which are easily dislodged from the outer orbit and shifted to other atoms.

It is sufficient to state here that the electrons around the nucleus of an atom are arranged in levels called "shells" as indicated in Fig. 10·2 and that the electrons which make up the electric current come from the

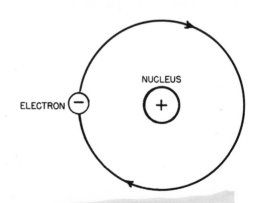

Figure 10·1 Diagram of a hydrogen atom.

200

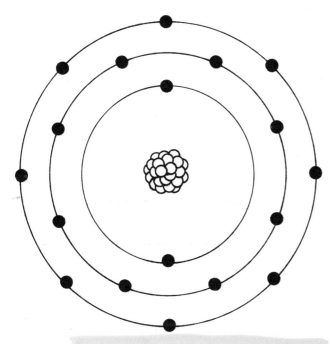

Figure 10·2   Arrangement of electrons around the nucleus of an atom.

outer shells of the atoms. These electrons which move from one atom to another are called **"free" electrons.** A substance which contains many free electrons is a good **conductor** of electric current, and a substance with very few free electrons is an **insulator.** That is, it will not carry an electric current easily. Most metals have many free electrons and are therefore good conductors. The best conductors are silver and copper. Aluminum is also a very good conductor and is often used in place of copper because the weight of aluminum is about one-third that of copper.

Electrical charges

Before we pursue the study of electrical current, we must know something of electrical charges. An electrical charge may be **negative** or it may be **positive.** Since the basic component of electricity is the electron and the electron carries a negative charge, a body which possesses a **negative charge** has an excess of electrons. This means that there are more electrons than there are protons in the body. If the body has a deficiency of electrons, it carries a **positive charge.** When a negatively charged body is connected to a positively charged body with a conductor, the excess electrons of the negative body will flow to the positive body until the charges are equalized. We find, therefore, that the flow of an electric current is normally from negative to positive.

Any person who has ridden in an automobile many times will have experienced an electric shock as the result of electrical charges. These charges are developed when his clothing slides along the plastic covering of the seat. If the person touches the metal handle of the car door after the charge is developed, a small spark will jump between the door handle and the hand or other part of the body which touches the door handle.

Any two dissimilar dry substances when rubbed together will be likely to generate electrical charges, one substance becoming negative and the other becoming positive. If a piece of fur is used to rub a glass rod, the fur will acquire a positive charge and the glass rod will have a negative charge.

A simple experiment will serve to demonstrate the effects of small electrical charges. With some dry tissue paper, rub a fountain pen or other plastic object. Now hold the pen close to small bits of the tissue paper. The paper will be attracted to the pen and will adhere to it. The paper is attracted to the pen because the pen and paper have unlike charges.

If two objects have like charges, they will repel each other. This is demonstrated when a person combs dry hair with a plastic comb. After vigorous combing, the hairs repel one another and stand out from the head. The repulsion of like charges can also be demonstrated by using two small pith balls suspended together as shown in Fig. 10·3. If a glass rod is charged by rubbing it with fur and then the glass rod is touched simultaneously to both balls, the balls will spring apart.

Electrical charges are generated by friction because one substance gives up electrons more easily than the other. When the two are rubbed together, electrons from one substance move to the other substance, thus leaving one negatively charged and the other positively charged.

The **static electrical charges** described above often create problems in the operation of aerospace vehicles. They cause radio interference, they may start fires when sparks occur in a flammable atmosphere, and they build up on aircraft in flight to the extent that a very strong spark discharge could take place when the aircraft lands. The charge on an airplane is usually dissipated by means of static discharge devices and static conducting tires, which are treated to make them reasonably good conductors of electricity.

When a static charge exists on a body, an **electro-**

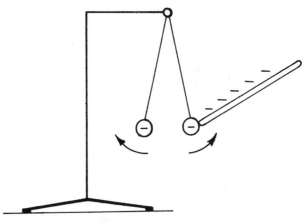

Figure 10·3   Charging pith balls with a glass rod.

static field exists around the body. This field consists of invisible lines of force which have a definite direction. When two bodies having unlike charges are brought near each other, the electrostatic field is comparatively strong. If the charges are sufficiently great, they will cause a spark discharge between the two bodies. Such a discharge can be observed in the familiar flash of lightning when the charge on a cloud becomes so great that it discharges to the ground or to another cloud. Actually, the flash of lightning may jump from the cloud to the earth or from the earth to the cloud, depending upon the nature of the charges.

Voltage, amperage, and resistance

When we speak of the electricity used in an electric circuit, we must be able to express certain values with respect to the electricity if we are to know what it will do in the circuit. The first value we must consider is the force which causes the electricity to flow in the circuit. This force is measured in **volts,** and it may be considered **electrical pressure.** It is called **electromotive force** and abbreviated emf. Most of us are familiar with the effects of pressure in a water system, and we know that it causes water to flow out of a faucet or hose nozzle when the valve controlling it is opened. If the pressure is high, there is a comparatively great flow of water, and if the pressure is low, the flow is small. In a given electrical circuit, an increase of voltage (electrical pressure) will cause an increase in the flow of electric current.

The electric current is a movement of electrons through a conductor, and it may be compared with a flow of water through a pipe. There is a difference, however, which must be well understood. An electric circuit must normally form a complete loop or path. In effect, we may say that the electricity must start at a point and return to that point. An electric current will not flow out the end of a conductor in the same manner that water will flow out of a hose. In an electric circuit, the electricity must start at the generator or battery and then must have a complete path back to the generator or battery.

The flow of electricity through a conductor is measured in **amperes.** The ampere represents a flow of one **coulomb** of electricity past a certain point in a circuit in one second. The **coulomb** is said to be equal to approximately 6.24×10^{18} electrons. Observe carefully that the ampere is a **rate of flow** and not a quantity. If we consider the flow of a liquid, we may say that it is flowing at a rate of so many **gallons per second.** The gallon is the quantity and the gallons per second is the **rate of flow.** In like manner, the coulomb is the **quantity** and the ampere is the **rate of flow.**

Another factor which is most important in the operation of electric circuits is **resistance** because resistance is found in every circuit. In simple terms, resistance may be called "electrical friction" and compared with mechanical friction. Resistance may be defined as the property of a substance which opposes the flow of an electric current. The unit of resistance is the **ohm.**

The relationship among voltage, amperage, and resistance is explained by **Ohm's law.** Ohm's law may be stated in several ways; however, the following is considered suitable for our purpose: **The current flow in a given circuit is directly proportional to the voltage and inversely proportional to the resistance.** Another statement which may be used to explain Ohm's law is: **One volt of electromotive force will cause one ampere to flow through a circuit having one ohm of resistance.**

From Ohm's law we see that current flow will increase as voltage increases in a given circuit and will decrease as resistance increases. Any one of the values in a circuit can be determined through the use of the formula for Ohm's law when the other two values are known. The formula is

$$I = \frac{E}{R} \qquad R = \frac{E}{I} \qquad E = IR$$

where I = current, amp
E = electromotive force, volts
R = resistance, ohms

Each of the foregoing formulas is a different arrangement of the same formula.

The relative effects of voltage, amperage, and resistance can be understood by considering the simple water system shown in Fig. 10·4. The pump and pressure regulator represent a generator and voltage regulator. The valve represents a variable resistance. If we increase the pressure (voltage) by adjusting the pressure regulator, the rate of flow (amperage) will increase provided that the valve opening is not changed. If we decrease the opening of the valve (increase resistance) while the pressure remains constant, the rate of flow will decrease. Thus we see that we can change the amperage in an electric circuit by changing either the voltage or resistance. An increase in voltage increases the amperage, while an increase in resistance decreases the amperage.

A thorough understanding of Ohm's law is important to the aviation maintenance technician because it is often necessary for him to install electric circuits and components or to replace portions of electric circuits. If the technician knows the voltage used for a given circuit and the current flow which is likely to exist in the circuit under operating conditions, he can easily determine the correct size of wire and values of circuit breakers to be used in the circuit.

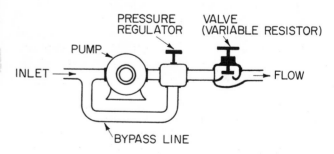

Figure 10·4 Demonstration of effects of voltage and resistance.

Electrical power

Power is the rate of doing work. As previously explained, 1 hp is equal to 33,000 ft-lb per min or 550 ft-lb per sec. In electricity, the unit of power is the **watt,** and it is equal to about 0.00134 hp. We may also state that 746 watts is equal to approximately 1 hp.

Using the electrical units already defined, we can determine the power consumed in a circuit with the following formula:

$$W = IE$$

where W = power, watts
I = current, amp
E = electromotive force, volts

If a current of 20 amp is flowing in a circuit in which the voltage is 110, the power being consumed in the circuit is 2200 watts. To obtain horsepower we divide 2200 by 746 to obtain about 2.95 hp.

Electric circuits

A simple electric circuit consists of a source of electric power, a load, and conductors to carry the current from the power source to the load and back to the power source. Such a circuit is shown in Fig. 10 · 5. The circle at the left represents a generator, and the circle at the right represents a motor which is the load. The arrows indicate the direction of the current through the conductors. Observe that one conductor carries the current to the load and another conductor carries the current from the load back to the generator.

Another simple electric circuit is shown in Fig. 10 · 6. In this circuit the load is an electric lamp and the circuit is controlled by means of a switch. When the switch is closed, the current can flow and the lamp

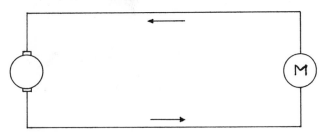

Figure 10 · 5   A simple electric circuit.

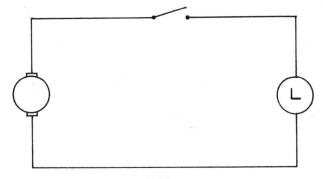

Figure 10 · 6   Circuit with a switch.

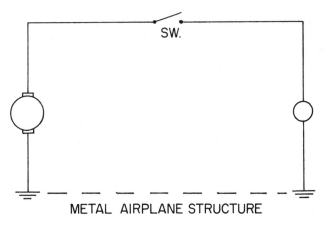

Figure 10 · 7   A single-wire circuit.

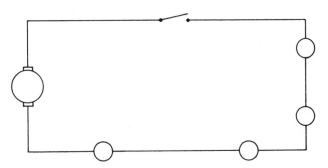

Figure 10 · 8   A series circuit.

will operate. When the switch is off (open), the circuit is "open" and no current can flow.

On an airplane it is common practice to utilize "grounded" circuits in order to save wire and reduce weight. In a grounded circuit the metal structure of the airplane is used as one of the conductors. Such a circuit is shown in Fig. 10 · 7. This circuit is also called a single-wire circuit because a single wire is used to carry the current in one direction and a switch in the single wire is used for control. A system made up of single-wire circuits is called a **single-wire** system.

There are several different types of circuits, named according to the arrangement of the components in the circuits. The first of these circuits which we shall consider is the **series circuit.** In a series circuit the units are arranged so the current flowing through one unit must flow through all the other units in the circuit. The simple circuits previously described may be considered as series circuits because all the current must flow through each of the units in the circuit. In Fig. 10 · 6 the current flows from the generator, through the switch, through the lamp and back to the generator. In Fig. 10 · 8 is a series circuit having four lamps in series. It will be noted in this circuit that all the current in the circuit must flow through each of the lamps. If one lamp should burn out, the current flow would stop and all the lamps would go out. This type of circuit is familiar to most persons because Christmas-tree lights are often connected in series.

A **parallel circuit** is commonly used for lighting and

203

power purposes and is arranged so each load unit can operate independently of the others. Figure 10·9 illustrates the circuit arrangement for a parallel circuit. In this diagram it will be noted that each of the lamps is connected separately between the power leads and one lamp is not dependent upon another. Therefore if one lamp burns out, the others will continue to operate. If the switch is open, all the lights will go out because the path to the power source is broken. In this circuit a battery is used as a power source. The battery symbol is shown at the left of the figure.

Still another combination of circuitry is the **series-parallel** circuit. In this arrangement, some of the load units are connected in series and others are connected in parallel. A circuit of this type is shown in Fig. 10·10. In this circuit it will be observed that three of the lamps are in series with one another but that the three lamps as a unit are in parallel with the two other lamps.

Solution of circuit values

The technician should be able to determine the values in standard circuits through the use of Ohm's law. In a circuit such as that shown in Fig. 10·11, if the generator voltage and the resistance of the lamp are known, it is easy to compute the current flow in the circuit. Assume that the voltage of the generator is 28 and the resistance of the lamp is 7 ohms. The amperage (current flow) can then be determined as follows:

$$I = \frac{E}{R} = \frac{28}{7} = 4 \text{ amp}$$

When several different units are connected in series or parallel or both, the total resistance of the circuits can be determined by the use of standard formulas. When resistances (loads) are connected in series, the total resistance is the sum of the resistances. This is shown by the formula

$$R_t = R_1 + R_2 + R_3 + \cdots$$

In the circuit of Fig. 10·12, the total resistance is the sum of the resistances in the circuit. Since the values for the resistances are given, the formula will appear thus:

$$R_t = 2 + 5 + 3 + 6 = 16 \text{ ohms}$$

In stating resistance values, instead of spelling out the word **ohms,** we may use the Greek letter omega (Ω). This symbol is often used to indicate ohms. The symbol for a resistance (resistor) in a circuit is the zigzag line shown in the diagrams.

In a parallel circuit the total resistance of a group of resistances is equal to **the reciprocal of the sum of the reciprocals of the resistances.** The **reciprocal** of a number is that number divided into the number 1. For example, the reciprocal of 2 is ½ and the reciprocal of 50 is ⅟₅₀. When a number is multiplied by its reciprocal, the product is 1.

The formula for resistances connected in parallel is

$$\frac{1}{R_t} = \frac{1}{R_1} + \frac{1}{R_2} + \frac{1}{R_3} + \cdots$$

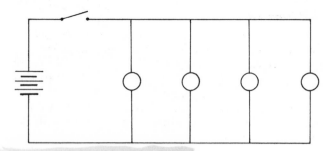

Figure **10·9**   A parallel circuit.

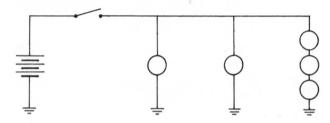

Figure **10·10**   A series-parallel circuit.

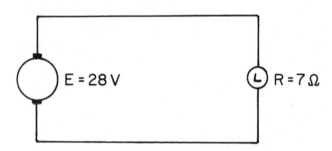

$E = 28$ V $R = 7\,\Omega$

Figure **10·11**   Circuit to illustrate Ohm's law.

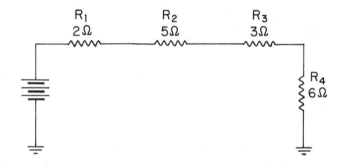

R_1 $2\,\Omega$ R_2 $5\,\Omega$ R_3 $3\,\Omega$ R_4 $6\,\Omega$

Figure **10·12**   Circuit with resistance loads in series.

or
$$R_t = \frac{1}{1/R_1 + 1/R_2 + 1/R_3 + \cdots}$$

The correctness of the foregoing formula can be easily demonstrated by using a typical example. In the circuit of Fig. 10·13, if $R_1 = 6$ ohms, $R_2 = 12$ ohms, and $R_3 = 8$ ohms, with a battery voltage of 24, by Ohm's law we can determine that the current through R_1 is 4 amp, through R_2 it is 2 amp, and through R_3 it is 3 amp. Then the total current flowing from the battery is $4 + 2 + 3 = 9$ amp. Again, by Ohm's law, since $E = 24$ and $I = 9$, $R = {}^{24}\!/\!_9 = 2.667$ ohms.

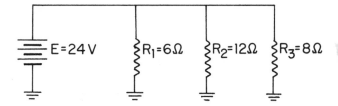

Figure 10·13   Circuit with resistances in parallel.

Now, by the formula for parallel resistances,

$$\frac{1}{R_t} = \frac{1}{6} + \frac{1}{12} + \frac{1}{8} = \frac{4}{24} + \frac{2}{24} + \frac{3}{24} = \frac{9}{24}$$

Then $R_t = \frac{24}{9} = 2.667$ ohms

From the solution we see that the total resistance value is the same regardless of how we work the problem. Many students have difficulty in understanding why the total resistance in a circuit decreases when more resistances are connected in parallel. We must remember that each resistance connected in parallel provides an additional path for the current flow; hence more current can flow with a greater number of paths. When more current can flow with a given voltage, it is obvious that there is less total resistance in the circuit.

The principal reason why it is important to know the current value in an electrical circuit is so that the proper size of conductor (electrical cable) will be installed to carry the current in a particular circuit. Generally speaking, we can use copper electrical cable of the sizes shown in the following table:

Table 10·1

Load	AWG (American Wire Gage) size
Less than 10 amp	18
10–15 amp	14
15–20 amp	12
20–30 amp	10
30–40 amp	8
40–50 amp	6
60–80 amp	4
80–100 amp	2

For the very heavy, intermittent loads such as those in a starter system, it is usually wise to install cable of 0 size upward to 2/0 or 3/0, depending upon the value of the load. A safe practice is to install wire at least as large as that originally furnished by the manufacturer.

Alternating current

Thus far in this section we have dealt principally with **direct current,** that is, current which always flows the same direction in the circuit. It is well, however, for the powerplant technician to understand **alternating current** because this type of current will be encountered from time to time in work with powerplants and their associated circuits.

Alternating current periodically changes direction and continuously changes in magnitude. To illustrate alternating current we may use the **sine** curve shown in Fig. 10·14. The sine curve is developed as shown in the illustration and is so named because it represents the values of the sines of all the angles through a complete circle. In trigonometry, the **sine** of an angle is the ratio of the side of a right triangle opposite the angle to the hypotenuse of the triangle. In the diagram, the sine of the 35° angle AOB is AB/AO. If the radius of the circle has a value of 1, the sine of the angle is then merely AB. If we plot the values of the sines for the various angles from 0 to 180° as shown in the drawing, we shall produce a sine curve. Alternating-current values usually follow a sine curve when plotted with a time base such as BCD in the illustration. This means, of course, that the value of an alternating current will be at zero, then increase to a maximum at 90°, back to zero at 180°, to a maximum in the opposite direction at 270°, and again to zero at 360°. The changes in value from 0 to 360° represent 1 cycle of alternating current.

The number of cycles which occur per second in an alternating current is the **frequency** of the current. The frequency of the current used in most city power systems is 60 cycles per second (cps). One-half of a cycle is one **alternation.** In the diagram of Fig. 10·14 the curve from B to C is one alternation and the curve from C to D is one alternation. During the second alternation the current flow is in a direction opposite that of the current for the first alternation. The sine curve is used to represent either current or voltage in an a-c circuit.

One of the principal values of alternating current lies in the fact that the voltage can be stepped up or stepped down by means of a transformer. Thus it is possible to transmit the electrical power at a high voltage and low amperage through comparatively small conductors. At the point where the power is to be used, the voltage is reduced to the desired level with a transformer before being delivered to the load. It must be remembered that the voltage drop in a conductor increases in proportion to the current flow. For this reason, there will be a smaller voltage drop in a circuit where the voltage is high and the current low than there will be in a similar circuit where the voltage is low and the current is high.

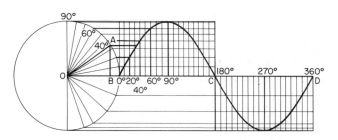

Figure 10·14   Development of a sine curve.

MAGNETISM

Magnetism is one of the oldest electrical phenomena known to man. It is believed that Chinese sailors used the **lodestone,** a magnetic oxide of iron, as early as the tenth century A.D. for navigational purposes. The lodestone when freely suspended will align itself with the earth's magnetic field and will therefore assume a position pointing generally north and south. Magnetism may be defined as the property of a substance which causes it to attract other magnetic substances.

The nature of magnetism

A magnetized substance is surrounded by a **field** of force which has both direction and magnitude. If a magnet is in the shape of a bar as shown in Fig. 10·15, the magnetic field at one end of the bar will be in a direction opposite that of the other end. In order to establish laws or rules for magnetism, the magnet is said to have **poles** and these poles are named according to the direction of the magnetic field at the pole. When a bar magnet is freely suspended, one end of the bar will point toward the north magnetic pole of the earth and the other end will point toward the south magnetic pole. This is because the earth is a large magnet and the bar magnet aligns itself with the earth's magnetic field.

The end of a bar magnet which points toward the north pole of the earth is called a "north-seeking" pole or the "north" pole, and the other end is called the "south-seeking" or "south" pole. Although the actual direction of the magnetic field is not known, by definition, magnetic force is said to travel from the north pole of a magnet to the south pole. For this reason it is often called magnetic **flux.**

When the north pole of one magnet is placed near the south pole of another magnet, there is a very strong attraction between the two poles. On the other hand, when the north pole of one magnet is placed near the north pole of another magnet, there is a repulsion between them. We may therefore state that **opposite poles attract and like poles repel.** Since the north pole of a bar magnet is attracted by the earth's magnetic pole, we know that the magnetic pole near the north geographic pole of the earth is actually a south magnetic pole. The magnetic field of the earth will therefore be in a direction from the geographic south pole to the geographic north pole.

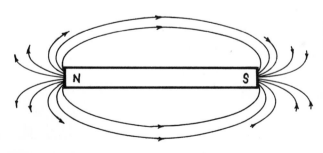

Figure **10·15**   Bar magnet and field.

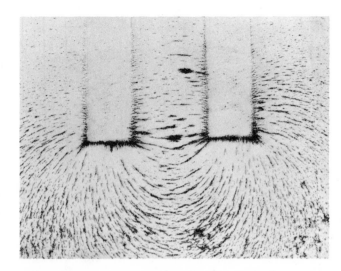

Figure **10·16**   Demonstrating magnetic field with iron filings.

The theory of magnetism can be explained when we consider that atoms may have magnetic polarity as the result of the electrons in orbit about them and the atoms thus give polarity to the molecules of the substance. If the molecules are aligned in such a manner that their magnetic forces combine, the substance which they form will have magnetic polarity.

It is also said that a group of billions of molecules may make up a **domain** which has magnetic polarity. In a magnetized substance, such as a permanent magnet, the polarized domains are arranged in such a manner that their individual magnetic fields are aligned to reinforce each other. In a nonmagnetized substance the domains are arranged at random and their magnetic fields cancel each other.

When we speak of magnetic fields, we often refer to "magnetic lines of force." Actually, there are no individual lines of force, but we can see what are apparent lines when we perform the experiment shown in Fig. 10·16. When a piece of paper is placed over a horseshoe magnet and iron filings are sprinkled on the paper, the pattern of the magnetic field can be made to appear. The iron filings take positions in lines, so it is natural to refer to the field as being composed of lines of force. As stated before, we assume that these lines of force are in a direction from north to south. The strength of the magnetic field may also be referred to as the "amount of magnetic flux."

Magnetic fields are encountered wherever a flow of electrical current exists, and for this reason among others the technician must have an understanding of their nature and their effects. The strength of a magnetic field is determined by its intensity and the intensity is given in **gauss.** One gauss intensity is one line of force per square centimeter.

Magnets

Magnets today are of many sizes and shapes and are made of a variety of materials. One of the most common metals used for permanent magnets is hardened steel. A permanent magnet is one which retains its magnetism indefinitely. Exceptionally strong permanent magnets are made from special alloys, such as alnico and Permalloy. Some of the metals which are used in the alloys are nonmagnetic in the pure state. Permanent magnets are used to provide the fields for magnetos.

Temporary magnets are usually made of soft iron, and they retain their magnetic properties only while within a magnetic field. The field may be produced by an electrical coil or by a permanent magnet. In our present study, temporary magnets are used chiefly for solenoids and relays and to produce generator fields. These will be explained as we proceed with discussions of the accessories with which they are associated.

Electromagnets

An **electromagnet** is a magnet produced by means of an electric current. As mentioned previously, whenever there is a flow of an electric current, a magnetic field is produced. In Fig. 10·17, if a current is flowing through a wire as shown, magnetic lines of force will surround the wire in the direction indicated. Actually, the field around the wire is much more extensive than shown in the diagram. The field around a current-carrying wire extends indefinitely, becoming weaker as the distance from the wire increases. The strength of the field is inversely proportional to the square of the distance from the wire.

The direction of the magnetic field around a current-carrying wire can be determined by the **left-hand rule for conductors.** If the conductor is grasped in the left hand with the thumb pointing in the direction of current flow as shown in Fig. 10·18, the fingers will be encircling the conductor in the direction of the mag-

netic field. This can be verified by using a compass needle as shown in Fig. 10·19. If a small compass is placed over the current-carrying wire, the needle will point in the direction of the field above the wire.

The effect of the magnetic field around a current-carrying conductor may be multiplied many times by winding the conductor into a coil. When this is done, the magnetic fields of the separate turns are added together and the combined magnetic field passes through the coil as shown in Fig. 10·20. Under these conditions the coil will have the properties of a magnet and will draw magnetic substances toward the center of the coil. When we place a bar of soft iron inside the

Figure **10·19** Use of compass needle to show field direction.

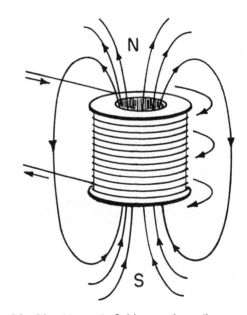

Figure **10·20** Magnetic field around a coil.

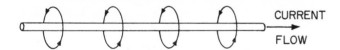

Figure **10·17** Field around a current-carrying conductor.

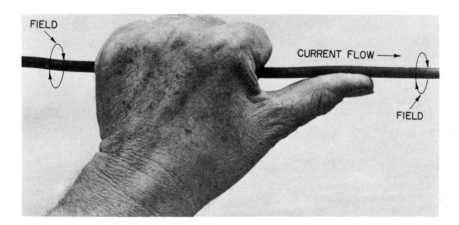

Figure **10·18** Left-hand rule for conductors.

207

coil, the effect of the coil is greatly increased because magnetic lines of force pass through soft iron much more easily than they do through the air. The coil with a soft iron core is called an **electromagnet.** When current is flowing in the coil, the core is magnetic, and when the current is shut off, the core loses its magnetism.

The strength of an electromagnet is determined by the number of turns of insulated wire in the coil and the current flow through the wire. The product of these two quantities is called **ampere-turns.** If the coil of an electromagnet has 200 turns of wire and a current of 5 amp is flowing in the coil, the magnetizing force **(magnetomotive force)** is 1000 amp-turns.

The polarity of an electromagnet can be determined by means of the **left-hand rule for coils.** If the left hand is closed and held so the fingers point in the direction of current flow in the coil, the extended thumb will point in the direction of the field of the electromagnet; that is, the thumb will be pointing toward the north pole. This is illustrated in Fig. 10·21.

It must be remembered that only a few of the metals are magnetic. In general, it is safe to say that most ferrous (iron-base) metals are magnetic; however, there are many metal alloys which contain iron and are not magnetic. Typical of these are the stainless steels. Such metals as aluminum, brass, copper, zinc, silver, and gold are completely nonmagnetic.

The ability of a substance to carry magnetic lines of force is called **permeability.** The permeability of air and other materials which are not magnetic is given a value of approximately 1. Pure annealed iron has a permeability of 6000 to 8000. This means that it will carry magnetic lines of force 6000 to 8000 times as easily as will air. An alloy of nickel and iron, called **Permalloy,** has a permeability of more than 80,000. The opposition of a substance to magnetic lines of force is called **reluctance.** This may be compared with resistance in an electrical circuit. If we wish to state a formula for the values in a magnetic circuit, it will appear thus:

$$\text{Magnetic flux} = \frac{\text{magnetomotive force}}{\text{reluctance}}$$

It is not intended that the foregoing formula be used to compute magnetic strength for the purpose of this text because it is not required that the powerplant technician perform this type of problem. If the student desires to pursue the study of magnetism further, he may find additional information in a good college physics text. It is sufficient to know that an increase in the number of turns of wire in a coil or an increase in the current through the coil will cause an increase in the magnetic effect of the coil.

ELECTROMAGNETIC INDUCTION

General principles

The transfer of electrical energy from one circuit to another without the aid of conductors is called **induction.** The transfer of electrical energy from one circuit to another by means of a magnetic field is called **electromagnetic induction.** It has been explained that, whenever a current flows through a conductor, a magnetic field exists around the conductor. It is also true that, when a conductor is "cut" by a changing magnetic field, a voltage will be produced in the conductor.

Purely **magnetic induction** occurs when an unmagnetized magnetic substance is placed within a magnetic field. For example, if a piece of soft iron is placed near a permanent magnet, as shown in Fig. 10·22, the magnetic lines of force will pass through the iron and the iron will become magnetic. As shown in the illustration, the iron will then have the power to attract other magnetic substances.

In the diagram of Fig. 10·23, the conductor is moved upward through the magnetic field. As it moves, it cuts across the magnetic lines of force and a voltage is induced which causes current to flow in the direction

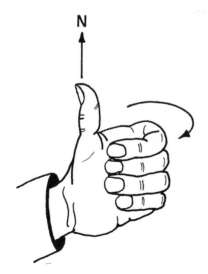

Figure **10·21** *Left-hand rule for coils.*

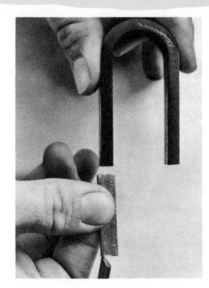

Figure **10·22** *Magnetic induction.*

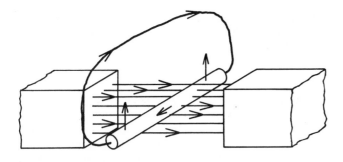

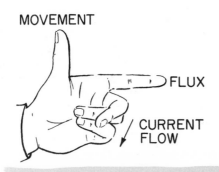

Figure **10·23** *Determining direction of an induced current.*

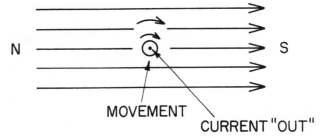

Figure **10·24** *Another method for determining direction of an induced current.*

shown by the arrows. If the conductor were moved downward, the current flow would be in the opposite direction. The direction of current flow in a conductor moving across a magnetic field can be determined by use of the **left-hand rule.** When the left hand is held so the thumb, forefinger, and middle finger are at right angles to each other as shown in Fig. 10·23, with the thumb pointing in the direction of conductor movement and the forefinger pointing in the direction of the magnetic field, then the middle finger will be pointing in the direction of current flow.

Another method for finding the direction of induced current flow is illustrated in Fig. 10·24. If we assume that a conductor is moving upward through a magnetic field and that the lines of force are bent around the conductor as shown, we can hold the left hand so the fingers are pointed in the direction of the curved lines of force around the conductor and the thumb will be pointing in the direction of the induced current flow.

Electromagnetic induction takes place whenever there is a relative movement between a magnetic field and a conductor or conductors such that the conductors cut across (link with) the magnetic lines of force. If the conductors move parallel to the lines of force, there will be no induction. The voltage produced by electromagnetic induction is proportional to the number of lines of force cut per second. When lines of force are being cut at the rate of 10^8 per second, the induced emf will be 1 volt.

Lenz's law

An important principle governing electromagnetic induction is called Lenz's law, named for a German physicist of the nineteenth century, H. F. Emil Lenz.

This law may be stated thus: **An induced current is in a direction which produces a magnetic field opposing the change in the field which causes it.** This may be illustrated by the diagrams of Fig. 10·25. In diagram *A* a bar magnet is being moved toward a coil of wire. The field of the bar magnet induces a current in the coil as shown by the meter *M*, and the field produced by this current is such that the north end of the coil field is toward the north end of the bar magnet. Since like poles repel, the field of the coil is opposing the movement of the magnet toward it. When the bar magnet is moved away from the coil, the direction of current flow in the coil and the field of the coil are reversed as shown in diagram *B*.

One of the methods by which electromagnetic induction takes place has been illustrated in Fig. 10·25. This is the case where the field is moving and the coil is stationary and is called "transformer action." When the field is stationary and the coil (conductors) is moving, the induction is called "generator action." In a conventional generator the conductors rotate with a drum called the armature and the field is produced by stationary electromagnets.

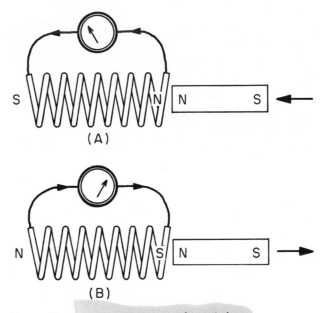

Figure **10·25** *Demonstration of Lenz's law.*

In a simple **transformer** separate coils of wire are wound on a common iron core or on cores arranged so the magnetic field traverses the separate cores. Two different arrangements for transformers are shown in Fig. 10·26. In the illustration at (a), two windings called the **primary** and the **secondary** are placed on one common core. In the illustration at (b), the primary and secondary windings are placed on separate sections of a core which is in a square configuration.

In a transformer, the winding into which the current is fed is called the **primary winding** and the winding from which the output is taken is called the **secondary winding**. The output voltage is proportional to the turns ratio of the primary and secondary. This is shown by the formula

$$\frac{E_p}{E_s} = \frac{N_p}{N_s}$$

where E_p = primary voltage
E_s = secondary voltage
N_p = number of turns in primary winding
N_s = number of turns in secondary winding

Example: An alternating current with an emf of 12 volts is fed to a transformer having 200 turns in the primary winding and 2000 turns in the secondary winding. What is the output voltage? By the foregoing formula,

$$\frac{12}{E_s} = \frac{200}{2000}$$

Then $\quad 200E_s = 24{,}000$

$$E_s = \frac{24{,}000}{200} = 120 \text{ volts}$$

From the above example, we note that the secondary winding has ten times as many turns as the primary. The output voltage is therefore ten times the input voltage.

The transformer used in the example is called a **step-up** transformer because the output voltage is higher than the input voltage; that is, the transformer steps the voltage up. If the secondary winding has fewer turns than the primary winding, the transformer is a **step-down** transformer because the output voltage is less than the input voltage.

Because the total power output of a transformer cannot be greater than the total power input, there must be a decrease in output current when there is an increased output voltage. If a transformer could be 100 percent efficient, we could use the following formula:

$$E_p I_p = E_s I_s$$

Remember that the power in an electrical circuit is equal to the voltage times the current. By the above formula we see that the power in the primary circuit is equal to the power in the secondary circuit when efficiency is 100 percent. Commercial transformers have efficiencies of 95 to 99 percent.

As mentioned previously, a transformer must be operated on an alternating current in order to have a moving magnetic field. If a direct current is connected to a transformer, there will be a momentary surge of voltage at the output terminals during the time that the magnetic field is being built up. Since the direct current is steady, there will be no further change in the field until the direct current is disconnected. At this time there will be a surge of voltage in the reverse direction. In some cases where no alternating current is available, a direct current is rapidly interrupted by vibrating contacts and then fed to the primary of a transformer. The output of the transformer will then be an alternating current having the frequency of the vibrating contact points. This principle has been used for many years to provide the plate voltage for radio sets which must operate from a d-c power source.

An important feature of the transformer is the core material. The core must be made of a special soft iron which has low reluctance so the magnetic field can change rapidly. Furthermore, it must be made of thin laminations which are insulated from each other to prevent the flow of **eddy currents** which would otherwise develop and cause the core to overheat. In a solid core, the changing magnetic field induces eddy currents in the core material and these currents cause a substantial loss of power as well as heating.

A most important feature of a standard transformer is the fact that it can remain connected to a power source and, if no current is being drawn from the secondary, there will be practically no current flow in the primary. This occurs because the current flow in the primary induces a back voltage in the primary almost equal to the input voltage. This **back emf** prevents any appreciable flow of current in the primary. When a load is connected to the secondary winding, the current flow in the secondary opposes the magnetic field caused by the primary current, and the back voltage in the primary therefore decreases. This allows enough current flow in the primary to supply the required output power. Thus we see that the transformer is self-regulating. If an excessive load is placed on the transformer, the primary current may be so great that the windings will burn out.

Transformers are manufactured in many sizes and types, and for any particular application, the transformer must have the capacity to handle the power applied to it, it must have the proper turns ratio to provide the amount of "step-up" or "step-down" re-

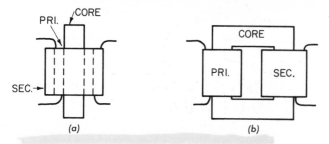

Figure 10·26 *Arrangements for transformers.*

quired, and it must be sufficiently well insulated to withstand the voltages applied to it. It is the responsibility of the technician to see that the transformer he selects for a particular job has the proper characteristics to fulfill its purpose.

CAPACITANCE, INDUCTANCE, AND REACTANCE

Capacitors

It has been pointed out that various substances can be given a negative or positive charge by adding or removing electrons from them. A **capacitor (condenser)** is a device designed to store electrical charges. When two metal plates are placed adjacent to each other with an air gap between them as shown in Fig. 10·27, a simple capacitor is formed. If one plate is connected to the negative terminal of a battery and the other plate is connected through a switch to the positive terminal of the battery, the capacitor will be charged. During the charging process, electrons flow from the negative terminal of the battery to one plate. The excess of electrons on this plate repels electrons from the other plate, and these repelled electrons will flow to the positive terminal of the battery. Now, if the switch is opened, the capacitor will remain charged for a long period of time unless an electrical connection is made between the plates. This is because the positive charge on one plate holds the electrons on the other plate. Between the plates is an **electrostatic field** which may be considered a field of force. The electrostatic field exists between the plates of any charged capacitor.

When the capacitor is disconnected from the battery and the plates connected by a conductor, the electrons from the negative plate will flow to the positive plate until the charges are equalized. This action is illustrated in Fig. 10·28.

The insulating material between the plates of a capacitor is called the **dielectric.** It may consist of air, waxed paper, mica, glass, or a variety of other in-

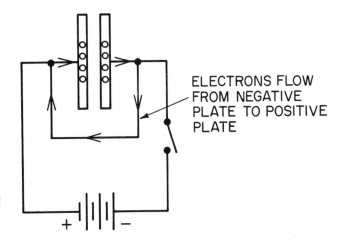

Figure 10·28 Action of a capacitor.

sulating materials. The most important requirement for a dielectric is that it be a good insulator and be able to withstand the **dielectric stresses** imposed by the applied voltages. If the dielectric breaks down, an electrical discharge will take place through it and the capacitor will become useless.

The **capacity** of a capacitor is normally measured in **microfarads.** A microfarad (μf) is one-millionth of a **farad.** The capacity is 1 farad when the capacitor will store 1 coulomb of electricity under an emf of 1 volt. One farad is a very high value of capacitance; hence capacitors rated in microfarads are used for most purposes in a standard electrical system.

The capacitors most often encountered by the powerplant technician are the mica type and the rolled-paper type. The mica capacitor is constructed by stacking very thin plates of metal (foil) with thin sheets of mica dielectric between each pair of plates. This construction is illustrated in Fig. 10·29. The paper capacitor consists of two long strips of foil separated by waxed paper or a similar material and rolled into a cylindrical shape. The foil is usually positioned so the edge of one strip can be contacted at one end of the roll and the edge of the other strip is contacted at the opposite end. The roll is sealed in a paper or metal case for protection.

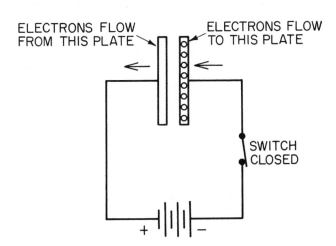

Figure 10·27   A simple capacitor.

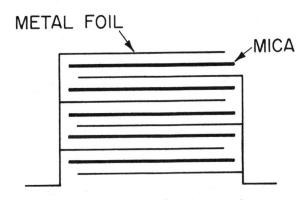

Figure 10·29   Construction of a mica capacitor.

211

Variable capacitors are constructed so one set of plates can be inserted into the other set to any degree desirable by means of a control knob. The plates are spaced so they do not touch each other, and the air between the plates serves as the dielectric. Variable capacitors are commonly used in electronic circuits.

The capacity, or **capacitance,** of a capacitor is determined by the area of the plates, the distance between the plates, and the **dielectric coefficient** of the insulating material between the plates. In simple terms, the **dielectric coefficient** of a material is a measure of its ability to convey the effect of electric charges through itself. The dielectric coefficient of a vacuum is 1, and that of other substances is more than 1.

To provide an example of the nature of a capacitor we may consider a sphere separated into two sections by an elastic diaphragm as shown in Fig. 10·30. If the two chambers thus formed are connected by pipe to a piston pump as shown and the system is filled with fluid, the sphere may be "charged" first in one direction and then the other. When the pump handle is moved to the left, the chamber A will be filled with fluid and the fluid will be removed from chamber B. This may be compared with the addition of electrons to one plate of a capacitor and the removal of electrons from the other plate. The pump shown in the drawing serves as the battery or generator for this illustration. If the valve is closed after the sphere is charged, the charge will hold. When the valve is opened, the pressure of the diaphragm will drive the fluid from chamber A and fluid will flow back into chamber B, provided that the pump is free to move back to the neutral position.

In an a-c system, it appears that a capacitor allows current to flow through it. It is true that the capacitor allows the current to flow, but it does not flow through the capacitor. If the handle of the pump in Fig. 10·30 is moved back and forth, we can see that the fluid will move back and forth in the system. No fluid will actually flow through the sphere. Fluid will flow into one chamber and out of the other chamber, and then the flow will reverse. A similar effect takes place in an a-c circuit with a capacitor. The electrons flow **in** to one plate and **out** from the other plate. When the current reverses, the electrons flow in the opposite direction. In a d-c circuit, the electrons will flow momentarily until the capacitor is charged and then no more flow can take place because the pressure (voltage) is always in the same direction.

The total capacitance in a circuit where two or more capacitors are connected can be determined by simple computations. If two capacitors are connected in **parallel** as shown in Fig. 10·31, it is merely necessary to add the individual capacitances to determine the total. That is,

$$C_t = C_1 + C_2 + C_3 + \cdots$$

When capacitors are connected in series, the total capacitance is reduced because the effective distance between the plates is increased. If two capacitors of equal value are connected in series as shown in Fig. 10·32, the total capacitance is one-half the value of one of the capacitors. If the distance between the plates of one of the capacitors is d, the effective distance is increased to $2d$ when the two capacitors are connected in series. The formula for computing total capacitance when capacitors are connected in series is

$$C_t = \frac{1}{1/C_1 + 1/C_2 + 1/C_3}$$

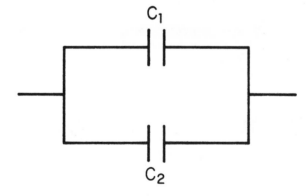

Figure 10·31   Capacitors in parallel.

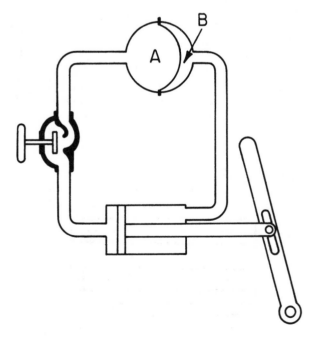

Figure **10·30**   Diagram to illustrate operation of a capacitor.

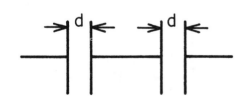

Figure **10·32**   Capacitors in series.

According to the formula, the total capacitance in a circuit where capacitors are connected in series is equal to the reciprocal of the sum of the reciprocals of the individual capacitances.

Example: Three capacitors having values of 2, 4, and 6 μf, respectively, are connected in series. What is the total capacitance? By the formula,

$$C_t = \frac{1}{\frac{1}{2} + \frac{1}{4} + \frac{1}{6}}$$

$$= \frac{1}{\frac{6}{12} + \frac{3}{12} + \frac{2}{12}}$$

$$= \frac{1}{\frac{11}{12}} = \frac{12}{11} = 1\frac{1}{11} \mu f$$

The principal value of a capacitor (condenser) in a powerplant circuit is to store surges of current and then release them when the voltage drops. Capacitors are essential to the operation of ignition systems as will be explained in the next chapter of this text.

In order to prevent radio interference caused by surging voltages and currents, filter capacitors are used. The effect of these capacitors is to reduce the peaks of voltage and to fill in the low points. This smooths the current flow and reduces the emanation of electromagnetic waves which cause radio interference.

Inductors

An **inductor,** or inductance coil, is simply a coil of wire whose turns are insulated from one another. The coil may have a magnetic core or an air core, depending upon the amount of inductance needed. As explained under electromagnetic induction, the moving of magnetic lines of force across a conductor will induce a voltage in the conductor. Self-induction occurs when the magnetic field of a conductor induces a voltage in the conductor. Every conductor has a certain amount of inductance, and this inductance is increased by winding the inductor into a coil. An inductance coil is shown in Fig. 10·33.

The effect of an inductance coil is to resist changes in current flow. If the current increases in an inductor, the magnetic field produced by the inductor is increased in strength. This increasing field induces a back voltage in the coil which opposes the increase in current flow. If the current flow is reduced, the change in the magnetic field will produce a voltage which tends to maintain the current flow. This is in accordance with Lenz's law. The value of inductance L is expressed in

a unit called the **henry.** One henry is the amount of inductance possessed by a coil when a change in current flow of one ampere per second will induce a back emf of one volt. Since the henry is a rather large value of inductance, small inductance coils are rated in **millihenrys.** One millihenry is one-thousandth of a henry.

Reactance

The effect of a capacitor in an a-c circuit is called **capacitive reactance** X_C, and it is measured in ohms because it opposes the flow of current. The effect of an inductor is called **inductive reactance** X_L, and it is also measured in ohms. Capacitive reactance in an a-c system causes the current to lead the voltage. This is illustrated in Fig. 10·34. While the capacitor is charging, the voltage is held down but the current is flowing. As the capacitor approaches the charged condition, the voltage increases, and when the voltage of the capacitor has reached maximum, no more current can flow into the capacitor. This means that the current is zero as shown at A in the diagram and the voltage is maximum. As the voltage begins to drop, the current flows out of the capacitor; that is, it is flowing in a direction opposite to that in which it flowed previously. The current flow reaches a peak value at B, and as the voltage increases in the opposite direction, the current flow again decreases and returns to zero as the voltage reaches a peak at C. If an a-c circuit contained only capacitance, the current would lead the voltage by 180°. Since every circuit contains some resistance, the lag between voltage and current cannot be as much as 180°.

Inductance in an a-c circuit has an effect opposite that of capacitance. This is, inductive reactance cancels capacitive reactance. If an a-c circuit has 100 ohms of capacitive reactance and 100 ohms of inductive reactance, the net reactance will be zero. When the reactances are equal, the circuit is said to be **resonant.**

Inductive reactance in an a-c circuit causes the current to lag the voltage. In a purely inductive circuit the voltage would lead the current by 180° as shown in Fig. 10·35. As the voltage rises, the current is held back by the induced back voltage. When the applied

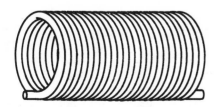

Figure 10·33 An inductance coil.

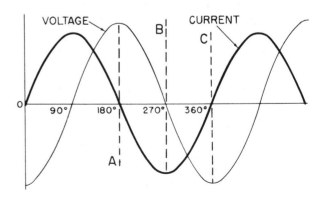

Figure 10·34 Current leading the voltage.

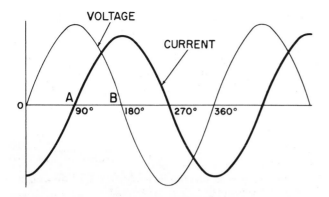

Figure 10·35   Voltage leading the current.

voltage reaches a peak, the current flow can increase because the field is not inducing a back voltage.

A further understanding of inductance in a circuit may be gained by considering the diagram of Fig. 10·36. A long spring handle is attached to the shaft supporting a heavy wheel. If the handle is moved quickly, the movement of the wheel will not follow the handle immediately but will lag. After the handle is moved a certain distance and then moved back in the opposite direction, there will be a period when the handle is moving in one direction and the wheel is moving in the opposite direction. This same condition can be seen in the diagram of Fig. 10·35, where current is flowing in one direction and voltage force is in the opposite direction.

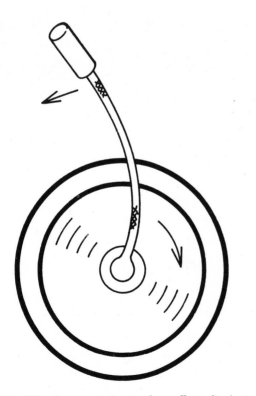

Figure 10·36   Demonstration to show effect of inductance.

214

The formulas used for determining capacitive reactance X_C, inductive reactance, X_L, and the frequency of resonance are as follows:

$$X_C = \frac{1}{2\pi f C}$$
$$X_L = 2\pi f L$$
$$f = \frac{1}{2\pi \sqrt{LC}}$$

where X_C = capacitive reactance, ohms
X_L = inductive reactance, ohms
f = frequency, cps
C = capacitance, farads
L = inductance, henrys

From the foregoing formulas it is apparent that the reactance in an a-c circuit is dependent upon the frequency. As frequency increases in a particular a-c circuit, capacitive reactance will decrease and inductive reactance will increase. From this we can see that a capacitor will allow more current flow when the frequency is high and an inductor will allow more current when the frequency is low.

The use of the foregoing formulas can be demonstrated by solving typical problems. Assume that we wish to determine the capacitive reactance in a circuit when the frequency is 400 cps and the capacitance in the circuit is 0.5 μf. We apply the formula as follows:

$$X_C = \frac{1}{2\pi f C}$$
$$= \frac{1}{6.28 \times 400 \times 0.0000005}$$
$$= \frac{1}{0.001256}$$
$$= 796.17 \text{ ohms}$$

In the foregoing problem it must be noted that capacitance is given in microfarads. Then, in the formula, 0.5 μf is equal to 0.0000005 farad or 5×10^{-7} farad.

To solve a problem in inductance, we shall assume that a circuit contains 10 mh (millihenry) of inductance and the frequency is 400 cps. Substituting in the formula for inductive reactance,

$$X_L = 6.28 \times 400 \times 0.010$$
$$= 25.12 \text{ ohms}$$

With any combination of inductance and capacitance in an a-c circuit, there is always one frequency where the capacitive reactance is equal to the inductive reactance. As explained previously, this condition is called **resonance**. To find the frequency where a circuit is resonant when the capacitance is 0.5 μf and the inductance is 10.0 henrys, we apply the formula for the frequency of resonance.

$$f = \frac{1}{2\pi \sqrt{LC}}$$

$$= \frac{1}{6.28 \times \sqrt{0.010 \times 0.0000005}}$$

$$= \frac{1}{6.28 \times \sqrt{0.000000005}}$$

$$= \frac{1}{6.28 \times 0.00001 \times \sqrt{50}}$$

$$= \frac{1}{0.00001 \times 44.4}$$

$$= \frac{1}{0.000444} = 2252.2$$

In the foregoing problems, the decimal figures can be expressed in terms of powers of 10. For example, 0.5 μf can be expressed as 5×10^{-7} farad because 10^{-7} = one ten-millionth or 0.0000001. Whenever it becomes necessary to work problems involving long decimals, it is often more convenient to use the powers of 10 for computation when one is familiar with the process.

MULTIPHASE A-C SYSTEMS

It is beyond the scope of this text to give a detailed explanation of multiphase systems; however, we shall give definitions and explanations sufficient for the student to have some understanding of the principles involved. A **multiphase** system has two or more interrelated systems of currents and voltages operating together in three or more conductors.

Values in three-phase system

The curves of Fig. 10·37 illustrate the values in a three-phase system and the schematic wiring diagram for a delta-connected alternator and motor. If we assume that phase 1 is at a potential of 0 volt beginning at 0°, we find that phase 2 is at 86.6 percent of maximum voltage negative and phase 3 is at 86.6 percent of maximum voltage positive. When the rotor of the alternator has turned 30°, phases 1 and 3 are both at 50 percent of maximum voltage positive and phase 2 is 100 percent of maximum voltage negative. At a rotation of 60°, phase 1 is at 86.6 percent of maximum voltage positive, phase 2 is again at 86.6 percent of maximum voltage negative, and phase 3 is at 0 voltage. As we continue to note the values at various degrees of rotation, we can see that the voltages change steadily in a uniform sequence such that the sum of the negative voltages is always equal to the sum of the positive voltages.

Even though we have used voltage values in the foregoing example, we could also use current values and get the same results. It is true, however, that the current may lead or lag the voltage an amount depending upon how much capacitance or inductance is in the circuit.

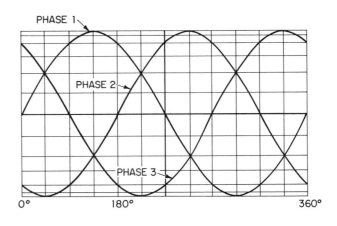

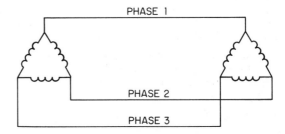

Figure 10·37 A three-phase electrical circuit.

Alternators and motors

A three-phase system provides the most efficient distribution of power for motors. In modern aircraft systems, both the alternators and the motors are constructed without brushes or slip rings (sliding contacts), thus greatly reducing the problems that often exist with d-c equipment.

A three-phase alternator consists of a stator (stationary winding) in the form of a drum or cylinder with a magnetic rotor. As the rotor turns, the magnetic field of the rotor induces voltages in the windings of the stator as previously explained. If the output of the alternator is connected to a three-phase stator of an a-c motor, the current flow in the windings of the stator will set up a rotating field which turns at the same rate as the rotor of the alternator. This rotating field is employed in the a-c motor to develop torque forces in the rotor, thus causing the motor to run.

Use of a-c power

Alternating-current power has a number of advantages over d-c power. The principal advantage is that a-c power can be transmitted at a higher voltage and lower current, thus making it possible to use smaller diameter conductors. This principle can be illustrated by the following example where it is desired to transmit 2000 watts of power. If a d-c voltage of 25 volts is employed, it will require 80 amp to provide the desired power. When an a-c voltage of 250 is used, only 8 amp is needed. This means that the a-c power will require a conductor with only one-tenth the cross-sectional area required for the d-c power.

215

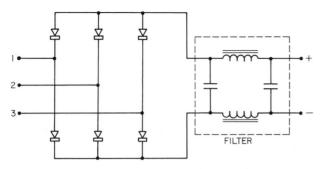

Figure 10·38   A three-phase full-wave rectifier circuit.

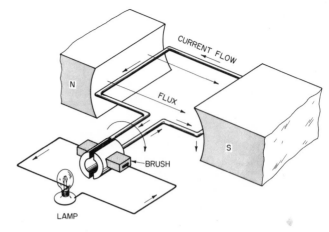

Figure 10·39   A simple d-c generator.

Alternating-current can be reduced or increased instantly and efficiently by means of transformers, thus making it possible to provide the various voltages required for different types of equipment. Furthermore, when a d-c voltage is needed, the alternating current can be changed to direct by means of diode rectifiers and filters. Direct current cannot be increased or decreased by means of transformers. Hence in a d-c system, if higher or lower voltages are required, it is necessary to employ dynamotors or inverters, which are very inefficient and expensive.

When it is desired to operate single-phase equipment from a three-phase source of power, it is merely necessary to connect the load across two of the three phases. In practice, it is attempted to divide single-phase loads among the three phases so that the loads on the different legs of the system are as nearly equal as possible. If the loads are greatly out of balance, the efficiency of the system decreases.

When direct current is needed for certain types of equipment, all three phases of the a-c system may be connected to a three-phase full-wave rectifier. The circuit for such a rectifier is shown in Fig. 10·38. It will be noted that the six-diode rectifier units will provide for a continuous flow of current from the three legs of the a-c system; hence a maximum of available power will be supplied to the d-c circuit. The ripples which would otherwise be present in the direct current are removed by the filter.

DIRECT-CURRENT GENERATORS AND CONTROLS

Generator theory

A generator, either for direct current or for alternating current, operates on the principle of electromagnetic induction. The conventional design for a d-c generator provides that a rotating armature be placed in a stationary magnetic field, the field being produced, usually, by field windings on field poles. Figure 10·39 is a simplified drawing of a d-c generator. As the armature rotates in the field, the conductors of the armature winding cut across the lines of magnetic flux, thus causing a voltage to be induced in the armature winding. The windings of the armature are connected to the

commutator from which the current is taken by means of brushes.

The direction of the induced voltage in the armature windings depends upon the direction of the magnetic field and the direction in which the moving conductor is moving. In the drawing of Fig. 10·40 a conductor is moving downward as it cuts across magnetic lines of force. The direction of the lines of force is from left to right. We may apply the left-hand rule to determine

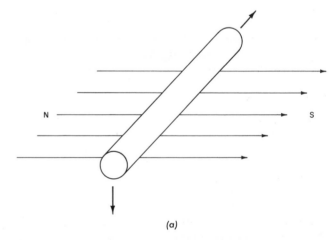

(a)

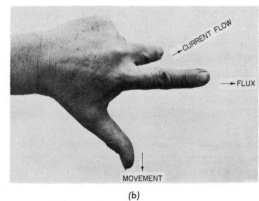

(b)

Figure 10·40   Left-hand rule for generators.

216

the direction of voltage or current flow. When the thumb, index finger, and middle finger of the left hand are placed at right angles as shown in the illustration, with the thumb pointing in the direction of conductor movement relative to the field and the index finger pointing in the direction of the magnetic flux, the middle finger will point in the direction of induced voltage. This principle is called the **left-hand rule for generators.** In using the left-hand rule, we assume that the electric current (electrons) moves from negative to positive.

The strength of the voltage produced in the armature of a generator depends upon three factors: (1) the strength of the magnetic field, (2) the number of turns of wire on the armature, and (3) the rate at which the armature is turning. Assuming a standard value for each "line of magnetic force," an electromotive force of 1 volt will be induced when 100,000,000 lines of force are being cut per second.

Construction of a generator

The construction of a d-c generator is illustrated in Fig. 10·41. The essential electrical parts of this generator are the **field poles, armature, commutator,** and **brushes.** The field poles are electromagnets each having a soft iron core surrounded by a **field coil.** Their function is to provide the varying magnetic field necessary for the induction of a voltage in the armature windings. The armature consists of a laminated, soft iron core with longitudinal slots which carry the field windings (see Fig. 10·42). As the armature rotates in the magnetic field between the field poles, voltages are

Figure 10·42   Armature for a d-c generator.

induced in the windings. The commutator is composed of a series of copper bars, insulated from one another and mounted in a cylindrical arrangement at the end of the armature. The copper bars are connected to the ends of the armature windings and serve as the electrical contacts through which the current from the armature is delivered to the brushes. The generator brushes are made of hard carbon or a composition of carbon and other materials which improve the conducting and wearing qualities of the brushes. The brushes are mounted to make contact with the commutator at points where the voltage differential is the greatest, as shown in Fig. 10·43. The plane cutting through these points is called the **neutral plane,** because at these points there is very little potential difference between adjacent bars of the commutator. If the brushes are not located on the neutral plane, adjacent bars of the commutator under the brushes will have a potential difference and will be short-circuited by the brushes. This will result in arcing of the brushes, loss of power, pitting of the commutator, and rapid wear of the brushes.

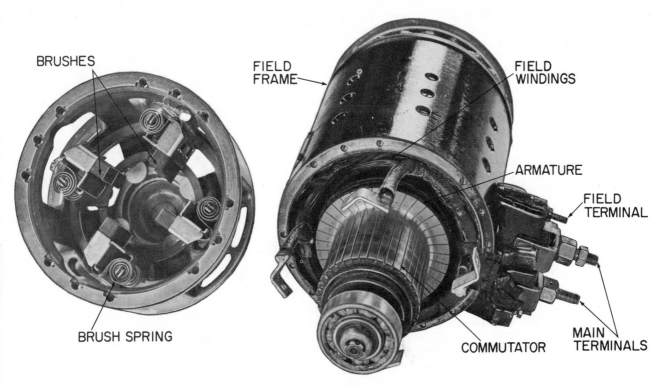

BRUSHES

FIELD FRAME

FIELD WINDINGS

ARMATURE

FIELD TERMINAL

BRUSH SPRING

COMMUTATOR

MAIN TERMINALS

Figure 10·41   Construction of a d-c generator.

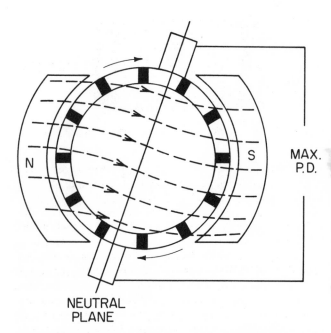

Figure **10 · 43** *Location of brushes on commutator.*

The principal structural parts of a generator are the **field frame, drive-end frame, commutator end frame, brush rigging, bearings,** and possibly other parts. The **field** frame is usually an iron cylinder inside which the field pole pieces are mounted and held in place by large screws. The field frame provides a portion of the magnetic circuit between the field poles. The two end frames are attached to the field frame, either by screws or by long bolts which extend from one end of the generator to the other. A recess is usually machined in each end frame to hold the bearing in which the armature shaft is supported.

The purpose of the brush rigging is to provide a mounting for the brush holders and springs. The **negative** brush holder is usually attached directly to the rigging with metal-to-metal contact for grounding purposes. The **positive** brush holder must be insulated from the generator frame to prevent short circuiting. The positive brush is connected to the positive output terminal, which is also insulated from the frame by means of a phenolic bushing and washers. So they may always maintain a good contact with the commutator, it is necessary that the brushes be free to move in the brush holders with the brush springs providing constant pressure.

The electric circuit for a **shunt-type** generator is shown in Fig. 10 · 44. A shunt-type generator has the field windings connected in parallel with (shunted across) the armature. A variable resistor is connected in series with the field windings to control the field current. It will be observed in the drawing that the current taken from the armature flows from one brush to the other through the field winding to provide the magnetic field.

Operation of the generator

Since the production of voltage in the armature of the generator is dependent upon the magnetic field and the magnetic field is dependent upon current from the armature, we may ask where the process of electrical generator begins. What actually starts the process? Fortunately the iron from which the field poles are made has the capability of holding a small amount of magnetism indefinitely, even though there is no current flow through the field windings. This is called **residual magnetism,** and it provides the starting energy for the generator. As the armature starts to rotate, it cuts across the few lines of magnetic force produced by the residual magnetism of the field poles. This is sufficient to induce a voltage in the armature; hence a current starts to flow from the regulator. The current through the field windings quickly builds up the magnetic field, and the generator voltage increases until limited by the voltage regulator.

Voltage-control systems

As mentioned previously, the voltage of a generator depends upon the speed of the armature, the number of windings in the armature, and the strength of the field. In order to regulate the voltage to compensate for changes in load and variation of engine speed, it is necessary that one of the voltage-controlling factors be changed. The only one of these factors which can be changed conveniently is the strength of the field, and this is accomplished by changing the current flow through the field windings by means of an automatically variable resistance.

For many of the light airplane systems, the voltage control unit is of the vibrator type, similar to those used in conventional automobile systems. A schematic diagram of such a system is shown in Fig. 10 · 45. This diagram is simplified to show only the voltage control.

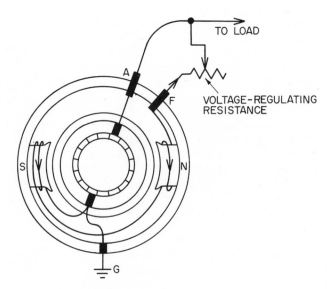

Figure **10 · 44** *Circuit of a shunt generator.*

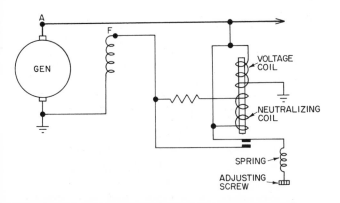

Figure 10·45   Vibrator-type voltage-control unit.

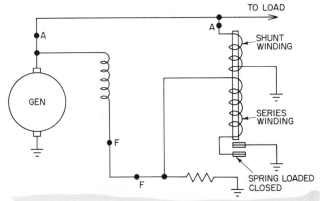

Figure 10·46   Regulator to control ground circuit of field.

This particular voltage control is designed to regulate the current in the positive path of the field circuit. The voltage coil is connected directly across the generator output and continually senses generator voltage. If the voltage becomes greater than the value for which the voltage regulator is adjusted, the strength of the magnetic field produced by the voltage coil in the regulator will overcome the spring pressure which holds the contact points together and the points will open. This will break the direct path to the field of the generator and will cause a resistance to be inserted in the circuit. The current flow through the field windings will be reduced, thus weakening the generator field strength. When this occurs, the generator voltage must decrease. It will be noted that, when the contact points in the regulator are open and current is flowing through the field, the current must also flow through the neutralizing coil. Since this coil is wound in a direction opposite that of the voltage coil, the magnetic effect of this coil is to reduce the magnetism of the electromagnet. At the same time, since the generator voltage is dropping, the magnetic field produced by the voltage coil is reduced. It is obvious then that the total magnetic strength will be quickly reduced and the contact points will be closed by the spring.

The cycle just described occurs many times a second, the actual number being determined by the total load on the circuit and the rpm of the generator. In some regulators the vibration rate is from 50 to 200 cps.

Another commonly employed vibrator-type regulator is used in the ground circuit of the field windings. A schematic diagram of this regulator is shown in Fig. 10·46. In this diagram it can be seen that the field circuit is complete to ground through the series winding when the contact points are closed. At this time maximum current will be flowing through the field coils of the generator. When the generator voltage exceeds the value for which the regulator is adjusted, the current flowing through the two coils in the regulator will produce sufficient magnetic strength to open the contact points. When this occurs, the direct path from the ground to the generator field winding will be broken and the field current will be required to flow through the resistor. This reduces the field current, thus reducing the generator field strength and the output voltage. When the contact points open, current flow through the series winding of the regulator is stopped and the magnetic strength of the regulator electromagnet is greatly reduced. As generator voltage drops, the current flow through the shunt winding drops proportionally, thus further reducing the electromagnet strength. All this occurs in a very small fraction of a second, and the contact points close again. This cycle is repeated many times per second as explained in the previous description.

Reverse-current cutout

Every generator system must have an automatic means for disconnecting the generator from the battery when the generator voltage becomes less than battery voltage. This condition occurs sometimes when an engine is idling, and it always occurs when the engine is stopped. If the battery were left connected to the generator, current from the battery would flow through the generator and probably burn out the armature. If the armature did not burn out, the battery would discharge through the generator.

The **reverse-current cutout** serves as an automatic switch to open the main generator circuit whenever generator voltage drops slightly below battery voltage. A schematic diagram of the cutout relay is shown in Fig. 10·47. In this drawing it will be noted that the electromagnet of the relay has two windings. The series winding consists of a few turns of heavy wire so it can carry the entire output current of the generator. This winding is connected to the contact points through which the current flows to the battery and the electrical load of the system. These contact points are spring loaded in the normally open position. The shunt winding, also called the voltage winding, consists of many turns of fine wire, thus providing sufficient resistance to limit the current flow to a fraction of 1 amp. This low current draw is necessary because the shunt winding is continuously connected across the generator output when the generator is operating.

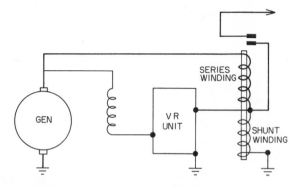

Figure 10·47   Reverse-current cutout relay.

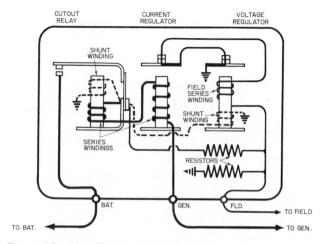

Figure 10·48   Three-unit regulator.

When the generator first starts turning, the reverse-current cutout relay points are open. As voltage builds up to the value determined by the voltage-regulator setting, the shunt winding of the relay produces a magnetic field strong enough to close the relay points. This connects the generator to the system. As long as the generator voltage remains above that of the battery, the relay remains closed and the generator supplies current to charge the battery and for all the system loads. When the engine driving the generator is stopped, the generator voltage falls below battery voltage and the battery voltage causes current to feed backward through the cutout relay series winding. Since this current is opposite in direction to its normal flow, it will produce a magnetic field which opposes the field of the shunt winding. This reduces the total magnetic strength and allows the spring to open the contact points. It must be explained that the shunt winding will continue to produce a magnetic field when the generator voltage drops because it will be supplied by the battery as long as the relay contact points are closed. The series winding is therefore necessary to produce a field opposing the field of the shunt winding.

Current regulator

The three-unit regulator unit used with many generator systems includes a **current regulator** to prevent the generator current output from becoming excessive. This condition can occur when excessively heavy loads are applied to the system. The current regulator is shown in the schematic diagram of Fig. 10·48, which illustrates the complete three-unit regulator arrangement. A study of this diagram will reveal that the current-regulator section of the generator control unit consists of an electromagnet with a series winding through which the entire load current flows and a set of contact points which are connected in series with the voltage-regulator control circuit. When generator output current exceeds the preset value, the magnetic field of the current regulator will become strong enough to open the contact points. This will break the direct ground circuit of the generator field winding and cause the field current to flow through the ground resistor. When this occurs, generator field current will decrease substantially and reduce generator voltage. The re-

duction in voltage will cause a drop in generator output current and a weakening of the magnetic field produced by the current regulator coil. The current regulator contact points will close, and the cycle will repeat in a manner similar to that of the voltage regulator.

Carbon-pile voltage regulator

The most commonly employed type of voltage regulator for d-c electrical systems on larger aircraft is called the **carbon-pile** type because it utilizes a stack of carbon disks as a variable-resistance element for controlling generator field current. A photograph of such a regulator is shown in Fig. 10·49, and a schematic diagram of the circuit is given in Fig. 10·50. In this regulator the variable resistance element is connected in series with the field circuit so any change in the resistance will be accompanied by a change in field current and a corresponding change in generator voltage. The carbon pile consists of alternate disks of hard and soft carbon pressed together by means of a radial leaf spring at one end of the stack. When the

Figure 10·49   Photograph of carbon-pile voltage regulator.

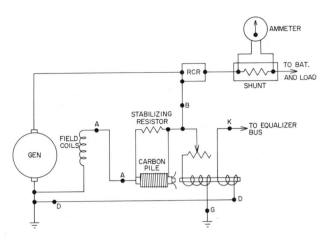

Figure 10·50 *Schematic diagram of carbon-pile regulator circuit.*

disks are pressed together with maximum spring force, the resistance of the pile is low and current flow through the stack will be correspondingly high. At the spring end of the carbon pile is an electromagnet which is shunted across the generator to sense generator voltage. If the voltage becomes excessive, the strength of the electromagnet will exceed the strength of the spring compressing the carbon disks and the pressure will be released. This results in an immediate increase in the resistance of the carbon pile and a reduction of field current. This, of course, reduces the generator voltage. During normal operation of the carbon-pile regulator, when the electrical load is steady, a balanced condition will exist in which the strength of the electromagnet in the regulator will equal the strength of the carbon-pile spring. Any change in electrical load or generator speed will result in a quick adjustment of the regulator to accommodate the new conditions.

In the diagram of Fig. 10·50 is shown a variable resistor connected in series with the voltage coil of the electromagnet. This variable resistor, also called a rheostat, is used to make fine adjustments in the voltage-regulator setting when the system is in operation. Normally the regulator is set, prior to installation, for a voltage value of 28 volts. The adjusting rheostat is in the center position when this value is established. Then, when the regulator is installed and in operation, the generator voltage can be adjusted to balance with other generators connected in the same system.

The stabilizing resistor connected across the carbon pile in the regulator is provided to reduce the surge effect of sudden changes in load and to help reduce arcing between the carbon disks.

An equalizing circuit is usually provided when two or more generators are connected in the same system. This circuit utilizes a winding in each regulator by which the regulator voltage setting will be slightly increased or decreased automatically if the generator is not in balance with the other generators in the system. For example, if a generator is carrying more than its share of the load, current will flow in the equalizer winding in a direction which will strengthen

the magnetic field of the voltage coil. This added magnetic strength will reduce the pressure of the spring on the carbon pile and increase the resistance of the coil. When this occurs, the field current of the generator is reduced and the voltage must decrease. The reduced voltage will cause the generator to drop a part of the load, and the other generators in the system will assume the part of the load dropped by the generator which had previously carried too much.

Differential reverse-current relay

Typical of reverse-current relays utilized in 24-volt d-c systems is the **differential reverse-current relay.** A schematic diagram of the circuit for such a unit is shown in Fig. 10·51. This relay acts as both a master switching device and a reverse-current relay. When the generator is operating, there will be a differential voltage between the GEN terminal and the BAT terminal of the relay. If the contact points in the differential voltage coil circuit are closed, a current will flow in such a direction that the **pilot points** will close. When the generator switch is turned on, the DV points will close, thus completing the DV coil circuit. The current flowing in the DV coil will close the polarized pilot points. When contact points are "polarized," they are magnetized so they will close when subjected to a field of one polarity and will open when a field of the opposite polarity is applied. The pilot points in the diagram are polarized to close when the generator voltage is higher than the battery voltage and to open the differential voltage is in the opposite direction.

In the diagram of Fig. 10·51, it can be seen that the generator switch must be turned on to close the DV points. Then, if the generator voltage is higher than battery voltage, the DV coil will cause the pilot points to close. At this time, current can flow through the main contactor coil, thus causing the main contact points to close and connect the generator to the battery.

If the generator speed is reduced to a point where the battery voltage is higher than the generator voltage, there will be a current flow through the DV coil and

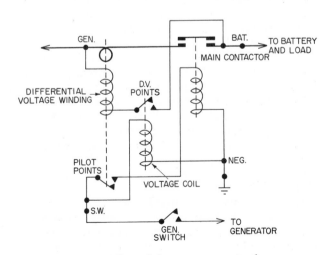

Figure 10·51 *Differential reverse-current relay.*

221

the reverse-current coil in a direction which will cause the pilot points to open. As soon as the pilot points open, the main contactor coil is deenergized and the main contact points open. This disconnects the generator from the battery.

The purpose of the DV points in the DV coil circuit is to disconnect the circuit completely so battery voltage will not bleed back through the DV circuit when the generator is not operating. The DV points are always open when the generator switch is turned off.

Maintenance and adjustment of generator control units

It must be emphasized that some adjustment of the control units described in this section must not be made while the unit is mounted on the aircraft. Other adjustments can be made in accordance with manufacturer's service instructions.

The operation of the vibrator-type voltage and current regulators depends upon the spring tension which normally holds the contact points closed and the air gap between the armature and magnet. If the generator voltage is too low, it can be increased by increasing the spring tension on the voltage points. This can usually be accomplished by bending the tabs to which the armature springs are attached or by adjusting the screw which controls the spring tension. If the air gap is not correct, it can be adjusted by loosening screws and adjusting the contact bracket position.

The cutout relay may require three adjustments. These are the air gap, the point opening distance, and the point closing voltage. The air gap and the point opening adjustments must be made with the battery disconnected. The air gap is adjusted by loosening the screws which hold the armature bracket and raising or lowering the armature. The point opening distance is checked by placing a feeler gage between the contact points when they are open. The opening can be adjusted by bending the upper armature stop or by some other method recommended by the manufacturer.

The closing voltage is checked by connecting a precision voltmeter between the generator terminal of the control unit and ground. The engine speed is then increased until the relay closes. The reading of the voltmeter at this time will give the closing voltage. The closing voltage is adjusted by means of a screw which controls the spring tension on the armature.

A carbon-pile voltage regulator should not be adjusted on the aircraft except with the voltage rheostat. If the generator voltage cannot be adjusted satisfactorily by this means, the regulator should be removed and taken to an electrical shop, where the pile screw and air-gap adjustments can be made in accordance with the indications of precision measuring instruments.

Polarizing the generator field

It has been explained that voltage is induced in the armature windings of a generator when the windings are cutting across lines of magnetic force, that is, a magnetic field, as the armature rotates. It has been further pointed out that the magnetic field is produced as the result of current flow through the field windings. Since the direction (polarity) of the generator output is dependent upon the direction (polarity) of the magnetic field, we can see that the field must be established in the proper direction if the generator is to function correctly.

Occasionally the field poles of a generator will lose their residual magnetism or will have their polarity reversed as the result of an accidental reversal of current through the field windings. In such cases it is necessary to reestablish the correct polarity by "flashing the field." This can be done by various means, but the principle is the same in each case. It is merely necessary to pass a current through the field windings in the proper direction.

For a generator system which completes the ground circuit of the field through the voltage regulator, it is merely necessary to connect a jumper momentarily from the BAT terminal of the regulator to the GEN terminal. This will cause a current to flow through the generator and field in the correct direction to reestablish the field polarity.

If the generator has the field grounded within the generator case, a positive voltage must be applied to the external field terminal. This is accomplished by connecting a jumper momentarily from the BAT terminal to the FLD terminal of the regulator.

When it is necessary to repolarize the field of a generator in a system utilizing a carbon-pile voltage regulator, the regulator should be removed before a positive voltage is applied to the field terminal. The positive voltage can be obtained from the BAT terminal of the reverse-current relay or from any other terminal which has direct connection to the positive terminal of the battery. A jumper should be connected from the positive battery source to the A (field) terminal of the regulator base or to the field terminal of the generator. If the system incorporates a field switch or a field relay in the field circuit, it will be necessary to close the switch or relay contact to allow current to reach the field terminal of the generator when the jumper is connected from the positive battery source to the A terminal of the regulator base. In all cases, the jumper should be connected for only a fraction of a second.

Generator troubleshooting

Generator troubleshooting by the technician depends upon a thorough understanding of the principles explained in this chapter. We may summarize these principles as follows:

1. Generator voltage and current are produced according to the principles of electromagnetism; that is, when a conductor cuts across (links with) a magnetic field, a voltage is induced in the conductor.
2. The voltage produced by a generator is dependent upon the strength of the field, the speed of rotation, and the number of conductors in the armature.
3. The magnetic field for a generator is developed as a result of current flow through the field windings of the generator.
4. Generator voltage is usually governed by means of a voltage regulator which controls the amount of current flowing in the field windings.

5. The reverse-current cutout relay is necessary to disconnect the generator from the battery when the generator voltage is lower than that of the battery.
6. The reverse-current relay closes when the generator voltage reaches a predetermined value and opens when reverse current flows from the battery to the generator. The reverse current value is preset by adjustment of the relay and is usually between 10 and 20 amp.
7. The commutator of a generator acts as a switching device to carry current from the rotating armature to the brushes and thence to the external circuit. The commutator also acts as rectifier to change the alternating current in each winding of the armature to a direct current in the external circuit.
8. The brushes are made of carbon or a carbon compound and maintain constant contact with the commutator under

TROUBLESHOOTING CHART

Trouble	Probable cause	Remedy
Generator produces voltage but ammeter reads zero when a load is turned on.	Generator switch not turned on.	Turn on the switch.
	Main generator circuit breaker open.	Reset circuit breaker.
	Defective or improperly connected ammeter.	Check wiring to ammeter. Replace ammeter if necessary.
	Defective reverse-current relay.	Repair or replace reverse-current relay.
No voltage or amperage from generator.	Polarity of field reversed or lost.	Repolarize the field.
	High resistance between the brushes and commutator.	Repolarize the field. Clean the commutator.
	Generator armature burned out.	Replace generator.
	Generator drive shaft broken.	Replace generator.
	Armature grounded.	Replace generator.
	Terminal connections faulty.	Correct faulty condition.
	Brushes binding.	Remove and clean brushes.
	Brush spring tension too low.	Adjust or replace brush springs.
Residual voltage only.	Faulty connections at voltage regulator.	Correct faulty connections.
	Open circuit in voltage regulator.	Replace voltage regulator.
	Open field circuit or open field in generator.	Check field circuit and continuity of generator field.
	Generator field circuit grounded.	Replace generator or correct grounded circuit.
Voltage too high.	Voltage regulator not properly adjusted.	Adjust voltage regulator.
	Contact points in voltage regulator stuck.	Repair or replace points.
	Open circuit to voltage coil in regulator.	Replace regulator.
	Open circuit in ground lead of regulator (for generator with positive field terminal).	Repair regulator ground.
Generator voltage too low.	Regulator not correctly adjusted.	Adjust voltage regulator.
	Faulty regulator.	Replace regulator.
	Faulty voltmeter.	Replace voltmeter.
	Defective armature.	Replace generator.
Voltage fluctuates.	Loose or dirty connections in field circuit.	Clean and tighten connections.
	Voltage-regulator contact points dirty or pitted.	Repair contact points.
	Regulator base contacts loose or dirty.	Clean and tighten base contacts.
	Generator brushes worn or binding.	Replace or clean brushes.
	Commutator dirty or pitted.	Clean or repair commutator.
Excessive arcing at brushes.	Worn or binding brushes.	Clean or replace brushes.
	Brushes not correctly located.	Adjust location of brushes on commutator.
	Dirty, rough, or eccentric commutator.	Clean or resurface commutator.
	Brush spring tension too low.	Adjust or replace brush springs.
Generator burned out after operation.	Main contact points in reverse-current relay stuck closed.	Replace main contact points and replace generator.
	Generator load too high.	Install generator with capacity for load.
Battery has low charge.	Generator capacity too low.	Install generator with capacity for load.
Improper division of load in a parallel system.	Generator switch not turned on.	Turn on all generator switches.
	Voltage adjustments not properly balanced.	Adjust regulators to balance load.
	Equalizer circuit defective.	Correct faulty conditions in equalizer circuit.

pressure of brush springs. The brushes must be located on the neutral plane of the commutator to prevent short-circuiting between commutator bars and arcing at the brush contact.

When generator trouble exists, the technician should "think through" the possible causes and then eliminate these causes one by one until the difficulty is located. As an example of a trouble which may be encountered, the generator voltage for a particular system may reach a maximum value of 3 volts, regardless of the engine speed. Since a small voltage is being produced, the technician will know that the generator is operating on residual magnetism only and that there is no current flowing through the field circuit. The first unit to check is the voltage regulator because it controls the current through the field. He may find that a wire to the regulator is broken or that the regulator is loose on its base and is not making contact at all points. If the regulator and its connections are found to be satisfactory, then it will be necessary to trace the field circuit from the regulator to the generator. If this circuit is intact, it will probably be necessary to trace the circuit within the generator. This can be done with a continuity tester and ohmmeter or test light. As a last resort, the generator must be removed and repaired.

For troubleshooting generator systems it is useful to employ a troubleshooting chart. The following chart is typical of troubleshooting charts for d-c generator systems.

Generator inspections, maintenance, and repairs

Between engine overhaul periods the generators should require a minimum of service. Normal service usually includes lubrication of bearings (except for generators with sealed bearings), periodic inspections of circuitry, and checking of output. If inspections reveal that brushes are worn beyond acceptable limits, the brushes should be replaced. If the commutator shows signs of arcing or pitting, the cause should be determined and the commutator resurfaced.

A commutator which is slightly pitted or dirty may be resurfaced by the use of fine sandpaper or an abrasive stick designed for the purpose. The sandpaper is placed over the square end of a small wooden stick and then applied to the commutator while the generator is running. The abrasive will clean the surface of the commutator and will also be carried under the brushes, thus grinding the faces of the brushes to fit the contour of the commutator. The abrasive stick will serve the same purpose. Emery cloth must not be used for this purpose because the emery grit is conductive and will lodge between the commutator bars, thus short-circuiting the bars and causing arcing.

The brush springs should be checked with a brush-spring scale to determine whether the spring tension is correct. The hook end of the scale is placed under the brush spring, and the scale lifted until the pressure is completely off the brush. The scale is read at this time to find the brush-spring tension. If the tension is not sufficient, the springs should be adjusted or replaced.

Principles of the d-c motor

A typical d-c motor is constructed in much the same manner as a d-c generator. In fact, some d-c motors can be used either as generators or as motors.

The basic principle of a d-c motor is illustrated in Fig. 10·52. In the first diagram the current flow is such that the armature has a north polarity at the top and a south polarity at the bottom. Since like poles repel and unlike poles attract, it is apparent that the armature will rotate in a clockwise direction. As it turns to a point almost in alignment with the field poles, the commutator switches the connections to the power source and the polarity of the armature is reversed. The like poles are repelled again, and the armature continues to rotate in a clockwise direction.

The armature of a conventional d-c motor is an iron cylinder made up of a stack of laminations. The laminations prevent the flow of eddy currents in the armature, thus preventing overheating and loss of power. The windings of the armature are placed in slots on the surface in the manner described for a generator armature. The ends of the windings are connected to commutator bars so that the windings are in series with one another. When electrical power is connected to the commutator on opposite sides, the current flow through the commutator windings will be such that one side of the armature will have a **north** polarity and the other side will have a **south** polarity. This is illustrated in the drawing of Fig. 10·53. When this condition exists, the side of the armature with the north pole will be repelled from the north field pole and attracted to the south field pole. The same set of conditions exists with respect to the opposite side of the armature. Since the connections to the armature are continuously changing as the commutator turns, the top of the armature in the drawing will always have a north polarity and the bottom will always have a south polarity. Thus the motor will continue to rotate as long as power is applied.

Direct-current motors are often constructed with four field poles. In a motor of this type the armature must be wound in such a manner that four poles will be produced when electric current is flowing through the windings. A schematic diagram illustrating the field of a four-pole armature is shown in Fig. 10·54. This armature is wound so the two sides of each

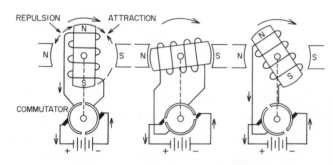

Figure **10·52** Principle of the d-c motor.

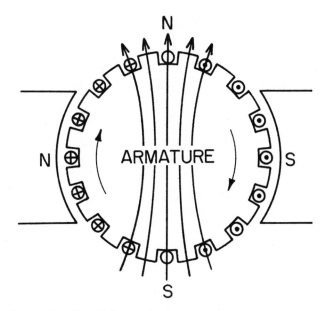

Figure 10·53 *Polarity of a motor armature.*

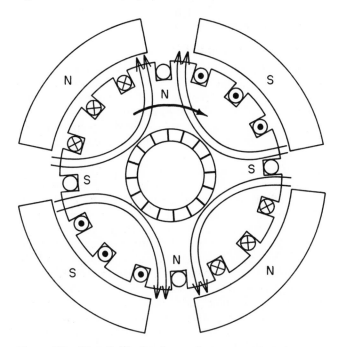

Figure 10·54 *Field of a four-pole motor armature.*

armature coil are 90° apart. Hence, current flowing into the drawing in one winding will be coming out at a point 90° from the point of entrance. The location of the four brushes on the armature is such that the armature poles will be produced at a position with respect to the field poles where the greatest forces of repulsion and attraction are developed. The brushes are alternately negative and positive; that is, brushes 180° apart are of the same polarity and are connected together.

Types of motors

Electric motors are generally designed in three different types. These are **shunt-wound, series-wound,** and **compound-wound.** The electrical arrangement of each of these types is shown in Fig. 10·55.

The shunt-wound motor is also referred to as a **constant-speed** motor because it will always operate at nearly the same rpm, even under a wide variety of loads. When the motor is first started, it will draw a comparatively large surge of current because the armature windings provide a low resistance. However, a voltage will be induced in the armature windings as it rotates because the windings are cutting across the magnetic field produced by the field poles. This induced voltage in the armature is opposite to the voltage being applied from the outside power source. Hence, as the armature speed increases, the induced back voltage (back emf) in the armature will also increase. When the back emf is approximately equal to the applied voltage, the armature speed will no longer increase because the armature field has decreased almost to zero. If a mechanical load is applied to the motor, the armature will tend to slow down and the back emf will decrease. This will allow more current to flow through the armature from the outside power supply, and the armature magnetic field will increase. This, of course, will increase the torque of the armature, and the motor will drive the load if the load is not beyond the capacity of the motor. As the mechanical load to the motor is increased, the current flow through the motor will also increase.

The shunt-wound motor produces a comparatively low starting torque because the current flow through the field windings is low when the motor is first started. This is because the armature windings take the major portion of the current. As the motor speed increases, the armature current decreases and the field current increases, thus increasing the torque. Because of the low starting torque, the shunt-wound motor is not used where the mechanical load is high at the time the motor is started.

The series-wound motor produces a high starting torque because all the current must pass through both the field and the armature windings. For this reason the series motor is used for starting engines and in other applications where a high starting torque is required.

In general, a series motor should not be allowed to operate without a mechanical load applied. If the motor is not driving a load, the rpm may continue to increase until the centrifugal force in the armature causes it to fly apart. This is because the back emf generated in the armature is not sufficient to balance the applied voltage.

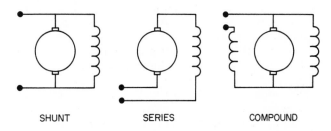

SHUNT   SERIES   COMPOUND

Figure 10·55 *Circuits for different types of motors.*

225

The series motor cannot be used with loads requiring a constant speed because the series motor speed varies according to load. When the mechanical load is high, the motor speed will be low and vice versa.

The compound-wound motor incorporates features of both the shunt and series motors. Since it has a series field, it will produce a good starting torque, and because of the shunt field, it will have a reasonably stable speed characteristic. Compound motors are therefore employed where a substantial starting load exists and a steady rpm is desired.

Inspection and maintenance of motors

The inspection and maintenance of electric motors are similar to those required for generators. Very little maintenance is normally required with the possible exception of bearing lubrication. If the motor has sealed bearings, no lubrication is required. Periodic inspections of the brushes and commutator will enable the technician to correct any discrepancies before failure occurs.

AIRCRAFT STORAGE BATTERIES

Theory of electrochemical action

The production of an electric current through electrochemical action is based upon the fact that dissimilar metals, when placed in a particular chemical solution, will react with the solution and with each other, causing at least one of the metals to be decomposed and free electrons to be released.

If we place a strip of zinc and a strip of copper in a glass container so the strips of metal do not touch each other and then pour a solution of sulfuric acid in the container, we note that chemical action takes place at the zinc strip while the copper strip is apparently not affected. The action at the zinc strip is shown by the formation of hydrogen bubbles which break free and rise to the surface of the liquid. These bubbles are the result of the combination of zinc ions with the sulfate ions of the sulfuric acid to form zinc sulfate. As each zinc ion combines with a sulfate ion, two electrons are released at the zinc strip. At the same time, hydrogen is released from the sulfuric acid molecules, and this hydrogen forms in bubbles at the zinc plate. The chemical action which takes place may be expressed as follows:

$$Zn + H_2SO_4 = ZnSO_4 + H_2$$

Since electrons are released on the zinc strip, the strip becomes negatively charged. If we connect the zinc strip and the copper strip to a voltmeter as shown in the drawing of Fig. 10·56, we observe that there is a potential difference of more than 1 volt between the two strips. When the two strips are connected together, the electrons will flow from the zinc strip to the copper strip.

All ordinary batteries, including dry cells and storage batteries, operate accordingly to the principle explained above. If the battery elements are consumed,

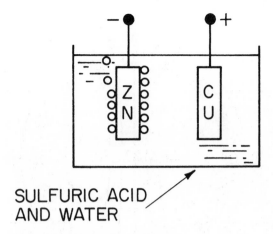

SULFURIC ACID AND WATER

Figure 10·56 Electrochemical action.

as in the case of the zinc strip, the battery cannot be recharged. On the other hand, some combinations of materials make it possible to reverse the chemical action which takes place when the battery is discharging. A battery or cell of this type is commonly called a **storage** or **secondary** battery.

The lead-acid storage battery

The **lead-acid** storage battery is so named because the active materials are lead, lead peroxide, and sulfuric acid. The positive plates of the battery are composed of a compound of lead peroxide (PbO_2), and the negative plates are composed of pure, spongy lead (Pb). The active materials are held in lead grids, thus forming the plates.

The chemical action which takes place in a storage battery as the battery discharges involves the combining of sulfuric acid with the active material in the plates to form lead sulfate and water. The sulfuric acid (H_2SO_4) breaks up into hydrogen ions (H_2) and sulfate ions (SO_4). The sulfate ions combine with the lead of the negative plate to form lead sulfate ($PbSO_4$) and with the lead peroxide (PbO_2) of the positive plate to form lead sulfate and oxygen. The combining of the lead in the negative plate with the SO_4 ions releases electrons on the negative plate. This, of course, is what makes the plate assume a negative charge. The oxygen combines with the hydrogen ions in solution to form water. When the oxygen ions leave the positive plate, they remove electrons from the plate, thus causing it to assume a positive charge.

The potential difference between the plates of a lead-acid storage cell is about 2.2 volts when there is no load on the cell. Three cells are connected in series to make a 6-volt battery, and six cells in series to make a 12-volt battery. Thus, a storage battery of any desired voltage can be produced by connecting the correct number of secondary cells in series.

Construction of storage batteries

A typical storage battery is composed of parts such as those illustrated in Fig. 10·57. These are the **battery case,** made of hard rubber or plastic; the **cell containers,**

VENT CAP   TERMINAL   PLATE STRAP   CELL COVER
CELL CONNECTOR
CASE
SEPARATOR   PLATE

Figure **10·57** *Construction of a lead-acid storage battery. (Electric Storage Battery Co.)*

which may be integral with or separate from the battery case; the **plates** joined by **plate straps** to form **plate groups;** the **plate separators,** composed of wood, porous rubber, or glass fiber; the **terminal posts,** attached to the plate straps; the **separator protector;** the **cell covers** in which are placed the **vent caps;** the **cell connectors;** and the **electrolyte.**

As previously mentioned, the plates of the lead-acid cell consist of lead grids in which is held the active material. The active material for the positive plate is lead peroxide, and for the negative plate it is spongy lead. The lead material for the grid includes additional elements to strengthen and improve the conductivity of the plates. Among the elements commonly used in the grids are antimony and silver.

The plates are assembled into plate groups and are connected together by means of the plate straps. The negative group includes one plate more than the mating positive group in order to provide a negative plate on the outside of each of the assembled groups. Since the positive plates are softer and less durable than the negative plates, the outer negative plate in each cell group serves to protect the positive plates.

The plate groups are assembled into cell groups with separators between each pair of plates. The separators are made of wood, or they may include glass-fiber wool mats together with wood or porous rubber separators. The separators must allow a free passage of electrolyte so they will not interfere with the electrical and chemical action which must take place within the cell. When wood separators are employed, the ribbed side of each separator is placed next to the

positive plates to permit the shedding of decomposed active material.

Cell containers are designed to provide support for the assembled plate groups and hold the electrolyte. These containers are made of hard rubber composition or plastic. In the bottom of each cell container are four ribs to serve as plate supports. Two of these ribs support the positive plates, and two support the negative plates. This arrangement leaves a space underneath the plates for the accumulation of sediment which would otherwise tend to short-circuit the plates.

Cell covers are sealed into the tops of the cell containers with a special sealing compound. The compound is applied in a molten condition so it will completely fill the space between the cover and the container. When the compound cools, it remains sufficiently soft to provide a cushioning effect between the cover and the container and between the separate cells.

The terminal posts extend through holes in the cell covers to provide means for connecting the cells to one another. Usually a lead strap called the cell connector is fused into the terminal posts to connect the negative post of one cell to the positive post of the next, thus providing a series circuit. The spaces around the terminal posts are sealed to prevent the leakage of electrolyte.

The vent caps which are screwed into openings in the cell covers are designed to prevent the leakage of electrolyte and also to allow gases to escape from the cells. Common types of nonspill vent caps are illustrated in Fig. 10·58. This illustration shows the tubular vent cap used in a battery which has a large space above the plates to hold the electrolyte when the battery is on its side or inverted. The open tip of the cap is positioned where it can never be covered by the electrolyte. The other type of cap shown is hollow and contains a lead valve which closes the vent hole whenever the battery is in a position where the electrolyte could flow out the vent. It must be emphasized that each battery cell must be vented to allow the escape of hydrogen gas. During the charging process, especially when the battery is near full charge,

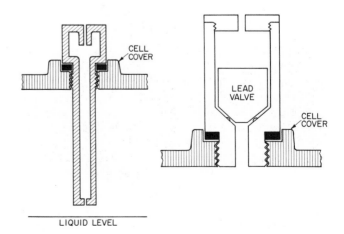

CELL COVER
LEAD VALVE
CELL COVER
LIQUID LEVEL

Figure **10·58** *Nonspill vent caps.*

227

a substantial amount of hydrogen gas is released from the electrolyte. This gas must be vented to prevent a pressure explosion of the cell.

A recently designed battery vent cap incorporates a sintered alumina (aluminum oxide) plug in the top of the cap. This plug is sufficiently porous to allow the escape of gas, but it will not allow the passage of electrolyte.

Some aircraft storage batteries are constructed with an integral metal case on the outside of the rubber or plastic case. This metal case, which is usually made of aluminum, protects the battery from damage and also serves as a radio shield. The metal cover of the case provides a sealed compartment which is vented to the outside of the airplane, thus providing for the removal of explosive hydrogen and corrosive acid fumes.

The main battery terminals are usually brass studs to which cables can be attached by means of washers and wing nuts. In many instances, smooth prongs are screwed on the terminal studs to provide for quick-disconnect fittings. A quick-disconnect fitting manufactured by the Cannon Electric Company is shown in Fig. 10·59. This plug-type fitting is quickly connected or disconnected merely by turning the large knob on the outside of the fittings.

Alkaline batteries

The alkaline-type secondary (storage) battery provides a very long life with great dependability; how-

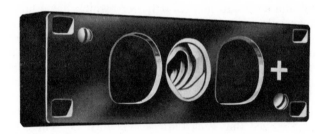

BASE—ATTACHED TO BATTERY CASE

PLUG ASSEMBLY—ATTACHED TO CABLES

Figure 10·59 A quick-disconnect plug.

ever, the cost is greater than that of the lead-acid cell. The nickel-cadmium battery is considered one of the best of the alkaline cells, and it is manufactured in a wide variety of sizes and shapes. The positive plates of the cell are composed of nickel hydroxide mixed with a special type of graphite, and the negative plates are made of a mixture of cadmium oxide and iron oxide. The electrolyte is potassium hydroxide dissolved in water. Cell containers are constructed of nickel-plated steel.

The working voltage of the nickel-cadmium cell is about 1.2 volts; hence a 6-volt battery contains five cells. As is true of the lead-acid battery, the capacity of the nickel-cadmium battery is dependent upon the total plate area and the thickness of the plates.

One of the principal advantages of the nickel-cadmium battery is its long life. The battery can be left in any state of charge for several years without any appreciable deterioration.

Storage battery capacity and ratings

Storage batteries are rated according to voltage and ampere-hour capacity. The ampere-hour rating is usually based upon a discharge period of 5 hr; hence when we state that a particular battery is rated at 34 amp-hr, we mean that the fully charged battery can furnish current at the rate of approximately 6.8 amp for a period of 5 hr before the battery is discharged. The total amount of power a battery can supply is affected by the rate of discharge. If a battery is discharged at a rate greater than the 5-hr rate, the total power furnished will be less than it would at the 5-hr rate. On the other hand, if the battery is discharged at less than the 5-hr rate, the total power available will be greater than it would at the 5-hr rate.

As previously mentioned, the capacity of a battery depends upon the total area of the plates and the thickness of the plates. As a rule, when the plates are the same size and thickness, the capacity will be proportional to the number of plates.

Testing lead-acid storage batteries

The most common method for testing the state of charge in a storage battery is to use a hydrometer and test the specific gravity of the electrolyte. The electrolyte for a fully charged battery should have a specific gravity of 1.300. As a battery ages, this will slowly decrease, partially because of hard sulfate formation in the plates and partially because a small amount of the sulfuric acid is carried away as fumes. It is common practice to consider the battery fully charged if the specific gravity of the electrolyte is between 1.275 and 1.300.

If the specific-gravity reading is less than 1.240 for an aircraft battery, the charge is considered low because at this level the battery will not carry a heavy sustained load, such as that required for starting the engine, for more than a very few minutes. The procedure for testing a storage battery with the hydrometer is as follows and is illustrated in Fig. 10·60:

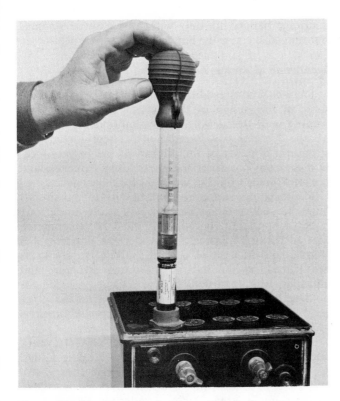

Figure 10·60   Testing a battery with a hydrometer.

1. Remove the cell cap, and insert the tip of the hydrometer into the electrolyte.
2. Squeeze the bulb of the hydrometer, and release it to draw the electrolyte into the tube.
3. When sufficient electrolyte has entered the tube to float the hydrometer indicator, hold the tube vertically so the indicator will float free.
4. Read the numerical indication at the liquid level on the float stem.

To test the general condition of a storage battery, a **high-rate discharge tester** is often used. This tester consists of a heavy load resistance and a voltmeter. The prongs of the instrument are pressed against the two terminals of the cell being tested, and the reading of the voltmeter is noted. Normally, for a good cell which is fully charged, the reading may be as low as 1.7 volts, and this reading will hold steady for the short time that the tester is connected. If the reading is somewhat lower than 1.7 volts and starts to decrease immediately, it is known that the cell is either discharged or worn out. If all the cells of a battery give the same reading, it is an indication that the battery is in good condition.

Another simple but effective test is to connect a nominal load (10 to 15 amp) to the battery and then read the voltage of each cell with a voltmeter. Cells in poor condition will read lower than the good cells, and a cell which is short-circuited will give a reverse reading.

Charging storage batteries

Storage batteries can be charged by either one of two methods. On the aircraft or in any system utilizing a voltage regulator to control the generator voltage, the battery is charged by the **constant-voltage** method. This means that the charging source is adjusted to provide a voltage slightly above that of the battery. In a 24-volt system, the battery is nominally rated at 24 volts and the generator is set to deliver 28 volts. The actual voltage of the battery will rise to about 26.4 volts as it reaches the fully charged condition; hence the difference between the battery voltage and the generator voltage will be only 1.6 volts when the battery is fully charged. This small voltage is enough to maintain the charge of the battery, but it will not cause it to overcharge or gas excessively.

During the operation of an airplane the electrical power system is subjected to a variety of electrical loads. As loads, such as radio or lights, are turned on, there is a very slight voltage drop in the generator output. This is quickly sensed by the voltage regulator, which then causes more current to flow through the generator field, thus bringing the generator voltage back to the required level. When this occurs, the generator amperage is increased to take care of the additional electrical load, and the battery is not required to supply power for the circuit.

It should be noted that the battery does not supply any power for the aircraft electrical system during normal operation of the aircraft. In flight the battery could be completely disconnected and the aircraft electrical system would continue to operate satisfactorily. The battery does serve to stabilize the electrical system by absorbing voltage surges and filling in when the voltage drops momentarily as a result of turning on a heavy motor load.

The constant-voltage system may be employed to charge a large number of batteries provided that the capacity of the source is sufficient to maintain the voltage at a constant level and provided that the batteries all have the same voltage rating. When this system is employed, all the batteries are connected in parallel as shown in Fig. 10·61. The ampere-hour rating of a battery makes little difference when charging by the constant voltage method. The low-rated battery will charge more rapidly then the others, but when it is fully charged, it will draw very little current from the system.

In **constant-current** charging, the batteries must have the same ampere-hour rating because they are con-

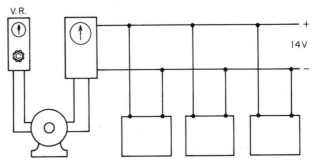

Figure 10·61   Charging with a constant-voltage system.

nected in series and all receive the same current. If some batteries have a lower capacity than others, the low-capacity batteries will be charged first and will gas furiously as the charging current continues to pass through them.

The usual procedure for constant-current charging is to set the charging source to a given amperage for a specified number of hours and then reduce the amperage in steps as the batteries near the fully charged state. The batteries must not be charged too rapidly, or they will become overheated and boil. This will cause the loss of electrolyte and may buckle the plates, thus seriously damaging the battery. In general, it is good practice to keep the battery temperature below 110°F when charging.

Safety precautions

There are three principal sources of danger when handling and servicing storage batteries. These are (1) the presence of hydrogen gas, (2) the corrosive and burning action of the sulfuric acid in the electrolyte, and (3) the possibility of short-circuiting the terminals.

There have been many battery explosions as the result of igniting the hydrogen gas which is constantly present in the space above the electrolyte. This danger is particularly acute in the vicinity of batteries which are on charge or which have recently been on charge. The technician handling batteries should be constantly alert to this danger and make sure that no open flames or sparks are permitted in the vicinity of batteries. It is especially important that all electrical loads and power sources be turned off before connecting or disconnecting a storage battery. If a load is on the circuit, or if a charging source is turned on, sparks will be emitted when the battery is connected or disconnected, and these sparks can easily ignite the hydrogen gas.

The handling of sulfuric acid and electrolyte requires great care to avoid the possibility of being burned by the acid. When acid and water are being mixed to provide an electrolyte of the correct specific gravity, the acid should be poured into the water carefully and never the reverse. The acid may boil and spit if water is added, and this can result in severe burns. The acid not only will burn the skin but will also eat holes in the clothing and cause severe corrosion of many metals. Therefore, whenever acid is spilled, it should be rinsed away with water and neutralized with an alkaline solution such as baking soda and water. Finally, the area should be rinsed with clear water and dried.

A storage battery is capable of delivering a current of several hundred amperes when short-circuited. Care must be taken, therefore, that metal tools, wires, and similar conductive items are not dropped or laid on a battery where they may contact the terminals. If a battery is short-circuited with a pair of pliers or a screwdriver, the arc at the point of contact will melt both the terminal and the tool. A small wire connected between the terminals of a storage battery will immediately become white hot and melt. Short-circuiting

a storage battery not only will cause external damage but may also cause the battery plates to warp.

Installation of storage batteries

The conditions established by an aircraft manufacturer in the design of the battery installation must comply with the airworthiness requirements set forth by the Federal Air Regulations. These include the structural integrity of the aircraft at the battery location and the provision for eliminating explosive and noxious fumes from the vicinity of the battery.

The structure supporting the battery in the aircraft must be such that no damage will occur under any possible operating condition. It must be remembered that a battery represents considerable concentrated weight, and in case of a hard landing, severe loads are placed on the battery mounting structure and adjacent aircraft structure. The means provided for holding the battery in place must also meet the structural requirements. The hold-down bolts and brackets must withstand all possible operating loads.

The battery compartment must be suitably ventilated to remove hydrogen gas and electrolyte fumes. As previously explained, the hydrogen gas is explosive and the acid fumes will corrode all unprotected metal surfaces in the area. If nickel-cadmium batteries are installed in the aircraft, the alkaline electrolyte (potassium hydroxide) will also present corrosion problems; hence the compartment must be protected against corrosion.

The metal aircraft structure in the vicinity of the battery can be protected by the application of bituminous acidproof paint. If the battery is located in a sealed compartment, the entire area within the compartment should be coated with acidproof paint. The compartment should be provided with a venting system to carry away the gases and fumes from the battery. A small ram air scoop on one side can be used to bring air into the compartment, and an outlet vent on the opposite side, headed away from the wind, is satisfactory for the removal of the gases and fumes. The venting system should be designed so the hydrogen concentration will never exceed 1 percent under any flight conditions.

A battery which is enclosed in a metal case is provided with vent connections to permit the attachment of vent tubes. One tube is connected to a ram air scoop, and the other leads to an outlet which carries the gases outside and clear of the aircraft structure. In some cases a neutralizing sump is placed in the line between the battery case outlet and the tube leading outside the aircraft. This neutralizing sump contains a felt pad saturated with a solution of baking soda to neutralize the acid fumes.

The top of the battery should be kept clean and dry to prevent the slow leakage of current. The battery electrolyte is conductive; hence current will leak slowly between the battery terminals if electrolyte is permitted to remain on the area between the terminals.

The cable terminals of the battery should be inspected frequently to observe any formation of corrosion. When corrosion is found, the cable should be disconnected from the terminal and all corrosion residue should be removed. After the parts have been thoroughly cleaned and dried, they should be coated with petrolatum and reconnected. The petrolatum will prevent the further formation of corrosion for several weeks.

REVIEW QUESTIONS

1. Of what is an electric current composed?
2. What is a *free* electron?
3. What is the difference between a conductor and an insulator?
4. Explain *negative* and *positive* charges.
5. What is a *static* charge?
6. Explain *voltage* and *amperage*.
7. Define *coulomb*.
8. Express Ohm's law in two different ways.
9. If 24 volts is applied to a circuit having a resistance of 6 ohms, what will be the current flow?
10. If a current of 5 amp is flowing through a resistor with a value of 3 ohms, what will the voltage drop be across the resistor?
11. How much electrical power is consumed by a motor which draws a current of 10 amp in a 12-volt system?
12. What is the total resistance in a circuit when resistors of 3, 6, and 8 ohms are connected in series?
13. Find the total resistance in a circuit having resistors of 4, 8, and 12 ohms connected in parallel.
14. In Fig. 10·62, what is the total resistance?
15. In the same circuit, what is the voltage drop across R_3?
16. In the same circuit, what is the current through R_1?
17. What size electrical cable would you use in a 28-volt circuit for a 1-hp motor which is 75 percent efficient?
18. Define alternating current.
19. What is a magnetic substance? A magnetized substance?
20. How can we explain magnetism?
21. What is an electromagnet?
22. How would you determine the magnetic strength of a coil?
23. How would you determine the direction of the magnetic field of a coil?
24. Explain electromagnetic induction.
25. State the principle of Lenz's law.

26. Describe a transformer, and tell how the output can be determined.
27. What effect is produced by capacitance in an a-c circuit?
28. Compare the effect of capacitance with that of inductance.
29. How is a capacitor constructed?
30. What is the total capacitance when two 100-μf capacitors are connected in series?
31. Find the capacitive reactance when a 5-μf capacitor and a 10-μf capacitor are connected in parallel in a 400-cycle a-c circuit.
32. How much inductance must be placed in the foregoing circuit to produce a condition of resonance?
33. What is a three-phase a-c circuit?
34. Why is a-c power often superior to d-c for a power circuit?
35. What electrical principle is used in a generator?
36. Name the principal parts of a generator.
37. What part of a generator circuit is employed for voltage control?
38. Explain the difference between the operation of a vibrator-type voltage regulator and a carbon-pile type.
39. Why is a reverse-current cutout relay required in a generator circuit?
40. Describe the operation of a differential reverse-current relay.
41. How would you *polarize,* or "flash," a generator field?
42. Where would you look for trouble if the generator output was 3 volts with the generator operating at normal speed?
43. What trouble would be indicated if you found a generator armature overheated or burned out after normal operation?
44. How do you seat generator brushes?
45. What may be wrong if there is excessive arcing at the brushes?
46. Why is a series motor used where starting loads are high?
47. What may happen if a series motor is operated with no load?
48. What type of motor is used for constant-speed operations?
49. Explain electrochemical action.
50. What is the open circuit voltage of a lead-acid cell?
51. Describe the construction of a lead-acid cell.
52. What is the full charge reading of a hydrometer for a lead-acid cell?
53. What electrolyte is used in an alkaline battery?
54. How is the capacity of a lead-acid battery indicated?
55. What precautions must be taken in handling the electrolyte?
56. Give two methods for testing lead-acid cells.
57. What is meant by constant-voltage charging?
58. What are the requirements for the battery compartment in an airplane?
59. What precautions must be taken in the vicinity of batteries which are being charged?
60. Describe a battery vent system.
61. What treatment is recommended for the prevention of corrosion at the battery terminals?

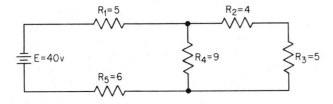

Figure 10·62

Ignition Systems and Magneto Timing

CHAPTER 11

PRINCIPLES OF IGNITION

Ignition event in the four-stroke cycle

During the first event of the four-stroke five-event cycle, the piston moves downward as a charge of combustible fuel and air is admitted into the cylinder. This is the **intake** or **admission stroke.** During the second event, which is the **compression stroke,** the crankshaft continues to rotate and the piston moves upward to compress the fuel/air mixture.

As the piston approaches the top of its stroke within the cylinder, an electric spark jumps across the points of the spark plugs and ignites the compressed fuel/air mixture. This is the **ignition event,** or the third of the five events. Having been ignited, the fuel/air mixture burns and expands, and the resulting gas pressure drives the piston downward. This causes the crankshaft to revolve. Since it is the only stroke and event that furnishes power to the crankshaft, it is usually called the **power stroke,** and it is the fourth event. The **exhaust stroke** is the fifth event. These facts have been presented before, but they must be reviewed briefly in order to understand aircraft-engine ignition.

The electric spark jumps between the electrodes (points) of a spark plug that is installed in the cylinder head or combustion chamber of the engine cylinder. The ignition system furnishes sparks periodically to each cylinder at a certain position of piston and valve travel.

Essential parts of an ignition system

The essential parts of an ignition system are a source of high voltage, a timing device to cause the high-voltage source to function at the set position of piston travel, a distributing mechanism to route the high voltage to the various cylinders in the correct sequence, spark plugs to carry the high voltage into the cylinders of the engine and ignite the fuel/air mixture, control switches, and the necessary wiring. The source of the high voltage may be either a **magneto** driven by the engine or an **induction coil** connected to a battery or a generator. In general, it is correct to state that the source of high voltage on most piston-type aircraft powerplants is a magneto, although some have a combination of magneto and battery ignition. Regardless of the source of high voltage, the purpose is to ignite the fuel/air mixture.

Gas-turbine engines utilize ignition systems principally for starting because the fuel/air mixture is self-igniting after it is first started. It is common practice to turn the ignition on during takeoff and sometimes at high altitudes so the engine will restart immediately if a flameout should occur.

All parts of the aircraft ignition system are enclosed in either flexible or rigid metal covering called **shielding.** This metal covering "receives" and "grounds out" radiations from the ignition system, which would otherwise cause interference (noise) in the radio receiving equipment installed in the airplane.

Magneto ignition

Magneto ignition is superior to battery ignition because it produces a hotter spark at high engine speeds and it is a self-contained unit, not dependent upon any external source of electrical energy.

The magneto is a special type of generator that produces electric pulsations of high voltage for purposes of ignition. When an aircraft engine is started, the engine turns over too slowly to permit the magneto to operate; hence, it is necessary to use a **booster coil vibrating interrupter,** or **impulse coupling** for ignition during starting.

The impulse coupling is designed to give the magneto a momentary high rotational speed. This coupling is a springlike mechanical linkage between the engine and magneto shaft which "winds up" and "lets go" at the proper moment for spinning the magneto shaft, thus supplying the necessary high voltage for ignition. During the "winding-up" process, the starter impulse coupling also retards the spark a predetermined amount to prevent backfiring.

When two magnetos fire at the same or approximately the same time through two sets of spark plugs, this is known as a **double, or dual, magneto-ignition system.** The principal advantages of the dual magneto-ignition system are the following: (1) If one magneto or any part of one magneto system fails to operate, the other magneto system will furnish ignition until the disabled system functions again, and (2) two sparks, igniting the fuel/air mixture in each cylinder simultaneously at two different places, give a more complete and quick combustion than a single spark; hence, the power of the engine is increased. The magnetos, which are identical, may be turned on separately (for testing) or both at the same time (during normal operation), by means of an ignition switch. On radial engines, it has been a standard practice to use the right-hand magneto for the front set of spark plugs and the left-hand magneto for the rear set of spark plugs. All certificated reciprocating engines must be equipped with dual ignition.

Dual ignition may be set to operate at the same instant (synchronized) or at slightly different intervals (staggered). When **staggered** ignition is used, each of the two sparks occurs at a different time. The spark plug on the exhaust side of the cylinder always fires first because the slower rate of burning of the expanded and diluted fuel/air mixture at this point in the cylinder makes it necessary to have an advance in the ignition timing.

The magnetic circuit

The magnetic circuit of the magneto may be designed in different ways. One type of design uses **rotating permanent magnets** having two, four, and even eight magnetic poles. These magnets are often made of **alnico,** an alloy of aluminum, iron, nickel, and cobalt that retains magnetism for an indefinite period of time. The magnets rotate under **pole pieces,** which complete a magnetic circuit through a coil core.

Another type of magneto design makes use of **stationary permanent magnets** and a system of rotating inductors which complete the magnetic circuit through the coil core by two different paths, thereby providing two directions through the coil core for the magnetic flux.

The first type of design is called the **rotating-magnet type,** and the second is called the **inductor-rotor type.** The rotating-magnet type is more widely used in aircraft ignition.

Principles of the rotating-magnet type of magneto

The properties of the common horseshoe magnet are present in the rotating magnet of the magnetos manufactured by the Scintilla Division of the Bendix Corporation. These magnetos are typical examples of the rotating-magnet type.

The horseshoe-shaped permanent magnet shown in Fig. 11·1 has a magnetic field that is represented by many individual paths of invisible magnetic flux, commonly known as "lines" of flux. Each of these lines of flux within the magnet itself extends from the north pole of the magnet (marked with the letter *N*) through the intervening air space to the south pole (marked with the letter *S*), thereby forming the closed loop indicated in the drawing. These lines of magnetic flux are invisible, but their presence can be verified by placing a sheet of paper over the magnet and sprinkling

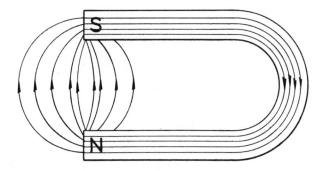

Figure 11·1   Permanent magnet and field.

the paper with iron filings. The iron filings will then arrange themselves in definite positions along the lines of flux which compose the magnetic field represented by the solid lines containing arrows.

The lines of flux repel one another; hence, they tend to spread out in the air space between the poles of the magnet, as shown in Fig. 11·1. They also tend to seek the path of least resistance between the poles of the magnet. A laminated soft-iron bar provides an easier path for the lines of flux flowing between the poles than air; consequently the lines will crowd together if such a bar (sometimes called a **keeper**) is provided near the magnet. The lines of flux then assume the locations and directions shown in Fig. 11·2, where they are concentrated within the bar instead of being spread out as they were in the air space of Fig. 11·1. This heavy concentration of lines of flux within the bar is described as a condition of high "density."

The direction taken by the lines of flux in the laminated soft-iron bar placed in a magnetic field is determined by the polarity of the permanently magnetized horseshoe magnet. For example, in Figs. 11·1 and 11·2, the direction of flow is from the north pole to the south pole. The direction would be reversed if the north pole were the upper pole in the illustrations and the south pole were the lower pole of the pictures.

If the permanent magnet is made of **alnico, permalloy,** or some hardened steel, it can retain a large portion of the magnetism induced in it when it was originally

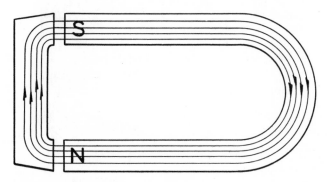

Figure 11·2   Permanent magnet with flux passing through an iron bar.

magnetized. Since the laminated iron bar is of magnetically "soft" iron, it does not retain much of the magnetism when magnetic lines of flux pass through it. This makes it possible to change the direction of the lines of flux by turning the magnet over so that the north pole of the magnet in Figs. 11·1 and 11·2 is at the top instead of the bottom of the picture.

Current induced in a coil

A horseshoe magnet can be used to show that a current can be generated or **induced** in a coil of wire. The coil for demonstration purposes should be made with a few turns of heavy copper wire and connected to a **galvanometer,** an instrument that indicates any flow of current by the deflection of its needle (pointer), as shown in Fig. 11 · 3.

The lines of flux of the horseshoe magnet pass through or "link" the turns of wire in the coil when in the position shown in Fig. 11 · 3. When one line of flux passes through one turn of a coil, it is called one **flux linkage.** If one line of flux passes through five turns of a coil, five flux linkages are produced. If five lines of flux pass through five turns of a coil, there are 25 flux linkages, and so on.

In Fig. 11 · 3a, if the horseshoe magnet is brought toward the coil from a remote position to the position shown in the drawing, the number of lines of flux, which are linking the coil, constantly increases during the motion of the magnet. In more technical language, there is a change in **flux linkages** as the horseshoe magnet moves toward the coil, and this change induces a voltage in the coil of wire. This voltage, or electromotive force (emf), causes an electric current to flow

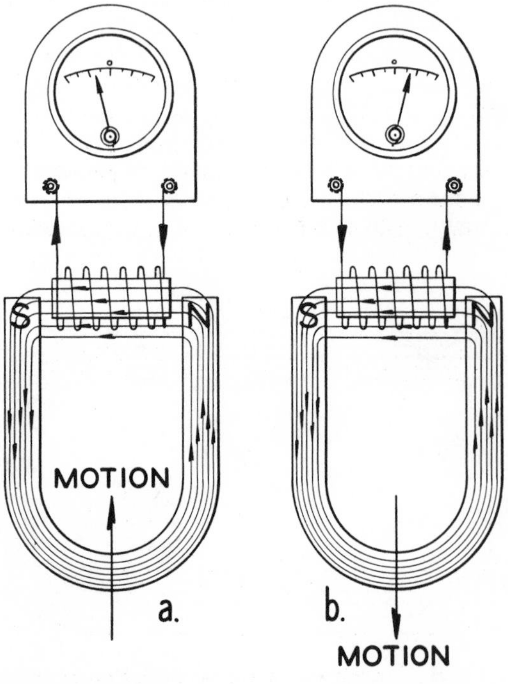

Figure 11 · 3   Inducing current with magnetic field.

around through the circuit, and this is indicated by the deflection of the galvanometer needle.

In Fig. 11 · 3b, if the horseshoe magnet is moved back away from the coil, the flux linkages constantly decrease during this movement, and this change in flux linkages induces a current in the coil of wire **in the opposite direction,** as indicated by the movement of the galvanometer needle.

The voltage induced in the coil of wire is proportional to the **rate of change of flux linkages.** The flux linkages can be increased by adding more turns in the coil of wire or by using a stronger magnet having more lines of flux. The **rate** involves an element of time and can be increased by moving the horseshoe magnet near the coil faster, thus increasing the speed of flux change. When any of these methods for increasing the rate of change of flux linkages are tried during an experiment, the galvanometer needle deflection indicates the magnitude of the induced current.

There must be a change in flux linkages to induce a voltage. Voltage is not induced in the coil of wire if the horseshoe magnet is held stationary, regardless of the strength of the magnet or the number of turns of wire in the coil. This principle is applied to the magneto because the lines of flux must have a magnetic path through the coil in the first place and then **there must be a movement of either the coil or the magnet** to produce the change in flux linkages. A voltage in the same proportions could be induced in the coil of wire by holding the horseshoe magnet stationary and moving the coil. This would provide the necessary relative movement to produce the change of flux linkages.

We have previously stated that magnetos can be divided into two types or classes: (1) the rotating-magnet type and (2) the inductor-rotor type. The above explanation of the two methods of changing the flux linkages to induce voltage should clarify this earlier statement. However, we shall continue our discussion of the rotating-magnet type of magneto as exemplified by the Bendix Scintilla aircraft magnetos.

Whenever there is a current passing through a coil of wire, a magnetic field is established, which has the same properties as the magnetic field of the horseshoe or permanent magnet previously described. An example is the ordinary electromagnet with which almost everyone is familiar, one of its more common applications being an electric doorbell.

Lenz's law

Lenz's law can be stated in terms of induced voltage thus: **An induced voltage, whether caused by self-inductance or mutual inductance, always operates in such a direction as to oppose the source of its creation.**

The same thing can be stated in simpler terms thus: When a change in flux linkages produces a voltage which establishes a current in a coil of wire, the direction of the current is always such that its magnetic field opposes the motion or change in flux linkages which produced the current. Lenz's law is of the greatest importance to the operation of the magneto, as explained further in this text.

In Fig. 11·3, when the magnet is moved toward the coil, the current flows up the left-hand wire, through the galvanometer, and down the right-hand wire, as shown by the arrows in Fig. 11·3. When the magnet is moved away from the coil, the current flows up the right-hand wire, through the galvanometer, and down the left-hand wire, as shown in Fig. 11·3b. In this experiment, the coil must be wound exactly as shown in the picture and the poles of the magnet must be as they are in Fig. 11·3.

Left-hand rule

The polarity of a magnetic field can be determined when the direction of the current and the direction of the winding of a coil are known. If the wire is grasped with the left hand, and if the fingers of the left hand extend around the coil in the direction of the current, the thumb will always point in the direction of the flux, or the north end of the field. This is called the **left-hand rule.**

If the left-hand rule is applied to the current in Fig. 11·3, it will be found that the field which the current establishes opposes the **increase** or change of flux linkages. While the magnet is being moved up toward the coil in Fig. 11·3a, the usual tendency is to **increase** the flux through the coil core in the direction from right to left of the illustration, as shown by the arrows. However, as soon as the flux starts to increase, a current begins to flow in the coil, it establishes a field of direction from left to right, and this field opposes the increase of magnetic flux and actually exerts a small mechanical force that tends to push the magnet away from the coil.

In Fig. 11·3b, when the magnet is moving away from the coil, the current flows up the right-hand wire, through the galvanometer, and down the left-hand wire. In accordance with the statement of the left-hand rule, the field of the coil is now helping the field of the magnet. As the magnet is moved away from the coil, the flux linkages decrease, but as soon as the flux linkages begin to decrease, a current flows in the coil and sets up a magnetic field that opposes the change, following the principle of Lenz's law. However, the change is now a decrease; hence, the field of the coil now helps the magnetic field, aiding it in its effort to avoid decreasing. A small mechanical pull is actually exerted on the magnet by the coil tending to resist the motion of the magnet away from the coil.

If the circuit of the coil is opened, no current can flow in the wire because there is not enough voltage to force the current across the gap where the wire in the circuit is broken or disconnected. To jump the gap requires high voltage, and this would make it necessary to increase greatly the rate of change of flux linkages. We have already discussed the methods of increasing the rate of change of flux linkages. In the case of the simple horseshoe magnet and single coil of Fig. 11·3, if the size of the coil and the size of the magnet were both increased and the rate of movement of the magnet were also increased, the power required to move the magnet rapidly enough to produce the high rate of

change of flux linkages would be so great that we would find that our simple experimental device would not be practical. Therefore, the basic design must be changed to provide the compact, efficient source of high voltage required for igniting the fuel/air charge in the engine cylinder. The following pages of this text will tell how this is done.

Rotating magnet

Figure 11·4 shows a four-pole rotating magnet, similar to those used in some models of Bendix-Scintilla aircraft magnetos. The lines of flux of the rotating magnet, when it is not installed in the magneto, pass from its north pole through the air space to its south pole, in a manner similar to the flow of the lines of flux in the simple horseshoe magnet in Fig. 11·1.

In Fig. 11·5, the pole shoes and their extensions are made of soft-iron laminations cast in the magneto housing. The coil core is also made of soft-iron laminations and is mounted on top of the pole-shoe extensions. The pole shoes D and their extensions E, together

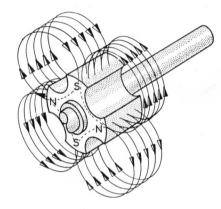

Figure **11·4**   A four-pole rotating magnet.

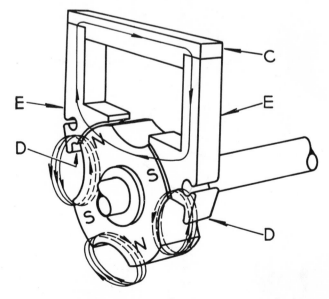

Figure **11·5**   Arrangement of rotating magnet, pole shoes, and core of coil in a magneto.

with the coil core C, form a magnetic path similar to that made by the laminated soft-iron bar (keeper) shown with the ordinary horseshoe magnet in Fig. 11·2. When the magnet is in the position shown in Fig. 11·5, the magnetic path produces a concentration of flux in the core of the coil.

In Fig. 11·6, notice that the rotating magnet has rotated from the position it had in Fig. 11·5. The neutral position of any rotating magnet is that position where one of the pole pieces is centered between the pole shoes in the magneto housing, as shown in Fig. 11·6. When the rotating magnet is in its neutral position, the lines of flux do not pass through the coil core because they are short-circuited by the pole shoes.

Notice especially that primary and secondary windings are **not** shown on the coil core of Figs. 11·5 and 11·6. They are omitted to make it easier to understand the magnetic action. Having learned the action without windings, the reader will find it easier to understand the functions of the windings explained later in this text.

The curve in Fig. 11·7 shows how the flux in the coil core changes when the magnet is turned with no windings present. This curve is called the **static-flux curve** because it represents the stationary or normal condition of the circuit. If the magnet is turned with no windings on the coil core, the flux will build up through the coil core in first one direction and then the other, as indicated by the curve.

This curve represents both the direction of the flux and its concentration. When the curve is above the horizontal line, the flux is passing through the coil in one direction, and the higher the curve above the line, the greater the number of lines of flux in the core.

When the curve is below the horizontal line, the flux is passing through the coil in the opposite direction, and the lower the curve below the line, the greater the number of lines of flux passing through the core in this other direction.

Whenever the magnet passes through a neutral position, the flux in the coil core falls to zero, and this is shown by the point where the curve touches the horizontal line. Having fallen to zero, the flux then builds up again in the opposite direction, as shown in the curve. Therefore, the greatest change in the flux occurs when the magnet is passing through the neutral position. Note that the curve of Fig. 11·7 has a steep slope at the points corresponding to the neutral positions of the magnet, that is, wherever the curve crosses the horizontal line.

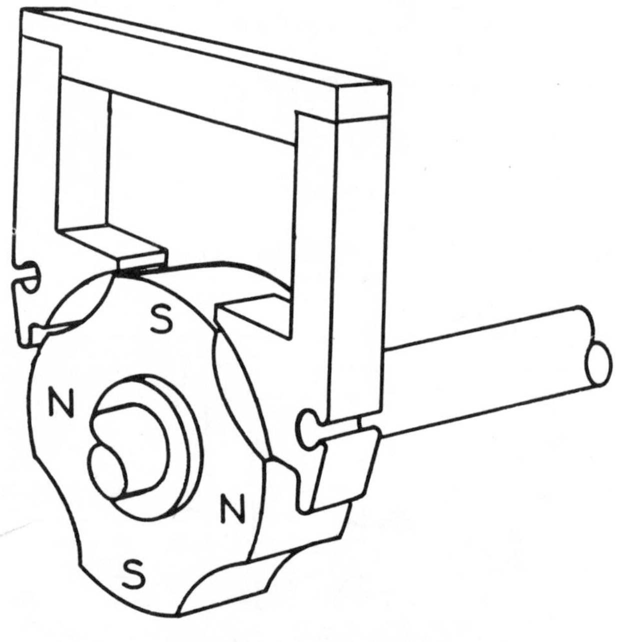

The coil assembly

The typical coil assembly consists of a laminated soft-iron core around which is placed a **primary** winding and a **secondary** winding. The primary winding consists of a comparatively few turns of insulated copper wire and the secondary winding consists of several thousands of turns of very fine wire. The coil is covered with a case of hard rubber, bakelite, or varnished cambric, according to the design requirements of the manufacturer. A primary condenser (capacitor) may be built into the coil between the primary winding and the secondary winding, or it may be connected in the external circuit.

The ends of the coil core extend beyond either end of the coil assembly so they can be secured to the pole shoe extensions. One end of the primary winding is usually grounded to the core, and the other end is brought out to a terminal connection or to a short length of connecting wire having a terminal on the end. This end of the primary coil is connected in the magneto to the breaker points, and provision is also made for a connection to the ignition switch lead. Note carefully that, when the breaker points are closed, current flows from the coil to ground and back from ground to the coil in a complete circuit. This direction of flow alternates with the rotation of the magnet.

One end of the secondary winding is grounded inside the coil, and the other end is brought to the outside of the coil to provide a contact through which the high-tension (high-voltage) current can be carried to the distributor.

This description of a magneto coil does not necessarily apply to all magnetos, but is does give an overall explanation of coil-assembly design and construction. A magneto coil is illustrated in Fig. 11·8.

Figure 11·6   Rotating magnet in neutral position.

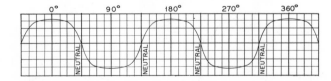

Figure 11·7   Static-flux curve.

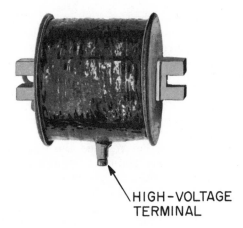

HIGH-VOLTAGE
TERMINAL

Figure 11·8   Magneto coil assembly.

Magneto speed

Figure 11·9 is a schematic illustration of an aircraft ignition system using a rotating-magnet type of magneto. Notice the cam on the end of the magnet shaft. It is **not** a compensated cam; hence, it has as many lobes as there are poles on the magnet; that is, it has four in this case. The number of high-voltage impulses produced per revolution of the magnet is equal, therefore, to the number of poles. The number of cylinder firings per complete revolution of the engine is equal to one-half the number of engine cylinders. Therefore, the ratio of the magneto-shaft speed to that of the engine crankshaft is equal to the number of cylinders divided by twice the number of poles on the rotating magnet. This can be stated in the form of a formula in this manner:

$$\frac{\text{No. of cylinders}}{2 \times \text{No. of poles}} = \frac{\text{magneto-shaft speed}}{\text{engine-crankshaft speed}}$$

For example, if the uncompensated cam has four lobes, since there are four poles on the magnet, and if the engine has 12 cylinders, then

$$\frac{12 \text{ cylinders}}{2 \times 4 \text{ poles}} = \frac{12}{8} = 1\frac{1}{2}$$

Hence, the magneto speed is 1½ times the engine crankshaft speed.

It should be remembered that a four-stroke-cycle engine fires each cylinder once for each two turns of the crankshaft. Therefore we know that a 12-cylinder engine will fire six times for each revolution of the crankshaft. Also, a magneto having four lobes on the cam will produce four sparks for each turn of the cam. In the magneto under discussion, the cam is mounted on the end of the magneto shaft, so we know that the magneto produces four sparks for each revolution of the magneto shaft. Then, in order to produce the six sparks needed for each revolution of the crankshaft, the magneto must turn 1½ times.

Breaker assembly

The **breaker assembly** consists of contact points actuated by the rotating cam. This assembly is shown in the illustration of Fig. 11·9.

Some early magnetos have lever-type breaker point assemblies with a movable contact mounted on a pivot arm and actuated by a cam follower. Later models have a pivotless-type breaker assembly with the movable point mounted on a spring. The contact points are made of platinum-iridium alloy or some other heat-

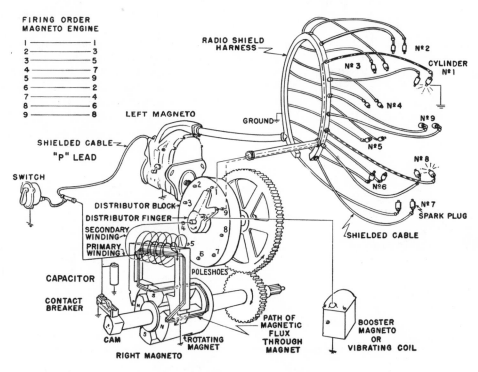

Figure 11·9   A high-tension magneto ignition system.

237

and wear-resistant material. When the points are in good condition, they have a frosty appearance.

The cam and cam follower are lubricated by means of a felt pad on the cam follower. This pad is saturated with lubricating oil at service periods.

The breaker contact points are electrically connected across the primary coil, and the magneto breaker mechanism is arranged so that the contact points close at the position where there is a maximum of flux, as shown in Fig. 11·10. At this time there is a minimum of **flux change.**

When the magnet is turned toward the neutral position, the amount of flux starts to decrease. This decrease or change in flux linkages induces a current in the primary winding. Since a current-carrying coil produces its own magnetic field, the current induced in the primary winding establishes a magnetic field of its own.

The magnetic field established by this current induced in the primary winding opposes the change of flux linkages, inducing the current. This is in accord with Lenz's law, and it is graphically represented in Fig. 11·10. If there were no current flowing in the primary winding, the flux in the coil core would drop to zero as the magnet was turned to neutral and then it would start to increase in the opposite direction, as shown by the dotted static-flux curve in Fig. 11·10. However, the field established by the primary current prevents the flux from changing, as stated before, and it temporarily holds the field in the coil core instead of allowing it to change. This is represented by the "resultant-flux" curve.

The process just described causes great stress in the magnetic circuit by the time the magnet has reached the position where the contact points are about to open, a few degrees past the neutral position.

The E-gap angle

The number of degrees between the neutral position and the position where the contact points open is called the **E-gap angle** and is usually shortened to simply **E gap.** The manufacturer of the magneto determines, for each model, how many degrees beyond the neutral position a pole of the rotor magnet should be in order to obtain the strongest spark at the instant of breaker-point separation. This angular displacement from the neutral position, which is the E-gap angle, varies from 5 to 17°, depending upon the make and model, but for a representative type of four-pole magneto, such as the one we are discussing here, the correct E gap is 12°. Notice that the rotating magnet will be in the E-gap position as many times per revolution as there are poles.

When the magnet has reached the position where the contact points are about to open, a few degrees past the neutral position, the primary current is maintaining the original field in the coil core while the magnet has already turned past neutral. The primary current is now attempting to establish a field through the coil core in the opposite direction. The magnetic circuit at this instant is shown in Fig. 11·11.

When the contact points are opened, the primary circuit is broken. This interrupts the flow of the primary current and causes an extremely rapid change in flux linkages. In an exceedingly short period of time, the field established by the primary current falls to zero and is replaced by the field of the opposite direction established by the magnet. This process is represented by the almost vertical portion of the resultant-flux curve.

The secondary winding

The secondary winding consists of many turns of fine wire, often about 13,000, wound over the primary on the coil core. The large number of turns in the secondary winding and the very rapid change in flux together cause a high rate of change of flux linkages, which in turn produces the high voltage in the secondary winding. A curve representing the current flowing in the secondary winding during the high-voltage discharge is shown in Fig. 11·10.

The extremely rapid flux change represents the dissipation of the energy involved in the stress that existed in the magnetic circuit before the contact points opened. The flux in the coil core would normally change as represented by the static-flux curve in the illustration, but the primary current prevents this

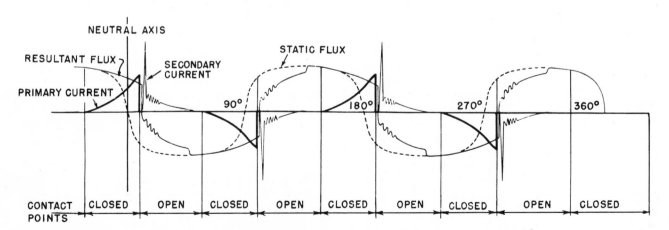

Figure 11·10   Flux and current curves for a high-tension magneto.

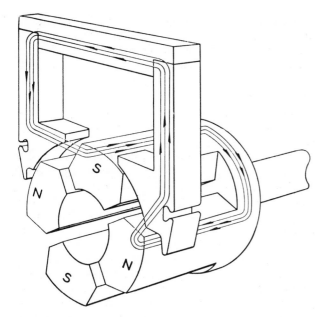

Figure 11·11 *Magnetic field produced by primary current.*

actual operating conditions, when the spark discharge takes place under pressure in a cylinder, indicate that the secondary current flow stops before the breaker points reach the closing position, thus preventing the development of the negative current.

Polarity or direction of sparks

Fundamentally the magneto is a special form of a-c generator, modified to enable it to deliver the high voltage required for ignition purposes. In Fig. 11 · 10, the high rate of change of flux linkages represented by the almost vertical portion of the resultant-flux curve is responsible for the high voltage which produces the secondary spark. From the curves it is apparent that the rapid flux change is downward, then upward, alternating in direction at each opening of the contacts. Since the direction of an induced current depends on the direction of the flux change which produced it, the sparks produced by the magneto are of alternate polarity, that is, they jump from one way and then the other, as represented by the secondary current curve in the illustration, which is first above and then below the line, indicating alternate polarity.

The primary capacitor

In addition to producing the high voltage in the secondary winding, the flux change also causes a current to flow in the primary winding. This is owing to the fact that the mechanical process of opening the contacts is relatively slow compared with the extremely rapid change in flux linkages. Between the time when the contacts start to open and the time when they are actually separated, sufficient change in flux linkage occurs to cause a rapid rise of voltage in the primary. This rapid rise of voltage would cause an arc between the contact points at the moment of separation, causing them to pit and burn if nothing was done to prevent arcing.

A primary capacitor is always connected across the contact points to prevent arcing, as shown in Fig. 11 · 12. It absorbs the shock of the rapid rise of voltage during the time that the contact points are separating and in this manner prevents arcing. Its action can be compared with that of an elastic diaphragm, as illustrated in the water analogy of Fig. 11 · 12, where the elastic diaphragm prevents the valve from "banging" when the water is suddenly turned off. The elastic diaphragm absorbs the shock caused by the inertia of the water. In a like manner, the primary capacitor prevents arcing between the contact points as they open by absorbing the "inertia" current induced in the primary coil by the collapse of the electromagnet field established by primary current. This field "cuts" the turns of the primary winding as it collapses. The underlying principle is commonly called the **self-inductance of the primary winding.**

The primary capacitor is always connected across the points, but its shape and location vary on different magneto models. It may be round, square, or some other shape. It may be located in the coil housing, in

change and holds back the flux change while the magnet turns. The stress in the magnetic circuit represented by the vertical distance between the resultant-flux curve and the dotted static-flux curve can be compared with the tension of a spring. When the points open, the action is comparable to the releasing of the trigger that holds a spring under tension, allowing the spring to fly forward violently.

When the high voltage in the secondary winding discharges, a spark jumps across the gap in the spark plug to ignite the fuel/air mixture in the engine cylinder. Each spark actually consists of one peak discharge, after which a series of small oscillations take place, as represented by the secondary current curve in Fig. 11 · 10, and they continue to occur until the voltage becomes too low to maintain the discharge. Current flows in the secondary winding during the time that it takes for the spark to discharge completely.

A magnetic field is established as soon as the current flows in the secondary winding, and this field opposes the change in flux that produced it. Therefore, the flux change is retarded, as indicated by the tapering portion of the resultant-flux curve. Regardless of the "slowing up" of the flux change, the spark completely discharges in the two-pole and four-pole magnetos before the next closing of the contact points. In other words, the energy or stress in the magnetic circuit is completely dissipated by the time the contacts close for the production of the next spark. Figure 11 · 10 shows that the resultant-flux curve has tapered off so that it coincides with the static-flux curve before the contact points close. However, in eight-pole magnetos the secondary current appears to be still flowing at the time that the contact points close, and it was believed for a period of time that this resulted in a negative current being developed. Analyses of magneto performance under

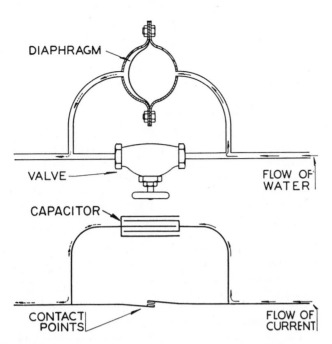

DIAPHRAGM

VALVE

FLOW OF WATER

CAPACITOR

CONTACT POINTS

FLOW OF CURRENT

Figure 11·12   Diagrams to illustrate operation of primary capacitor.

the breaker housing with the breaker points, or on top of the coil. Briefly stated, its function is to absorb self-induced current flowing in the primary circuit.

HIGH-TENSION IGNITION SYSTEM

Figure 11·9 illustrates a complete high-tension ignition system for an aircraft engine. This system utilizes a Bendix-Scintilla rotating-magnet type of magneto. It consists of two magnetos, a radio-shield harness, spark plugs, a booster magneto, and a switch. One magneto is shown completely assembled and is illustrated in skeleton form to show the magnetic and electric circuits.

One end of the primary winding is grounded to the magneto, and the other end is connected to the insulated contact point. The other contact point is grounded. The capacitor is connected across the contact points.

The ground terminal on the magneto is electrically connected to the insulated contact point. A wire called the **P lead** connects the ground terminal on each magneto with the switch. When the switch is in the OFF position, this wire provides a direct path to the ground for the primary current. Therefore, when the contact points open, the primary current is not interrupted, thus preventing the production of high voltage in the secondary winding.

One end of the secondary winding is grounded to the magneto, and the other end terminates at the high-tension insert on the coil. The high-tension current produced in the secondary winding is then conducted to the central insert of the distributor finger and across

a small air gap to the electrodes of the distribution block. High-tension cables in the distributor block then carry it to the spark plugs where the discharge occurs in the engine cylinder.

The distributor

The distributor finger of Fig. 11·9 is secured to the large distributor gear, which is driven by a smaller gear located on the drive shaft of the rotating magnet. The ratio between these gears is always such that the distributor finger is driven at **one-half engine-crankshaft speed.** This ratio of the gears ensures the proper distribution of the high-tension current to the spark plugs in accordance with the firing order of the particular engine.

In general, the distributor rotor of the typical aircraft magneto is a device that distributes the high-voltage current to the various connections of the distributor block. This rotor may be in the form of a finger, disk, drum, or other shape, depending upon the judgment of the magneto manufacturer. In addition, the distributor rotor may be designed with either one or two distributing electrodes. When there are two distributing electrodes, the leading electrode, which obtains high voltage from the magneto secondary, makes its connection with the secondary through the shaft of the rotor, while the trailing electrode obtains a high-tension voltage from the booster by means of a collector ring mounted either on the stationary distributor block or on the rotor itself.

It must be explained that the distributors with the trailing finger are not employed on late-model aircraft magnetos, although they may be encountered from time to time on magnetos used on older engines. The early systems utilized booster magnetos or high-tension booster coils to provide a strong spark when starting the engine, and the trailing finger of the distributor provided a retarded spark to prevent the engine from kicking back.

Magneto sparking order

Almost all aircraft engines operate on the four-stroke five-event-cycle principle. For this reason, the number of sparks required for each complete revolution of the engine is equal to one-half the number of cylinders in the engine. The number of sparks produced by each revolution of the rotating magnet is equal to the number of its poles. Therefore the ratio of the speed at which the rotating magnet is driven to the speed of the engine crankshaft is always one-half the number of cylinders on the engine divided by the number of poles on the rotating magnet, as explained before.

The numbers on the distributor block tell the **magneto sparking order** and not the firing order of the engine. The distributor-block position marked 1 is connected to the No. 1 cylinder; the distributor-block position marked 2 is connected to the second cylinder to be fired; the distributor-block position marked 3 is connected to the third cylinder to be fired; and so on.

Some distributor blocks or housings are not numbered for all high-tension leads. In these cases the lead socket for the No. 1 cylinder is marked and the others follow in order according to direction of rotation.

Coming-in speed of magneto

To produce sparks, the rotating magnet must be turned at or above a specified number of revolutions per minute, at which speed the rate of change in flux linkages is sufficiently high to induce the required primary current and the resultant high-tension output. This speed is known as the **coming-in speed** of the magneto; it varies for different types of magnetos but averages about 100 to 200 rpm.

TYPES OF MAGNETOS

There are many ways of classifying magnetos. They may be (1) low-tension or high-tension, (2) rotating-magnet or inductor-rotor, (3) single or double, and (4) base-mounted or flange-mounted.

Low-tension and high-tension magnetos

A **low-tension magneto** delivers current at a low voltage by means of the rotation of an armature, wound with only one coil, in the field of a permanent magnet. Its low-voltage current must be transformed into a high-tension (high-voltage) current by means of a transformer.

A **high-tension magneto** delivers a high voltage, and it has both a primary winding and a secondary winding. An outside induction coil is not needed because the double winding accomplishes the same purpose. The low voltage generated in the primary winding induces a high-voltage current in the secondary winding when the primary circuit is broken.

Rotating-magnet and inductor-rotor magnetos

In a magneto of the **rotating-magnet** type, the primary and secondary windings are wound upon the same iron core. This core is mounted between two poles, or inductors, which extend to "shoes" on each side of the rotating magnet. The rotating magnet is usually made with four poles, which are arranged alternately north and south in polarity.

As the magnet rotates, first it sends a magnetic field through the inductors to the core of the coil and back to the opposite pole of the magnet, and then the rotation of the magnet causes the field to reverse. This action was explained in an earlier portion of this chapter and is illustrated in Figs. 11·5, 11·6 and 11·11. A review of these sections will aid in an understanding of the operation.

The **inductor-rotor** type of magneto has a stationary coil (armature) just as the rotating-magnet type does. The difference lies in the method of inducing a magnetic flux in the core of the coil. The inductor-rotor magneto has a stationary magnet or magnets. As the rotor of the magneto turns, the flux from the magnets is carried through the segments of the rotor to the pole shoes and poles, first in one direction and then in the other.

Single- and double-type magnetos

Two single-type magnetos are commonly used on most radial engines. The **single-type** magneto is just what its name implies—one magneto.

The **double-type** magneto is generally used on in-line engines, but this type is also made for radial engines. When made for radial engines, it is essentially the same as the magneto made for in-line engines except that two **compensated cams** are employed. The compensated cam is explained later in this chapter.

The **double-type** magneto is essentially two magnetos having one rotating magnet common to both. It contains two sets of breaker points, but the high voltage is distributed by two distributors mounted elsewhere on the engine, and not by distributors forming part of the magneto proper. Since there are two sets of breaker points, an equal number of sparks will be produced by each coil assembly per revolution of the magneto drive shaft.

Base-mounted and flange-mounted magnetos

A **base-mounted** magneto is attached to a mounting bracket on the engine by means of cap screws, which pass through holes in the bracket and enter tapped holes in the base of the magneto.

A **flange-mounted** magneto is attached to the engine by means of a flange on the end of the magneto. The mounting holes in the flange are not circular; instead, they are slots that permit a slight adjustment, by rotation, in timing the magneto with the engine.

The single-type magneto may be either base-mounted or flange-mounted. The double-type magneto is always flange-mounted.

Symbols used to describe magnetos

Magnetos are technically described by means of letters and figures which indicate make, model, type, etc., as follows:

Example 1: The type DF18RN is a double-type magneto, flange-mounted, for use on an 18-cylinder engine designed for clockwise rotation and made by Scintilla.

Example 2: The type SF14LU-7 is a single-type magneto, flange-mounted, for use on a 14-cylinder engine, designed for counterclockwise rotation and made by Bosch, seventh modification.

Note: Each manufacturer uses a dash followed by a letter or a numeral after the symbol for his product to indicate a change made or new feature added in the magneto.

Magneto safety gap

Magnetos are sometimes equipped with a **safety gap** to provide a return ground when the secondary circuit is open. It is connected in series with the secondary circuit and hence protects it against shorts or open circuits. One electrode of the safety gap is screwed into the high-tension brush holder, while the grounded electrode is on the safety-gap ground plate. Thus, the safety gap protects against damage from excessively

Table 11 · 1

Order of designation	Symbol	Meaning
1	S	Single type
	D	Double type
2	B	Base mounted
	F	Flange mounted
3, 9, 12, 14, etc.		Number of distributor electrodes
4	R	Clockwise rotation as viewed from drive-shaft end
	L	Counterclockwise rotation as viewed from drive-shaft end
5	G	General Electric
	N	Scintilla
	A	Delco Appliance
	U	Bosch
	C	Delco-Remy (Bosch design)
	D	Edison-Splitdorf

high voltage in case the secondary circuit is accidentally broken and the spark cannot jump between the electrodes of the spark plugs. In such a case, the high-tension spark jumps the safety gap to the ground connection, thereby relieving the voltage in the secondary winding of the magneto.

IGNITION BOOSTERS

If it is impossible, under certain conditions, to rotate the engine crankshaft fast enough to produce the **coming-in speed** of the magneto, a source of external high-tension current is required for starting purposes. The various devices used for this purpose are called **ignition boosters.**

An ignition booster may be in the form of a booster magneto, a high-tension coil to which primary current is supplied from a battery, or a vibrator which supplies intermittent direct current from the battery directly to the primary of the magneto. Another device used for increasing the high-tension voltage of the magneto for starting is called an **impulse coupling.** It gives a momentary high rotational speed to the rotor of the magneto during starting.

The booster coil

A booster coil is a small induction coil. Its function is to provide a shower of sparks to the spark plugs until the magneto fires properly. It is usually connected to the starter switch. When the engine has started, the booster coil and the starter are no longer required; hence they can be turned off together.

When voltage from a battery is applied to the booster coil, magnetism is developed in the core until the magnetic force on the soft-iron armature mounted on the vibrator overcomes the spring tension and attracts the armature toward the core. When the armature

moves toward the core, the contact points and the primary circuit are opened. This demagnetizes the core and permits the spring again to close the contact points and complete the circuit. The armature vibrates back and forth rapidly, making and breaking the primary circuit as long as the voltage from the battery is applied to the booster coil.

The use of booster coils as described here is limited to a few of the older aircraft which are still operating. Most of the modern aircraft employ the **induction vibrator.**

The induction vibrator

A circuit for an induction vibrator as used with a high-tension magneto is shown in Fig. 11·13. This circuit applies to one engine only, but it is obvious that a similar circuit would be used with each engine of a multiengine airplane. The induction vibrator is ener-

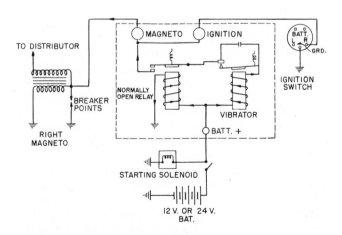

Figure 11 · 13   Circuit for induction vibrator.

242

gized from the same circuit which energizes the starting solenoid. It is thus energized only during the time the engines are being started.

One advantage of the induction vibrator is that it reduces the tendency of the magneto to "flash over" at high altitudes, since the booster finger can be eliminated. The function of this induction vibrator is to supply interrupted low voltage for the magneto primary coil, which induces a sufficiently high voltage in the secondary for starting.

The vibrator sends an interrupted battery current through the primary winding of the regular magneto coil. The magneto coil then acts like a battery ignition coil and produces high-tension impulses, which are distributed through the distributor rotor, distributor block, and cables to the spark plugs. These high-tension impulses are produced during the whole time that the magneto contact points are open. When the contact points are closed, sparks cannot be generated, although the vibrator continues to send interrupted current impulses through the magneto contact points without harm to the vibrator or any part of the circuit.

When the ignition switch is in the ON position and the engine starter is engaged, the current from the battery is sent through the coil of a relay which is normally open. The battery current causes the relay points to close, thus completing the circuit to the vibrator coil and causing the vibrator to produce a rapidly interrupted current.

The rapidly interrupted current produced by the vibrator is sent through the primary winding of the magneto coil. By induction, high voltage is created in the secondary winding of the magneto coil, and this high voltage produces high-tension sparks which are delivered to the spark plugs through the magneto distributor-block electrodes during the time that the magneto contact points are open.

This process is repeated each time that the magneto contact points are separated, because the interrupted current once more flows through the primary of the magneto coil. The action continues until the engine is firing because of the regular magneto sparks, and the engine starter is released. It should be understood that the vibrator starts to operate automatically when the engine-ignition switch is turned to the ON position and the starter is engaged. The vibrator stops when the starter is disengaged.

A simplified diagram of the induction vibrator designed for use with light aircraft engine magnetos is shown in Fig. 11·14. Observe that, when the starter switch is closed, battery voltage is applied to the vibrator coil through the vibrator contact points and through the **retard contact points** in the left magneto. As the coil is energized, the breaker points open and interrupt the current flow, thus deenergizing the coil VC. The contact points close and again energize the coil, causing the points to open. Thus the contact points of the vibrator continue to make and break contact many times per second, sending an interrupted current through both the main and retard contact points of the magneto. When the magneto turns to its normal

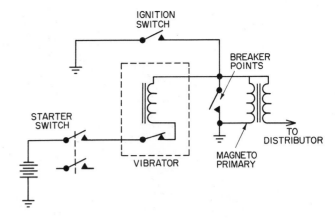

Figure 11·14 Induction vibrator circuit for light aircraft engine.

firing position, the main contact points open. However, the retard points are still closed and vibrator current flows to ground through these points. When the magneto has turned to the preset retard position, the retard points open and the vibrator current then flows to ground through the primary winding of the magneto. This induces a high-tension current in the secondary winding, thus providing the necessary retarded spark for starting the engine. A further discussion of this vibrator will be given in the explanation of the complete magneto system.

BENDIX HIGH-TENSION MAGNETO SYSTEM FOR LIGHT AIRCRAFT ENGINE

General description

A typical ignition system for a light aircraft engine consists of two magnetos, a starter vibrator, combination ignition and starter switch, and harness assembly. These parts are illustrated in Fig. 11·15. This illustration shows the components of the system associated with the Bendix S-200 series magneto.

Magneto

The Bendix S-200 magneto is a completely self-contained unit incorporating a two-pole **rotating magnet,** a **coil unit** containing primary and secondary windings, a **distributor assembly, main breaker points, retard breaker points,** a **two-lobe cam,** a **feed-through**-type **capacitor,** housing sections, and other components necessary for assembly.

The rotating magnet turns on two ball bearings, one located at the breaker end and the other at the drive end. A two-lobe cam is secured to the breaker end of the rotating magnet. In a six-cylinder magneto, the rotating magnet turns 1½ times engine speed. Thus, six sparks are produced through 720° of engine rotation, that is, two revolutions of the crankshaft. In a four-cylinder magneto, the rotating magnet turns at engine speed, thus producing four sparks through two revolutions of the crankshaft.

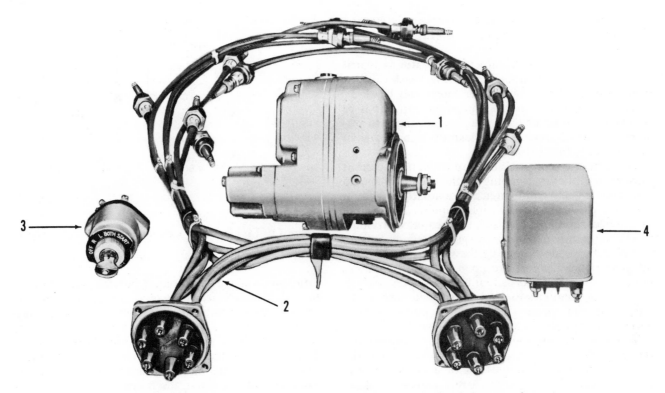

Figure **11·15** *Components of high-tension ignition system for light aircraft engine: (1) magneto, (2) harness assembly, (3) combination switch, (4) vibrator. (Bendix-Scintilla)*

As mentioned previously, the dual breaker magneto incorporates a retard breaker. This breaker is actuated by the same cam as the main breaker and is so positioned that its contacts open a predetermined number of degrees after the main breaker contacts open. A battery-operated starting vibrator used with this magneto provides retarded ignition for starting, regardless of engine cranking speed. The retard ignition is in the form of a shower of sparks instead of a single spark like that produced by an impulse coupling. It must be remembered that the slow cranking speed of an engine during starting makes it necessary that the ignition be retarded to prevent "kickback." At starting speed, if advanced ignition is supplied, the full force of the combustion will be developed before the piston reaches TDC and the piston will be driven back down the cylinder, thus rotating the crankshaft in reverse of the normal direction.

Starting vibrator

The starting-vibrator assembly consists of a electromagnet acting upon contact points which make and break the circuit through the electromagnet. This, of course, causes the points to vibrate rapidly, thus developing an interrupted battery current to the primary of the magneto. This interrupted current induces a high voltage in the secondary winding of the magneto coil, thus providing the high-tension current necessary for firing the spark plugs. The starting vibrator is supplied with battery power only while the starting switch is turned on.

Operation of the system

The operation of the Bendix S-200 magneto system can be understood by studying the diagram of Fig. 11 · 16. In this circuit the starting vibrator unit includes both a **vibrator** and a **control relay.** The interrupted battery current supplied by the vibrator is controlled by the retard breaker points in the left magneto. The control relay grounds the right magneto during the time that the starter switch is turned on, thus preventing an advanced spark from being applied to the spark plugs.

The vibrator assembly which includes the control relay is used with a **standard** ignition switch. The elec-

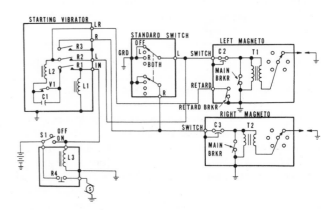

Figure **11·16** *Diagram of Bendix S-200 magneto system. (Bendix-Scintilla)*

trical operation of this switch can be seen in the diagram of Fig. 11·16. In the diagram all the switches and contact points are shown in their normal OFF position.

With the standard ignition switch in its BOTH position and the starter switch turned on, the starter solenoid $L3$ and the relay coil $L1$ are energized, thus causing them to close their relay contacts $R4$, $R1$, $R2$, and $R3$. Relay contact $R3$ connects the right magneto to ground, rendering it inoperative during starting procedures. Battery current flows through relay contact $R1$, vibrator points $V1$, coil $L2$, through the retard breaker of the left magneto to ground, through the relay contact $R2$, and through the main breaker to ground. The flow of current through the coil $L2$ establishes a magnetic field which opens the vibrator points $V1$ and starts the vibrating cycle. The interrupted battery current thus produced is carried to ground through both sets of breaker points in the left magneto.

When the engine reaches its normal advance firing position, the main breaker opens. However, the current is still carried to ground through the retard breaker, which does not open until the starting **retard position** of the engine is reached. When the retard breaker opens (the main breaker is still open), the vibrator current flows through the primary of transformer $T1$ (magneto coil), producing a rapidly fluctuating magnetic field around the coil. This causes a high voltage to be induced in the secondary, thus firing the spark plug to which the voltage is directed by the distributor. A shower of sparks is therefore produced at the spark plug owing to the opening and closing of the vibrator points while the main and retard breaker points are open.

When the engine fires and begins to pick up speed, the starter switch is released, thus deenergizing the relay coil $L2$ and the starter relay $L3$. This opens the vibrator circuit and the retard breaker circuit, thus rendering them inoperative. The single breaker magneto (right magneto) is no longer grounded; hence both magnetos are firing in the full advance position.

The schematic diagram of Fig. 11·17 illustrates the operation of a system utilizing a **combination starter-**

ignition switch and a starting vibrator which does not include the control relay. When the combination switch is placed in the START position, the right magneto is grounded, the starter solenoid $L1$ is energized, and current flows through the vibrator $L2$ to both magneto breaker points and thence to ground if the points are closed. It must be pointed out that all contacts in the combination switch are moved to the **starting** position; hence they will not be in the position shown in the diagram.

When the engine reaches its normal advance firing position, the main breaker points will open; however, the vibrator current is still carried to ground through the retard breaker, which does not open until the starting retard position of the engine is reached. When the retard breaker opens, the vibrator current flows through the primary of the magneto coil $T1$, thus inducing a high voltage as explained previously. This voltage provides the retard spark necessary for ignition until the engine speed picks up and the starter switch is released. The combination switch automatically returns to its BOTH position, thus removing the starting vibrator and starter solenoid from the circuit. A study of the switch diagram will also show that the **switch** circuits of both magnetos are ungrounded; hence both magnetos will be firing.

The combination switch used with a magneto system has five positions and is actuated by either a switch or a key. The five positions are (1) OFF—both magnetos grounded and not operating; (2) R-right magneto operating, left magneto off; (3) L-left magneto operating, right magneto off; (4) BOTH—both magnetos operating; and (5) START—starter solenoid is operating and the vibrator is energized, causing an intermittent current to flow through the retard breaker on the left magneto while the right magneto is grounded to prevent advanced ignition. The START position on the switch is a **momentary** contact and is **on** only while being held in this position. When the switch is released, it automatically reverts to the BOTH position.

It will be observed in the diagram that the magnetos are equipped with flow-through-type capacitors C_2 and C_3, which reduce arcing at the breaker contacts, help to eliminate radio interference, and cause a more rapid collapse of the magnetic field when the breaker points open during normal operation. A capacitor C_1 is also necessary in the starter vibrator circuit to produce similar results during the production of the intermittent vibrator current.

Magneto timing

As we have explained in the general discussion of magnetos, every magneto must be timed to produce a spark for ignition at a precise instant. Furthermore, the magneto breaker points must be timed to open when the greatest magnetic field stress exists in the magnetic circuit. This point is called the **E gap** or **efficiency gap**, and it is measured in degrees past the neutral position of the magnet. The magneto distributor must be timed to deliver the high-tension current to the proper outlet terminal of the distributor block. The timing procedure

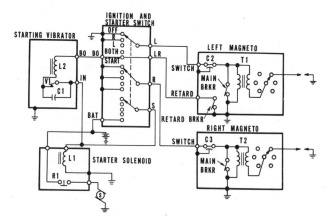

Figure 11·17 Ignition system with combination starter-ignition switch.

varies to some extent for different types of magnetos; however, the principles are the same in every case.

Distributor timing is usually accomplished during the time the magneto is being assembled. The illustration of Fig. 11·18 shows the matching of the chamfered tooth on the distributor drive gear with the marked tooth on the driven gear. In the illustration the magneto is being assembled for right-hand (clockwise) rotation. The direction of rotation refers to the direction in which the magnet shaft rotates, facing the drive end. When the teeth of the gears are matched as shown, the distributor will be in the correct position with respect to the rotating magnet and breaker points at all times. The large distributor gear also has a marked tooth which can be observed through the timing window on the top of the case to indicate when the distributor is in position for firing No. 1 cylinder. This mark is not sufficiently accurate for timing the opening of the points, but it does show the correct position of the distributor and rotating magnet for timing to No. 1 cylinder.

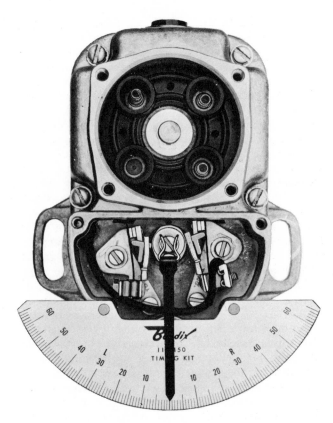

Figure 11·19   Use of timing kit.

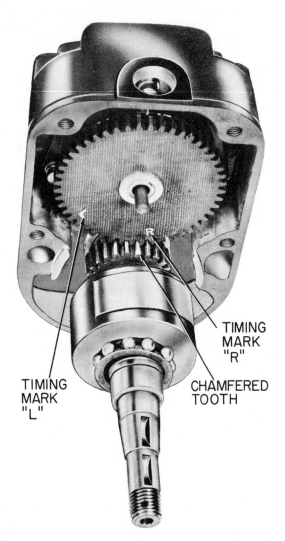

Figure 11·18   Matching marks on gears for distributor timing.

The following steps are taken to check and adjust the timing of the breaker points for the Bendix S-200 magneto, which does not have timing marks in the breaker compartment:

1. Remove the timing inspection plug from the top of the magneto. Turn the rotating magnet in its normal direction of rotation until the painted, chamfered tooth on the distributor gear is approximately in the center of the inspection window. Then turn it back a few degrees until the magnet is in its neutral position. Because of its magnetism, the rotating magnet will hold itself in the neutral position.
2. Install the timing kit as shown in Fig. 11·19, and place the pointer in the zero position. If the manufacturer's timing kit (Bendix 11-8150) is not available, a substitute can be fabricated using a protractor to provide accurate angular measurement.
3. Connect a suitable timing light across the main breaker points, and turn the magnet in its normal direction of rotation 10° as indicated by the pointer. This is the E-gap position. The main breaker points should be adjusted to open at this point.
4. Turn the rotating magnet until the cam follower is at the high point on the cam lobe, and measure the clearance between the breaker points. This clearance must be 0.018 in. ±0.006 in. If the breaker-point clearance is not within limits, the points must be adjusted for correct setting. It will then be necessary to recheck and readjust the timing for breaker opening. It the breaker points cannot be adjusted to open at the correct time, they should be replaced.

On dual breaker magnetos (those having retard breakers), the retard breaker is adjusted to open a predetermined number of degrees after the main breaker opens, within +2° −0°. The amount of retard in degrees for any particular magneto is stamped in the bottom of the breaker compartment. In order to set the retard breaker points correctly, it is necessary to add the degrees of retard indicated in the breaker compartment to the reading of the timing pointer when the main breaker points are opening. For example, if the main breaker points open when the timing pointer is at 10° and the required retard is 30°, then the 30° should be added to 10°. The rotating magnet should therefore be turned until the timing indicator reads 40°. The retard breaker points should be adjusted to open at this time.

If an engine is designed for ignition at 20° BTC under normal operating conditions, the retard ignition should be set at least 20° later than the normal ignition. At this time the piston is close enough to TDC so it is not likely to kick back when ignition occurs.

Timing for magneto with "cast-in" timing marks

Some models of the S-200 magneto have timing marks cast in the breaker compartment. These are illustrated in Fig. 11·20. On each side of the breaker compartment there are timing marks indicating E-gap position and various degrees of retard breaker timing. The marks on the left-hand side, viewed from the breaker compartment, are for clockwise rotating magnetos, and the marks on the right-hand side are for counterclockwise rotating magnetos. The rotation of the magneto is determined by viewing the magneto from the drive end.

The point in the center of the E-gap boss, shown at E in the drawing, indicates the exact E-gap position if the indicator is first set to zero with the magnet in the neutral position. The width of the boss on either side of the point is the allowable tolerance of ±4°. In addition to these marks, the cam has an indented line across its end for locating the E-gap position of the rotating magnet. This position is indicated when the mark on the cam is aligned with the mark at the top of the breaker housing.

The procedure for checking the timing of the magneto is as follows:

1. Disconnect the harness assembly from the magneto, and remove the timing window plug.
2. Turn the engine crankshaft in the direction of normal rotation until the painted chamfered tooth of the distributor gear is just becoming visible in the timing window. Continue turning the crankshaft until the line on the end of the cam is aligned with the mark at the top of the breaker housing.
3. Install a suitable pointer (Bendix No. 11-8149) on the cam screw so that it indexes with the center of the E-gap mark. The magnet is now at the E-gap position. The position of the cam and pointer should be as shown in Fig. 11·20.
4. Connect a timing light across the main breaker, and adjust the breaker to open at this point. Now turn the engine crankshaft until the cam follower is on the high point of the cam lobe. With a thickness gage, check the clearance between the breaker points to see that the clearance is 0.018 in. ±0.006 in. If the clearance is not correct, the points must be adjusted and then rechecked for correct opening.
5. To set the retard breaker points, first note the number of degrees required for retard breaker opening. This number is marked in the breaker compartment as shown. Turn the engine back to the position where the main breaker points open. Position the pointer at the 0° mark. Now turn the engine in the normal direction of rotation until the pointer is over the required retard degree mark. Using the timing light, adjust the retard breaker contacts to open at this point. Continue turning the crankshaft until the cam follower is on the high point of the cam lobe and measure the clearance for 0.018 in. ±0.006 in.

Installation of S-200 magneto

When the S-200 magneto is installed on an engine for the first time, it is necessary to install a switch terminal connection for the timing light in the following manner:

1. Strip ⅛ in. of insulation from the end of the shielded wire to be connected to the terminal. Strip the metallic shielding back about 0.672 in. from the end of the insulation as shown in the drawing of Fig. 11·21.
2. Using Bendix Kit No. 10-157209, slide the coupling nut, shouldered bushing, insulating bushing, and flat washer over the end of the stripped wire.
3. Fan the strands of wire over the washer and solder, using

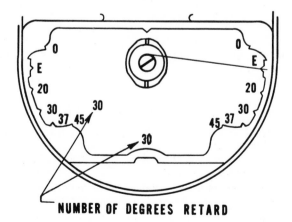

Figure 11·20 Timing marks in breaker compartment.

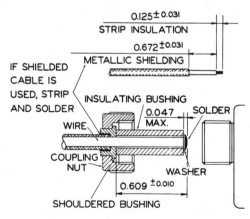

Figure 11·21 Preparing connector for magneto-switch terminal.

50/50 solder. The washer and solder should not exceed a thickness of 0.047 in. The fitting is now ready for connecting to the switch terminal of the magneto.

Before the magneto is installed on the engine, it should be checked to make sure that it has the correct direction of rotation. Then proceed as follows:

1. Remove the timing inspection plug from the top of the magneto, and turn the magneto in the normal direction of rotation until the painted chamfered tooth of the distributor gear is approximately in the center of the window. The magneto is now in the correct advance position for firing the No. 1 cylinder.
2. Turn the engine to the No. 1 cylinder full advance firing position (compression stroke) with the use of a **Time-Rite** piston-position indicator or with a timing disk and top-center indicator.
3. Install the magneto on the engine, and tighten the mounting bolts sufficiently to hold the magneto in position but loose enough so it can be rotated.
4. Connect the timing light to the magneto switch terminal using the previously prepared terminal connection.
5. If the timing light is out, rotate the magneto housing in the direction of its magnet rotation a few degrees beyond the point where the light comes on. Then slowly turn the magneto in the opposite direction until the light just goes out. Secure the magneto to the engine in this position by tightening the mounting bolts. Recheck the timing of the breaker points by turning the engine in reverse and then rotating it forward until the light goes out. The light should go out when the engine reaches the advance firing position as shown on the timing disk.
6. Remove the timing-light connection, and install the switch wire connection to the switch terminal of the magneto.

WARNING: *It is most important to note that the magneto is in the "switch on" condition whenever the switch wire is disconnected. It is therefore necessary to have the spark-plug wires disconnected when timing the magneto to the engine. Otherwise the engine could fire and cause injury to personnel.*

Installation of high-tension harness

The high-tension spark-plug leads are secured to the proper outlets in the magneto by means of the **high-tension outlet plate** and a rubber **grommet** or **terminal block.** The shielding of the cables is secured in the outlet plate by means of a ferrule, sleeve, and coupling nut. The ferrule and sleeve are crimped on the end of the shielding to form a permanent coupling fitting.

The high-tension cables are inserted through the outlet plate and into the grommet after the insulation has been stripped for about ½ in. back from the end of the wire. The bare wires are extended through the grommet and secured by means of a small brass washer as shown in Fig. 11·22. A suitable method for securing copper high-tension cable is illustrated in Fig. 11·23. In this method, the wires are cut off even with the insulation and the cable is then inserted into the grommet. A metal-piercing screw is used with a washer to hold the cables in place. The screws penetrate the ends of the stranded copper cable and form threads. The screws must not be turned too tight or they will strip

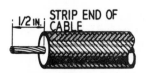

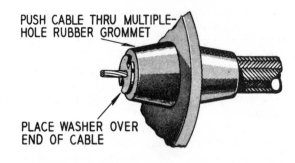

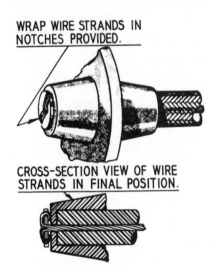

Figure **11·22** *Connecting high-tension leads to magneto.*

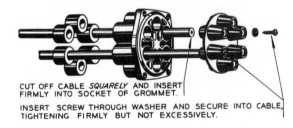

Figure **11·23** *Use of screws for attaching copper high-tension cable.*

out. The arrangement of the harness assembly and distributor blocks is shown in Fig. 11·24.

During the assembly of the high-tension harness, it is essential to note that the high-tension leads are installed in the outlet plate in the order of engine firing. The order of magneto firing for different magnetos is shown in Fig. 11·25; however, the spark-plug leads must not be connected in the same order. Since the

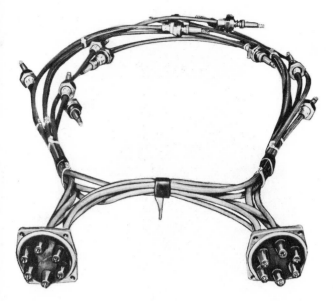

Figure 11·24   Harness assembly with distributor block.

firing order of a typical six-cylinder opposed engine is 1-4-5-2-3-6, the magneto outlets must be connected to spark-plug leads as follows:

Table 11·2

Magneto outlet	Spark-plug lead
1	1
2	4
3	5
4	2
5	3
6	6

In the practice of connecting the leads for dual magneto systems, the right magneto fires the top spark plugs on the right-hand side of the engine and the bottom spark plugs on the left-hand side of the engine. The left magneto is connected to fire the top spark plugs on the left side of the engine and the bottom spark plugs on the right side of the engine. A circuit

diagram for this arrangement is shown in Fig. 11·26. This is the ignition circuit for a Continental 0-470 engine.

Maintenance

It is recommended that S-200 magnetos be inspected after the first 25 hr of operation and every 50 hr thereafter. A typical inspection and check are performed as follows:

1. Remove the screws which hold the breaker cover, and loosen the cover sufficiently to allow removal of the feed-through

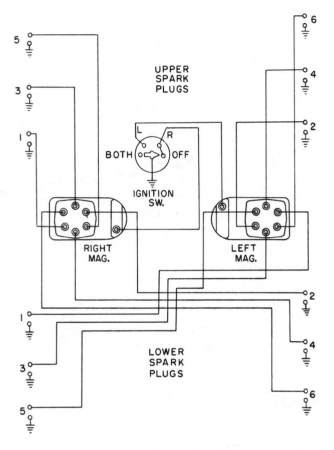

Figure 11·26   Wiring diagram for high-tension ignition system on a six-cylinder opposed engine.

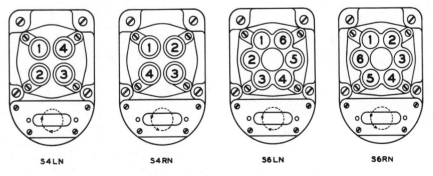

Figure 11·25   Magneto firing order.

249

capacitor and retard lead terminals from the breakers. The feed-through capacitor and retard leads will remain in the breaker cover when the cover is removed from the magneto.

2. Examine the breaker contact points for excessive wear or burning. Points which have deep pits or excessively burned areas should be discarded. Examine the cam follower felt for proper lubrication. If the felt is dry, apply 2 or 3 drops of Scintilla 10-86527 lubricant or the equivalent. Blot off any excess oil. Clean the breaker compartment with a clean, dry cloth.

3. Check the depth of the spring contact in the switch and retard terminals. The spring depth from the outlet face should not be more than ½ in.

4. Visually check the breakers to see that the cam follower is securely riveted to its spring. Check the screw that holds the assembled breaker parts together for tightness.

5. Check the capacitor mounting bracket for cracks or looseness. Test the capacitor for a minimum capacitance of 0.30 μf with a suitable capacitor tester.

6. Remove the harness outlet plate from the magneto, and inspect the rubber grommet and distributor block. If moisture is present, dry the block with a soft, dry, clean lintfree cloth. Do not use gasoline or any solvent for cleaning the block. The solvent will remove the wax coating and possibly cause electrical leakage.

7. Reassemble all parts carefully.

The foregoing directions are indicative of the checks and inspections that should be made, especially if there is any indication of magneto trouble. If possible, the manufacturer's manual should be employed to make sure that no important details are omitted.

THE SLICK MAGNETO FOR LIGHT AIRCRAFT ENGINES

The Slick series 600 magneto is manufactured for use with six-cylinder opposed aircraft engines and is quite similar in operation to the Bendix magneto previously described. This magneto, however, is not designed with retard breaker points for use with a starting vibrator but is normally equipped with an **impulse coupling** which enables it to produce a re-

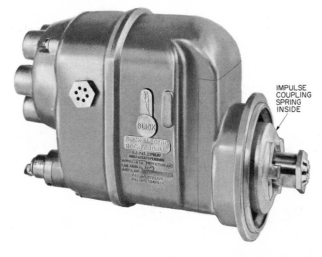

Figure 11·27 Magneto with impulse coupling. (Slick Electro, Inc.)

250

Figure 11·28 Alignment of breaker cam and drive gear.

tarded spark for starting purposes. Figure 11·27 is a photograph of the magneto with the impulse coupling mounted on the drive shaft.

General description

The Slick series 600 magneto incorporates a two-hole rotating magnet, a coil which includes both primary and secondary windings, nylon distributor gears, a single set of breaker points, a coaxial capacitor, and other parts necessary for the production and distribution of high-tension current for ignition. The principle of operation is the same as for other similar magnetos, and the timing is arranged to provide for breaker opening at the E-gap position in order to produce the greatest electrical effect.

Timing the magneto

Figure 11·28 shows the alignment of the drive gear and breaker cam with the magnet shaft. Note that the drive gear must be aligned with the mark on the shaft. This is the first step in internal timing. The main shaft should now be turned to a position where a timing pin can be inserted in the small hole in the bottom of the main frame near the drive end. The timing pin engages the rotating magnet shaft to hold the magnet in the E-gap position. The breaker assembly is now installed and adjusted so the points are just beginning to open. This is illustrated in Fig. 11·29.

The distributor gear is installed with the arrow mark for the proper direction of rotation aligned with the marked tooth on the distributor gear. Direction of rotation is determined from the drive end of the magneto. When the drive turns clockwise, the rotation is **right hand.**

The positioning of the distributor gear is illustrated

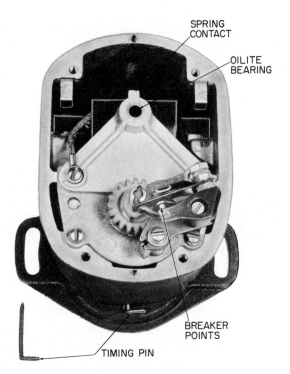

Figure 11·29   Installation of breaker points.

in Fig. 11·30. The gear in the illustration is installed for right-hand rotation.

Since both gears in the magneto are made of nylon, there is a substantial backlash in the gears at room temperature. After the magneto has warmed to operating temperature, the expansion of the gears reduces the clearance to the proper amount.

The cam oiler pad should be saturated with heavy (SAE 70) oil when the assembly is installed. Two or

three drops of the oil are sufficient to provide adequate lubrication. The pad touches the cam lightly at the corner to transfer the lubricant. If excessive oil is applied to the oiling pad, some may flow to the breaker points and cause a poor contact. For this reason, all excess oil must be wiped off the mechanism.

The impulse coupling

The **impulse coupling** installed on the drive shaft of the Slick magneto or the Bendix magneto is designed to provide a retarded spark for starting the engine. The coupling consists of a **shell, spring,** and **hub.** The hub is provided with weighted dogs which enable the assembly to accomplish its purpose. These are illustrated in Fig. 11·31.

When the impulse coupling is installed on the drive shaft of the magneto, the shell of the coupling may be rotated by the engine drive for a substantial portion of one revolution while the rotating magnet remains stationary. While this is taking place, the spring in the coupling is being wound up. At the point where the magneto must fire, the dogs are released and the spring unwinds to give the rotating magnet a rapid rotation in the normal direction. This, of course, causes the magneto to produce a strong spark at the spark plug. As soon as the engine begins to run, the weighted dogs are held in the released position by centrifugal force and the magneto fires in its normal advanced position. During starting, the retard spark is produced when the magneto rotation is held back by the impulse coupling.

Harness installation

The high-tension leads to the spark plugs are installed in a manner similar to that described for the Bendix magneto. The leads are inserted through the distributor-block housing to a position where they contact the terminals in the distributor block. The leads are held in place by means of coupling nuts. The arrangement of the distributor block in the housing is shown in Fig. 11·32.

Installation on the engine

The installation of the Slick magneto on the engine is similar to the installation of any other magneto.

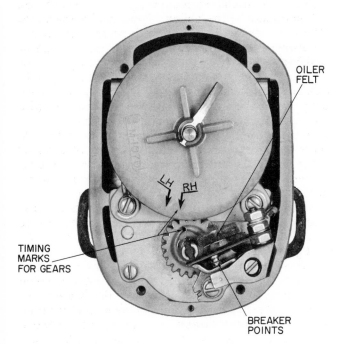

Figure 11·30   Position of distributor gear.

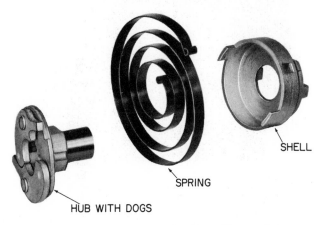

Figure 11·31   Components of an impulse coupling.

DISTRIBUTOR BLOCK

HIGH TENSION FINGER

CAPACITOR

CAPACITOR CONNECTIONS

Figure 11·32   Arrangement of distributor block.

First, the magneto is placed in the position for firing No. 1 cylinder. This is accomplished by rotating the magneto shaft until the timing lines are in position as shown in Fig. 11·33. The timing pin, previously mentioned, is then inserted through the hole in the bottom of the case near the drive end. The engine is placed in the firing position for No. 1 cylinder as explained in the previous section, and the magneto is installed. Slotted holes in the mounting flange permit final adjustment at installation.

OTHER HIGH-TENSION MAGNETOS

Numerous types of high-tension magnetos have been designed for use on aircraft engines; however, it is not deemed essential that all types be described. The basic principles are the same for all such magnetos, and it is only necessary to determine how each is timed internally and timed to the engine. If the technician has a good understanding of the principles of operation and timing, he can usually adjust any magneto for satisfactory operation. If there is any question concerning

SPARK OCCURS AT THIS TOWER

WHEN 2 RED MARKS ARE IN LINE TIMING PIN (6 PENNY NAIL) WILL FIT THROUGH HOLE IN FRAME AND ROTOR SHAFT. THIS HOLDS MAGNETO FOR TIMING TO ENGINE.

TIMING PIN IN PLACE

Figure 11·33   Timing lines in position for No. 1 cylinder.

a particular magneto and its installation, the manufacturer's manuals for the magneto and the engine should be consulted.

Among popular magnetos not described in this text are the Bendix SF6LN-21 and the Eisemann LA-6 and LA-4 types. The Bendix magneto is very much like the S-200 (SFLN-200) series and can be adjusted and installed in the same manner. The harness installation is the same for both types. The Eisemann magnetos employ a different method for securing the high-tension spark-plug cables from those previously described. The distributor cap is designed for screw connections, and eyelets are installed on the ends of the cables. Thus the cable ends are attached to the proper terminals of the distributor cap by means of screws through the cable eyelets.

LOW-TENSION IGNITION

Reasons for development of low-tension ignition

There are several very serious problems encountered in the production and distribution of the high-voltage electricity which is used to fire the spark plugs of an aircraft engine. High-voltage electricity causes corrosion of metals and deterioration of insulating materials. Also, it has a marked tendency to escape from the routes provided for it by the designer of the engine.

There are four principal causes for the troubles experienced in the use of high-voltage ignition systems: (1) flashover, (2) capacitance, (3) moisture, and (4) high-voltage corona.

Flashover is a term used to describe the jumping of the high voltage inside a distributor when an airplane ascends to a high altitude. The reason for this is that the air is less dense at high altitudes and hence has less dielectric, or insulating, strength.

Capacitance is the ability of a conductor to store electrons. In the high-tension ignition system, the capacitance of the high-tension leads from the magneto to the spark plugs causes the leads to store a portion of the electrical charge until the voltage is built up sufficiently to cause the spark to jump the gap of a spark plug. When the spark has jumped and established a path across the gap, the energy stored in the leads during the rise of voltage is dissipated in heat at the spark-plug electrodes. Since this discharge of energy is in the form of a relatively low voltage and high current, it causes burning of the electrodes and shortens the life of the spark plug.

Moisture, wherever it exists, increases conductivity. Thus it may provide new and unforeseen routes for the escape of high-voltage electricity.

High-voltage corona is a phrase often used to describe a condition of stress which exists across any insulator (dielectric) exposed to high voltage. When the high voltage is impressed between the conductor of an insulated lead and any metallic mass near the lead, an electrical stress is set up in the insulation. Repeated application of this stress to the insulation will eventually cause failure.

Low-tension ignition systems are designed in such a manner that the high voltage necessary to fire the spark plugs is confined to a very small portion of the entire circuit. The greater part of the circuit involves the use of low voltage; hence the term **low-tension ignition** is used to describe the system.

Operation of the low-tension ignition system

The low-tension ignition system consists of (1) a **low-tension magneto,** (2) a **carbon brush distributor,** and (3) a **transformer** for each spark plug. Figure 11·34 is a diagram showing the principal parts of a simple low-tension system. The distributor is not shown because in this diagram only one spark plug is used. Figure 11·35 is a schematic drawing of a low-tension ignition system, showing the location in the system of the carbon brush distributor.

During the operation of the low-tension system, surges of electricity are generated in the magneto generator coil. The peak surge voltage is never in excess of 350 volts and probably is nearer 200 volts on most installations. This comparatively low voltage is fed through the distributor to the primary of the spark-plug transformer.

While the complete process by which the transformer coil accomplishes its purpose is not a simple one, the following explanation is sufficiently accurate for the technician or other persons who are not responsible for the design of such systems.

At the instant of opening of the breaker contacts which are connected across the magneto generator coil, a rapid flux change takes place in the generator coil core, causing a rapid rise of voltage in this coil. As has

already been explained, it is the capacitor connected across the breaker points which actually stops the flow of current when the breaker opens.

The primary capacitor and magneto generator coil of a low-tension system are connected through the distributor directly across the primary winding of the transformer coil as shown in Fig. 11·35. Therefore, during the time that the voltage across the primary capacitor is rising, as the breaker points open, the natural tendency is for current to start flowing out through the distributor and the primary of the transformer coil.

When this condition has been achieved, we have the situation of a primary capacitor charged to nearly 200 volts connected across the primary of the transformer. The result is a very rapid rise of current in the primary, accomplished by a very rapid change in flux linkages (magnetic field) in both coils. The rapid change in the flux linkages in the secondary induces the voltage which fires the spark plug. As soon as the spark gap has been "broken down" (broken through and ionized), current also starts to flow in the secondary circuit.

The transformer of the low-tension system is purposely designed to have an appreciable resistance in the primary winding (5 ohms or more). When the secondary current increases, the resistance of the primary coil prevents a corresponding increase of current in that winding, so that, as soon as the voltage originally generated in the secondary has been lowered by the flow of secondary current, the spark is extinguished and no further action takes place. From this it will be clear that the duration of the spark in a high-tension system is several times that of a comparable low-tension system. After the secondary current has stopped, the energy stored in the form of a charge in the primary capacitor continues to drain away at a comparatively slow rate through the primary of the transformer coil.

The rather high resistance of the transformer primary winding, which is characteristic of all low-tension transformer coils, helps to bring the primary current to a stop after the spark has been produced. If this were not done, the primary current would continue to flow through the circuit until the distributor finger carbon brush reached the edge of the distributor contact segment, at which time the current would be stopped by the interruption of the contact as the carbon brush moved off the segment. This would cause pitting and burning of the distributor segments.

It should be clear that the spark voltage is produced by the growth of a magnetic field in the transformer core and not by the collapse of the field as is the case in conventional ignition coils. This fact sometimes raises the question as to why the subsequential collapse or decay of the field in the transformer does not produce a second spark at the spark plug. The reason for this is that the rate of decay of the magnetic field in the transformer is determined by the rate of decay of the primary current. It has already been pointed out that the primary current results from the discharge of the

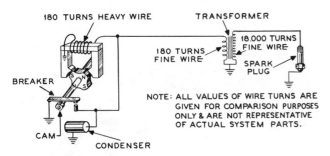

Figure 11·34 Diagram illustrating low-tension ignition system.

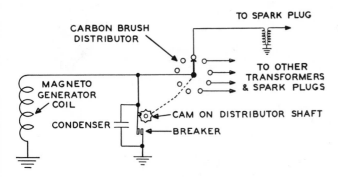

Figure 11·35 Low-tension system with distributor.

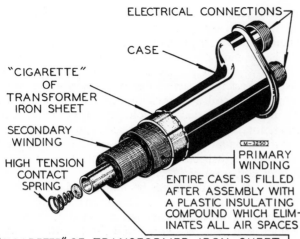

Figure 11·36 Transformer coil for low-tension system.

ELECTRICAL CONNECTIONS

CASE

"CIGARETTE" OF TRANSFORMER IRON SHEET

SECONDARY WINDING

HIGH TENSION CONTACT SPRING

M-3250

PRIMARY WINDING

ENTIRE CASE IS FILLED AFTER ASSEMBLY WITH A PLASTIC INSULATING COMPOUND WHICH ELIMINATES ALL AIR SPACES

"CIGARETTE" OF TRANSFORMER IRON SHEET

its case) to show the design. This coil consists of a primary and a secondary winding with a "cigarette" of transformer iron sheet in the center and another cigarette of transformer iron sheet surrounding the primary winding, which is on the outside of the secondary winding. Usually the transformer unit contains two transformers, one for each spark plug in the cylinder.

The complete transformer assembly provides a compact, lightweight unit convenient for installation on the cylinder head near the spark plugs. This permits the use of short high-tension leads from the transformer to the spark plugs, thus reducing to a large extent the opportunities for leakage of high-tension current.

primary capacitor and that this current tapers off at a rather slow rate after the secondary current stops. Since the rate of decay of the magnetic field is the same as that of the primary current, it is too slow to produce enough voltage for a second spark at the plug.

The transformer coil

Figure 11·36 is a drawing of a typical low-tension transformer coil "telescoped" (that is, pulled out of

LOW-TENSION SYSTEM FOR LIGHT AIRCRAFT ENGINES

General description of system

The low-tension system commonly employed on engines for light aircraft is the S-600 series developed by the Scintilla Division of the Bendix Corporation. The model numbers are S6RN-600 for the dual-breaker magneto and S6RN-604 for the single-breaker magneto. These magnetos are also designed for left-hand rotation.

The components of the S-600 low-tension system are shown in Fig. 11·37. This system is designed for

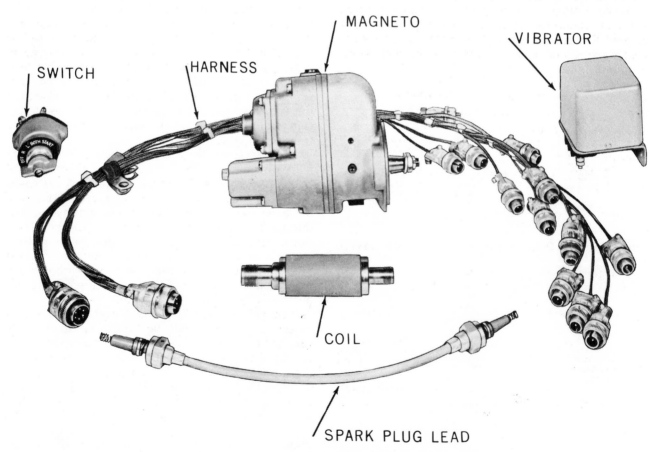

SWITCH

HARNESS

MAGNETO

VIBRATOR

COIL

SPARK PLUG LEAD

Figure 11·37 Components of S-600 low-tension system. (Bendix-Scintilla)

use on a six-cylinder opposed engine. Each installation consists of a retard-breaker magneto, single-breaker magneto, starting vibrator, harness assembly, transformer coils, high-tension leads, and either a combination ignition and starter switch or a standard ignition switch.

This system is designed to generate and distribute low-voltage current through low-tension cables to individual high-voltage transformer coils mounted on the engine crankcase. The low voltage is stepped up to a high voltage by the individual transformer coils and then conducted to the spark plug by short lengths of high-tension cable. Both the low-tension and high-tension cables are shielded to prevent radio interference.

Magneto

The magneto for the S-600 system is almost identical with the S-200 magneto described earlier in this chapter. The principal exceptions in construction are the coil assembly and the distributor assembly. The coil contains one winding only for the generation of the low-tension current. Instead of the high-voltage distributor described for other magnetos, the low-tension magneto employs spring-loaded carbon brushes in the distributor block to bear against metal ring segments on the face of the large distributor gear. The small segment is connected electrically to the carbon brush at the center of the gear which bears against the coil contact.

The magneto has a two-pole rotating magnet and a two-lobe breaker cam on the end of the magnet shaft. The S-600 magneto incorporates a retard breaker in addition to the main breaker. The retard breaker is actuated by the same cam as the main breaker and is so positioned that its contacts open at a predetermined number of degrees after the main breaker contacts open.

A battery-operated starting vibrator used with this magneto provides retarded ignition for starting regardless of engine cranking speed. The retard ignition is in the form of a shower of sparks instead of a single spark obtained by the impulse coupling. This is similar to the operation described for the S-200 high-tension magneto.

A capacitor is required in both the high-tension and low-tension magnetos for the low-voltage circuit. In the magneto under discussion a feed-through-type capacitor is connected across the main breaker points. This capacitor reduces arcing of the points, stores current which feeds to the transformer primary coil shortly after the breaker points open, and aids in reducing radio interference.

Harness assembly

The harness assembly for the low-tension system is shown in Fig. 11·37. This assembly comprises two sections, one for each magneto. Each section consists of six shielded low-tension cables which terminate in connectors for the primary end of the transformer coils. The magneto end of each section has one connector plug with six connecting pins. These mate with six-pin sockets in the female section of the connector which is on the magneto.

Transformer coils

The transformer coils contain primary and secondary windings, with the primary connection on one end of the assembly and the secondary connection on the other end. Both windings are grounded through the metal case. The resistance of the primary winding is between 15 and 25 ohms, and the resistance of the secondary winding is between 5500 and 9000 ohms.

Spark-plug leads

The spark-plug leads are short lengths of shielded high-tension cable provided with fittings at the ends by which they are secured to the high-tension ends of the transformer coils and to the spark plugs. The leads must be of different lengths so they can reach to the spark-plug locations.

Operation of the low-tension system

A schematic diagram of the circuit for a low-tension system is shown in Fig. 11·38. It will be observed that this circuit is very similar to the circuit for the high-tension S-200 system. The system in Fig. 11·38 illustrates the use of the starting vibrator with a control relay and a standard ignition switch. In the diagram all switches and relays are shown in their normal OFF position before operation commences.

When the starter switch S_3 is turned on, the starter solenoid L_3 and the coil L_1 are energized, thus closing contacts R_1, R_2, R_3, and R_4. With the magneto switch in the L position, battery current flows through contact R_1, the vibrator points, coil L_2, contact points R_2, and through the main breaker to ground. The magnetic field built up around coil L_2 from this current causes the vibrator points to open. Vibration starts and continues as previously explained, and the interrupted current is carried to ground through the main and retard breaker points.

When the engine reaches its normal advance firing position, the main breaker of the magneto opens. However, the vibrator current is still carried to ground through the retard breaker. When the retard position

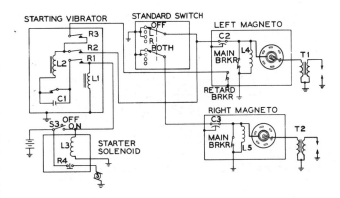

Figure 11·38 *Circuit for low-tension ignition system.*

of the engine is reached, the retard breaker opens and the vibrator current flows through coil L_4 to ground, thus producing a rapidly changing field around the coil. The build-up and collapse of the field around coil L_4 cause a high surge of current to flow through the distributor and the primary winding of the transformer T_1. This surge of current in the primary induces a high voltage in the secondary, thus providing the voltage necessary for firing the spark plug.

When the engine fires and begins to pick up speed, the starter switch is released. This deenergizes relay L_1 and the starter solenoid L_3, thus opening the vibrator circuit and the retard breaker circuit. The switch is then turned to the BOTH position, and this permits both magnetos to operate.

Timing the magneto

For magnetos which do not have timing marks in the breaker compartment, the three raised marks on the drive end of the magneto should be used. These marks are in the recess of the mounting pilot as shown in Fig. 11 · 39. The center mark is used for the **neutral position** when timing the magneto. The outer two marks are for the exact E-gap (10°) position, depending on the direction of rotation.

To time the magneto, the rotor is turned in the direction of normal rotation until the painted chamfered tooth is aligned with the center of the inspection window. It is then turned back a few degrees until it locates in its neutral position. Remember, the magnet will tend to place itself in the neutral position when it has been rotated to a position near neutral.

To construct a pointer for timing, a piece of soft wire is bent around the drive shaft as shown in Fig. 11 · 39. This wire should be bent to a position where it is aligned with the center timing mark while the magneto is still in the neutral position. The magneto is now turned in the direction of normal rotation until the wire pointer is aligned with the outer timing mark. The magneto is now in the exact E-gap position.

The breaker points should be adjusted to open while the pointer is within 7/64 in. of the timing mark. The opening is indicated with a suitable timing light. When the magneto is turned to a position where the cam follower is on a high point of the cam, the breaker-point clearance should be 0.018 in. ±0.006 in.

Adjusting retard breakers

On magnetos having retard breakers, it is necessary to set the retard breaker to open a predetermined number of degrees after the main breakers open, within +2° −0°. This can be accomplished by inscribing a line on the mounting flange at the proper distance from the center mark in the pilot recess. On S-600 series magnetos, the line should be scribed 5/64 in. from the center line as shown in Fig. 11 · 39.

The retard line on the flange can be scribed in the correct position by the use of a divider. Set the divider to the correct dimension (5/64 in.), and place one point directly over the center mark on the OD of the pilot. Now scribe a line on the surface of the flange where the other point of the divider touches the OD of the pilot.

After the main breaker has been set to open at E gap, the wire pointer is shifted to index over the center mark without allowing the shaft to move from its position where the main breaker points just open. The shaft is now rotated until the pointer indexes with the scribed line on the flange. By means of the timing light, the retard breaker is adjusted to open at this point.

Timing magnetos with timing marks in the breaker compartments

Magnetos with timing marks in the breaker compartment can be timed as described for the S-200 magneto. Figure 11 · 40 illustrates a pointer attached to the cam screw and located with the shaft in the neutral position. The main breaker points should be adjusted to open when the pointer is turned to the E-gap position. The retard breaker should open at 30° after the E-gap position. This is accomplished by resetting the pointer at 0° when the rotor is at E-gap position. Then the rotor is turned until the pointer is at the 30° mark. At this point the retard breaker should open.

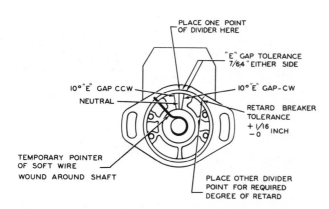

Figure 11 · 39   Installation of timing pointer.

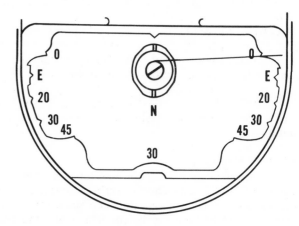

Figure 11 · 40   Timing pointer on magneto with timing marks.

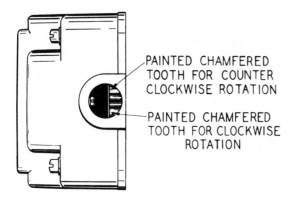

PAINTED CHAMFERED
TOOTH FOR COUNTER
CLOCKWISE ROTATION

PAINTED CHAMFERED
TOOTH FOR CLOCKWISE
ROTATION

Figure **11·41** *Setting magneto in position for timing to engine.*

Installation

The installation of the S-600 magneto is very similar to the installation of other Bendix magnetos; however, we shall describe the procedure here for emphasis.

1. Check the magneto for direction of rotation to see that the magneto is correct for the engine.
2. Remove the inspection plug from the top of the magneto.
3. Turn the magneto drive shaft in the direction of rotation until the first of the two painted chamfered teeth is aligned approximately with the center of the inspection hole (see Fig. 11·41). The magneto is now in the No. 1 cylinder firing position. (**Note:** The timing mark on the distributor gear is only for timing reference and is not to be used as a reference for adjusting the breaker point opening).
4. Turn the engine to the No. 1 cylinder firing position as previously explained.
5. Install the magneto on the engine, and tighten the mounting bolts sufficiently to hold the magneto in position and yet allow it to be rotated.
6. Connect a suitable timing light to the switch (P lead) connection, and connect the common lead of the timing light to a good ground on the engine.
7. If the timing light is out, rotate the magneto housing in the direction of its magnet rotation a few degrees beyond the point where the light comes on. Then slowly turn the magneto in the opposite direction until the light just goes out. Secure the magneto housing in this position, and recheck the setting. Connect the switch wire (P lead) to the switch terminal on the breaker cover, and connect the retard wire to the retard connection in the same manner. The fittings for connecting these wires are available through the manufacturer, and they are identified as Kit No. 10-157209 for the switch lead and Kit No. 10-157208 for the retard lead. These are the same kits supplied for the S-200 magneto.

Maintenance for the S-600 low-tension system

After the first 25- and 50-hr periods of operation and every 50 hr thereafter, the breaker assemblies should be checked. Points which have deep pits or excessively burned areas should be discarded.

The oiler felt should be checked for effectiveness. If the fingers are not moistened with oil after squeezing the felt, 2 or 3 drops of oil should be placed on the felt. This oil should be Scintilla 10-186527 or equivalent. After the oil has been allowed to soak in (about 30 min), all excess oil should be blotted off with a clean

cloth. Too much oil may foul the breaker contacts and cause excessive burning.

If engine operating troubles develop and they appear to be caused by the ignition system, it is advisable to check the spark plugs, transformer coils, and wiring before working on the magnetos. The transformer coils may be checked with an ohmmeter. The primary resistance should be between 15 and 25 ohms, and the secondary resistance should be between 5500 and 9000 ohms. The resistance is checked between the end terminal of the coil and the metal case.

If the magneto seems to be the source of trouble, a visual inspection may be conducted. Uncouple the magneto connector, and separate the harness from the magneto. Remove the four adapter plate screws, and separate the adapter from the distributor housing. Inspect for the presence of moisture and foreign matter, and remove any that is found. Check for broken leads or damaged insulation. If either is present, remove the magneto and replace it with one known to be in satisfactory condition.

LOW-TENSION IGNITION SYSTEMS FOR LARGE AIRCRAFT ENGINES

General description

In this section we shall describe the low-tension, high-altitude ignition system designed by the Scintilla Division of the Bendix Corporation for use with the Pratt & Whitney R-2800 aircraft engine. The system consists of a magneto, a harness with nine detachable primary leads, two distributors, 18 double high-tension coils, and 36 high-tension leads. As shown in Fig. 11·42, the appearance of these parts on the engine

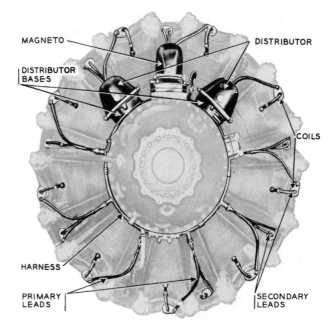

Figure **11·42** *Low-tension system on R-2800 engine. (Bendix-Scintilla)*

257

does not differ radically from that of a conventional high-tension system. Electrically, however, the low-tension system is quite different from the high-tension system as explained previously.

Type DLN-10 magneto

The designation DLN means that the magneto is the dual type, left-hand rotating (counterclockwise), and manufactured by Bendix. It is illustrated in Fig. 11·43. Actually, this magneto can be described as a double, double magneto because it has four coils. Two four-pole magnets are mounted on the magnet shaft, with the poles of one magnet staggered 45° from those of the other. Each magnet operates in conjunction with two pairs of pole shoes molded in the housing. A coil is mounted upon each pair of pole shoes, making four coils in all. Each coil consists of a single primary winding of relatively few turns of heavy wire. There are no secondary windings. One end of each coil winding is grounded to the magneto housing, and the other end is connected through a four-pin electrical connector into the harness.

The magneto is mounted on the front of the engine by means of a standard four-bolt flange. It is driven at one and seven-eighths engine crankshaft speed. The magnet shaft is supported on two ball bearings. The housing and cover are of cast-magnesium alloy and are precision machined and secured together with a special clamping ring to provide adequate radio shielding. A timing plunger is provided which, when depressed, engages a notch cut in the magnet shaft. This facilitates setting of the magneto in its exact firing position when the magneto is timed to the engine.

Harness assembly and primary leads

The harness for this system is a tubular metal manifold. Two permanent distributor bases, nine primary lead outlets, one magneto connection, and one switch connection are integral parts of the manifold. The complete assembly is shown in Fig. 11·44. The outlet connections are four-pin plug-in electrical connectors.

There are 44 low-tension primary wires in the mani-

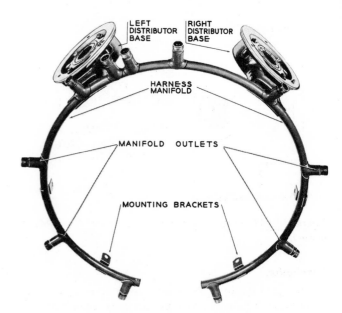

Figure 11·44   Distributor base and harness assembly.

fold. These function as follows: 4 run from the magneto connector to the distributors (2 to each), 4 run from the switch connector to the distributors (2 to each), and 36 run from the contact segments of the distributors to the primary lead outlets.

Figure 11·45 is a chart of the electrical connections of the system showing the pin-letter designations of the various electrical connectors. All wires within the manifold are No. 18 gage, insulated with rubber and fabric. Since these wires carry only a few hundred volts, the insulation requirements are not critical.

The distributor bases contain the distributor connection plates over which the carbon brushes of the distributor finger travel in making the proper distribution of current to the engine cylinder coils. Short lead wires attached to each segment plate make the electrical connections to the distributors which fit within the distributor bases of the harness.

The detachable primary leads connect the harness outlets to the transformer coils. Each primary lead is of forked construction as shown in Fig. 11·46, having a four-pin electrical connector at each of the branches which lead to the two coils. For purposes of identification, the manifold outlets are numerically designated as shown in Fig. 11·44. The distributor bases are designated as left and right, as viewed from the cockpit or antipropeller end of the engine.

Within each distributor base an oil seal is mounted. The sealing ring of the oil seal assembly mates against a lapped washer on the drive shaft of the distributor unit, thereby preventing the engine oil from entering the distributor.

Distributor assemblies

The **distributor assemblies** fit within the distributor bases of the harness assembly. They are of clockwise rotation as viewed from the drive end. This means that the rotation is counterclockwise as one looks into the

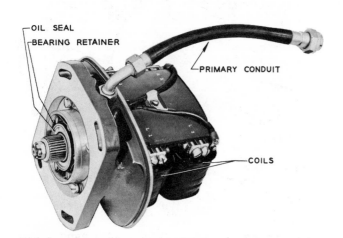

Figure 11·43   Low-tension magneto.

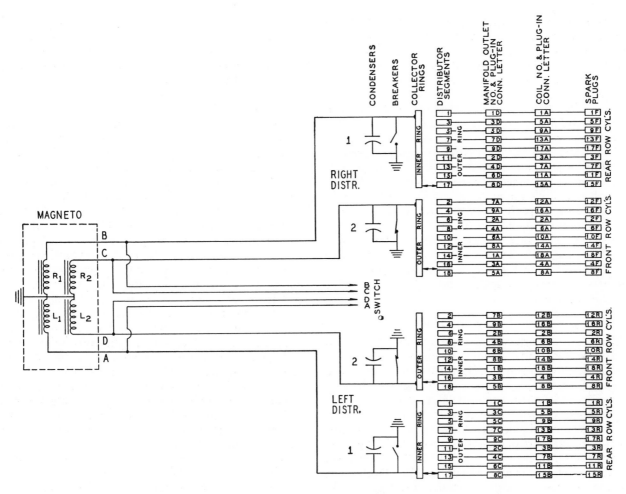

Figure 11·45   Chart showing electrical connections for low-tension system.

distributor base at the segment plate. Each distributor is secured in position with three screws and is provided with a precision-machined cover. The cover is secured with a clamping ring which ensures an electrically tight seal, preventing radio interference.

The distributor shaft carries two nine-lobe **compensated breaker cams,** a **distributor finger,** and the **drive coupling.** It also carries a lapped washer which mates against the sealing member of the oil seal in the distributor base.

The breakers are mounted adjacent to the cams and are secured to a breaker plate mounted on the distributor housing. A capacitor (condenser) is connected

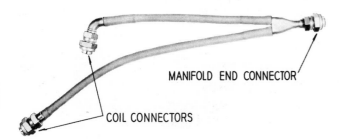

MANIFOLD END CONNECTOR

COIL CONNECTORS

Figure 11·46   A primary lead assembly.

across each breaker and is mounted to the housing with clamps.

The molded **collector plate** is mounted directly over the **distributor rotor.** The two collector rings in this plate make contact with the two carbon brushes on the upper surface of the distributor rotor. The upper brushes are connected through the rotor to the lower brushes, which make contact with the **distributor connection plates** in the distributor base section of the harness.

As mentioned previously, the breaker cams are of compensated design. This means that there is a separate lobe for each cylinder of the engine. The No. 1 lobe of each cam is marked with a dot. Each cam is also engraved with an arrow to show the direction of operating rotation. The two cams are mounted on the same shaft with the No. 1 cam and breaker in the top position. The No. 1 breaker of the right distributor fires the front plugs of the rear row of engine cylinders, and the No. 1 breaker of the left distributor fires the rear plugs of the rear row of cylinders. The No. 2 cams fire the front and rear plugs of the front row (even numbered) of cylinders. The connections for the spark plugs can be traced in Fig. 11·45.

The distributor shaft turns on two ball bearings and

is driven at one-half engine speed. It should be noted that all distributor rotors turn at one-half engine speed for a four-stroke-cycle engine because one complete revolution of the rotor fires all plugs once and this occurs in two revolutions of the crankshaft. Since a compensated cam has one lobe for each cylinder fired, the cam also turns at one-half engine speed and can therefore be driven by the same shaft that drives the distributor rotor.

The drive end of the distributor shaft carries a coupling of standard 17-tooth design. The upper end of the shaft is machined to provide a timing step which is used in conjunction with two timing marks to indicate the opening positions of the two breakers. Figure 11·47 shows the method of locating the opening position of No. 1 breaker by using a straightedge to align the shaft step with the No. 1 timing mark. The drive coupling of the distributor is provided with vernier ratchets to permit accurate setting of the distributor when it is timed to the engine.

Transformer coils and high-tension leads

Each coil (transformer) assembly consists of two transformer coils permanently assembled into a single case and wired to suitable electrical connections. The coil units are mounted on special brackets secured to the baffle plates of the engine cylinders.

A two-pin electrical connector forms the input connection to the coil assembly. One pin of the connector leads to the primary of each transformer coil. The other end of each primary is grounded to the case. One end of each secondary is also grounded. The other end of each secondary winding terminates at a high-tension contact socket at each end of the coil case.

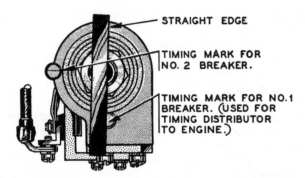

STRAIGHT EDGE

TIMING MARK FOR NO. 2 BREAKER.

TIMING MARK FOR NO.1 BREAKER. (USED FOR TIMING DISTRIBUTOR TO ENGINE.)

Figure 11·47   Use of a straightedge with timing step and timing marks.

Each high-tension lead fits directly into one of the high-tension contact sockets of its respective coil. The leads are short, thereby reducing energy losses in the system. Figure 11·48 shows one of the coil assemblies with its high-tension lead.

Magneto operation

A simplified schematic diagram of the high-altitude low-tension system for an 18-cylinder radial engine is shown in Fig. 11·49. In the diagram it can be seen that the magneto has two four-pole magnets mounted on the same shaft but staggered in position so the poles of one magnet are aligned with the pole shoes when the poles of the other magnet are in the neutral position. Thus the magnets are staggered 45°. Also in the magneto are two sets of double-pole shoes and four primary coils. As each magnet rotates one revolution, it produces in each of the two coils on its pole shoes four impulses of current. Since the magnets are staggered 45° from each other, there are eight current impulses per revolution of the shaft. Because each impulse is generated in two coils, each is of a dual nature; that is, they are two separate but simultaneous pulses of low-voltage current. During operation, a pair of pulses will fire the front and rear plugs of one cylinder.

The magnet shaft is driven at one and one-eighth engine speed. This produces nine double spark impulses per engine revolution, which is the requirement for an 18-cylinder four-stroke-cycle engine, such as the Pratt & Whitney R-2800.

Harness and distributors

The low-voltage impulses from the magneto coils are transmitted through the harness to the distributors. The impulses from the two right-hand coils in the magneto, R_1 and R_2, are carried to the right-hand distributor which fires the front plugs in each cylinder. The two left-hand coils in the magneto, L_1, and L_2, are connected to the left-hand distributor and fire the rear plugs of each cylinder. As long as the breaker points are closed, there are two completed circuits in each distributor. One is through the breaker points to ground and back to the grounded coil in the magneto. The other is out through the distributor into the primary winding of the high-tension coil. This second circuit has a relatively high resistance, so most of the current flows through the breaker points to ground. When the magneto low-tension current reaches its peak value, the cam separates the breaker points and interrupts the circuit.

Figure 11·48   Coil assembly with high-tension lead.

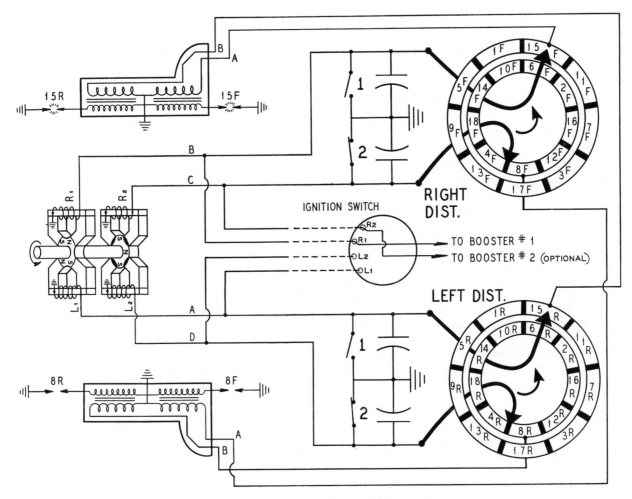

Figure 11·49   Schematic diagram of low-tension system.

As the breaker points open, the capacitor connected across the points is charged. The capacitor charge plus the remaining current from the magneto coil then surges through the distributor contacts and into the primary coil of the high-tension coil where it induces the high-voltage in the secondary winding. This voltage breaks down the gap between the spark-plug electrodes and produces the spark to ignite the fuel/air mixture. The surge of secondary current is quite short-lived and falls away rapidly. Then the points close again and reconnect the low-resistance circuit to ground. Meanwhile, of course, the rotor of the distributor has made contact with the proper segment of the distributor block so that the surge is directed to the particular spark plug which it is required to fire. As the magnet rotates and another impulse is building up in the magneto circuit, the rotor moves to the next distributor segment, and the next plug in the firing order will receive the coming surge of high voltage. Also, the two distributors are synchronized, and when the right one is firing a front plug, the left is firing the rear plug in the same cylinder. Therefore, the two plugs in any one cylinder are each receiving a high-voltage spark at the same moment, assuring proper ignition of the fuel/air mixture in the cylinder.

Distribution of the magneto output

An examination of the diagram of Fig. 11·49 will further clarify the action of these circuits at the instant of firing a cylinder. Assume that the No. 15 cylinder is being fired. This cylinder is the seventeenth in the firing order. Coils L_1 and R_1 are generating impulses in the magneto. The current goes through the harness to the distributors, L_1 to the left distributor and R_1 to the right distributor. Since the breaker points are opened, the current flows into the distributor rotor, through the carbon brushes and to the No. 17 segment which is connected to the coil for the No. 15 cylinder. It then flows through the harness to the coil for the No. 15 cylinder where it is transformed into high-voltage current and passes through the high-tension lead to the spark plug, causing a spark at the gap. The current from the left distributor is transmitted to the rear plug, and the current from the right distributor is transmitted to the front plug. After this surge of current has ceased, the distributor rotor will progress from No. 17 segment to No. 18 segment and coils L_2 and R_2 in the magneto will be generating impulses which will be transmitted to cylinder No. 8, which is the eighteenth cylinder in the firing order. Note that the firing order for the

R-2800 engine is 1-12-5-16-9-2-13-6-17-10-3-14-7-18-11-4-15-8. On an 18-cylinder twin-row radial engine, the even-numbered cylinders are in the front row and the odd-numbered cylinders are in the rear row.

THE COMPENSATED CAM

Reason for compensated cam

In a radial engine, because of the mounting of the link rods on the flanges of the master rod, the travel of the pistons connected to the link rods is not uniform. Normally we would expect that the pistons in a nine-cylinder radial engine would reach top center 40° apart. That is, for each 40° the crankshaft turns, another piston would reach TDC. Since the master rod tips from side to side while it is carried around by the crankshaft, the link rods follow an elliptical path instead of the circular path required for uniform movement. For this reason there is less than 40° of crankshaft travel between the TDC positions for some pistons and more than 40° of travel between the TDC positions of other pistons.

In order to obtain ignition at precisely 25° BTC it is necessary to compensate the breaker cam in the magneto by providing a separate cam for each cylinder of the engine.

Design of the compensated cam

A compensated cam for a nine-cylinder radial engine is shown in Fig. 11·50. The cam lobe for the No. 1 cylinder is marked with a dot, and the direction of rotation is shown by an arrow. A careful inspection of the cam will reveal that there is a slight difference in

NO. 1 LOBE

Figure 11·50 A compensated cam.

the distance between the various lobes. This variation is designed into the cam in order to compensate for the nonuniform movement of the pistons. The variation may be as much as 2.5° more or less than 40° for a nine-cylinder radial engine.

The compensated cam turns at one-half crankshaft speed because it produces a spark for each cylinder during each complete revolution. Since the crankshaft must rotate through two turns to fire all the pistons, the cam can turn only one-half crankshaft speed. The compensated cam is normally mounted on the same shaft that drives the distributor because the distributor also can turn only one-half crankshaft speed.

IGNITION SHIELDING

Since the magneto is a special form of high-frequency generator, it acts like a radio transmitting station while it is in operation. Its oscillations are called **uncontrolled** because they cover a wide range of frequencies. The oscillations of a conventional radio transmitting station are waves of a **controlled** frequency. For this reason the ignition system must be **shielded.**

Shielding is difficult to define in general terms. Aircraft **radio shielding** is the metallic covering or sheath over all electric wiring and ignition equipment, grounded at close intervals and provided for the purpose of eliminating any interference with radio reception.

If the high-tension cables and switch wiring of the magneto are not shielded, they can serve as antennas from which the uncontrolled frequencies of the magneto oscillations are radiated. The receiving aerial on an airplane is comparatively close to the ignition wiring; hence, the uncontrolled frequencies are picked up by the aerial along with the controlled frequencies from the aircraft radio station, thus causing interference (noise) to be heard in the radio receiver in the airplane.

The magneto has a metallic cover that is made of a nonmagnetic material. The cover joints are fitted tightly to prevent dirt and moisture from entering. Since it is necessary to cover the cables completely, fittings are provided on the magneto to attach a shielded ignition harness. Provision is made for ventilation to remove condensation and the corrosive gases formed by the arcing of the magneto within the housing.

Ignition wiring system

The **low-tension wiring** on a high-tension magneto consists of a single shielded conductor from the primary coil to the engine-ignition switch. Its circuit passes through the fire wall with a connector plug, frequently of a special design, which automatically grounds the magnetos when the plug is disconnected.

High-tension cable differs from low-tension cable in that the high-tension cable has a conductor of small cross section and insulation of comparatively large cross section whereas low-tension cable has a conductor of large cross section and insulation of comparatively small cross section. The reason for this difference is that the capacity to carry current is the primary requisite of low-tension cable whereas dielectric strength (insulating property) is the most important requirement of high-tension cable.

The modern high-tension cable consists of several strands of small wire, a layer of rubber or synthetic rubber, a glass braid covering, and a neoprene sheath. It is available in several sizes, the most common being 5, 7, and 9 mm.

High-tension wiring is always placed in the special conduit arrangement known as the **ignition harness,** mentioned before. This harness, which includes both flexible and rigid conduits, is made so that its shielded portion can be fastened directly to the magneto shield and also to the shielded portion of the spark plug.

THE TIMING LIGHT

Timing lights for the synchronizing of magneto breaker points may be simply "hot" test lights, or they may be more complex. If an ordinary hot test light is used for checking the opening of breaker points, it is necessary to disconnect the primary lead from the breaker points. This is because the light will burn regardless of whether the points are open or closed owing to the low resistance of the primary windings. There may be a slight dimming when the breaker points open, but it is not appreciable. If the primary circuit is disconnected from the points, the light will go out when the points are open because the current path is open. This is illustrated in Fig. 11·51.

The circuit for another type of test light is shown in Fig. 11·52. In this test unit a vibrator produces an interrupted current, and this is converted to an alternating current by means of a transformer. The alternating current is supplied to the lamp when the unit is connected to the breaker points. When the breaker points of the magneto are closed, the lamp will be on because there is a complete circuit through the secondary of the transformer and the lamp. When the breaker points open, the primary of the magneto is in series with the lamp and the inductive reactance of the primary coil will reduce the current, thus causing the lamp to go out or glow very dimly.

A test unit incorporating two circuits such as that shown in Fig. 11·52 may be constructed in one box for convenience in synchronizing magneto timing. In a dual test unit such as this, a common black wire is used for ground and the two red leads are connected to the "hot" sides of the breaker points.

SPARK PLUGS

The function of the spark plug

The spark plug is that part of the ignition system in which the electrical energy of the high-voltage current produced by the magneto or other high-tension device is converted into the heat energy required to ignite

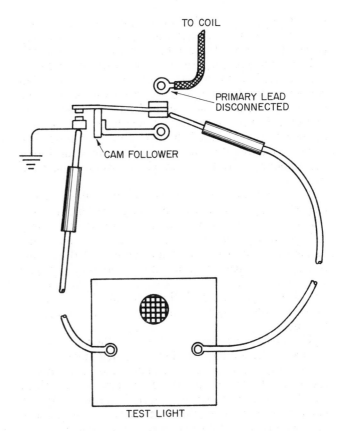

Figure 11·51   Use of timing light.

the air/fuel mixture in the engine cylinders. The spark plug provides an air gap across which the high voltage of the ignition system produces a spark to ignite the mixture.

Construction of spark plugs

A modern aircraft spark plug fundamentally consists of three major parts: (1) the electrodes, (2) the ceramic insulator, and (3) the metal shell.

Figure 11·53 shows the constructional features of a typical modern aircraft spark plug manufactured by

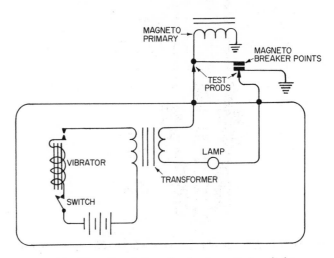

Figure 11·52   Circuit for vibrator-type timing light.

the Champion Spark Plug Company. In the illustration, the assembly shown in the center of the spark plug is the inner electrode assembly consisting of the terminal contact, spring, resistor, brass cap, a conductor (not labeled in the illustration), and the nickel-clad copper electrode. The insulator is shown between the electrode assembly and the shell and is made in two sections. The main section extends from the terminal contact to a point near the tip of the electrode. The barrel-insulating section extends from near the top of the shielding barrel far enough to overlap the main insulator.

The outer section of the spark plug, illustrated in Fig. 11 · 53, is a machined steel shell. The shell is often plated to eliminate corrosion and to reduce the possibility of thread seizure. In order to prevent the escape of high-pressure gases from the cylinder of the engine through the spark-plug assembly, internal pressure seals, such as the sillment seal and the glass seal, are used between the outer shell and the insulator and also between the insulator and the center electrode assembly.

The shell of the spark plug includes the radio-shielding barrel. In some spark plugs, the shell and shielding barrel are made in two sections and are screwed together. The two parts should never be disassembled by the technician because during manufacture the correct pressure is applied to provide a gastight seal. Any disturbance of the seal may cause leakage.

The shell and the radio-shielding barrel complete the ground circuit for the radio shielding of the ignition harness. The shell is externally threaded on both ends so that it can be joined to the radio shielding of the ignition harness at the top and can be screwed into the cylinder head at the bottom.

Spark plugs are manufactured with many variations in construction to meet the demands of modern aircraft engines. **Resistor-type** spark plugs were designed to reduce the burning and erosion of the electrodes in engines having shielded harnesses. The capacitance between the high-tension cable and the shielding is sufficient to store electrical energy in quantities which produce a comparatively high-current discharge at the spark-plug electrodes. The energy is considerably greater than is necessary to fire the fuel/air mixture; hence it can be reduced by means of a resistor in order to provide greater spark-plug life.

Another improvement which leads to greater dependability and longer life is the use of platinum-alloy firing tips and high-temperature alloys in the main center electrode. A spark plug with this type of construction is illustrated in Fig. 11 · 54.

Unshielded spark plugs are still used in a few light aircraft engines. An unshielded spark plug is shown in Fig. 11 · 55.

Classification of shell threads

Shell threads of spark plugs are classified as 14 or 18 mm diameter, **long reach** or **short reach,** thus:

Diameter	Long Reach	Short Reach
14 mm	½ in.	⅜ in.
18 mm	13⁄16 in.	½ in.

Terminal threads at the top of the radio-shielded spark plugs are either ⅝ in.–24 thread or ¾ in.–20 thread. The latter type are particularly suitable for high-altitude flight and in other situations where flashover within the sleeve might be a problem.

The designation numbers for spark plugs provide an indication of the characteristics of the plug. The

CERAMIC INSULATOR

TERMINAL CONTACT

CEMENT

SPRING

RESISTOR

GLASS SEAL

COPPER SLEEVE

COPPER CORED ELECTRODE

Figure 11 · 53   Shielded spark plug. (Champion Spark Plug Co.)

SILVER - CORED CENTER ELECTRODE

PLATINUM ELECTRODES

Figure 11 · 54   Spark plug with platinum electrodes.

Figure 11·55 Unshielded spark plug.

Champion Spark Plug Company utilizes letters and numbers to indicate whether the spark plug contains a resistor, the barrel style, mounting thread, reach, hex size, heat rating range, gap, and electrode style. The designations are as follows:

1. No letter or an R. The R indicates a resistor-type plug.
2. No letter, E, or H. No letter—unshielded; E—shielded ⅝ in.-24 thread; H—shielded ¾ in.-20 thread.
3. Mounting thread, reach and hex size.
   A—18 mm, ¹³⁄₁₆ in. reach, ⅞ in. stock hex
   B—18 mm, ¹³⁄₁₆ in. reach, ⅞ in. milled hex
   D—18 mm, ½ in. reach, ⅞ in. stock hex
   J—14 mm, ⅜ in. reach, ¹³⁄₁₆ in. stock hex
   L—14 mm, ½ in. reach, ¹³⁄₁₆ in. stock hex
   M—18 mm, ½ in. reach, ⅞ in. milled hex
4. Heat rating range. Numbers from 26 to 50 indicate coldest to hottest heat range. Numbers from 76 to 99 indicate special application aviation plugs.
5. Gap and electrode style. E—two-prong aviation; N—four-prong aviation; P—platinum fine wire; B—two-prong massive, tangent to center; R—push wire, 90° to center.

Spark-plug heat range

The **heat range** of a spark plug is the principal factor governing aircraft spark-plug performance under various service conditions. The term **heat range** refers to the classification of spark plugs according to their ability to transfer heat from the firing end of the spark plug to the cylinder head.

Spark plugs have been classified as "hot," "normal," and "cold." However, these terms may be misleading because the heat range varies through many degrees of temperature from extremely hot to extremely cold. Thus the word "hot" or "cold" or "normal" in itself does not necessarily tell the whole story.

Since the insulator is so designed as to be the hottest part of the spark plug, its temperature can be related to the preignition and fouling regions as shown in Fig. 11·56. Preignition is likely to occur if surface areas in the combustion chamber exceed critical limits or if the spark-plug core nose temperature exceeds 1630°F. On the other hand, fouling or shorting of the plug due to carbon deposits is likely to occur if the insulator tip temperature drops below approximately 800°F. Thus, spark plugs must operate between fairly well-defined temperature limits, and this requires that plugs be supplied in various heat ranges to meet the requirement of different engines under a variety of operating conditions.

From the engineering standpoint, each individual plug must be designed to offer the widest possible operating range. This means that a given type of spark plug should operate as hot as possible at slow speeds and light load and as cool as possible at cruise and takeoff power. Plug performance therefore depends upon the operating temperature of the insulator nose, with the most desirable temperature range falling between 1000 and 1250°F.

Fundamentally, an engine which runs "hot" requires a relatively cold spark plug, whereas an engine which runs "cool" requires a relatively hot spark plug. If a hot spark plug is installed in an engine which runs hot, the tip of the spark plug will be overheated and cause **preignition**. If a cold spark plug is installed in an engine which runs cool, the tip of the spark plug will collect unburned carbon, causing **fouling** of the plug.

A discussion of hot, normal, and cold plugs is technically correct, but it should be emphasized that different heat ranges of aircraft spark plugs cannot be substituted arbitrarily, as is common in automotive practice, because the selection of aircraft spark plugs is governed by the aircraft engine manufacturers' and Federal Aviation Agency approvals governing the use of a particular spark plug in any aircraft engine.

The principal factors governing the heat range of aircraft spark plugs are (1) the distance between the copper sleeve around the insulator and the tip of the insulator, (2) the thermal conductivity of the insulating material, (3) the thermal conductivity of the electrode,

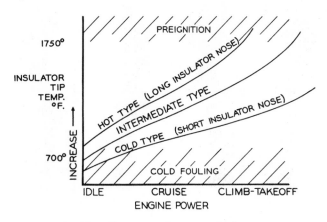

Figure 11·56 Chart to show spark-plug temperature ranges.

(4) the rate of heat transfer between the electrode and the insulator, (5) the shape of the insulator tip, (6) the distance between the insulator tip and the shell, and (7) the type of outside gasket used. Hot- and cold-plug construction is illustrated in Fig. 11·57.

Other features of spark-plug construction may affect the heat range to some extent. However, the factors we have mentioned are those of primary consideration.

Servicing aircraft spark plugs

Scheduled servicing intervals are normally determined by the individual aircraft operator. These intervals will vary according to operating conditions, engine models, and spark-plug types. The principal determining factor in the removal and servicing of spark plugs is the width of the spark gap, that is, the distance between the electrodes where the spark is produced. This spark-plug gap increases in width with use until the distance becomes so great that the spark plug must be removed and either regapped or replaced. If the spark-plug gap becomes too wide, a higher secondary voltage must be developed by the ignition system in order to create a spark at the gap. This higher voltage will tend to leak through the insulation of the ignition wiring, thus eventually causing failure of the high-tension leads.

The correct spark-plug gap for a particular spark-plug installation is established by the manufacturer. No spark plug should be operated with a gap greater than that specified in the manufacturer's instructions.

Servicing procedure

It must be emphasized that an aircraft operator must either follow the manufacturer's instructions for the servicing of aircraft spark plugs or adopt an adequate procedure of his own.

In general, the servicing of aircraft spark plugs is accomplished according to the following sequence:

1. **Removal.** Shielded terminal connectors are removed by loosening the elbow nut with the proper size crowfoot or open-end wrench. Care must be taken to avoid damaging

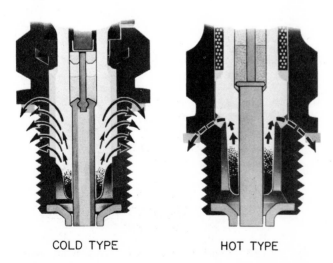

COLD TYPE   HOT TYPE

Figure **11·57** *Construction of cold and hot spark plugs.*

the elbow. Terminal sleeve assemblies must be pulled out in a straight line to avoid damaging either the sleeve or the barrel insulator.

The spark plug is loosened from the cylinder bushing by the use of the proper size deep-socket wrench. It is recommended that a six-point wrench be used because it provides a greater bearing surface than a twelve-point wrench. The socket must be seated securely on the spark-plug hexagon to avoid possible damage to the insulator or connector threads.

As each spark plug is removed, it should be placed in a tray with numbered holes so that the engine cylinder from which the spark plug has been removed can be identified. This is important, because the condition of the spark plug may indicate impending failure of some part of the piston or cylinder assemblies.

If a spark plug is dropped on a hard surface, cracks may occur in the ceramic insulation which are not apparent on visual examination. **Any spark plug which has been dropped should be rejected or returned to the manufacturer for reconditioning.**

In case the threaded portion of a spark plug breaks off in the cylinder, great care must be exercised in the removal of the broken section. Normally it will be necessary to remove the cylinder from the engine. Before an attempt is made to remove the section, a liquid penetrant should be applied around the threads and allowed to stand for at least 30 min. If the broken part is tapped lightly with the end of a punch while the penetrant is working, the vibration will help the liquid to enter the space between the threads. The electrodes of the plug should be bent out of the way with a pin punch or similar tool in order to permit the insertion of a screw extractor (Easy out). A steadily increasing force on the screw extractor should remove the broken part.

If the foregoing process is not successful, it will be necessary to remove the part by cutting with a small metal saw. Such a saw can be made by cutting a hacksaw blade to a size which can be inserted inside the spark-plug section. The saw is carefully manipulated to cut three slots inside the section without cutting deeply enough to touch the threads of the cylinder. The three sections of the part can then be broken out by means of a punch and a light hammer. The blows should be directed toward the center of the spark-plug hole.

After the broken portion of the spark plug has been removed, the threads in the cylinder should be checked carefully for damage. Usually the threads can be cleaned by means of a thread chaser. If there is appreciable damage to the threads, a Heli-Coil insert should be installed. See instructions in the chapter on overhaul practices.

2. **Preliminary inspection.** Immediately after the spark plugs have been removed, they should be given a careful visual inspection and all unserviceable plugs should be discarded. Spark plugs with cracked insulators, badly eroded electrodes, damaged shells, or damaged threads should be rejected.

3. **Degreasing.** All oil and grease should be removed from both the interior and the exterior of the spark plugs according to the degreasing method approved for that particular type of spark plug. Either vapor degreasing or the use of solvents, such as Stoddard solvent, is usually recommended. **Carbon tetrachloride should not be used in cleaning spark plugs** because it is likely to cause corrosion and is poisonous.

4. **Drying.** After they have been degreased, spark plugs should be dried, both inside and out, to remove all traces of solvent. Drying may be accomplished by the use of dry compressed air or by placing the spark plugs in a drying oven.

5. **Cleaning.** During operation of an aircraft engine, lead and carbon deposits form on the ceramic core, the electrodes, and the inside of the spark-plug shell. These deposits are most readily removed by means of an abrasive blasting machine especially designed for cleaning spark plugs.

The use of an abrasive blast spark-plug cleaner is shown in Fig. 11·58. Instructions for the use of the cleaning unit are as follows:

a. Install the proper size rubber adapter in the cleaner, and press the firing end of the spark plug into the adapter hole.

b. Move the control lever to ABRASIVE BLAST, and slowly wobble the spark plug in a circular motion for 3 to 5 sec. The wobbling motion angle should be no greater than 20° from vertical to permit the abrasive materials freely to enter the firing end opening and facilitate cleaning.

c. Continue the wobbling motion, and move the lever to AIR BLAST to remove the abrasive particles from the firing bore.

d. Remove the plug and examine its firing end. If cleaning is incomplete, repeat the cleaning cycle for 5 to 10 sec. If cleaning is still incomplete, check the cleaner and replace the abrasive. For complete service information, refer to the manufacturer's service manual.

Several companies offer spark-plug cleaning machines with the abrasive supported in liquid. This is an excellent cleaning method, but the operator must make sure that the abrasive is of the **aluminum oxide** type. **Silica** abrasive can contribute to later plug fouling. Immediately after cleaning by the wet blast method, the plugs should be oven-dried to prevent rusting and to ensure a satisfactory electrical test.

Excessive use of the abrasive blast is avoided to prevent too much wear of the electrodes and insulators. Spark-plug threads are cleaned by means of a wire wheel with soft bristles. Threads which are slightly nicked may be cleaned by using a chasing die.

The connector seat at the top of the shielding barrel must be cleaned to provide a proper seating surface for the gasket and nut at the end of the ignition harness. If necessary, fine-grained garnet paper or sandpaper may be used to smooth the seat. Emery paper should not be used because

Figure 11·59 Types of electrode construction.

the emery compound conducts electricity and may establish a path for leakage of high-voltage current. After the seat is cleaned, the shielding barrel should be thoroughly blown out with an air blast.

6. **Regapping.** The tools and methods used to set spark-plug gaps will vary with the shape, type, and arrangement of electrodes. In Fig. 11·59, four typical forms of electrode construction are illustrated. These are the single-ground electrode, the two-prong "fine-wire" electrodes, the two-prong ground electrodes, and the four-prong ground electrodes.

The main precaution to be taken in regapping a spark plug is to avoid putting any pressure on the center electrode. If force is applied to the center electrode in any way, it is likely to crack the ceramic insulator and render the spark plug useless.

The gap in any spark plug is measured by the use of round wire gages. These gages are supplied in two sizes for each gap to measure both the minimum and the maximum width for the gap. For example, a spark-plug-gap gage will have two wires, one of which is 0.011 in. and the other 0.015 in. When the spark-plug gap is being tested, the smaller dimension gage must pass through the gap and the larger dimension gage must be too large to pass through the gap. A gage for checking the gap clearance of a spark plug is shown in Fig. 11·60.

If a spark-plug gap is too large, it is closed by means of a special gap-setting tool supplied by the manufacturer and used according to the manufacturer's instructions. A gap-setting tool is shown in Fig. 11·61.

If the gap of a four-prong or two-prong spark plug has been closed beyond limits, no effort should be made to open the gap. In such a case the plug should be returned to the manufacturer for adjustment.

Single-electrode and two-prong wire electrode plugs are so constructed that the gap can be either opened or closed without danger of cracking the ceramic insulator. A special tool for adjusting the gap of such a plug is shown in Fig. 11·62.

7. **Inspection and testing.** The final step in preparing a used spark plug for service is the inspection and test. Visual inspection is accomplished by means of a magnifying glass. It is essential that good lighting be provided. The following items are examined: threads, electrodes, shell hexagons ("hex"), ceramic insulation, and the connector seat.

Spark plugs are tested by applying high voltage, equiva-

Figure 11·58 Use of abrasive spark-plug cleaner.

Figure 11·60 Spark-plug gap tool.

Figure 11·61 Gap-setting tool. (Champion Spark Plug Co.)

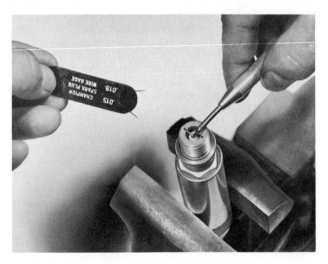

Figure 11·62 Setting gap on platinum electrode spark plug.

lent to normal ignition voltage, to the spark plug while the plug is under pressure. This test has commonly been called the "bomb" test. Modern testing devices have been designed by spark-plug manufacturers to apply the correct pressure and voltage to the spark plug for this test. Spark plugs are tested under pressure to simulate to some extent the operating conditions of the spark plug. A spark plug that fires satisfactorily under normal atmospheric conditions may fail under pressure because of the increased resistance of the air gap under these conditions. The testing of a spark plug in a pressure tester is shown in Fig. 11·63. Instructions for operation are included with the test unit.

Spark plugs which fail to function properly during the pressure test should be baked in an oven for about 4 hr at 225°F. This will dry out any moisture within the plug. After it has been baked, the plug should be tested again, and if it

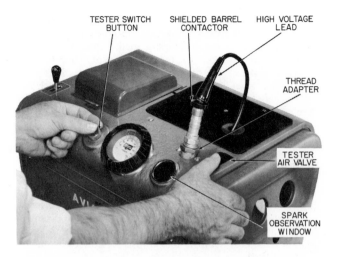

Figure 11·63 Pressure testing a spark plug.

fails under the second test, it should be rejected or returned to the manufacturer.

8. **Gasket servicing.** One of the most important and yet unrecognized essentials of spark-plug installation involves the condition of the solid-copper gasket used with the spark plug. When spark plugs are installed, either a new gasket or a reconditioned gasket should be used.

Used spark-plug gaskets should be annealed by being heated to a cherry red and immediately quenched in light motor oil. After the quenching, the oil should be removed with a solvent and the gaskets immersed in a solution of 50 percent water and 50 percent nitric acid to remove oxides. After the acid bath, the gaskets should be carefully rinsed in running water and dried.

Even though good reconditioned spark-plug gaskets may be available, it is recommended that new gaskets be installed with new or reconditioned spark plugs. The additional cost which may be involved is so small that it cannot offset the advantage of new gasket reliability.

9. **Installation.** Before installing spark plugs, the technician must make sure that he has the proper type of plug for the engine. Two of the most critical factors are the **heat range** and the **reach.** The effect of improper heat range has been described previously. Briefly, if the plug is too hot, preignition and detonation may occur; if the plug is too cold, it will become fouled.

If a long-reach plug is installed in an engine which is designed for a short-reach plug, some of the threads of the plug will extend into the combustion chamber. In this position, the threads and the end of the plug may become overheated and thus cause preignition. This will result in loss of power, overheating, and possible detonation. The threads will be subject to high-temperature corrosion, and this will cause the plug to stick in the cylinder. The sticking tendency will be aggravated by the formation of carbon and lead residue at the end of the plug. When this condition exists, damage may be caused to the cylinder threads and to the spark plug at the time of removal.

Regardless of the care exerted by the technician in carrying out all the steps previously explained, his best efforts are in vain if he fails to install the spark plugs properly. The first step is to inspect the spark plug and the cylinder bushing. The threads of each should be clean and free of damage. A light coating of approved **antiseize compound** should be applied to the

268

threads of the spark plug. It should not, however, be applied to the first two threads because the material may run down on to the electrodes when hot, thus shorting the electrodes of the spark plug.

The spark plug is then installed together with the gasket in the cylinder bushing. It should be possible to screw the spark plug into the cylinder bushing by hand. The spark plug is tightened by means of a deep-socket wrench with a torque handle. It is very important that the spark plug be tightened to the torque specified by the manufacturer. The usual torque for 18-mm spark plugs is 360 to 420 in.-lb, and the torque for 14-mm plugs is 240 to 300 in.-lb. Overtightening a spark plug may damage the threads and make the spark plug difficult to remove or, in extreme cases, may change the gap setting. Overtightening will also cause the spark plug to stick in the cylinder.

The ignition lead is connected to the spark plug by inserting the terminal sleeve in a straight line into the shielding barrel and tightening the terminal nut to the top of the shielding barrel. The terminal sleeve must be clean and dry and must not be touched by the hands, as moisture or acid might eventually cause failure.

The terminal nut at the top of the spark plug should be tightened as far as possible by hand and then turned about one-quarter turn with the wrench. A good snug fit is all that is required. Overtightening may cause damage to the elbow and the threads.

After a complete set of spark plugs has been installed, it is wise to run the engine and perform a magneto check to determine the general condition of the ignition system. A drop in engine rpm beyond the specified limit will require a check of the magneto, ignition cables, or spark plugs.

TURBINE IGNITERS

Although a gas-turbine engine **igniter** serves the same purpose as a spark plug, the design and configuration of these units are considerably different from the spark plugs for reciprocating engines. Furthermore, the sizes and shapes of igniters have not been standardized appreciably; hence there are no fixed rules for service and maintenance. In every case it is essential that the manufacturer's recommendations for cleaning and reconditioning be followed.

Figure 11·64 illustrates different types of igniter plugs. Since the igniters are designed to operate at a lower surrounding pressure than the spark plug, the spark gaps are greater. The power source for the igniter supplies a very high level of energy; hence the spark produced is of relatively high amperage and resembles a white-hot flame rather than a spark. This spark discharge causes a much more rapid erosion of the electrodes than the spark of a spark plug. However, the igniter operates each time just long enough to start the engine, and the total erosion over a long period of engine operation is not great. In some cases the igniter also operates during takeoff of the airplane in order to assure a restart if the engine should flame out.

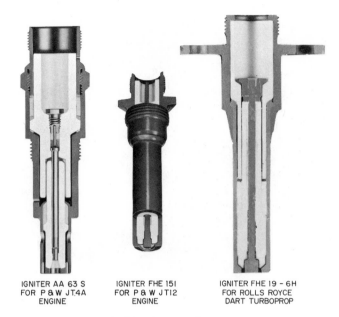

IGNITER AA 63 S FOR P & W JT-4A ENGINE

IGNITER FHE 151 FOR P & W JT12 ENGINE

IGNITER FHE 19 - 6H FOR ROLLS ROYCE DART TURBOPROP

Figure 11·64   Turbine igniter plugs.

Service and inspection

The igniter is inspected visually for burning and erosion of the electrode or shell, cracking of the ceramic insulator, and damage to threads, hex, or flange. If damage is apparent, the igniter should be discarded.

The inside of the shell may be cleaned with a swab dampened with a standard petroleum cleaning solvent conforming to P-S-661 specification. If the inside of the barrel insulator is stained, a nonconductive abrasive powder such as Bon Ami may be used with the solvent and swab. After cleaning, all traces of the abrasive should be removed with a clean swab dampened in solvent.

The connector seat at the top of the barrel should be cleaned to assure a good contact between the harness connector and the barrel. If necessary, a finely grained garnet or sandpaper can be used. Care should be taken to see that abrasive particles do not enter the barrel.

The firing end of the igniter can be cleaned only if a cleaning procedure is approved by the manufacturer. Some igniters have semiconductor materials at the firing end, and these can be damaged if normal cleaning procedures are followed.

THE ENGINE IGNITION ANALYZER

Functions of the ignition analyzer

The **engine ignition analyzer** is an electronic instrument designed to assist the technician or flight engineer in the detection and diagnosis of ignition troubles in the aircraft engine. The ignition analyzer not only will detect ignition troubles but will indicate other engine troubles which may affect the ignition system and be reflected in the behavior of the ignition voltages. Figure 11·65 is an illustration of an ignition analyzer

Figure 11·65   Bendix ignition analyzer.

manufactured by the Scintilla Magneto Division of the Bendix Aviation Corporation.

The ignition analyzer is fundamentally an **oscilloscope** especially modified to receive electrical indications from the ignition system and to show these indications graphically on the screen of the cathode-ray tube. The **cathode-ray** tube is the key to the operation of the ignition analyzer, even as it is the key to the operation of a television receiver.

Principles of operation

A cathode-ray tube contains an electron "gun" which directs a beam of electrons against a fluorescent screen. When the electron beam strikes the screen, it causes a small, brilliant spot to appear. This is sometimes called the "writing" spot. The electron beam must pass between two sets of plates on its way to the screen. The electrons can thus be deflected either horizontally or vertically by changing the value of the charges on the plates. In this way the spot can be caused to trace a pattern on the screen. The form of this pattern will depend on the signals imposed upon the deflection plates in the tube.

Figure 11·66 is a block diagram of the ignition analyzer illustrated in Fig. 11·65. This diagram shows the relative position of the various components in the circuit of the analyzer. A careful study of the diagram will aid in understanding the operation.

As previously discussed in this text, the high voltage necessary to fire the spark plugs in the engine is produced by the secondary coil of the magneto when the primary field reverses as a result of the opening of the breaker points. During the time that the breaker points are open and the spark discharge is occurring across the gap of the spark plugs, the ignition analyzer receives the signals which indicate the conditions existing throughout the ignition system. The high-tension current discharging across the spark-plug gap sets up electrical oscillations (waves or vibrations) in both the

secondary and the primary circuits of the magneto. The nature of these oscillations is affected by the conditions existing within every part of both circuits. If any part of the system is not normal, the characteristics of the oscillations will change in frequency, magnitude, or rate of damping.

Research has shown that most of the normal malfunctions encountered in an ignition system will produce significant changes in the oscillatory characteristics of the circuit. The ignition analyzer provides a means for observing these changes and identifying the cause of the changes. It is only necessary to compare the wave form of a normal circuit with that of a malfunctioning circuit to detect the difference.

It is easily understood that the pattern on the screen of the ignition analyzer must be produced by two different signals from the engine. One of these signals moves the electron beam in the cathode-ray tube horizontally, and the other signal moves the beam vertically.

In order to produce a signal or voltage which will cause the electron beam to move from one side of the screen to the other, a voltage differential must be built up between the horizontal deflection plates in the tube. This voltage differential must increase at a uniform rate so that the beam will traverse the screen at a uniform rate. When the beam has completed its travel or sweep across the screen, the charge on the deflection plates is discharged and the beam moves instantaneously to the opposite side of the screen.

When the analyzer is in operation, the timing of the horizontal sweep is accomplished by a pickup device on the engine. The action is timed so that one sweep of the beam will include one complete cycle of engine cylinder firing.

A study of the block diagram in Fig. 11·66 will show the three methods by which the timing signal is obtained from the engine. When an analyzer is permanently installed in an airplane for operation during flight, either the three-phase generator or the breaker pickup is used. These units are installed on the engine in the same manner as any other accessory and are driven so that a signal is produced for each two revolutions of the engine. When the analyzer is connected to an engine temporarily, the signal is picked up by induction from the high-tension leads of one of the cylinders.

The timing signals obtained from the engine are converted to triggering pulses which are delivered to the sweep generator. The sweep generator produces the sweep signal, which is amplified and then imposed upon the horizontal deflection plates of the tube.

The vertical deflection of the electron beam in the cathode-ray tube is controlled by the voltages present in the primary of the ignition system being tested. A lead is connected directly from the primary of the magneto to the vertical deflection amplifier. In this manner the voltages in the primary circuit control the amount of vertical deflection of the electron beam.

The combined effect of the horizontal and vertical signals in the cathode-ray tube is to trace a pattern on

270

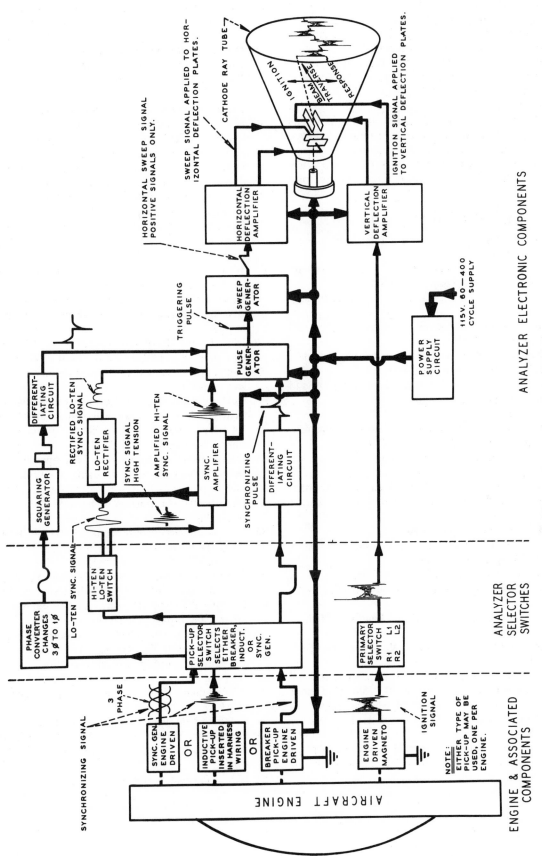

Figure 11·66 Block diagram of ignition analyzer.

the fluorescent screen of the tube. Since the horizontal sweep is triggered by the engine, the pattern at the left side of the tube will begin with the signal from the first cylinder firing after the triggering impulse. Patterns for each cylinder will follow from left to right in the order in which the cylinders fire. Thus it is easy to determine which circuit is producing each pattern.

The ignition analyzer is equipped with controls which enable the operator to concentrate the patterns from the entire engine on the screen, or he may enlarge any single pattern so that it will occupy the entire space on the face of the tube. This permits him to study the patterns individually or collectively as he may desire.

REVIEW QUESTIONS

1. At what point in the four-stroke cycle does the ignition event take place?
2. Name the essential components of an ignition system.
3. Explain the function of ignition shielding.
4. Describe the construction of a typical high-tension magneto.
5. How can you determine how many sparks a magneto will produce in one revolution?
6. How does the primary current affect the magnetic field immediately before the breaker points open?
7. How do you determine the magneto speed with respect to the crankshaft speed of the engine?
8. Explain E gap.
9. Give two reasons why the secondary voltage of a magneto is so much greater than the primary voltage.
10. Explain the function of the primary capacitor.
11. Describe the construction of the magneto coil.
12. Compare magneto sparking order with engine firing order.
13. If a magneto carries the model designation SF9LN-3, what can you tell about the magneto?
14. Describe three types of ignition boosters.
15. Explain the purpose of the retard breaker on some Bendix magnetos for light aircraft engines.
16. Describe a combination ignition-starter switch.
17. Describe the timing procedure for the Bendix S-200 magneto.
18. Tell how you would install and time a Bendix S-200 magneto to the engine.
19. What are the two key points in installing and timing any magneto?
20. How are the high-tension leads anchored in the distributor grommet on a Bendix magneto for light aircraft engine?
21. What precaution must be observed when a magneto is installed on an engine and the switch lead (P lead) is disconnected?
22. What spark-plug leads are connected to what spark plugs on a six-cylinder opposed engine? Include both top and bottom plugs.

23. Describe the inspection procedure for a magneto?
24. Describe the Slick series 600 magneto.
25. Explain the timing procedure for the Slick 600 magneto.
26. How is the breaker cam lubricated?
27. Explain the operation of an impulse coupling.
28. What problems are reduced through the use of a low-tension system?
29. Explain the operation of a low-tension ignition system.
30. Why is the primary winding of the transformer coil in a low-tension ignition system designed with greater resistance than the winding in the magneto coil?
31. Describe the construction of a typical transformer coil for a low-tension ignition system.
32. Compare the S-600 low-tension magneto with the S-200 high-tension magneto.
33. Describe the distributor system for the S-600 magneto.
34. Describe the harness assembly for the S-600 low-tension ignition system.
35. What are the resistances of the primary and secondary windings in the transformer coils for the S-600 system?
36. Describe the timing procedure for the S-600 magneto.
37. Give the procedure for timing the S-600 magneto to the engine.
38. Describe the distributor assembly for the Bendix low-tension ignition system used on the R-2800 engine.
39. Explain the construction of one of the detachable primary lead assemblies.
40. How are the compensated breaker cams mounted, and at what speed do they rotate with respect to the crankshaft?
41. By what means is the distributor position established when it is timed to the engine?
42. Explain the reason for the use of a compensated cam.
43. Describe two types of timing lights, and explain the use of each.
44. Describe the construction of a modern shielded aircraft spark plug.
45. What is the purpose of the resistor in a spark plug?
46. What should be done with a spark plug which has been dropped?
47. Explain the difference between a *hot* and a *cold* spark plug.
48. What is the advantage of platinum electrodes?
49. Describe the complete procedure for removing, reconditioning, and installing spark plugs.
50. What precaution must be taken in regapping a spark plug?
51. What may result if a long-reach spark plug is installed in an engine designed for a short-reach plug?
52. Why are spark plugs tested under pressure?
53. What damage may be caused by overtorquing a spark plug?
54. Compare a turbine igniter with a spark plug.
55. Describe the purpose of an engine ignition analyzer.
56. Why does an ignition analyzer give an indication of trouble?
57. How is the analyzer timed to the engine?

CHAPTER 12

Engine Starting Systems

TYPES OF STARTING SYSTEMS

Starters for reciprocating engines

The types of starting systems which have been installed in aircraft for starting reciprocating engines may be classified as follows: (1) direct hand cranking; (2) direct cranking, either hand or electric; (3) hand inertia; and (4) combination hand and electric inertia.

The first two mentioned above may be described as direct-cranking systems, and the second two may be referred to as inertia-type cranking systems.

Starters for gas-turbine engines

Starters for gas-turbine engines may be classified as air-turbine (pneumatic) starters, electric starters, fuel-air combustion starters, and cartridge-type starters. The most commonly used starter is the air-turbine type. This type of starter requires a high-volume air supply which may be provided by a ground starter unit, a compressed-air bottle on the airplane, or compressor bleed from other engines on the aircraft. This starter will be described later in this chapter.

DIRECT-CRANKING SYSTEMS

Direct hand-cranking starter

The **direct hand-cranking starter** is sometimes described as a **hand-turning gear-type starter**. It consists of a worm-gear assembly that operates an automatic engaging and disengaging mechanism through an adjustable-torque overload-release clutch. It has an extension shaft that may be either flexible or rigid, depending upon the design. To prevent the transmission of any reverse motion to the crank handle in case the engine "kicks" backward while it is being cranked, a ratchet device is fitted on the hand crankshaft.

This type of starter can be used with a gear ratio of 6:1 for any engine rated at 250 hp or less. It has a comparatively low weight, and it is simple to operate and maintain. It was extensively used on early airplanes which had low-horse-power engines and no source of electric power for starting. On seaplanes, where it was very difficult to start the engine by swinging the propeller, it was especially popular. However, it has been entirely supplanted by more efficient designs.

Direct-cranking electric starter

When the direct-cranking method is used, either hand or electric, there is no preliminary storing of energy in the fly-wheel as there is in the case of the inertia-type starters. The starter of the direct type, when electrically energized, provides instant and continuous cranking. The starter fundamentally consists of an electric motor, reduction gears, and an automatic engaging and disengaging mechanism, which is operated through an adjustable torque overload-release clutch. The engine is therefore cranked directly by the starter.

The motor torque is transmitted through the reduction gears to the adjustable torque overload-release clutch, which actuates a helically splined shaft. This, in turn, moves the starter jaw outward, along its axis, and engages the engine-cranking jaw. Then, when the starter jaw is engaged, cranking starts.

When the engine starts to fire, the starter automatically disengages. If the engine stops, the starter automatically engages again if the current continues to energize the motor.

The automatic engaging and disengaging mechanism operates through the adjustable torque overload-release clutch, which is a multiple-disk clutch under adjustable spring pressure. When the unit is assembled, the clutch is set for a predetermined torque value. The disks in the clutch slip and absorb the shock caused by the engagement of the starter dogs. They also slip if the engine kicks backward. Since the engagement of the starter dog is automatic, the starter disengages when the engine speed exceeds the starter speed.

INERTIA STARTERS

Although inertia-type starters are not in common use today, the technician is likely to encounter them from time to time on older aircraft. For this reason it is deemed proper to retain a brief description of inertia starters in this text.

Types of inertia starters

There are two types of inertia starters: (1) the hand-cranking type, commonly called the **hand inertia starter,** in which the flywheel is accelerated by hand only; and (2) the electric type, commonly called the **combination inertia starter** and sometimes referred to as the **combination hand and electric inertia starter,** in which the flywheel is accelerated by either a hand crank or an electric motor. All movable parts, including the flywheel, are set in motion during the energizing of an inertia starter of either type.

Principles governing the operation of the inertia starter

Newton's first law states: **Every body continues in its state of rest or uniform motion in a straight line unless it is compelled to change that state by some external force.** This is also known as a statement of the property of **inertia.**

The cranking ability of an **inertia starter** for an airplane depends upon the amount of energy stored in a rapidly rotating flywheel. The energy is stored in the flywheel slowly during the energizing process, and then it is used very quickly to crank the engine rapidly, thus obtaining from the rotating flywheel a large amount of power in a very short time.

Under ordinary conditions, the energy obtained from the flywheel is great enough to rotate the engine crankshaft three or four times at a speed of 80 to 100 rpm. In this manner, the inertia starter is used to obtain the starting torque needed to overcome the resistance imposed upon the cranking mechanism of the engine by reason of its heavy and complicated construction.

The speed at which the engine crankshaft is rotated may be less than the **coming-in speed for the magneto,** which is the minimum crankshaft speed at which the magneto will function satisfactorily. Therefore, if the engine uses magnetos for ignition, as practically all modern engines do, an ignition booster of some type must be provided. It is usually installed near the engine and operated while the inertia starter is cranking the engine.

Hand inertia starter

In using the **hand inertia starter,** when a hand crank is placed in the crank socket and the crank rotated, a gear relationship between the crank and the flywheel makes it possible for a single turn of the hand crank to cause the flywheel to turn many times. For example, one revolution of the hand crank may cause the flywheel to revolve 100 or more times, depending upon the make, model, etc., of the starter. The speed of all movable parts is gradually increased with each revolution of the hand crank, and most of the energy imparted to the crank is stored in the rapidly rotating wheel in the form of kinetic energy.

Figure 12·1 is a sectional diagram of a hand inertia starter. The crank socket, flywheel, engaging lever, mounting flange, starter driving jaw, torque overload-release clutch, springs, disks, and barrel are labeled on the drawing.

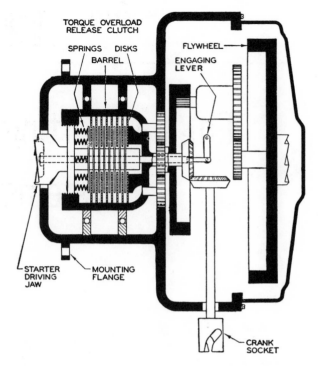

Figure **12·1** *Sectional diagram of hand inertia starter.*

One type of clutch consists of one set of disks fastened to the shaft and another set of disks, made of a different kind of metal, fastened to the barrel. The disks are pressed together by springs. The retaining ring compresses the springs and can be adjusted to set the value of the slipping torque. This feature is important because the normal operation of the clutch is to slip momentarily after the starter and engine jaws are meshed. During the process of slipping, a torque is exerted on the crankshaft until the initial resistance of the engine is overcome and the clutch is again able to hold. The maximum holding torque is called the **breakaway.** This breakaway and the slipping torque depend upon the size of the engine being cranked.

Figure 12·2 illustrates an early type of inertia starter with cranking and engaging controls. In this illustration the following parts are labeled: (1) starter crank, (2) extension crank, (3) adapter and universal assembly, (4) lever, (5) starter pull rod, (6) spring link, (7) spring, (8) starter, (9) bolt, (10) nut, (11) bolt, and (12) nut. When the starter crank is inserted through the left side of the airplane, it can be turned to crank the mechanism and start the engine.

The clutch prevents any injury to the starter caused by an engine kickback or a sudden overload. If the engine crankshaft does not rotate for any reason, the clutch slips until the flywheel ceases to turn.

Combination hand and electric inertia starter

A **combination hand and electric inertia starter** may consist of a hand inertia starter with an electric motor attached, and the gear and clutch arrangement may be like that of the hand inertia starter. The flywheel may

274

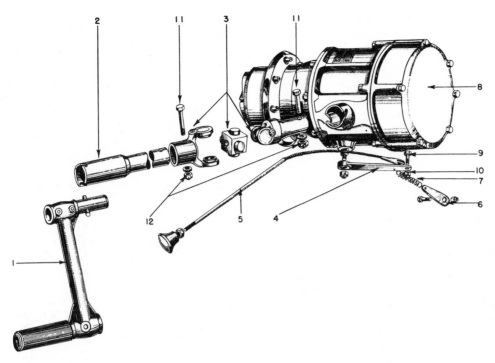

Figure 12·2   Early type of inertia starter with controls.

be accelerated by either a hand crank or the electric motor. When the starter is energized by hand cranking, the motor is mechanically disconnected and it does not operate.

When the motor is operated, a movable jaw on a helically splined shaft engages the motor directly to the inertia-starter flywheel in one type of inertia starter called a **jaw-type starter motor-engaging mechanism,** illustrated in Fig. 12·3.

On some starters of this general type, the starter jaw tends to remain at rest when the motor armature starts to rotate, but as the shaft turns, the jaw moves

forward along the splined shaft until it engages the flywheel jaw. Ordinarily, there is no trouble with this type of mechanism, but if the jaw binds on the shaft, it will not engage the flywheel, and this permits the motor to race. When the engine fails to start, the operator must not continue to attempt cranking. If he does, the teeth may be stripped on either the flywheel or the motor jaw or both. The correct procedure is to wait until the starter flywheel comes to rest before energizing the motor in a second attempt to crank. This avoids both the racing of the motor and the stripping of the teeth.

Electric motors for inertia starters

The typical electric motor for an inertia starter is either a 12- or a 24-volt series-wound d-c motor with windings of low resistance. The reason for the low resistance of the windings is that, when the starter switch is closed, there is a great amount of current drawn in order to deliver a powerful starting torque. When the motor gains speed, the induced electromotive force (emf) causes a smaller amount of current to flow. For example, an inertia starter motor, which draws about 350 amp at starting, may draw only about 75 amp at high speed.

This can be explained in another manner by saying that a counter emf is established when the motor gains speed.

An inertia starter motor is never operated at full voltage unless there is a load imposed upon it. If there is no load, and if the motor has a small amount of internal friction, it will "race" and the armature may fly apart ("burst") because of the centrifugal stresses.

Figure 12·4 is a simple schematic diagram of a series

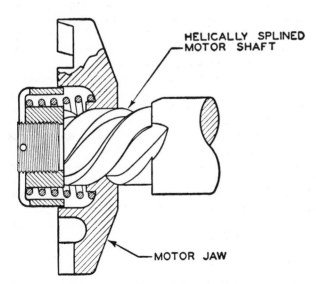

HELICALLY SPLINED MOTOR SHAFT

MOTOR JAW

Figure 12·3   Starter engaging jaw and mechanism.

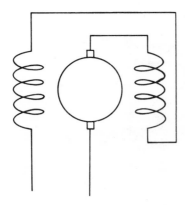

Figure 12·4   Schematic diagram for a series motor.

motor. The field coils are connected in series with the armature. Since all the current used by the motor must flow through both the field and the armature, it is apparent that the flux of both the armature and the field will be strong. The greatest flow of current through the motor will take place when the motor is being started; hence, the starting torque is high. Series-wound motors are used wherever the load is continually applied to the motor and is heavy when the motor first starts. In addition to starting motors, those motors used to operate landing gear, cowl flaps, and similar equipment are of this type.

DIRECT-CRANKING STARTERS FOR LIGHT AIRCRAFT ENGINES

Starter motor

A typical direct-cranking motor is illustrated in Fig. 12·5. The armature winding is of heavy copper wire capable of withstanding very high amperage. The windings are insulated with special heat-resistant

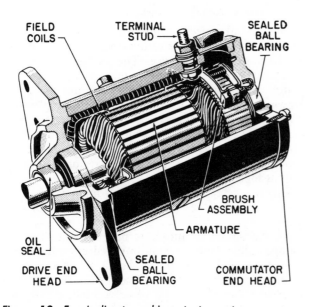

Figure 12·5   A direct-cranking starter motor.

enamel, and after being placed in the armature, the entire assembly is doubly impregnated with special insulated varnish. The leads from the armature coils are staked in place in the commutator bar and then soldered with high-melting-point solder. An armature constructed in this manner will withstand severe loads imposed for brief intervals during engine starting.

The field-frame assembly is of cast-steel construction with the four field poles held in place by countersunk screws, which are threaded into the pole pieces. Since a motor of this type is series wound, the field coils must be wound with heavy copper wire to carry the high starting current.

The end frames are of cast aluminum and are attached to the field frames by means of screws threaded into one end. The ball bearings are of the sealed type and are pressed into recesses in the end frames. An oil seal is placed in the drive end frame to prevent engine oil from entering the motor.

The brush assemblies are attached to the commutator end frame. The brushes are not held in brush holders in the particular motor illustrated but are attached with screws to a pivoted brush arm. This arm is provided with a coil spring which holds the brush firmly against the commutator.

The field frame is slotted at the commutator end to provide access to the brushes for service and replacement. A cover band closes the slots to protect the motor from dirt and moisture.

The positive terminal extends through the field frame. It is insulated from the frame by means of a composition sleeve and washers of similar material. The negative side of the power supply comes through the field frame.

The overrunning clutch

In order to engage and disengage a starter from an engine it is necessary to employ some type of an engaging mechanism. In the discussion of inertia starters the starter jaw mounted on a helically splined shaft was mentioned as the means for engaging the starter to the engine. Various types of mechanisms have been designed for light engine starters, and one of the most popular is called the **overrunning clutch.**

A typical overrunning clutch arrangement is shown in Fig. 12·6. It will be observed that the clutch consists of an inner collar; a series of rollers, plungers, and springs enclosed in a shell assembly; and the shaft upon which the assembly is mounted. The hardened steel rollers are assembled into notches in the shell. The notches taper inward with the result that the rollers seize the collar when the shell is turned in such a direction that the rollers are moved toward the small end of the notches. Thus, when the shell is turned in one direction, the collar must turn with it; however, when it is turned in the opposite direction, the collar can remain stationary.

Complete starter assembly

A starter assembly employing a manually operated switch and a shift lever is shown in Fig. 12·7. This

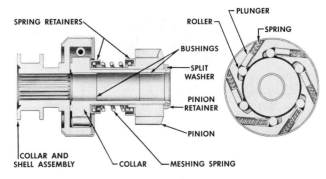

SPRING RETAINERS
ROLLER
PLUNGER
SPRING
BUSHINGS
SPLIT WASHER
PINION RETAINER
PINION
COLLAR AND SHELL ASSEMBLY
COLLAR
MESHING SPRING

Figure 12·6 An overrunning clutch.

starter assembly makes use of an overrunning clutch similar to that described above, and it also incorporates a pair of gears so that there is a gear reduction between the motor armature and drive pinion. This gear reduction provides an increase in cranking torque at the drive pinion.

The shift lever is operated by means of a cable or wire control from the airplane cockpit. The control has a return spring with sufficient tension to bring the lever to the fully released position when the control is released.

When the control is operated to start the engine, the lower end of the shift lever thrusts against the clutch assembly and causes the overrunning clutch drive pinion to move into mesh with the engine starter gear. If the drive pinion and starter gear teeth butt against each other instead of meshing, the **meshing spring** inside the clutch sleeve compresses to spring-load the drive pinion against the starter gear. Then, as soon as the armature begins to turn, engagement and cranking take place. In the unit illustrated, the overrunning

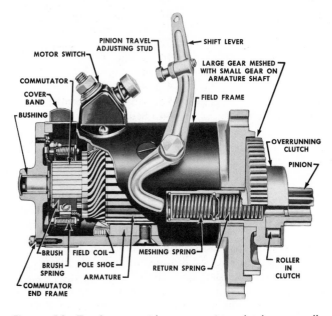

PINION TRAVEL ADJUSTING STUD
MOTOR SWITCH
SHIFT LEVER
LARGE GEAR MESHED WITH SMALL GEAR ON ARMATURE SHAFT
COMMUTATOR
COVER BAND
BUSHING
FIELD FRAME
OVERRUNNING CLUTCH
PINION
BRUSH
BRUSH SPRING
FIELD COIL
POLE SHOE
ARMATURE
MESHING SPRING
RETURN SPRING
ROLLER IN CLUTCH
COMMUTATOR END FRAME

Figure 12·7 Starter with overrunning clutch, manually operated switch and clutch lever. (Delco-Remy Div., General Motors Corp.)

clutch drive pinion is supported on a stub shaft which is part of the engine. As the drive pinion is moved into mesh, the stub shaft causes the **demeshing spring** inside the sleeve to be compressed. The demeshing spring produces demeshing whenever the shift lever is released. After the engine starts, overrunning clutch action permits the pinion to overrun the clutch and gear during the brief period that the pinion remains in mesh. Thus, high speed is not transmitted back to the cranking motor armature.

Starter assembly with 90° adapter drive

The complete starter assembly, adapter, and clutch assembly for a six-cylinder opposed engine is shown in the exploded view of Fig. 12·8. The starter is mounted on a right-angle drive adapter which is attached to the rear end of the crankcase. The tongue end of the starter shaft mates directly with the grooved end of the worm shaft. The worm shaft (43) is supported between a needle bearing (44) at its left end and a ball bearing (41) which is retained in the adapter by a Truarc snap ring. The worm (39) is driven by the shaft through a Woodruff key. The worm wheel (34) is attached by four bolts to a flange on the clutch drum (36) which bears on the shaft-gear (35). Two dowels center the wheel on the drum and transmit the driving torque. A heavy helical spring (30) covers both the externally grooved drum and a similarly grooved drum machined on the shaftgear just ahead of the clutch drum. The spring is retained on the clutch drum by an in-turned offset at its rear end which rides in a groove around the drum, just ahead of the flange. The in-turned offset of the clutch spring is notched, and the clutch drum is drilled and tapped for a spring retaining screw. The front end of the spring fits closely in a steel sleeve, pressed into the starter adapter. When the starter is energized, friction between the clutch spring and the adapter sleeve and between the spring and the clutch drum, which is turned by the worm wheel, tends to wind up the spring on the clutch and shaftgear drums, locking them together so that the shaftgear rotates and turns the crankshaft. As soon as the engine starts, the shaftgear is driven faster than the clutch spring and tends to unwind it, thus increasing its inside diameter so that the shaftgear spins free of the starter drive. The generator drive pulley is mounted on the rear end of the shaftgear and driven through a Woodruff key, so it always turns at shaftgear speed.

STARTERS FOR RADIAL ENGINES

Early-type radial engines were often equipped with hand inertia starters or electric hand inertia starters. These starters were effective. However, there was some inconvenience associated with their use because of the necessity of accelerating the starter and then engaging it to the engine for the start. If the energy stored in the flywheel was dissipated before the engine started, then it was necessary to accelerate again. The inertia starter was, therefore, more complex in system, construction, and operation than a direct-cranking electric starter;

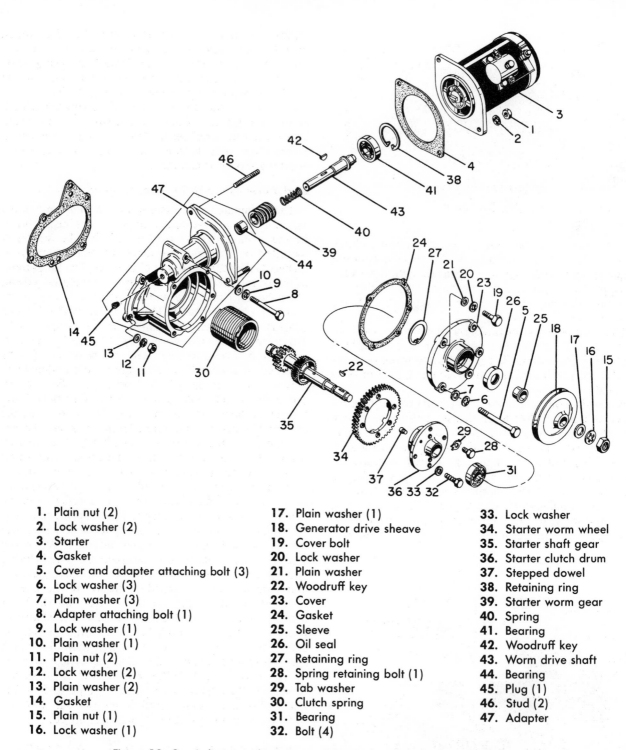

1. Plain nut (2)
2. Lock washer (2)
3. Starter
4. Gasket
5. Cover and adapter attaching bolt (3)
6. Lock washer (3)
7. Plain washer (3)
8. Adapter attaching bolt (1)
9. Lock washer (1)
10. Plain washer (1)
11. Plain nut (2)
12. Lock washer (2)
13. Plain washer (2)
14. Gasket
15. Plain nut (1)
16. Lock washer (1)
17. Plain washer (1)
18. Generator drive sheave
19. Cover bolt
20. Lock washer
21. Plain washer
22. Woodruff key
23. Cover
24. Gasket
25. Sleeve
26. Oil seal
27. Retaining ring
28. Spring retaining bolt (1)
29. Tab washer
30. Clutch spring
31. Bearing
32. Bolt (4)
33. Lock washer
34. Starter worm wheel
35. Starter shaft gear
36. Starter clutch drum
37. Stepped dowel
38. Retaining ring
39. Starter worm gear
40. Spring
41. Bearing
42. Woodruff key
43. Worm drive shaft
44. Bearing
45. Plug (1)
46. Stud (2)
47. Adapter

Figure 12·8   A direct-cranking starter with a spring-type clutch and 90° drive.

hence designers and manufacturers eventually developed direct-cranking starters which were convenient and effective in operation.

The Bendix type 756 starter

A typical direct-cranking starter for radial engines with a displacement not to exceed 985 cu in. is shown in Fig. 12·9. This is the Bendix type 756 starter and has the capacity for starting engines as large as the Pratt & Whitney R-985 nine-cylinder radial engine.

The starter consists basically of a heavy-duty series-wound electric motor, reduction gearing, multiple-disk clutch, automatic engaging and disengaging device, and a driving jaw. Since the motor is series wound and designed for intermittent duty, it develops a very high starting torque.

Figure 12·9 *The Bendix type 756 direct-cranking starter. (Utica Division, Bendix Corp.)*

The reduction gearing for this starter has a ratio of 69:1; hence the motor can turn at more than 8000 rpm while the starter is cranking the engine at a little more than 100 rpm. Torque overload protection is provided by means of a multiple-disk lubricated clutch.

The starter jaws may be designed with either 3 or 12 teeth, depending upon the requirements of the

engine. The jaw is automatically engaged with the engine jaw when the starter is energized and disengaged when the engine starts. Jaw travel from the retracted position to the extended position is about 1$\frac{1}{32}$ in.

The average performance of the type 756 starter is shown in the chart of Fig. 12·10. This chart shows efficiency, voltage, current, jaw rpm, and brake horse-power for various values of torque.

The type 756 starter is designed for use with a standard 24-volt d-c power supply. Batteries employed with the system must have sufficient capacity to supply the starter motor for several starting operations. Since the starter will draw a very high amperage when it first is energized, the power is controlled through a solenoid switch. The solenoid is energized when the starter switch is closed, thus causing the heavy current-carrying contacts to be closed. The winding of the solenoid is usually of the intermittent type and should not remain energized for more than 1 or 2 min at any one time. The windings heat rapidly and will burn out if the control switch remains on for more than a few minutes.

The clutch adjustment for the starter is of particular importance. If the torque setting is too low, the clutch will slip and will not provide satisfactory rotation of the engine. If the setting is too high, the shock upon engagement will be too great and the engaging jaws may be damaged. The clutch may be tested by means of a prony brake or other torque-testing device. It is adjusted by increasing or decreasing the clutch spring pressure.

The Jack and Heintz direct-cranking starter

The Model JH-6C starter shown in Fig. 12·11 is used with commercial airplanes equipped with engines of 1000- to 3500-cu-in. displacement. It incorporates three principal assemblies. These are (1) the series motor, (2) the reduction gears, and (3) the multiple-disk clutch.

The series motor is built to withstand very high

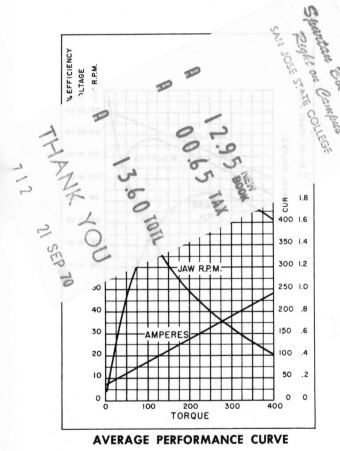

AVERAGE PERFORMANCE CURVE

Figure 12·10 *Chart to show performance of the type 756 starter.*

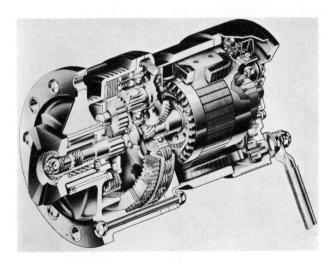

Figure 12·11 *Jack and Heintz JH-6C direct-cranking starter.*

rotational speeds. This is a necessary feature, since the motor speed must be reduced many times to deliver the correct speed and torque at the starter jaw. The gear ratio between the motor and the starter jaw, or "dog," is 167.4:1 in the JH-6CE and JH-6CF starters. This means that, when the jaw is turning at 90 rpm, the starter motor is turning at more than 15,000 rpm. The brushes of the starter motor are constructed of extremely durable material, since they must carry a current of more than 250 amp when the starter first begins to rotate the engine.

The reduction gearing of a JH-6C starter is accomplished by a combination of spur gears and a planetary system. A small helical spur gear on the end of the armature shaft engages a larger gear. This gear drives another small spur gear, which in turn engages the internal teeth of a bell gear. The bell gear carries the planetary gears.

The movable disks of the clutch assembly are constructed with teeth on the inner edge. These teeth engage the planetary gears. As the bell gear carries the planetary gears around the internal gear teeth of the clutch plates, the planetary gears rotate and transmit their torque to the gear which drives the starter jaw.

The multiple-disk clutch of the starter is compressed by a series of helical springs. These springs are adjusted to give a maximum breakaway torque of 1100 lb-ft. The maximum slipping torque is 900 lb-ft.

ELECTRICAL CIRCUITS FOR STARTING SYSTEMS

System for electric inertia starter

Figure 12·12 is a diagram of a typical inertia-starter electric system. If the ignition switch is placed in the BOTH position, the battery current can flow to the cockpit control switch. If that switch is placed in the ENERGIZE position, the current closes the starter relay and the inertia starter begins to pick up speed. When the inertia starter has attained the desired speed of rotation, the control switch is turned to ENGAGE, thus enabling the current to actuate the meshing solenoid and, at the same time, energize a booster coil that

delivers high voltage to the trailing distributor finger on the right-hand magneto until the pilot releases the switch.

Starter circuit for light twin airplane

The battery control and starter circuit for the Cessna 310 airplane is shown in Fig. 12·13. This is an actual circuit diagram for certain models of the airplane, and it includes the wire identification numbers. It will be observed that the battery solenoid must be closed before power can reach the bus which supplies the starter solenoids. The battery control switch is in the ground circuit of the battery solenoid.

The starter solenoids are controlled by means of button-type starter switches through which power is supplied to the solenoid windings. Electrical power for the starter switches is taken from the right fuel boost switch or the right auxiliary pump switch.

Starter circuit for Beech Super 18 airplane

The circuit of Fig. 12·14 is designed for the operation of the starters in the Beech Super 18 twin-engine airplane. The circuit diagram includes the wire identification numbers used on the airplane.

This circuit incorporates one button-type starter switch which is shifted to either engine by means of the **booster and starter selector switch.** It will be observed that the starter solenoids in this circuit are controlled through their ground circuits. Power for operating the solenoids is taken from the "hot" side of the main

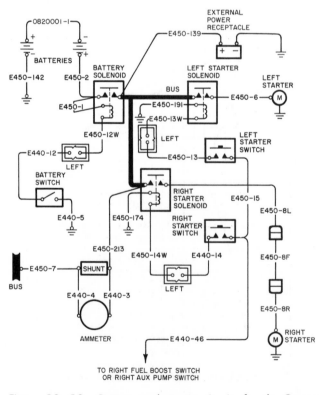

Figure 12·13 Battery and starter circuits for the Cessna 310 airplane. (Cessna Aircraft Co.)

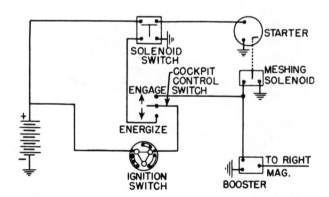

Figure 12·12 Electric circuit for inertia-type starter.

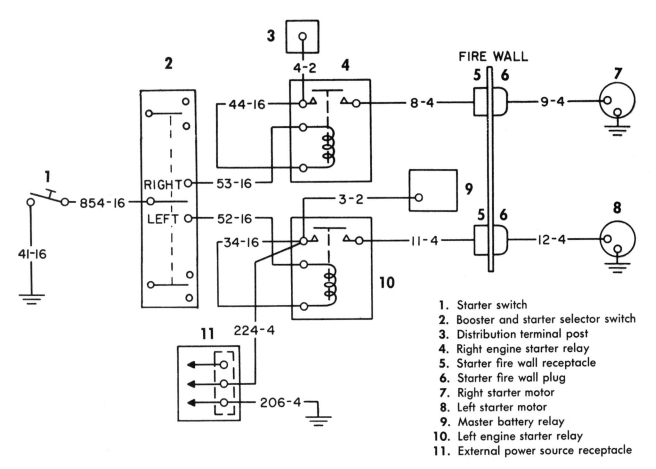

1. Starter switch
2. Booster and starter selector switch
3. Distribution terminal post
4. Right engine starter relay
5. Starter fire wall receptacle
6. Starter fire wall plug
7. Right starter motor
8. Left starter motor
9. Master battery relay
10. Left engine starter relay
11. External power source receptacle

Figure **12·14** *Starter circuit for Beech Super 18 airplane. (Beech Aircraft Co.)*

power circuit on each solenoid. Power for the left starter is taken from the master battery relay (solenoid) which is shown at (9) in the drawing, and power for the right starter is taken from the distribution terminal post shown at (3) in the drawing.

TYPICAL STARTING PROCEDURE FOR LARGE ENGINES

For the starting of any particular aircraft engine, it is essential that the technician or pilot carefully follow the procedures established by the aircraft manufacturer or operator. The procedures described in the following paragraphs are typical of the methods employed by an airline in starting the engines of a Convair Model 340.

Procedure

1. Always obtain a clearance signal from a member of the ground crew before rotating the engine with the starter. Make sure that the starting selector switch is set for the engine being started. Return the switch to OFF after the engines are started.
2. Whenever the left engine is being started or run, the passenger door must be closed and locked. The right engine may be started and run with the passenger steps extended and the nose wheel blocked.

3. The engines must be rotated with the starter while the magneto switch is off until 12 propeller blades have passed a fixed point. If the propeller is seen to stop suddenly during the starting operation, the starter switch must be released immediately. Sudden stoppage indicates a hydraulic lock in the lower cylinders, which must be cleared.
4. During the starting procedure, if the engine has backfired and caused an induction fire, the starting switches must be released immediately, the throttle closed, the mixture returned to IDLE CUTOFF, the fuel booster pump turned off, and the ignition switch turned off. An induction fire is indicated by a rapid rise in carburetor air temperature. This temperature should be watched closely.
   Thirty seconds or more after the above procedure has been followed, the starting operation may be repeated.
5. If an engine does not start after 30- to 45-sec rotation with the starter, wait at least 3 min before attempting again to start the engine. Turn the fuel booster pump and ignition switch off during the waiting period. It is necessary to allow the starter to cool because of the rapid heating that takes place while the starter is rotating the engine.
6. If engine oil pressure and primary-compressor oil pressure are not indicated within 30 sec after the engine starts, the engine must be stopped immediately. The oil-pressure indicators should be closely watched during starting.
7. Steps in starting:
   a. Obtain an "all clear" signal from the ground crew. Start No. 2 engine first. For pressure carburetors, see that mixture control is at IDLE CUTOFF.

b. Turn the fuel booster pump on. Wait 10 to 15 sec before proceeding.

c. See that the ignition switch is off. Set the starting selector switch to the engine being started. Set the throttle to 1½ in. open.

d. Press the START and START SAFE switches to ON. Watch the propeller, and rotate the engine until 12 blades have passed a fixed point.

e. Continue holding the switches. Turn the ignition switch to BOTH, and press the BOOST switch to ON. Press the PRIME switch as required. If the engine is hot, allow it to turn one or two revolutions; then apply prime lightly.

f. As soon as the engine fires, continue to hold the PRIME switch on and adjust the throttle until the engine is running at 500 to 800 rpm on prime alone. Slowly advance the mixture control to AUTO LEAN. If the engine starts to die, return the mixture control to IDLE CUTOFF at once. Do not move the throttle rapidly, since this may cause damage to the carburetor balance diaphragm.

g. Set the throttle to hold the rpm at 900 to 1000.

h. Turn the fuel booster pump off.

i. Immediately check and call aloud the oil pressure for the engine being started.

Any person who is starting an engine of a modern transport airplane, such as those used by the airlines, must exercise extreme care and attention to avoid damaging the engine. Overheating the starter, backfiring and induction fires, and lack of oil pressure may all cause damage which will result in extensive delays and costly repairs.

TROUBLESHOOTING AND MAINTENANCE

In this section we shall discuss the usual troubles found in the operation of typical, conventional starters installed on modern airplanes. Although the instructions are broad in their application, they will cover the situations normally encountered. The study of manuals and handbooks issued by manufacturers and those responsible for inspection and maintenance is always recommended in order that the equipment may be serviced in accordance with its own particular design characteristics.

Failure of starter motor to operate

When the starter switch on an airplane is placed in the START position and the starter fails to operate, the trouble can usually be traced to one of the following: (1) electrical power source, (2) starter control switch, (3) starter solenoid, (4) electric wiring, or (5) the starter motor itself. A check of each of these items will usually reveal the trouble.

The electrical power source for a light airplane is the battery. If the starter fails to operate or if a "click" is heard, the battery charge may be low. This can be quickly checked by means of a hydrometer. A fully charged battery will give a reading of 1.275 to 1.300 on the hydrometer scale. When the battery is low, the starter solenoid may click or chatter and the starter motor will fail to turn or it may turn very slowly. The solution to this problem is, of course, to provide a fully

charged battery. In many cases the technician will merely connect a fully charged battery externally in parallel with the battery in the airplane. When this is done, it is important to see that the external battery is of the same voltage as the battery of the airplane and that the terminals are connected positive to positive and negative to negative.

If the battery of the airplane is found to be fully charged, the fault may be in the control switch. This can be checked by connecting a jumper across the switch terminals. If the starter operates when this is done, the switch is defective and must be replaced.

If the starter control switch in the cockpit appears to be functional, trouble may be in the starter solenoid. The solenoid can be checked in the same manner described for the starter control switch. In this case, a heavy jumper must be used because the current flow across the main power circuit of the solenoid is much greater than that in the control circuit. If the starter operates when the jumper is connected across the main solenoid terminals, it is an indication that the solenoid is defective. Before the solenoid is replaced, however, the solenoid control circuit should be thoroughly checked out. The circuit breaker or fuse in the control circuit may be failing, or the wiring may be defective.

If the power source, wiring, control switch, and starter solenoid are all functioning properly, it is apparent that the trouble lies with the starter motor. In this case, the band covering the brushes of the motor should be removed and the condition of the brushes and commutator checked. If the brushes are badly worn or the spring tension is too weak, the brushes will not make satisfactory contact with the commutator. This trouble can be corrected by replacing the brushes and/or the brush springs as required. If the commutator is black, dirty, or badly worn, it should be cleaned with No. 000 sandpaper or the starter should be removed for overhaul. Usually it is not necessary to overhaul a starter between engine overhauls.

Failure of starter to engage

If, when attempting to start an engine, the starter motor turns but does not turn the engine, it is apparent that the overrunning clutch, the disk clutch, or engaging mechanism has failed. In this case it is necessary to remove the starter and correct the trouble. If the starter is engaged by means of the Bendix-type mechanism in which the engaging gear is moved into mesh by means of a heavy spiral thread on the screw shaft, cold oil or grease on the thread will cause the gear to stick, thus preventing the gear from meshing. When this occurs, the problem can be solved by cleaning the spiral shaft and applying light oil for lubrication.

Troubles with inertia starters

Inertia starters are subject to some problems which are not encountered with a direct-cranking starter. Among these are (1) failure to energize satisfactorily, (2) failure to engage when the meshing switch or mechanical control is operated, (3) failure of the starter jaw to disengage when the mesh control is released, and (4) interference between the starter and engine jaws.

When the starter fails to energize properly, the remedies suggested for the direct-cranking starter may be applied. In addition, if oil has leaked into the flywheel case, the drag created by the oil will prevent acceleration of the flywheel to the speed required for starting.

If the starter fails to engage, the trouble is likely to be in the meshing solenoid or the mechanical meshing linkage. The exact source of the trouble can be found by an examination of the meshing system.

Failure of the starter to disengage may occur because the disengaging spring is weak or broken. If this difficulty is encountered, it is necessary to remove the starter for repair.

Interference between the starter and engine jaws will take place when there is insufficient clearance between the jaws. The clearance can be increased by adding shims or gaskets between the engine mounting pad and the mounting flange of the starter. Whenever a jaw-type starter is installed on the engine, the jaw clearance should be checked. This applies to inertia starters and to large direct-cranking starters such as those described previously in this section.

STARTERS FOR GAS TURBINES

The comparatively small gas-turbine engines (under 6000 lb thrust) utilized between World War II and the Korean conflict were usually equipped with heavy-duty electric starters or starter generators. These were simply electric motors or motor-generator units which produced a very strong starting torque because of the large amount of electric power which they consumed. Even though these starters required expensive auxiliary power units to supply the low-voltage high-amperage direct current necessary for operation, they were satisfactory for the size of engine in use at that time.

As engines increased in size, it was soon apparent that electric starters could not meet the starting power requirements of the larger engines; hence turbine starters of various types were developed. Among the turbine starters used for modern gas-turbine engines are low-pressure air turbines, high-pressure air turbines, fuel/air combustion starters, and solid-fuel combustion starters.

Low-pressure air-turbine starter

The low-pressure air-turbine starter is designed to operate with a high-volume low-pressure air supply, usually obtained from an external turbocompressor unit mounted on a ground service cart or from the airplane low-pressure air supply. The air supply must produce a pressure of about 35 psig and a flow of more than 100 lb per min.

A drawing of the AiResearch 383042-1 air-turbine starter designed for use on the Boeing 707 airliner is shown in Fig. 12·15. This starter is a lightweight turbine air motor equipped with a **rotating assembly, reduction-gear system, splined output shaft, cutout switch mechanism,** and **overspeed switch mechanism.** The

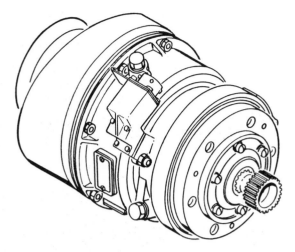

Figure 12·15 AiResearch air-turbine starter. (AiResearch Mfg. Div. of Arizona)

complete unit is mounted within a **scroll assembly** and **gear housing.** It includes a mounting flange designed to mate with a standard AND-20002, type XII-S engine drive pad.

A cross-sectional drawing of the starter is shown in Fig. 12·16. A careful study of this drawing will enable the student to understand the construction and operation of the unit. The low-pressure air is introduced into the scroll (5) through a 3-in. duct which is not shown in the illustration. From the scroll the air passes through nozzle vanes to the outer rim of the turbine wheel (4). Since this is an inward-flow turbine design, the air expands radially inward toward the center of the wheel and then is expelled through the exducer (3). The exhausted air passes through the screen (1) and out to the atmosphere. The expansion of the air from a pressure of about 35 psig to atmospheric pressure imparts energy to the turbine wheel, causing it to reach a speed of about 55,000 rpm. This low-torque high speed is converted to a high-torque low speed by means of the 23.2:1 reduction gearing.

The **rotating assembly** of the starter consists of the turbine wheel, a spacer, a spur gear (9), and a nut. The turbine wheel assembly is an integral wheel and shaft with an exducer pinned on the exhaust end of the shaft against the front face of the wheel. The spacer, gear, and nut are installed on the opposite end of the shaft, which also provides for the installation of the two ball bearings in which the rotating assembly is mounted. The spacer, bearings, and gear are held on the shaft by the nut, which is secured by a rollpin through the shaft.

The **heat barrier and oil seal** (36) are positioned to provide the correct clearance between the turbine wheel assembly and the heat barrier. The heat barrier and the oil seal installed on the heat barrier prevent the passage of compressed air from the scroll into the housing or the passage of lubricating oil from the housing into the scroll.

The **oil seal assembly** (36) consists of a rotor mounted on the turbine wheel shaft and a stator placed in the

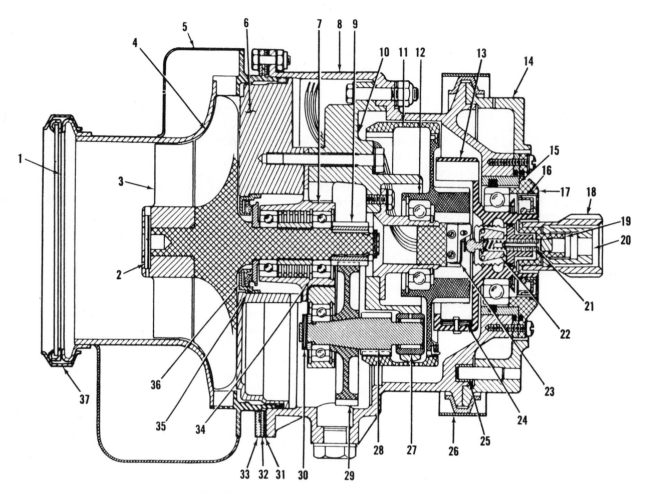

Figure 12·16 Cross-sectional drawing of air-turbine starter.

heat barrier. The rotor serves as an oil slinger. The carbon stator, containing an O-ring packing, is spring-loaded against the rotor, providing sealing against the passage of compressed air or lubricating oil.

The **bearing carrier** (7) supports the two ball bearings in which the rotating assembly is mounted. The bearing carrier and heat barrier with the oil seal are bolted to the gear carrier of the reduction-gear system.

The **reduction-gear system** consists of a **gear carrier** (10), three **spur gear-shaft assemblies** (only one assembly shown at 28 and 29), an **internal gear** (11), and an **internal** gear hub (12). The gear carrier assembly is a matched pair of forgings brazed together and is bolted inside the housing. The gear carrier provides for the installation of a ball bearing and a needle bearing in which each of the spur gear-shaft assemblies rotate and a ball bearing on which the internal gear hub rotates. Each of the three spur gear-shaft assemblies consists of an integral spur gear and tapered shaft (28), planet spur gear (29), bearing, and nut. The planet spur gear has a tapered bore and is friction-mounted on the tapered shaft, being held in position by the bearing and nut. The nut is secured on the shaft by a rollpin through the shaft. The planet spur gears mesh with and are driven by the spur gear of the rotating assem-

bly. The internal gear is mounted over the spur gear-shaft assemblies in mesh with and driven by the three spur gears of the gear-shaft assemblies. The internal gear hub is installed in and attached to the internal gear by means of a lockring. The internal gear hub rotates on the ball bearing installed on the gear carrier assembly and is integral with the jaw of the engagement mechanism.

The **engagement mechanism** consists of a drive hub (12) and a drive-shaft assembly (13). The drive hub has a series of ratchet teeth equally spaced about the outside diameter, and these teeth engage the three pawls which are mounted inside the drum of the drive-shaft assembly. The arrangement of the pawl and spring drive assembly is shown in Fig. 12·17. The drive shaft is internally threaded for installation of the switch-actuating governor (22 in Fig. 12·16) and internally splined for installation of the output shaft (18) and provides a sealing surface for the drive-shaft seal (16) which is installed in the housing. Each pawl spring assembly (24) is a series of leaf-type springs of varying length as also shown in Fig. 12·17. Each spring assembly is riveted inside the drive-shaft drum.

The operation of the engagement mechanism is such that the drive-shaft pawls are disengaged from the

284

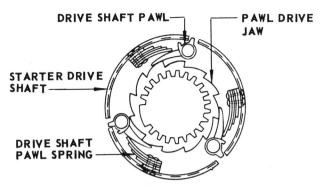

DRIVE SHAFT PAWL — — PAWL DRIVE JAW

STARTER DRIVE SHAFT —

DRIVE SHAFT PAWL SPRING —

Figure 12·17 Engaging mechanism for AiResearch air-turbine starter.

teeth of the ratchet (pawl drive jaw) when the engine is running. Before and during starting, at low rotational speeds, the pawl springs in the drive shaft force the drive-shaft pawls into engagement with the ratchet teeth of the drive hub. This engagement transmits the rotation of the drive hub through the drive-shaft assembly and the output shaft to the engine on which the starter is installed. When engine light-off occurs and the drive-shaft speed exceeds that of the drive hub, a ratcheting action takes place between the drive-shaft pawls and the ratchet teeth. This ratcheting action serves to disengage the starter from the engine as the engine overspeeds the starter drive hub. As engine speed continues to increase, the starter drive pawls assume the function of flyweights as centrifugal force overcomes the force of the pawl springs and the pawls are completely withdrawn from engagement with the drive hub.

Before disengagement of the drive-shaft pawls from the drive hub and as the starter output shaft speed approaches the predetermined cutoff point, centrifugal force causes the flyweights of the switch-actuating governor to move outward. This actuates the snap-action switch in the gear carrier of the starter reduction-gear system to open the control circuit. This initiates the sequence of operations to interrupt the flow of compressed air, and the starter then becomes inoperative.

Operation of the low-pressure air-turbine starter

Any one of the four engines on a Boeing 707 airliner may be started from the low-pressure external air supply. To furnish the necessary air for low-pressure starting, a turbocompressor outlet duct is connected to the airplane at the pneumatic ground service connection.

To initiate a start, the **ground start selector switch** is placed in the LOW PRESS (MANIFOLD) position and the start switch for the engine being started is placed in the GROUND START position. This causes 28-volt d-c power to flow to the solenoid which controls the **starter low-pressure air shutoff valve.** The valve is operated by a pneumatic actuator which is controlled by the solenoid. As the low-pressure air valve opens, air flows to the starter turbine and rotates the N_2 rotor of the

engine through the drive from the engine accessory section where the starter is mounted.

The start switch is held in the start position until lightoff occurs and the output shaft speed reaches the calibrated cutoff point. At this point, interruption of the flow of inlet air pressure to the starter is automatic, and disengagement of the starter from the engine takes place as the engine drives the output shaft to a higher speed. The **ground start** switch is then released.

Release of the ground start switch at any time will shut off the flow of compressed air to the starter, and no attempt must be made for another starting operation until the engine has completely stopped all rotation. To make certain that the engine has stopped turning, the operator should wait for 15 sec after the engine tachometer shows zero rpm.

The normal duty cycle for the starter is 30 sec **on** followed by 1 min **off.** When the engine is cold and the starter has not been operated for at least 60 min, the time **on** may be extended to 1 min at speeds up to the starter cutoff, which is approximately 2400-rpm output shaft speed. After a 1-min cooling period another 1-min start attempt may be made, after which a 5-min cooling period must be allowed.

Starter operation is discontinued by releasing the ground-start switch which deenergizes the solenoid in the air-pressure shutoff valve. Operational sequence of the valve and starter is then broken so that the flow of compressed air to the starter is shut off and operation of the starter is discontinued.

High-pressure air-turbine starters

A high-pressure air-turbine starter is essentially the same as the low-pressure starter except that it is equipped with an axial-flow turbine in place of the radial, inward-flow turbine previously described. The high-pressure starter is fitted with both low-pressure and high-pressure air connections to provide for operation from either type of air supply.

The usual air supply for the high-pressure starter operation is a high-pressure air bottle mounted in the airplane. This air bottle is charged to a pressure of about 3000 psi and is used for starting one of the engines when an external low-pressure source is not available. On the Boeing 707 airplane, both the Nos. 2 and 3 engines are equipped with high-pressure starters, so either one or both can be started from the high-pressure system. After one of these engines is started, the low-pressure air from the turbocompressors is fed to the airplane manifold, thus making it possible to start the other engines from the low-pressure air supply of the airplane.

Combustion starters

The two principal types of combustion starters are the **fuel/air combustion** starter and the **cartridge-type** starter. The turbine-operating section of these starters is similar to or identical with the air-turbine starters.

A fuel/air combustion starter is actually a small turboshaft engine. The engine fuel supply is a small fuel accumulator mounted on the starter, and the air supply is a high-pressure (3000-psi) air bottle near the engine. The fuel accumulator is refilled as needed from the aircraft fuel supply, and the air bottle is recharged by means of a compressor mounted in the airplane.

The air supply to the fuel/air combustion starter is reduced to the proper level for turbine operation by means of a pressure regulator. Typical operating air pressure is about 300 psi.

The fuel/air combustion starter has the advantage of being a completely airplane-contained unit which is used for starting engines when no external service units are available. The operation of the starters is reliable and effective.

The principal disadvantage of these starters is the weight. The fuel/air combustion starter weighs between 50 and 60 lb, and an air-turbine starter with the same capacity weighs from 25 to 35 lb.

The **cartridge-type** starter may be considered as an air-turbine starter which is operated by means of hot gases from a solid fuel cartridge instead of using compressed air as the energy source. As a matter of fact, some air-turbine starters can be adapted to cartridge operation merely by installing a cartridge combustion chamber and gas duct to the air-turbine starter.

The advantage of the cartridge-type starter is that it is a self-contained unit and does not require an external power source. The two principal disadvantages are the cost of the fuel cartridges and the erosion of the turbine parts by solid particles in the hot gases.

Inspection and maintenance of turbine engine starters

Routine inspections of turbine starters are similar to those of other accessories. These include security of mounting, freedom from oil leaks, and security of air and gas ducts, liquid lines, and electrical wiring. Special inspections required for particular units are listed in the manufacturer's **operation and service instructions.**

Maintenance and service include the changing of the lubricant in the gear housing. Since the starter is attached to the engine, it is likely to be exposed to very high temperatures. For this reason, the lubricant used is of the high-temperature type such as MIL-L-7808C. Even this type of lubricant will lose its lubricating qualities after a time; hence it must be changed regularly. The presence of metal particles in the lubricant is checked whenever a change is made in order to detect an incipient failure. Very small particles are normal, but particles which produce a sandy feel to the lubricant are a definite indication of internal damage in the starter.

Overhaul of turbine starters should not be necessary normally at less than 2000 hr of engine service; however, the life of a starter is largely dependent upon the skill and knowledge of the flight engineer or pilot who operates it. Under no circumstances should anyone but a well-trained and informed individual be permitted to operate the starting system.

REVIEW QUESTIONS

1. Name four types of starters which may be found on reciprocating engines.
2. Describe a direct-cranking electric starter.
3. How is cranking energy stored in an inertia starter?
4. What protective device is installed in a starter to prevent damage when the starter is engaged to the engine?
5. What type of electric motor is used for a starter?
6. If a starter motor is operated without a load, what precaution must be taken?
7. What precaution must be taken with respect to the length of time a starter is operated? Why?
8. Describe an overrunning clutch.
9. Describe a starter system with a 90° drive.
10. Why is reduction gearing required for a direct-cranking starter?
11. How is the torque setting for a direct-cranking starter adjusted?
12. What type of device is used as a switch to handle the heavy current required by a starter?
13. Draw a diagram of a typical starter circuit including the essential components.
14. List the causes for failure of a starter motor to operate.
15. How would you test a starter solenoid for operation?
16. How can the starter-to-engine jaw clearance be increased?
17. Name four types of starters for gas-turbine engines.
18. Describe an air-turbine starter.
19. What pressure and flow of air is required for a low-pressure air-turbine starter?
20. Describe the engagement mechanism for an AiResearch air-turbine starter.
21. If, while starting a gas-turbine engine, the starting switch is momentarily released, what should be done?
22. How long may the air-turbine starter be operated at one time?

CHAPTER 13

Engine Performance

FACTORS GOVERNING PERFORMANCE

Earlier in this text we discussed engine **power, mean effective pressure, rpm, displacement,** and other factors involved in the measurement of engine performance. It is our purpose here to explore these areas in greater depth because the reader will have obtained a fuller understanding of engine operation, having studied the intervening chapters describing engine construction, carburetion, fuels, and systems.

Manifold pressure

As we have explained previously, **manifold pressure** (MP) is the absolute pressure of the fuel/air mixture immediately before it enters the intake port of the cylinder. **Absolute pressure** is the pressure above a complete vacuum and is often indicated in **pounds per square inch absolute** (psia) or in **inches of mercury** (in. Hg). The pressure we read on an ordinary pressure gage is the pressure above ambient atmospheric pressure and is often called gage pressure or **pounds per square inch gage** (psig). Manifold pressure is normally indicated on a pressure gage in inches of mercury rather than pounds per square inch gage; hence the reading on a manifold gage at sea level when an engine is not running will be about 29.92 in. Hg when conditions are standard. When the engine is idling, the gage may read from 10 to 15 in. Hg because the manifold pressure will be considerably below atmospheric pressure.

Manifold pressure is of primary concern to the operator of a high-performance engine because such an engine will often be operating at a point near the maximum allowable pressure. It is essential, therefore, that any engine which can be operated at an excessive manifold pressure be equipped with a manifold pressure gage so the operator can keep the engine operation within safe limits.

The operator of an aircraft engine must take every precaution to avoid operating at excessive manifold pressure because such operation will result in excessive cylinder pressures and temperatures. Excessive cylinder pressures will overstress the cylinders, pistons, piston pins, valves, connecting rods, and crankshaft journals. Excessive pressure usually is accompanied by excessive temperature, and this leads to detonation, preignition, and loss of power. Detonation usually results in engine damage if continued for more than a few moments. Damage may include piston failure by cracking or burning, failure of cylinder base studs, cracking of the cylinder head, and burning of valves.

Naturally-aspirated engines using variable-pitch propellers must be equipped with MP gages in order to assure safe operation.

Mean effective pressure

Mean effective pressure is a computed pressure derived from power formulas in order to provide a measuring device for determining engine performance. For any particular engine operating at a given rpm and power output, there will be a specific **indicated mean effective pressure** (imep) and a corresponding **brake mean effective pressure** (bmep).

Mean effective pressure may be defined as an average pressure inside the cylinders of an internal-combustion engine based on some calculated or measured horsepower. It increases as manifold pressure increases. Imep is the mean effective pressure derived from indicated horsepower, and bmep is the mean effective pressure derived from brake horsepower output.

The pressure in the cylinder of an engine throughout one complete cycle is indicated in the curve of Fig. 13·1. This curve is not derived from any particular engine, but it is given to show the approximate pressures that exist during the various events of the cycle. It will be observed that ignition takes place shortly before TDC and then there is a rapid pressure rise which reaches maximum shortly after TDC. Thus the greatest pressure on the cylinder occurs during the first 5 to 12° after TDC. By the end of the power stroke there is very little pressure left and this is being rapidly dissipated through the exhaust port.

The indicated horsepower (ihp) of an engine is the result of the imep, the rpm, the distance through which the piston travels, and the number of cylinders in the engine. The formula for this computation was previously given as

$$\text{ihp} = \frac{PLANK}{33,000} \qquad (1)$$

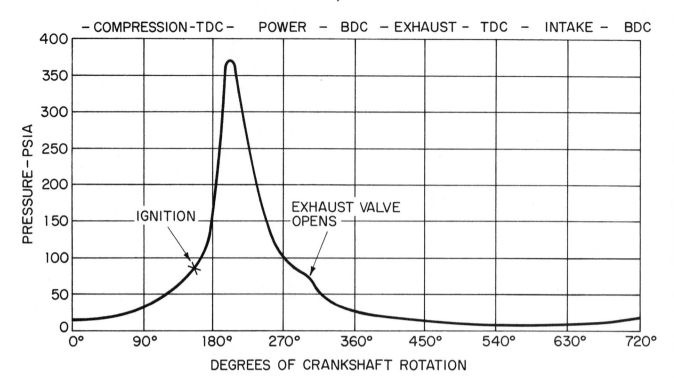

Figure 13·1 Curve to show cylinder pressure.

where P = imep
     L = length of the stroke, ft
     A = area of the piston
     N = rpm divided by 2
     K = number of cylinders

The foregoing formula is also given as

$$\text{ihp} = \frac{PLAN}{33,000} \qquad (2)$$

where N is the number of power strokes per minute. The number of power strokes per minute is equal to the rpm/2 times the number of cylinders. In this latter formula the N includes both the N and K of the previous formula.

If we can obtain the brake horsepower output of an engine by means of a dynamometer or prony brake, we can determine the bmep by means of a formula derived from the power formula given above. By simple transposition the formula set up for brake horsepower becomes

$$P(\text{bmep}) = \frac{33,000 \times \text{bhp}}{LAN} \qquad (3)$$

In order to simplify the use of the formula, we can convert the length of the stroke and the area of the piston to the displacement of one cylinder and then multiply by the number of cylinders to find the total displacement of the engine. In the formula L is equal to the length of the stroke in feet, A is the area of the piston, and N is the number of cylinders times the rpm divided by 2. Since we must multiply the area of the piston by the length of the stroke in inches in order to

obtain piston displacement in cubic inches, we may use S in place of L and express S in inches. Then $S/12$ is equal to L because L is expressed in feet. For example, if the stroke is 6 in. (S), then it is equal to $\frac{6}{12}$ or $\frac{1}{2}$ ft. With these adjustments in mind we find that LAN becomes

$$\frac{SA}{12} \times \text{No. of cylinders} \times \frac{\text{rpm}}{2}$$

or

$$\frac{SA \times \text{No. of cylinders} \times \text{rpm}}{12 \times 2}$$

Since $SA \times$ No. of cylinders is the total displacement of the engine, we can express the above value as

$$\frac{\text{Displacement} \times \text{rpm}}{12 \times 2}$$

Substituting this value in formula (3),

$$\begin{aligned}
\text{bmep} &= \frac{33,000 \times \text{bhp}}{(\text{disp} \times \text{rpm})/(12 \times 2)} \\
&= \frac{24 \times 33,000 \times \text{bhp}}{\text{disp} \times \text{rpm}} \\
&= \frac{792,000}{\text{disp}} \times \frac{\text{bhp}}{\text{rpm}} \qquad (4)
\end{aligned}$$

If an R-1830 engine is turning at 2750 rpm and developing 1100 hp, we can find the bmep as follows;

$$\begin{aligned}
\text{bmep} &= \frac{792,000}{1830} \times \frac{1100}{2750} \\
&= 173 \text{ psi}
\end{aligned}$$

288

For any particular engine computation, the value of 792,000/disp may be considered as a constant for that engine and given the designation K. Formula (4) then becomes

$$\text{bmep} = K \times \frac{\text{bhp}}{\text{rpm}}$$

The constant K is often called the **K factor** of the engine.

It must be noted that the foregoing formula may be used for imep as well as bmep by using ihp in the formula instead of bhp. It is easy to determine the bhp of an engine by means of a dynamometer or prony brake; hence the bmep computation is more commonly employed to determine engine performance.

Power and efficiency

The efficiency of an engine is the ratio of output to input. For example, if the amount of fuel consumed should produce 300 hp according to its rating in Btus, and the output is 100 hp, then the thermal efficiency is $^{100}\!/_{300}$ or 33 ⅓ percent.

An engine producing 70 hp burns about 30 lb per hr of gasoline or ½ lb per min. One-half pound of gasoline has a heat value of about 10,000 Btu, and since 1 Btu can do 778 ft-lb of work, the fuel being consumed should produce $778 \times 10,000$ ft-lb of work per min. Then

$$\text{Power} = \frac{778 \times 10,000}{33,000} = 235 \text{ hp.}$$

The fuel being consumed has a total power value of 235 hp, but the engine is producing only 70 bhp. The thermal efficiency is then $^{70}\!/_{235}$ or approximately 30 percent.

We may ask the question, what happens to the other 70 percent of the fuel energy? The answer is that the largest portion of the fuel energy is dissipated as heat and friction. The distribution of the fuel energy is approximately as indicated in the following:

Brake horsepower	30 percent
Friction and heat loss from engine	20 percent
Heat and chemical energy in exhaust	50 percent

Brake specific fuel consumption

One of the measures of engine performance is **brake specific fuel consumption** (bsfc). Bsfc is the number of pounds of fuel burned per hour for each bhp produced. The bsfc for modern reciprocating engines is **usually** between 0.40 to 0.50 lb per hp per hr. The bsfc depends upon many elements of engine design and operation volumetric efficiency, rpm, bmep, friction losses, etc. In general, we may say that bsfc is a direct indicator of overall engine efficiency. The best values of bsfc for an engine are obtained at a particular cruising setting, usually at a little over 70 percent of maximum power. During takeoff the bsfc may increase to a value almost double what it is at the best economy setting. This is because a richer mixture must be used for takeoff and because engine efficiency decreases with the higher rpm needed for maximum power.

Weight/power ratio

Another important indicator of engine performance is the **weight/power ratio.** This is the ratio of the weight of the engine to the bhp at **best power** settings. For example, if the basic weight of the engine is 150 lb and the power output is 100 hp, the weight/power ratio is 150:100 or 1.5 lb per hp. Since weight is a prime consideration in the design of any aircraft, the weight/power ratio of the engine is always an important factor in the selection of the airplane powerplant. Weight/power ratios for reciprocating engines vary between 1.0 and 2.0 lb per hp, with the majority of high-performance engines having ratios between 1.0 and 1.5 lb per hp.

ENGINE PERFORMANCE CURVES

A large number of different curves may be developed for an engine to indicate a wide variety of operating conditions. For the purpose of this text we shall employ those curves which deal with specific fuel consumption, power output, manifold pressure, rpm, air density, and propeller load.

Manifold pressure and rpm

The effects of manifold pressure and rpm on the power output of an engine are shown in the curves of Fig. 13·2. These values were developed from the performance of Continental 0-470-K and -L engines with

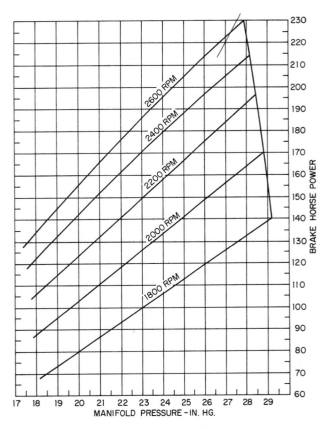

Figure **13·2** *Bhp vs. intake manifold pressure vs. rpm.*

289

atmospheric conditions at the sea-level standard of pressure P_s and temperature T_s. From this chart the horsepower of the engine can be determined for any normal values of rpm and manifold pressure. For example, if the engine is operating at 23 in. Hg manifold pressure and 2200 rpm, the power delivered is about 149 hp. For full power output at 2600 rpm and 27.9 in. Hg manifold pressure, the power is 230 hp.

It is of interest to note from the chart that volumetric efficiency decreases as rpm increases above 1800. At 1800 rpm the manifold pressure can be as high as 29.2 in. Hg, but as rpm increases, the maximum manifold pressure decreases to 27.9 at 2600 rpm. Volumetric efficiency (VE) decreases as rpm increases because the velocity of the air or fuel/air mixture increases with a resultant increase in air friction and gas-inertia effects through the manifold passages.

Maximum VE is always less than 100 percent for a naturally aspirated engine and at full power is likely to be about 75 percent. VE is greatly increased by valve overlap, up to the point where valve overlap would allow exhaust pressure to act against intake pressure or where there would be a reversal of exhaust flow back into the cylinder.

The power values shown in the chart of Fig. 13·2 will be as indicated only at sea-level standard conditions. If temperature or pressure changes, there will be a corresponding change in power output at a given rpm and manifold pressure.

Propeller load

It can be readily understood that it requires more power to drive a propeller at high speeds than it does to drive it at low speeds and that a certain propeller being driven at a given speed will absorb a specific amount of power. Actually, the power required to drive a propeller varies as the cube of the rpm. This is expressed in the formula

$$hp = K \times rpm^3$$

where K is a constant whose value depends upon the propeller type, size, pitch, and number of blades. Another formula which can be used to express the same principle is

$$hp_2 = hp_1 \left(\frac{rpm_2}{rpm_1}\right)^3$$

This means that it will require eight times as much power to drive a propeller at a given speed than it will require to drive it half that speed. Also, if the speed of a propeller is tripled, it will require 27 times as much power to drive it than it did at the original speed.

Propeller load curves are shown in the chart of Fig. 13·3. This chart shows the manifold pressure, the power output, and the bsfc at different rpms when the engine is operated at full throttle with a particular fixed-pitch propeller.

At the top of the chart, it will be noted that manifold pressure decreases at full throttle as rpm increases. This is in keeping with the observation made from the chart of Fig. 13·2. From the prop load curve at the top

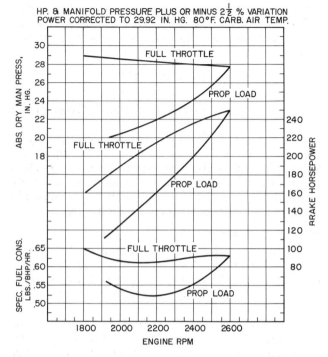

Figure 13·3 *Bhp, intake manifold pressure, and bsfc vs. rpm at full throttle and propeller load.*

of the chart we can see that the propeller can be turned at 1950 rpm with a manifold pressure of 20 in. Hg, at 2200 rpm at a manifold pressure of 22 in. Hg, and at 2600 rpm with a manifold pressure of 27.8 in. Hg. This is the maximum output available with this propeller because the load curve meets the manifold pressure curve at this rpm.

From the curves at the middle portion of the graph we can see that the engine power output increases as rpm increases. The increase is not proportional because of the decrease in manifold pressure which takes place as rpm increases. We also note from the prop load curve that the propeller can be driven at 2100 rpm with 142 hp, at 2400 rpm with 202 hp, and at 2600 rpm with 248 hp. Another way of saying the same thing is that the propeller absorbs 248 hp at 2600 rpm.

The curves at the bottom of the graph in Fig. 13·3 show the specific fuel consumption under various conditions of rpm and prop load. It will be observed that the best fuel consumption takes place at approximately 2200 rpm when the propeller is absorbing 160 hp. The bsfc at this point is about 0.52 lb per hp per hr. If the engine were operated at full throttle with the rpm at 2200, the bsfc would be about 0.61 lb per hp per hr.

Effects of altitude on performance

It has been mentioned previously that air density will affect the power output of an engine at a particular rpm and manifold pressure. Since air density depends upon pressure, temperature, and humidity, these factors must be taken into consideration in determining the exact performance of an engine. In order to obtain the power of an engine from a power chart, it is necessary to find what corrections must be made. In the first place, the **density altitude** must be determined by applying approximately corrections to the pressure altitude as shown on a standard barometer. A chart for converting pressure altitude to density altitude is shown in Fig. 13·4. If the temperature at a particular altitude is the same as standard (T_s) at that altitude, no correction for density will be required unless humidity is a factor.

The charts of Fig. 13·5 are used to determine the power output of a Continental 0-470-M engine at altitude. The chart at the left shows engine output at sea-level standard conditions with no ram air pressure applied to the carburetor intake. The chart at the right shows the effect of altitude and is used in conjunction with the first chart. The points corresponding to engine rpm and manifold pressure are located on both charts. The horsepower indicated on the sea-level chart is transferred to an equivalent point C on the altitude chart. Then a straight line is drawn from the point A to the point C to establish the altitude correction. The intersection of this line with the density altitude line (D in the example) establishes the power output of the engine. The horsepower should be corrected by adding 1 percent for each 6°C temperature decrease below T_s and subtracting 1 percent for each 6°C temperature increase above T_s.

Effects of fuel/air ratio

Thus far we have considered engine performance under fixed conditions of fuel/air ratio and without

reference to other variables which exist under actual operating conditions. There are two fuel/air ratio values which are of particular interest to the operator of an engine. These are the **best power** mixture and the **best economy** mixture. The actual fuel/air ratio in each case will also depend upon engine rpm and manifold pressure. The chart of Fig. 13·6 illustrates how the **best power** mixture will vary for different power settings. It will be observed that there is a very narrow range of fuel/air ratios for the best power mixture. For example, the setting for 2900 rpm is 0.077, for 3000 rpm it is 0.082, and for 3150 rpm it is 0.091. Any other fuel/air ratios than those given will result in a rapid falling off of power.

The **best economy** mixture is the fuel/air ratio which gives the lowest value for bsfc. This is the setting which would normally be used by a pilot in attempting to obtain maximum range for a certain amount of fuel. The chart of Fig. 13·7 provides a graphic illustration of the difference between **best economy mixture** and **best power mixture**. This chart is based upon a constant-throttle position with a constant rpm. The only variable is the fuel/air ratio. With a very lean fuel/air ratio of about 0.055, the engine delivers 292 bhp with a fuel flow of 140 lb per hr and the bsfc is about 0.48 lb per bhp per hr. The **best economy mixture** occurs when the fuel/air ratio is approximately 0.062. At this point the bhp is 324 and the fuel flow is 152 lb per hr. The bsfc is then 0.469 lb per bhp per hr. As the strength of the fuel/air mixture is increased, a point is reached where the engine power has reached a peak and will begin to fall off. This is the **best power mixture,** and it is shown to be approximately 0.075 or 1:13.3. At this point the bhp is 364 and the bsfc is 0.514 with a fuel flow of 187 lb per hr.

We have now established the effects of fuel/air ratio when other factors are constant, and we can see that the mixture in the operation of the engine will have a profound effect on the performance. We must, however, explore the matter further because engine operating temperature must be considered. If an engine is operated at full power and at the best power mixture, as shown in the upper curve of the chart in Fig. 13·6, it is likely that the cylinder-head temperature will become excessive and detonation will result. For this reason, at full power settings, the mixture will be enriched beyond the best power mixture. This is the function of the **economizer** or **enrichment valve** in the carburetor or fuel control as explained previously. The extra fuel will not burn but will vaporize and absorb some of the heat developed in the combustion chamber. At this time the manual mixture control is placed in the **full-rich** or **automatic-rich** position and the fuel/air ratio will be at or above the **rich best power** mixture.

When operating under cruising conditions of rpm and manifold pressure, it is possible to set the mixture at the **lean best power** value in order to save fuel and still obtain a maximum value of cruising power from the engine. If it is desired to obtain maximum fuel economy at a particular cruise setting, the manual mixture control will be used to lean the mixture to the

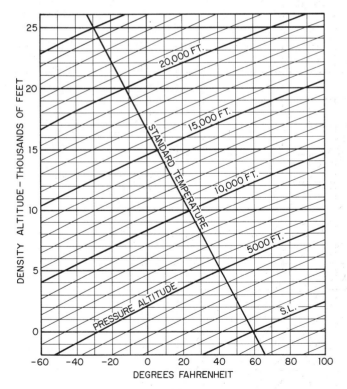

Figure 13·4   Chart to convert pressure altitude to density altitude.

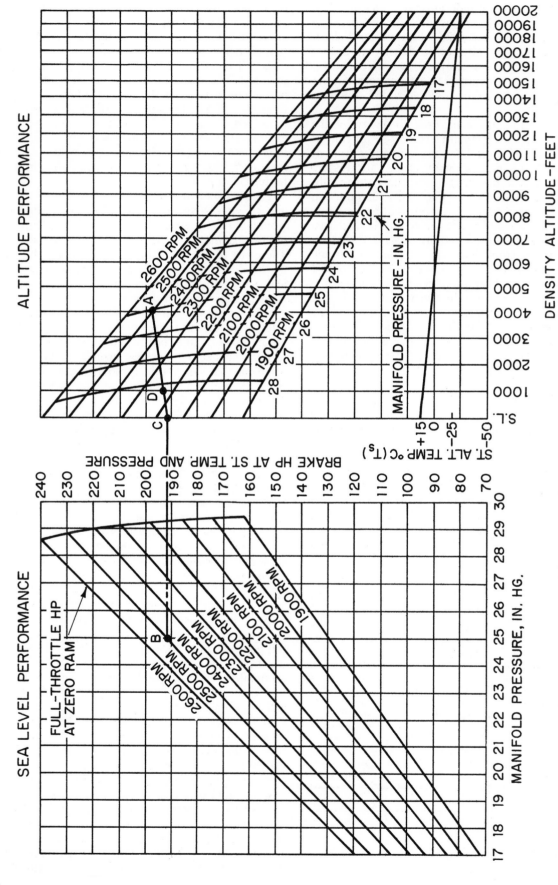

Figure **13·5** *Finding actual horsepower from sea-level and altitude charts.*

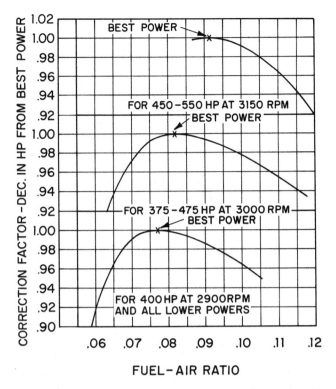

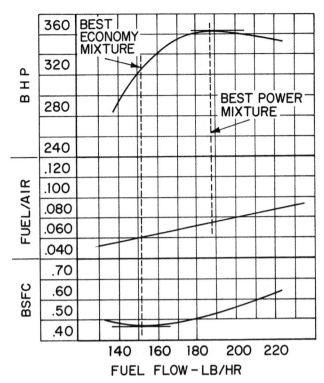

Figure **13·6** *Chart to show best power mixture for different power settings.*

Figure **13·7** *Best economy mixture and best power mixture at constant throttle and constant rpm.*

best economy F/A ratio. This will save fuel but will result in a power reduction of as much as 15 percent.

Other variables affecting performance

The performance of an aircraft engine is affected by a number of conditions or design features not yet mentioned. However, these must be taken into account if an accurate evaluation of engine operation is to be made. Among these conditions are **carburetor air-intake ram pressure, carburetor air temperature (CAT), exhaust back pressure,** and **water-vapor pressure.**

Ram air pressure at the carburetor air scoop is determined by the design of the scoop and the velocity of the air. Ram air pressure has the effect of supercharging the air entering the engine; hence the actual power output will be greater than it would under standard conditions of rpm, pressure, and temperature. An empirical formula for ram is

$$\text{Ram} = \frac{V^2}{2045} - 2$$

where ram is in inches of water and V is air velocity in miles per hour.

Carburetor air temperature (CAT) is of considerable importance because it affects the density, hence the quantity, of the air taken into the engine and, if it is too high, will result in detonation.

If an engine is equipped with a supercharger, the manifold mixture temperature should be observed rather than carburetor air temperature because the temperature of the mixture actually entering the engine

is the factor governing engine performance. A standard rule to correct for the effects of temperature is to add 1 percent to the chart horsepower for each 6°C below T_s and subtract 1 percent for each 6°C above T_s.

Water-vapor pressure effects must be determined when an engine is required to operate at near maximum power output under conditions of high humidity. In extreme cases an engine may lose as much as 5 percent of maximum rated power; hence an allowance must be made for takeoff distance and other critical factors. At altitudes above 5000 ft, water-vapor pressure is considered inconsequential.

Exhaust back pressure has a decided effect on the performance of an engine because any pressure above atmospheric at the exhaust port of a cylinder will reduce volumetric efficiency. The design of the exhaust system is therefore one of the principal items to be considered by both the engine manufacturer and the manufacturer of the exhaust system. Exhaust back pressure effect begins at the cylinder with the exhaust port. Both the size and shape of the opening and passages will affect the pressure. From the exhaust port onward the exhaust stacks and sound-reduction devices will produce varying amounts of back pressure depending upon design.

Engineers have developed exhaust augmenting systems to assist in reducing exhaust back pressure and to utilize the ejected exhaust gases for the production of additional thrust. These devices have proved effective for increasing engine performance on the airplane. Such systems usually consist of one or more tubes into which the exhaust stacks from the engine are directed. The engine exhaust passing through the tubes through which ram air is also flowing results in a reduced pressure against the exhaust and an increased thrust because the "jet" of exhaust gases is directed toward the rear of the aircraft.

ENGINE OPERATION

Operating requirements

The operation of any reciprocating engine requires that certain precautions be observed and that all operations be kept within the limitations established by the manufacturer. Among the conditions which must be checked during the operation of an engine are the following:

1. Engine oil pressure.
2. Oil temperature.
3. Cylinder-head temperature.
4. Engine rpm.
5. Manifold pressure.
6. Drop in rpm when switching to single magneto operation.
7. If a constant-speed or controllable-pitch propeller is used with the engine, the engine response to propeller controls should be checked.

No engine should be operated unless the engine oil pressure and temperature are within satisfactory limits. For this reason a reciprocating engine must be properly warmed up before full-power operation is undertaken. When the engine is started, the oil pressure gage should be observed to see that the oil pressure system is functioning satisfactorily. **If no oil pressure is indicated within 30 sec after starting, the engine must be shut down and the malfunction located.** If the engine is operated without oil pressure for much more than 30 sec, damage is likely to result.

Generally speaking, if an engine has been warmed up for a few minutes and it can be accelerated to full power and rpm without showing excessive oil pressure, and if it operates smoothly, it is likely that a safe takeoff can be made. In any event, however, the directions given in the Airplane Owner's Handbook should be followed.

Prior to takeoff, the reciprocating engine should be given an ignition check and a full power test. This is usually done while the airplane is parked just off the end of the takeoff runway in a warm-up area. For the magneto check the throttle is moved slowly forward until the engine rpm is at the point recommended by the manufacturer. This is usually from 1500 to 1600 rpm, although it may vary from this range. To make the check, the ignition switch is turned from the BOTH position to the LEFT MAGNETO position and the tachometer is observed for rpm drop. The amount of drop is noted, and then the switch is turned back to the BOTH position for a few seconds until the engine is again running smoothly at the full test rpm. The switch is then turned to the RIGHT MAGNETO position for a few seconds so the rpm drop can be noted. The engine should not be allowed to operate for more than a few

seconds on a single magneto because of possible plug fouling.

The permissible magneto drop varies, but it is usually in the range between 50 and 125 rpm. In all cases the instructions in the operator's manual should be followed. Usually the magneto drop will be somewhat less than the maximum specified in the instructions.

When the magnetos are checked on an airplane having a constant-speed or controllable-pitch propeller, it is essential that the propeller be in the full **high-rpm** (low-pitch) position. Otherwise a true indication of rpm drop may not be obtained.

After the magneto check is completed, the engine should be given a brief full-power check. This is done by slowly advancing the throttle to the full forward position and observing the maximum rpm obtained. If the rpm level and the manifold pressure are satisfactory and the engine runs smoothly, the throttle is slowly retarded until the rpm has returned to the desired idling speed.

When making the full-power check, the pilot must make sure that the airplane is in a position which will not direct the propeller blast into another airplane or into any other area where damage or inconvenience to another person may be caused. He should also make sure that his brakes are on and the elevator control pulled back if the airplane has conventional landing gear.

Power settings and adjustments

During the operation of an airplane the engine power settings must be changed from time to time for various types of operation. The principal power settings are those for **takeoff, climb, cruise** (from maximum to minimum), **letdown,** and **landing.**

The methods for changing power settings differ according to the type of engine, type of propeller, whether the engine is equipped with a supercharger, type of carburetion, and other factors. The operator's manual will give the proper procedures for a particular airplane-engine combination.

The following rules generally apply to most airplanes and engines:

1. Always move the throttle slowly for either a power increase or power decrease. "Slowly" in this case means that the throttle movement from **full open** to **closed** or the reverse should require 2 or 3 sec rather than the fraction of a second required to "jam" the throttle forward or "jerk" it closed.
2. Reduce the power setting to the **climb** value as soon as practical after takeoff. Continued climb at maximum power can easily produce excessive cylinder-head temperatures and detonation. This is particularly true if the airplane is not equipped with a cylinder-head temperature gage.
3. Do not reduce power suddenly when the cylinder-head temperature is high (at or near the red line on the cylinder-head temperature gage). The sudden cooling which occurs when power is reduced sharply will often cause the cylinder head to crack. When preparing to let down, it is well to reduce the power slowly by increments to allow for a gradual reduction of temperatures.

4. When operating an airplane with a constant-speed propeller, always reduce manifold pressure with the throttle before reducing rpm with the propeller control. Conversely, always increase rpm with the propeller control before increasing manifold pressure. If the engine rpm setting is too low and the throttle is advanced, it is possible to develop excessive cylinder pressures with the consequences explained previously. The operator of an engine should become thoroughly familiar with the maximums allowable for the engine and then make sure that the engine is operated within these limits. It must be remembered that a constant-speed propeller holds engine rpm to a particular value in accordance with the position of the propeller control. When the throttle is moved forward, the propeller blade angle increases and the manifold pressure increases but the rpm remains the same.

5. During a prolonged glide with power low (throttle near closed position) "clear the engine" occasionally to prevent spark-plug fouling. This is done by advancing the throttle to a medium-power position for a few seconds. If the engine runs smoothly, the power may be reduced again.

6. Always place the manual mixture control in the FULL RICH position when the engine is to be operated at or near full power. This is to aid in preventing overheating. The engine should be operated with the mixture control in a LEAN position only during cruise in accordance with the instructions in the operator's manual. When power is reduced for letdown and preparatory to landing, the mixture control should be placed in the FULL RICH position. Some mixture controls and carburetors do not include a full-rich setting. In this case the mixture control is placed in the RICH position for high power and takeoff.

7. If there is any possibility of carburetor icing at the time that power is reduced for a letdown preparatory to landing, it is necessary to place the carburetor heat control in the HEAT ON position. This is a precautionary measure and is common practice for all engines in which carburetor icing may occur.

8. At high altitude, adjust the mixture control to a position less rich than that used at low altitudes. The density of the air at high altitudes is less than it is at lower altitudes; hence the same volume of air will contain less oxygen. If the engine is super-charged, the increase in altitude will not be of particular consequence until the capacity of the super-charger is exceeded. Usually the manifold pressure gage will provide the information needed for proper adjustment of mixture control.

CRUISE CONTROL

Cruise control is the adjustment of engine controls to obtain the results desired in range, economy, or flight time. Since an engine consumes more fuel at high power settings than it does at the lower settings, it is obvious that maximum speed and maximum range or economy cannot be attained with the same power settings. If a maximum distance flight is to be made, it is desirable to conserve fuel by operating at a low power setting. On the other hand, if maximum speed is desired, it is necessary to use maximum power settings with a decrease in range capability.

Range and speed charts

The charts of Fig. 13·8 were developed for the operation of the Piper PA-23-160 Apache aircraft. The chart on the left shows the effects of power settings on

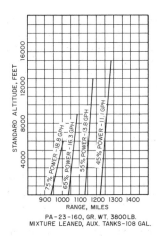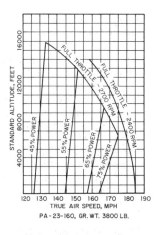

PA-23-160, GR. WT. 3800LB.
MIXTURE LEANED, AUX. TANKS-108 GAL.

PA-23-160, GR. WT. 3800 LB.

Figure 13·8 Charts to show range and airspeed in relation to power settings. (Piper Aircraft Co.)

range, and the chart on the right shows how power settings and true airspeed (TAS) are related. From these charts we can easily determine the proper power settings for any flight within the range of the airplane, taking into consideration the flight altitude, distance of the flight, and desired flight time.

If we wish to make a flight of 900 miles at an altitude of 6500 ft, we can determine the flight values for maximum speed or maximum range or we can choose to select a compromise setting. If we wish to make the flight in the shortest possible time, we must use 75 percent of the engine power. With this setting (2400 rpm and full throttle) the TAS will be about 175 mph and the flight will take 5.14 hr, assuming no tail wind or head wind. At this setting the fuel consumption will be 18.8 gph; hence the flight will require 96.7 gal of fuel. If we wish to make this same flight with maximum economy, we may operate the engines at 45 percent of power with the mixture control leaned as far as good engine operation will permit. At this power setting, the TAS will be about 128 mph and the fuel required for the trip will be about 77.7 gal. The time required for the flight is about 7 hr.

We would seldom actually operate the engine at the extremes mentioned above because the recommended power setting for cruise conditions is 65 percent of power. Flying at an altitude of 9500 ft, this would provide a TAS of about 166 mph. If we wished to operate more economically or with greater range, we would probably use a power setting of about 55 percent of maximum.

Power settings

In order to set the controls of an engine for a particular power output, we adjust manifold pressure and rpm according to density altitude when the airplane is equipped with constant-speed propellers. Table 13·1 shows the settings for the Lycoming O-320-B six-cylinder opposed engine. This table is adjusted for the use of **pressure altitude** at standard temperature T_s instead of **density altitude.** Observe the following facts regarding the settings for manifold pressure and rpm:

1. At a given rpm and a given power setting, manifold pressure must be decreased as altitude increases. This is because the T_s of the air decreases and the density therefore increases. Thus, a given volume of air at a certain pressure will have a greater weight as altitude increases, and manifold pressure must be reduced in order to maintain constant power.
2. When the engine is operated at a higher rpm, a lower manifold pressure is used in order to maintain the same power.
3. At a certain level of altitude the manifold pressure can no longer be maintained because of the reduction in atmospheric pressure. This is the point in the chart shown as *FT*, meaning full throttle.
4. At 55 percent rated power, the power can be maintained up to 15,000 ft pressure altitude. An output of 75 percent power can be maintained only up to about 7000 ft pressure altitude.
5. Manifold pressure settings must be adjusted to maintain a particular power output if outside air temperature is above or below the standard given in the chart.

For large engines equipped with torquemeters, a power table of the type shown in Table 13·1 is not required. In this case a conversion chart is used to change the torquemeter readings to horsepower. The formula used with the Pratt & Whitney R-2800 engine is bhp = torque pressure × rpm × torque constant.

ENGINE STARTING AND STOPPING

Starting procedures

The starting of an aircraft engine is a relatively simple procedure; however, certain precautions must be taken in order to obtain the best results and to avoid damage to the engine.

Before an engine is started prior to flight, the airplane should be given a standard preflight inspection in accordance with the operator's handbook. During this inspection a small amount of fuel should be drained from each drain valve to remove sediment and water. The fuel and oil quantity should be checked to make sure all tanks are properly filled. The ground or pavement near the propellers should be checked for loose items which might be drawn into the propellers.

After all preliminary inspections and cockpit checks have been made, the engine may be started according to the procedure set forth in the operator's manual. The following starting procedure is recommended for the engines on a Cessna 310F airplane:

1. Turn ignition switches **on.**
2. Open the throttle approximately ½ in.
3. Set the propeller pitch lever full forward for HIGH RPM.
4. Set the mixture lever full forward for FULL RICH.
5. Clear the propeller.
6. Turn the auxiliary fuel pump switch to PRIME position. Avoid leaving the auxiliary fuel pump switch in either the PRIME or ON position for more than a few seconds unless the engine is running.
7. Turn the ignition switch to START when the fuel flow reaches 2 to 4 gph. (Read the fuel pressure gage.) If the engines are warm, turn the ignition switch to START first, then turn the auxiliary pump switch to PRIME.
8. Release the ignition switch as soon as the engine fires.
9. Turn off the auxiliary fuel pump switch when the engine runs smoothly.

    During very hot weather, if there is an indication of vapor in the fuel system (indicated by fluctuating fuel flow) with the engine running, turn the auxiliary fuel pump switch to ON until the system is purged.

Table 13 · 1   Power setting table—Lycoming Model O-320-B, 160-hp engine

Press. alt. 1000 ft	Std. alt. temp., °F	88 hp—55% rated Approx. fuel 7 gal/hr rpm & man. press.				104 hp—65% rated Approx. fuel 8 gal/hr rpm & man. press.				120 hp—75% rated Approx. fuel 9 gal/hr rpm & man. press.		
		2100	2200	2300	2400	2100	2200	2300	2400	2200	2300	2400
SL	59	22.0	21.3	20.6	19.8	24.4	23.6	22.8	22.1	25.9	25.2	24.3
1	55	21.7	20.0	20.3	19.6	24.1	23.3	22.5	21.8	25.6	24.9	24.0
2	52	21.4	20.7	20.1	19.3	23.8	23.0	22.3	21.5	25.0	24.3	23.5
3	48	21.1	20.5	19.8	19.1	23.5	22.7	22.0	21.2	25.3	24.6	23.8
4	45	20.8	20.2	19.6	18.9	23.1	22.4	21.7	21.0	24.7	24.0	23.2
5	41	20.5	19.9	19.3	18.6	22.8	22.1	21.4	20.7	FT	23.7	23.0
6	38	20.2	19.6	19.0	18.4	22.5	21.8	21.2	20.5		FT	22.7
7	34	19.9	19.3	18.8	18.2	22.2	21.5	20.9	20.2			FT
8	31	19.5	19.0	18.5	18.0	FT	21.2	20.6	19.9			
9	27	19.2	18.8	18.3	17.7		FT	20.3	19.7			
10	23	18.9	18.5	18.0	17.5			FT	19.4			
11	19	18.6	18.2	17.8	17.3				FT			
12	16	18.3	17.9	17.5	17.0							
13	12	FT	17.6	17.3	16.8							
14	9		FT	17.0	16.6							
15	5			FT	16.3							

To maintain constant power, correct manifold pressure approximately 0.15 in. Hg for each 10°F variation in carburetor air temperature from standard altitude temperature. Add manifold pressure for air temperatures above standard; subtract for temperatures below standard.

10. Check for an oil-pressure indication within 30 sec in normal weather and 60 sec in cold weather. If no indication appears, shut off the engine and investigate.
11. Disconnect the external power source if used.
12. Warm up the engine at 800 to 1000 rpm.

Starting procedures will vary to some extent for different types of engine installations. There are certain general rules which almost always apply, however, and these should be noted carefully.

1. The propeller control should be placed in the HIGH-RPM position.
2. The mixture control should be placed in the FULL RICH position.
3. If the engine cowling is equipped with cowl flaps, the flaps should be open.
4. A radial engine should always be turned through several revolutions before attempting to start in order to clear cylinders of possible hydraulic lock due to oil drainage in the lower cylinders. It is good practice to turn any engine through a few times if the engine is cold in order to provide a small amount of prelubrication to the moving parts. Ignition switch must be checked **off.**
5. If the engine is equipped with oil cooler flaps which have a manual control, the control should be placed in the CLOSED position until the engine is warm.

Stopping procedure

Usually an aircraft engine has cooled sufficiently for an immediate stop because of the taxi time required to move the airplane into the parking area. It is good practice, however, to observe the cylinder-head temperature gage to see that the CHT is somewhat under 400°F before stopping. If the engine is equipped with an idle cutoff on the mixture control, the engine should be stopped by placing the control in the IDLE CUTOFF position. Immediately after the engine stops, the ignition switch must be turned off. If the airplane is equipped with cowl flaps, the flaps should be left in the open position until after the engine has cooled.

If an airplane is equipped with a Hamilton Standard counterweight-type propeller, the propeller should be placed in the LOW-RPM (high-pitch) position shortly before stopping the engine in order to move the propeller cylinder forward where it will cover the piston. This will prevent corrosion of the piston and will also prevent sand and other dirt from collecting on the piston surface. In the LOW-RPM position the cylinder is rearward and the oil in the cylinder has been returned to the engine. This helps to prevent the congealing of oil in the cylinder during very cold weather.

After stopping the engine, check all switches in the cockpit to OFF. This is especially important with respect to the ignition switches and the master battery switch.

REVIEW QUESTIONS

1. What damage to the engine may occur if the engine is operated with excessive manifold pressure?
2. If an R-2800 engine is delivering 2000 hp at 2700 rpm, what is the bmep?
3. Approximately what power output would you expect to obtain from a good aircraft engine consuming 60 lb (10 gal) per hr of gasoline? Figure the heat value of the fuel as 20,000 Btu per lb.
4. At approximately what percent of full power output is an engine likely to be most efficient?
5. If you operate a Continental O-470-K engine at 2200 rpm and 25 in. Hg manifold pressure, what power would the engine develop at sea level (standard conditions)?
6. Why is the volumetric efficiency of a naturally aspirated engine always less than 100 percent?
7. If it requires 50 hp to drive a certain fixed-pitch propeller at 600 rpm, what power is required to drive it at 1800 rpm?
8. Compare *density altitude* with *pressure altitude*.
9. If a Continental O-470-M engine is operated at 5000 ft, density altitude, with a power setting of 2400 rpm and 23 in. Hg MP, what is the actual power output?
10. Explain the difference between *best power mixture* and *best economy mixture*.
11. Discuss the effects of carburetor air temperature on engine operation.
12. How does exhaust back pressure decrease engine power?
13. What conditions must be observed when an aircraft engine is operated?
14. In the operation of an engine with a variable-pitch propeller, what sequence must be followed in changing power settings?
15. What precaution is taken to prevent carburetor icing when power is reduced for a letdown?
16. What is meant by *cruise control*?
17. How is maximum range obtained in the operation of an aircraft engine?
18. Give the general rules which apply to the starting of an aircraft engine.

Engine Overhaul Practices

CHAPTER 14

In the operation of any aviation flight activity, one of the most critical segments of the operation is the maintenance of the airplanes and powerplants, and of these two, the powerplant is certainly a major consideration. Every man responsible for the maintenance or overhaul of a certificated aircraft engine or any of its parts bears a serious responsibility to the public, to himself, and to his organization. He must perform his work in such a way that, when he has completed a particular repair or overhaul job, he can say, "This part (or this engine) will not fail."

THE NEED FOR OVERHAUL

The young person first entering the field of aviation maintenance may wonder why engine overhaul is necessary, what it consists of, and how often it must be done and may have a variety of other questions in his mind. These questions are not difficult because experience has provided the answers.

After a certain number of hours of operation, an engine undergoes various changes, and it is these changes which make the overhaul necessary. The most important of these are as follows:

1. Critical dimensions in the engine are changed as a result of wear and stresses, thus bringing about a decrease in performance, increase in fuel and oil consumption, and an increase in engine vibration.
2. Foreign materials including sludge, gums, corrosive substances, and abrasive substances accumulate in the engine.
3. The metal in critical parts of the engine may be crystallized owing to constant application of recurring stresses.
4. One or more parts may actually fail.

Experience with a particular make and model of engine establishes the average period of time this model may be operated without expectation of failure. On the basis of this experience a normal period of overhaul is established. The operator of a privately owned airplane may choose to operate his engine beyond the normal overhaul period, especially if he has operated the engine in such a manner that it has not been overheated or overstressed in any manner.

The actual time that an engine can be operated between overhauls is determined largely by the manner in which it has been operated. If the operator is careful and continuously observes the rules for good engine operation, he may extend the life of the engine for several hundred hours. On the other hand, careless operation, such as extended climb at full power, may create a need for engine overhaul in much less than the normal period. If the engine is operated with excessive cylinder-head temperature for a short time, the piston rings may become "feathered" and will lose their capacity to seal the cylinder. This results in loss of compression and high oil consumption. A good piston ring has sharp, square edges where contact with the cylinder wall is made. If the ring is overheated, these edges are damaged and the ring is said to be "feathered." Cases are known where a new engine has been installed in an airplane and the first flight has resulted in ring feathering because the pilot failed to reduce power soon enough on the initial climb. In such cases, the cylinders of the engine must be removed and new rings installed.

With respect to engines used in commercial air transport airplanes, the engine overhaul period is determined by experience and is approved by the Federal Aviation Agency. Typical overhaul periods range from 800 to 1500 hr. The overhaul periods for modern jet engines used in commercial service may be more than 3000 hr.

Definition of overhaul

The dictionary definition of **overhaul** is "the disassembly, inspection, and repair of an integrated mechanism." For an aircraft engine this expands into the complete disassembly of the engine, cleaning and stripping of all parts, thorough inspection of every part, checking of measurements for all bearings and other fitted parts according to the manufacturer's Table of Limits, repair or replacement of parts as required, reassembly of the engine according to the manufacturer's instructions, preparation of a complete record of the overhaul, and a test run of the engine as specified by the manufacturer.

THE OVERHAUL SHOP

Organization

In order to provide for efficient overhaul operations so engine overhaul can be accomplished with a minimum cost to the engine owner, an overhaul shop must be well organized. The type of organization largely depends upon the size of engines to be overhauled and the volume (number of engines to be overhauled in a given period of time). Overhaul shops may be established to handle comparatively few small engines, or they may be large companies which overhaul hundreds of small and large engines each year. A sample organization chart for a medium-sized overhaul operation is shown in Fig. 14·1.

As can be observed from the organization chart, the Production Department is serviced by all the other departments. This is because the production of overhauled engines is the business of the organization.

The Accounting Department handles all financial records, including costs of production, payment of invoices, billing of customers, tax reports, payroll preparation, etc. An effective accounting department is essential, not only to perform the routine accounting operations but also to keep management informed regarding the financial condition of the organization.

It is the function of the Purchasing, Receiving, and Shipping Department to maintain a smooth flow of engines and materials in to the facility and finished engines out to the customer. It will be noted that this department maintains direct communication with some of the subdepartments in Production.

The major functions of the Production Department are indicated in the chart. The success of the operation depends upon the quality of work done in the subdepartments and the efficiency with which each operates. It must be remembered that the organization is responsible for the quality of the product and must answer to both the Federal Aviation Agency and the customer if the overhaul work is not airworthy.

The Federal Aviation Agency requires that official inspections for quality of production be accomplished by a separate inspection individual or group who will make an objective appraisal of all work performed. It is the responsibility of the Inspection (or Quality Control) Department to see that all the parts of an engine meet approved specifications before they are installed in the engine. They are also required to check repair operations and assembly procedures. The assembly inspection is particularly important because every nut and bolt must be tightened to the proper torque and then safetied by approved methods.

The function of **receiving inspection** is to inventory each engine as it is received, making records of the general condition of the engine, the accessories included with the engine, the serial numbers of the engine and its accessories, and any other information which may be essential to the satisfactory completion of the engine overhaul. These records are necessary for the satisfaction of the customer and to provide information for any subsequent investigation of the history of the engine.

In the **disassembly and cleaning** section the engine is given a preliminary cleaning to remove external dirt and grease. This may be done by careful steam cleaning, by means of a petroleum solvent wash, or by the use of an emulsion cleaner. After this external cleaning, the engine is started through the disassembly procedure in accordance with the manufacturer's instructions in

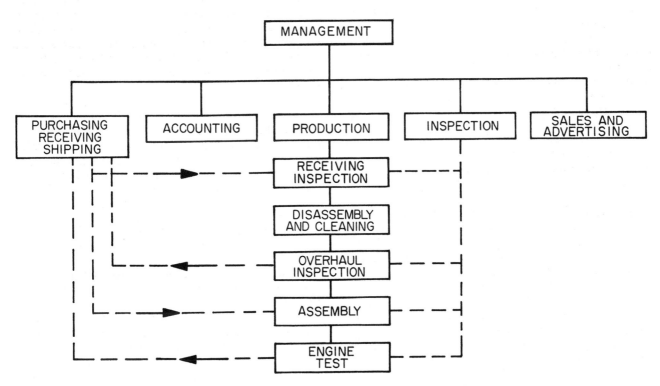

Figure 14·1 Organization chart for an overhaul shop.

the overhaul manual. In all cases, it is important that the operator in charge of cleaning make sure that the cleaning material being used will not harm the engine or its parts. Manufacturers of cleaning chemicals can furnish information regarding their products and instructions regarding methods for using the products correctly.

For disassembly, the engine should be mounted on a suitable disassembly stand (overhaul stand) so the engine will be held in a position for convenient handling. As each part is removed from the engine, a metal tag with the work order number should be attached to the part.

After the engine is disassembled, the parts are given the final cleaning and stripping treatment. The purpose of this operation is to remove all grease, paint, carbon, and any other material which coats or covers the bare metal. This is necessary to allow for an adequate inspection.

The **overhaul inspection** division determines what damage and wear have occurred in the engine, thereby providing information needed for repair and replacement of parts. This division utilizes all the inspection methods necessary to assure that the engine and its parts are brought up to airworthy standards. At this time the quality-control inspectors will provide assistance.

During the overhaul inspection, records are made indicating whether parts must be replaced or what type of repair or rework is required. The various parts may be sent to different sections of the shop for particular types of work. For example, a special section may be devoted exclusively to cylinder repair, another section may handle crankcases, etc. The number of special sections in the shop is determined by the volume of work handled by the shop.

Replacement parts for an engine are drawn from the stock room and charged to the work order number or are ordered through the Purchasing Department. A shop which overhauls a substantial number of the same type of engine will usually maintain a stock of the most commonly required parts.

The **assembly division** receives the airworthy parts of the engine, including new parts and repaired parts, and proceeds with the assembly of the engine according to the manufacturer's overhaul manual, Airworthiness Directives, Type Certificate Data Sheet, manufacturers' bulletins, and other applicable instructions. During and after assembly the quality-control inspector checks each step of assembly for compliance with pertinent requirements.

Upon completion of assembly and inspection, the engine is installed in an engine test stand and is operated according to the approved run-in schedule. During run-in the operation of the engine is carefully observed for rpm, temperatures, vibration, power output, manifold pressure, etc. If the engine does not perform according to specifications, the reason for the unsatisfactory performance must be determined and corrected.

The larger overhaul organizations will usually have a Sales and Advertising Department. It is the function of this department to bring the overhaul business to the organization by means of advertising, offering bids, and direct contact with potential customers. A good Sales Department is often the difference between the success and failure of an overhaul business.

One of the most critical functions of the Sales Department, working in cooperation with the Accounting Department, is to determine the cost of engine overhaul jobs and to offer realistic bids for jobs to be done. Some companies list flat rates for certain engine overhaul jobs, and others bid on the basis of a flat rate for labor only. In the latter case the parts required for the engine are listed and charged for separately.

Another type of overhaul service offers rebuilt engines at a given price provided that a suitable trade-in engine is supplied. In this case, the trade-in engine must meet certain rigidly established specifications before full credit is allowed.

The pricing of an engine overhaul job must be such that all costs and a reasonable amount of profit are provided for. The costs include labor, parts, and overhead. The overhead includes all costs of operating the business, including administration, sales, staff services, cost of buildings and equipment, and various other charges. A certain percentage of the income from each engine overhaul job must be applied to the overhead charge.

Certification of the overhaul station

In order to provide overhaul services for certificated aircraft engines, an overhaul agency should be certificated as an **FAA certificated repair station** with ratings to cover all types of overhaul work performed. A **certificated repair station** is defined by Federal Air Regulations as **"a facility for the maintenance, repair, and alteration of airframes, powerplants, propellers, or appliances, holding a valid repair station certificate with appropriate ratings issued by the Administrator."** Certification by the FAA as a certificated repair station permits the repair station to perform major overhaul on all items for which appropriate ratings are held. This certification also permits the repair station to approve the overhauled items for return to service. Further details regarding the responsibilities and privileges of a certificated repair station are given in the applicable parts of the Federal Air Regulations.

RECEIVING THE ENGINE

Receiving inspection

The purpose of the **receiving inspection** is to determine the general condition of the engine when it is received and to provide an inventory of the engine and all its accessories and associated parts. It is most essential that every part be accounted for because an owner may not be aware that certain parts or accessories have been removed before the engine was delivered to the overhaul facility. The receiving inspection report should be made on a standardized form, and a copy of this form should be provided for the owner.

Included in the receiving inspection report should be the make, model, and serial number of the engine and all its accessories. In addition, all parts such as cylinder baffles, ducting, brackets, etc., should be listed so there will be no question regarding the responsibility for these parts after the engine is completed.

The general condition of the engine should be carefully noted on the receiving report. If the engine has been in a crash, fire, or other situation where damage may have been caused, it is necessary that such conditions be recorded. The cost of overhauling an engine which has suffered damage, other than normal wear, will be considerably greater than usual. In many cases it is not economically feasible to overhaul such an engine.

Records

Federal Air Regulations require that a permanent record of every maintenance (except preventive maintenance), repair, rebuilding, or alteration of any airframe, powerplant, propeller, or appliance shall be maintained by the owner in a logbook or other permanent record satisfactory to the Administrator (FAA Administrator), which shall contain at least the following information: (1) an adequate description of the work performed; (2) the date of completion of the work performed; (3) the name of the individual, repair station, manufacturer, or air carrier performing the work; and (4) the signature and, if a certificated mechanic or certificated repairman, the certificate number of the person approving as airworthy the work performed and authorizing the return of the aircraft or engine to service.

All major repairs and major alterations to an airframe, powerplant, propeller, or appliance must be entered on a form acceptable to the Administrator. Such form must be executed in duplicate and must be disposed of in such manner as, from time to time, may be prescribed by the Administrator.

All major alterations must be entered on Form ACA-337, the approved major repair and alteration form. This form must be executed in accordance with pertinent instructions, and the original copy given to the owner of the unit altered or repaired. The repair station should retain a copy for its permanent record, and one copy must be sent to the local FAA office within 48 hr of the time that the powerplant or other unit is returned to service.

The Administrator will accept, in lieu of Form ACA-337 for major repairs made only in accordance with a manual of specifications approved by the Administrator, the customer's work order upon which repairs are recorded by the repair station. The original copy of the work order must be furnished the owner or purchaser, and the duplicate copy must be retained at least 2 years by the repair station.

The owner of a powerplant which has been overhauled must be supplied with a copy of a **maintenance release.** This release must accompany the engine until it is installed in the aircraft, and at that time the installing agency will make the release available to the owner for incorporation in the permanent record of the aircraft. The maintenance release may be included as a part of the work order, but it must contain the complete identification of the engine including the make, model, and serial number. The following statement must also be included:

> The engine identified above was repaired and inspected in accordance with current Federal Air Regulations and was found airworthy for return to service.
>
> Pertinent details of the repair are on file at this agency under Work Order No. _____.

Date _____

Signed _____ for
(Signature of authorizing individual)

_____
(Agency name)   (Certificate No.)

_____
(Address)

In addition to the formal records and statements required by FAA regulations, the repair station should maintain a complete record of all repair operations and inspections accomplished on each engine or component overhauled. This record should contain an account of every repair operation, every inspection made, and every replacement of a part. The inspection record should show the dimensions of each part measured and all fits and clearances. These measurements are compared with the manufacturer's Table of Limits so that repairs and replacements can be made to restore worn parts to the required specification.

The inspection record should show the types of inspection procedures employed such as magnetic inspection, fluorescent penetrant inspection, dye penetrant inspection, X-ray inspection, and any other approved process employed to determine the airworthiness of the engine and its parts. If any of these inspections are performed by another agency, the certificate of that agency must be included in the overhaul record.

From time to time, special **bulletins** are issued by the manufacturer of an engine to require alterations or parts replacements designed to improve the performance and reliability of the engine. During the overhaul of an engine bulletins must be complied with, and a statement of such compliance must be made in the overhaul record. The FAA issues **Airworthiness Directives** pertaining to aircraft and engines whenever it appears that certain changes should be made in order to correct discrepancies or to improve the reliability of the unit. During the overhaul of an engine, all Airworthiness Directives pertaining to the engine should be checked to make sure that such directives are complied with, and a statement to that effect should be entered in the overhaul record.

In addition to the special bulletins and Airworthiness Directives, the FAA Engine Specification or Type

Certificate Data Sheet covering the particular engine should be checked for **notes** or other information relating to the engine. If the performance of special operations or changes is required, these must be accomplished and a record made to show what has been done.

The preparation of adequate overhaul records cannot be overstressed. These records are particularly important for the protection of the overhaul agency in the event of an engine failure. If the record is complete and properly prepared, the overhaul agency can show that all overhaul work was accomplished in accordance with the manufacturer's overhaul manual and that all required operations were performed. This type of record will usually absolve the overhaul agency of responsibility in case of engine failure.

CLEANING PROCESSES

During the overhaul of an aircraft engine it is necessary to clean the engine externally before disassembly and also to clean the parts after disassembly. Great care must be taken during the cleaning processes because the engine parts can be seriously damaged by improper cleaning or the application of the wrong types of cleaners to certain parts of the engine. In every case, the person in charge of the cleaning processes should study the engine manufacturer's recommendations regarding the cleaning procedures to be used for various parts of the engine and also comply with the directions provided by the manufacturer of the cleaning agent or process.

In general, we may say that there are three types of cleaning required when an engine is overhauled. These are degreasing, removal of soft types of dirt and sludge, and the removal of hard carbon deposits. The removal of grease and soft types of residues is relatively simple; however, hard carbon deposits require the application of rather severe methods. It is during this type of cleaning that the greatest care must be exercised in order to avoid damaging the engine parts.

External degreasing

When an engine is first received for overhaul, it usually has oil and dirt on various parts of the exterior. In some cases the dirt and oil mixture is "baked" on to the extent that it is not entirely removable with an ordinary solvent. Usually, however, the oil and loose dirt can be removed by means of a petroleum solvent such as mineral spirits, kerosene, or other approved petroleum solvent. Some operators steam-clean the engine, thus removing oily deposits and caked dirt. When steam cleaning is done, the engine should be washed off with plain hot water afterward to remove all traces of the alkaline steam-cleaning solution. This is necessary in order to prevent the corrosion of aluminum and magnesium parts.

Degreasing after disassembly

After the engine is disassembled, all oil should be removed from the parts before further cleaning is attempted. The reason for this is that the additional cleaning processes are much more effective after the surface oil is removed. Two of the principal methods for removing the residual lubricating oil and loose sludge are washing in a petroleum solvent and employing a vapor degreaser.

Cleaning with a petroleum solvent can be accomplished in a special cleaning booth where the parts are supported on a wooden grill and sprayed with a solvent gun using an air-pressure source of 50 to 100 psi. The spray booth should be provided with a ventilating system to carry away the vapors left in the surrounding air, and the operator should wear adequate protective clothing. A drain should be provided underneath the wooden grill to collect the used cleaning solvent. During the cleaning process particular care should be applied to make sure that all crevices, corners, and oil passages are cleaned.

Vapor degreasing is accomplished with equipment especially designed for this type of cleaning. A vapor degreaser consists of an enclosed booth in which a degreasing solution such as tricholethylene is heated until it vaporizes. The engine parts are suspended above the hot solution, and the hot vapor dissolves the oil and soft residue to the extent that they flow off the parts and drop into the container below. The vapor degreaser should be operated only by a person who is thoroughly familiar with the equipment and the manufacturer's instructions regarding its use.

Stripping

The stripping process is employed to remove paint and various resinous varnishes which have formed in the engine during its operation. Some stripping solutions are also effective in removing some of the harder carbon deposits. A number of solutions suitable for stripping have been developed by manufacturers of chemical cleaning agents, but each solution must be used according to proper direction, or damage may be inflicted on the engine parts. In all cases the person responsible for cleaning and stripping the parts must be thoroughly familiar with the solution used and must know what engine parts may be cleaned safely with the solution. Alkaline (caustic) solutions will attack aluminum, magnesium, and some of the alloys employed in aircraft engines. For this reason, the operator must make sure that he does not expose such parts to a strongly alkaline solution. In order to prevent electrolytic action in the stripping solution dissimilar metals should not be placed in the solution at the same time. Cold strippers are available which are neutral in their effect on metals but will produce good results in removing paint and engine varnishes. They also tend to soften hard carbon, thereby aiding the process of soft grit blasting.

A typical cold-stripping process involves the immersion of parts, such as the engine crankcase, in a vat containing the solution for several hours or overnight. The parts are then removed and steam-cleaned to remove all traces of the stripping solution and all material which has been loosened by the solution. After steam cleaning, the parts are washed with clear hot water and all openings, oil passages, crevices, etc., are checked for cleanliness. This is particularly important because the clogging of one oil passage can cause failure of the engine.

It is inadvisable to soak aluminum and magnesium parts in solutions containing soap because some of the soap will become impregnated in the surface of the material even though it is washed thoroughly after soaking. Then during engine operation, the heat will cause the soap residue to contaminate the engine oil and cause severe foaming. This will result in loss of oil and possible damage to the engine.

Vapor blast

Vapor blasting is employed for special cleaning jobs and is accomplished by means of specially designed equipment and materials. The vapor solution is used with a fine abrasive and should be applied in an enclosed booth. The vapor is hot and is applied with a high-pressure air gun.

The use of vapor blasting is limited to parts and areas of parts which will not be damaged by a small amount of material erosion. It may be used on the tops of pistons, on the outside of cylinders, and in almost any area which is not a bearing surface of some type. In all cases, the manufacturer's instructions must be followed.

Grit blast

For the removal of hard carbon from the inside of cylinders and the tops of pistons, soft **grit blasting** offers one of the most satisfactory processes. The blasting material (grit) consists of ground walnut shells, ground fruit seeds, and other organic materials. The grit is applied by means of a high-pressure air gun in an enclosed booth as shown in Fig. 14·2. The operator extends his hands and arms into sleeves and gloves sealed into the machine. In this way he is fully protected as he manipulates the gun and the parts being cleaned. He can observe his work through a window in the front of the booth.

In the application of grit blasting for the removal of hard carbon, paint, and other residues, the operator must use care to avoid damage to highly polished surfaces and to avoid the plugging of oil passages. If crankcases are grit-blasted, it is advisable to plug all the small openings into which the grit may enter. Some operators do not use the grit blast on parts having oil passages.

In general, **sandblasting** is not employed in the cleaning of engine parts except the valve heads. This is because a sandblast will erode the metal so rapidly that serious damage may be done before the operator is aware of it. Furthermore, sand tends to embed itself in soft metals and will later become a source of abrasion in the operating engine. Under some circumstances, such as preparation for metallizing of cylinders, the outside of the cylinder is carefully sandblasted before the application of the metal spray. Special uses of sandblasting may be approved for particular purposes; however, this may be done only by a thoroughly trained operator and then only within the limits specified for the process.

Figure 14·2 Grit blasting an engine part. (Pangborn Co.)

ENGINE DISASSEMBLY

Tools and equipment

Before the powerplant maintenance technician attempts to overhaul an aircraft engine, he should see that he has all the essential tools and equipment required for the engine which he plans to overhaul. Engine manufacturers design special tools and fixtures to be used for the overhaul of their engines; however, it is not necessary to have every tool listed in the overhaul manual. Many standard tools such as wrenches, gear pullers, arbors, lifting slings, reamers, etc., can be used in place of similar tools which may be available from the manufacturer. If a particular overhaul shop is likely to receive many engines of the same type for overhaul, it is a good plan to equip the shop with most of the tools designed for the overhaul of that type of engine.

Among the tools and equipment needed for engine overhaul are the following:

Engine Shop Equipment

Arbors of several sizes	Cylinder fixtures or holding blocks
Arbor press	Drill press
Cleaning equipment	Generator test stand
Crankshaft thread cap	Heating equipment
Crankshaft wrench	Lifting sling
Magnetic inspection equipment	Penetrant inspection equipment
Magneto test stand	Test stand and propeller
Magneto timing tools	Timing disk or Time-Rite equipment
Overhaul stand	Timing lights
Parts trays	Vises

Connecting-rod alignment tools	Valve guide tools
Cylinder base wrench	Valve refacing equipment
Gear pullers	Valve seat-grinding equipment
Ignition harness tools	Valve spring compressor
Piston-ring compressor	Valve spring tester
Reamers	

Hand Tools

Box wrenches	Pliers
Bushing reamers	Safety wire tools
Counterbores	Screw extractors
Diagonal cutters	Spanner wrenches
Drifts of several sizes	Spot facers
Drill motor	Stud drivers
End wrenches	Stud pullers
Heli-Coil tools	Torque wrenches

Precision Measuring Tools

Depth gages	Small hole gages
Dial gages	Surface plate
Height gages	Telescope gages
Micrometers	V blocks

In addition to the listed tools and equipment, it is likely that the engine will have certain features which require the use of manufacturer's special tools. It is therefore necessary to obtain these special tools for each different type of engine overhauled.

Manufacturer's manual

Every engine overhaul should be accomplished in accordance with the instructions given in the manufacturer's overhaul manual. Usually the manufacturer's manual will give specific steps for the disassembly of the engine, and by following these steps the technician will avoid many problems.

Procedures

For a typical small aircraft engine, the disassembly follows a sequence beginning with the installation of the engine on the overhaul stand. The overhaul manual then specifies that parts be removed or disassembled in the following order:

1. Ignition system
2. Priming system
3. Generator
4. Magneto and accessory drives
5. Oil cooler
6. Carburetor and manifold riser
7. Starter and drive adapter assembly
8. Oil-pump assembly
9. Oil filler neck
10. Fuel pump
11. Valve rocker covers
12. Intake and balance tubes
13. Oil sump and oil suction tube
14. Valve mechanism
15. Cylinders and pistons
16. Accessory case
17. Crankcase

The foregoing order of disassembly established for a particular engine, the Continental O-470, and the details of each operation are given in the overhaul manual. If the technician has carefully noted each step and carried out the operations as given, the engine will be completely disassembled and ready for the first visual inspection.

During disassembly the operator should identify and mark all parts. This is often done by attaching small aluminum tags to each part with soft safety wire. The metal tags are stamped with the work order number. Further identification is needed for certain parts which must be reinstalled in the same location from which they are taken. This applies to cylinders, pistons, connecting rods, valves, etc. The overhaul manual specifies which parts must be replaced in their original locations. These parts may be identified by attaching additional tags to show the location. Nuts and bolts may be strung on safety wire in groups which are identified for location.

Cylinders, pistons, connecting rods, valve lifters, and other parts requiring exact location should be clearly marked to show the location in the engine. For example, the piston from the No. 1 cylinder should be marked with the number 1. Usually this number will be stamped on the head of the piston. Connecting rods have numbers stamped on the big end. Careful marking and identification of the parts will assure proper assembly and will provide for correct fits and clearances when measurements for wear are made.

It is recommended that all parts be given a preliminary visual inspection as they are removed or before they are cleaned. Parts that are obviously damaged beyond repair should be discarded and marked so they will not be reused. A record of all parts thus discarded should be made for the overhaul file.

Cleaning

When the engine is disassembled, all small parts should be placed in metal wire baskets in order to prevent the loss of any part during the cleaning process. The first cleaning operation is the removal of oil and sludge by washing in solvent or in a vapor degreaser. This is to prevent the dilution and contamination of the stripping solution during the next phase of cleaning.

As mentioned previously, great care must be taken during the stripping and decarbonizing process. The operator must be familiar with the characteristics of the cleaning solution, and he must follow the recommendations of the manufacturer. Magnesium parts are particularly susceptible to damage in alkaline solutions, and prolonged exposure to such solutions must be avoided.

Care must be exercised in the handling of decarbonizing (stripping) solutions to prevent the material from contacting the skin because these solutions will usually cause severe irritation or burning. The operator should therefore wear goggles, rubber gloves, and protective clothing while working with these solutions.

After the required soaking time in the stripping solution, the engine parts should be steam-cleaned and then washed with clear hot water. Oil passages and other small apertures should be examined to see that all sludge and other residues are removed. The parts are then dried with compressed air, and those requiring further cleaning are routed to the next operation. Steel parts which are clean should be coated with a rust-inhibiting oil immediately after the cleaning operation is completed.

Except as permitted by the instructions in the overhaul manual, wire wheels, steel scrapers, putty knives, or abrasives should not be used for cleaning parts or removing carbon. The use of these items may leave scratches on the parts which will lead to stress concentrations and ultimate failure.

Hard carbon is removed from piston heads and from the inside of cylinder heads by means of a soft grit blast. The carbon which has collected inside the piston head and in the ring lands is the most difficult to remove. After the part has been soaked in the decarbonizing solution, the carbon can usually be removed by grit blasting, although it is sometimes necessary to use a soft scraper. The operator must be careful not to damage the piston-ring lands or remove any metal from the small radii between the ring lands and the bottom of the ring grooves. The glazed surfaces on the piston and the piston pin should not be removed.

INSPECTIONS

Use of manufacturer's overhaul manual

Although we have explained the importance of using the manufacturer's overhaul manual previously, we must reemphasize this essential policy. The manufacturer of an aircraft engine has all the information relating to the construction and design of engine parts and has made numerous tests of the assembled engine and its parts. The overhaul manual prepared by the manufacturer is therefore the most valid source of information available for a particular make and model of engine.

The overhaul manual provides information on all procedures of a special nature and also general procedures for disassembly, cleaning, inspection, repair, modifications, assembly, and testing of engines. These procedures must be followed in order to assure that the engine is overhauled in a manner which will provide the required reliability.

Table of Limits

The **Table of Limits** found in the manufacturer's overhaul manual supplies the information necessary to determine the degree of wear for various parts. A portion of the Table of Limits for the Continental O-470 engine is shown in Fig. 14·3.

In the Table of Limits it will be noted that three dimensions for each measurement are usually given. These are the **serviceable limit, new minimum,** and **new maximum.** If a measurement exceeds the serviceable limit, the part is no longer suitable for the engine and must not be used. If the dimension is between the serviceable limit and the new maximum, the part can

be used but should not ordinarily be reinstalled in an engine being given a major overhaul. The correct dimension for parts installed in a newly overhauled engine should fall between the new minimum and new maximum dimensions.

To illustrate the use of the Table of Limits we shall assume that the clearance for the rocker shaft in the rocker-arm bearing is being measured. First we use a telescoping gage in the rocker-arm bearing as shown in Fig. 14·4 to measure the minimum inside diameter of the bearing. It is well to take the measurement several times using different diameter locations in the bearing. When the telescoping gage has been locked at the correct dimension, we measure the extension of the gage with a micrometer caliper as shown in Fig. 14·5. The micrometer must not be tightened on the telescoping gage but should touch each end of the gage lightly. The reading of the gage is noted and recorded on the inspection sheet. In this case we shall assume that the reading is 0.7195 in. We then measure the rocker shaft in the center at several different diameters with the micrometer and find that the dimension is 0.7205 in. We record this dimension in the inspection record and then note the difference between the two dimensions. This is the clearance of the rocker shaft in the bearing, and since it is 0.0010 in., we accept it as satisfactory because it is within the limit given in the table.

Some engine parts require that a number of measurements be taken, for example, the cylinders and pistons. All the dimensions shown in the table must be measured and recorded.

It will be observed that some of the dimension figures in the table are followed by the letter L or T. The L stands for **loose** and indicates a clearance between the parts. The letter T stands for **tight** and indicates a "pinch" or "interference" fit. This usually means that one part must be shrunk into the other. In the case of the valve guides, the limits shown are 0.001T to 0.0025T. That is, the valve guide must have a diameter of 0.001 to 0.0025 in. larger than the hole into which it is installed. Installation is usually accomplished by heating the cylinder head and then pressing or driving the cold valve guide into place with the proper type of driving tool.

Manufacturer's bulletins

As mentioned in an earlier part of this section, the manufacturers of aircraft engines issue bulletins when it becomes apparent that changes or modifications should be made in certain parts of an engine. Such a bulletin may require the installation of a new type of camshaft at the next overhaul, an immediate replacement of all rocker shafts, the drilling of a new oil passage, or any number of operations. The purpose of the change is to increase the reliability and airworthiness of the engine. In many cases the changes described in the bulletins are mandatory, and in other cases the changes are recommended but not required. During the overhaul of an engine the technician must check all bulletins which have been issued for the make and model of engine with which he is working.

TABLE OF LIMITS

O-470-K, L, M

Ref. No.	Chart No.	Model	Description	Serviceable Limit	New Parts Min.	New Parts Max.
			CYLINDER AND HEAD ASSEMBLY			
1	1	K,L,M	Cylinder bore (lower 4-1/4" of barrel) . . . . diameter:	5.006	5.001	5.003
2	1	All	Cylinder bore (top of barrel) . . . . diameter:	5.000	4.989	4.993
3	1	All	Cylinder bore choke (from 3.25" above flange to top) . . . . taper:	.006	.010	.012
4	1	All	Cylinder bore out of round . . . . :	.003	–	.002
5	1	All	Cylinder bore (reground .015) . . . . . allowable o' size:	5.021	5.016	5.018
6	1	All	Cylinder bore surface roughness . . . (micro in. RMS):	–	30	40
7	1	All	Cylinder barrel in crankcase . . . . diameter:	–	.004L	.010L
8	1	All	Intake valve seat insert in cylinder head . . . diameter:	–	.009T	.012T
9	1	All	Intake valve guide in cylinder head . . . . . . diameter:	–	.001T	.0025T
10	1	All	Exhaust valve guide in cylinder head . . . . . diameter:	–	.001T	.0025T
11	1	All	Exhaust valve seat insert in cylinder head . . diameter:	–	.007T	.010T
12	1	All	Intake valve seat . . . . .width:	–	.107	.156
13	1	All	Exhaust valve seat .width:	–	.120	.171
14	1	All	Valve seat (to valve guide axis) . . . . .angle:	–	45°	45°30'
			ROCKER ARMS AND SHAFTS			
15	1	All	Rocker shaft in cylinder head bosses . . . . . diameter:	.003L	.000	.0015L
16	1	All	Rocker shaft in rocker arm bearing . . . . . diameter:	.004L	.001L	.0025L
17	1	All	Rocker arm bearing in rocker arm . . . . diameter:	–	.002T	.004T
18	1	All	Rocker arm . . . . side clearance:	.019	.005	.015
19	1	All	Intake valve in guide . . . . diameter:	.005L	.0012L	.0032L
20	1	All	Exhaust valve in guide . . . . diameter:	.008L	.003L	.005L
21	1	All	Intake valve face (to stem axis) . . . . angle:	–	45°	45°30'
22	1	All	Exhaust valve face (to stem axis) . . . . angle:	–	45°	45°30'
23	1	All	Intake valve (max. tip regrind .015) . . . . . . length:	4.789	4.804	4.824
24	1	All	Exhaust valve (max. tip regrind .015) . . . . . . length:	4.791	4.806	4.826
25	1	All	Intake and exhaust valve (full indicator reading) warpage . . . . :	.004	.000	.002
			PISTONS, RINGS AND PINS — See footnote also			
26	1	K & L	Piston (bottom of skirt) in cylinder . . . . diameter:	.021L	.006L	.009L
		M	Piston (bottom of skirt) in cylinder . . . . diameter:	.022L	.007L	.010L
27	1	K & L	Piston (below third ring groove) in cylinder . diameter:	.026L	.016L	.019L
		M	Piston (below third ring groove) in cylinder . diameter:	.028L	.017L	.021L
28	1	All	Top piston ring in groove . . . . side clearance:	.015	.007	.0085
29	1	All	Second piston ring in groove . . . . . . side clearance:	.014	.0065	.008
30	1	All	Third piston ring in groove . . . . side clearance:	.008	.0035	.005
31	1	All	Top and second ring (ring in cylinder barrel) . . . . gap:	.065	.0381	.0544
32	1	All	Third ring (ring in cylinder barrel) . . . . gap:	.060	.0331	.0494
33	1	All	Top piston ring (standard gap) comp. ring . . .tension*:	12 lbs.	13 lbs.	17 lbs.
34	1	All	Second piston ring (standard gap) comp. ring. .tension*:	12 lbs.	13 lbs.	17 lbs.
35	1	All	Third piston ring (standard gap) . . . . .tension†:	10 lbs.	11 lbs.	16 lbs.
36	1	All	Plug in piston pin (before swaging) . . . . diameter:	–	.0005T	.001L
37	1	All	Piston pin in piston . . . . diameter:	.002L	.0005L	.0012L
38	1	All	Piston pin and plug in cylinder . . . . end clearance:	.090L	.036	.048L
39	1	All	Piston pin in connecting rod bushing . . . . . . diameter:	.004L	.0018L	.0022L
40	1	All	Bushing in connecting rod . . . . diameter:	–	.0025T	.0050T
41	1	All	Connecting rod bearing on crankpin (tri-metal bearing) . . . . diameter:	.006L	.0009L	.0034L

† Measure piston ring (oil ring) tension on diameter perpendicular to gap when ring is compressed to .030 - .040 inch gap.

* Measure piston ring (top and second compression ring) tension on diameter perpendicular to gap when ring is compressed to .035 - .045 inch gap.

Piston (Models K & L) . . . . :			
Fourth ring (in cylinder barrel) . . . . gap :	.060	.0331	.0494
Fourth ring in groove . . . . side clearance :	.014	.0065	.008

Figure 14·3 Table of Limits. (Continental Motors Co.)

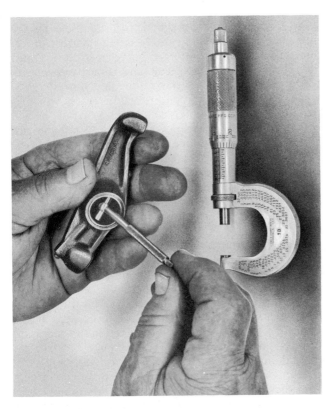

Figure 14·4   Using a telescoping gage.

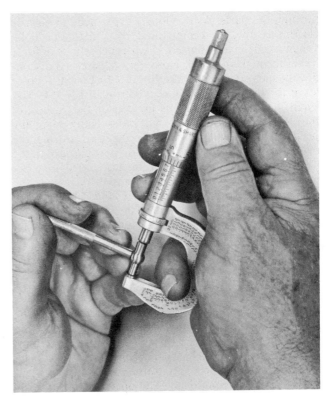

Figure 14·5   Measuring the dimension of a telescoping gage.

Airworthiness Directives

Airworthiness Directives are issued by the FAA to specify changes or modifications required for aircraft, engines, propellers, accessories, or parts. These directives are therefore similar in purpose to the manufacturers bulletins, and in many cases the change required by an Airworthiness Directive is also required by a manufacturer's bulletin issued within a short time after the AD is issued. As is the case with the bulletins, all the ADs for an engine must be checked when the engine is overhauled to make sure that required changes and modifications are made.

Engine specifications and type certificate data sheets

Pertinent information regarding certificated engines is listed for each engine on an **Engine Specification Sheet** or a **Type Certificate Data Sheet** issued by the FAA. The information for engines certificated prior to **January 1, 1959,** is given on the Engine Specification Sheet, and information for engines subsequent to the above date is shown on the Type Certificate Data Sheet. For engines certificated before World War II, engine specifications are given in a document called the Aircraft Engine Listing.

The Overhaul technician should study the specifications given for the engine which he plans to overhaul, paying particular attention to the "Notes" given with the specifications. The Notes provide information essential to the proper operation of the engine or its accessories.

Inspection procedures

The inspection processes and procedures for engine parts may vary somewhat from one overhaul shop to another; however, the primary function of inspection must always be accomplished. This function is to assure that all parts installed in an engine are airworthy.

Detailed inspection forms should always be used to record the results of inspections, and these forms become a permanent part of the overhaul file. A description of each type of inspection should be recorded together with the results of each inspection.

Inspections fall into three principal categories: (1) **visual inspection,** which involves a visual examination of parts to note any defects which are visible to the eye; (2) inspection with special aids such as **magnetic inspection, fluorescent penetrant inspection,** and **dye penetrant inspection;** and (3) **dimensional inspection** accomplished with micrometers, gages, and other measuring devices.

Visual inspection is accomplished by direct examination and with the use of a magnifying glass. In each case a strong light should be used to aid in revealing all possible defects. During visual inspection special attention is given those areas of the engine and its parts where experience has shown damage to be most likely. Visual inspection will usually reveal cracks, corrosion, nicks, scratches, galling, scoring, and other disturbances of the metal surfaces.

Magnetic inspection is applied to steel parts which can be magnetized by passing a strong electric current through the parts. As previously explained, an electric current is always accompanied by a magnetic field. When a part is magnetized, the magnetic lines of force travel through the steel. However, if there is a discontinuity such as a crack, the lines of force will tend to leave the metal at the crack as shown in Fig. 14·6. A small magnetic field is thus created at the surface of the metal, and this field will attract the magnetic particles which are applied to the part during the magnetizing process. The magnetic particles are in the form of a powder, either dry or suspended in a petroleum fluid. When a fluid is used in which the magnetic particles are suspended, the part is magnetized and the fluid is applied to the part by means of a fluid nozzle. As the fluid flows over the part, the magnetic particles will adhere to any area where the magnetic lines of force leave the surface of the metal. The concentration of magnetic particles will reveal the presence of a crack or other possible defect.

Magnetic inspection is accomplished by means of special equipment such as that manufactured for the purpose by the Magnaflux Corporation. Parts requiring magnetic inspection may be sent to an authorized inspecting agency, or the inspection may be performed by a person who is thoroughly trained in the use of magnetic inspection equipment. The operator must under-stand the nature of the magnetic fields employed in the magnetic inspection and must use the correct procedures and techniques for each part inspected. He must understand that the magnetic field is perpendicular to the current flowing through the part and that the inspection is not likely to reveal a crack which is parallel to the magnetic field. Because of this, he will realize that it is sometimes necessary to remagnetize a part in order to produce fields in different directions. For example, a crankshaft may be inspected for longitudinal cracks by passing a current through the shaft lengthwise as shown in Fig. 14·7. In order to detect cracks in other directions it may be necessary to employ a coil or solenoid as shown in the inspection of the cylinder (Fig. 14·8).

Since the current available from a Magnaflux machine may be more than 3000 amp, the operator must use care to avoid overheating the parts. If a small part is subjected to 3000 amp, it will quickly become heated and the contact areas may be burned. Thus the part will be rendered useless and must be discarded. If the operator follows the instructions given in the operation manual for the equipment, he will not be likely to cause damage to the parts being inspected.

After parts have been subjected to magnetic inspection, they must be demagnetized. If this is not done, the parts will pick up and hold small steel particles which can cause serious damage within the engine during operation. Demagnetization is accomplished by passing the parts slowly through a strong alternating magnetic field and then moving the parts slowly out of the field. The parts will not be demagnetized if current for the demagnetizing coil is turned off while the parts are still in the field. The use of a demagnetizing coil is shown in Fig. 14·9.

Upon completion of magnetic inspection, engine parts should be washed in clean petroleum solvent and dried with compressed air. Following this, they should

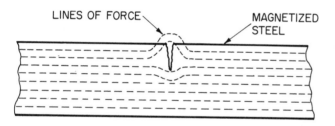

Figure **14·6** Magnetic lines of force leaving surface of metal.

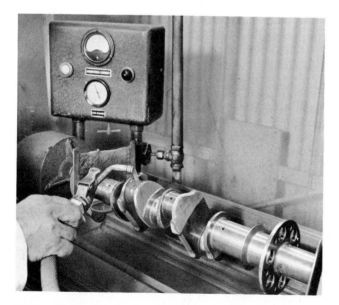

Figure **14·7** Magnetic inspection of a crankshaft.

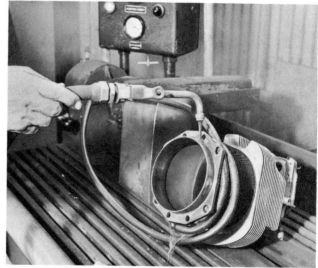

Figure **14·8** Using a coil for magnetic inspection.

Figure 14·9 Demagnetizing a part.

be coated with a thin layer of corrosion-inhibiting oil.

Engine parts made of aluminum alloy, magnesium alloy, bronze, or any other metal which cannot be magnetized are usually inspected by means of a **fluorescent penetrant** or a **dye penetrant.**

Inspection by means of a penetrant should include the testing of the parts, the tabulation of the nature and extent of the discontinuities found, and the final decision regarding the suitability of the parts for further service. The operator should be a specialist who has been thoroughly trained to evaluate correctly the various indications which may be found.

The process of fluorescent penetrant inspection involves the immersion of the thoroughly cleaned parts in the penetrant solution for sufficient time to allow the penetrant to enter all cracks and other discontinuities. The time may be from 10 to 45 min depending upon the nature of the part. The heating of parts before immersion will increase the sensitivity of the process. After the part is removed from the penetrant, it is placed upon a drain rack for a short time to allow excess penetrant to drain back into the vat, and then the part is washed with warm water and dried.

The development of fluorescent penetrant indications will occur after a relatively short time without any further treatment. However, the development will be hastened and improved by the application of a dry developing powder which is dusted over the surface of the part. All excess powder is brushed off, and then the part is placed under an ultraviolet light in a darkened booth. At all points where the penetrant has seeped out of cracks or other discontinuities, a bright line or spot will appear. It is then up to the inspector to determine if the indication represents a defect which requires

that the part be rejected, if the part can be repaired, or if the indication is of no consequence.

Dye penetrant inspection serves the same purpose as fluorescent penetrant inspection; however, it has the advantage of being performed without the special equipment required for the fluorescent penetrant inspection. Dye penetrant inspection is accomplished by application of a highly penetrating dye to the surface of a part. Excess dye is washed off with the specified solvent, and the part is dried. A developer is then brushed or sprayed on the surface of the part and allowed to dry. Since the developer forms a pure white porous coating on the part, the penetrant will be revealed in a bright red line or spot wherever it has entered a crack or other opening in the surface.

Dimensional inspections are employed to determine the degree of wear for parts of the engine where moving surfaces are in contact with other surfaces. If the wear between surfaces exceeds the amount set forth in the manufacturer's Table of Limits, the parts must be replaced or repaired in accordance with approved methods.

It is well for the inspector to know that parts are usually manufactured with dimensions in sixteenths of inches. This is in accordance with a practice established by the Society of Automotive Engineers many years ago. A correctly dimensioned part will therefore measure $x/16$ in. $+ 0.000$ minus an amount up to the tolerance. The decimals for sixteenths of an inch are as follows:

$\frac{1}{16} = 0.0625$	$\frac{7}{16} = 0.4375$	$\frac{12}{16} = 0.7500$
$\frac{2}{16} = 0.1250$	$\frac{8}{16} = 0.5000$	$\frac{13}{16} = 0.8125$
$\frac{3}{16} = 0.1875$	$\frac{9}{16} = 0.5625$	$\frac{14}{16} = 0.8750$
$\frac{4}{16} = 0.2500$	$\frac{10}{16} = 0.6250$	$\frac{15}{16} = 0.9375$
$\frac{5}{16} = 0.3125$	$\frac{11}{16} = 0.6875$	$\frac{16}{16} = 1.0000$
$\frac{6}{16} = 0.3750$		

The dimensions of shafts, crankpins, main bearing journals, piston pins, and similar parts are measured with a micrometer caliper as shown in Fig. 14·10. The micrometer should be equipped with a vernier scale so measurements can be taken to the nearest ten-thousandth. A micrometer having a ratchet sleeve or stem is recommended to assure that the measuring pressure between the anvil and stem is uniform for all measurements.

The inside diameters of bushings, bearings, and similar openings are measured with telescoping gages. While the gage is in the opening, it is locked in place to preserve the dimension. The dimension of the telescoping gage is then measured with a micrometer as explained previously. If a hole is too small to receive a telescoping gage, a **small-hole gage** is used. Gages of this type are also called **ball gages.** The ball end of the gage is inserted in the hole and expanded until it fits the hole snugly as shown in Fig. 14·11. It is then removed and measured with a micrometer to obtain the dimension of the hole.

Engine manufacturers often supply **plug gages** or **"go and no-go"** gages to measure the dimensions of certain holes or openings. These gages are used ac-

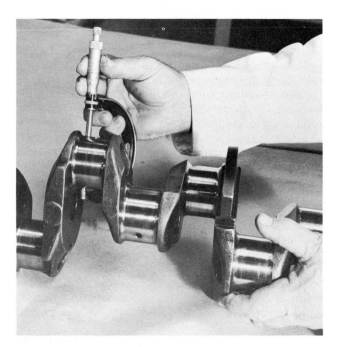

Figure 14·10 *Measuring a crankpin with a micrometer caliper.*

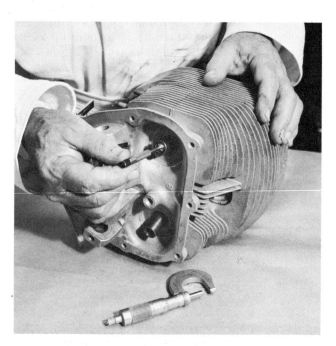

Figure 14·11 *Using a small-hole gage.*

cording to the instructions given by the manufacturer.

Cylinder barrels are measured with a cylinder-bore gage as shown in Fig. 14·12. This gage will show the wear, out-of-roundness, and taper. The cylinder bore is measured by sliding the gage from the top to the bottom of the cylinder in the direction of piston thrust and also at 90° to this direction. In this way the out-of-roundness can be checked for the full length of the barrel. Before the gage is placed in the cylinder barrel,

Figure 14·12 *Measuring the cylinder bore.*

the gage needle is set at zero with the basic dimension of the barrel. Deviations from the basic dimension will be shown as the needle moves in a positive or negative direction.

Connecting rods must be measured for bearing and bushing dimensions and also for alignment. The methods used for checking the alignment (twist and convergence of bearing with bushing) will be given later in this section.

The dimensions of small gaps, such as the clearance between piston rings and ring lands, is measured with a **thickness gage.** If a gage of the specified thickness will enter the gap without the use of undue force, it is evidence that the gap is at least as great as the gage

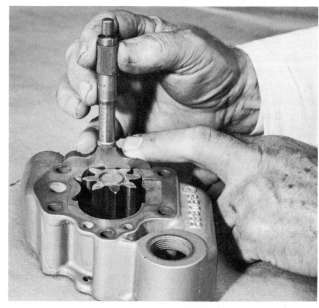

Figure 14·13 *Use of a depth gage.*

dimension. Thickness gages are used to measure side clearances, end clearances, valve clearances, and other similar dimensions.

The **depth gage** is used to provide an accurate indication of the distance between fixed surfaces such as the distance of the parting surface of an oil pump housing to the end of the gear. The use of a depth gage is shown in Fig. 14·13.

Dial gages are particularly useful for checking the alignment or out-of-roundness of rotating parts. The use of a dial gage in checking the alignment of a crankshaft is described later in this section.

We have mentioned a variety of measuring instruments or gages in this section; however, engine manufacturers often provide special gages to be used with their particular engines. These gages are described in the manufacturer's overhaul manual for the engine concerned and should be used according to the instructions given.

CYLINDER OVERHAUL

The repair operations required for cylinders depend upon the wear and damage which may be found during inspection. Some operations are performed at each overhaul, and others are performed only if required in order to restore the cylinder to an airworthy condition.

If an engine is being overhauled for the first time, it is quite likely that the only operations required on the cylinders will be routine inspections after cleaning, reseating the valves by grinding and lapping, and breaking the glaze on the cylinder walls by means of a cylinder hone.

When cylinders have been overhauled several times, it is probable that the cylinder bore will have to be ground oversize or chrome-plated and ground to standard dimensions. Valve guides will need to be replaced, and if the valve seats have been ground a number of times, it may be necessary to replace the seats. Rocker shaft bosses which incorporate bushings must be rebushed from time to time to retain the dimension specified in the Table of Limits.

Cylinder bore

The cylinder bore is inspected for dimensions, corrosion, and scoring. Mild corrosion or scoring can sometimes be removed by means of No. 400 wet-or-dry sandpaper followed by the use of crocus cloth. The dimensions of the bore should be measured after it has been sanded and polished. If the dimensions are not within suitable limits, the bore must be ground to 0.010, 0.015, or 0.020 in. oversize, depending upon how much metal must be removed in order to clean the old metal. Cylinder grinding must be done only with the proper type of equipment and by an operator who is thoroughly trained in its operation. Many operators of small overhaul shops send the cylinders to approved shops which specialize in the grinding of cylinders rather than invest in the costly grinding machines required for this operation.

Another repair commonly employed for cylinders which are worn beyond limits is to plate the bore with porous chrome and then grind the bore to standard dimensions. This operation should be accomplished only by an operator whose process has been approved by the FAA. The advantage of porous chrome plating is that the cylinder bore will show very little wear between overhauls and they usually remain serviceable with standard dimensions for several thousand hours of operation.

When the cylinders of an engine have been chromeplated, the piston rings used in these cylinders **must not** be chrome-plated. The overhaul technician must determine whether cylinders have been plated, and if so, the piston rings must be unplated cast iron or steel.

Cooling fins

During inspection of the cylinder it may be found that some of the cooling fins have been damaged. The fins on the cylinder head are made as integral parts of the cast-aluminum-alloy head; hence they are brittle and easily cracked or broken. Broken head fins should be filed smooth at the broken edges to eliminate roughness and sharp edges. If it becomes necessary to cut out a vee notch to stop a head fin crack, a slotted drill bushing to fit over the fin may be used with a 3/16-in. twist drill to cut the notch. The apex of the notch and the edges of the cut should be rounded to reduce the possibility of further cracking. If repairs and previous damage have removed as much as 10 percent of the total head fin area, the cylinder assembly is considered beyond repair.

Steel barrel fins which have been bent can be straightened with a long-nose plier or a special slotted tool designed for the purpose.

Studs

The studs by which the exhaust pipes are attached to the cylinder head are usually subject to severe corrosion because of heat and the chemical effects of the exhaust gases. It is, therefore, often necessary to replace these studs. During inspection the threads of the studs should be carefully examined, and if appreciable erosion is noted, the studs should be replaced. Stud replacement is described in the section covering crankcase repair.

Skirt and flange

During the handling of cylinders care must be exercised to avoid damaging the skirt. Approved practice calls for mounting the cylinder on a wooden cylinder block when it is not being worked on. If cylinder blocks are not available, the cylinder may be placed on its side on a wooden rack. If pushrod housings are attached, the cylinder must be placed on its side in a manner to avoid putting a stress on the housings. The cylinder must not be lifted or carried by grasping the pushrod housings.

If the cylinder is handled properly, there is no reason why the skirt should become damaged. Usually such damage is caused by carelessly allowing the skirt to strike a hard metal object. If a small nick or scratch should be found on the skirt, it can be removed by careful stoning and polishing.

The cylinder mounting flange must be examined for cracks, warping, damaged bolt holes, and bending. A very small amount of warp can be removed by lapping the bottom of the flange on a cylinder surface plate. Otherwise, any appreciable defects require that the cylinder be discarded.

The cylinder flange should be given an especially careful examination if any of the cylinder hold-down bolts or nuts were found to be loose at the time of disassembly. A loose hold-down nut or bolt will cause exceptional stresses to be imposed on the flange and also on the crankcase.

Valve guides, seats, and valves

If inspection reveals that valve guides are oversize or damaged in any way, it is necessary that they be replaced. Valve guides should be removed according to the manufacturer's instructions, and the method usually requires driving with a special piloted drift or using a valve-guide puller. Since the valve guide has a flange on the outside end, it is necessary to drive it from the inside of the cylinder. Before it is driven or pulled, the inner end of the guide should be cleared of all hard carbon to prevent scoring of the guide hole. Some operators recommend heating the cylinder head to about 450°F before removing the valve guides because this tends to expand the valve-guide hole and permit easier removal. In all cases the cylinder should be properly supported on a cylinder-holding fixture while valve-guide removal and replacement are being done.

If equipment is not available to pull or drive the valve guide from inside the cylinder, it is possible to cut away the outer end and flange of the guide by means of a spot facer and then drive the guide to the inside of the cylinder. Care must be taken to avoid cutting into the guide flange seat.

After the valve guides are removed, the guide holes must be inspected for scoring, roughness, and diameter. If the hole size is not within specified limits, it will be necessary to ream or broach to an oversize dimension. The actual size of the hole should be approximately 0.002 in. smaller than the outside diameter of the guide to be installed. The Table of Limits for typical opposed engines establishes limits of 0.001 to 0.0025 in. interference (T) fit. Valve guides are made in oversizes of 0.005 and 0.020 in.

Guide holes which are within the required dimensional limits and are not scored or damaged in any way do not require repair. It is merely necessary to install new valve guides by driving with a suitable installing tool. The guide must be carefully aligned with the hole before driving. Valve seats must be reground after replacing valve guides in every case.

Valve seats can usually be repaired by grinding with specially designed seat-grinding equipment. A typical valve-seat grinder is shown in Fig. 14·14. As can be observed in the illustration, the valve-seat grinder con-

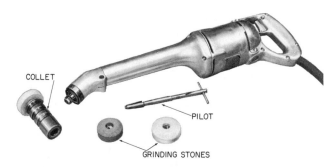

Figure 14·14 *A valve seat grinder.*

sists of an electric motor equipped with an angle drive to permit grinding of the seats at the angle in which they are installed in the cylinder. The grinding wheel is mounted on a collet equipped with a pilot which fits into the valve guide. The pilot holds the grinding wheel in exact alignment with the valve seat. The valve seat is ground by inserting the pilot of the grinder into the valve guide and placing the face of the grinding stone on the seat. The stone angle must be correct for the particular seat being ground. Some engines have a 30° seat for the intake valve and a 45° seat for the exhaust valve. After the grinding stone is in place, the end of the drive unit is placed in the socket and the seat is ground.

When grinding valve seats, the operator must make sure that he has the correct stone (angle, hardness, grit size) and that he removes only sufficient material to provide a smooth seat of the correct width. The width of the seat is adjusted by using a 15° stone to reduce the outer diameter and a 75° stone to increase the inside diameter. The width and diameter of the seat after it is ground must be within the dimensions specified by the manufacturer.

If a valve seat has been reground so many times that the entire face of the 15° narrowing wheel must be brought into contact with the seat in order to grind to the required dimension, the seat is beyond limits and must be replaced.

A valve seat is removed by cutting it out with a special counterbore suitable for the purpose while the cylinder is mounted in a fixture which holds it at the proper angle under the spindle of a drill press. The drill press is used to rotate the counterbore, thus cutting the valve seat from its recess. This is a precision operation and must be performed by an experienced operator.

After the seat is removed, the inside diameter of the valve-seat recess must be measured to determine which oversize seat is to be installed. The recess must then be cut to the correct oversize dimension as specified in the Table of Limits. This is accomplished by means of a valve recess cutter available from the manufacturer.

The cylinder is then heated to 600 to 650°F, and the new valve seat is driven into the recess with the replacement drift. After replacement the new valve seats are ground to the proper face dimension as previously explained. The manufacturer's manual must be consulted to ascertain the correct temperature to be used.

Valves are inspected for burning, erosion, stretch, diameter of stem, cracking, scoring, and warping. Because of the high temperatures to which exhaust valves are exposed, these valves often need to be replaced even though the intake valves are still in serviceable condition. The valves are subjected to many thousands of recurring tension loads, as the valve is opened by cam action and closed by the valve springs. This, of course, tends to stretch the valves, and the effects of stretching are commonly noted with exhaust valves. Figure 14·15 shows how a valve is examined for stretch with a valve stretch gage.

The valves are refaced by means of a standard valve refacing machine. This operation is illustrated in Fig. 14·16. The refacing machine rotates the valve while the grinding wheel is moved back and forth across the face. The surface of the grinding wheel should be dressed to a smooth finish before the operation is started.

Before the valve is inserted in the chuck of the machine, the stem should be examined for cleanliness and alignment. If it is not perfectly smooth and straight, the valve head will wobble and the face will not be true. The operator must make sure that he is using the proper type of grinding wheel and that the machine is set for the correct grinding angle. If the manufacturer's instructions call for an **interference fit,** the valve face angle will be as much as 1° less than the corresponding seat in the cylinder.

Testing valve springs

Valve springs are visually inspected for evidence of over-heating and for pitting caused by corrosion. They are then placed in a valve spring compression tester as shown in Fig. 14·17, and the compression load is checked when the spring is compressed according to instructions. The outer spring will normally have a greater compression strength than the inner spring.

Installation of valves

Valves are installed by inserting the stems through the valve guides from inside the cylinder and then holding them in place while the cylinder is placed over a cylinder block. The block bears against the valve heads and holds the valves on the valve seats. The lower spring seat is installed over the valve stem, and the valve springs are placed on the seat. Assembly instructions should be checked to see if there is a difference between the ends of the springs and the springs are compressed by means of a valve spring

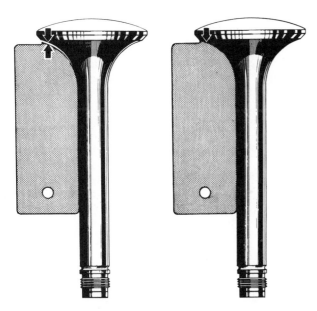

Figure 14·15   Inspecting a valve for stretch.

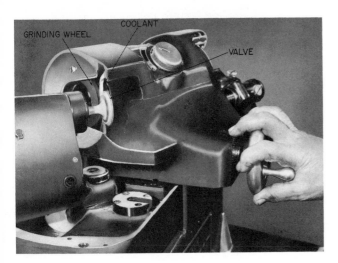

Figure 14·16   Refacing a valve.

Figure 14·17   Testing the compression of a valve spring.

313

compressor. The valve retaining keys are installed in the groove around the valve stem, and the spring compressor is then released.

Rocker arms, shafts, and bushings

Valve rocker arms are inspected for wear on both ends, cracks, dimension of bushing, corrosion, and any other condition which may render them unsuitable for use. Frequently the rocker arms need no repair, and sometimes the only repairs required are replacement and reaming of the bushing. These are accomplished by means of a suitable arbor and arbor press by which the old bushing is pressed out and a new bushing is pressed in. The bushing hole should be examined for condition before the new bushing is pressed in. Special attention must be given the position of the oil hole in the bushing to make sure that it is aligned with the oil hole in the rocker arm.

Rocker shaft bushings in the cylinder head must be replaced if they are worn beyond limits. If the bushing is held in place with a dowel pin, the pin must be drilled out before the bushing is removed. Removal of the bushing is accomplished with a drift or arbor. The cylinder must be properly supported while removing the rocker shaft bushings in order to prevent damage.

After the rocker shaft bushings have been removed, each bushing hole must be checked for size, with either a telescoping gage or a special plug gage. If the bushing hole dimension is above the maximum limit, it is necessary to install an oversize bushing. When it has been decided which oversize bushing is required, the hole is reamed to the correct size for the bushing. The new rocker shaft bushing is installed with an installation drift or similar tool in accordance with the manufacturer's instructions. If the bushing is held in place with a dowel pin, it will be necessary to drill a new hole in the bushing for the dowel pin and then install a pin of the correct size. Special instructions relating to this operation are provided by the manufacturer for the engines in which dowel pins are employed.

After rocker shaft bushings are installed in the cylinder head, it is necessary to check them for dimension and ream them to size if required. The final cut should be made with a finish reamer to produce a very smooth surface.

PISTONS AND RINGS

Pistons

Pistons are inspected for cleanliness, wear, scoring, corrosion, cracks, and any other apparent damage. Oil holes are checked for freedom from carbon. Wear is checked by means of a large micrometer caliper taking the measurements specified in the Table of Limits. The measurements taken on the pistons are compared with cylinder bore measurements to determine piston clearances.

If a piston is found to have deep scoring on the sides, it must be discarded. Very shallow scoring is not cause for rejection and may be left on the piston. No attempt should be made to remove light scoring with sandpaper or crocus cloth because this may change the contour of the skirt.

The piston-ring lands are inspected for cracks or scratches which may lead to cracks. The ring lands must be smooth, and the grooves free from carbon or damage of any kind.

The pin bore is checked with a telescoping gage, and the dimension is checked against the corresponding piston pin to determine the clearance. Piston pins are usually dimensioned to provide a push fit.

Piston rings

New piston rings are installed when the engine is overhauled. These rings must be approved for the installation and must be inspected for fit. The end clearance (gap) is checked by inserting the ring in the skirt of the cylinder and pushing it in with the head of a piston to ensure that the ring is square with the bore. At a point inside the cylinder even with the flange the gap of the piston ring is measured as shown in Fig. 14·18. This gap must be within the tolerance given in the Table of Limits. The piston-ring gap is necessary to prevent seizure of the rings in the cylinder as the pistons and rings expand with the high temperatures of operation.

Piston-ring tension is measured at a point 90° from the gap when the ring is compressed to the normal gap. This tension must conform to the approved specifications.

After the piston-ring gap is measured, the rings are installed on the pistons in the proper grooves for inspection of side clearance. The installation of the rings may be accomplished with a ring expander, or it can be done by hand. Some operators prefer hand installation because they feel that it is less trouble.

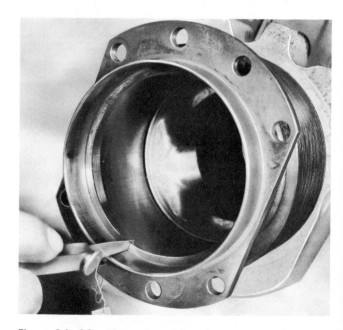

Figure 14·18 Measuring piston-ring gap.

Figure 14·19   Measuring piston-ring side clearance.

The side clearance of the piston rings is measured with a thickness gage as shown in Fig. 14·19. The specified ring clearance is necessary in order to ensure free movement of the rings in the ring grooves and a free flow of oil behind the rings.

CRANKSHAFTS

The crankshaft of an engine is without question one of the most critical parts. The dimensions of the journals, the balance, and the alignment of the shaft must be within tolerances, or the engine will vibrate and may ultimately fail. It is easily understood that the crankshaft is subjected to extremely rigorous treatment during the operation of an engine because it must bear the constant hammering of the connecting rods as they transfer the force of the piston thrust to the connecting rod journals. The inspection and repair of the crankshaft must therefore be accomplished with great care and precision if it is to perform reliably for the hundreds of hours between overhauls.

Magnetic inspection

After the crankshaft is disassembled and cleaned, it should be inspected by the magnetic method. It may be magnetized radially by mounting it lengthwise in the Magnaflux machine and magnetized longitudinally by means of a heavy coil. To accomplish a thorough inspection, the shaft should be magnetized by both methods. During the inspection the radii of crankpins and main bearing journals should be checked carefully for cracks. In many cases these cracks are extremely fine and can be detected only by the magnetic method. The entire shaft should be examined from end to end for cracks or other possible defects. After the magnetic inspection is completed, the shaft must be demagnetized.

Crankpins and main journals

Crankpin journals and main bearing journals are checked for dimension with a micrometer caliper. The "mike" should be placed at four different diameters of the journal to make certain that the measurement is correct. If the journal is found to be oval (out-of-round) more than 0.0015 in., the crankshaft must be discarded or the journals must be reground to not more than 0.010 in. undersize and renitrided. During the measurement of the crankpins and main journals, the dimensions must be recorded in the overhaul file. These same dimensions are compared with the bearing measurements at a later time to determine bearing clearances.

During the inspection of crankshaft journals, if a small amount of roughness is noted, the journal surface should be smoothed with crocus cloth. It is best to do this while the shaft is being rotated slowly in a lathe.

Crankshaft journals should be reground undersize by an experienced operator in a shop which is properly equipped for grinding and renitriding. It is recommended that shafts which require regrinding be returned to the manufacturer for this repair.

When a crankshaft is reground, the exact radii of the original journal ends must be preserved in order to avoid the possibility of failure during operation. If a small ledge or step is left in the metal at the radius location, the shaft is likely to develop cracks which may lead to failure of the journal.

Crankshaft alignment

Crankshaft alignment is checked by mounting the shaft on vee blocks placed on a level surface plate and rotating the shaft while a dial gage is used to measure the runout. This operation is shown in Fig. 14·20. The crankshaft runout should be checked at the center main journals while the shaft is supported at the thrust and rear journals. It should also be checked at the propeller flange or at the front propeller bearing seat. Permissible runout tolerances are given in the Table of Limits.

Counterweights

The crankshafts of many engines are dynamically balanced by means of counterweights mounted on

Figure 14·20   Checking crankshaft alignment (runout).

extensions of the crank cheeks. The size and mounting of these counterweights are such that they dampen out (reduce) the torsional vibration which occurs as the result of the connecting rod thrust. The proper method for removing and replacing the counterweights differs with various types and models of engines; hence the overhaul technician should make sure that he follows the exact procedure outlined in the overhaul manual for the model of engine upon which he is working.

Sludge chambers and oil passages

Some crankshafts are manufactured with hollow crankpins which serve as sludge removers. Drilled oil passages through the crank cheeks carry the oil from inside the main journals to the chambers in the crankpins. The sludge chambers may be formed by means of spool-shaped tubes pressed into the hollow crankpins, or they may be formed by sludge plugs mounted in each end of the crankpin.

The sludge chambers of a crankshaft must be disassembled and cleaned during overhaul to remove the soft-carbon sludge which has collected. If the sludge chambers are formed by means of tubes pressed into the hollow crankpins, the overhaul technician must make certain that the tubes are reinstalled correctly to avoid covering the ends of the oil passages.

The oil passages in the crankshaft should be cleaned at the time that the shaft was originally cleaned; however, they should be checked again before the crankshaft is declared ready for reassembly in the engine. Soft copper wire passed through the passages will verify that they are clear of dirt or other obstruction.

CAMS AND VALVE TAPPETS

Camshaft alignment

The camshaft of an opposed or in-line engine can be checked for alignment in the same manner as that described for a crankshaft. The shaft is mounted in the vee blocks at the end bearings, and the runout is measured at the center bearing.

Camshaft journals

Camshaft journals are measured with a micrometer caliper, and the measurements are recorded for later comparison with the measurement of the camshaft bearing bores in the crankcase. The clearances are specified in the Table of Limits. The camshaft journals should be examined for scratches, scoring, and other damage. Defects which are not apparent to the unaided eye will usually be revealed during the magnetic inspection.

Cam surfaces

The surfaces of the cams must be examined with a magnifying glass to detect incipient failure. Any obvious wear, spalling, pitting, surface cracks, or other damage is cause for rejection of the camshaft. If ex-

amination with a magnifying glass reveals small pores in the surface, this also requires that the shaft be discarded.

Cam gear

The cam gear is inspected for wear, cracks, and other damage. If any defects are found, the gear must be replaced. At the time of assembly the cam gear backlash with the crankshaft gear is checked. If the backlash exceeds the value given in the Table of Limits, the gears must be replaced.

Valve tappets

Valve tappets are inspected for wear, spalling, pitting, scoring, and other damage. Defective tappets must be replaced. The OD of the tappet body is compared with the ID of the bore in the crankcase to determine the clearance. This value must be within approved limits.

Hydraulic lifters or tappets are disassembled and inspected for wear. If any appreciable wear is noted as evidenced by a feathered edge of worked metal at the shoulder in the tappet body, the entire tappet assembly must be discarded. The hydraulic tappet cylinder and plunger assembly must be checked to see that no burrs or binding exist and that the ball check valve is not leaking. A leaking check valve can be tested as follows: Make sure that the cylinder and plunger assembly are dry, and hold the lifter cylinder between the thumb and middle finger in a vertical position with one hand. Then place the plunger in position so that the plunger just enters the lifter cylinder. When the plunger is depressed quickly with the index finger, it should return to approximately its original position. If the plunger does not return but remains in a collapsed position, the ball check valve is not seating properly. The cylinder should be recleaned and then checked again. If the check valve still does not seat, the unit is defective and the entire cylinder and plunger assembly must be discarded.

Hydraulic cylinder and plunger parts cannot be interchanged from one assembly to another, and if a part of any assembly is defective, the entire assembly is discarded. The cylinder and plunger (hydraulic unit) assemblies can be interchanged in lifter bodies provided that the clearances are within the approved limits.

CONNECTING RODS

The inspection and repair of connecting rods involve (1) visual inspection for nicks, cracks, bending, corrosion, and other damage; (2) magnetic inspection; (3) checking of alignment for parallelism and convergence between the bearing end and the piston end; (4) rebushing; and (5) replacement of bearings. Visual inspection is accomplished in the usual manner, directly and with a magnifying glass. A rod which obviously has been bent or twisted must be discarded. Connecting rods should be weighed to see that all weights are the same within ¼ oz.

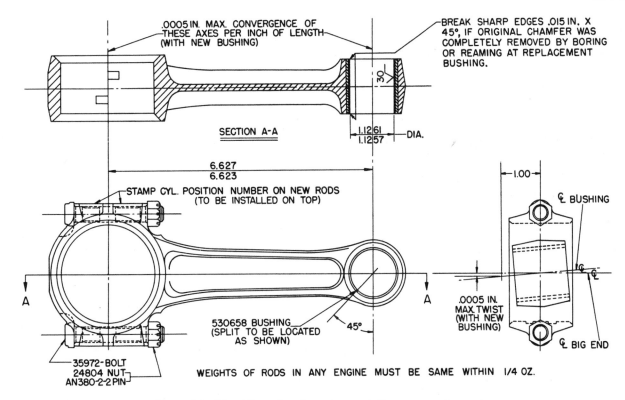

.0005 IN. MAX. CONVERGENCE OF THESE AXES PER INCH OF LENGTH (WITH NEW BUSHING)

BREAK SHARP EDGES .015 IN. X 45°, IF ORIGINAL CHAMFER WAS COMPLETELY REMOVED BY BORING OR REAMING AT REPLACEMENT BUSHING.

SECTION A-A

1.1261 / 1.1257 DIA.

6.627 / 6.623

STAMP CYL. POSITION NUMBER ON NEW RODS (TO BE INSTALLED ON TOP)

530658 BUSHING (SPLIT TO BE LOCATED AS SHOWN)

45°

35972-BOLT
24804 NUT
AN380-2-2 PIN

WEIGHTS OF RODS IN ANY ENGINE MUST BE SAME WITHIN 1/4 OZ.

1.00

℄ BUSHING

.0005 IN. MAX. TWIST (WITH NEW BUSHING)

℄ BIG END

Figure 14·21   Dimensional requirements for a connecting rod.

The requirements for a connected rod to be used in a Continental O-470 engine are shown in the drawing of Fig. 14·21. This drawing illustrates the dimensions as well as the tolerances for twist and convergence.

Checking alignment

The twist of a connecting rod is checked by installing push-fit arbors in both ends and supporting the rod by means of the arbors on parallel steel bars resting on a surface plate. Measurements are then taken with a thickness gage at each supporting point to determine the amount of twist. This check is shown in the photograph of Fig. 14·22. The clearance between the sup-

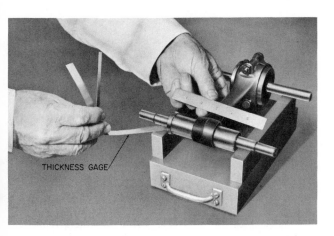

THICKNESS GAGE

Figure 14·22   Checking twist of a connecting rod.

port bar and the arbor in the small end of the rod is measured and divided by the number of inches from the center of the rod to the point where the measurement is taken. The twist must not exceed 0.0005 in. per inch of distance from the center line.

The arbor in the large end of the connecting rod may be supported by matched vee blocks rather than on the steel bars. Either method will give the desired results.

To check convergence, the difference in the distance between the arbors is measured at a given distance on each side of the connecting-rod center. This is accomplished by installing a precision measuring arm with a ball end on one end of the arbor in the small end of the connecting rod. The distance of the measuring arm from the center line of the rod is noted, and the measuring arm is adjusted so the ball just touches the arbor in the big end of the rod. The measuring arm is then moved to the opposite end of the arbor, and the difference in distance is checked with a thickness gage as shown in Fig. 14·23. If the distances are checked at points 3 in. from the center line of the connecting rod, the total distance between the measuring points is 6 in. Therefore, if the difference in the distances between the arbors on each side of the connecting rod is less than 0.003 in., the convergence is within limits.

Bushing replacement

If the piston-pin clearance in the connecting-rod bushing is excessive, it is necessary to replace the bushing. This is accomplished by pressing out the old bushing and pressing in a new bushing with an arbor press. The new bushing should be lubricated before it

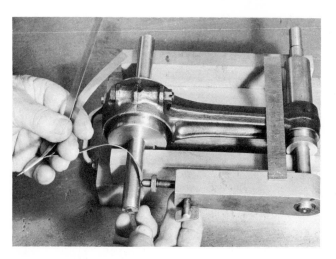

Figure 14·23   Checking convergence of connecting-rod ends.

is installed and must be perfectly parallel with the bore into which it is pressed. After a new piston-pin bushing is installed in the connecting rod, it is usually necessary to ream or bore the bushing to the correct size. This operation is particularly critical because the alignment of the bushing must be held within 0.0005 in. per inch as previously explained. The bushing may be bored with special equipment designed for this purpose, or it may be bored with the use of an engine lathe as shown in Fig. 14·24. For this method the connecting rod is mounted on a faceplate as shown so it is exactly perpendicular to the axis of lathe rotation. The boring tool is then brought into contact with the inner surface of the bushing while the lathe is turning at a slow rate. A small cut is taken with a smooth cutting tool for as many passes as necessary to provide the desired dimension.

Figure 14·24   Line boring a connecting-rod bushing.

Connecting-rod bearings

New connecting-rod bearing inserts are installed when an engine is overhauled. Bearing measurements are taken with the bearings installed in the connecting rods before the rods are assembled to the crankshaft and with the connecting-rod bolts reasonably tight. These measurements are then checked against the dimensions of the crankpins previously recorded. The operator should make sure that the original location of each connecting rod is maintained during the clearance check and at final assembly.

Replacements

At the time of engine overhaul, all connecting-rod bolts, nuts, washers, and cotter pins are replaced. As mentioned above, new connecting-rod bearings are also installed.

CRANKCASE

Crankcases are inspected for cracks, warping, damage to machined surfaces, worn bushings and bearing bores, loose or bent studs, corrosion damage, and any other condition which may lead to failure in service. Two-piece crankcases are manufactured with matched parts; hence if one half must be discarded, the entire crankcase is replaced.

Inspection

Since the majority of crankcases are made of aluminum-alloy castings, a fluorescent penetrant or dye penetrant provides a suitable method for detecting cracks, porosity, and similar defects. These inspections should be made by a person experienced in the use of the method selected.

Visual inspection with a 10-power magnifying glass over the entire surface of the crankcase will reveal most of the defects mentioned previously and will also lead to detection of all but the very fine cracks. If minor nicks and abrasions are discovered, they can usually be removed by filing, stoning, and with crocus cloth.

Replacement of studs

Studs which are damaged, bent, or broken must be removed and replaced with new studs. Studs which are not broken can be removed with a **stud remover** or with a small pipe wrench. The stud should be turned slowly to avoid heating the casting. Broken studs which cannot be gripped by a stud remover or pipe wrench are removed by drilling a hole in the center of the stud and inserting a **screw extractor.** The screw extractor may have straight splines or helical flutes. The Easyout extractor has helical flutes as shown in Fig. 14·25.

After a stud is removed, the coarse thread end should be examined to determine whether the stud is standard or oversize. This is indicated by machined or stamped markings on the coarse thread end. Identification markings are shown in Fig. 14·26. The replacement stud should be one size larger than the stud removed. If the threads in the case are damaged, or if the old

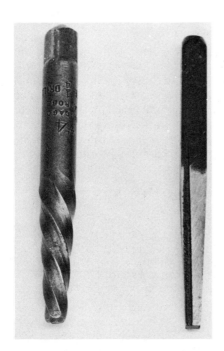

Figure **14·25** An Easyout and a straight-fluted screw extractor.

stud was maximum oversize, it will be necessary to retap the hole and install a Heli-Coil insert for a standard size stud.

Before the new stud is installed, the coarse threads should be coated with a compound specified by the manufacturer. This compound serves to lubricate and protect the threads and may also seal the threads to prevent the leakage of lubricating oil from inside the engine. The stud should be installed with a **stud driver** and screwed into the case a distance specified by the manufacturer.

Heli-Coil inserts

A Heli-Coil insert is a helical coil of wire having a diamond-shaped cross section. When this coil is properly installed in a threaded hole, it provides a durable thread to receive standard studs or screws.

When a threaded hole has been damaged or oversized beyond accepted limits, it can be repaired by retapping and installing a Heli-Coil insert. The tap and installing tools are provided by the manufacturer of the Heli-Coil inserts and must be used according to instructions. The inserts are used in cylinders for spark-plug holes and stud holes and in other parts for stud holes and screw holes.

Heli-Coil inserts may be removed and replaced if they become worn or damaged. The special extracting tool provided by the manufacturer must be used for removal. Heli-Coil inserts and tools are illustrated in Fig. 14·27.

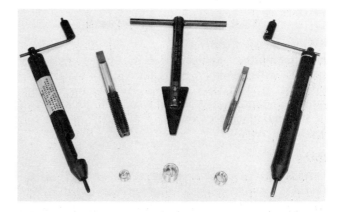

Figure **14·27** Heli-Coil inserts and tools.

Typical part no.	Oversize on pitch dia. of coarse thread, in.	Optional identification marks on coarse thread end		Identification color code
		Stamped	Machined	
XXXXXX	Standard	None		None
XXXXXXP003	0.003			Red
XXXXXXP006	0.006			Blue
XXXXXXP009	0.009			Green
XXXXXXP007	0.007			Blue
XXXXXXP012	0.012			Green

Figure **14·26** Identification data for oversize studs.

319

Measuring bearing bores

During the overhaul of an engine it is important to determine the clearances of crankshaft main bearings and camshaft bearings. This is accomplished by temporarily assembling the crankcase with the main bearing inserts installed. The through bolts which hold the crankcase together are installed and tightened sufficiently to remove all clearance between the parting surfaces. The main bearings and camshaft bearing bores are then measured, and the measurements are compared with the corresponding crankshaft and camshaft measurements to determine the clearances. These clearances are compared with the Table of Limits to ensure that they are satisfactory.

The bores which receive the valve tappet bodies and all other bearing bores in the crankcase section are measured and compared with the parts or shafts to be installed to determine that clearances are within limits. All clearances are recorded in the overhaul file for the engine.

ACCESSORY SECTION

Since the accessory sections for various engines differ considerably for various models and types of engines, specific instructions for overhaul will not be given in this text. It is stressed, however, that the inspections, repair operations, and assembly operations described in the manufacturer's overhaul manual must be followed carefully.

Gears

Accessory gears are examined for wear, overheating, scoring, pitting, and alteration of the tooth profile. Any appreciable damage is cause for rejection of the part. Steel gears and gear shafts can be magnetically inspected for cracks in accordance with approved methods. After inspection the parts must be demagnetized.

Shafts and bushings

The fits and clearances of gears on shafts and shafts in bushings must be checked to see that they are within the tolerances specified in the Table of Limits. If shaft clearances in bushings are excessive, it is necessary to remove, replace, and ream new bushings. In each case these operations must follow the manufacturer's directions. In many cases of bushing replacement it is necessary to drill out dowel pins which hold the bushings in place. This is a critical operation and must be executed with great care to avoid damage to the engine. Manufacturers often supply drill jigs or bushings to guide the drill, thus reducing the possibility of drilling at the wrong angle or in the wrong position. Another precaution which must be emphasized is the alignment of oil holes in bushings. If a bushing is installed where an oil passage emerges, the position of the bushing must be checked as it is pressed into place, and the oil hole in the bushing must be checked after installation to see that it coincides with the hole in the bore.

Accessory case

The procedures described for the inspection and repair of crankcases are generally applicable to accessory cases when the cases are made of aluminum alloy. Some accessory cases, however, are magnesium castings, and these require special treatment because of the greater possibility of corrosion damage. The treatment for magnesium cases should follow the manufacturer's instructions as given in the overhaul manual.

ENGINE ASSEMBLY

The assembly of an engine must follow a sequence recommended for the particular model of engine being assembled. Since the "core" of an engine is the crankshaft, assembly usually starts with the installation of connecting rods on the shaft.

Before assembly is started, the engine parts are checked for cleanliness because dust and other foreign matter will often collect during the inspection, repair, and storage of parts. Parts may be washed with a petroleum solvent and then dried with compressed air in order to remove accumulated dirt. They should then be coated with a corrosion-inhibiting oil.

Use of safety wire

During the final assembly of an engine and the installation of accessories, it is often necessary to **safety wire** (lock-wire) drilled head bolts, cap screws, fillister head screws, castle nuts, and other fasteners. The wire used for this purpose should be soft stainless steel, brass, or other wire specified by the manufacturer.

The principal requirement for lockwire installation is to see that the tension of the wire tends to tighten the bolt, nut, or other fastener. The person installing safety wire must therefore see that the wire pull is on the correct side of the bolt head or nut to exert a tightening effect.

A length of safety wire is inserted through the hole in the fastener, and the two strands are then twisted together by hand or with a special safety-wire tool as shown in Fig. 14 · 28. The length of the twisted portion is adjusted to fit the installation. One end of the wire is then inserted through the next hole, and the two ends are again twisted together. The wires are twisted tightly with pliers but not so much that the wire is weakened. After the job is completed, the excess wire is cut off to leave a stub end of about ½ in. The stub should be bent back toward the nut. Typical examples of lockwiring are shown in Fig. 14 · 29.

Self-locking nuts

Self-locking nuts may be used on aircraft engines if all the following conditions are met:

1. Their use is specified by the manufacturer
2. The nuts will not fall inside the engine should they loosen and come off
3. There is at least one full thread protruding beyond the nut
4. Cotter pin or locking-wire holes in the bolt or stud have been rounded off so they will not cut the fiber of the nut

Figure 14·28   Using a safety-wire twisting tool.

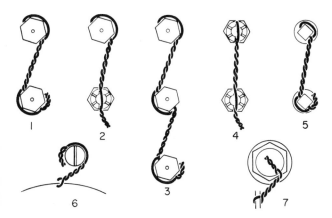

Figure 14·29   Examples of lockwiring.

5. The effectiveness of the self-locking feature has been checked and found to be satisfactory prior to its use

Engine accessories should be attached to the engine by means of the types of nuts furnished with the engine. On many engines, however, self-locking nuts are furnished for such use by the engine manufacturer for all accessories but the heaviest, such as starters and generators.

On many engines, the cylinder baffles, rocker box covers, drive covers and pads, and accessory and super-charger housings are fastened with fiber insert locknuts which are limited to a maximum temperature of 250°F because above this temperature the fiber will char and consequently lose its locking characteristic.

Most engines require some specially designed nuts to provide heat resistance; to provide adequate clearance for installation and removal; to provide for the required degrees of tightening or locking ability which sometimes requires a stronger, specially heat-treated material, a heavier cross section, or a special locking means; to provide ample bearing area under the nut to reduce unit loading on softer metals; and to prevent loosening of studs when nuts are removed.

Palnuts

Palnuts are made of thin sheet steel and are used as locking devices for plain nuts. After the plain nut is properly torqued, the Palnut is screwed onto the bolt fingertight. It is then turned about one-fourth turn with a wrench to lock it in place. Excessive turning of the Palnut will damage the threads and render the nut ineffective.

Washers

Flat washers (AN-960) are used under hex nuts to protect the engine part and to provide a smooth bearing surface for the nut. Such washers may be reused provided that they are inspected and found to be in good condition. Washers which are grooved, bent, scratched, or otherwise damaged should be discarded.

Lock washers may be used in some areas but only with the approval of the manufacturer. Lock washers should not be used where a part must be removed frequently because of the damage which occurs each time that the nut or bolt is loosened.

Connecting rods

New connecting-rod bearing inserts should be snapped into the rods and rod caps with the tangs of the inserts fitted into the cutouts provided. Each bearing is lubricated with approved oil, and then the rod and cap are installed on the crankpins according to the numbers stamped on the rods and caps. The position numbers should be on the upper side when the engine is in the horizontal position.

Since different manufacturers of engines do not necessarily designate engine cylinder numbers from the same end of the engine, the overhaul technician must make sure that he uses the correct order when installing parts according to cylinder number. For example, the Lycoming O-480 engine has the cylinders numbered with No. 1 being the right front cylinder, whereas the No. 1 cylinder of the Continental O-470 engine is the right rear cylinder. In both cases the **front** of the engine is the propeller end.

The connecting rods are installed with new bolts, washers, nuts, and corrosion-resistant cotter pins, and each nut is tightened to the torque specified using a suitable torque wrench. A nut must not be "backed up" in an effort to obtain a certain torque value but should always approach the correct value while being tightened. If the cotter-pin hole cannot be aligned with the nut when the nut has been torqued properly, it may be necessary to substitute nuts or bolts until the correct position can be attained. When the cotter pin is installed, one tang is bent back on the side of the nut and the other is bent out over the end of the bolt.

Some manufacturers specify the use of roll pins instead of cotter pins. When these are called for, the pin holes in the connecting-rod bolts must be of the proper diameter for the pins used.

After a connecting rod is installed on the crankpin, the side clearance should be checked with a thickness gage to see that it is within approved limits. The rod should rotate freely on the crankpin, but there should be no noticeable play when tested manually.

Assembling the crankcase

The crankcase of an opposed engine can be assembled to the crankshaft assembly either while the shaft is mounted in a vertical assembly stand or with the crankcase supported on a workbench. The procedure depends upon the type of equipment available in the overhaul shop.

If the crankcase is assembled on a workbench, it must be supported so the cylinder pads are about 6 in. above the surface of the table. The right or left section of the case, as designated by the overhaul manual, should be placed on the supports, and all preliminary assembly operations specified should be completed.

The parting flange of the crankcase is coated with a thin layer of an approved sealing compound, care being taken not to apply so much that it will run inside the engine upon assembly. A single strand of No. 50 silk thread is then placed along the parting flange inside the bolt holes as specified by the manufacturer.

Prior to installation of the crankshaft and connecting-rod assembly in the crankcase, the front oil seal is installed on the crankshaft. The crankshaft gear can be installed either before or after the connecting rods.

The crankshaft is lifted carefully by two persons so the correctly numbered connecting rods will be down and the others up. It is placed into the crankcase, care being used to see that the crankshaft seal fits into the seal recess without damage. The upper connecting rods are then laid gently to the side so they rest on the crankcase flange.

If the engine construction is such that valve tappet bodies cannot be installed after the crankcase is assembled, these must be installed before the camshaft is placed in the assembly position.

The valve tappet bodies are lubricated on the outside and installed in the tappet bores of the opposite half of the crankcase. The camshaft with the cam gear installed is then placed in position and wired in place with brass or soft steel wire.

Before the opposite half of the crankcase is placed in the assembly position, the end clearances of the crankshaft and camshaft are checked with a feeler gage. This is to ensure that the end play is within specified limits.

If required, the valve tappet bodies are installed in the crankcase section in which the crankshaft assembly has been placed. The other section of the crankcase in which the camshaft has been placed is now mated with the first section, care being taken to see that all parts fit together properly and that the cam gear timing marks are aligned with the timing marks on the crankshaft gear. This automatically times the camshaft to the crankshaft. The two halves are then partially bolted together as specified in the overhaul manual, and the wire holding the camshaft is removed.

It must be emphasized at this time that the foregoing procedures are usually followed for the assembly of the crankcase of an opposed engine. However, there is considerable variation in procedure for different makes and models, and the most desirable method is usually that described by the manufacturer in the overhaul manual.

When an assembly stand is employed which holds the crankshaft in a vertical position, the two halves of the crankcase are assembled simultaneously on the crankshaft and connecting-rod assembly. Regardless of which method is employed, care must be exercised to prevent damage to any part. After the crankcase halves are bolted together, the connecting rods should be supported by means of rubber bands or cords to prevent them from striking the edges of the cylinder pads.

Pistons and cylinders

Before installation, the piston and piston pin are generously coated with a preservative oil. This oil should be worked into the ring grooves so all piston rings are thoroughly lubricated. Each piston is numbered and must be installed on the correspondingly numbered connecting rod. The piston is positioned so the number on the head is in the location specified by the manufacturer, assuming that the engine is in its normal horizontal position. For radial engines, it must be remembered that the cylinder with the master rod is removed **last** during disassembly and installed **first** during assembly. This is to provide adequate support for the master rod assembly and to hold the link rods and pistons in such a position that the lower piston ring will not be below the skirt of the cylinder.

Before a piston is installed, the crankshaft should be turned so the connecting rod for the cylinder being installed is in the TDC position. Installation of the piston is accomplished by placing the piston in the proper position over the end of the connecting rod and pushing the piston pin into place through the piston and connecting rod. A piston-ring compressor is then hung over the connecting rod to be in readiness for the installation of the cylinder. Prior to installation the cylinders should be checked for cleanliness and the inside of the barrel coated with preservative oil. A base flange packing ring is installed around the skirt at the intersection of the skirt and flange. The correctly numbered cylinder is lifted into position, and the cylinder skirt is placed over the piston head. The ring compressor is then placed around the piston and upper piston rings, and the rings are compressed into the piston grooves. The cylinder can then be moved inward so the skirt slides over the piston rings as the compressor is pushed back. When all the piston rings are inside the cylinder skirt, the compressor is removed and the cylinder flange stud holes are carefully moved into place over the studs. The base flange packing ring is then checked for position, and the cylinder is pushed into place. Cylinder hold-down nuts are screwed onto the studs and tightened lightly. The upper nuts are installed first in order to provide good support for the cylinder. After all the nuts are in place, they are tightened moderately but not torqued to the full value. A torque handle is installed on the cylinder base wrench, and the nuts are torqued in the sequence specified in the overhaul manual. It is of the utmost importance that the cylinder hold-down nuts be tightened evenly and to the correct value to prevent warping and undue strain on one side of the flange. Some manufacturers require that all cylinders be installed before the final torquing of cylinder hold-down nuts. Cylinder hold-down nuts are secured by means of safety wire or with Palnuts.

Valve mechanism

Since the valve mechanisms for engines of different makes and models vary considerably, we shall not describe any particular method of installation or assembly in this text. We shall stress, however, that the assembly must be in the sequence described by the manufacturer in order to avoid omitting any required operation. All parts should be perfectly clean before installation and should be coated with clean lubricant. This is particularly true of the valve lifter cylinder and plunger assembly. It is especially important to see that the pushrod socket is in place in the tappet body before the pushrod is installed.

After the complete valve-operating mechanism has been assembled, the clearance between the rocker arm and valve stem should be checked with the cylinder at TDC on the compression stroke. If the valve clearance is not within the limits specified, it must be adjusted by installing a pushrod of a slightly different length.

Upon completion of the valve mechanism installation the rocker cover is installed with a gasket and safetied. If self-locking nuts are specified, no further safetying is required.

REVIEW QUESTIONS

1. Describe the changes which take place in an aircraft engine during operation eventually making an overhaul necessary.
2. What is accomplished during an overhaul of an engine?
3. Briefly describe the organization of an overhaul shop.
4. Why is a separate inspection (quality-control) department required in an overhaul shop?
5. List the functions of a receiving inspection.
6. Discuss the need for complete records of an engine overhaul.
7. Describe the cleaning operations required during engine overhaul.
8. What precautions must be taken when stripping engine parts in a chemical stripping solution?
9. What is the principal value of grit blasting?
10. To what documents should an overhaul technician refer during the overhaul of an aircraft engine?
11. What is an *Airworthiness Directive?*
12. Briefly describe magnetic inspection.
13. Describe the process of dye penetrant inspection.
14. For what purpose is the *Table of Limits* used?
15. What instrument is used to measure the cylinder bore?
16. Describe the use of a telescoping gage, small-hole gage, and micrometer caliper.
17. What should the approximate dimension of a valve guide be compared with the hole into which it is to be installed?
18. Describe the installation of valve guides.
19. What condition requires the replacement of a valve seat?
20. How is the correct width of a valve seat obtained during the grinding process?
21. What precaution must be taken before the stem of a valve is inserted into the chuck of a refacing machine?
22. What is meant by *interference fit* of a valve face and seat?
23. What inspections are made on valve springs?
24. How are piston to cylinder-bore clearances obtained?
25. Describe the clearance checks required for piston rings.
26. What may happen if the piston-ring gap is not adequate?
27. Why is it advisable to return a crankshaft to the manufacturer for regrinding of the crankpins and main journals?
28. Describe the procedure for checking crankshaft runout.
29. What is the function of counterweights?
30. How are sludge chambers cleaned?
31. How can oil passages be checked for freedom from obstructions?
32. What conditions require the rejection of a camshaft?
33. How would you check the hydraulic unit of a valve tappet assembly for satisfactory operation?
34. List the inspections required for connecting rods.
35. Describe the procedure for checking the twist and convergence of a connecting rod.
36. What condition must be maintained when reaming or boring a connecting-rod bushing?
37. How is the clearance of connecting-rod bearings determined?
38. What should be done if it is found that one section of a two-piece crankcase must be discarded?
39. Describe the replacement of studs.
40. Explain the use of Heli-Coil inserts.
41. Discuss the replacement of bushings in the accessory section.
42. What check should be made immediately before parts are assembled?
43. Explain the proper use of safety wire.
44. Under what conditions may self-locking nuts be used on an engine?
45. What precaution must be taken with respect to the location of connecting rods during engine assembly?
46. Discuss the tightening and torquing of cylinder holddown nuts.
47. How would you check the valve clearance after an engine is assembled?

CHAPTER 15

Engine Control Systems

Purpose

The purpose of engine control systems is to provide a means by which the pilot, copilot, or flight engineer can control the engine and engine accessories from the pilot's compartment or the flight engineer's station. The modern airplane engine has many control mechanisms. Some operate the throttle, the fuel/air mixture, and the ignition, while others operate the oil-cooler shutters, the cowl flaps, etc. If all these mechanisms could be operated directly, it would be an ideal situation, but it is apparent that they must be controlled at a distance from their location.

Desirable characteristics

Each part or unit of the engine which is subject to control and each engine accessory must be controlled not only as an individual unit but also in consideration of its effect on all the other parts, units, and accessories. Therefore, engine control systems must be accurate in their manipulation, positive, reliable, and effective regardless of the distance between the controlled unit and the control in the pilot's conpartment or the flight engineer's station.

Principal types of control systems

The three general types of engine control systems are (1) **push-pull rods** with bellcranks and levers, (2) **cable and pulley systems,** and (3) **flexible push-pull wires encased in a coiled wire sheath.** Frequently aircraft-engine control systems embody combinations of the above systems. These are basic control systems. They may or may not be included in the hydraulic, electric, or electronic control systems installed in modern airplanes.

It is also possible to classify engine controls thus: (1) manually operated, (2) semiautomatic, and (3) auto-matic. The rapid advancement in engine design, the use of a higher power output in many powerplants, the installation of superchargers and turbosuperchargers, the introduction of highly controllable propellers, and the need for accurate fuel schedules in the operation of gas-turbine engines are some of the factors calling for the adoption of automatic or semiautomatic controls, although a method of manual control is almost always retained to provide for the possible failure of automatic or semiautomatic control mechanisms.

Automatic and semiautomatic control may be accomplished by hydraulic, electric, or electronic mechanisms. In this connection, the word **electronic** is distinguished from the words **electric** and **electrical** by the simple fact that any **electronic** circuit must, by definition, contain vacuum tubes or transistors. However, in the broad usage of the words, **electric** and **electrical** are words that include **electronic** devices as a lesser included subdivision of the general field.

Push-pull tube characteristics

The rods or tubing used to transmit control lever movements are generally called **push-pull rods.** The amount of force to be exerted on a push-pull rod determines its diameter and its wall thickness if it is a hollow tube, since it must withstand both compression and tension. Compression tends to increase a bend, and tension tends to decrease it; hence, bends are avoided, for if they were present, they would tend to change the length and therefore the adjustment of the mechanism under control.

Guides for rods and tubing

Guides are often provided for the tubing or rods to prevent flexing and to give them mechanical support where needed. The tubing or rod must slide through the guides smoothly and without friction, especially where the rods or tubing are long. Guides may be made of fiber, plastic, hard rubber, a composition such as micarta, or other material of similar characteristics. The plastic called Teflon makes an excellent guide because of its almost complete freedom from friction.

Types of attachment for control rods

There are four types of attachment for the ends of control rods: (1) clevis and pin, (2) ball bearing, (3) ball joint, and (4) threaded. If properly inspected and adjusted when necessary, these various rod ends will not be responsible for the so-called "give and slack" which causes much of the improper operation of control-system linkage. Clevis-rod ends may be screwed on the tube or flexible joint and locked with a jam nut. A clevis pin, washer, and cotter pin may be used to fasten the rod end to the control arm or bellcrank. When the control-tube movement is not in line with the control arm movement, a ball-joint end is used on the control tube to allow an angle (usually up to 15°) between the two parts. Screw ends permit adjusting the length of the tube by screwing it in or out. Obviously, when a tube is screwed in, it is shorter and less thread is exposed.

Figure 15·1 shows a clevis-rod end, locknuts, a push-pull control rod cut apart in the drawing to reduce the length, the threaded end of a rod, an inspection hole, and a straight beam which is sometimes called a "walking beam." It is definitely not a bellcrank.

Figure 15·2 emphasizes the bellcrank, which has two arms approximately at right angles to each other. A ball-bearing rod end is also illustrated.

Bellcranks

A **bellcrank** is a double lever or crank arm in which there are two cranks approximately at right angles to each other. The purpose of a bellcrank is to provide a means of changing the direction of motion, that is, to transmit the motion around some obstacle. For example, it may be necessary to change a forward movement to a rearward movement or to change a horizontal movement to a vertical movement. In this manner, it is possible to obtain the desired relative movement between the engine control lever in the pilot's compartment or at the flight engineer's station and the engine unit which it controls.

If the arms of a bellcrank are of equal length, the change of movement is accomplished without any gain or loss in the movement of the linkage, but if the arms are not of equal length, a gain or a loss in movement is obtained. For example, it is possible to produce a relatively great movement of an engine-unit adjustment by means of a comparatively small movement of the cockpit control. The reverse is also true. A comparatively great movement of the cockpit control may produce a relatively small movement of the engine-unit adjustment. The results obtained depend upon the original design of the bellcrank, its installation, and the way it is rigged to the engine units. Regardless of the transmission of movement, it must be supported by bearings that will reduce the friction to a minimum. Ball bearings are generally used for this purpose.

Cable-and-pulley control systems

A **pulley** is essentially a wheel, usually grooved, mounted in a frame or block so that it can readily turn upon a fixed axis. Two or more wheels may be mounted in the same frame, either on the same axis or on different axes. When two or more wheels are mounted in the same frame, the pulley is described as having two or more **sheaves.**

A single **fixed pulley** is a lever of the first class and has a mechanical advantage of only 1. A single pulley gains neither force nor speed. Its only purpose is to change the direction in which the force is applied.

A single **movable pulley** is a lever of the second class and has a mechanical advantage of 2 because its diameter is twice its radius; hence, it can be used to gain force, to gain speed, or to change direction. Pulleys can be combined in different ways to obtain various results in force, speed, and change of direction. A detailed discussion of the laws governing pulleys is beyond the scope of this text.

The installation of cable and pulley systems in a multiengine airplane is often a complicated procedure. In a single-engine airplane, where the distance between the control levers and the engine units is short, a push-pull control rod may be used, but the great distances and the need for changes of direction in a multiengine airplane make it essential to use cables and pulleys.

Figure 15·3 illustrates various types of pulley clusters. All the types illustrated and even more may be found on a typical multiengine airplane.

Pulleys for aircraft control systems are usually made of a phenolic or micarta composition, plastic, or aluminum alloy. They are often supported on antifriction bearings. Typical aircraft pulleys are shown in Fig. 15·4.

The cables are usually of flexible steel, attached to the outer edges of certain pulleys at some points in the system, guided and supported by **fairleads** (phenolic or micarta blocks with holes in them to admit the cables) at other points in the system, and also guided and supported by other pulleys which may also change the direction of the cable movement.

In some powerplant installations, the cables extend

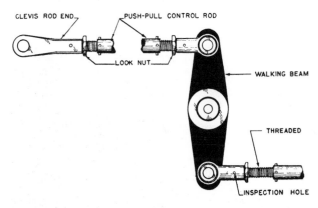

Figure 15·1   Beam and rod end.

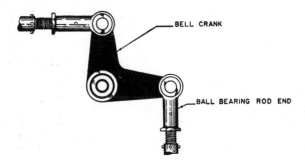

Figure 15·2   Bellcrank and rod end.

325

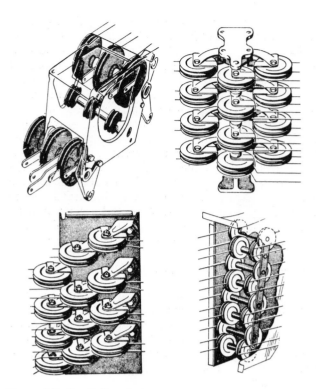

Figure 15·3   Pulley clusters.

from the control levers to the engine units, but in other installations the cables extend only from the control levers to the fire wall of each engine nacelle and are there connected to push-pull control rods that transmit the movement to the engine units.

Various devices are used for adjusting the tension and the length of the cables, such as turnbuckles, adjustable pulley clusters, and adjusting links. The manufacturer's instructions for each installation prescribe how the cables will be adjusted so that the control handles in the pilot's compartment reach their fore-and-aft stops just after the stops in the engine sections are reached.

The control quadrant

The word **quadrant** means a fourth part, usually the fourth part of a circle, or 90°. The engine **control quadrant** in an airplane is usually a control lever which pivots back and forth over a base through a 90° arc, but it also may refer to the base on which the lever is mounted. For example, the **throttle quadrant** is the base upon which the throttles are mounted in the pilot's compartment or at the flight engineer's station of a multiengine airplane. A control quadrant is shown in Fig. 15·5.

The control pedestal

The control pedestal is a frame or mount on the floor of the cockpit or pilot's compartment in a multiengine airplane where some of the engine controls are connected. The control pedestal supports one or more control quadrants. Figure 15·6 illustrates a control pedestal for a twin-engine airplane. The control quad-

Figure 15·4   Aircraft pulleys. (Tansey Aircraft Pulley Co.)

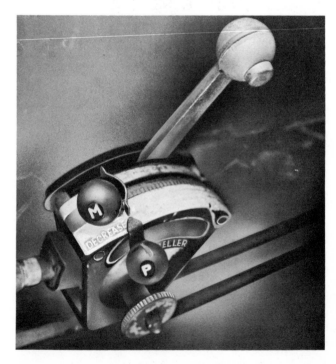

Figure 15·5   Control quadrant. (Cessna Aircraft Co.)

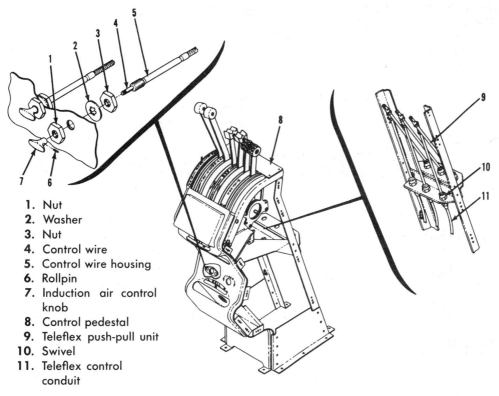

1. Nut
2. Washer
3. Nut
4. Control wire
5. Control wire housing
6. Rollpin
7. Induction air control knob
8. Control pedestal
9. Teleflex push-pull unit
10. Swivel
11. Teleflex control conduit

Figure 15·6 Control pedestal. (Cessna Aircraft Co.)

rant on this pedestal has controls for the throttle, engine rpm (propeller), and carburetor mixture.

It will be observed that the quadrant levers are attached to Teleflex push-pull cable units which are mounted so they can swivel with the movement of the lever.

Control assemblies

The control assemblies in the pilot's compartment or cockpit of a single-engine airplane are much simpler than those installed in a multiengine airplane. A single-engine airplane may have only one control quadrant, which is used to control the throttle, the fuel/air mixture, the propeller, and possibly a supercharger. Individual control levers may be provided for such powerplant accessories as the carburetor air heater, the cowling shutters, the oil-cooler shutters, and possibly the radiator in the case of a water-cooled engine.

In a multiengine airplane, the complexity of the controls installed in the pilot's compartment may make it necessary to have two or more control quadrants mounted on a control pedestal where most of the engine controls are located to afford a central point of operation for the convenience of the operator.

A pilot may sometimes observe a **springback** at either end of the control quadrant when he is testing the adjustment of the engine controls. The engine control system is then readjusted so that there will be the same amount of springback at each end of the quadrant. A small amount of springback is usually required to ensure that the unit being controlled moves through its complete range of travel.

Another problem encountered in the operation of a control quadrant is the tendency of the controls to creep out of the position in which they are placed. This is partly overcome by providing a reasonable amount of friction in the quadrant assemblies, but it is also met by mechanical locking devices, which temporarily hold the controls in the positions where they are placed by the operator until he is again ready to move them.

Flexible push-pull controls

Flexible push-pull controls are used for a variety of remote-control situations in aircraft. This is particularly true for light aircraft, where the distance through which the control must operate is not so great that friction becomes a problem.

The construction of a simple push-pull control is shown in Fig. 15·7. This control is mounted on the instrument panel and may be used for carburetor air heat, cabin heater, or other similar function. The knob is attached to a **plunger** into which a steel spring wire is secured. The plunger is inserted into the **sleeve** which serves as a guide. At the forward end of the sleeve is a threaded section and a **faceplate** to provide for mounting on the panel. The assembly is inserted through a hole in the panel and is mounted firmly by means of a locknut and washer on the rear of the panel.

The steel wire of the control is enclosed in a $\frac{3}{16}$-in. galvanized-wire casing which is in the form of a coil or

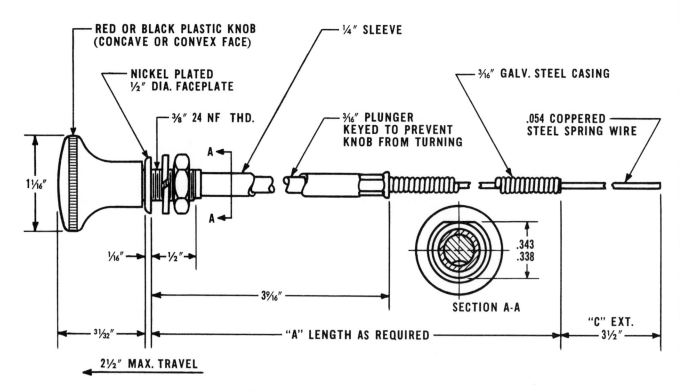

Figure **15·7** _A push-pull control._

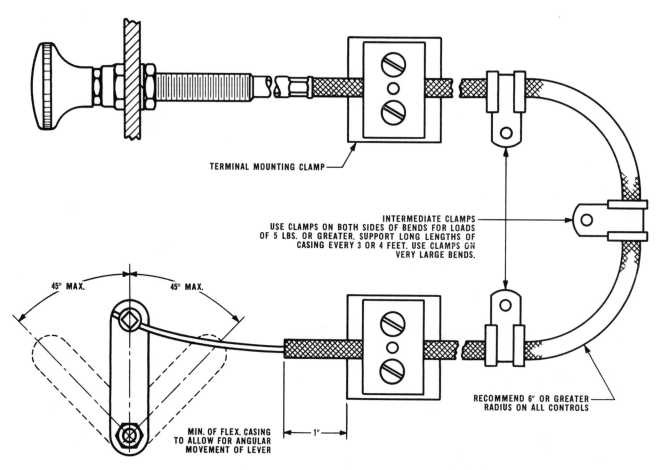

Figure **15·8** _Mounting of a push-pull control. (Ahrens Controls, Inc.)_

spiral. The casing guides the control wire to the operating mechanism.

The method by which the control should be mounted in the aircraft is shown in Fig. 15·8. Note that each end of the flexible casing is securely mounted with terminal mounting clamps so there will be no slack or play in the operation. Intermediate clamps must be used on both sides of bends to prevent flexing and a resultant loss of movement. The control should be adjusted so there is a small amount of springback at the full in position of the knob to ensure that the operated lever has moved through its full range.

Vernier push-pull control

A **vernier** push-pull control is constructed to provide for a coarse adjustment and a fine (vernier) adjustment, especially for the throttle and propeller controls. A unit of this type is shown in Fig. 15·9. When it is desired to make a fine adjustment, the plastic knob is rotated to the right for increase and to the left for decrease. To make a coarse adjustment the lock button is depressed and the knob is pushed in or pulled out. The fine adjustment is used when precise power settings are made. The approximate engine rpm is set by moving the propeller control in or out as required. Then the final adjustment is made by rotating the knob. After the rpm is set, the manifold pressure is adjusted with the throttle control, first with the coarse adjustment and then with the vernier.

Control for use with quadrant

Push-pull wire-type controls are often used with control quadrants on the pedestal. A simplified dia-gram to show how this is accomplished is shown in Fig. 15·10. The end of the control unit is connected to the arm of a quadrant lever instead of a knob. The sleeve is secured to a bracket with a swivel fitting to allow a few degrees of side movement as the quadrant lever position is changed. The engine end of the control assembly is connected to the controlled unit with a clevis or other suitable device.

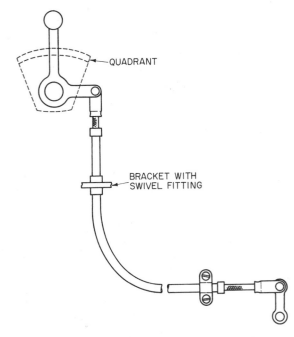

Figure **15·10** Lever-operated push-pull control.

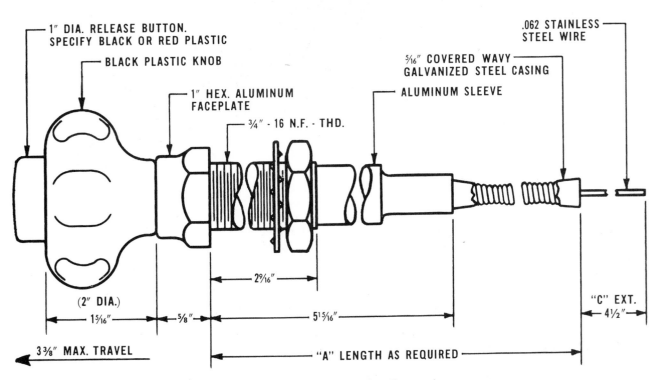

Figure **15·9** Vernier push-pull control.

Construction of a control quadrant

To illustrate the detailed construction of a control quadrant for a modern light twin airplane, an exploded view is shown in Fig. 15·11. This is the control quadrant assembly for a Cessna Model 310 airplane. The quadrant includes two levers for the throttles, two for rpm (propeller pitch) control, and two for the mixture control. Observe that spacers, washers, and

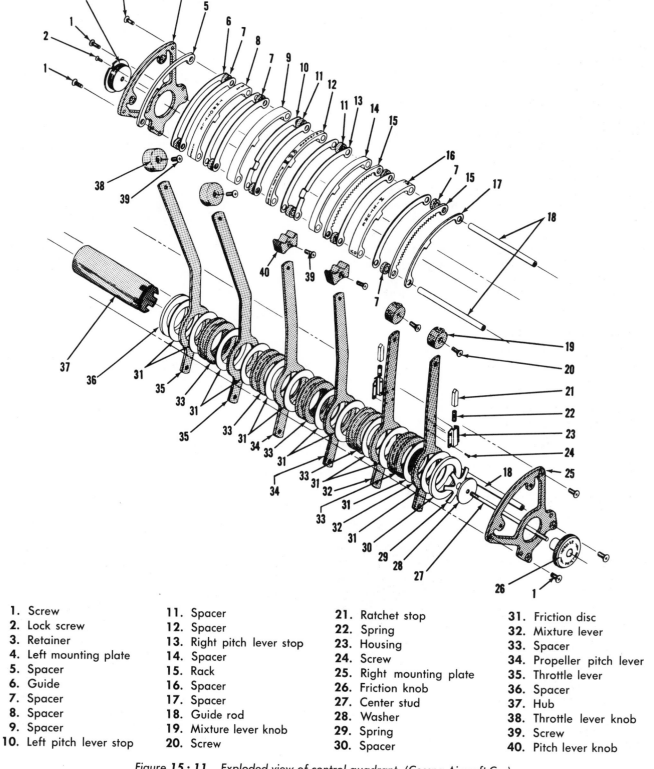

1. Screw	11. Spacer	21. Ratchet stop	31. Friction disc
2. Lock screw	12. Spacer	22. Spring	32. Mixture lever
3. Retainer	13. Right pitch lever stop	23. Housing	33. Spacer
4. Left mounting plate	14. Spacer	24. Screw	34. Propeller pitch lever
5. Spacer	15. Rack	25. Right mounting plate	35. Throttle lever
6. Guide	16. Spacer	26. Friction knob	36. Spacer
7. Spacer	17. Spacer	27. Center stud	37. Hub
8. Spacer	18. Guide rod	28. Washer	38. Throttle lever knob
9. Spacer	19. Mixture lever knob	29. Spring	39. Screw
10. Left pitch lever stop	20. Screw	30. Spacer	40. Pitch lever knob

Figure 15·11   Exploded view of control quadrant. (Cessna Aircraft Co.)

friction disks are installed between the levers to provide for friction to prevent creeping of the levers. This friction is adjusted by means of the friction knob at the right side of the quadrant.

ENGINE CONTROL FUNCTIONS

A variety of engine mechanisms require control from the cockpit of the airplane, and many of these can be controlled manually by means of the devices previously explained. We shall not attempt to explain the electrical or electronic controls often used with modern power-plants but shall confine our discussion to the units and devices controlled manually.

Throttle

The throttle control knob or lever is probably the most conspicuous of all controls, and by some persons it is considered to be the most important because it controls engine power. The throttle lever is marked with the letter T or the word **throttle,** and its direction of operation in indicated by the words **open** and **closed.** The throttle knob is a thick disk, flat on each side, to comply with the standard requirements of the FAA. Throttle movement is always such that forward movement will open the throttle valve and rearward movement will close the valve.

Propeller control

The propeller control is also of great importance in engine power adjustment for airplanes equipped with constant-speed or controllable propellers. The propeller control lever and linkage must be precise in its operation to provide for accurate control of rpm. The control lever is linked to the propeller governor, thus establishing the rpm at which the engine is to operate. Engine power is determined by the combined settings of rpm and manifold pressure in accordance with the throttle and propeller control lever positions.

The propeller control lever knob is quadrant shaped and scalloped on the top. This is to provide a distinctive shape which the pilot will quickly recognize. Forward movement of the lever will increase rpm, and rearward movement will decrease rpm.

Mixture control

The mixture-control lever on the quadrant is used to adjust the fuel/air mixture through the mixture-control lever on the carburetor or fuel-control unit. The lever positions are usually marked for FULL RICH, LEAN, and IDLE CUTOFF. Some airplanes have markings for AUTO RICH and FULL RICH to provide two rich settings. The FULL RICH setting provides a maximum rich condition which is not affected by the automatic mixture control.

The mixture-control lever is arranged so a forward movement will provide a richer adjustment. The knob on the quadrant lever is distinctively shaped for recognition. It is a thick disk like the throttle knob; however, it has a raised diamond pattern on the periphery.

Carburetor air heat

The control lever or knob for the carburetor air heat may or may not be mounted on the pedestal. It is usually not a lever of the type used for the previously described controls but may be a push-pull knob on the front of the pedestal or on the instrument panel. The function of this control is to operate a gate valve in the air induction system to provide either cold air or heated air for the carburetor. Heated air is required for the engine when there is danger of carburetor icing.

Miscellaneous engine controls

In addition to the controls described in the foregoing paragraphs, engines may require several other controls depending upon the design of the engine and aircraft. Among others are controls for the cowl flaps, oil coolers, superchargers, and intercoolers. All such controls must be marked to show their functions and must be easily accessible to the pilot.

ENGINE CONTROL SYSTEMS FOR LARGE AIRCRAFT

The engine control systems for large aircraft are rather complex; however, they utilize cable and pulley mechanisms in much the same manner as those for smaller aircraft. To provide an example of large aircraft control systems we shall describe the throttle (thrust lever) system of the Boeing 720 jet airliner.

General description

The Boeing 720 airliner is equipped with four separate engine throttle systems to provide for individual control of each engine. The starting of each engine is accomplished by the use of a single lever to energize the ignition system and to initiate the flow of fuel to the engine. Another lever assembly controls both forward and reverse thrust by regulating fuel flow and actuating the thrust reverser. An interlocking mechanism prevents simultaneous initiation of forward and reverse thrust for each engine.

The throttle system consists of an engine start lever and a thrust lever assembly for each engine, connected by a series of throttle-control cables and mechanical linkages to the fuel-control units on the engine. This system is illustrated in Fig. 15·12. A thrust lever friction brake applies a braking force to all thrust lever assemblies during forward thrust operation.

The engine start lever is connected by cables to an engine control drum-and-shaft assembly in a nacelle strut. The arrangement of this assembly and the associated linkages is shown in Fig. 15·13. The drum-and-shaft assembly is connected by a rod and bellcrank installation on the right side of the engine to the fuel-control unit. Advancing the engine start lever actuates an ignition switch to energize the ignition system. Further movement of the start lever opens a pilot shutoff valve in the fuel-control unit.

The thrust lever assembly is connected by cables to the drum-and-shaft assembly as shown in the illustra-

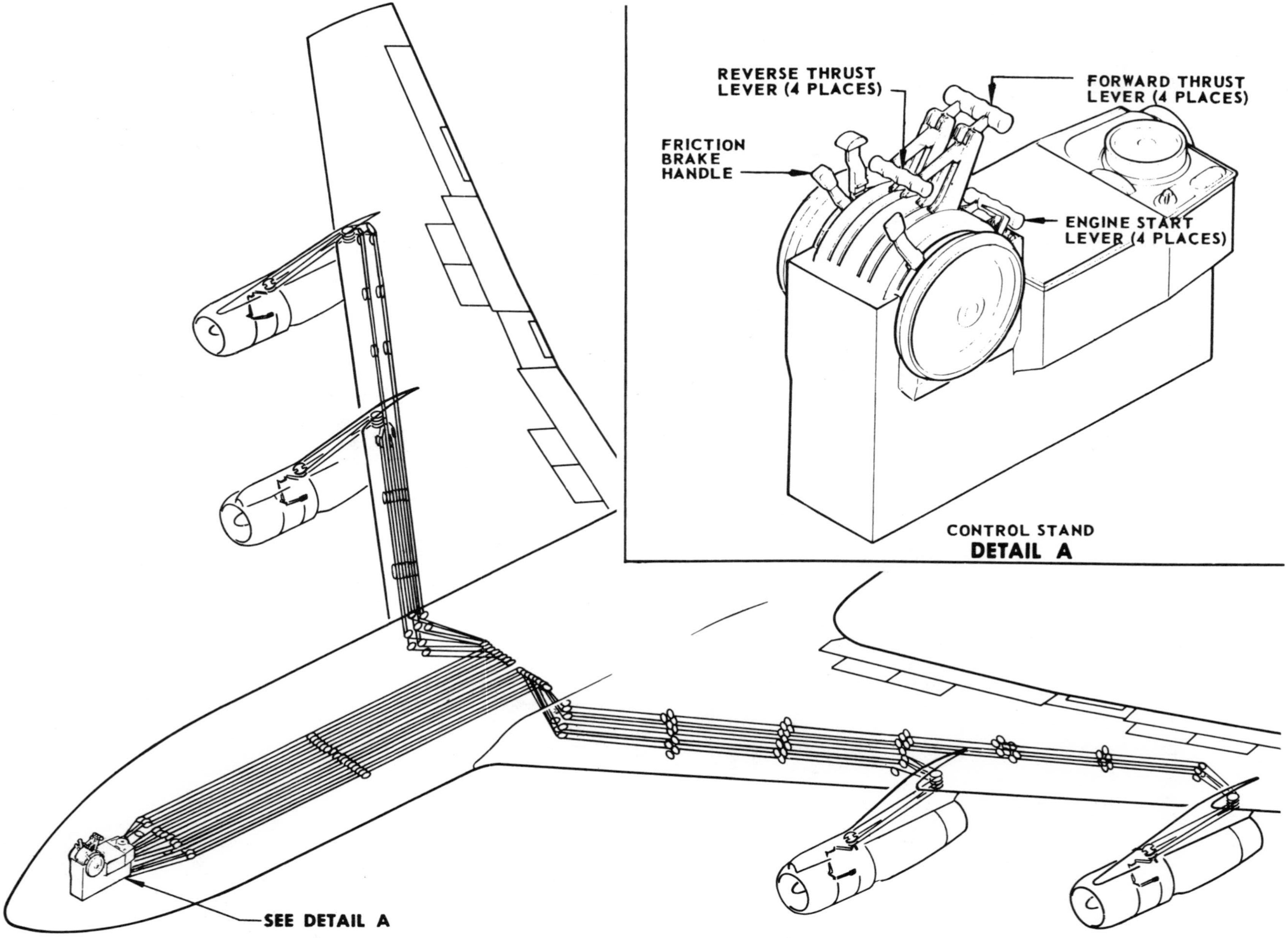

FORWARD THRUST
LEVER (4 PLACES)

ENGINE START
LEVER (4 PLACES)

REVERSE THRUST
LEVER (4 PLACES)

FRICTION
BRAKE
HANDLE

CONTROL STAND
DETAIL A

SEE DETAIL A

Figure 15·12 Throttle system for jet airliner. (The Boeing Co.)

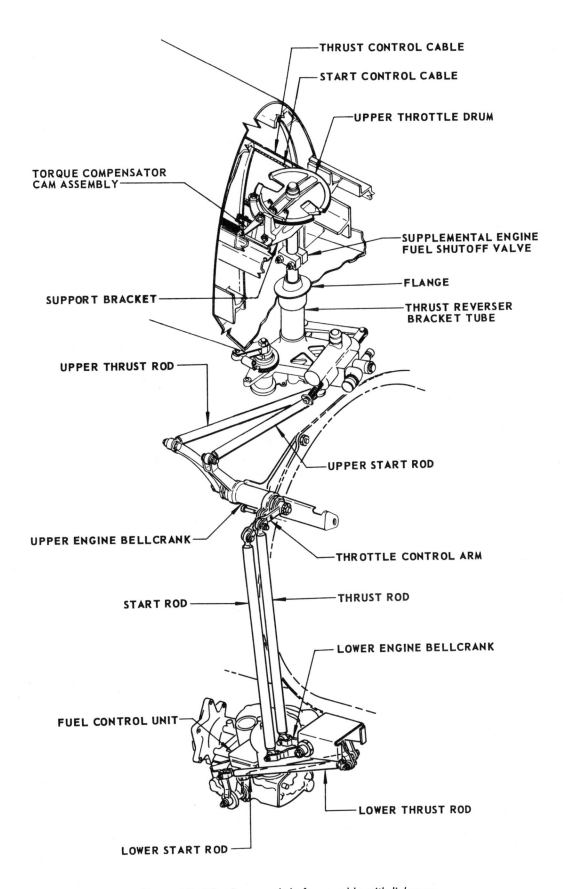

THRUST CONTROL CABLE

START CONTROL CABLE

UPPER THROTTLE DRUM

TORQUE COMPENSATOR CAM ASSEMBLY

SUPPLEMENTAL ENGINE FUEL SHUTOFF VALVE

FLANGE

SUPPORT BRACKET

THRUST REVERSER BRACKET TUBE

UPPER THRUST ROD

UPPER START ROD

UPPER ENGINE BELLCRANK

THROTTLE CONTROL ARM

START ROD

THRUST ROD

LOWER ENGINE BELLCRANK

FUEL CONTROL UNIT

LOWER THRUST ROD

LOWER START ROD

Figure 15·13   Drum-and-shaft assembly with linkages.

tion. Movement of the thrust lever is therefore transmitted through the bellcrank and rod linkages to the fuel-control unit.

Actuation of the thrust lever assembly regulates fuel flow in the fuel-control unit, subject to the automatic limiting features incorporated in the unit. For reverse thrust, the lever assembly movement actuates the thrust reverser before increasing fuel flow. It should be noted that the direction of travel of the thrust-control cables and drums is the same for decreasing forward thrust as it is for increasing reverse thrust.

Thrust lever assembly

Four thrust lever assemblies on the control stand (pedestal) quadrant control the forward and reverse thrust of the engines. Each thrust lever assembly consists of a forward thrust lever, a reverse thrust lever, a reverse thrust-control link, a pawl, a brake drum, and a thrust-control drum. The forward thrust lever, with the reverse thrust lever attached to it, is mounted on the brake drum. One end of the control link is riveted to the reverse thrust lever, and the opposite end is attached to the thrust-control drum. Various positions of the assembly are shown in Fig. 15·14.

As either thrust lever is advanced from the idle position, the control link rotates the thrust-control drum to actuate the fuel-control unit to increase thrust. The forward thrust idle position is against an idle stop on the quadrant, and full forward thrust is obtained before the lever is all the way forward. The reverse thrust lever, when in the idle position, is against an idle stop on the forward thrust lever.

An interlock mechanism prevents simultaneous actuation of the forward and reverse thrust levers to ensure positive forward or reverse thrust control. The ability of each lever to move depends on the position of the other lever. If the forward thrust lever is more than 2° from the idle position, the reverse thrust lever cannot be moved more than 12° from idle. However, if the reverse thrust lever is advanced more than 12° from idle, the forward thrust lever cannot be moved. The interlock between the levers is a pawl riveted to the forward thrust lever with the pawl between the thrust lever and the control link. When the forward thrust lever is 2° or less from the idle position, the pawl is aligned with a lockout hole in the web of the thrust lever cover. As the reverse thrust lever is moved from the idle position, the control link forces the pawl into the hole to lock the forward thrust lever in the idle position. As the reverse thrust lever is returned to the idle position, the control link pushes the pawl from the hole to unlock the forward thrust lever. When the forward thrust lever is more than 2° from the idle position, the pawl is not aligned with the lockout hole. The web then opposes the force of the control link on the pawl so that the reverse thrust lever cannot be moved more than 12° from idle.

Engine start levers

Four engine **start levers** on the control stand quadrant are used to start the engines. Each lever controls ignition and fuel as explained previously. The start lever is provided with a spring-loaded detent catch which may be released by lifting the knob. The detent secures the lever in the CUTOFF and IDLE positions. An additional detent is provided between these two positions. This catch is provided to ensure that a throttle left insecurely in the IDLE position will not creep to the CUTOFF position and cause an unintentional engine shutdown. A stop gate and detent are provided at the START position.

Throttle-control cables

The throttle-control cables are 7 by 7, ³⁄₃₂-in., flexible steel with standard swaged attachment fittings and Boeing Aircraft fittings. They serve as thrust and start cables to connect the fuel-control unit on each engine to the respective engine start lever and thrust lever assembly. The cables are routed under the floor from the control stand through the lower nose compartment and above the forward cargo compartment ceiling. From the cargo compartment the cables are routed along the wing leading edge to the nacelle struts. In each strut the cables are routed to the drum-and-shaft assembly, which is linked to the fuel-control unit.

Thrust lever friction brake

A thrust lever friction brake on the control stand quadrant applies a variable braking force to all thrust levers during forward thrust operation. The friction brake is used to select manually the proper amount of braking force in order to prevent throttle creep during flight. The friction brake consists of a brake handle mechanically linked to two leaf springs and four brake shoes.

The brake handle, mounted to the right of the thrust levers, is connected by a brake link and an eyebolt to a brake crank. Bolted to the crank are the leaf springs and the brake shoes. As the brake handle is advanced, friction between the brake shoes and the brake drums is increased. A ratchet locks the brake handle in any position.

Engine control drum-and-shaft assembly

The engine control drum-and-shaft assembly in the nacelle strut of each engine is a mechanical link in the throttle system which provides for independent control of the fuel-control unit by the thrust and engine start levers. The assembly consists of concentric engine start and thrust-control shafts, a thrust-control drum, engine start drum, engine thrust-control crank, and an engine start crank. These are illustrated in Fig. 15·13. The start drum and the start crank are mounted on each end of the engine start shaft. The thrust drum and thrust crank are mounted on each end of the thrust-control shaft, which is mounted inside the start shaft. The assembly is supported by a bracket on the strut aft of the forward engine mount. The start lever contacts the strut bracket to provide a mechanical stop for the engine start control system at cutoff. A lug on the strut bracket provides a stop for the thrust system at both 100 percent forward and reverse thrust.

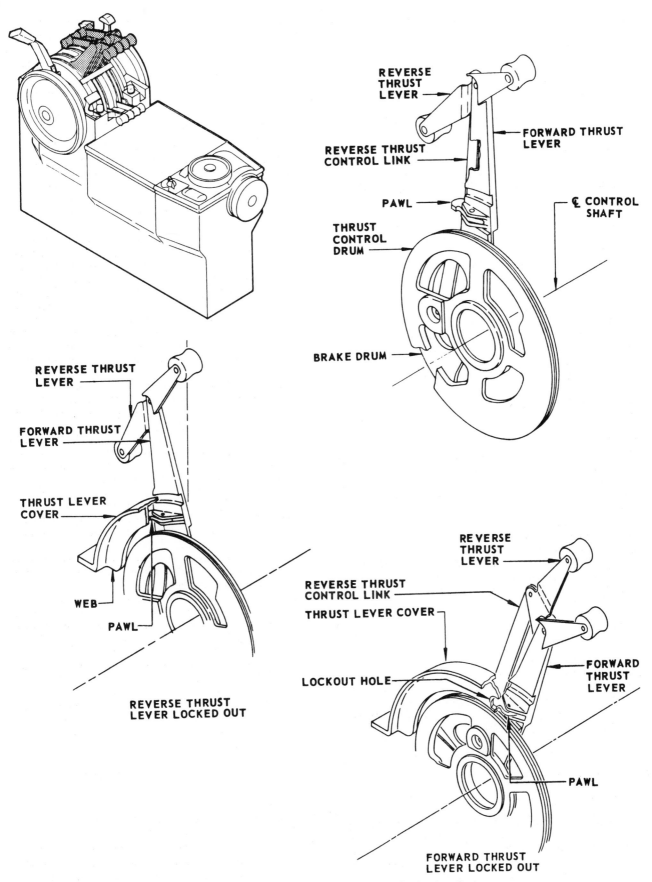

REVERSE THRUST LEVER

REVERSE THRUST CONTROL LINK

PAWL

THRUST CONTROL DRUM

FORWARD THRUST LEVER

₵ CONTROL SHAFT

BRAKE DRUM

REVERSE THRUST LEVER

FORWARD THRUST LEVER

THRUST LEVER COVER

WEB

PAWL

REVERSE THRUST LEVER LOCKED OUT

REVERSE THRUST LEVER

REVERSE THRUST CONTROL LINK

THRUST LEVER COVER

LOCKOUT HOLE

FORWARD THRUST LEVER

PAWL

FORWARD THRUST LEVER LOCKED OUT

Figure 15·14   *Thrust lever assembly. (The Boeing Co.)*

INSPECTION AND MAINTENANCE

Rods and tubing

1. Operate the system slowly, and watch for evidence of any strain on the rods and tubing that will cause bending or twisting.
2. Examine each rod end that is threaded, and observe whether or not the rod is screwed into the socket body far enough to be seen through the inspection hole.
3. Eliminate any play by making certain that all connections are tight.
4. Examine the guides to see if the rods bind too much on the guides, but do not mistake any binding for springback. Reinstall any guides that cause binding.
5. Adjust the length of screw-end rods by screwing into the control end or backing out. Retighten the locknuts.
6. If any rod is removed, mark it to show its location on reassembly.
7. Replace any ball-bearing rod ends that cause lost motion.

Bellcranks

1. Examine for security of mounting, wear, and the proper lubrication.
2. Replace any bellcrank bearings that are causing lost motion.
3. Mark each part that is removed, and reassemble in the correct order.

Cables

1. Inspect for frayed or broken cables.
2. Clean the cables where they pass through fairleads or over pulleys, and then cover them with the prescribed rust preventive.
3. Maintain the correct tension constantly, not merely at the prescribed inspection intervals. Use a tensiometer to obtain an accurate reading of the cable tension, and check it against the approved tension given in the manufacturer's instructions.
4. Inspect all turnbuckles, adjusting links, and other devices used to maintain tension in the cables. Safety such devices after each adjustment.
5. If any cables are removed, mark them to show their location in the system. When new cables are installed, apply any required code markings in the same manner as they were on the original cables.

Pulleys

1. Inspect each pulley to be sure that it is properly mounted and securely fastened.
2. Operate the system to observe how the cables pass through the pulleys. Where necessary, adjust or replace to obtain the proper clearance and tension. Correct any misalignment.
3. Check pulley bearings or bushings for excessive play, and replace pulleys in which the bearings are found to be defective. Pulleys which do not have prelubricated bearings or impregnated bushings should be lubricated with oil.

Flexible push-pull controls

1. Inspect push-pull controls for wear and smoothness of operation.
2. If controls stick or are hard to operate, disconnect the control wire or cable from the controlled unit and pull the wire out of the casing or conduit. Clean all grease, rust, or dirt from the wire, and lubricate it with low-temperature grease. If it appears that the casing contains dirt or rust, it can be cleaned by pushing a cleaning wire through it two or three times.

3. Inspect the casing for damage at bends or where abrasion may have occurred. Replace casings which are broken or badly worn.
4. Lubricate the plungers and sleeves with oil or other lubricant specified in the maintenance manual.
5. Adjust the travel of the control to allow the amount of springback required for the controlled unit.

Miscellaneous inspections

1. Examine the control unit in the cockpit or pilot's compartment or at the flight engineer's station for free operation, for the correct travel of the control levers through their extreme range of movement, for security of mounting, and for lost motion.
2. With a helper at the control unit in the pilot's compartment, go to the point of application of each of the engine controls and check there for any lost motion while the helper operates the control levers. Then, while the helper continues to operate the control levers slowly, trace back each control system to the control unit in the pilot's compartment, observing each subordinate part or unit en route.
3. Throughout all control systems, look for proper safetying, broken or misaligned pulleys, missing or loose nuts or bolts, dirty connections, and lack of lubrication. Either remedy each defective condition as it is found, or record it on a check sheet and then remedy the unsatisfactory conditions in a systematic manner; that is, you may accomplish all the lubrication jobs in one session, etc.
4. All through the engine control system, examine for any play. Be sure that all mounting bolts, shaft bolts, rods, check nuts, etc., are tight.

    Having accomplished an inspection with the engines stopped, operate the engines and check all the controls for each engine, one engine at a time. When this is done, check the operation with all engines operating.
5. Pay particular attention to the adjustment of the throttle levers, especially in a multiengine airplane. They should be together at equal positions of the throttle valves in the carburetors. This may require an individual adjustment of each throttle valve.
6. Check the fuel/air mixture control system to be certain that it operates in accordance with the prescribed limits given in the manufacturer's instruction book.
7. Operate the carburetor air heating system, and check the controls carefully to be certain that all play is eliminated. See that the carburetor air-heater valve in the carburetor intake is tightly closed when the control lever is in the OFF, CLOSED, or COLD position. Be sure that hot air does not leak past the valve and mix with the cold air in the induction system, leading to loss of engine power and increased fuel consumption.
8. Review the "squawk sheets" filled out by the flight crew for the past several flights, and be certain that all defects have been remedied.

REVIEW QUESTIONS

1. Define the purpose of engine control systems.
2. Name three basic types of engine control systems.
3. Describe the components of a push-pull rod system.
4. What means is used to prevent the flexing of long rods?
5. Name the types of attachments for push-pull rod systems.
6. What condition requires the use of pulley and cable systems?
7. Describe a typical pulley used in a control system.

8. What method is used to support long cables between pulleys?
9. Describe a control quadrant.
10. Why is a control pedestal employed in multiengine aircraft?
11. Why are controls rigged to allow **springback** in the control lever?
12. How are the control levers prevented from creeping during operation?
13. Describe a flexible push-pull control.
14. What are the requirements for mounting a flexible push-pull control in an airplane?
15. What is meant by **vernier** as applied to a push-pull control?
16. What engine systems or devices are usually controlled from the cockpit?
17. Briefly describe the throttle-control system for a typical jet airliner.
18. Name the principal points of inspection for a push-pull rod system.
19. What inspections should be given cables?
20. Describe service and maintenance for flexible push-pull controls.
21. How can the technician be certain that threaded rod end fittings have sufficient thread engagement?

CHAPTER 16

Engine Installation, Test, Inspection, and Troubleshooting

TYPES OF INSTALLATION

Since the engine installation for an airplane depends upon the type of airplane and the type of engine installed, specific instructions cannot be given which will cover all installations. Types of engine installations include (1) radial engines, (2) horizontal engines, (3) in-line air-cooled engines, (4) in-line water-cooled engines, (5) turboprop engines, and (6) turbojet engines. Within each of these classifications are a number of different configurations, so it is obvious that the airplane manufacturer's instructions must be followed in each case.

For conventional reciprocating engines there are many similarities in engine installation, and for the purposes of this chapter we shall confine the discussion to the general practices to be observed for radial and opposed-type engines. Examples of procedures to be employed with specific engines will be given to emphasize the details involved.

ENGINE INSTALLATION

Preparation for installation

If an engine has been stored in an engine case, special instructions relating to unpacking the engine will usually be included in the case. The case should

be placed in the correct position (top side up) so the engine case cover can be lifted off. After the attaching bolts are removed, the cover is carefully lifted to avoid damage to the engine.

If the engine has been properly preserved and packed to prevent corrosion damage while moving from the factory overhaul shop to the purchaser, it will be sealed in a plastic envelope. The magnetos will probably be mounted on the engine together with the ignition harness. The carburetor may be in a separate package within the case.

The engine will be bolted to the supports built into the case, and it will be necessary to remove bolts and other attachments before the engine can be removed. The technician in charge of unpacking the engine must exercise great care to prevent damage and the loss of small parts. He should first locate all paper work such as overhaul records and unpacking instructions and then proceed according to instructions.

When the engine cover is removed, a hoist should be attached to the lifting eye and sufficient tension placed on the hoisting cable to remove most of the weight from the mounting brackets. The mounting bolts should then be removed, and the engine hoisted and placed on a suitable stand. This is necessary because there are usually a number of fittings and parts which must be assembled to the engine before it is ready to be installed in the airplane.

When the engine is firmly mounted on the stand, all shipping and preservative plugs are removed. These plugs, with the exception of drain plugs, should be replaced immediately with the proper fitting for engine operation. Fittings include oil pressure fitting, manifold pressure fitting, crankcase vent fitting, oil-temperature bulb fitting, and others. The desiccant plugs should be removed from the spark-plug holes and from the oil sump. At this time the engine should be rotated a few times to permit drainage of the preservative oil.

New spark plugs and washers of the correct type should be installed, and the plugs should be tightened to the following torques: 14-mm plugs, 200 to 245 in.-lb; 18-mm plugs, 260 to 300 in.-lb. Before the spark plugs are installed, a small amount of approved anti-seize thread lubricant should be applied to the upper threads of the plugs. Care must be taken to prevent thread lubricant from getting on the electrodes of the spark plugs.

When fittings having pipe threads are installed, the threads of the fittings should be lightly coated with an approved thread lubricant and the fittings should be installed with proper torque to prevent damage to the threads.

Following installation of the spark plugs the ignition

harness elbows are attached to the plugs. Care must be taken to insert the sleeves ("cigarettes") into the spark plugs in good alignment to prevent damage. The elbow nuts are then screwed into place by hand until finger-tight. After this they are torqued only enough to prevent them from turning during operation. Excessive torque will bend and collapse the spark-plug elbows.

If the carburetor is of the pressure type and has been packed and preserved separately, it is necessary to "condition" it before placing it in operation. This is accomplished as follows: Remove the inlet strainer and all plugs leading to fuel chambers, and drain all the preserving oil from the carburetor. Wash the inlet strainer in clean fuel, and replace it. Also, replace the plugs.

With the throttle lever in the WIDE-OPEN position and the manual mixture control in the FULL-RICH position, inject clean fuel through the fuel inlet connection at the proper pressure for the carburetor until clean fuel flows from the discharge nozzle. Close the throttle, and place the manual mixture control in the IDLE CUTOFF position. Disconnect the fuel supply line, and install a plug in the fuel inlet to retain the fuel in the carburetor. Permit the carburetor to soak with the fuel for at least 8 hr before placing it into service.

During the preceding operation care must be taken to see that fuel does not enter the air sections of the diaphragm chambers.

Before the engine is installed in the airplane, it should be inspected thoroughly. Both the engine manual and the airplane manual should be consulted to make sure that all fittings, baffles, and accessories are securely fastened and safetied as necessary. A careful check at this time may save much time and trouble later.

Installation in the airplane

The installation of the engine in the airplane should follow the directions given by the manufacturer. An example of the instructions given for the installation of an engine in a light twin airplane is given here to show the details of a typical operation. These instructions are given in the manufacturer's manual for the Cessna 310 airplane. Reference numbers are omitted.

a. Hoist the engine to a point just above the nacelle.
b. Install the IO-470-D engine on engine mounts as follows:
   1. Temporarily install mount pads, spacers, and pins to all four engine mounts using AN7-24 bolts and suitable washers. See that the pins are in a position which will align them with the slots at the side of the holes in the engine mount brackets.
   2. Be certain that the propeller control conduit and bracket are outside the engine mounts.
   3. Lower the engine slowly into place on the engine mount brackets.
   4. Remove the temporary bolts and washers. Install the spacer, mount pad, washer, and bolt. Torque the bolts to 40 ±3 lb-ft.
c. Fasten the engine ground strap to the left aft engine mount bracket.
d. Connect wires and cables as follows:

1. Attach the wire bundle to the right manifold intake pipe with three clamps and the generator cables to the left intake manifold pipe with two clamps.
2. Route the oil temperature wires forward along the right side of the engine, below the cylinders and behind the intake manifold pipe. Use a sump attachment bolt to attach a clip to the engine crankcase. Fasten the oil temperature wires to this clip with a wire clamp. Attach the connector to the oil temperature bulb, located directly below the oil cooler, and safety. Connect the ground wire to the nacelle just below the forward right engine mount bracket.
3. Route the magneto ground wires forward through the right rear engine baffle.

WARNING: *These magnetos DO NOT have internal grounding springs. Ground the magnetos to the crankcase to prevent accidental firing. DO NOT connect the aircraft ground wires to the magnetos at this time.*

4. Connect the starter cable to the starter.
5. Attach the tachometer generator electrical connector to the tachometer generator, and safety.
6. Route the cylinder-head temperature bulb wires forward along the left side of the engine, below the cylinders and behind the intake manifold pipe. Install the cylinder-head temperature bulb in No. 4 cylinder. Attach the cylinder-head temperature bulb ground wire to the nacelle just below the left aft engine mount bracket.
7. Attach the generator cables to the generator. Ground the generator cable shielding to the lower stud of the air-oil separator bracket.
8. Attach the wiring at the radio noise filter.
9. Attach the wiring at the fuel pressure switch.
e. Connect lines and hoses as follows:
   1. Connect the crankcase breather line.
   2. Connect the vacuum line to the vacuum pump.
   3. Connect the air-oil separator exhaust line at the air-oil separator.
   4. Connect the fuel vapor return line and fuel pressure gage line to the fuel/air control unit.
   5. Connect the manifold pressure hose and the two manifold drain lines.
   6. Route the oil pressure hose aft through the lightening hole in the canted bulkhead, and attach to the oil pressure fitting at the inboard nacelle rib. Fasten the oil pressure hose to the canted bulkhead with a clamp.
   7. Connect the fuel-pump supply line at the fuel pump.
   8. Connect the ram air tube at the fuel strainer shroud, and clamp.

Note: If anti-ice and/or oil-dilution systems are installed, connect the anti-ice hose at the fitting below No. 1 cylinder and connect the oil-dilution hose at the crankcase fitting just below the fuel pump.

f. Attach the propeller-control bracket with two clamps. Connect the propeller control at the governor. Rig the propeller control in accordance with appropriate instructions.
g. Connect the induction air control, the mixture control, and the throttle control. Rig these controls as directed in the pertinent section of this manual.
h. Install the exhaust stack centering springs.
i. Install the propeller in accordance with propeller instructions.
j. Connect the battery cable.
k. Inspect the installation for safeties, loose connections, missing bolts, clamps, screws, or nuts; for proper routing of cables, hoses, and lines; and for correct connection.
l. Make a magneto switch ground-out and continuity check. Connect the magneto ground wires to the magnetos.

m. Service the engine in accordance with lubrication instructions.

n. Install the engine cowling.

Installation inspection

After an engine installation is completed, it is required that a complete installation inspection be made. The following check list names the inspections to be accomplished after the installation of the IO-470-D engine in the Cessna 310 airplane:

1. Propeller mounting bolts safetied
2. Engine mounts secure
3. Oil temperature bulb electrical connector secure and safetied; ground wire connection tight
4. Oil pressure-relief valve plug safetied
5. Tachometer generator electrical connector secure and safetied
6. Starter cable connection secure and insulating boot in place.
7. Cylinder-head temperature bulb installed and ground wire connection tight
8. Generator cable connections secure and cable shielding grounded
9. All wiring securely clamped in place
10. Fuel-pump connections tight
11. Manifold pressure hose connections tight
12. Oil pressure connections clamped and tight
13. Fuel-injection nozzles tight
14. Fuel-injection lines clamped and tight
15. Fuel manifold secure
16. All flexible tubing in place and clamped
17. Crankcase breather line connections secure
18. Air-oil separator exhaust line and return oil hose connections secure
19. Vacuum line and vacuum-pump outlet hose connections secure
20. Oil-dilution hose connections tight
21. Propeller anti-ice hose connections tight
22. Engine controls properly rigged
23. Oil drain plugs tight and safetied
24. Oil quantity check, 12 qt in each engine
25. Hoses and lines secure at fire wall
26. Fuel/air control unit and air-intake box secure
27. Shrouds installed on engine-driven fuel pump, fuel filter, and fuel-control unit; ram air tubes installed and clamped
28. Induction system clamps tight
29. Exhaust system secure
30. Spark plugs tight, ignition harness connections tight, and harness properly clamped
31. Magneto ground wires connected and safetied
32. Engine nacelle for loose objects (tools, rags, etc.)
33. Cowling and access doors for security

The foregoing listings of instructions for a specific engine and airplane are given to emphasize the many important details involved in engine installation. The installer and the inspector must follow the check lists to make sure that no operation is left incomplete.

Installation in the test stand

If an engine has just been overhauled but has not been tested and run-in as required, it should be installed in a suitable test stand and run in according to the test schedule to make sure that it is operating to specifications. Small engines are sometimes run in on an airplane, but the standard run-in procedure must be modified to some extent if this is done.

An engine test stand should be mounted in a test cell equipped with necessary controls, instruments, and special measuring devices required for fuel consumption, power output, oil consumption, heat rejection to the oil, and standard engine performance data. The following instruments and devices will usually be required:

1. Fuel tank with adequate capacity (at least 50 gal)
2. Oil tank with capacity of 10 gal or more
3. Fuel flowmeter
4. Scales for weighing oil
5. Cylinder-head temperature gages
6. Manifold pressure gage
7. Tachometers (one which counts revolutions)
8. At least two oil temperature gages (inlet and outlet)
9. Fuel pressure gage
10. Oil pressure gage
11. Manometer to test crankcase pressure
12. 12-volt battery or other power source
13. Fuel pressure pump, either manual or electrical
14. Engine test propeller
15. Magneto switch
16. Suitable starter controls
17. Control panel for mounting instruments and controls
18. An accurate clock for checking run-in time
19. Throttle control
20. Mixture control

The control room of the test cell should be provided with a safety-glass window located so the operator has a good view of the engine during the run-in procedure. The safety-glass window should be adequate to prevent any flying object from entering the control room. The area in which the engine is installed should be protected with gates or doors to prevent personnel from entering the propeller area while the engine is running; however, provision must be made for the operator to gain access to the rear part of the engine in order to make necessary adjustments.

The actual installation of the engine in the test stand depends partly upon the design of the test stand. The following installation steps may be considered typical.

1. See that the test stand is equipped with all items necessary for testing the make and model of engine to be installed.
2. Hoist the engine into place, and align mounting brackets.
3. Install mounting bolts, washers, lock washers, and nuts. Tighten the nuts to proper torque.
4. Install short exhaust stacks with gaskets to cylinder exhaust ports.
5. Connect the fuel-supply line to the engine-driven pump inlet or to the carburetor as required. Make sure the supply pressure is correct for the carburetor or fuel unit. The pressure will vary for gravity-fed float-type carburetors, pump-fed float-type carburetors, injection carburetors, or direct fuel-injection units.
6. Connect the oil supply and return lines if the engine is the dry-sump type.

7. Attach cylinder-head temperature-sensing units (thermocouples or temperature bulbs) as required.
8. Connect the magneto switch wires to the magnetos.
9. Connect the pressure line for the oil pressure gage.
10. Connect the pressure line for the fuel pressure gage.
11. Connect the oil temperature gage line (electric or capillary).
12. Connect the manifold pressure line.
13. Connect the throttle control.
14. Connect the mixture control.
15. Connect the electric cable to the starter.
16. Connect the tachometer cable or electric lines as required.
17. Install a suitable cooling shroud for the engine.
18. Install the test propeller (test club). Make sure that the test propeller is of the correct rating for the engine being tested.
19. Service the engine with the proper grade of lubricating oil. If the engine is to be stored for a time after the test, use a preservative-type lubricating oil.
20. Perform a complete inspection of the installation to make sure that all required installation procedures have been completed.

ENGINE TEST AND RUN-IN

Preoiling

Before the engine is actually started for the first time, it should be preoiled to remove trapped air in oil passages and lines and to make sure that all bearing surfaces are lubricated.

Preoiling can be accomplished in several ways, one of these being the use of a pressure oil container. With this method, the oil pressure unit is connected to the oil inlet line for the engine. Oil under pressure (about 20 psi) is then applied to the inlet while the engine is rotated through several turns with the starter. This is continued until a generous flow of oil comes from the oil **out** line. Prior to preoiling, one spark plug should be removed from each cylinder to reduce the load on the starter. The engine should not be rotated with the starter for periods longer than 30 sec.

If an oil pressure tank is not available, the engine may be preoiled by connecting the normal test-cell oil supply to the engine inlet after making sure that the line from the tank to the engine is free of air. It will be necessary to rotate the engine more than is required with the pressure tank; however, preoiling can be accomplished satisfactorily in this manner.

Starting procedure

Before the engine is actually started, the engine area should be checked for loose objects which could be picked up by the propeller. The engine itself should be checked for tools, nuts, washers, and other small items which may be lying loose.

The following steps are typical of engine starting in the test cell:

1. Turn on the master power switch.
2. Turn on the fuel pump, and check the fuel pressure.
3. Open the throttle about one-tenth of the total distance.

4. Press the starter switch, and allow the engine to turn through three or four revolutions.
5. Turn the magneto switch onto the magneto having the impulse coupling or induction vibrator.
6. Place the mixture control into FULL RICH position.
7. As soon as the engine starts running smoothly, adjust the throttle for the desired rpm, usually 1000 rpm or less for a newly overhauled engine.
8. Immediately check for oil pressure. If oil pressure does not register within 30 sec, shut down the engine and check for the trouble.
9. If the engine operates properly, shut off the fuel booster pump.
10. As soon as the engine is operating smoothly, turn the magneto switch off **momentarily** in order to determine whether the engine can be shut off with the switch in case of emergency.
11. If the engine is operating satisfactorily, continue with the test run as specified by the manufacturer. The following instructions are given for the testing of a Lycoming GSO-480 engine:

A log should be kept, and the instrument readings recorded every 15 min. The log sheet should also include the date of the test, the engine number, the type and nature of the test, along with the total number of hours of engine operation. All periods during the test run when the engine was not in operation should be recorded, along with the reason. If for any reason it should be necessary to replace any part, the complete reason for the rejection of the part should also be recorded.

Oil-consumption run

An oil-consumption check run may be made at the end of the test if desired in the following manner: Record the oil temperature. Stop the engine in the usual manner. Place a previously weighed container under the external oil tank, and remove the drain plug. Allow the tank to drain for 15 min. Replace the drain plug. Weigh the oil and container. Record the weight of oil (i.e., total weight less weight of container). Replace the oil in the tank. Start the engine, warm up to 2600 rpm ±20, and operate at this speed for 1 hr. At the conclusion of 1 hr of operation and with the oil temperature the same as recorded at the time of previous draining (it is important to keep this oil temperature as constant as possible), again drain the oil in the same manner as before. The difference in oil weights at the start and at the end of the run will give the amount of oil used during 1-hr operation. The oil consumption for 1 hr on an overhauled engine with new rings installed should not exceed 1 lb for GO-480-D engines, 1.5 lb for GO-480-C1B6 and -G1B6 engines, 1.8 lb for GSO-480 engines, and 2 lb for IGSO-480 engines.

Run-in test schedule

The manufacturer's overhaul manual provides a run-in schedule to be followed for newly overhauled engines. The schedule for a Lycoming GSO-480 engine is given in Table 16·1.

It will be observed that the manifold pressure shown

Table 16·1   Run-in test schedule

RPM	Manifold pressure, in. Hg	Time, min
1000	14.0–14.5	15
1200	14.5–15.0	15
1400	15–16	15
1600	16–17	15
1800	17–18	15
2000	18–19	30
2200	21–22	30
2400	24–25	15
2600	27–28	15
2800	31–33	15
3000	38–40	30
3200	43–45	30
2200	21–22	**
2600 ± 20*	27–28	60

* Oil consumption check—1 hr mandatory, 2 to 3 hr recommended.

** Check magneto dropoff, which should not exceed 100 rpm on either magneto.

in the run-in test schedule of Table 16·1 reaches values well above atmospheric pressure. This is because the GSO-480 engine is equipped with a supercharger. An unsupercharged engine will seldom exceed 27.5 or 28 in. Hg manifold pressure.

ENGINE PRESERVATION

If an engine is to be stored for a time after having been run in, it should be preserved against corrosion. This is particularly important with respect to the interior of cylinders, where the products of combustion will start corrosion of the bare cylinder walls within a very short time.

Preservation run-in

As previously mentioned, an engine which is to be stored should be run in with a preservative oil as the lubricant. In addition, if possible, the last 15 min of operation should be done with clear (unleaded) gasoline at about two-thirds of full rpm. This will tend to remove the accumulation of corrosive residues which are in the cylinders and combustion chambers.

Interior treatment

Upon completion of the run-in, all necessary adjustments of valves, magneto timing, and other operations which will require turning of the crankshaft should be accomplished before preservation is begun. The engine can then be started and idled, using clear gasoline, while preservative oil is sprayed into the carburetor inlet. The spray should not be heavy enough to choke the engine and should continue only until heavy white smoke issues from the exhaust. The engine should then be shut down immediately.

When the engine is stopped, the preservative oil should be drained from the crankcase or the sump. Spark plugs are then removed from the cylinders, and preservative oil is sprayed into the cylinders as the engine is rotated, several times for each cylinder. The rotation can be accomplished with the starter.

After all cylinders have been sprayed, dehydrator plugs are installed in the spark-plug holes and in the sump drain. The dehydrator plugs will absorb the moisture within the engine, thus reducing the tendency for the interior to corrode.

The short exhaust stacks should be removed, and preservative oil sprayed into the exhaust ports. The ports should then be covered with metal plates and gaskets to seal them against moisture.

Exterior treatment

All openings into the engine should be sealed with air-tight plugs or with waterproof tape. If the carburetor is removed for separate preservation, a dehydrator bag can be placed in the carburetor opening before it is sealed. The bag should be tied to an exterior fitting so it can be easily removed when the engine is prepared for operation.

After the engine is completely sealed, it may be sprayed lightly with preservative oil or other approved coating. If the engine is to be stored for as long as 6 months, it should be sealed in a waterproof plastic bag. The bag is first placed over the mounting bolts in the engine case, and the engine is installed in the case with the mounting bolts sticking through the bag. The bag is sealed at the engine mounting bolts when the bolts are tightened.

After a number of dehydrator bags are placed in the bag with the engine, the bag should be sealed according to the directions furnished. An indicator is also placed in the bag with the desiccant exposed through a window to show when the humidity level in the bag has reached a point where it is necessary to represerve the engine. When the desiccant loses its blue color and begins to turn pink, the preservation is no longer effective.

Inspection after storage

When an engine is removed from storage after having been preserved, certain inspections should be made to ascertain that it has not been damaged by corrosion. The exterior inspection consists of a careful examination of all parts to see if corrosion has taken place on any bare metal part or under the enamel. Corrosion under enamel will cause the enamel to raise in small mounds or blisters above the smooth surface.

Interior inspection should be accomplished in all areas where it is possible to insert an inspection light. The most vulnerable area is inside the cylinders where the bare steel of the cylinders has been exposed to the combustion of fuel. Inspection of the cylinders is accomplished by removing the spark plugs from the cylinders and inserting an inspection light in one of the spark-plug holes. The inside of the cylinder can then be seen by looking through the other spark-plug hole. If rust is observed on the cylinder walls, it is necessary to remove the cylinder and dispose of the rust. If the cylinder walls are badly pitted, it will be necessary to regrind the cylinders and install oversize pistons and rings.

The rocker box covers should be removed to inspect for corrosion of the valve springs. Pitted springs will be likely to fail in operation owing to stress concentrations caused by the pitting.

When the exhaust port covers are removed to permit installation of the exhaust stacks, the ports and the valve stems can be examined for corrosion. A small amount of corrosion on the cast aluminum inside the exhaust port is not considered serious; however, if the valve stem is rusted, the rust must be removed or the valve replaced.

PREFLIGHT INSPECTION

In order to provide an example of an actual preflight engine-check procedure recommended by a manufacturer, the following instructions are taken from the owner's handbook for the Piper PA-23-160, Model G, light twin airplane.

Preflight

Before each flight, visually inspect the airplane, and/or determine that:

1. The tires are satisfactorily inflated and not excessively worn.
2. The landing-gear oleos and shock struts operate within limits.
3. The propellers are free of detrimental nicks.
4. The ground area under the propeller is free of loose stones, cinders, etc.
5. The cowling and inspection opening covers are secure.
6. There is no external damage or operational interference to the control surfaces, wings, or fuselage.
7. The windshield is clean and free of defects.
8. There is no snow, ice, or frost on the wings or control surfaces.
9. The tow bar and control locks are detached and properly stowed.
10. The fuel tanks are full and are at a safe level of proper fuel.
11. The fuel-tank caps are tight.
12. The fuel-system vents are open.
13. The fuel strainers and fuel lines are free of water and sediment by draining all fuel strainers once a day.
14. The fuel tanks and carburetor bowls are free of water and sediment by draining sumps once a week.
15. There are no obvious fuel or oil leaks.
16. The engine oil is at the proper level.
17. The brakes are working properly.
18. The radio equipment is in order.
19. The weather is satisfactory for the type of flying you expect to do.
20. All required papers are in order and in the airplane.
21. Upon entering the airplane, ascertain that all controls operate normally, that the landing gear and other controls are in proper position, and that the door is locked.

Starting

Before starting the engine, the pilot should set the parking brake and turn on the master switch and the electric fuel pumps. Each pump should be individually checked for operation. When the engine is cold (under 40°F), prime three to five strokes, making sure fuel valves are on, cross-feed off, fuel pressures normal, and fuel quantity checked. Push mixture controls to FULL RICH, carburetor heat off, and open throttles about ¼ in. If the engines are extremely cold, they should be pulled through by hand four to six times.

Next turn all ignition switches on and engage starter on left engine first. After the engine starts, idle at 800 to 1200 rpm and start the right engine. If the battery is low, before starting the right engine, run the left engine over 1200 rpm to cut in the generator. This will produce extra power for starting the right engine. If the engine does not start in the first few revolutions, open the throttle on that engine while the engine is turning over with the ignition on. When the engine starts, reduce the throttle.

If the above procedure does not start the engine, reprime and repeat the process. Continue to load cylinders by priming or unload by turning the engine over with the throttle open. If the engine still does not start, check for malfunctioning of the ignition or fuel systems.

Priming can be accomplished by pumping the throttle controls. However, care must be used because excessive pumping may overprime the engine, making starting difficult.

When the engines are warm (over 40°F), do not prime but turn the ignition switches both on before engaging the starter. The engines should start after rotating through about four compression strokes.

Warm-up and ground check

As soon as the engines start, the oil pressure should be checked. If no pressure is indicated within 30 sec, stop the engine and determine the trouble.

Warm up the engines at 800 to 1200 rpm for not more than 2 min in warm weather or 4 min in cold weather. If electrical power is needed from the generator, the engines can be warmed at 1200 rpm, at which point the generator cuts in. The magnetos should be checked at 2000 rpm with 15 in. Hg MP, the drop not to exceed 125 rpm. The engines are warm enough for takeoff when the throttles can be opened without the engine faltering.

Carburetor heat should be checked during the warm-up to make sure the heat-control operation is satisfactory and to clear out the carburetor if any ice has formed. It should also be checked in flight occasionally when outside-air temperatures are between 20 and 70° to see if icing is occurring in the carburetor. In most cases when an engine loses manifold pressure without apparent cause, the use of carburetor heat will correct the condition.

The propeller controls should be moved through their normal ranges during the warm-up to check for proper operation, then left in the full low pitch (high-rpm) positions. Full feathering checks on the ground are not recommended because of the excessive vibration caused in the powerplant installations. However, feathering action can be checked by momentarily pulling the propeller controls into the feathering position and allowing the rpm to drop not lower than 1500, then returning the controls to a normal operating position.

The electric fuel pumps should be turned off after starting or during warm-up to make sure that the engine-driven pumps are operating. Prior to takeoff the electric pumps should be turned on again to prevent loss of power during takeoff due to fuel-pump failure.

Stopping the engine

Aircraft engines are today usually equipped with carburetors or fuel-control units having an IDLE CUTOFF control by which the fuel flow into the engine may be stopped. After a flight and a few minutes of taxiing, the engine can usually be stopped almost immediately by placing the mixture control in the IDLE CUTOFF position. If the engine is exceptionally hot as indicated by the cylinder-head temperature gage and the oil-temperature gage, it is good practice to allow the engine to idle for a short time before shutdown.

After the engine is stopped, the magneto switch should be placed in the OFF position and all other switches should then be turned off.

ENGINE TROUBLESHOOTING

A good understanding of engine theory and the function of all parts and systems is essential to skillful engine troubleshooting. Engine operational malfunctions can usually be traced to one or more of three basic causes. These are (1) ignition malfunctions, (2) fuel-system malfunctions, and (3) engine parts malfunctions. We shall consider each of these types of malfunction separately.

Ignition malfunctions

Ignition troubles may be traced to defective magnetos, defective transformers in a low-tension system, improper timing, spark plugs which are burned or otherwise damaged, poor insulation on the high-voltage leads, short-circuited or partially grounded primary or switch (P) leads, burned breaker points, or loose connections.

Missing at high speeds. Misfiring of the engine at high speeds can be caused by almost all the foregoing defects in varying degrees. If the engine is operating at high speeds and high loads, the manifold pressure and the cylinder pressure will be high. As previously explained, it requires more voltage at the spark-plug gap to fire the plug when the pressure at the gap is increased. This means that at high engine loads the ignition voltage will build up higher than at low engine loads. This higher voltage will seek to reach ground through the easiest path, and if there is a path easier to follow than through the spark-plug gap, the spark plug will not fire and the spark will jump through a break in the insulation or it may follow a path where dampness has reduced the resistance.

If the airplane is operating at high altitudes, the high-voltage spark will be still more likely to leak off the high-tension leads instead of going through the spark plug. The lower air pressure at high altitudes permits the spark to jump a gap more readily than it will at the higher pressure near sea level.

A weak breaker-point spring will also cause misfiring at high speeds. This is because the breaker points do not close completely after they are opened by the cam. This condition is called **floating points** because the cam follower actually does not maintain contact with the cam but "floats" at some points between the cam lobes.

Engine fails to start. If the engine will not start, the trouble can be in a defective ignition switch. Since aircraft engines have dual ignition systems, it is rare that both systems would become inoperative at the same time. It is possible, however, that, in some magneto switches, both magnetos could be grounded through a short circuit inside the switch.

If it is the recommended practice to start the engine on one magneto only and the engine will not start, an attempt should be made to start the engine on the other magneto. If the cause of the trouble is in the first magneto system, the engine will fire on the other magneto.

The checking of magnetos during engine test will usually reveal malfunctions in one magneto or the other before a complete failure occurs. The defective magneto can then be removed and repaired before serious trouble occurs.

Defective spark plugs. Defective spark plugs are usually detected during the magneto check. If one spark plug fails, the engine rpm will show an excessive rpm drop when it is checked on the magneto supplying the defective plug. The bad plug may be located by the "cold-cylinder" check. This is accomplished as follows: Start and run the engine for a few minutes on both magnetos. Perform a magneto check, and determine which magneto indicates a high rpm drop. Stop the engine, and let it cool until the cylinders can be touched without burning the hand. Start the engine again, and operate on the one magneto for which the high rpm drop was indicated. Run the engine for about 1 min at 800 to 1000 rpm, and then shut it down. Immediately feel all cylinders with the hand, or use a "magic wand" to determine which is the cold cylinder. This cylinder will have the defective spark plug. The magic wand is a temperature gage operated by means of a thermocouple on the end of the wand. When the thermocouple is placed against the cylinder, a temperature indication is produced on the dial of the instrument.

The foregoing procedure for locating a defective spark plug is particularly important for a large engine having 14 to 18 cylinders. The time and expense involved in removing and replacing all the spark plugs to correct one defective plug can be avoided by pinpointing the defective plug through a cold-cylinder check.

FUEL SYSTEM TROUBLES

Indication	Cause	Remedy
Engine will not start.	No fuel in tank. Fuel valves turned off. Fuel line plugged. Defective or stuck mixture control. Pressure discharge nozzle valve diaphragm ruptured. Primer system inoperative.	Fill fuel tank. Turn on fuel valves. Starting at carburetor, check fuel line back to tank. Clear obstruction. Check carburetor for operation of mixture control. Replace discharge nozzle valve. Repair primer system.
Engine starts, runs briefly, then stops.	Fuel-tank vent clogged. Fuel strainer clogged. Water in the fuel system. Engine fuel pump inoperative or defective.	Clear the vent line. Clean fuel strainer. Drain sump and carburetor float chamber. Replace engine-driven fuel pump.
Black smoke issues from exhaust. Red or orange flame at night.	Engine mixture setting too rich. Primer system leaking. At idling speed, idle mixture too rich. Float level too high. Defective diaphragm in pressure carburetor.	Correct the fuel/air mixture adjustment. Replace or repair primer valve. Adjust idle mixture. Reset carburetor float level. Replace pressure carburetor.

Fuel-system troubles

Fuel systems, carburetors, fuel pumps, and fuel-control units can cause a wide variety of engine malfunctions, some of which may be difficult to analyze. A thorough understanding of the system and its components is essential if the technician hopes to resolve the problems of a particular system effectively. The chart shown above lists some of the most common problems encountered with fuel systems and suggests remedies.

The foregoing chart does not cover all symptoms which may develop with fuel systems and carburetors because of the many different designs involved. The technician, in each case, should analyze the type of system upon which he is working and make himself familiar with the operation of the carburetor or fuel-control unit used in the system.

Oil-system troubles

Oil-system troubles are usually revealed as leaks, no oil pressure, low oil pressure, high oil pressure, and high oil consumption. The correction of oil leaks is comparatively simple in that it involves tracing the leak to its source and then applying the indicated repair procedure. If oil has spread over a large area of the engine, it is sometimes necessary to wash the engine with solvent and then operate it for a short period to find the leak.

A check for oil pressure when an engine is first started is always a standard part of the starting procedure. If the oil pressure does not show within about 30 sec, the engine is shut down. Lack of oil pressure can be caused by any one of the following conditions: no oil in the tank; no oil in the engine oil pump, hence no prime; an air pocket in the oil pump; an oil plug left out of a main oil passage; an inoperative oil pump; an open pressure-relief valve; a plugged oil-supply line; or a broken oil line. If a condition of no oil pressure exists, the technician should start with the most likely cause first and then check each possibility until the trouble is located.

Low oil pressure can be caused by a variety of discrepancies including the following: oil pressure-relief valve improperly adjusted, broken oil relief valve spring, sticking pressure-relief valve, plug left out of an oil passage, defective gasket inside the engine, worn oil pressure pump, worn bearings and/or bushings, dirty oil strainer, excessive temperature, wrong grade of oil, and leaking oil-dilution valve. The cause of low oil pressure is often more difficult to ascertain than some of the other oil problems; however, a systematic analysis of the problem by the technician will usually lead to a solution. One of the first questions that the technician must ask is, "Did the condition develop gradually, or did it show up suddenly?" He should also check to see how many hours of operation the engine has had. Another most important consideration is the actual level of the oil pressure. If it is extremely low, the technician will look for an "acute" condition, and if it is only slightly low, the likely cause will be different.

High oil pressure can be owing to only a few causes. These are improper setting of the relief valve, sticking relief valve, improper grade of oil, low temperature of oil and engine, and plugged oil passage. The cause can usually be located easily except in the case of a newly overhauled engine where a relief valve passage may be blocked.

High oil consumption is usually the result of wear or leaks. If blue oil smoke is emitted from the engine breather and exhaust, it is most likely that the piston rings are worn with the result that blowby occurs. The pressure built up in the crankcase causes the oil spray inside the crankcase to be blown out the breather. The worn rings will also allow oil to pass the piston and enter the combustion chamber, where it is burned. This, of course, produces blue smoke at the exhaust. Another cause of high oil consumption is a worn master rod bearing in a radial engine. This permits an excessive amount of oil to be sprayed from the bearing and into the cylinder bores. If the scavenger pump is defective, the oil will not be removed from the sump as rapidly as required, and this also will lead to excessive oil consumption.

Operating an engine at high power settings and high temperatures will increase the oil consumption. If an apparently normal engine is using more oil than it should, the pilot should be questioned regarding his operation of the engine in flight.

Backfiring

The condition known as **backfiring** occurs when the flame from the combustion chamber burns back into the intake manifold and ignites the fuel/air mixture before it enters the engine. It often occurs when starting a cold engine because of poor (slow) combustion. The fuel/air mixture in the cylinder is still burning at the time the intake valve opens and the flame burns back through the intake valve. This sometimes causes a fire in the induction system.

Any defect in the carburetor or fuel-control system which causes an excessively lean mixture can lead to backfiring. If the condition is persistent after an engine is warmed up, it will be necessary to follow a systematic procedure to locate the cause.

Another cause of backfiring is sticking intake valves. This does not usually occur with a new or newly overhauled engine but is likely to be encountered with an older engine which is operated at high temperatures. If a sticking intake valve remains open, it can cause the engine to stop and may cause considerable damage to the induction system.

Ignition troubles often cause backfiring. If high-tension current leaks at the distributor block, it can cause firing of plugs out of time with the result that the mixture may fire in a cylinder when the intake valve is open. If a newly overhauled engine is being started for the first time and backfiring persists, the technician should check for ignition timing and for proper connection of the spark-plug leads. Ignition out of time can also cause afterfiring through the exhaust.

Afterfiring

Afterfiring is the burning of fuel/air mixture in the exhaust manifold after the mixture has passed through the exhaust valve. It is characterized by explosive sounds as well as large flames trailing outward from the exhaust stacks (torching). Afterfiring is usually caused by excessive fuel (rich mixture) in the exhaust to the extent that the fuel continues to burn after the mixture leaves the cylinder. The condition may be caused by overpriming, excessively rich mixture, poor ignition, and improper timing. Since there are comparatively few causes for afterfiring, the condition is usually easy to correct.

Compression testing

Since engine compression is a primary factor in the proper operation of an engine and its ability to develop full power, the technician will be called upon from time to time to check the compression of engine cylinders. The procedure is not difficult, but it does require that the technician have a good understanding of the procedure to be followed.

The compression test reveals whether the valves, piston rings, and pistons are adequately sealing the combustion chamber. If leakage of pressure is excessive, it is obvious that the cylinder cannot develop its full force.

A simple method for checking the compression of the cylinders for small engines is "pulling through" the propeller. First the engine should be operated until it is thoroughly warmed up. Immediately after stopping the engine (ignition switch off), the propeller is pulled through and the back pressure of each cylinder is noted. The person pulling the propeller stands clear of the blades so he cannot be injured if the engine should happen to fire. An experienced technician can feel any appreciable difference in the compression of the cylinders. If the compression for any cylinder seems to be weak, the exhaust stacks are checked for a hissing sound as the propeller is rotated. If such a sound is heard, it is known that an exhaust valve is leaking.

If only one cylinder shows poor compression, it will probably be advisable to correct the trouble by making the repair required. To determine which cylinder has weak compression, one spark plug is removed from No. 1 cylinder. The thumb is then placed over the spark-plug hole, and the engine is rotated until pressure on the thumb indicates that the piston is approaching TDC on the compression stroke. This fixes the position of the crankshaft with respect to firing order. The engine is then rotated, and the number of each cylinder in the order of firing is noted as back pressure on the propeller indicates that it is passing the compression stroke. The number noted when the weak cylinder reaches the compression stroke indicates the cylinder to be repaired.

In some cases the weak compression is caused by a valve which has an accumulation of carbon on the stem and is therefore not closing completely. This condition can sometimes be corrected by removing the rocker box cover and tapping the valve-stem end of the rocker arm sharply with a soft hammer to remove the carbon from the stem or the valve seat. The success of the operation is checked by pulling the engine through. If the valve still leaks, it will be necessary to remove the cylinder and recondition the valves and seats.

The compression of large engines is usually checked by means of a **compression tester.** This is a device which applies a controlled air pressure to the cylinder through a spark-plug hole so the leakage can be determined by comparing the readings of two gages. The procedure for checking the compression of a cylinder is as follows:

1. Warm up the engine to operating temperature.
2. Remove the front spark plug from the cylinder to be checked, and place the piston of the cylinder at TDC on the compression stroke.
3. Connect the compression tester to an air-pressure source of 100 to 120 psi.
4. Install the cylinder pressure line fitting into the spark-plug hole. Attach the air-pressure line to the fitting in the cylinder.
5. Have two men hold the propeller blade so the piston will remain at TDC position.
6. Adjust the pressure regulator of the compression tester to show the correct pressure (about 80 psi) on the fixed pressure gage.
7. Open the air valve slowly to allow time for the men holding the propeller to make sure that the piston is at TDC. If the piston is not at TDC, the propeller will tend to turn because of the air pressure on the piston.
8. Turn the air valve full on, and note the reading of the cylinder pressure gage. The difference between this pressure and the pressure of the fixed pressure gage will show the amount of leakage from the cylinder. If the difference in pressure exceeds that shown in the table for the engine, the cylinder should be repaired.

The compression tester employed in the foregoing procedure operates on the principle of pressure differential across a metering orifice as shown in the diagram of Fig. 16·1. If a regulated pressure of 80 psi is applied on one side of the orifice and there is no leakage on the other side of the orifice, both pressure gages will read 80 psi. However, as leakage increases on the cylinder side of the orifice, the cylinder pressure gage reading will decrease. When the difference between the two readings exceeds a certain value, the cylinder compression is considered unsatisfactory.

It must be noted that the procedure for checking cylinders with compression testers may vary to some extent, depending upon the design of each tester. The procedure described in this section is to provide an understanding of how the operation is accomplished and is not to be used with a particular tester unless it happens to agree with the instructions for the tester being employed.

REVIEW QUESTIONS

1. List the essential steps in unpacking and removing an engine from the shipping case.

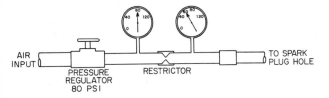

Figure 16·1 Diagram to illustrate the principle of a compression tester.

2. Describe a general procedure for removing an engine from preservation and placing it in service.
3. What torque should be used for the installation of 14-mm spark plugs? 18-mm plugs?
4. Describe the installation of a fitting having pipe threads.
5. After a pressure-type carburetor has been in preservation, what treatment should be applied to it before service?
6. What inspections should be made following an engine installation?
7. What information should be obtained during the engine test run in a test cell?
8. Describe the preoiling procedure for a newly overhauled engine.
9. List the steps in a typical engine starting procedure.
10. Describe a method for preservation of an engine after it has been run in on a test stand.
11. Why is unleaded gasoline useful in engine preservation?
12. What material is used to remove moisture from inside the engine?
13. What sections of the engine should be inspected for rust after a long period of storage?
14. What should be done if an engine is overprimed during an attempt to start?
15. What important check must be made immediately after an engine is started?
16. If the battery is found to be low after starting one engine on a twin-engine airplane, how can the other engine be started?
17. Describe the procedure for checking magnetos.
18. How can you check the feathering system for the propeller?
19. When should carburetor heat be checked?
20. Why should electric fuel pumps be turned on during take-off?
21. When a carburetor is equipped with an *idle cutoff*, what is the procedure for shutting down the engine?
22. List six ignition malfunctions.
23. What are the likely causes when an engine misfires at high speed?
24. Why is an engine more likely to misfire at high altitudes than at sea level?
25. Describe the procedure to be followed if an engine will not start owing to a fuel-system discrepancy.
26. What may be the trouble if an engine starts, runs briefly, and then stops?
27. What condition causes black smoke to be emitted from the engine exhaust?
28. What condition causes blue or whitish smoke to be emitted from the engine exhaust and the engine breather?
29. List five possible causes for low oil pressure.
30. List five causes for high oil pressure.
31. Explain the reasons for backfiring.
32. What damage can be caused by backfiring?
33. If an engine which has been running normally suddenly begins to backfire violently, what is the likely cause?
34. Explain the reasons for afterfiring.
35. Describe a simple method for checking the compression of a small aircraft engine.
36. Describe the use of a compression tester for a large engine.

CHAPTER 17

Propeller Fundamentals

DESCRIPTION AND NOMENCLATURE

The **aircraft propeller** normally consists of two or more blades and a central hub by means of which the blades are attached to a shaft driven by the engine. The purpose of the propeller is to pull the airplane through the air. It does this by means of the thrust obtained by the action of the rotating blades on the air.

Nomenclature

In order to explain the theory and construction of propellers, it is necessary first to define the parts of various types of propellers and give the nomenclature associated with propellers. Figure 17·1 is a fixed-pitch one-piece wood propeller designed for light aircraft. Note carefully the **hub, hub bore, bolt holes, neck, shank, blade, tip,** and **metal tipping.** These are the common terms applied to a wood propeller.

The cross section of a propeller blade is shown in Fig. 17·2. This drawing is shown to illustrate the **leading edge** of the blade, the **trailing edge,** the **cambered side** or **back,** and the **flat side** or **face.** From this illustration it is apparent that the propeller blade has an airfoil shape similar to that of an airplane wing.

Since the propeller blade and the wing of an airplane are similar in shape, each blade of an aircraft propeller may be considered as a rotating wing. It is true that it is a small wing, which has been reduced in length, width, and thickness, but it is still a wing in shape. At one end this midget wing is shaped into a shank, thus forming a propeller blade. When the blade starts rotating, air flows around the blade just as it flows around the wing of an airplane, except that the wing, which is approximately horizontal, is lifted upward while the blade is "lifted" forward.

The nomenclature for an **adjustable** or **ground-adjustable** propeller is illustrated in Fig. 17·3. This is a metal propeller with two blades clamped into a steel **hub assembly.** The hub assembly is the supporting unit for the blades, and it provides the mounting structure by which the propeller is attached to the engine propeller shaft.

The propeller hub is split on a plane parallel to the plane of rotation of the propeller to allow for the installation of the blades. The blade **root** consists of machined ridges which fit into grooves inside the hub. When the propeller is assembled, the sections of the hub are held in place by means of **clamping rings** secured by means of bolts. When the clamping ring bolts are properly tightened, the blade roots are held rigidly so the blades cannot turn and change the **blade angle.**

Figure 17·4 shows two views and various cross sections of a propeller blade. The **blade shank** is that portion of the blade which is near the butt of the blade. It is usually thick to give it strength, and it is cylindrical where it fits the hub barrel, but the cylindrical portion of the shank contributes little or nothing to thrust. In an attempt to obtain more thrust, some propeller blades are designed so that the airfoil section (shape) is carried all the way along the blade from the tip to the hub. In other designs, the airfoil shape is carried to the hub by means of blade **cuffs,** which are thin sheets of metal or other material, which function like cowling as shown in Fig. 17·5.

In the illustration of Fig. 17·4 the tip section, the center of the hub, and the **blade butt** are shown. The **blade butt** or **base** is merely the end of the blade which fits into the hub.

Figure 17·1   Fixed-pitch one-piece wood propeller.

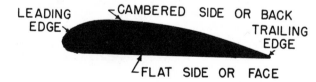

Figure 17·2   Cross section of a propeller blade.

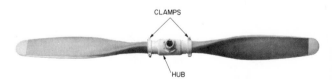

Figure 17·3   A ground-adjustable propeller.

TIP
SECTION

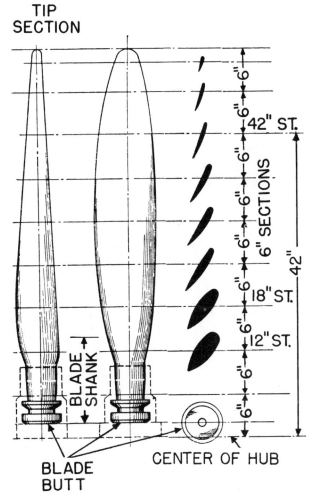

BLADE
BUTT

CENTER OF HUB

Figure 17·4   Propeller blade showing blade construction and sections.

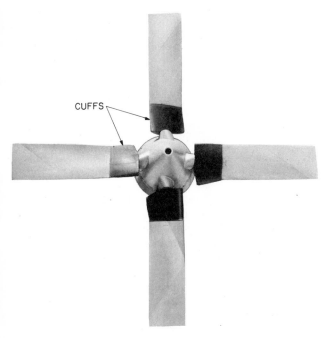

CUFFS

Figure 17·5   Propeller with blade cuffs.

The blade-element theory

The first satisfactory theory for the design of aircraft propellers was known as the **blade-element theory.** This theory was evolved in 1909 by a Polish scientist named **Dryewiecki;** hence, it is sometimes referred to as the **Dryewiecki theory.**

This theory assumes that the propeller blade from the end of the hub barrel to the tip of the propeller blade is divided into various small, rudimentary airfoil sections. For example, if a propeller 10 ft in diameter has a hub 12 in. in diameter, then each blade is 54 in. long and can be divided into fifty-four 1-in. airfoil sections. Figure 17·6 shows one of these airfoil sections located at a radius r from the axis of rotation of the propeller. This airfoil section has a span of 1 in. and a chord C. At any given radius r, the chord C will depend upon the plan form or general shape of the blade.

According to the blade-element theory, the many airfoil sections, or **elements,** being joined together side by side, unite to form an airfoil (the blade) that can create thrust when revolving in a plane about a central axis. Each element must be designed as part of the blade to operate at its own best angle of attack to create thrust when revolving at its best design speed.

The thrust developed by a propeller is in accordance with Newton's third law of motion: **For every action, there is an equal and opposite reaction, and the two are directed along the same straight line.** In the case of a propeller, the first action is the acceleration of a mass of air to the rear of the airplane. This means that, if a propeller is exerting a force of 200 lb to accelerate a given mass of air, it is, at the same time, exerting a force of 200 lb tending to "pull" the airplane in the direction opposite that in which the air is accelerated. That is, when the air is accelerated rearward, the airplane is pulled forward. The quantitative relationships among mass, acceleration, and force can be determined by the use of the formula for Newton's second law: $F = ma$, or **force is equal to the product of mass and acceleration.** This principle is discussed further in the chapter explaining the theory of jet propulsion.

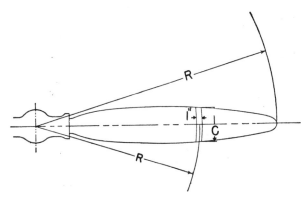

Figure 17·6   The blade element of a propeller.

349

A **true pitch propeller** is one that makes use of the blade-element theory. Each element (section) of the blade travels at a different rate of speed, and hence the tip sections travel faster than the sections close to the hub. When the elements (sections) are arranged so that each is set at the proper angle to the relative airstream, they all advance the same distance during any single revolution of the propeller.

Blade stations

Blade stations are designated distances along the blade as measured from the center of the hub or from some reference line marked near the tip. In Fig. 17·4 the stations are measured from the center of the hub. If a blade is divided into 6-in. intervals, as it is in this case, the 6- to 12-in. blade section is between the 6- and 12-in. stations; the 12- to 18-in. blade section is between the 12- and 18-in. stations; etc.

This division of a blade into sections separated by stations provides a convenient means of discussing the performance of the propeller blade, locating blade markings, finding the proper point for measuring the blade angle, and locating antiglare areas.

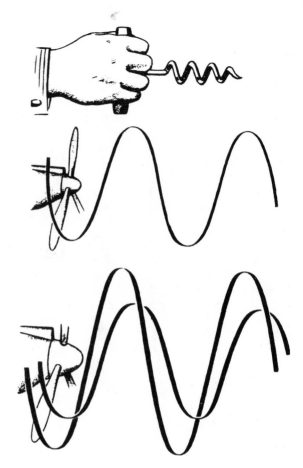

Figure **17·8**   Path of the propeller through the air.

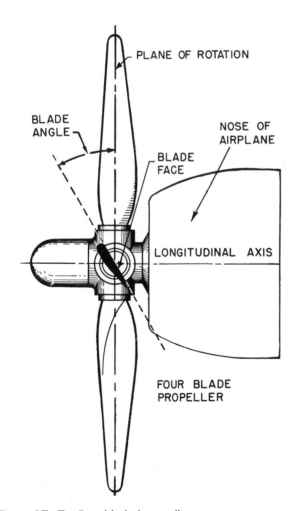

Figure **17·7**   Four-bladed propeller.

Blade angle

Technically, the **blade angle** is defined as the angle between the face or chord of a particular blade section and the plane in which the propeller blades rotate. Figure 17·7 is a drawing of a four-blade propeller, but only two blades are fully shown in order to simplify the presentation. The blade angle, the plane of rotation, the blade face, the longitudinal axis, and the nose of the airplane are all designated in this illustration. The plane of rotation is perpendicular to the crankshaft.

In order to obtain thrust, the propeller blade must be set at a certain angle to its plane of rotation, in the same manner that the wing of an airplane is set at an angle to its forward path. While the propeller is rotating in flight, each section of the blade has a motion that combines the forward movement of the airplane with the circular or rotary movement of the propeller. Therefore, any section of a blade has a path through the air that is shaped like a spiral or a corkscrew, as illustrated in Fig. 17·8.

An imaginary point on a section near the tip of the blade traces the largest spiral, a point on a section midway along the blade traces a smaller spiral, and a point on a section near the shank of the blade traces the smallest spiral of all. In one turn of the blade, all sections move **forward** the same distance, but the sections near the tip of the blade move a greater **circular** distance than the sections near the hub.

If the spiral paths made by various points on sections of the bl~~ace~~d, with the sections at their most ~~eff~~... ~~en~~ each individual section must be ~~...structed~~ so that the angles become ~~...~~ d the tip of the blade and larger ~~...~~ gradual change of blade section ~~...~~ **stribution** and accounts for the ~~...~~ propeller blade, as illustrated ~~...~~ blade is actually a twisted ~~...~~ any particular section of a ~~...~~ t from the blade angle of ~~...~~ ne blade.

~~...~~red at one selected station ~~...~~ hub, depending upon the ~~...~~ ade angle at this station ~~...~~ s should be correct if the ~~...~~ signed and accurately

~~...~~tant that a change in ~~...~~ t the rpm of a direct- ~~...~~ pm. The effect that it ~~...~~ peller gear reduction ~~...~~ ratio. In some installa- ~~ti...~~ or less of blade-angle setting is ~~occ...~~ permitted by specific instructions, but ~~this...~~ by no means a common practice.

The reason for a variation of the propeller blade angle from the hub to the tip of a blade can be understood by examining the illustrations of Fig. 17·10. The three triangles show the relative movement of the airplane and a particular section of the propeller blade during flight at 150 mph with the propeller turning at 2000 rpm. The triangle at *a* represents the movement of the blade section 36 in. from the propeller hub.

The diameter of the circle traversed by the blade section at 36 in. from the hub is 3 ft $\times$ 2π, or 18.85 ft.

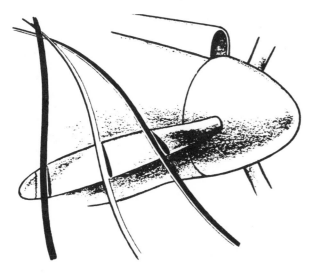

Figure **17·9** *Pitch distribution.*

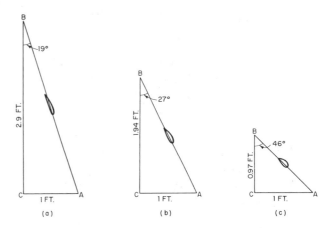

Figure **17·10** *Demonstrating reason for change of blade angle from hub to tip.*

With the propeller turning at 2000 rpm, the section of the blade travels 37,700 ft per min or about 628 ft per sec.

If the airplane is traveling at a true airspeed of 150 mph, it is moving through the air at 220 ft per sec. This means, then, that the airplane travels 220 ft while the blade section is moving 628 ft. From these data we can determine that, while the airplane is moving 1 ft, the propeller blade section at 36 in. from the hub is moving slightly less than 2.9 ft. This is illustrated in triangle *a*, which shows blade section distance in its plane of rotation as *BC* and the airplane distance as *CA*. The actual track of the propeller blade section is *BA*, and the relative wind direction is along the line *AB*. The angle of attack of the propeller blade is the difference between the angle of *AB* with respect to the plane of rotation and the propeller blade angle.

From a table of tangents or by measuring, we can find that the angle *ABC* is a little more than 19°. If the blade angle is set at 22°, the angle of attack of the blade will be somewhat more than 3°.

The triangle *b* in Fig. 17·10 represents the travel of a blade section at 24 in. from the hub when the airplane is moving at 150 mph TAS and the propeller is turning at 2000 rpm. By using the same methods of computation, we find that the angle at *B* is about 27°, and to provide an angle of attack of 3°, the blade angle would have to be set at 30°. Under the same conditions we will find that a blade section at 12 in. from the hub will move at an angle of 46° from the plane of rotation as shown in triangle *c*.

It is apparent that a fixed-pitch propeller will be efficient only through a narrow range of operating conditions. Fixed-pitch propellers are therefore designed to operate most efficiently at the cruising speed of the airplane on which they are installed.

Blade angle and angle of attack in flight and on the ground

The **angle of attack of a propeller blade section** is the angle between the face of the blade section and the direction of the relative airstream, as illustrated in Fig.

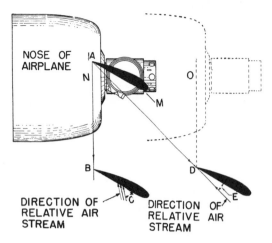

Figure **17·11** *Blade angle with aircraft at rest and in flight.*

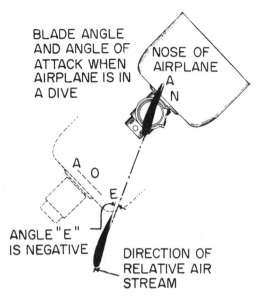

BLADE ANGLE AND ANGLE OF ATTACK WHEN AIRPLANE IS IN A DIVE

NOSE OF AIRPLANE

ANGLE "E" IS NEGATIVE

DIRECTION OF RELATIVE AIR STREAM

Figure **17·13** *High speed results in negative angle of attack.*

17·11. The direction of the relative airstream depends upon the direction that the airfoil moves through undisturbed air.

The relative air motion is along the pitch angle; hence the angle of attack is added to the pitch angle to obtain the blade angle as the sum of the two angles. In Fig. 17·11 the blade airfoil section *M* of the rotating propeller travels from *A* to *B* when the airplane is parked on the ground. The trailing edge of the propeller determines the plane of rotation represented by the line *AB*.

The **relative wind** is the direction of the air with respect to the movement of the airfoil, as shown in Fig. 17·12. When the airplane is in the air, the relative wind results from the forward motion of the airplane and the circular motion of the propeller blade sections. When the engine is run on the ground, there is no forward movement of the airplane (on the assumption that the airplane is standing) but there is a relative wind caused by the air flowing through the propeller. There is also a certain amount of pitch angle of the air motion with regard to the blade sections. The angle of attack is therefore represented in Fig. 17·11 by the angle *C*.

This is the angle at which the propeller section meets the relative airstream.

Continuing to refer to Fig. 17·11, in flight the airplane moves forward, and as it moves forward from *N* to *O*, the airfoil section *M* will travel from *A* to *D*. The trailing edge follows the path represented by the line *AD*, which represents the relative airstream. The angle of attack then becomes smaller and is represented by *E* in the illustration.

The normal angle of attack in flight of the propeller blades for many airplanes varies from 0 to 15°. Referring to Fig. 17·13, in a power dive the acceleration due to the force of gravity may give the airplane a speed which is greater than the speed which the propeller tends to reach. The angle of attack, represented by the letter *E*, is then negative and tends to hold back the airplane.

In a steep climb with the forward speed reduced, the angle of attack is increased, as shown in Fig. 17·14.

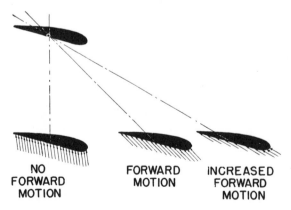

NO FORWARD MOTION   FORWARD MOTION   INCREASED FORWARD MOTION

Figure **17·12** *Relative wind with respect to propeller blade.*

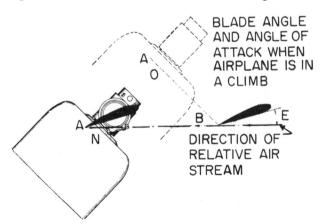

BLADE ANGLE AND ANGLE OF ATTACK WHEN AIRPLANE IS IN A CLIMB

DIRECTION OF RELATIVE AIR STREAM

Figure **17·14** *Increased angle of attack as airplane climbs.*

Whether the airplane is in a power dive or in a steep climb, the aerodynamic efficiency of the propeller is low.

It will be noted that the propeller blade angles in the foregoing illustrations appear to be high. In actual practice the blade angle is less than shown, but for the purpose of illustration the angles have been exaggerated in these views.

PROPELLER OPERATION

The actual operation of propellers in flight depends upon a number of factors. Among these are aircraft design, engine design, the nature of aircraft operation desired, conditions of flight, performance required, and various others. If an airplane is required to fly great distances with a maximum of economy, the propeller should be of an automatic type which will adjust blade angle to meet the power and speed values selected by the pilot. For airplanes used in short, local flights, the extra cost of an automatic propeller system is not usually justified.

Pitch

The **effective pitch** is the actual distance the airplane moves forward during one revolution (360°) of the propeller in flight. **Pitch** does not mean the same as **blade angle,** but the two terms are commonly used interchangeably because they are so closely related. Figure 17·15 shows two different pitch positions. The heavy black airfoil drawn across the hub of each represents the cross section of the propeller to illustrate the blade setting. When there is a small blade angle, there is a low pitch and the airplane does not move very far forward in one revolution of the propeller. When there is a large blade angle, there is a high pitch and the airplane moves forward farther during a single revolution of the propeller.

A **fixed-pitch propeller** is a rigidly constructed propeller on which the blade angles may not be altered without bending or reworking the blades. A **controllable-pitch** propeller is one provided with a means of control for adjusting the angle of the blades during flight.

The propeller somewhat resembles the gearshift of an automobile when the pitch is adjustable. When only fixed blade-angle propellers were used on airplanes, the angle of the blade was chosen to fit the principal purpose for which an airplane was designed. If it was designed for fast climbing and quick takeoff, it had a comparatively low blade-angle propeller, although it was no more suitable for high-speed flying or diving than the low gear on an automobile is adapted to high-speed driving on the highway.

With a fixed blade-angle propeller, an increase in engine power causes increased rotational speed, and this causes more thrust, but it also creates more drag from the airfoil and forces the propeller to absorb the additional engine power. In a similar manner, a decrease in engine power causes a decrease in rotational speed and consequently a decrease in both thrust and drag from the propeller.

When an airplane with a fixed blade-angle propeller **dives,** the forward speed of the airplane increases. Since there is a change in the direction of the relative wind, there is lower angle of attack, thus reducing both lift and drag and increasing the rotational speed of the propeller.

On the other hand, if the airplane goes into a climb, the rotational speed of the propeller will decrease, the change in the direction of the relative wind increases the angle of attack, there is more lift and drag and less forward speed for the airplane.

The propeller can absorb only a limited amount of excess power by increasing or decreasing its rotational speed. Beyond that, the engine will be damaged. For this reason, as aircraft-engine power and airplane speeds both increased, the engineers found it necessary to design propellers with blades that could rotate in their sockets into different positions to permit changing the blade-angle setting to compensate for changes in the relative wind brought on by the varying forward speeds. This made it possible for the propeller to absorb more or less engine power without damaging the engine. The first step in this development produced a propeller with two different blade-angle settings. One gave a low angle for takeoff and climb. The other gave a high blade angle for cruising and driving.

Geometrical pitch and zero-thrust pitch

A distinction is made between effective pitch and other kinds of pitch. The **geometrical pitch** is the distance an element of the propeller would advance in one revolution if it were moving along a helix (spiral) having an angle equal to its blade angle. Geometrical pitch can be calculated by multiplying the tangent of the blade angle by $2\pi r$, r being the radius of the blade station at which it is computed. For example, if the blade angle of a propeller is 20° at the 30-in. station, we can apply the formula thus:

$$2\pi \times 30 \times 0.364 = 68.58 \text{ in.}$$

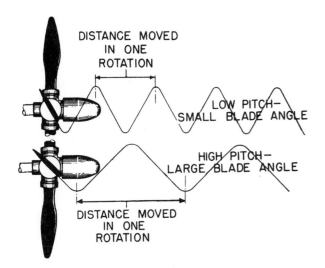

Figure 17·15   Low pitch and high pitch.

(The tangent of 20° is 0.364.) The geometrical pitch of the propeller is therefore 68.58 in. This is the distance the propeller would move if it were going forward through a solid medium.

The **zero-thrust pitch,** also called the **experimental mean pitch,** is the distance a propeller would have to advance in one revolution to give no thrust.

The **pitch ratio** of a propeller is the ratio of the pitch to the diameter.

Slip

Slip is defined as the difference between the geometrical pitch and the effective pitch of a propeller. It may be expressed as a percentage of the mean geometrical pitch or as a linear dimension.

The **slip function** is the ratio of the speed of advance through undisturbed air to the product of the propeller diameter and the number of revolutions per unit time. This may be expressed as a formula thus: V/nD, where V is the speed through undisturbed air, D is the propeller diameter, and n is the number of revolutions per unit time.

The word **slip** is rather loosely used by many people in aviation to refer to the difference between the velocity of the air behind the propeller (caused by the propeller) and that of the aircraft with respect to the undisturbed air well ahead of the propeller. It is then expressed as a percentage of this difference in terms of aircraft velocity.

If there were no slippage of any type, and if the propeller were moving through an imaginary solid substance, then the geometrical pitch would be the calculated distance that the blade element at two-thirds the blade radius would move forward in one complete revolution of the propeller (360°). This set of assumptions is entirely theoretical and of little or no interest to a mechanic unless he wants to learn the terminology of the engineers so that he can better understand technical discussions of propellers.

Types of propellers

In designing propellers, the engineers try to obtain the maximum performance of the airplane from the horsepower delivered by the engine under all conditions of operation, such as takeoff, climb, cruising, and high speed. Practically all propellers may be classified under four general types, as follows:

1. **Fixed pitch.** The propeller is made in one piece. Only one pitch setting is possible because of its design. It is usually a two-blade propeller and is often made of wood, although other materials, such as aluminum alloy, steel, and even phenolic compounds, are used.
2. **Adjustable pitch.** The pitch setting can be adjusted only with tools on the ground when the engine is not operating. This type usually has a split hub. The propeller may be removed from the engine when the pitch is being adjusted on some airplanes, but on others this is not necessary. It has at least two blades and often more. Wood may be used in its construction, but it is generally made of steel or aluminum alloy.
3. **Controllable pitch.** The pilot can change the pitch of the

propeller in flight or while operating the engine on the ground by means of a pitch-changing mechanism that may be mechanically (manually) operated, hydraulically operated, or electrically operated. The blades may be made of aluminum alloy, steel, wood, or one of the resin-bonded materials.
4. **Constant-speed.** The constant-speed propeller utilizes a hydraulically or electrically operated pitch-changing mechanism which is controlled by a governor. The setting of the governor is adjusted by the pilot with the rpm lever in the cockpit. During operation, the constant-speed propeller automatically changes its blade angle to maintain a constant engine speed. In straight and level flight, if engine power is increased, the blade angle is increased to make the propeller absorb the additional power while the rpm remains constant. The pilot selects the engine speed required for any particular type of operation.

Terms used in describing pitch change

The principal terms used in describing propeller-pitch change are as follows: (1) **two-position,** which makes available only two pitch settings; (2) **multiposition,** which makes any pitch setting within reasonable limits possible; (3) **automatic,** which provides a pitch-setting control by some automatic device; (4) **automatic, selective,** which enables the pilot to select and control, during flight, the exact conditions at which he wants the automatic features to operate; and (5) **automatic, nonselective,** which provides for pitch control entirely independent of the pilot.

Forces acting on a propeller in flight

The forces acting on a propeller in flight are (1) **thrust,** which is the component of the total air force on the propeller which is parallel to the direction of advance and induces bending stresses in the propeller; (2) **centrifugal force,** which is caused by the rotation of the propeller and which tends to throw the blade out from the central hub and produces tensile stresses; and (3) **torsion or twisting forces** in the blade itself, caused by the fact that the resultant air forces do not go through the neutral axis of the propeller, producing torsional stresses.

Stresses to which propellers are subjected at high speeds

Figure 17·16 illustrates the three general types of stresses to which propellers rotating at high speeds are subjected. These stresses are bending stresses, tensile stresses, and torsional stresses, explained in detail as follows:

1. The **bending stresses** are induced by the thrust forces. These stresses tend to bend the blade forward as the airplane is moved through the air by the propeller. Bending stresses are also caused by other factors, such as the drag caused by the resistance of the air, but these are of small importance in comparison with the bending stresses caused by the thrust forces.
2. **Tensile stresses** are caused by centrifugal force. This always tends to throw the blade out from the central hub. The hub resists this tendency, and hence the blades "stretch" slightly.
3. **Torsional stresses** are produced in rotating propeller blades by two twisting moments. One of these stresses is caused by

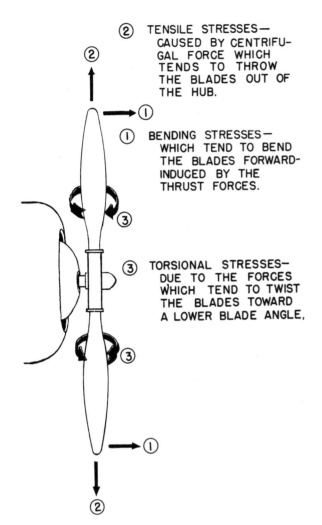

② TENSILE STRESSES—
CAUSED BY CENTRIFU-
GAL FORCE WHICH
TENDS TO THROW
THE BLADES OUT OF
THE HUB.

① BENDING STRESSES—
WHICH TEND TO BEND
THE BLADES FORWARD-
INDUCED BY THE
THRUST FORCES.

③ TORSIONAL STRESSES-
DUE TO THE FORCES
WHICH TEND TO TWIST
THE BLADES TOWARD
A LOWER BLADE ANGLE.

Figure 17·16 Forces and stresses on propeller blades during operation.

the air reaction on the blades and is called the **aerodynamic twisting moment.** The other stress is caused by centrifugal force and is called the **centrifugal twisting moment.** During ordinary propeller operation, the centrifugal force tends to turn the blades to a lower angle. In some propeller control mechanisms, this centrifugal twisting moment is employed to aid in turning the blades to a lower angle when necessary to obtain greater propeller efficiency in flight, thus putting a natural force to work.

Torsional stresses increase with the square of the rpm. For example, if the rpm is doubled, the stresses will be four times as great.

Tip speed

Flutter or vibration may be caused by the tip of the propeller blade traveling at a rate of speed approaching the speed of sound, thus causing excessive stresses to develop. This condition can be overcome by operating at a lower speed or by telescoping the propeller blades, that is, reducing the propeller diameter without changing the blade profile.

Tip speed is actually the principal factor deter-

mining the efficiency of high-performance airplane propellers of conventional two- or three-blade design. It has been found by experience that it is essential to keep the tip velocity below the velocity of sound, which is about 1120 ft per sec (1116.4 ft per sec at standard sea-level pressure and temperature) and varies with temperature and altitude. At sea level the velocity of sound is generally taken as about 1120 ft per sec, but is decreases about 5 ft per sec for each increase in altitude of 1000 ft.

The efficiency of high-performance airplane propellers of conventional two- or three-blade design may be expressed in terms of the ratio of the tip speed to the velocity of sound. For example, at sea level, when the tip speed is 900 ft per sec, the maximum efficiency is about 86 percent, but when the tip speed reaches 1200 ft per sec, the maximum efficiency is only about 72 percent.

It is often necessary to gear the engine so that the propeller will turn at a lower rate of speed in order to obtain tip ratios below the velocity of sound. For example, if the engine is geared in a 3:2 ratio, the propeller will turn at two-thirds the speed of the engine.

When the propeller turns at a lower rate of speed, the airfoil sections of the blades strike the air at a lower speed also, and they therefore do not do so much work in a geared propeller as they would do in one with a direct drive. It is necessary in this case to increase the blade area by using a larger diameter or more blades.

Ratio of forward velocity to rotational velocity

The efficiency of a propeller is also influenced by the ratio of the forward velocity of the airplane in feet per second to the rotational velocity of the propeller. This ratio can be expressed by a quantity called **the V over nD ratio,** which is sometimes expressed as a formula: V/nD, where V is the forward velocity of the airplane in feet per second, n is the number of revolutions per second of the propeller, and D is the diameter in feet of the propeller. Any fixed-pitch propeller is designed to give its maximum efficiency at a particular value of forward speed of the airplane, which is usually the cruising speed in level flight, and at a particular engine speed, which is usually the speed employed for cruising. At any other condition of flight where a different value of the V/nD ratio exists, the propeller efficiency will be less.

Propeller efficiency

Some of the work performed by the engine is lost in the slipstream of the propeller, and some is lost in the production of noise, neither of which can be converted to horsepower for turning the propeller. We have already examined the effect of tip speed on propeller efficiency. In addition, it is well known that the maximum propeller efficiency that can be obtained in practice under the most ideal conditions, using conventional engines and propellers, has been only about 92 percent, and in order to obtain this efficiency it has been necessary to use thin airfoil sections near the tip of the propeller and very sharp leading and trailing

355

edges. Such airfoil sections are not practical where there is the slightest danger of the propeller picking up rocks, gravel, water spray, or similar substances that might damage the blades.

The **thrust horsepower** is the actual amount of horsepower that an engine-propeller unit transforms into thrust. This is less than the **brake horsepower** developed by the engine, since propellers are never 100 percent efficient.

In the study of propellers, two forces must be considered: **thrust** and **torque.** The thrust force acts parallel to the axis of rotation of the propeller, and the torque force acts parallel to the plane of rotation of the propeller. The thrust horsepower is less than the torque horsepower. The **efficiency** of the propeller is the ratio of the thrust horsepower to the torque horsepower, expressed thus:

$$\text{Propeller efficiency} = \frac{\text{thrust horsepower}}{\text{torque horsepower}}$$

Feathering

The term **feathering** refers to the operation of rotating the blades of a propeller to an edge-to-the-wind position for the purpose of stopping the rotation of the propeller whose blades are thus feathered and to reduce drag. Therefore, a **feathered blade** is in an approximate in-line-of-flight position, streamlined with the line of flight. Some, but not all, propellers can be feathered.

Feathering is necessary when an engine fails or when it is desirable to shut off an engine in flight. The pressure of the air on the face and back of the feathered blade is equal, and the propeller will stop rotating. If it is not feathered when its engine stops driving it, the propeller will "windmill" and cause drag.

Another advantage of being able to feather a propeller is that a feathered propeller creates less resistance (drag) and disturbance to the flow of air over the wings and tail of the airplane. Furthermore, a feathered propeller prevents additional damage to the engine if the failure was caused by some internal breakage, and it also eliminates the vibration which might damage the structure of the airplane.

The importance of feathering the propeller for an engine which has failed on a multiengine airplane cannot be over-emphasized. If the propeller cannot be feathered in such a case, it is likely that the engine will "run away," that is, overspeed to the point where great damage may be caused. The lubrication system of the engine may fail because of the excessive speed, and this will cause the engine to "burn up." The heat generated may set the engine on fire, in which case the airplane itself may be destroyed. The excessive speed of the engine may cause the propeller to lose a blade, thus bringing about an unbalanced condition which will cause the engine to be wrenched from its mounting. Numerous cases of runaway engines which caused airplane crashes are on record.

Summing up some of the advantages of feathering a propeller when an engine failure occurs, there is not only less drag, but there is a better performance on the part of the remaining engines, better speed, a higher ceiling, better powerplant control, and the airplane can be flown safely to a point where an emergency landing can be made.

Reverse thrust

When propellers are reversed, their blades are rotated below their positive angle, that is, through "flat" pitch, until a negative blade angle is obtained in order to produce a thrust acting in the opposite direction to the forward thrust normally given by the propeller.

The feature is helpful in handling multiengine flying boats in restricted areas and during landing operations of large airplanes, in reducing the length of landing runs, which in turn reduces the amount of braking needed and materially increases the life of the brakes and tires. Reverse propeller thrust is used in almost every case where a four-engine transport-type aircraft is landed. This applies to turboprop-equipped aircraft as well as the conventional types. Jet-propelled transport aircraft utilize jet engines which are equipped with jet reversing devices for the purpose of reducing the landing roll.

REVIEW QUESTIONS

1. Name the principal parts of a single-piece wood propeller.
2. Compare the cross section of a propeller blade with the cross section of a wing.
3. What is meant by a *ground-adjustable* propeller?
4. Define *blade root.*
5. Explain the purpose of blade cuffs.
6. What is the *blade-element* theory?
7. What law of motion explains propeller thrust?
8. Why does the blade angle change from the hub to the tip?
9. Why is a fixed-pitch propeller limited in its range of operation?
10. Discuss the angle of attack of a propeller blade with respect to airplane speed.
11. Explain the difference between a ground-adjustable propeller and a controllable propeller.
12. What is the *geometrical pitch* of a propeller?
13. Define propeller *slip.*
14. Explain the operation of a constant-speed propeller.
15. Explain the effect of each of the three principal forces acting on a propeller in flight.
16. What is the limiting factor with respect to the rpm at which a propeller may be operated?
17. Explain *propeller efficiency.*
18. Give the reasons why it is essential to use feathering propellers on multiengine aircraft.
19. Describe the process of propeller *reversing.*
20. What is the value of reverse thrust?

CHAPTER 18

Propellers for Light Aircraft

WOOD PROPELLERS

In the early days of aviation, all propellers were made of wood, but the development of larger and higher-horsepower aircraft engines made it necessary to adopt a stronger and more durable material; hence, metal is now extensively used in the construction of propellers for all types of aircraft. Some propeller blades have been made of plastic materials, specially treated wood laminations, and plastic-coated wood laminations. For most purposes, however, the metal propellers have been most satisfactory where cost is not a primary consideration.

In spite of the successful development of metal propellers, wood is still used for some propellers for lower horsepower engines where less strength is required. Wood propellers are lighter in weight, are easier to manufacture, have less tendency to vibrate than metal propellers of the same power rating, and cost less. For these reasons, solid wood propellers and propellers

with wooden blades are still used for many light, privately owned airplanes.

Stabilized nature of wood-propeller construction

Fixed-pitch wood propellers have gone through such a long stage of development that it has been possible to establish certain minimum standards for material, procedures, processes, manufacturing tolerances, inspection methods, and repair methods. All these must be of the best possible quality because of the highly stressed condition of a propeller and its relative importance as a unit of the powerplant. For these reasons, this text presents the subject in phraseology that has been universally adopted by propeller specialists.

Construction

The first consideration in the construction of a wood propeller is the selection of the right quality and type of wood. It is especially important that all lumber from which the propeller laminae (layers) are to be cut should be kiln dried. A wood propeller is not cut from a solid block but is built up of a number of separate layers of carefully selected and well-seasoned hardwoods, as illustrated in Fig. 18·1.

Many types of wood have been used in making propellers, but the most satisfactory are sweet or yellow birch, sugar maple, black cherry, and black walnut. In some cases, alternate layers of two different woods have been used to reduce the tendency toward warpage. This is not considered necessary, however, because the use of laminations of the same type of wood will effectively reduce the tendency for a propeller to warp under ordinary conditions of use.

The spiral or diagonal grain of propeller wood should have a slope of less than 1 in 10 when measured from the longitudinal axis of the laminae.

Propeller lumber should be free from checks, shakes, excess pinworm holes, unsound and loose knots, and decay. Sap stain is considered a defect. The importance of selecting a high grade of lumber cannot be too strongly emphasized in order to reduce the effect of internal variations present in all wood.

The wood laminations (layers) should be laid out with the longitudinal axis parallel to the grain of the boards from which they are to be cut. The boards may be glued edge to edge to provide laminations or hub sections of the desired width. The edges to be joined should be approximately parallel to the direction of the grain as indicated on the face of the board, and in no case should the slope of the grain with respect to the edge to be glued be greater than 1 in 15.

Edge joints may be plain or serrated. The edges should be accurately and smoothly fitted not more than 4 hr before gluing. If serrated, the pitch should

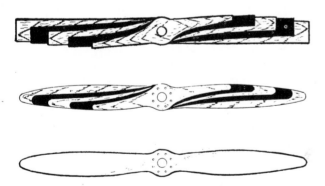

Figure 18·1   Construction of a typical wood propeller.

be not less than ⅛ in. and not greater than ¼ in. The gluing technique employed in making these edge-to-edge joints should be the same as that later used in gluing the laminations together, as described below.

Edge-glued laminations should remain in the clamps at least 4 hr after gluing. After removal from the clamps, such laminations should be conditioned for a period of not less than 72 hr at temperatures of not less than 70°F before the final surfacing operation.

Laminae thickness may vary on the drawings. Laminae of the same thickness should be used in a propeller except for outside laminae. Prior to assembly for gluing, the laminae should be separated into three classes: light, medium, and heavy. Only laminae of one class should be assembled in a single propeller. These should be individually balanced and assembled with the heavy ends of adjacent laminae at opposite ends to facilitate balancing. Laminae should be prepared for gluing by smoothly and accurately planing all surfaces to be glued not more than 4 hr before gluing.

Defects in laminae that are causes for rejection include such conditions as checks, shakes, rot, dotes, pronounced burls or curls, wormholes, discoloration streaks, etc. Knots which are causes for rejection are (1) round knots over ½ in. in diameter, (2) small knots which are not so sound as the surrounding wood and which are present in large numbers, and (3) knots in parts of the finished blade less than ½ in. thick or within 18 in. of the tip of either blade.

For standard one-piece wood propellers, from five to nine separate wood laminations about ¾ in. thick are used. On the other hand, some propeller blades are made of a very large number of laminations about ¹⁄₁₆ in. thick. The several layers of the wood propeller are cut to the proper shape and then are glued together with a waterproof phenolic resin glue or some other type which has been approved for this purpose.

The glue is applied in accordance with the manufacturer's instructions, Gluing is done in an enclosed room which is light, clean, and free from drafts and dust. No gluing should be done when the temperature of the gluing room or wood is below 21°C (70°F). Particular care should be taken to spread the glue evenly and to the correct thickness. The use of a glue spreader is recommended.

The propeller manufacturer should so control the temperature of the gluing room, the amount of glue spread, and the time that elapses between the spreading of the glue and the application of pressure, that the glue joints will be of maximum strength. Either a jack press or C clamps can be used to apply pressure. After the propeller has been removed from the press or clamps, a conditioning period of at least 2 days should be allowed.

After conditioning, the propeller should be roughed out to within not closer than ¼ in. of the finished surface, either by hand or with a profiling machine.

When the "blank" has been roughed to the approximate shape and size of the finished product, the propeller is conditioned for an additional 7 days or more at about 70°F or not less than 3 days at 120°F. It is allowed to hang during this period in order to permit the moisture content of the layers to be equalized. This additional period of seasoning prevents cracking and warping that might occur if the blank were carved immediately.

The propeller is then carefully finished by hand. It should be carved and worked to a final size, using suitable templates and bench protractors to obtain the proper contour and blade angle at all stations. During this process the propeller is balanced.

Final operations should include a smooth sanding. The propeller is rigidly mounted for this and the other final processes. The change in pitch angle from station to station should be smooth and true throughout the blade length with no irregularities in contour. At this stage, a set of metal bench templates, suitably stamped, should be available. All checking with templates should be accomplished with the propeller in the "white" and before applying the metal tips.

The hub holes should be drilled with extreme accuracy, using a suitable jig and taking care to ensure that the holes are perpendicular to the hub faces.

Tipping

Propeller tipping is a protective covering of the blade of a propeller near the tip. Metal tipping extends from the tips along the leading edges for a considerable distance toward the hub. The purpose of tipping is to prevent injuries to the wood which otherwise might occur during warm-up and run-up periods on the line and which might be made during takeoffs and landings by small stones, bits of wood, and sometimes small pieces of metal picked up by the propeller. In addition, injuries to the wood may be caused by tall weeds in landing and by birds, insects, rain, snow, and hail in flight. Any of these can injure any part of a propeller blade, but the damage to the tips is especially great because they have the smallest cross-sectional area and travel at a high rate of speed.

Metal tipping may be made of a good-grade brass, monel metal, stainless steel, terneplate, or the equivalent. Copper is not used because it does not wear well. The recommended thickness is 0.019 in. Figure 18·2 illustrates a metal-tipped propeller.

The metal tip should be applied over at least one coat of **finish.** Since wood is subjected to warping, swelling, and shrinking when there is any excessive change of moisture content, these adverse conditions are avoided by the application of a protective coating. The usual procedure is to apply several coats of water-repellent clear varnish (such as a high-quality spar varnish or its equivalent), wait for it to dry, and then mount the propeller on a spindle where it is balanced.

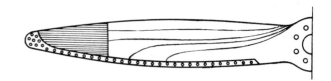

Figure 18·2   A metal-tipped propeller blade.

Very small variations in balance can be corrected by adding varnish at various places on the propeller.

The finish having been applied, the small piece of metal used for the tipping should be applied to the camber face of the tip first. The ends of the large piece of metal are then so lapped over the small piece as to eff___ a continuous piece of metal along the leading

___tal should be secured by No. 4 brass or ___ flathead wood screws, ½ and ⅜ in. long, ___ thin section near the blade tip, where ___ brass or copper rivets should be used. ___ be bored for the screws and counter-___ ds. The countersunk holes should ___ ective finish, such as a high-___ equivalent. ___ countersunk to take the ___ mpled into the counter-___ thod that avoids split-___ e holes for the rivets ___ and wood with the ___ l tipping should ___ be removed, ___ d a protective co___ screws. The metal shou___ ly dimpled into the counte___ ng. Rivet holes should be drilled ___ the rivets so that the rivets can be pre___ d, since they should not be driven in pla___ completed, the metal tipping should fit snug___ ainst the wood. Buckling or lifting of the metal is a cause for rejection.

Solder should be filled in over the heads of the rivets and screws to prevent loosening and then filed down to the smooth surface of the metal tip. In soldering screws and rivets, there must not be any excessive heating and the wood should not be charred.

The metal tipping is vented by drilling three No. 60 (0.040 in.) holes ³⁄₁₆ in. deep in the tip end after assembly. The purpose of these small holes is to allow the moisture condensed on the tipping between the metal and the wood to drain away or be thrown out by centrifugal force. These drain holes must be open at all times.

A linen fabric is frequently applied to the surface for additional strengthening at the tip and for protection against abrasion and splintering along the grain. The fabric covering is applied to the outer area of each blade for a distance of 12 to 15 in. Cloth is wrapped around the blade, the seam is placed under the metal tipping, and the cloth sealed with a protective covering, such as two coats of transparent dope or varnish, but this finish need not be applied to the metal covering.

Procedure after tipping is applied

At least one coat of finish should be applied to the wood prior to and at least two coats after tipping. A priming coat of a paste wood filler may be applied initially. The hub bore should receive several coats of finish.

The propeller should be balanced after shaping and after each successive operation that might affect the balance. Final balance should be accomplished on a rigid, knife-edge balancing stand in a room free from air currents. No persistent tendency to rotate from any position on the balance stand should exist. A propeller on a balance stand is shown in Fig. 18·3.

Horizontal unbalance may be corrected by the application of finish or solder to the light blade. The light blade may be coated with a high grade of varnish allowing for a finishing coat. After each coat is allowed to dry 48 hr, the balance should be checked. Then it may be necessary either to remove the required amount of finish by careful sandpapering or to apply an additional coat. The balance must be rechecked and sandpaper or additional finish applied to accomplish the final balancing.

Vertical unbalance can be corrected by applying putty to the light side of the wood hub at a point on the circumference about 90° from the longitudinal center line of the blades. The putty should be weighed, and a brass plate weighing slightly more than the putty should be cut out. The thickness of this brass plate is from ¹⁄₁₆ to ⅛ in., depending on the final area, which must be sufficient for the required number of flathead attaching screws.

The plate may be made to fit on the hub face or to fit the shape of the light side of the wood hub and drilled and countersunk for the necessary screws. The plate is then attached, and all screws tightened. After the plate is finally attached to the propeller, the screws are secured to the plate by soldering the screwheads. The balance is checked, and all edges of the plate are beveled to reduce its weight. The drilling of holes in the propeller and the insertion of lead or other material to assist in balancing are not permitted.

Blade thickness and hub-hole dimensions

A pair of calipers may be used to measure the blade thickness. The hub bolt holes should be examined with an exact size "go" gage and a 0.015-in. oversize "no-go" gage. The tolerance on the roundness of hub holes is −0 +0.020 in.

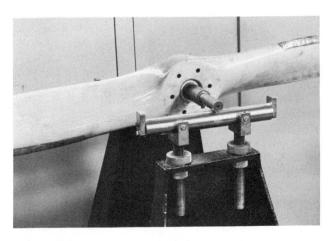

Figure 18·3   Propeller on a balance stand.

Track

The track is considered to consist of the corresponding points on two or more blades of a propeller lying in the same plane perpendicular to the axis of rotation within the required track tolerances.

Propeller track can be checked by mounting the propeller on a propeller surface table and then rotating the propeller tips past a fixed reference point as shown in Fig. 18·4. After the propeller is mounted on an engine installed in an airplane, the track can be checked by rotating the tip of the propeller by a fixed reference point attached to the landing gear of the airplane. This is shown in Fig. 18·5. The track of one blade should normally be within 1/16 in. of the other blade.

Face alignment

The face alignment is the distance from the center line of the blade to its thrust or working face as measured perpendicular to the chords of the cross

Figure 18·4 Checking propeller track on a surface table.

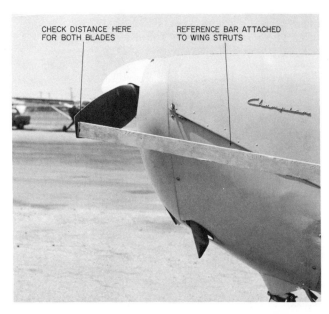

CHECK DISTANCE HERE
FOR BOTH BLADES

REFERENCE BAR ATTACHED
TO WING STRUTS

Figure 18·5 Checking propeller track on an airplane.

sections of the blade at various stations. An optional use of a projected face alignment is permitted when it is so specified on the drawing.

Edge alignment

The edge alignment is the distance parallel to the respective chords of the sections from the center line of the blade to the leading edge of the cross sections as designated on the drawing. An optional use of a projected edge alignment is permitted when so specified on the drawing.

Wood-propeller tolerances

Recommended tolerances for wood propellers are given below. Blades of the same propeller should be identical within the limits given, disregarding the plus and minus signs.

Table 18·1

Required dimension	Recommended tolerance
Blade length	±1/16 in.
Blade width—from shank to 24-in. station	±3/32 in.
—from 30-in. station to tip	±1/16 in.
Blade thickness—from shank to 24-in. station	+1/8, −1/16 in.
—from 30-in. station to tip	+3/64 in., −0 in.
Edge alignment	±1/16 in.
Face alignment	±1/8 in.
Template fit—from shank to 24-in. station	3/32 in.
—from 30-in. station to tip	1/32 in.
Blade angle—from shank to 18-in. station	±1.0°
—from 24- to 30-in. station	±0.5°
—from 36-in. station to tip	±0.4°
Track	1/16 in.
Thickness of hub	±1/32 in.
Diameter of hub	±3/32 in.
Hub bolt holes	+0.015 in. −0.000 in.
Hub bore	+0.020 in. −0.00 in.

REMOVAL AND INSTALLATION

Types of hubs

The propeller is mounted on its shaft by means of several attaching parts. The types of hubs generally used to mount a wood propeller on the engine crankshaft are (1) forged-steel hub fitting a splined crankshaft, (2) tapered forged-steel hub for connecting to a tapered crankshaft, and (3) hub bolted to a steel flange forged on the crankshaft.

Hubs fitting a tapered shaft

On some models having a hub fitting a tapered shaft, the hub is held in place by a retaining nut that screws on the end of the shaft. A locknut safeties the retaining nut, and a puller is required for removing the propeller from the shaft. The locknut screws into the hub and bears against the retaining nut. The locknut and the retaining nut are then safetied together with either a cotter pin or a lockwire.

A newer design has a snap ring instead of a locknut. When the propeller is to be removed, the retaining nut is backed off, it bears against the snap ring, and thus the propeller is started from the shaft. Holes in the retaining nut and the shaft are provided for safetying.

Hubs fitting a splined shaft

A retaining nut that screws on the end of the shaft is used to hold a hub fitting a splined shaft, as shown in Fig. 18·6. A front and rear cone are provided to seat the propeller properly on the shaft. The rear cone is made of bronze and is of one-piece construction. It seats in the rear-cone seat of the hub. The front cone is a two-piece split-type steel cone. A groove around its inner circumference makes it possible to fit the cone over a flange of the propeller retaining nut.

The front cone seats in the front-cone seat of the hub when the retaining nut is threaded into place. In order that the front cone will act against the snap ring and pull the propeller from the shaft when the retaining nut is unscrewed from the propeller shaft, a snap ring is fitted into a groove in the hub forward of the front cone. This snap ring must not be removed when the splined-shaft propeller is removed from its shaft because the snap ring provides a puller for the propeller.

When a hub is used which has a bronze bushing instead of a front cone, a puller may be required to start the propeller from the shaft.

A rear-cone spacer is provided with some designs to prevent the front cone from bottoming on the forward ends of the splines. If the rear cone is too far back, the front cone will come in contact with the splines before the propeller is secure.

The principal purpose of a retaining nut is to hold the propeller firmly on its shaft. A secondary purpose, in some designs, is to function as a puller with the snap ring to aid in removing the propeller.

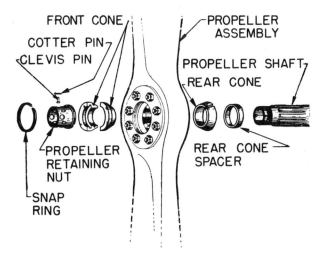

Figure **18·6** *Installation parts for a splined-shaft propeller.*

Removing a propeller from an integral-hub flange type of shaft

If the propeller has an integral-hub flange type of shaft, it can be taken off by simply removing the hub bolt nuts.

Removing a propeller from a splined shaft

In order to remove a propeller from a splined shaft, remove the cotter pins and clevis pin that secure the propeller retaining nut and then unscrew the propeller retaining nut. The front cone over the flange of the retaining nut presses against the snap ring in the hub and pulls the propeller away from the shaft for a short distance. When the propeller is loose, it is usually slipped off easily by hand, but if this is not possible with a reasonable amount of force, remove the snap ring, nut, and front cone. Then clean the threaded portion of the shaft and nut; lubricate the cone, nut, and shaft with clean engine oil; reassemble; and finally apply force to unscrew the nut. The rear cone and spacer are left with the engine if a new propeller is to be installed. A propeller puller is used to start the propeller from the shaft if there is a bronze bushing instead of a front cone.

Procedure before installing a wood propeller

Before installing any wood propeller, wipe the shaft and the inside of the hub with a clean, dry rag until they are free of dirt, grease, and other foreign substances. Using a fine file or a handstone with skill and discretion, remove any burrs or rough spots which might prevent the hub from slipping all the way on the shaft. Apply a thin coating of light engine oil to the shaft before the propeller is installed.

Safety precautions for propeller maintenance

The following rules are brief statements of important safe practices to be followed by all personnel engaged in the inspection, maintenance, overhaul, repair, or manufacture of all aircraft propellers:

1. Wear safety shoes.
2. When lifting a propeller manually, bend the knees, keep the shoulders back, and lift with the leg muscles but not with the back and abdominal muscles more than absolutely necessary. Take a deep breath, and hold it until the propeller is held in a comfortable position. Stand with the feet in line and reasonably separated. If the propeller is too heavy for the number of men assigned to lift it, they should get more men or use a hoist. This section of the rules is intended to prevent hernias (ruptures), back injuries, and similar disabling effects.
3. Do not stand under a propeller in position for hoisting or allow others to walk under it. Do not sling or hoist the propeller over the heads of others. Move it slowly. Be sure it is securely fastened to the hoisting device.
4. Stand clear of the rotating blades of a propeller when it is in a horizontal position on the assembly plate, when it is being balanced on a stand, or when it is rotating on an airplane.
5. If a pit is used for balancing propellers, keep it covered when not in use.
6. See that all personnel handling propellers are careful to

create no hazardous conditions that might hurt themselves or others. Do not allow anyone who is sleepy, inattentive, or careless to work around propellers.

7. Use only approved cleaning solvents for cleaning propeller parts. If such solvents must be used in accordance with special safe practices, instruct the necessary personnel in their care and use and then enforce the rules.

Installing a propeller on a tapered shaft

Before a propeller is installed on a tapered shaft, the fit of the propeller to the shaft should be checked. This may be done with **Prussian blue.** First, both the hub and the shaft are cleaned and all roughness removed. Then a thin coating of Prussian blue is applied to the shaft. The propeller hub is installed, and the retaining nut is tightened to the proper torque for normal installation. The hub is then removed, and the degree of surface contact inside the hub is shown by the transfer of Prussian blue. If the contact area is 70 percent or more, the fit is satisfactory. If the area of contact is less than 70 percent, the hub may be fitted to the shaft by lapping with a fine lapping compound. When the correct fit is attained, the lapping compound must be completely removed from both the hub and shaft, and then both surfaces should be coated with light engine oil.

The installation of a propeller on a tapered shaft depends upon the type of hub. If a locknut is used, lift the propeller into position. Be sure that the key on the shaft lines up with the keyway on the hub. Slide the propeller well back on the shaft. Unless there is something wrong, the hub will not bind as it slides on the tapered shaft. Screw the retaining nut on the end of the shaft. Note that a shoulder on the retaining nut bears against a shoulder in the hub and forces the hub on the shaft. Use the wrenches designated by the manufacturer for the final tightening, but do not apply any extra leverage.

Next, screw the locknut into the hub. Be careful in starting it that there is no "cross threading," because the thread on this nut is comparatively fine. Pull the locknut tight, but do not tighten it as much as the retaining nut. One of the locking-wire holes must be in line with a hole in the retaining nut. Finally, use either a lockwire or a cotter pin to secure the retaining nut and the locknut.

If the propeller is designed with a snap-ring puller, it is merely necessary to place the propeller in the proper position on the shaft, install and tighten the retaining nut, install the snap ring, and install the safety clevis pin or bolt.

Installation of a propeller on an integral-hub flange type of shaft

To install a propeller on an integral-hub flange type of shaft, first place the propeller on the stub shaft, then make certain that there are no metal chips or other particles of foreign substances on the threads of the bolts, and coat the threads with a light engine oil. Next, insert the bolts in the bolt holes. If necessary, use a soft-headed hammer to drive the bolts through the hub, but strike lightly. Apply the hub bolt nuts; draw them up evenly, tightening each only a little each time, tightening back and forth from one nut to another, thus avoiding any tendency to throw the propeller out of pitch and track. Finally, use a torque wrench to tighten the nuts to the values prescribed by the manufacturer, being careful not to injure the surface of the wood-propeller hub.

Installation of a propeller on a splined shaft

To install a propeller on a splined shaft, first install the rear-cone spacer if there is one on the assembly. Install the rear cone on the propeller shaft. Match the wide spline of the shaft with the wide groove of the hub, and slide the propeller well back against the rear cone. Next, assemble the front cone to the retaining nut, and screw the nut to the propeller shaft. A bar about 3 ft long is placed through the holes in the nut for the final tightening as specified in the maintenance manual. It is not necessary to pound the tightening bar. The snap ring is then installed in its groove in the hub. The retaining nut is safetied with a clevis pin and a cotter pin. If the propeller retaining nuts have elongated locking holes, a washer is placed under the cotter pin. The clevis-pin head should be to the inside, and the washer and cotter pin should be outside.

Inspection of a new propeller installation

When a new fixed-pitch propeller has been installed and operated, the hub bolts should always be inspected for tightness after the first flight and after 25 hr of flying. Thereafter, the bolts should be inspected and checked for tightness at least every 50 hr of operation. No definite time interval can be specified, since bolt tightness is affected by changes in the wood caused by the moisture content in the air where the airplane is flown and stored. During wet weather, some moisture is apt to enter the propeller wood through the drilled holes in the hub. The wood swells, but since expansion is limited by the bolts extending between the two flanges, some of the wood fibers are crushed. Later, when the propeller dries out during dry weather, a certain amount of propeller hub shrinkage takes place and the wood no longer completely fills the space between the two hub flanges. Accordingly, the shrinkage of the wood also results in loose hub bolts.

MAINTENANCE AND REPAIR OF WOOD PROPELLERS

Importance of propeller inspection, maintenance, and repair

Since the purpose of the propeller is to pull the airplane through the air, it is beyond question a vital part of the airplane that requires the highest degree of efficiency in its inspection, maintenance, and repair.

General nature of propeller repairs

When objects, such as stones, dirt, birds, etc., strike against the propeller blades and hub during flight or during takeoff and landing, they may cause a bend, cut, scar, nick, scratch, or some other defect in the blade or hub. If the defect is not repaired, local stresses are established which may cause a crack to develop, resulting eventually in the failure of the propeller or hub. For this reason propellers are carefully examined at frequent intervals, and any defects that are discovered are repaired immediately according to methods and procedures that will not further damage the propeller.

The terminology of propeller inspection, maintenance, and repair is very precise. Repairs and alterations are rigidly classified and assigned to certain types of repair agencies for accomplishment. After the work is assigned to the correct individuals or organizations, the propeller must be carefully cleaned before work is performed on it. Then the necessary inspections, repairs, alterations, and maintenance procedures may be accomplished. They are carefully regulated to prevent a technician from doing more harm than good.

Other inspection and maintenance operations include the checking of blade angles, field checking of a propeller for track, marking and coating of blades for identification purposes, servicing of the front cones, preparation of propeller shafts for installation, examining of hubs and blades for looseness, proper disposition of attaching parts, lubrication of the propeller assembly, and correct procedure after an accident involving a propeller.

Authorized repairs and alterations

The technician contemplating repair, overhaul, or alteration should be thoroughly familiar with the approved practices and regulations governing the operation which he expects to perform. All repairs or alterations of propellers must be accomplished in accordance with the regulations set forth in Federal Air Regulations and the pertinent manufacturer's manual.

Repairs and alterations on propellers are divided into four main categories: (1) **major alterations,** (2) **minor alterations,** (3) **major repairs,** and (4) **minor repairs.**

A **major alteration** is an alteration which may cause an appreciable change in weight, balance, strength, performance, or other qualities affecting the airworthiness of a propeller. Any alteration which is not accomplished in accordance with accepted practices or cannot be performed by means of elementary operations is also a major alteration.

A **minor alteration** is any alteration not classified as a major alteration.

A **major repair** is any repair which may adversely affect any of qualities noted in the definition of a major alteration.

A **minor repair** is any repair other than a major repair.

Classification of repair operations

Changes such as those in the following list are classified as major alterations unless they have been authorized in the propeller specifications issued by the Federal Aviation Agency.

1. Changes in blade design
2. Changes in hub design
3. Changes in governor or control design
4. Installation of a governor or feathering system
5. Installation of a propeller deicing system
6. Installation of parts not approved for the propeller
7. Any change in the design of a propeller or its controls

Changes classified as **minor alterations** are those similar to the types listed below.

1. Initial installation of a propeller spinner
2. Relocation or changes in the basic design of brackets or braces of the propeller controls
3. Changes in the basic design of propeller control rods or cables

Repairs of the types listed below are classified as propeller **major repairs,** since if they are improperly performed, they may adversely affect the airworthiness of the propeller.

1. Any repairs to or straightening of steel blades
2. Repairing or machining of steel hubs
3. Shortening of blades
4. Retipping of wood propellers
5. Replacement of outer laminations on fixed-pitch wood propellers
6. Inlay work on wood propellers
7. All repairs to composition blades
8. Replacement of tip fabric
9. Repairing of elongated bolt holes in the hub of fixed-pitch wood propellers
10. Replacement of plastic covering
11. Repair of propeller governors
12. Repair of balance propellers of rotorcraft
13. Overhaul of controllable-pitch propellers
14. Repairs involving deep dents, cuts, scars, nicks, etc., and straightening of aluminum blades
15. Repair or replacement of internal elements of blades

Propeller repairs such as those listed below are classified as propeller **minor repairs.**

1. Repairing of dents, cuts, scars, scratches, nicks, and leading-edge pitting of aluminum blades if the repair does not materially affect the strength, weight, balance, or performance of the propeller
2. Repairing of dents, cuts, scratches, nicks, and small cracks parallel to the grain of wood blades
3. Removal and installation of propellers
4. The assembly and disassembly of propellers to the extent necessary to permit (1) assembly of propellers partially disassembled for shipment and not requiring the use of balancing equipment, (2) the accomplishment of routine servicing and inspection, and (3) the replacement of parts other than those which normally require the use of skilled techniques, special tools, and test equipment
5. Balancing of fixed-pitch and ground-adjustable propellers
6. Refinishing of wood propellers

Persons and organizations authorized to perform repairs and alterations on propellers

The regulations governing the persons and organizations authorized to perform propeller repairs and alterations are subject to change, but in general, maintenance, minor repairs, or minor alterations must be done by a certificated repair station holding the appropriate rating, the manufacturer of the propeller, an appropriately rated technician (A & P) or a person working under the direct supervision of such a technician, or an appropriately certificated air carrier. Major repairs or alterations on propellers may be performed only by an appropriately rated repair station, manufacturer, or air carrier, in accordance with the regulations governing their respective operations.

Requirements governing persons or organizations authorized to perform maintenance and repairs on propellers are set forth in Federal Air Regulations.

It should be remembered that minor repairs and alterations are those which are not likely to change the operating characteristics of the propeller or affect the airworthiness of the propeller. All other repairs and alterations are major in nature and must be accomplished by the properly authorized agencies.

General inspection for defects

Wood propellers are inspected for such defects as cracks, bruises, scars, warp, oversize holes in the hub, evidence of glue failure, evidences of separated laminations, sections broken off, and defects in the finish. The tipping should be inspected for such defects as looseness or slipping, separation of soldered joints, loose screws, loose rivets, breaks, cracks, eroded sections, and corrosion. Frequently cracks do appear across the leading edge of the metal tipping between the front and rear slits where metal has been removed to permit easier forming of the tip curvature. These cracks are considered normal and are not cause for rejection.

The steel hub of a wood or composition propeller should be inspected for cracks and wear. When the hub is removed from the propeller, it should be magnetically inspected. Any crack in the hub is cause for rejection. The hub should also be inspected for wear of the bolt holes. If the bolt holes are appreciably worn, they may be repaired as described later in this chapter.

All propellers, regardless of the material of which they are made, should undergo regular and careful inspection for any possible defect. Any doubtful condition such as looseness of parts, nicks, cracks, scratches, bruises, or loss of finish should be carefully investigated, and the condition checked against repair and maintenance specifications for that particular type of propeller.

Causes for rejection

Propellers worn or damaged to such an extent that it is either impossible or uneconomical to repair them and make them airworthy should be rejected and scrapped. The following conditions are deemed to render a wood propeller unairworthy and are therefore cause for rejection.

1. A crack or deep cut across the grain of the wood
2. Split blades

3. Separated laminations, except the outside laminations of fixed-pitch propellers
4. More screw or rivet holes, including holes filled with dowels, than are used to attach the metal leading-edge strip and tip
5. An appreciable warp
6. An appreciable portion of wood missing
7. A crack, cut, or damage to the metal shank or sleeve of blades
8. Broken lag screws which attach the metal sleeve to the blade
9. An oversize shaft hole in fixed-pitch propellers
10. Cracks between the shaft hole and the bolt holes
11. Cracked internal laminations
12. Excessively elongated bolt holes

General repair requirements

Propellers should be repaired in accordance with the best accepted practices and the latest techniques. Manufacturers' recommendations should always be followed if such recommendations are available. It is recognized the manuals may not be available for some of the older propellers, and in such cases, the propellers should be repaired in accordance with standard practices and FAA regulations.

When a propeller is repaired or overhauled by a certificated agency, the Air Agency Certificate number or the name of the agency should be marked indelibly on the repaired propeller. It is recommended that a decalcomania giving both the repair agency's name and Air Agency Certificate number be used for this purpose. If the original identification marks on a propeller are removed during overhaul or repair, it is necessary that they be replaced. These include the name of the manufacturer and model designation.

Repairs for minor damage

Small cracks parallel to the grain in a wood propeller should be filled with an approved glue thoroughly worked into all portions of the cracks, dried, and then sanded smooth and flush with surface of the propeller. This treatment is also used with small cuts. Dents or scars which have rough surfaces or shapes that will hold a filler and will not induce failure may be filled with a mixture of approved glue and clean, fine sawdust, thoroughly worked and packed into the defect, dried, and then sanded smooth and flush with the surface of the propeller. It is very important that all loose or foreign matter be removed from the place to be filled so that a good bond of the glue to the wood is obtained.

Use of inlays

When damage to a wooden propeller is such that it cannot be classed as minor damage and still does not render the propeller unairworthy, inlays may be used to make the required repairs. Since these are major repairs, they must be accomplished by a repair agency which is certificated for major propeller repair.

The general requirements for propeller inlays are as follows:

1. The inlay must be of the same type of wood used in the original lamination and should be of approximately the same specific gravity.
2. The grain of the inlay material must be parallel with the grain of the propeller wood.
3. The taper of the inlay should be 10:1 or greater from the deepest point of damage to the featheredge of the inlay.
4. Inlays on the leading or trailing edge of a propeller should be made with a scarf, butt, or fish-mouth joint. The fish-mouth joint is preferred. A dovetail joint should not be used.
5. A trailing and a leading edge inlay should not overlap more than 25 percent.
6. The number of inlays should not exceed one large, two medium, or four small widely separated inlays per blade.
7. On blades with normal sections (thickness) from the mid-section to the tip, a cross-grain cut up to 20 percent of the chord in length and one-eighth of the section in thickness may be repaired. On blades with thin sections, this depth should not exceed one-twentieth (5 percent) of the section thickness.
8. The length of an inlay on the face or camber shall not exceed the chord length of the propeller at the center of the repair.
9. If inlays overlap lengthwise, the depth of each is limited to one-tenth the thickness at the deepest point of damage.

A drawing to illustrate inlays for the face or camber side of a wood propeller is shown in Fig. 18·7. Inlay repairs for leading and trailing edges are shown in Fig. 18·8.

Hub, neck, and shank repairs

The hubs, necks, and shanks of wood propellers may be repaired by the use of inlays within limits which will assure that the strength of the propeller is not impaired. Inlays in the sides of the hubs should not exceed in depth a value greater than 5 percent of the difference between the hub and bore diameters. For example, if the hub diameter is 6.5 in. and the bore diameter is 2.25 in., the difference is 4.25 in. and the inlay should not exceed a depth of 0.21 in.

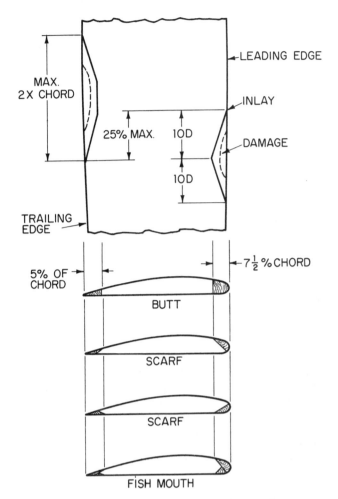

Figure **18·8**   Inlay repairs for leading and trailing edges.

In the portion of the blade where it fairs into the hub, allowable depths for inlays are dependent upon the general proportions. Where the width and thickness are both very large in proportion to the hub and blade, as shown in Fig. 18·9, maximum inlay depths of 7½ percent of the section thickness at the center of the inlay are permissible. The width and thickness of the propeller are determined as shown in Fig. 18·10.

Where the width and thickness of a propeller are excessively small, as shown in Fig. 18·11, maximum inlay depths of 2½ percent of the section thickness at the center of the inlay are permissible. For propellers rated for more than 50 hp, cuts 2½ percent deep may be filled with approved glue and fine sawdust. Propellers rated at less than 50 hp may have cuts 5 percent deep filled with glue and sawdust.

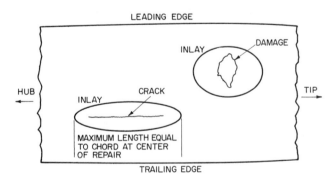

Figure **18·7**   Inlay repairs for face or camber of a wood propeller.

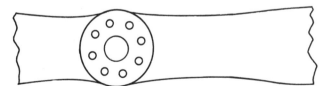

Figure **18·9**   Small hub with heavy neck and shaft.

365

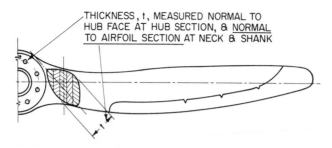

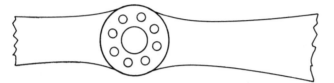

Figure 18·10 *Method for determining width and thickness.*

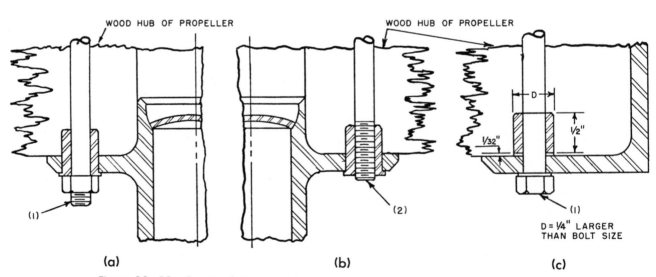

Figure 18·11 *Excessively small neck and shaft.*

Trailing-edge repairs

Narrow slivers up to ⅛ in. wide broken from the trailing edge at the wider portions of the blade may be repaired by sandpapering a new trailing edge, removing the least material possible, and fairing in a new trailing edge of smooth contour. Both blades should be narrowed by the same amount. Near the hub or tip an inlay should be used. The inlay should follow the specifications previously described for inlays on the trailing edge.

Repairs at or near the tip

In order to replace the wood worn away at the end of the metal tipping, enough of the metal should be removed to make the minimum repair taper 10:1 each

way from the deepest point. Because of the convex leading edge of the average propeller, this taper usually works out to about 8:1. The metal at the tip of the propeller may be removed by drilling out the rivets or screws and melting the solder where necessary. The solder should be melted with a soldering iron and not with a torch. Care must be taken not to weaken the wood by burning.

Repairs under the metal tipping should not exceed 7½ percent of the chord for butt or scarf joints or 10 percent for fish-mouth joints, with ¾ in. maximum depth for any repair.

The scarfing of wood tips onto a propeller to replace a damaged tip is not an acceptable repair. This is because it is not possible to test such a repair for strength, durability, and defective glue joints if such a repair remains undetected until failure occurs.

Separated laminations

Whenever the glue joint of an outside lamination of a fixed-pitch propeller is open, the propeller may be repaired by removing the loose lamination and gluing on a new lamination of kiln-dried wood of the same kind as the original. Outside laminations which have been crushed at the hub by excessive tightening of the hub bolts may be repaired by planing and sanding one hub face smooth and then removing the lamination on the other side of the propeller and replacing it with a thicker lamination. This will restore the propeller to its original thickness. It is permissible to replace both laminations if necessary.

Elongated bolt holes

It is permissible to repair elongated bolt holes by the insertion of a steel bushing around each bolt, as illustrated in Fig. 18·12. The bushing should be machined with an inside diameter to fit the bolt snugly and an

Figure 18·12 *Repair of elongated bolt holes. (a, b) Repair of damaged or elongated bolt holes in propeller hub flanges. (c) Repair of elongated bolt holes in propeller. (1) Drilled bolt with castellated nut or undrilled bolt with self-locking nut. (2) Bolt with head drilled for safety wiring. Note: These repairs are permitted only in the driving flange of the propeller hub and the adjacent face of the propeller.*

outside diameter approximately ¼ in. larger than the bolt size. The bushing should be about ½ in. long. The face of the hub should be drilled with a hole concentric with the bolt hole and only to a sufficient depth to accommodate the bushing so that it does not protrude above the surface of the wood hub. The bushing should not be driven onto the hub but should fit the hole in the hub with a clearance not exceeding 0.005 in. after moistureproofing. The bushing hole should be protected from moisture by two coats of aluminum paint, varnish, glue, or other moisture-resistant coating.

Plastic-covered blades

Small cracks, dents, scratches, and cuts in the plastic of plastic-covered propellers and blades may be repaired by using the special repair cement recommended by the manufacturer and by following manufacturer's directions. The instructions for the use of the cement and the method for making the repair should be followed carefully.

All repairs to composition blades are of a major nature, and damaged blades must be returned to the manufacturer for repair. However, where repairs to the metal cap and leading edge strip only are necessary, the methods and procedures prescribed by Federal Air Regulations may be followed.

Refinishing wood propellers

After repairing a propeller, it is usually necessary to refinish it. The material for refinishing should be of a type recommended by the manufacturer; however, two or three coats of approved spar varnish will usually be satisfactory. If it is necessary to remove the old finish, this may be done by applying a wax-free paint remover for a sufficient time to soften the varnish and then scraping the varnish from the blade. Care must be taken that the paint remover it not allowed to stay on the blade for a longer time than necessary and that it is not applied to the bare wood. After the propeller finish has been removed, the propeller may be sanded lightly with fine sandpaper until a smooth wood finish is obtained. A clear wood sealer should then be applied, followed by the required number of coats of spar varnish. Each coat of varnish should be allowed to dry thoroughly before the next coat is applied. During the application of the last two coats of varnish, it is well to check the balance of the propeller to make sure that balance is retained while the finish is applied.

Balancing a wood propeller

We have described the balancing of a propeller previously; however, because balancing is an important part of propeller repair, we shall explain the process further.

After a propeller has been repaired, the balance must always be checked. Balancing of a propeller should be done on a stand which is very stable and equipped with smooth knife-edge tracks. A mandrel of the correct diameter should be inserted in the hub or the hub boss of the propeller, and then the mandrel and propeller should be placed on the balancing stand.

It is essential that propeller balancing be performed

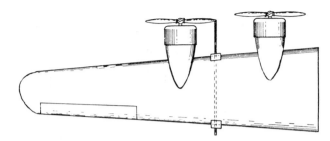

Figure 18·13   Checking propeller track in the field.

in a closed building to avoid any air currents which would give an erroneous indication. A correctly balanced propeller should have no tendency to turn from any position in which it is placed.

If a wood propeller is found to be out of balance horizontally, the condition may be corrected by adding a small amount of solder on the metal tipping. The solder should be spread on smoothly with the soldering iron and then filed and sanded to blend into the surrounding metal.

Vertical balance is corrected by attaching small brass plates to the hub boss on the light side. The plate must be exactly midway between the tips of the blades, or it will disturb the horizontal balance. Another method for correcting vertical balance is to attach metal weights between two hub bolts on the light side of the hub.

Checking and adjusting track

The **track** of a propeller is checked by locating a fixed reference point where it will just clear the rear face of the propeller at a point between 2 and 6 in. from the tip of the propeller, as shown in Fig. 18·13. As the propeller is rotated so that the blades pass the fixed reference point, the distance between the point and the propeller blade is measured. The out-of-track allowance for wood propellers is 1/16 in. A slightly out-of-track condition may be caused by unequal tension of the hub bolts. The trouble can be corrected by loosening the bolts and then retightening them a little at a time as evenly as possible. Care must be exercised to avoid overtightening of the hub bolts. If the propeller is as much as 3/8 in. out of track at the tips, the condition may be corrected by placing shims of suitable material between the hub boss and the rear flange. The shims should be placed on the side which has the rearward blade.

When the track of adjustable or controllable propellers is checked, the out-of-track limits should be checked against the manufacturer's specifications.

FIXED-PITCH METAL PROPELLERS

Description

A fixed-pitch metal propeller is usually manufactured by forging a single bar of aluminum alloy to the required shape. Typical of such propellers is the McCauley Met-L-Prop shown in Fig. 18·14. The pro-

Figure 18·14 McCauley Met-L-Prop. (McCauley Industrial Corp.)

peller shown carries the basic model numbers 1A90, 1B90, or 1C90.

The propeller shown in the illustration is provided with a center bore for the installation of a steel hub or adapter to provide for different types of installations. The six hub bolt holes are dimensioned to fit a standard engine crankshaft flange. The propeller is anodized to prevent corrosion.

Advantages

The advantages of a single-piece fixed-pitch metal propeller are (1) simplicity of maintenance, (2) durability, (3) resistance to weathering, (4) light weight, (5) low drag, and (6) minimum service requirements. The propellers are efficient for a particular set of operating conditions.

GROUND-ADJUSTABLE PROPELLERS

As previously mentioned, a ground-adjustable propeller is designed to permit a change of blade angle when the airplane is on the ground. This permits the adjustment of the propeller for the most effective operation under different conditions of flight. If it is desired that the airplane have a maximum rate of climb, the propeller blades are set at a comparatively low angle so the engine can rotate at maximum speed to produce the greatest power. The propeller blade, in any case, must not be set at an angle which will permit the engine to overspeed. When it is desired that the engine operate efficiently at cruising speed and at high altitudes, the blade angle is increased.

A ground-adjustable propeller may have blades made of wood or of metal. The hub is usually of two-piece steel construction with clamps or a large nut to hold the blades securely in place. When it is desired to change the blade angle of a ground-adjustable propeller, the clamps or blade nuts are loosened and the blade is rotated to the desired angle as indicated by a propeller protractor. The angle markings on the hub are not considered accurate enough to provide a good reference for blade adjustment; hence they are used chiefly for checking purposes.

Installation and adjustment

The installation for ground-adjustable propellers follows the practices previously described for fixed-

pitch propellers. The following steps may be considered typical for such an installation:

1. Make sure that the propeller being installed has been approved for the engine and aircraft on which it is being installed.
2. See that the propeller has been inspected for proper blade angle and airworthiness.
3. See that the propeller shaft and the inside of the propeller are clean and covered with a light coat of engine oil.
4. Install the rear-cone spacer (if used) and the rear cone.
5. Lift the propeller into place carefully, and slide it onto the shaft, making sure that the wide splines are aligned and that the splines are not damaged by rough handling of the propeller.
6. See that the split front cone and the retainer nut are coated with engine oil, assemble them, and install as a unit. (This step in the procedure will vary according to the design of the retaining devices. With some propellers the front-cone halves are installed, then the retainer nut, and finally a snap ring.)
7. Tighten the retainer nut to the proper torque as specified by the manufacturer or according to other pertinent directions. Usually a 3-ft bar will enable the technician to apply adequate torque for small propeller installations.
8. Install the safety pin or other safetying device.

Adjustment of the blade angle for a ground-adjustable propeller may be done on a propeller surface table as shown in Fig. 18·15. The propeller is mounted on a mandrel of the correct size, and the blade angle is checked with a large propeller protractor as shown in the illustration. The blade clamps or retaining nuts are loosened so the blades can be turned, and after the correct angle is established, the blades are secured in the hub by the clamps or blade nuts. The blade angle must be checked at a specified blade station as given in the pertinent instructions.

The method for checking the blade angle when the propeller is installed on the engine is the same as that used for other propellers and will be described later in this chapter.

Figure 18·15 Adjustment of blade angle on ground-adjustable propeller.

CONTROLLABLE-PITCH PROPELLERS

As the name implies, a controllable-pitch propeller is one on which the blade angle can be changed while the aircraft is in flight. Propellers of this type have been used for many years on aircraft where the extra cost of such a propeller was justified by the improved performance obtained.

Advantages

The controllable propeller makes it possible for the pilot to change the blade angle of the propeller at will in order to obtain the best performance from the aircraft engine. At takeoff the propeller is set at a low blade angle so the engine can attain the maximum allowable rpm and power. Shortly after takeoff the angle is increased slightly to prevent overspeeding of the engine and to obtain the best climb conditions of engine rpm and airplane speed. When the airplane has reached the cruising altitude, the propeller can be adjusted to a comparatively high pitch for a low cruising rpm or to a lower pitch for a higher cruising rpm and greater speed.

Two-position propeller

A **two-position propeller** does not have all the advantages mentioned in the foregoing paragraph; however, it does permit a setting of blade angle for best takeoff and climb (low-pitch, high rpm) and for best cruise (high-pitch, low rpm).

One of the best known two-position propellers was manufactured by the Hamilton-Standard Propeller Division of the United Aircraft Company. This propeller was used extensively for training and utility aircraft during World War II and is still used on some of the older aircraft.

A schematic diagram of a two-position propeller pitch change mechanism is shown in Fig. 18·16. The principal parts of this assembly are the hub assembly, the counterweight and bracket assembly, and the cylinder and piston assembly. The blade angle is decreased by the action of the cylinder and piston assembly when

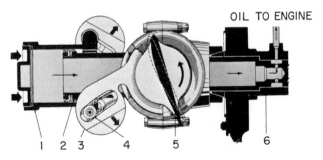

Figure 18·16 Diagram of two-position propeller mechanism. (1) Propeller cylinder, (2) propeller piston, (3) propeller counterweight and bracket, (4) propeller counterweight shaft and bearing, (5) propeller blade, (6) engine propeller shaft.

engine oil enters the cylinder and forces is forward. The cylinder is linked to the blades by means of a bushing mounted on the cylinder base and riding in a slot in the counterweight bracket. As the cylinder moves outward, the bracket is rotated inward, and since the bracket is attached to the base of the blade, the blade is turned to a lower angle.

When the oil is released from the cylinder by means of a three-way valve, the centrifugal force acting on the counterweights moves the counterweights outward and rotates the blades to a higher angle. At the same time, the cylinder is pulled back toward the hub of the propeller.

The basic high-pitch angle of the propeller is set by means of four blade-bushing index pins which are installed in aligned semicircular notches between the counterweight bracket and the blade bushing when the two are assembled. The pitch range is set by adjusting the counterweight adjusting screw nuts in the counterweight bracket.

Initial horizontal balance of the two-position counterweight-type propeller is adjusted by balancing washers installed in the base of the blades. Initial vertical balance is accomplished by means of balancing washers installed in the space provided in the barrel supporting block inside the hub barrel. Final balance is adjusted by installing lead wool in or removing it from the hollow assembly bolts.

A counterweight-type propeller may also be designed as a constant-speed propeller to be controlled by a propeller governor. In this case, the governor controls the flow of oil to and from the propeller cylinder in accordance with engine rpm. The governor is adjusted for the desired engine rpm by means of a control in the cockpit.

The foregoing brief discussion of counterweight-type propellers has been given to provide a basic understanding of their operation. Since these propellers will not often be encountered on many aircraft today, it is not deemed necessary to describe them in complete detail.

The Beech series 215 propeller

The Beech series 215 is a controllable-pitch propeller on which the blade angle is changed by means of an electric motor mounted on the **fixed sleeve** (1), Fig. 18·17. A pinion gear actuated by the motor through a gearbox drives the **ring gear** (3) in the illustration. The ring gear controls the position of the **pitch-control bearing** (2) by means of internal threads in the **ring-gear** hub (4). These threads engage lugs on the pitch-control bearing, thus causing it to move forward and rearward as the ring gear rotates. The lugs on the pitch-control bearing also engage slots in the fixed sleeve and prevent the external race of the bearing assembly from rotating with the propeller. The **control bolts** (7) attached to the inner race of the bearing assembly extend forward into the propeller hub and are attached to the **yoke** (11). The **bushing** (10) attached to the yoke engages a slot in the propeller blade butt. The fore-and-aft movement of the pitch-control bearing, as the ring

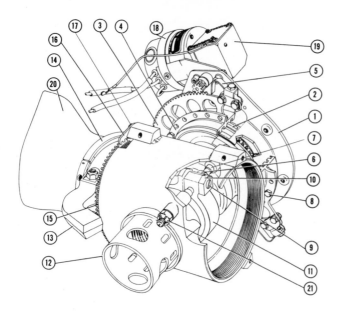

1. Fixed sleeve
2. Pitch control bearing
3. Ring gear
4. Ring gear hub
5. Spring stop
6. Yoke locknut
7. Control bolt
8. Ring gear attaching bolt
9. Actuator bolt
10. Bronze bushing
11. Yoke
12. Propeller retention nut
13. Counterweight arm
14. Balance ring
15. Blade retention nut
16. Blade retaining nut lock
17. Blade retaining nut lock bolt
18. Propeller motor mounting bracket
19. Propeller motor assembly
20. Propeller blade
21. Safety low pitch stop nut

Figure **18·17** *Pitch-changing mechanism for a Beechcraft series 215 propeller. (Beech Aircraft Co.)*

gear is turned, is transmitted through the control bolts to the yoke. The yoke moves fore and aft and rotates the blades by means of the bushing (10). An exploded view of the 215 propeller hub assembly is shown in Fig. 18·18.

Each blade assembly for the series 215 propeller consists of an aluminum-alloy blade, a steel sleeve, blade bearings, and blade retention nut. Thirty-one $7/16$-in.-diameter steel ball bearings ride in the bearing races of each blade. The blade retention nut, which remains as a permanent assembly on each blade, holds the blade ball bearings in their races and threads into the propeller hub to secure the entire blade assembly. A single slot on each blade butt is provided for the bronze actuator bushings.

The **hub assembly** consists of a pitch-control mechanism and a hub body. The hub body is constructed to make one piece. It is threaded to receive the blade retention nuts, and the center bore is splined to fit a 20-spline crankshaft. The hub body may be considered the foundation of the entire propeller. The propeller retention nut is designed so that, when it is loosened, the outer surface of the ridge on the aft end of the nut comes into contact with the snap ring in the hub body and acts as a puller to aid in removing the propeller. The hub body receives the centrifugal load of the rotating propeller blades through the threads for the blade retention nuts.

The **pinion and pitch-control gear assembly** consists of the internally threaded ring-gear hub, ring gear, stationary sleeve assembly, and a split lock ring. The pinion meshes with the ring gear and is an integral part of the motor which is mounted on the fixed sleeve. The ring gear is attached to the ring-gear hub which fits over the stationary sleeve assembly and is held in

place by means of the gear retainer ring. The sleeve contains slots so that the lugs on the outer race of the actuator bearing project through the sleeve and engage the internal threads of the ring-gear hub. The entire assembly is secured to the engine by bolting the stationary sleeve assembly to a plate on the nose case of the engine.

The **drive mechanism** consists of an electric motor, necessary gearing, and pinion gear. The electric motor is mounted on the fixed sleeve and provides the power for operating the blade-pitch actuating mechanism.

During operation of the propeller, the adjustment is controlled from the airplane cockpit by a three-position toggle switch. This switch is held in the INCREASE or DECREASE RPM position until the desired rpm is obtained, then it is returned to the center OFF position. When the engine is started, the propeller is adjusted to the HI RPM position (low pitch) by means of the toggle switch. This same position is used for takeoff. The desired cruising rpm is attained by moving the control switch to the LO RPM position and releasing it when the proper rpm is indicated. For approach and landing, the propeller is placed in the maximum high rpm position.

The removal, installation, inspection, and maintenance of the Beechcraft B215 propeller follows standard procedures established for other similar propellers. Special instructions are provided in the manufacturer's manual.

CONSTANT-SPEED PROPELLERS

As previously explained, a **constant-speed** propeller is controlled by a speed governor which automatically adjusts propeller pitch to maintain a selected engine

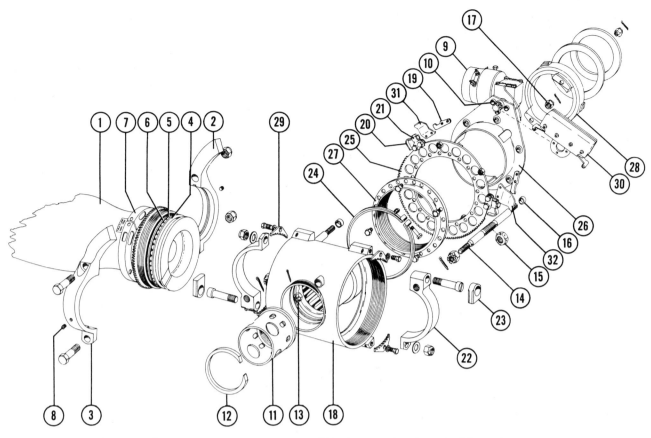

1. Blade assembly
2. Counterweight
3. Counterweight
4. Blade bearing race
5. Ball bearing
6. Blade bearing race
7. Balance ring assembly
8. Hex socket set screw
9. Motor assembly
10. Internal hex head screw
11. Propeller retention nut
12. Snap ring
13. Safety low pitch stop nut
14. Pitch control bolt
15. Yoke locknut
16. Pitch control bolt sleeve
17. Actuator bearing attaching nut
18. Hub
19. Ring gear clip tooth
20. Spring stop
21. Spring stop bracket
22. Yoke
23. Blade bushing
24. Gear retainer ring
25. Ring gear
26. Stationary sleeve
27. Gear hub
28. Actuator bearing assembly
29. Blade retention nut lock
30. Constant-speed switch assembly
31. Constant-speed switch actuator cam
32. Switch actuator cam

Figure 18 · 18 Exploded view of hub assembly for series 215 propeller.

speed. If the rpm of the propeller tends to increase, the governor senses the increase and responds by causing the propeller blade angle to increase. Also, when the propeller rpm tends to decrease, the governor causes a decrease in propeller blade angle. An increased blade angle will cause a decrease of rpm, and a decreased blade angle will cause an increase of engine rpm.

The pitch-changing devices for constant-speed propellers include electric motors, centrifugal force acting on flyweights, hydraulic cylinders, or a combination of these methods. The means by which these methods are applied will become clear as we examine some of the typical constant-speed propellers designed for light airplanes.

BEECHCRAFT MODEL 278 PROPELLER

The Beechcraft Model 278 propeller, shown in Fig. 18 · 19, is a hydraulically operated, constant-speed, all-metal propeller designed for use with Continental O-470 series engines. This engine has a flange-type

Figure 18·19 Beechcraft Model 278 propeller.

crankshaft, and the propeller installation is a simple, bolted, propeller-to-engine attachment. The propeller hub, blades, and spinner comprise the complete propeller assembly.

Propeller hub

The hub assembly for the Model 278 propeller, shown in the exploded view of Fig. 18·20, includes the hub body, machined from welded and copper-brazed steel forgings; the blade actuating mechanism; and retaining parts for the propeller blades. A piston and shaft assembly rides in the center of the hub, which is honed smooth and acts as a stationary cylinder. The piston shaft extends forward from the piston and is attached to a yoke, forward of the hub body, which links it with two actuator bolts. These bolts protrude from guides on opposite sides of the hub. Within the

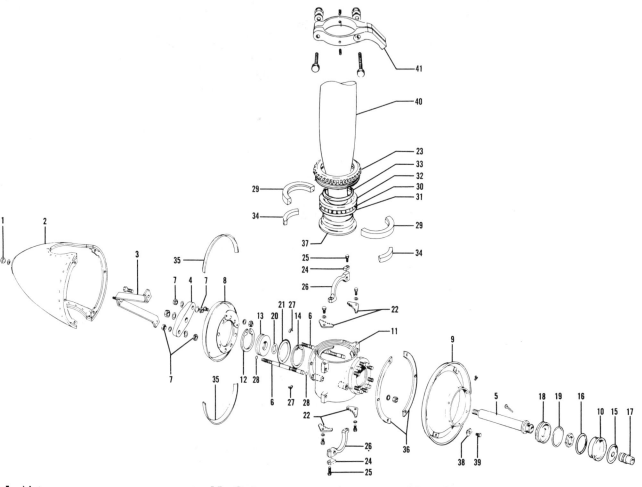

1. Nut	**15.** O ring	**29.** Balance ring assembly
2. Spinner shell assembly	**16.** O ring	**30.** Ball bearing
3. Spinner retainer bracket assembly	**17.** Oil transfer line connector tube	**31.** Thrust bearing inboard race assembly
4. Propeller front yoke	**18.** Propeller piston	**32.** Thrust bearing outboard race assembly
5. Propeller piston shaft assembly	**19.** O ring	**33.** Thrust bearing gasket
6. Propeller control bolt	**20.** O ring	**34.** Balance weight
7. Nut	**21.** O ring	**35.** Propeller shell bulkhead forward pad
8. Propeller spinner front bulkhead	**22.** Blade retention nut lock	**36.** Propeller shell bulkhead aft pad
9. Propeller spinner aft bulkhead	**23.** Retainer propeller blade nut	**37.** Propeller blade retainer
10. Oil retainer aft partition	**24.** Sliding actuator bushing	**38.** T nut
11. Propeller hub brazed assembly	**25.** Actuator bolt	**39.** Bolt
12. Snap ring	**26.** Propeller yoke	**40.** Propeller blade
13. Propeller piston guide	**27.** Control bolt lock	**41.** Counterbalance weight set
14. Snap ring	**28.** O ring	

Figure 18·20 Exploded view of Model 278 propeller.

hub the actuator bolts are linked together by a split yoke which fits around the outside of the stationary cylinder. The halves of the yoke are tied together by two pitch-control bolts with bronze actuator bushings fitted on their heads. Since the actuator bushings also fit into slots in the propeller blade butts, the axial piston motion moves the piston shaft and actuator bolt assembly, which in turn transmits a rotary motion to the propeller blades to change their pitch.

Blades

Each propeller blade assembly consists of an aluminum-alloy blade, steel sleeve, blade bearings, and a blade retention nut. Thirty-one $7/16$-in.-diameter steel ball bearings ride in the bearing races of each blade. The blade retention nut, which remains as a permanent assembly on each blade, holds the blade ball bearings in their races and threads into the propeller hub to secure the entire blade assembly. A single slot on each blade butt is provided for the bronze actuator bushings described before.

The spinner

A polished aluminum-alloy spinner streamlines the propeller installation and contributes to engine cooling. Except for the blade openings, the spinner shell completely encloses the propeller hub assembly. A retaining bolt at the front of the attaching bracket on the forward portion of the propeller hub flange is used to secure the spinner to the propeller. The spinner is supported by two aluminum-alloy bulkheads attached to the propeller hub. The forward bulkhead assists with spinner alignment, while the aft bulkhead bottoms the spinner and secures it from rotational slippage. Balancing bolts installed in nut plates on the aft bulkhead are used to balance the propeller assembly, and drain holes in the flange at the aft portion of the spinner shell prevent accumulation of moisture which could cause an out-of-balance condition.

Principles of operation

The blade-angle changes of the propeller are dependent upon the balance between governor boosted oil pressure and the inherent centrifugal tendency of the propeller blades to maintain a low pitch angle. The balance differential is maintained by the governor, which either meters oil pressure to or allows oil to drain from the propeller cylinder in the quantity necessary to maintain the proper blade angle for constant-speed operation. A drawing of the governor is shown in Fig. 18·21.

Within the governor, the L-shaped **flyweights** are pivoted on a disk-type **flyweight head** coupled to the engine gear train through a hollow drive-gear shaft. The **pilot valve plunger** extends into the hollow shaft and is so mounted that the pivoting motion of the rotating flyweights will raise the plunger against the pressure of the **speeder spring** or allow the spring pressure to force the plunger down in the hollow shaft. The positions assumed by the plunger determine the flow of oil from the governor to the propeller. Governor oil is directed to a transfer ring on the engine crank-

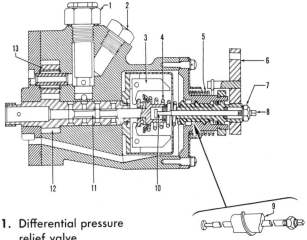

1. Differential pressure relief valve
2. High pressure relief valve
3. Flyweights
4. Speeder spring
5. Control lever spring
6. Speed adjusting control lever
7. Locknut
8. Lift rod adjustment
9. Speed adjusting worm
10. Pilot valve lift rod
11. Pilot valve
12. Governor pump drive gear
13. Governor pump idler gear

Figure 18·21 Woodward propeller governor. (Woodward Controls Corp.)

shaft and thence into the crankshaft tube which carries it into the rear side of the piston cylinder arrangement in the propeller hub. The linear motion of the piston is changed to rotary motion of the blades as shown in Fig. 18·22. Since the centrifugal twisting force of the propeller blades is transmitted to the propeller piston, the governor boosted oil pressure must overcome this force to change the engine rpm. Forward motion of the piston increases pitch and decreases engine rpm, while rearward motion of the piston decreases pitch and increases engine rpm.

The action of the pitch-changing mechanism is clearly shown in Fig. 18·22. As governor oil pressure enters the cylinder to the rear of the **piston,** the piston moves forward. This motion is transmitted through the **piston shaft** to the **forward yoke. Actuator bolts** are attached to each end of the yoke, and these bolts, being attached to the **split yoke,** carry the motion of the forward yoke to the split yoke. Each **actuator bushing** mounted on the split yoke fits into a groove on the butt of each blade, and when the bushings are moved forward by the split yoke, the blades are forced to rotate.

During operation of the propeller in flight, the governor flyweights react to engine rpm. If the engine is turning faster than the selected rpm, the flyweights will move outward and cause the pilot valve in the governor to move upward or toward the governor head. With this valve position the oil pressure from the governor pump is directed to the propeller and the propeller piston moves forward to increase the blade angle and decrease the rpm.

When the engine is "on speed," the governor flyweights are in a neutral position and the pilot valve

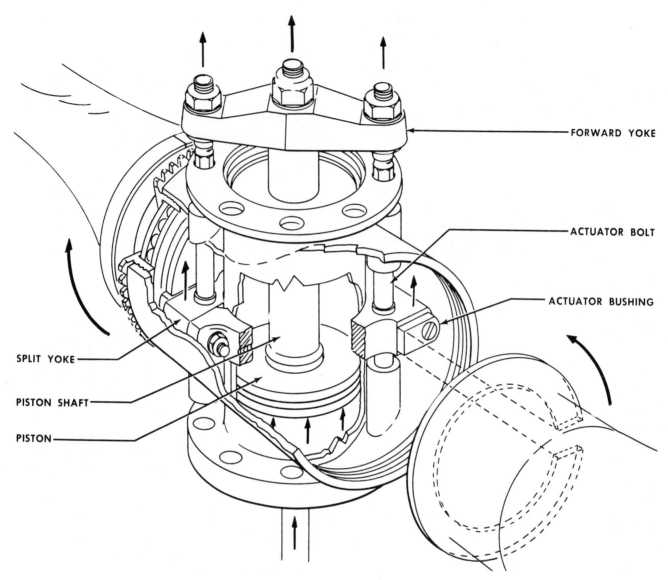

Figure **18·22** *Operation of Model 278 propeller.*

FORWARD YOKE

ACTUATOR BOLT

ACTUATOR BUSHING

SPLIT YOKE

PISTON SHAFT

PISTON

seals the oil pressure in the propeller system so there is no movement in either direction. The oil pressure prevents the piston from moving backward; hence the blade angle cannot decrease.

If engine rpm falls below the selected speed ("underspeed" condition), the flyweights of the governor move inward and allow the pilot valve to move toward the base of the governor. This position of the pilot valve opens a passage which permits the oil to flow from the propeller to the engine, thus allowing the blade angle to decrease and the rpm to increase. The blade angle tends to decrease because of the centrifugal twisting force as explained previously.

Propeller installation

The installation of the Model 278 propeller on the crankshaft flange of the engine is comparatively simple. The following procedure is recommended by the manufacturer:

1. Check the condition of the propeller and piston oil transfer tube at the engine crankshaft flange.
2. Align the two guide pins in the propeller hub with the corresponding holes in the engine crankshaft flange placing the No. 1 blade on the side of the TC (top center) mark on the engine flange, and install the propeller.
3. Install the retaining nuts and washers or retaining bolts and washers. Torque the propeller retention nuts to 600 to 800 in.-lb or the 278-395 retention bolts to 600 to 700 in.-lb.
4. Safety the nuts or bolts to the guide pins with safety wire.
5. Position the spinner on the propeller according to the marks made on removal, and install the spinner retaining nut. Tighten the nut until the flange at the rear of the spinner shell touches the rubber strip on the rear bulkhead completely around. Tighten the nut an additional two or three turns, and safety it with a cotter pin.

Maintenance and repair

The maintenance and repair of the Beechcraft Model 278 propeller should be performed according to the established methods employed for metal propellers. These methods comply with FAA regulations and with the instructions given in the manufacturer's overhaul manual. Specific instructions for the overhaul of the propeller are provided by the manufacturer, and overhaul should be accomplished in a properly certificated propeller repair station or by the manufacturer.

McCAULEY CONSTANT-SPEED PROPELLER

Operation

A McCauley Model 2A36C18 propeller is shown in Fig 18·23. This is an all-metal constant-speed propeller controlled by a single-acting governor. The blades are made of forged aluminum alloy, and the hub parts are made of steel.

A schematic diagram of the propeller hub mechanism is shown in Fig. 18·24. A careful study of this drawing will reveal the **cylinder** at the front of the propeller hub, the **piston** inside the cylinder, the hollow **piston rod** through which oil flows to and from the cylinder, the **blade actuating pin,** the **low-pitch return boost spring,** the **hub assembly,** and the **blade assembly.** During operation, when the piston is fully forward, the blades are in the low-pitch position. If the engine overspeeds, the governor will direct governor oil pressure through the crankshaft into the hollow piston rod

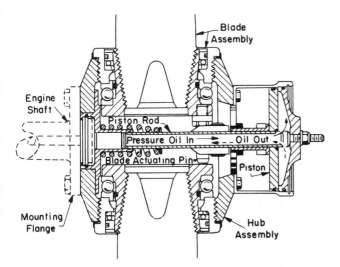

Figure *18·23* *McCauley propeller.*

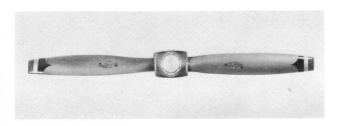

Figure *18·24* *Schematic diagram of hub mechanism.*

of the propeller. The oil flows through the piston rod and into the cylinder, forcing the piston to move back. The piston rod is linked to the blade butts through the **link assemblies** and the blade actuating pins, and as the piston rod moves backward, the blades are forced to rotate in the hub. This increases the pitch and reduces the engine speed. If the engine rpm falls below the value selected by the governor control, the governor pilot valve will move downward and open the passages which allow the oil in the propeller piston to return through the piston rod to the engine. The piston is pushed forward by the low-pitch return boost spring and by the centrifugal twisting of the rotating blades. When the propeller is "on speed," the oil pressure in the cylinder is balanced against the two forces tending to turn the blades to low pitch.

The detailed construction of the hub assembly, pitch-changing mechanism, and the blade assemblies is shown in the exploded view of Fig. 18·25.

BEECHCRAFT MODEL 279 FULL-FEATHERING PROPELLER

The Beechcraft Model 279 propeller is a hydraulic, constant-speed, full-feathering propeller with a flanged hub. It employs an engine-driven hydraulic governor for control. The governor is double acting in that it directs oil under boost pressure to the propeller for both increase and decrease rpm adjustments. The governor is similar to that described for the Model 278 propeller and is adjusted by means of a control in the cockpit.

Operation

The operation of the Model 279 propeller can be understood by examining Fig. 18·26. It will be observed that the hub of the propeller contains a sleeve inside which is a movable cylinder. Inside the movable cylinder is a stationary piston mounted at the end of the **piston rod,** and inside the piston rod is the **oil-distributor tube** which directs oil to either side of the piston, depending upon action of the governor. When governor-boosted oil pressure is directed to the forward side of the piston, the cylinder moves forward to increase the blade angle. If the oil pressure is directed to the rear side of the piston, the cylinder moves back and decreases the blade angle.

The yoke, mounted on the forward end of the movable cylinder, is linked to two rod assemblies extending around opposite sides of the hub. These rod assemblies are attached to arms mounted on the shank of each blade. As the cylinder is moved forward or backward, the linkage causes the blades to rotate. The blade-angle range is from full low pitch to a full-feathered position. The two rod assemblies, called the **propeller pitch-control link assemblies,** are shown in the drawing of Fig. 18·27. As the yoke is moved forward by the movable cylinder, the blades will rotate toward a higher blade angle until they finally reach the full-feathered position.

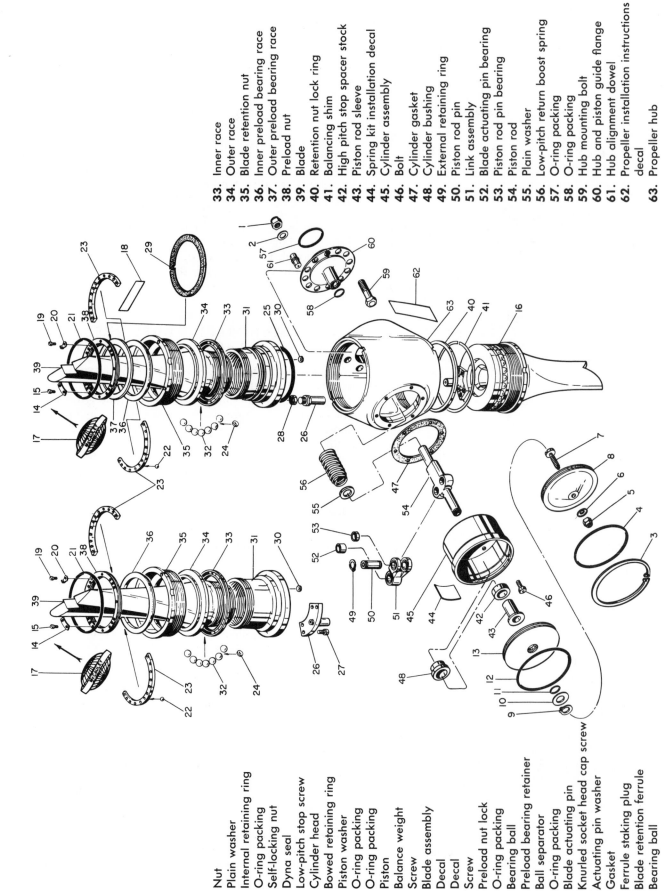

1. Nut
2. Plain washer
3. Internal retaining ring
4. O-ring packing
5. Self-locking nut
6. Dyna seal
7. Low-pitch stop screw
8. Cylinder head
9. Bowed retaining ring
10. Piston washer
11. O-ring packing
12. O-ring packing
13. Piston
14. Balance weight
15. Screw
16. Blade assembly
17. Decal
18. Decal
19. Screw
20. Preload nut lock
21. O-ring packing
22. Bearing ball
23. Preload bearing retainer
24. Ball separator
25. O-ring packing
26. Blade actuating pin
27. Knurled socket head cap screw
28. Actuating pin washer
29. Gasket
30. Ferrule staking plug
31. Blade retention ferrule
32. Bearing ball

33. Inner race
34. Outer race
35. Blade retention nut
36. Inner preload bearing race
37. Outer preload bearing race
38. Preload nut
39. Blade
40. Retention nut lock ring
41. Balancing shim
42. High pitch stop spacer stock
43. Piston rod sleeve
44. Spring kit installation decal
45. Cylinder assembly
46. Bolt
47. Cylinder gasket
48. Cylinder bushing
49. External retaining ring
50. Piston rod pin
51. Link assembly
52. Blade actuating pin bearing
53. Piston rod pin bearing
54. Piston rod
55. Plain washer
56. Low-pitch return boost spring
57. O-ring packing
58. O-ring packing
59. Hub mounting bolt
60. Hub and piston guide flange
61. Hub alignment dowel
62. Propeller installation instructions decal
63. Propeller hub

Figure 18·25 Exploded view of McCauley constant-speed propeller.

376

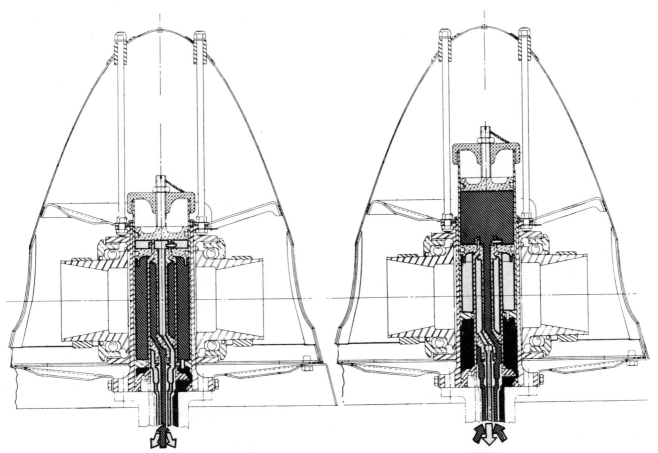

Figure 18·26 Operation of Beechcraft Model 279 propeller.

Construction

The construction and parts arrangement of the Model 279 propeller are illustrated in Fig. 18·28. When the propeller hub parts are assembled, the piston (19) is attached to the piston rod (13). The cylinder (26) is inside the hub (1). The piston and rod assembly is stationary inside the hub, and the cylinder is free to move forward and rearward. In the forward end of the cylinder is the **oil retainer partition** (21) which seals the cylinder. The **yoke** (27) is mounted on the forward end of the cylinder with the **propeller pitch-control link** (31) assemblies attached to each side. The ends of these link assemblies are connected to the blade actuator arm assemblies as shown in Fig. 18·29, which illustrates the construction of the blade assemblies at the butt.

The propeller blades are made of aluminum alloy and are shrunk into steel sleeves called **blade retainers.** The blade retainers cannot be removed without danger of damaging the blades. The arrangement and construction of the blade bearings are clearly shown in the illustration. When the blade is assembled, the bearing assembly is located between the flange of the blade retainer and the propeller blade retention nut.

The feathering system

The feathering system for the Model 279 propeller consists of a feathering pump, reservoir, a feathering time-delay switch, and a propeller feathering light located approximately in the center of the instrument panel. The propeller is feathered by moving the control in the cockpit against the low-speed stop. This causes the **pilot valve lift rod** in the governor to hold the pilot valve in a **decrease rpm** position regardless of the action of the governor flyweights. This causes the propeller blades to rotate through high pitch to the feathered position.

Maintenance and repair

The inspection, maintenance, and repair of the Beechcraft Model 279 propeller should be accomplished according to standard practice described elsewhere in this chapter and in accordance with the manufacturer's instructions. With the exception of minor repairs, routine inspections, and normal service, all work should be accomplished in a properly certificated repair station.

HARTZELL FULL-FEATHERING PROPELLER

Hartzell constant-speed, full-feathering propellers utilize hydraulic pressure to reduce the pitch of the blades and a combination of spring and counterweight force to increase the pitch. If the pitch is increased to the limit, the blades are in the feathered position.

377

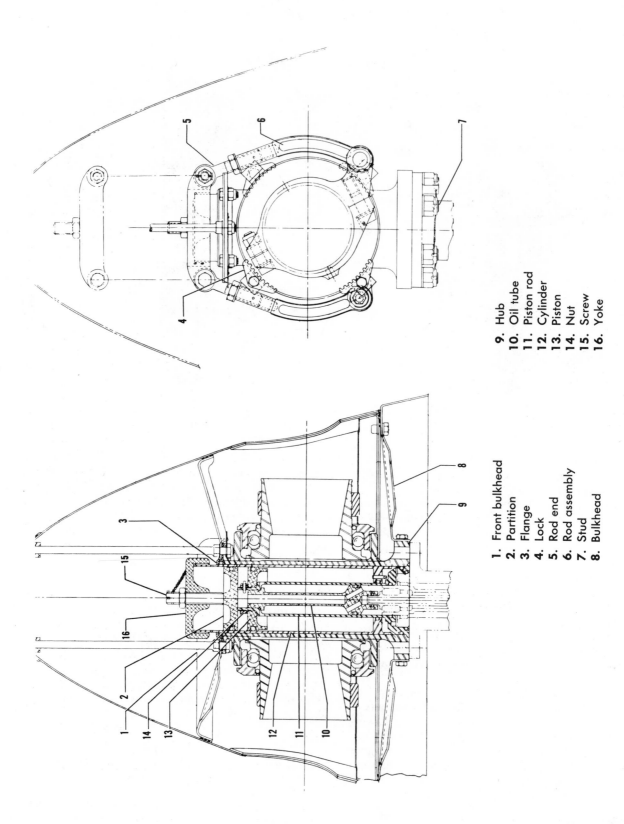

1. Front bulkhead
2. Partition
3. Flange
4. Lock
5. Rod end
6. Rod assembly
7. Stud
8. Bulkhead
9. Hub
10. Oil tube
11. Piston rod
12. Cylinder
13. Piston
14. Nut
15. Screw
16. Yoke

Figure **18 · 27**   Operating mechanism of Model 279 propeller.

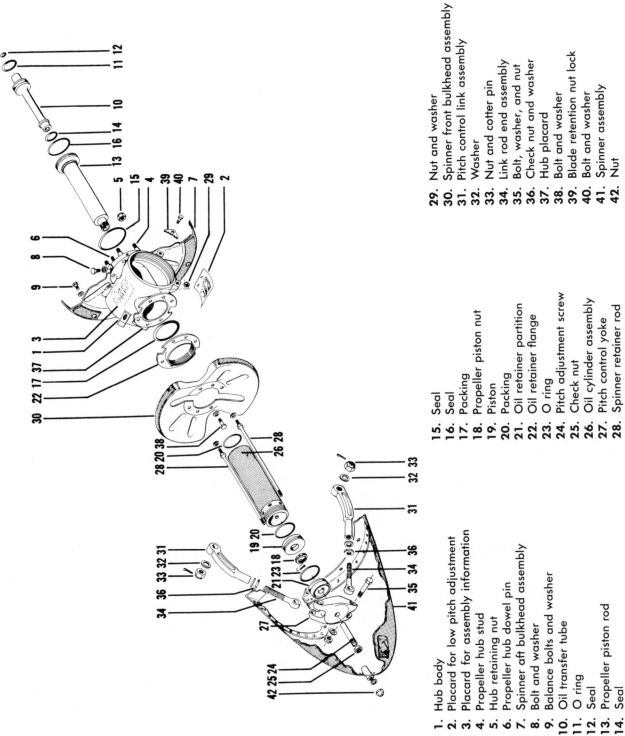

1. Hub body
2. Placard for low pitch adjustment
3. Placard for assembly information
4. Propeller hub stud
5. Hub retaining nut
6. Propeller hub dowel pin
7. Spinner aft bulkhead assembly
8. Bolt and washer
9. Balance bolts and washer
10. Oil transfer tube
11. O ring
12. Seal
13. Propeller piston rod
14. Seal
15. Seal
16. Seal
17. Packing
18. Propeller piston nut
19. Piston
20. Packing
21. Oil retainer partition
22. Oil retainer flange
23. O ring
24. Pitch adjustment screw
25. Check nut
26. Oil cylinder assembly
27. Pitch control yoke
28. Spinner retainer rod
29. Nut and washer
30. Spinner front bulkhead assembly
31. Pitch control link assembly
32. Washer
33. Nut and cotter pin
34. Link rod end assembly
35. Bolt, washer, and nut
36. Check nut and washer
37. Hub placard
38. Bolt and washer
39. Blade retention nut lock
40. Bolt and washer
41. Spinner assembly
42. Nut

Figure 18 · 28 Exploded view of Model 279 propeller hub assembly.

379

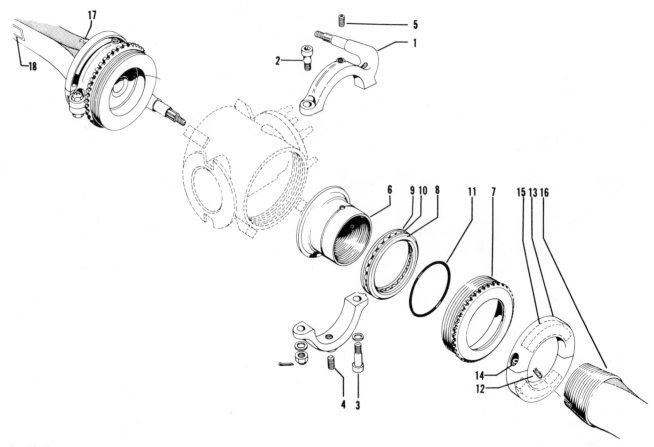

1. Blade actuator arm assembly
2. Bolt
3. Bolt, washers, and nut
4. Headless oval point set screw
5. Headless cup point set screw
6. Propeller blade retainer

7. Propeller blade retention nut
8. Blade thrust bearing race (outer)
9. Blade thrust bearing race (inner)
10. Ball (bearing)
11. Gasket
12. Headless cup point set screw

13. Balance ring assembly
14. Hex socket head cap screw
15. Balance weight
16. Propeller blade
17. Bearing information placard
18. Beechcraft propeller placard

Figure 18·29   Exploded view of Model 279 blade assembly.

Operation

Figure 18·30 is a schematic drawing of the Hartzell Model HC-82XF-2 propeller hub assembly to illustrate the pitch-changing mechanism. When the engine speed is below that selected by the pilot, the governor pilot valve directs governor oil pressure to the propeller. This pressure forces the cylinder forward and reduces the propeller pitch. When the cylinder moves forward, it also compresses the feathering spring.

If engine speed increases above the rpm selected, the governor opens the oil passage to allow the oil in the propeller cylinder to return to the engine. The feathering spring and the counterweight force cause the blades to rotate to a higher pitch position.

Feathering is accomplished by releasing the governor oil pressure, allowing the counterweights and feathering spring to feather the blades. This is done by pulling the governor pitch control back to the limit of its travel, thus opening up a port in the governor to allow the oil from the propeller to drain back to the

engine. The time necessary to feather depends upon the size of the oil passage from the propeller to the engine and the force exerted by the spring and counterweights. The larger the passages through the governor and the heavier the springs, the quicker is the feathering action. The elapsed time for feathering is usually between 3 and 10 sec.

Unfeathering the propeller is accomplished by repositioning the governor control to the normal flight range and restarting the engine. As soon as the engine cranks over a few turns, the governor starts to unfeather the blades and soon windmilling takes place, thus speeding up the process of unfeathering. In order to facilitate cranking of the engine, the feathering blade angle is set at 80 to 85° as the ¾ station on the blades. In general, restarting and unfeathering can be accomplished within a few seconds.

Special unfeathering systems may be installed with the Hartzell propeller when it is desired to increase the speed of unfeathering. Such a system is shown in Fig.

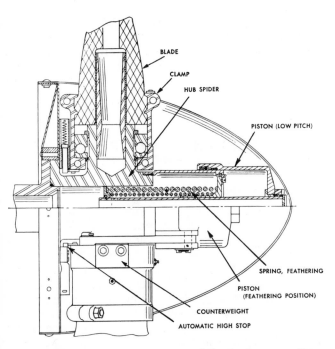

Figure **18·30** *Drawing of Hartzell feathering propeller.*

18·31. During normal operation the accumulator stores governor oil pressure, and when the propeller is feathered, this pressure is trapped in the accumulator because the accumulator valve is closed at this time. When the propeller control is placed in the normal position, the pressure stored in the accumulator is applied to the propeller to rotate the blades to a low pitch angle. It must be remembered that, when the propeller is feathered, there is no pressure available from the governor because the engine is stopped. The pressure stored in the accumulator is used in place of the pressure which would normally be supplied by the governor.

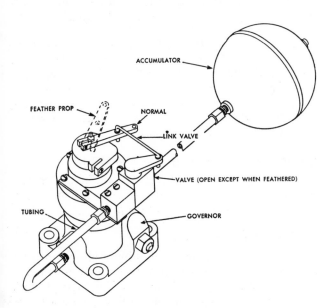

Figure **18·31** *Unfeathering system.*

Propeller governor

We have discussed the propeller governor and explained its operation to some degree in explaining the operation of constant-speed propellers; however, it will be beneficial to examine the illustration of Fig. 18·32 in order to gain a more complete understanding of governor operation.

The governor is geared to the engine in order to sense the rpm of the engine at all times. The speed sensing is accomplished by means of rotating **flyweights** in the upper part of the governor body. As shown in

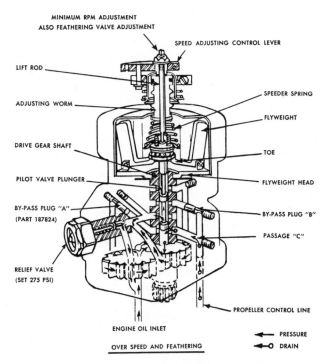

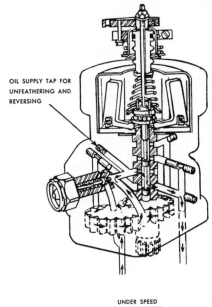

Figure **18·32** *Woodward propeller governor.*

the drawing, the flyweights are L-shaped and hinged at the outside where they attach to the **flyweight head.** The **toe** of each flyweight presses against the race of a bearing at the upper end of the **pilot valve.** Above the bearing are the **speeder spring seat** and the **speeder spring** which normally holds the **pilot valve plunger** in the down position. Above the speeder spring is the **adjusting worm,** which is rotated by means of the **speed-adjusting lever.** The speed-adjusting lever is connected to the propeller control in the cockpit. As the speed-adjusting lever is moved, it rotates the adjusting worm and increases or decreases the compression of the speeder spring. This, of course, affects the amount of flyweight force necessary to move the pilot valve plunger. If it is desired to increase the rpm of the engine, the speed-adjusting control lever is rotated in the direction to increase speeder spring compression. It is therefore necessary that the engine rpm increase in order to apply the additional flyweight force to raise the pilot valve plunger to an "on-speed position."

In the drawing of Fig. 18·32 the governor is in the "overspeed" condition. The engine rpm is greater than that selected by the control, and the flyweights are pressing outward. The toes of the flyweights have raised the pilot valve plunger to a position which permits oil pressure from the propeller to return to the engine. The propeller counterweights and feathering spring can then rotate the propeller blades to a higher angle, thus causing the engine rpm to decrease.

When the governor is in an "underspeed" condition, that is, with engine rpm below the selected value, the governor flyweights are held inward by the speeder spring and the pilot valve plunger is in the down position. This position of the valve directs governor oil pressure from the governor gear pump to the propeller cylinder and causes the propeller blades to rotate to a lower pitch angle. The lower pitch angle allows the engine rpm to increase.

The governor shown in the drawing is equipped with a lift rod to permit feathering of the propeller. When the cockpit control is pulled back to the limit of its travel, the lift rod in the governor holds the pilot valve plunger in an "overspeed" position. This causes the blade angle of the propeller to increase to the feathered position regardless of flyweight or speeder spring force.

It is important to observe the effect of the speeder spring on governor operation. If the speeder spring should break, the pilot valve plunger would be raised to the overspeed position, which would call for an increase of propeller pitch. This, of course, would allow the propeller to feather. If the speeder spring should break in a governor for a nonfeathering, constant-speed propeller, the propeller blades would rotate to maximum high pitch angle.

Propeller governors similar to the one described are also arranged for double-acting operation where governor pressure is directed to the propeller through different passages for both "increase" rpm and "decrease" rpm. This is accomplished merely by utilizing the oil passages in a different manner. A study of the diagram of Fig. 18·32 will show that some of the passages are plugged, and if the use of passages is changed, the governor may be adapted to different types of systems. The arrangement for any particular propeller system is shown in the manufacturer's manual for the propeller under consideration.

MAINTENANCE AND REPAIR OF METAL PROPELLERS

Hollow and solid-steel propellers

Damaged steel propeller blades should not be repaired except by the manufacturer. Welding or straightening is not permissible on such blades, even for very minor repairs, except by the manufacturer because of the special process employed and the heat treatment required. A blade developing a crack of any nature in service should be returned to the manufacturer for inspection. When a blade is considered non-repairable, a notice of rejection should be made out by the manufacturer and sent to the nearest inspector of the Federal Aviation Agency.

Inspection of steel blades

The inspection of steel blades may be either visual or magnetic. The visual inspection becomes easier to accomplish if the steel blades are covered with engine oil or rust-preventive compound. The full length of the leading edge, especially near the tip; the full length of the trailing edge; the grooves and shoulders on the shank; and all dents and scars should be examined with a magnifying glass to decide whether defects are scratches or cracks.

In the magnetic inspection of steel blades and propeller parts, the blade or part to be inspected is mounted in a machine, and then the blade is magnetized by passing a current through the blade or part, using a power supply of 2000 to 3000 amp at 6 volts. Either a black or a red mixture of iron filings and kerosene is poured over the blade or part at the time that it is magnetized. North and south magnetic poles are established on either end of any crack in the metal. The iron filings arrange themselves in lines within the magnetic field thus created. A black or a red line, depending upon the color of the mixture, will appear wherever a crack exists in the blade or part.

Repair of minor damage to steel blades

Minor injuries to the leading and trailing edges only of steel blades may be smoothed by handstoning provided that the injury is not deep.

Aluminum-alloy propellers

A seriously damaged aluminum-alloy propeller blade should be repaired only by the manufacturer or by repair agencies certified for this type of work. Such repair agencies should follow manufacturers' instructions.

Definition of damaged propellers

A damaged metal propeller is one that has been bent, cracked, or seriously dented. Minor surface dents, scars, nicks, etc., which are removable by field maintenance mechanics are not considered sufficient to constitute a damaged propeller.

If the model number of a damaged blade appears on the manufacturer's list of blades which cannot be repaired, the blade should be rejected.

Blades bent in face alignment

The extent of a bend in the face alignment of blades should be carefully checked by means of a protractor similar to the one illustrated in Fig. 18·33. Only bends not exceeding 20° at 0.15-in. blade thickness to 0° at 1.1-in. blade thickness may be cold-straightened. After straightening, the affected portion of the blade must be etched and thoroughly inspected for cracks and other flaws. Blades with bends in excess of this amount require heat-treatment and must be returned to the manufacturer or his authorized agent for repair.

Manufacturers often specify the maximum bends which can be repaired by cold-straightening on specific models of propellers. Figure 18·34 is a chart which shows the maximum allowable bend for cold repair of the McCauley Models 1A90, 1B90, and 1C90 fixed-pitch metal propellers. From the chart, for example, it can be determined that, if the propeller is bent at the 16-in. radius, the maximum degree of bend which can be straightened cold is 9°. At the 32-in. radius the blade can be repaired by cold-straightening if the bend is as great as 18.5°.

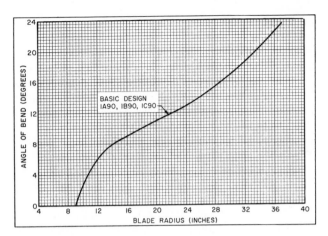

Figure 18·34   Chart to show maximum allowable bend for cold repair.

Blades bent in edge alignment

Blades which are bent in edge alignment should not be repaired by anyone except the manufacturer or a certificated repair station holding the appropriate rating.

Inspection and treatment of defects

Scratches and suspected cracks should be given a local etch, as explained elsewhere in this text, and then examined with a magnifying glass. **The shank fillets of adjustable-pitch blades and the front half of the undersurface of all blades from 6 to 10 in. from the tip are the most critical portions.**

Adjustable-pitch blades should be etched locally on the clamping portion of the shank at points ¼ in. from the hub edge in line with the leading and trailing edges and should be examined with a magnifying glass for circumferential cracks. The shank must be within drawing tolerance. Any crack is cause for rejection. The micarta shank bearing on controllable and hydromatic propeller blades should not be disturbed except by the manufacturer. Blades requiring removal of more material than that specified as permissible in this chapter under the heading "Repair of Pitted Leading Edges" should be scrapped.

Local etching

To avoid dressing off an excess amount of metal, checking by local etching should be accomplished at intervals during the progress of removing cracks and double-back edges of metal. Suitable sandpaper or fine-cut files may be used for removing the necessary amount of metal, after which, in each case, the surfaces involved should be smoothly finished with No. 00 sandpaper. Each blade from which any appreciable amount of metal has been removed should be properly balanced before being used.

When aluminum-alloy blades are inspected for cracks or other failures and for bends, nicks, scratches, and corrosion, the application of engine oil to the blades helps the inspector to see the defects, especially if he uses a magnifying glass. Then, if there is any

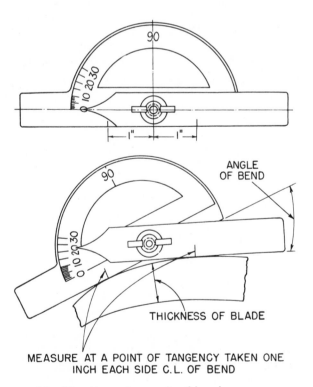

MEASURE AT A POINT OF TANGENCY TAKEN ONE INCH EACH SIDE C.L. OF BEND

Figure 18·33   Measuring angle of bend.

383

doubt about the extent of the defects, local etching is performed.

Local etching has four principal purposes: (1) It shows whether visible lines and other marks within small areas of the blade surfaces are actually cracks instead of scratches; (2) it determines, with a minimum removal of metal, whether or not shallow cracks have been removed; (3) it exposes small cracks that might not be visible otherwise; and (4) it provides a simple means for inspecting the blades without removing or disassembling the propeller.

The caustic soda solution is a 20 per cent solution prepared locally by adding to the required amount of water as much commercial caustic soda as the water will dissolve and then adding some soda pellets after the water has ceased to dissolve the caustic to be sure that the solution is saturated. The quantity required depends upon the amount of etching to be done. This caustic soda solution should reveal the presence of any cracks.

The acid solution is a 20 percent nitric acid solution prepared locally by adding 1 part commercial nitric acid to each 5 parts of water. This acid solution is used to remove the dark corrosion caused by the application of the caustic soda solution to the metal.

Keep the solutions in glass or earthenware containers. Do not keep them in metal containers, since they attack metal. If any quantity of either the caustic soda or the acid solution is spilled, flush the surface it hits with fresh water, especially if it is a metal surface.

Procedures for local etching

Clean and dry the area of the aluminum-alloy blade to be locally etched. Place masking tape around the area under suspicion to protect the adjoining surfaces. Smooth the area containing the suspected defect with No. 00 sandpaper. Apply a small quantity of the caustic soda solution with a small swab to the suspected area. After the suspected area becomes dark, wipe it off with a clean cloth dampened with clean water, but do not slop too much water around the suspected area or the water will remove the solution from the defect and spoil the test. If there is any defect in the metal, it will appear as a dark line or other mark. Examination under a microscope will show small bubbles forming in the dark line or mark.

It may require several applications of the caustic soda to reveal whether or not a shallow defect has been removed since a previous local etching was performed and a defect discovered. Immediately after the completion of the final test, all traces of caustic soda must be removed with the nitric acid solution. The blade is rinsed thoroughly with clean water, and then it is dried and coated with clean engine oil.

The inspection of aluminum-alloy propeller blades for cracks and flaws may be accomplished by means of a chromic acid anodizing process. This is superior to the caustic etching process and should therefore be used if facilities are available.

The blades should be immersed in the anodizing bath as far as possible, but all parts not made of aluminum alloy must either be kept out of the chromic acid bath or be separated from the blade by nonconductive wedges or hooks. The anodizing treatment should be followed by a rinse in clear, cold, running water for 3 to 5 min, and the blades should be dried as soon as possible after the rinse, preferably with an air blast. After the blades are dried, they should stand for at least 15 min before examination. Flaws, such as cold shuts and inclusions, will appear as fine black lines. Cracks will appear as brown stains caused by chromic acid bleeding out onto the surface.

The blades may be sealed for improved corrosion resistance by immersing them in hot water (180 to 212°F) for ½ hr. In no case should the blades be treated with hot water before the examination for cracks, since heating expands any cracks and allows the chromic acid to be washed away.

Inspection of aluminum-alloy propeller blades for cracks and other defects may also be accomplished by means of the fluorescent penetrant process or the dye penetrant process. These methods for the inspection of nonferrous metals are explained in the chapter covering inspection of engine parts.

Treatment of minor surface defects

Dents, cuts, scars, scratches, nicks, etc., should be removed or otherwise treated by means of fine sandpaper and fine-cut files provided that their removal or treatment does not materially weaken the blade, materially reduce its weight, or materially impair its performance or reduce the blade dimensions below the minimums established by the manufacturer. Minimums will usually be given in the manufacturer's service and overhaul manual.

The metal around longitudinal surface cracks, narrow cuts, and shallow scratches should be removed to form shallow saucer-shaped depressions, as illustrated in Fig. 18·35 by that portion of the drawing labeled C.

Blades requiring the removal of metal forming a finished depression more than 1/16 in. in depth at its

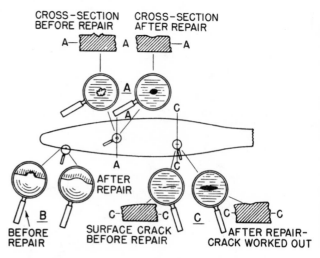

Figure 18·35   Repair of surface defects.

deepest point, ⅜ in. in width overall, and 1 in. in length overall should be rendered unserviceable.

The metal at the edges of defects requires careful treatment. Metal at the edges of wide scars, cuts, nicks, etc., should be rounded off, and the surfaces within the edges should be smoothed out as shown in Fig. 18·35 by that portion of the drawing marked with the letter B. Blades that require the removal of metal to a depth of more than ⅛ in. and a length of more than 1½ in. overall should be rendered unserviceable.

The **raised edges of scars** require a slightly different treatment. The raised edges at wide scars, cuts, nicks, etc., should be carefully smoothed to reduce the area of the defect and the amount of metal to be removed, as illustrated in Fig. 18·35 in that part of the drawing which is marked with the letter A. It is not permissible to peen down the edges of any defect. With the exception of cracks, it is not necessary to remove completely or "saucer out" all of a comparatively deep defect. Properly rounding off the edges and smoothing out the surface within the edges are sufficient, since it is essential that no unnecessary amount of metal be removed.

Number of defects allowable in blades

More than one defect falling within the above limitations is not sufficient cause alone for the rejection of a blade. A reasonable number of such defects per blade is not necessarily dangerous, if within the limits specified, unless their location with respect to each other is such to form a continuous line of defects that would materially weaken the blade.

Repair of pitted leading edges

Blades that have the leading edges pitted from normal wear in service may be reworked by removing sufficient material to eliminate the defects. In this case, the metal should be removed by starting at approximately the thickest section, as shown in Fig. 18·36, and working well forward over the nose camber so that the contour of the reworked portion will remain substantially the same, avoiding abrupt changes in section or blunt edges. Blades requiring the removal of more material than the permissible reduction in width and thickness from the minimum drawing dimensions should be rejected.

For repairing blades, the permissible reductions in width and thickness from the minimum original dimensions allowed by the blade drawing and blade-manufacturing specifications are shown in Fig. 18·37 for locations on the blade from the shank to 90 percent of the blade radius. The outer 10 percent of blade length may be modified as required.

Tolerances listed in blade-manufacturing specifications

The following are typical tolerances listed in the blade-manufacturing specifications and govern the width and thickness of new blades. These tolerances are to be used with the pertinent blade drawing to determine the minimum original blade dimensions to which the reductions of Fig. 18·37 may be applied.

Table 18·2

Dimension	Manufacturing tolerance, in.
Basic diameter less than 10 ft 6 in.:	
Blade width—from shank to 24-in. station	±³⁄₆₄
—from 30-in. station to tip	±¹⁄₃₂
Blade thickness	±0.025
Basic diameter 10 ft 6 in. to less than 14 ft 0 in.:	
Blade width—from shank to 24-in. station	±¹⁄₁₆
—from 30-in. station to tip	±¹⁄₃₂
Blade thickness—from shank to 24-in. station	±0.030
—from 30-in. station to tip	±0.025
Basic diameter 14 ft 0 in. and over:	
Blade width—from shank to 30-in. station	±³⁄₃₂
—from 36-in. station to tip	±¹⁄₁₆
Blade thickness—from shank to 30-in. station	±0.040
—from 36-in. station to tip	0.035

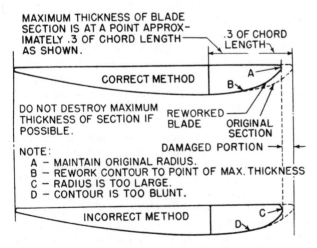

Figure 18·36 *Rework of propeller leading edge.*

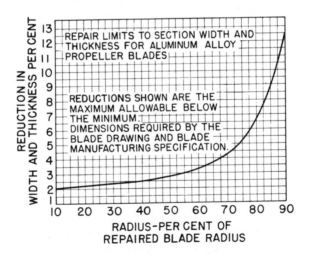

Figure 18·37 *Repair limits.*

Shortening of blades to remove defects

When the removal or treatment of defects on the tip necessitates shortening a blade, each blade used with it must likewise be shortened. Such sets of blades should be kept together. Figures 18·38 and 18·39 illustrate acceptable methods.

With some propeller blades, the length may be reduced substantially and the propeller can then be given a new model number in accordance with the manufacturer's specifications. The reduction in length may require an increase in the blade angle, and the length must agree with the specification for the new model number.

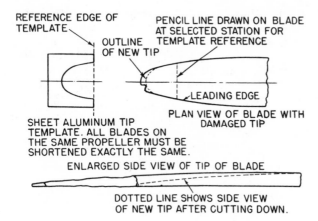

Figure **18·38** *Repair of a damaged tip.*

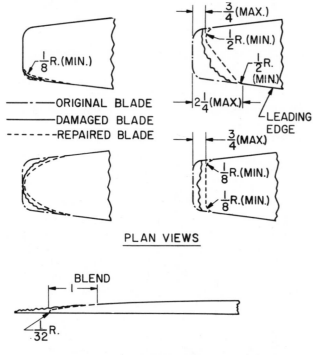

PLAN VIEWS

EDGE VIEW

NOTE: BLADE RADII AND TIP SHAPE SHOULD BE THE SAME FOR BOTH BLADES.

Figure **18·39** *Repair of damaged square tip.*

Causes for rejection

Unless otherwise specified in this text, a blade having any of the following defects must be rendered unserviceable: (1) irreparable defects, such as a longitudinal crack, cut, scratch, scar, etc., that cannot be dressed off or rounded out without materially weakening or unbalancing the blade or materially impairing its performance; (2) general unserviceability due to removal of too much stock by etching, dressing off defects, etc.; (3) slag inclusions in an excessive number or cold shuts in an excessive number or both; and (4) transverse cracks of any size.

CHECKING BLADE ANGLES

The blade angles of a propeller may be checked by using any precision protractor which is adjustable and is equipped with a spirit level. Such a protractor is often called a "bubble protractor."

The universal propeller protractor

The blade angles of a propeller may be accurately checked by the use of a **universal propeller protractor,** which is the same instrument used to measure the **throw** of control surfaces. An accurate check of blade angles cannot be made by referring to the graduations on the ends of the hub barrels or on the shanks of the blades of propellers; such references are suitable only for rough routine field inspections and emergency blade settings.

A **protractor** is merely a device for measuring angles. The propeller protractor consists of an aluminum frame in which a steel ring and a disk are mounted, as shown in Fig. 18·40. The principal, or "whole-degree," scale is on the disk. The vernier, or "fractional-degree," scale is on the ring. The zeros on these two scales provide reference marks which can be set at the two sides of an angle, thereby enabling the operator to read from zero to zero to obtain the number of degrees in the angle.

Two adjusting knobs provide for the adjustment of the ring and disk. The ring adjuster is in the upper right-hand corner of the frame; when it is turned, the ring rotates. The disk adjuster is on the ring; when this knob is turned, the disk rotates.

There are two locks on the protractor. One is the disk-to-ring lock, located on the ring. It is a pin that is held by a spring when engaged, but it engages only when the pin is pulled out and placed in the deep slot and when the zeros on the two scales are aligned. Under these conditions, the ring and disk rotate together when the ring adjuster is turned and when the ring-to-frame lock is disengaged. To hold the spring-loaded pin of the disk-to-ring lock in the released position, it is first pulled outward and then turned 90°.

Another lock, the ring-to-frame lock, is on the frame. It is a right-hand screw with a thumb nut. The disk can be turned independently of the ring by means of the disk adjuster when the ring is locked to the frame and the disk-to-ring lock is released.

There are two spirit levels on the protractor. One is

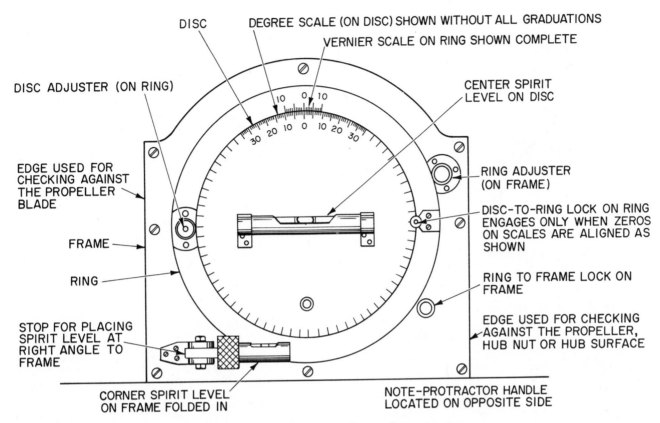

DISC | DEGREE SCALE (ON DISC) SHOWN WITHOUT ALL GRADUATIONS
VERNIER SCALE ON RING SHOWN COMPLETE

DISC ADJUSTER (ON RING)

CENTER SPIRIT LEVEL ON DISC

EDGE USED FOR CHECKING AGAINST THE PROPELLER BLADE

RING ADJUSTER (ON FRAME)

DISC-TO-RING LOCK ON RING ENGAGES ONLY WHEN ZEROS ON SCALES ARE ALIGNED AS SHOWN

FRAME

RING

RING TO FRAME LOCK ON FRAME

STOP FOR PLACING SPIRIT LEVEL AT RIGHT ANGLE TO FRAME

EDGE USED FOR CHECKING AGAINST THE PROPELLER, HUB NUT OR HUB SURFACE

CORNER SPIRIT LEVEL ON FRAME FOLDED IN

NOTE–PROTRACTOR HANDLE LOCATED ON OPPOSITE SIDE

Figure **18·40** *A universal propeller protractor.*

the center, or disk, level. It is at right angles to the zero graduation mark on the whole-degree scale of the disk; hence the zero graduation mark will lie in a vertical plane through the center of the disk whenever the disk is "leveled off" in a horizontal position by means of the disk level.

The other level is the corner spirit level, located at the lower left-hand corner of the frame and mounted on a hinge. This level is swung out at right angles to the frame whenever the protractor is to be used. It is used to keep the protractor in a vertical position for the accurate checking of the blade angle.

The whole-degree-scale graduations are in degrees.

The vernier-scale graduations are in tenths of a degree, as illustrated in Fig. 18·41. The number of whole degrees in the blade angle is determined by the number of degree-scale graduations between the zero of the degree scale and the zero of the vernier scale.

Ten points of the vernier scale are equivalent to nine points on the degree scale. The number of tenths of a degree in the blade angle is found by observing the number of vernier-scale spaces between the zero of the vernier scale and the vernier-scale graduation that comes closest to being in perfect alignment with a degree-scale graduation line. Always read tenths of degrees on the vernier scale in the same direction as the degrees are read on the degree scale.

How to measure the propeller blade angle

To measure the propeller blade angle, determine how much the flat side of the blade slants from the plane of rotation. If a propeller shaft is in the horizontal position when the airplane rests on the ground, the plane of propeller rotation, which is perpendicular to the axis of rotation or the propeller shaft, is vertical. Under these conditions, the blade angle is simply the number of degrees that the flat side of the blade slants from the vertical, as illustrated in Fig. 18·42.

However, an airplane may rest on the ground with its propeller shaft at an angle to the horizontal. The plane of propeller rotation, being perpendicular to the propeller axis of rotation, is then at the same angle to the vertical as the propeller shaft is to the horizontal, as represented by angle *A* in Fig. 18·43.

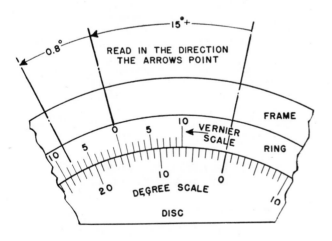

READ IN THE DIRECTION THE ARROWS POINT

FRAME

RING

VERNIER SCALE

DEGREE SCALE

DISC

Figure **18·41** *Reading the protractor scale.*

387

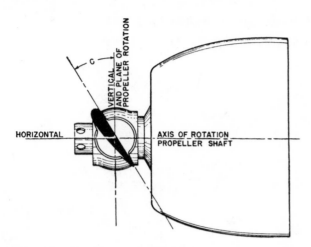

Figure **18 · 42**   *Measuring the blade angle.*

Under these conditions, the number of degrees that the flat side of the propeller blade slants from the vertical is the blade angle minus the ground angle of the airplane, or angle *B* in the same illustration. To obtain the actual blade angle, the ground angle of the airplane (which is also the angle at which the plane of rotation slants from the vertical) must be added to the angle at which the flat side of the blade slants from the vertical in the opposite direction, as represented by angle *C* in the same illustration.

Angles *A* and *B* are measured with a universal protractor and added in two related operations. It is then possible to read the total angle, or blade angle *C*, from the degree and vernier scales of the protractor.

Checking and setting blade angles when the propeller is on the shaft

The following steps are recommended when a universal propeller protractor is available for checking propeller blade angles while the propeller is installed on the shaft of the engine. If it is necessary to use

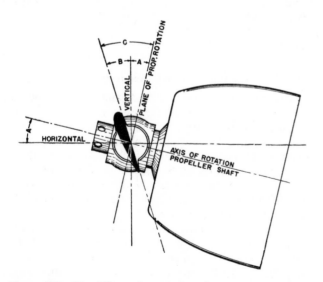

Figure **18 · 43**   *Effect of ground angle on measurement of blade angle.*

another type of protractor, the procedure to be followed will be modified.

1. Mark the face of each blade with a lead pencil at the blade station prescribed for that particular blade.
2. Turn the propeller until the first blade to be examined is in a horizontal position with its leading edge up.
3. Using a universal propeller protractor, swing the corner spirit level out as far as it will go from the face of the protractor.
4. Turning the disk adjuster, align the zeros of both scales and lock the disk to the ring by placing the spring-loaded pin of the disk-to-ring lock in the deep slot.
5. See that the ring-to-frame lock is released. By turning the ring adjuster, turn both zeros to the top. Refer to Fig. 18 · 40, which is a picture of the universal propeller protractor.
6. Hold the protractor in the left hand, by the handle, with the curved edge up. Place one vertical edge of the protractor across the outer end of the propeller retaining nut or any hub flat surface which is parallel to the plane of propeller rotation, which means that it is placed at right angles to the propeller-shaft center line. Using the corner spirit level to keep the protractor vertical, turn the ring adjuster until the center spirit level is horizontal. The zeros of both scales are now set at a point that represents the plane of the propeller rotation. This step can be understood better by referring to the illustration of the measurement of the blade angle in Fig. 18 · 44.
7. Lock the ring to the frame to fix the vernier zero so that it continues to represent the plane of propeller rotation.
8. Release the disk-to-ring lock by pulling the spring-loaded pin outward and turning it to 90°. This completes what is often called the **first operation,** shown in the left part of Fig. 18 · 44.
9. Change the protractor to the right hand, holding it in the same manner as before, and place the other vertical edge of the protractor, which is the edge opposite the first edge used, against the blade at the mark which was made by a pencil on the face of the blade. This is the beginning of the **second operation** and is illustrated by the picture of the protractor to the right in Fig. 18 · 44. Keep the protractor vertical by means of the corner spirit level. Turn the disk adjuster until the center spirit level is horizontal, as shown in the illustration. In this manner, the angle at which the flat side of the blade slants from the vertical is added to the angle at which the plane of rotation slants from the vertical in the opposite direction.
10. Read the number of whole degrees on the degree scale between the zero of the degree scale and the zero of the vernier scale. Read the tenths of a degree on the vernier scale from the vernier zero to the vernier-scale graduation that comes the closest to lining up with a degree-scale graduation. In this manner the blade angle is determined.
11. Obtain the required blade angle by making any necessary adjustments of the blade or the propeller pitch-changing mechanism.
12. Repeat this procedure for each of the remaining blades to be checked.

MISCELLANEOUS INSPECTION AND MAINTENANCE

Special inspections after accidents

If the propeller strikes or is struck by any object, examine it for damage. Disassemble any propeller that has been involved in an accident, and carefully inspect

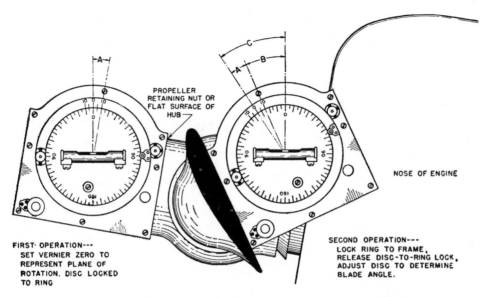

Figure 18·44   Measuring the blade angle in two operations.

the parts for damage and misalignment before using the propeller again. Examine all steel parts and otherwise serviceable steel propeller blades for minor injuries by means of a magnetic inspection supervised by competent personnel. Have aluminum-alloy blades which are otherwise serviceable given a general etching by competent operators.

Any accident which severely damages the propeller may also damage the engine. It is good practice, therefore, to check the alignment of the crankshaft after an accident in which the propeller has been damaged. Crankshaft alignment may be checked as follows:

1. Remove the propeller.
2. Install a dial gage on a mounting attached to the nose of the engine with the finger of the dial gage touching the smooth area of the crankshaft forward of the splines. With a flange-type shaft, the finger of the gage should be placed against the smooth surface of the flange on the outer edge.
3. Rotate the propeller shaft through a complete revolution, and observe the movement of the gage indicating needle. If the shaft runout is out of limits according to the manufacturer's specifications, the engine must be removed and overhauled.

Front cones

Since hub front-cone halves are machined in pairs, the original mated halves are always used together in the same installation. If one half becomes unserviceable, both halves are rejected. Before installation and use, the two halves of a front cone are held together by a thin section of metal left over from the manufacturing process. This metal must be sawed through with a hacksaw, and then the two separated halves gone over carefully with a handstone to remove all rough and fine edges and to round off the sharp edges where the cones were cut apart. After this process is completed, the two halves are always taped together when not installed.

Front-cone bottoming

A front cone sometimes "bottoms" against the outer ends of the propeller-shaft splines; that is, the apex of

the front cone hits the ends of the splines before the cone properly seats in its cone seat in the hub. The hub is loose because it is not seated properly and held tight by the cones, even though the retaining nut may be tight.

Whenever a splined hub is found to be loose, even though the retaining nut is tight, an inspection is made for front-cone bottoming unless there is a more probable cause of the trouble. Also, this condition may be manifested by excessive propeller vibration during preflight operations.

Inspection for front-cone bottoming

To check for front-cone bottoming, first apply a thin coating of Prussian blue to the apex of the front cone. Then install the propeller on the shaft and tighten the propeller retaining nut. Next, remove the retaining nut and front cone. See if the Prussian blue has been transferred to the ends of the splines of the propeller shaft. If it has not been transferred, the front cone is not bottoming and the Prussian blue can be cleaned off.

If the Prussian blue has been transferred to the ends of the shaft splines, install a steel spacer behind the rear cone to correct the condition of front-cone bottoming. Spacers for this purpose are generally made in any shop adjacent to the place where the work is being performed and are ⅛ in. thick.

The presence of the spacer moves the entire propeller assembly forward, causing the front cone to seat in the hub before its apex hits the end of the shaft spline. After the installation of the spacer, the Prussian-blue test should be made again. If bottoming is still indicated, inspect the hub-shaft end and all attaching parts for excessive wear or any other condition that might cause a failure to fit. Worn or defective parts should be replaced.

Shaft and hub splines

The splines on the propeller shaft and inside the propeller hub should be carefully inspected for damage

389

and wear. Wear of the splines should be checked with a single key "no-go" gage made to plus 0.002 in. of the base drawing dimensions for spline land width. If the gage enters more than 20 percent of the spline area, the part should be rejected.

Balancing controllable propellers

Upon completion of repairs, the horizontal and vertical balance of a propeller must be checked. If any unbalanced condition is found, correction must be made according to the manufacturer's instruction. Balancing methods include the installation of weights in the shanks of the blades, lead wool packed into holes drilled in the ends of the blades, lead packed into hollow bolts, and various others. In any event, the manufacturer's recommendations must be followed for any specific type of propeller. For some propellers, only the manufacturer is permitted to perform the balancing operations.

Anti-icing and deicing systems

Propeller anti-icing may be accomplished by spraying isopropyl alcohol along the leading edges of the blades. The anti-icing fluid is carried in a reservoir in the airplane in sufficient quantities for any possible demand. The fluid is pumped from the reservoir to the propeller by an electrically driven **anti-icing pump** which is controlled from the cockpit. The propeller is equipped with a **slinger ring** having nozzles aligned with the leading edge of each blade. When the pump is turned on, the fluid is forced out the nozzles of the slinger ring by centrifugal force and carried along the leading edges of the propeller blades.

Another anti-icing and deicing system which is extensively used is the heating of the blades by electrical heating elements. These elements are cemented in boots to the leading edge of the blades or are mounted within the blade. Power for the heating elements is transferred through slip rings at the rear of the propeller hub.

Servicing, inspection, maintenance, and repair of anti-icing and deicing systems for propellers will vary with different propellers and aircraft. It is therefore essential that the mechanic performing these operations follow the instructions furnished by the manufacturer of the aircraft and the manufacturer of the propeller.

REVIEW QUESTIONS

1. What are the principal advantages of a wood propeller?
2. Why is a wood propeller made up of laminations?
3. Briefly describe the construction of a wood propeller.
4. Describe the installation of tipping on a wood propeller.
5. What is the purpose of the small holes drilled in the metal tipping at the tip of a propeller?
6. Why is fabric sometimes applied to the tips of wood propellers?

7. Describe the procedure for checking and correcting horizontal and vertical balance of a wood propeller.
8. How would you check the *track* of a propeller?
9. What is the permissible variation in the track for wood propeller blades?
10. What is the purpose of the cones used with the installation of a propeller on a splined shaft?
11. Why is a rear-cone spacer used with some installations?
12. How does the retaining nut for a propeller serve as a puller when the propeller is removed?
13. Explain how the fit of a tapered hub and shaft is checked.
14. What precaution must be taken when the hub bolts of a wood propeller are tightened?
15. What authorization is required with respect to the major repair or alteration of a propeller?
16. What type of repair is that which does not materially affect the strength, weight, balance, or performance of a propeller?
17. What defects should be noted during the inspection of a wood propeller?
18. List the causes for rejection of a wood propeller.
19. Describe the repair of small cracks parallel to the grain of the wood.
20. Describe an inlay repair for a wood propeller.
21. What depth of inlay is permitted in the side of a propeller hub?
22. What repair is permitted for elongated bolt holes in the steel hub for a wood propeller?
23. Describe the refinishing of a wood propeller.
24. What is the principal advantage of a ground-adjustable propeller?
25. How is the blade-angle adjustment made on a ground-adjustable propeller?
26. Describe the pitch-changing mechanism for a Beech series 215 propeller.
27. Describe the feathering system for the Beech Model 279 propeller.
28. Explain the operation of the governor used with the Hartzell full-feathering propeller.
29. Who is authorized to repair damaged steel propeller blades?
30. How may minor injuries to the leading and trailing edges of a steel blade be repaired?
31. Define a *damaged* propeller blade.
32. What inspection should be made on an aluminum-alloy propeller blade which has been straightened?
33. Describe the method for inspecting cracks in an aluminum-alloy blade.
34. What is the purpose of *local etching?*
35. What material is used for local etching?
36. Describe the treatment of minor surface defects.
37. Discuss the shortening of blades to remove defects.
38. What device is used for checking propeller blade angle?
39. Describe the procedure for checking blade angle when the propeller is mounted on the aircraft.
40. After a propeller is damaged in an accident, what inspections should be made?
41. What inspection should be made on the engine after the propeller has been damaged in an accident?
42. How would you check a propeller for front-cone bottoming?

CHAPTER 19

Propellers for Large Aircraft

positions, but there are no intermediate settings possible.

During operation, when the propeller control is placed in the low-pitch position, the three-way valve directs engine oil pressure through the hollow propeller shaft and piston into the cylinder. This causes the cylinder to move forward, and as it does so, counterweight brackets and counterweights are pulled inward and the blades are rotated to the low-pitch position. The propeller blades will remain in this position as long as the oil pressure is maintained in the cylinder. When the control is placed in the high-pitch position, the three-way valve allows the oil from the propeller cylinder to drain back into the engine. The centrifugal force acting on the counterweights pulls the counterweight brackets outward, thus rotating the blades to the high-pitch position and drawing the cylinder back on the piston.

Constant-speed counterweight propeller

The constant-speed counterweight propeller is essentially the same as the two-position propeller with the exception of blade-angle range and controlling mechanism. The constant-speed propeller may have a range of either 15 or 20° depending upon the type of installation. This range is determined by the adjustment of the stops in the counterweight assembly. If the propeller is set for a 20° range, a return spring assembly is installed in the piston to assist the counterweights in returning the cylinder to the rearward position when the governor calls for increased pitch.

The control of the constant-speed propeller is accomplished by means of a propeller governor similar to those described previously. The governor operates by means of flyweights which control the position of a pilot valve. When the propeller is in an underspeed condition, with rpm below that for which the governor is set, the governor flyweights move inward and the pilot valve then directs engine oil pressure to the propeller cylinder through the engine propeller shaft. This moves the cylinder forward and reduces the propeller pitch. When the engine is in the overspeed condition, the governor action is opposite and the pilot valve allows oil to drain from the cylinder back to the engine.

The propeller control is in the cockpit of the airplane and is marked for INCREASE RPM and DECREASE RPM. **Increase rpm** means lower pitch, and **decrease rpm** means higher pitch. When the propeller is operating in an on-speed condition, the blade angle is usually somewhere between the extreme ranges. Control of the governor is accomplished by rotating a shaft through a cable linkage. Rotation of the shaft changes the compression of the governor speeder spring which controls the flyweight position.

HAMILTON STANDARD COUNTERWEIGHT PROPELLERS

Two-position propeller

Although the Hamilton Standard counterweight-type propellers are no longer in production, there are still some aircraft in operation which utilize these propellers. Hence a brief description is given here for the benefit of the technician who may encounter this type of equipment.

The two-position controllable propeller is operated by means of a control in the cockpit by which the pilot shifts the position of a three-way valve which is usually mounted on the nose of the engine. This valve directs engine oil pressure (70 to 80 psi) to the propeller cylinder to decrease the pitch, or it allows oil from the propeller cylinder to return to the engine as the pitch increases.

Attached to the butt of each blade is a **counterweight bracket.** A cam slot in the end of each bracket is engaged by a roller (bushing) which is attached to the base of the movable cylinder by means of the **counterweight bearing shaft.** Since the cam lot is at an angle with respect to the propeller's rotational axis, any movement of the cylinder forward or aft causes the propeller blades to rotate and change pitch. **Counterweights** are mounted on the end of each bracket in order to take advantage of centrifugal force for changing the blade angle.

The range of pitch change for the two-position propeller is about 10°. The low-pitch position is used for takeoff so the engine can develop its maximum rpm. After takeoff and climb, the propeller is placed in the high-pitch position for cruising. The propeller may be operated in either the high-pitch or the low-pitch

THE HYDROMATIC REVERSING PROPELLER

General description

In addition to the counterweight-type propellers, the Hamilton Standard Division of the United Aircraft Corporation has manufactured the constant-speed, full-feathering hydromatic propeller and the hydromatic propeller.

The steel-blade reversing hydromatic propeller is composed of three major assemblies: the hub assembly, the dome assembly, and the low-pitch stop-lever assembly. The hub assembly includes the blade assemblies and the barrel assembly. The blades are steel-alloy shells brazed to steel cores. The blade-shell cavities are filled with an organic sponge compound to reduce local vibration. The dome assembly is the pitch-changing mechanism in which is installed the low-pitch stop-lever assembly.

Principles of operation

Figure 19·1 illustrates the operation of the propeller pitch-changing mechanism for both underspeed and overspeed conditions.

The forces acting to control the blade angle of the propeller are **centrifugal twisting moment** and high-pressure oil. The centrifugal twisting moment tends to turn the blades to a lower angle. The high-pressure oil is directed to the propeller to change the blade angle in either direction.

The pitch-changing mechanism consists of a piston which moves forward and backward in the dome cylinder. Rollers on the piston engage cam slots in the cams. The cams are so arranged, one within the other,

that the rotation of one cam is added to the rotation of the other, thus doubling the movement that would be obtained from one cam alone. The outer cam is stationary, and the inner cam is rotated. This inner cam carries the bevel gear which meshes with the blade gears.

The blade angle of the propeller is controlled by means of a **double-acting governor** during constant-speed operation. The governor directs high-pressure oil to either side of the propeller piston as necessary to maintain the constant engine speed. If an underspeed condition exists, the oil is directed to the inboard side of the piston. This causes the piston to move outward and rotate the cam in a direction which will decrease the pitch of the blades. The opposite action takes place if an overspeed condition exists.

To reverse the blade angle of the propeller, the blades are rotated through the low-pitch position. The reversing operation makes use of the high-pressure oil from the feathering pump to force the piston to the full-forward position.

When it is desired to reverse the propellers after landing, the pilot pulls the throttles backward to the reverse position. The throttles actuate switches which set the system into operation.

The **pilot valve** of the governor is provided with two oil chambers which permit an artificial overspeed or underspeed condition to be imposed upon the governor. A solenoid valve on the governor is used to control the oil flow which actuates the pilot valve for the artificial conditions. When the solenoid is energized, as in reversing, it directs high-pressure oil to the positioning chamber and causes the pilot valve to move downward into the underspeed condition. The oil pressure overrides the normal control of the governor flyweights. When the pilot valve is in the DOWN position, it directs oil to the rear side of the propeller piston, causing it to move forward and reduce the propeller blade angle.

Normally the low-pitch angle of the propeller is limited by the **low-pitch stop levers;** however, when the propeller is reversed, these stop levers are released through the action of a servo piston in the low-pitch stop-lever assembly. The servo piston is actuated when the high-pressure oil from the feathering pump and governor pump reaches a pressure of 250 psi and opens the servo valve, directing oil to the servo piston. The servo piston then travels forward, removing the lever wedge and allowing the release of the stops, thus permitting the propeller piston to move into the full-forward, or reverse-pitch, position.

Unreversing the propeller is accomplished by moving the throttle forward from the reverse position. This movement actuates switches which deenergize the governor solenoid and start the auxiliary or feathering pump. The unreversing operation is essentially the same as the feathering operation, since both call for an increase of positive pitch.

Feathering of the propeller is accomplished by directing high-pressure oil from the feathering pump to the forward side of the propeller piston. This is accom-

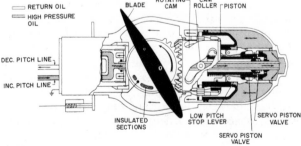

Figure 19·1 *Operation of pitch-changing mechanism.*

plished through the governor pilot valve. The high-pressure oil positions the pilot valve in an artificial **overspeed** condition, thus causing the oil flow to go to the forward side of the propeller piston.

The pilot starts the feathering operation by pushing in on the feathering button. This button is part of a cockpit-mounted feathering solenoid-switch assembly which, when closed, will remain closed until the propeller is feathered. At this time a pressure of approximately 650 psi is built up at the forward side of the propeller piston and thus at the governor cutout switch. The cutout switch is in the ground circuit of the feathering-switch holding coil and is opened by the oil pressure at approximately 650 psi. When the cutout switch opens, the feathering switch is released and the feathering operation is complete.

Unfeathering is accomplished by holding the feathering button in the OUT position for about 2 sec. This creates an artificial underspeed condition at the governor and causes high-pressure oil from the feathering pump to be directed to the rear of the propeller piston. As soon as the piston has moved outward a short distance, the blades will have sufficient angle to start rotation of the engine. When this occurs, the unfeathering switch can be released and the governor will assume control of the propeller.

The propeller governor

The double-acting propeller governor used with the reversing propeller, illustrated in Fig. 19·2, consists of a set of spring-loaded flyweights driven by the engine, a pilot valve actuated by the flyweights and high-pressure oil, a gear pump, and an electrically driven governor head which regulates the governor for constant-speed operation.

The centrifugal force acting on the flyweights is the primary regulating force of the governor. When the propeller overspeeds, the flyweights move outward and raise the pilot valve. This opens passages which direct

governor oil pressure to the outer or forward side of the propeller piston. The piston moves rearward and rotates the blades to a higher pitch, thus reducing the engine speed.

When an underspeed condition exists, the "speeder" spring holds the governor flyweights in an inward position. This places the pilot valve in a DOWN position and reverses the conditions of oil flow described for the overspeed condition. The propeller piston is moved forward and the blade angle is decreased, thus allowing the engine speed to increase.

In connection with the governor is a solenoid valve which controls high-pressure oil to the positioning chambers of the pilot valve. When the solenoid valve is open, the pilot valve is caused to move to the DOWN position. When the solenoid valve is closed, high-pressure oil from the feathering pump will raise the valve. As stated previously, the UP position of the pilot valve is an overspeed condition and the DOWN position of the valve is an underspeed condition.

Automatic synchronization

Any system used for synchronizing rotating units requires that a reference speed be established. In the synchronizing system used with the Hamilton Standard hydromatic reversing propeller, one of the aircraft engines is used as a "master" to set the pace for the other engines. Figure 19·3 is a schematic diagram of the synchronization circuit for the Hamilton Standard reversing propeller.

On the four-engine installation, the system is arranged so that either one of two engines may be used as the master engine. This provides a safety factor in case the engine being used should fail. On the Douglas DC-6 airplane, the system is arranged so that either No. 2 or 3 engine may be used as a master engine. The other engines are called "slave" engines. The master engine is selected by means of a toggle switch.

The "speed signal" for each engine is taken from the three-phase tachometer generators or alternators. This signal is in the form of a three-phase alternating current having a frequency proportional to engine speed. When

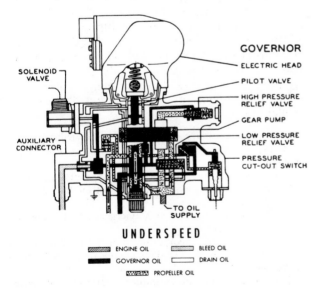

Figure 19·2 Diagram of propeller governor.

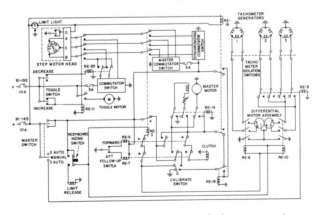

Figure 19·3 Schematic diagram of the automatic synchronization system.

this current is applied to the stator winding of a three-phase motor, it will establish a rotating field.

The output of the tachometer generator of the master engine is fed to the stators of the **differential motors** for the slave engines. The output of the tachometer generator of each slave engine is fed to the rotor of the differential motor for that engine. If the master engine and a slave engine are operating at the same speed, the fields produced in the differential motor rotor and stator will be rotating at the same speed. Under these circumstances the rotor of the differential motor will remain stationary. If the master engine and the slave engine are turning at different speeds, the rotor and stator fields in the differential motor will be rotating at different speeds. This will cause the rotor to turn at a speed necessary to lock the two fields together. Thus when any slave engine is not synchronized with the master engine, the differential motor for the slave engine will rotate. Each differential motor for a slave engine drives a **commutator switch** which is connected to the stator of the governor step motor. The governor step motor is the actuating unit which adjusts the force applied to the governor speeder spring for higher or lower engine rpm.

A schematic diagram of a commutator switch is shown in Fig. 19·4. The construction is such that each of three pairs of contacts is reversed in polarity alternately and in a definite sequence.

The commutator switch consists of three sets of contacts actuated by a cam with lobes spaced 120° apart. The contacts are arranged so that a single center contact is alternately pressed against the contact at each side. Thus the center contact will be alternately positive and negative.

The output of the commutator switch is connected to the three terminals of the delta-wound stator in the governor step motor. The effect is to produce a field in the stator which rotates by steps and turns the rotor in step with the field.

In some synchronizing systems, the differential motor, which rotates as a result of a difference in engine speeds, is replaced by a mechanical differential-gear system. The output of the tachometer generators is directed to synchronous motors. For each slave

engine, one motor, connected to the differential gear, is driven by the master signal. The other motor is driven by the slave-engine signal. If the engines are synchronized, there is no differential in speed and no rotation at the differential-gear output shaft. The output shaft is connected to the commutator-switch drive and drives the switch in the same manner as the differential motor previously described.

The operation of the automatic synchronization system may be summarized as follows:

The master engine is selected by the pilot to provide a reference speed for the slave engines. The tachometer alternator current from the master engine induces a rotating field in the stators of differential motors for each slave engine. This field reacts with the rotor field of each differential motor, and when there is a difference in speed, the differential motor will rotate the commutator switch for the "off-speed" slave engine. The output of the commutator switch causes the governor step motor to rotate and adjust the governor for a change of propeller blade angle to correct the engine speed.

The propeller control system has a number of safeguards to provide for operation in case some part of the synchronization system fails. Control can be taken away from the synchronization system at any time either by individual toggle switches or by a master switch. The system is designed to prevent the slave engines from following the master engine in case the master engine changes speed more than 3 percent. This is accomplished through devices called **limited-band mechanisms,** which permit an automatic change of only 60 to 70 rpm at the engine.

THE ALLISON TURBOPROPELLER

The Allison (formerly Aeroproducts) A6441FN-606 and 606A turbopropeller shown in Fig. 19·5 is a hydraulically controlled four-blade unit incorporating an integral hydraulic system. The hydraulic governing system operates independently of any of the other systems and maintains precise control during all operating conditions. Electrical power is supplied to the propeller for synchronizing and ice control. The propeller is designed for use with the Allison Model 501-D13 turbo-prop (prop-jet) engine as shown in Fig. 19·6.

Some of the important design features of the turbopropeller are as follows:

1. Four hydraulic pumps, driven by propeller rotation, provide the required flow and pressure to maintain propeller control.
2. An electrically driven feather pump provides hydraulic pressure for static operation as well as for feathering or unfeathering.
3. Auto-feathering, manual, and emergency feathering systems are provided.
4. Safety devices are incorporated for protection against excessive drag in the event of engine or propeller malfunctions.
5. The propeller provides uniform variation of thrust throughout the **beta range** with power lever movement.

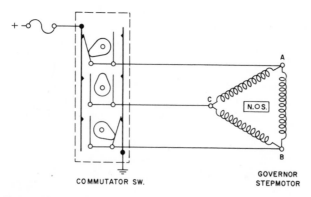

Figure 19·4 *Schematic diagram to illustrate the principle of a commutator switch.*

Figure 19·5 The Allison Model A6441FN-606 turbo-propeller. (Allison Division of General Motors Corp.)

Figure 19·6 Turbopropeller mounted on Allison Model 501-D13 gas-turbine engine. (Allison)

The Greek letter **beta** is used to denote blade angle. Beta range denotes that range of operation in which beta (blade angle) is scheduled.

6. The propeller is guaranteed up to at least 4500 shaft

horsepower (shp) at takeoff and 2500 shp at maximum reverse.

7. The propeller system is designed for primary reliability and fail-safe operation.

8. The propeller can be feathered at any rotational speed up to the propeller design limitation of 142 percent of rated rpm.

9. There is no limit on the number of times a propeller can be feathered or unfeathered in flight.

10. The propeller is designed to have an increase blade-angle change rate of 15° per sec and a decrease blade-angle change rate of 10° per sec at 1020 propeller rpm.

11. The feather pump will provide a static blade-angle change of 3° per sec.

12. When signaled to feather during operation, the initial blade-angle change rate is well in excess of 15° per sec but decreases as the rpm decreases.

Leading particulars

Number of blades	4
Propeller diameter	13.5 ft
Blade chord	18.5 in.
Governing speed	1020 prop rpm
Total weight installed including hydraulic fluid and grease	1038 lb max

Aerodynamic blade angles at 42 in. R station

Maximum reverse	−4°
Ground idle	1.5°
Start	7°
Flight idle	20°
Feather	94.7° + 0.2 − 0.1
Beta follow-up at takeoff	31.5° + 0.5 − 1.0
Mechanical low pitch stop	18.25° to 18.5°
Hydraulic low pitch stop	20°

Major assemblies and components

The propeller consists of five major assemblies mounted on the engine propeller shaft plus the control components and assemblies mounted in the aircraft. These major assemblies are (1) **hub**, (2) **blade and retention**, (3) **regulator**, (4) **feather reservoir,** and (5) **spinner.** The engine-driven propeller alternator, electronic controls for synchronization and phase synchronization, ice-control accessories, and necessary switches, relays, etc., complete the installation. The major assemblies are illustrated in Fig. 19·7.

Hub assembly

The **hub assembly** is the principal structural member of the propeller and consists of the hub, torque units, and master gear assembly. A cross-sectional drawing of the hub assembly is shown in Fig. 19·8. Note that each blade has a separate pitch-changing device called the **torque unit** and that the four blades are all meshed with the **master gear.** The master gear therefore ensures that all blades are at the same angle.

The hub, machined from a steel forging, provides mounting for the pitch-control mechanisms and the sockets for the retention of the blades. Splines and cone seats are machined on the inner diameter of the hub. The splines and cone seats provide the means of properly positioning the hub on the propeller shaft. The

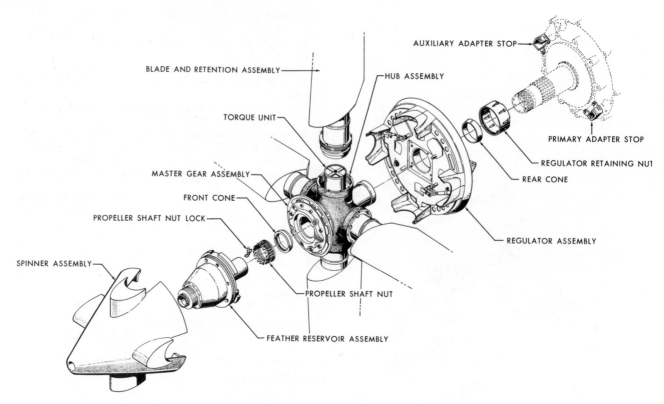

Figure 19·7   *Major assemblies of Allison turbopropeller. (Allison)*

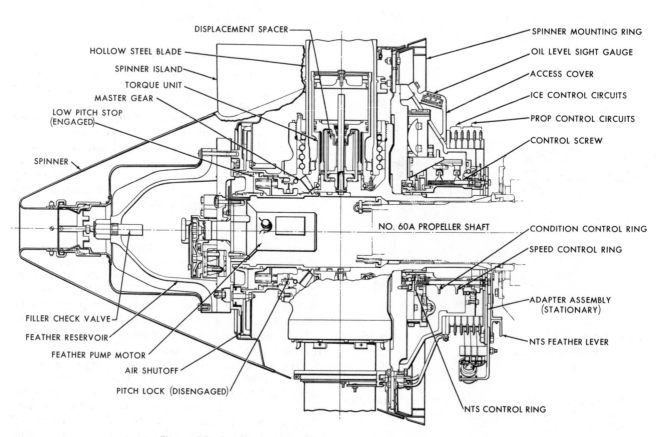

Figure 19·8   *Cross-sectional drawing of hub assembly. (Allison)*

hub contains hydraulic fluid passages which deliver oil, under pressure, from the regulator to the torque units, master gear assembly, and feather reservoir. The hub is shot-peened to increase the fatigue life, and it is cadmium plated to prevent surface corrosion.

Each hub socket contains a **torque unit** which consists principally of a fixed spline, a piston, and a cylinder. A retaining bolt, which secures the fixed spline to the hub, incorporates a tube to provide a passage for fluid to the outboard or **decrease-pitch** side of the piston. A port in the base of the fixed spline provides an oil passage to the inboard or increase-pitch side of the piston. Helical splines, machined on the components of the torque unit, convert linear motion of the piston to rotation of the cylinder. Cylinder rotation is transmitted to the blade through an indexing ring and matching splines on the cylinder and in the blade root. Figure 19·9 illustrates the construction of the torque unit assemblies.

The **master gear** assembly consists of a housing, master gear, mechanical low-pitch stop (MLPS), mechanical pitch lock, air shutoff, and feedback mechanism parts. The housing is splined and bolted to the front face of the hub and provides the mounting surface for the feather reservoir. The master gear coordinates the movement of the torque units so that all blades are maintained at the same aerodynamic blade angle. Splined to the housing are the parts which comprise the MLPS and the mechanical pitch lock. Feedback mechanism parts, actuated by blade-angle changes, operate the cooling-air shutoff mechanism, beta light switch, and feedback shaft which mechanically positions a part of the control linkage of the hydraulic governor.

As the blade angle approaches the feathered position, the master gear assembly feedback mechanism drives the air-shutoff shutter to its closed position. The shutter begins to move toward the closed position at 60° blade angle, and when the blade angle reaches approximately 75°, all airflow through the spinner is shut off. The air shutter is closed to prevent rapid cooling of the propeller operating mechanisms.

The beta light switch controls the cockpit beta light circuit. When the blade angle is below 18.5°, the beta light switch is closed by the master gear assembly feedback mechanism. When the switch is closed, the beta light is on in the cockpit to indicate that the propeller is operating in the beta range. At blade angles above 18.5°, the beta light switch is open and the beta light is out. This indicates that the propeller is not operating in the beta range; that is, the governor is in control of rpm.

Blade and retention assemblies

Each blade and retention assembly consists of a blade cuff, deicing element, cuff deicing slip ring, and integral ball-bearing set and is retained in its hub socket by a blade retaining nut.

The hollow steel blade consists of a **camber sheet** and **thrust member** which are brazed together. The camber sheet, formed from sheet steel, completes the camber surface of the blade. The thrust member, machined from a steel forging, constitutes the blade shank thrust face, longitudinal strengthening ribs, and leading- and trailing-edge reinforcements. Prior to brazing, the interior surfaces of the thrust member and camber sheet are ground and polished for maximum fatigue strength. The camber sheet and thrust member

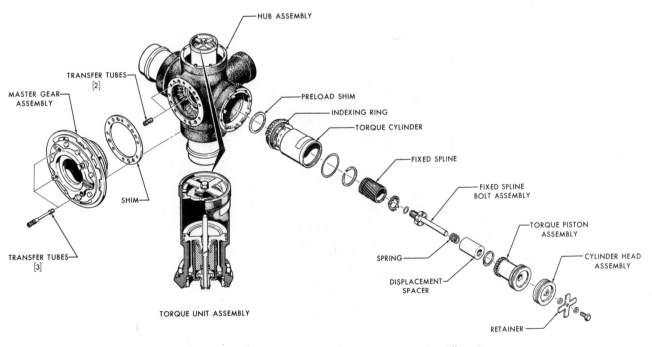

Figure **19·9** Hub assembly showing torque unit. (Allison)

are brazed together along the ribs and leading and trailing edges. This basic design provides maximum aerodynamic contours coupled with excellent structural qualities. The external surface of the blade is zinc plated and passivated electrochemically to obtain maximum corrosion protection. In addition to this, a portion of the blade tip and leading edge is "dull" chrome plated for abrasion resistance. Integral ball-bearing races are machined, locally hardened, and ground on the root portion of the blade. The outer races are ground and precision-fitted with balls and separators to obtain a blade bearing retention with maximum service life and optimum load distribution.

The foamed plastic structure of the cuff is covered by a fiberglass shell, neoprene fabric, and ice-control element which is flush mounted.

Regulator assembly

The **regulator assembly** which is mounted on the rear of the hub consists of the cover and housing assembly, pumps, valves, and hydraulic fluid required to provide controlled flow to the hub pitch-change and -control mechanisms. These parts, except for portions of the adapter assembly, are contained in the regulator cover and housing. The regulator assembly, except for the adapter assembly, rotates with the propeller. A drawing of the regulator assembly is shown in Fig. 19·10. Observe in particular the **shoes** (speed shoe and condition shoes) which straddle the control rings mounted on the front of the engine. As the rings are moved forward and backward in response to control from the airplane through the control screws and gears, the shoes are also moved backward and forward as they rotate around the edges of the rings. The movement of the shoes transmits signals to the components of the regulator.

When the propeller assembly is placed on the propeller shaft, two engine-mounted adapter stops engage with tangs on the adapter assembly. This prevents rotation of the adapter assembly when the propeller rotates. The adapter assembly is supported by two ball-bearing assemblies in the regulator. Seals, located in the regulator cover and housing, contact the adapter assembly to retain the hydraulic fluid.

The **adapter assembly** primarily consists of the mechanical control components which are coupled to the valves and pump power gear in the regulator and the accessory plate outside the regulator. Mechanical control movements from the engine or cockpit are transferred into the regulator to control the hydraulic operation of the propeller. This mechanical control is accomplished by movement of the propeller condition lever or negative torque signal (NTS) feather lever.

The accessory plate, which is attached to the adapter assembly, supports the brush block assemblies, the rotary actuator, a solenoid stop, and adapter stop tangs. Two brush block assemblies are provided, one for ice control and the other for control of the solenoid valve, beta light, and feather pump. Electrical power is supplied to and conducted through the brush block assemblies to the slip rings mounted on the regulator cover. Electrical power is also supplied to the rotary actuator.

Feather reservoir assembly

The **feather reservoir assembly,** installed on the forward face of the hub, consists of a feather motor, pump, pressure-control valve, check valve, and filler check

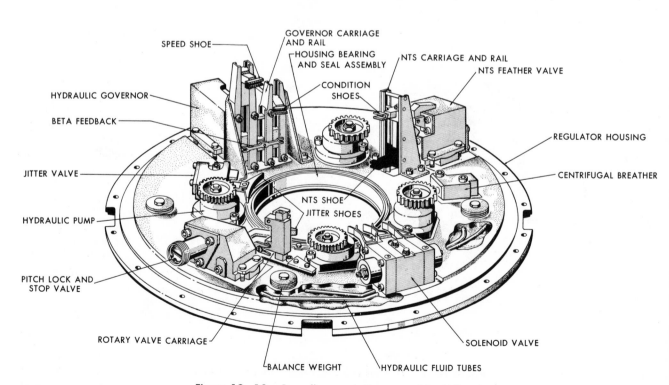

Figure 19·10   Propeller regulating assembly. (Allison)

valve mounted in a housing and cover assembly. A sufficient quantity of hydraulic fluid is available in the feather reservoir to accomplish feathering in the event the regulator hydraulic supply is depleted. This assembly also supplies hydraulic flow for stationary pitch-change operation and for completion of the feathering cycle. Air is admitted through the spinner nose and directed over the cover for cooling the hydraulic fluid.

Spinner assembly

The **spinner** is a one-piece aluminum-alloy assembly. It provides for the streamlined flow of air past the blade cuffs and over the feather reservoir, hub, and regulator. The spinner is positioned and supported by dowels on the regulator spinner mounting ring and retained to the feather reservoir by a nut in the nose of the spinner. Spray-mat-type ice-control circuits are on the external surface of the spinner. A schematic diagram of the anti-icing and deicing circuits for the spinner and cuffs is shown in Fig. 19·11.

Mechanical control system

The propeller must receive the following intelligence in order for it to function as desired: (1) power lever position, (2) emergency handle position, (3) feather solenoid energized or deenergized, and (4) NTS system actuated or not actuated.

The foregoing intelligence is provided the propeller by means of two linkage systems. One system is attached to the propeller condition control lever, and the other to the propeller NTS-feather lever.

The power lever and emergency handle are each connected by aircraft linkage to the engine **coordinator.** Linkage from the coordinator is attached to the propeller condition control lever. The purpose of the coordinator is to receive signals from the emergency handle and the power lever and transmit these signals

electrically and mechanically to the propeller-control system and to the fuel-control unit. Thus the fuel scheduling and propeller are controlled together to provide correct conditions for all power settings. The **power lever** operates through a range of 0 to 90° and has five basic positions. These are (1) MAXIMUM REVERSE, 0°; (2) GROUND IDLE, 9°; (3) START, 15 to 20°; (4) FLIGHT IDLE, 34°; and (5) TAKEOFF, 90°.

The coordinator contains a cam assembly called a **discriminator** which permits the power lever to control the linkage to the propeller if the emergency handle is in its normal (push in) position. The discriminator permits the emergency handle to override the action of the power lever in positioning the linkage to the propeller any time the emergency handle is pulled. The propeller condition control lever thus "informs" the propeller regulator of the power lever and emergency handle positions.

The feather solenoid and the engine NTS system are connected to the NTS linkage, which is attached to the propeller NTS-feather lever. The NTS-feather lever "informs" the propeller regulator of feather solenoid and NTS system requirements on the hydraulic system.

The **emergency handle** provides the means for shutting down an engine by a single action. Pulling the emergency handle will actuate mechanical linkage and electrical circuits to shut off the fuel and feather the engine.

The **feather solenoid,** secured to the reduction-gear assembly, is mechanically attached to the engine NTS linkage. When the solenoid is energized, it actuates the NTS linkage, which results in the propeller NTS-feather lever being moved to the feather position. Thus, the propeller is signaled to feather if the propeller NTS system is not blocked out owing to power lever setting. The NTS system is blocked out below the 21° position of the coordinator.

The reduction-gear NTS system is also mechanically attached to the engine NTS linkage. If negative torque is from −300 to −420 shp, the NTS system actuates the engine NTS linkage, which results in the propeller NTS-feather lever being moved to the feather position. Thus the propeller is signaled to feather. As the propeller blade angle increases, the negative torque produced by the propeller decreases to a point at which the reduction-gear NTS system no longer is actuated. The NTS system returns to the NORMAL position, which removes the feather signal to the propeller. The propeller hydraulic governor then regains control of the propeller and decreases the blade angle. If the negative torque again actuates the NTS system, the foregoing cycle repeats itself. The cycling of the NTS system from the actuated to the nonactuated position is called **NTSing.** If NTSing occurs during an approach with low power settings, a slight advance of the power lever will stop it. If NTSing is the result of engine failure, it can be stopped by feathering the propeller.

Hydraulic system

The propeller will function satisfactorily when the proper type of fluid is used in the system. Approximately 3 gal of hydraulic fluid is required per propeller.

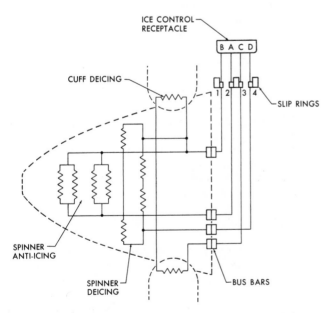

Figure 19·11 *Schematic diagram of anti-icing and deicing circuits. (Allison)*

This fluid is contained in the regulator reservoir and the feather reservoir. A visual oil lever sight gage is provided for quick, easy hydraulic fluid lever check. The propeller does not consume fluid. However, if replenishment is required, fluid may be added through a filler tube and check valve at the front of the feather reservoir without removing the spinner. The use of a pressure filling device is recommended because this will provide rapid filling and assure the use of only clean, filtered hydraulic fluid.

Any hydraulic fluid which drains into the regulator is called **uncontrolled drain.** Fluid which drains into the feather reservoir is called **controlled drain.** Except for a small amount of internal leakage, all oil pumped by the hydraulic pumps is directed to controlled drain. The airflow over the exterior of the feather reservoir provides for the cooling of the hydraulic fluid. The feather reservoir overflows the cooled fluid back into the regulator reservoir where the pumps again pick it up for recirculation. Thus, the controlled drain provides for cooling of the hydraulic fluid and keeps the feather reservoir full. In the event of a regulator hydraulic component malfunction which requires feathering of the propeller, the feather reservoir and pump can supply the flow of fluid required for feathering.

Four gear-driven hydraulic pumps, located in the propeller regulator, are driven only when the propeller is rotating. Their output volume is a function of propeller rpm. Thus if a propeller is signaled to feather during flight, the output of these pumps decreases as rpm decreases. An auxiliary source of hydraulic pressure is required to feather the propeller completely. If an auxiliary source of hydraulic pressure were not available, the propeller would not complete feathering but would continue to rotate at a high blade angle with low rpm and low drag.

The auxiliary source of hydraulic pressure is provided by an electrically driven pump. Operation of this pump is required for feathering, unfeathering, and static checks of the hydraulic system.

The components of the system mounted in the regulator are (1) four hydraulic pumps, (2) NTS-feather valve, (3) hydraulic pump, (4) jitter valve, (5) solenoid valve, (6) pitch lock and stop valve, and (7) the centrifugal breather.

The four hydraulic pumps supply the flow of hydraulic fluid for normal operation of the hydraulic system.

The NTS-feather valve responds to either an NTS signal or a feather signal by porting all fluid pumped by the hydraulic pumps to **increase beta** (blade angle) passages. Thus a rapid rate of blade-angle change required for feathering or NTS response can be effected.

The **hydraulic governor** is a hydromechanically controlled device used for both beta range and governing range operation. In the governing range the hydraulic governor effects blade angle changes required to maintain a constant engine rpm of 13,820. In this range of operation the propeller is classified as "nonselective and automatic." In the beta range the hydraulic gover-

nor provides the means by which blade angles may be selected by the power lever and the propeller is classified as "controllable and multiposition." The unit in the governor which acts automatically to regulate engine speed is the **speed-sensitive element.** This unit is affected by centrifugal force and spring pressure. When engine speed is excessive, the centrifugal force on the speed-sensitive element overcomes spring pressure and the element moves the distributor valve to route hydraulic fluid under pressure to the pitch-change (torque) units at the base of the propeller blades.

The **jitter valve** is used to "pulse" certain elements within the hydraulic governor to increase their sensitivity and response rate.

The **solenoid valve** is controlled by a phase synchronizer module to provide a means of trimming propeller speed by biasing the fluid flow from the hydraulic governor to the torque units.

The **pitch-lock and stop-valve assembly** contains the necessary valves required for the control of the mechanical low-pitch stop and pitch-lock mechanisms in the master gear assembly. It also incorporates a valve element which provides for the transition of the propeller operation from the beta range to the governing range or vice versa. The assembly contains a speed-sensitive unit which causes the blade angle to be locked if sufficient overspeed occurs. This prevents a further decrease in propeller pitch and helps to prevent a greater increase in engine speed.

The **feather pump** is mounted in the feather reservoir and provides an auxiliary source of hydraulic pressure for static ground operation of the propeller and for any feathering or unfeathering operation. During normal operation, the feather pump is not used. The pump is driven by an electric motor which is actuated for approximately 60 sec by the action of the feather pump motor timer. When the propeller is unfeathered, the motor is energized as long as the feather button is held in the unfeather position.

At the outlet of the feather pump is a check valve which allows the feather pump to deliver fluid into the hydraulic system but prevents the four regulator pumps from pumping fluid back through the feather pump.

During normal operation of the propeller, centrifugal twisting moment (CTM) tends to decrease blade angle. Thus greater pressures are required to increase the blade angle during propeller rotation than when the propeller is static. The feather pressure-control valve controls the discharge pressure of the feather pump as a function of rpm; that is, the higher the rpm, the greater the discharge pressure from the feather pump.

Safety features

Because of the design characteristics of turboprop (propjet) powerplants wherein high drag forces are associated with either engine or propeller failure, certain safety devices must be incorporated in the turbo-propeller to assure safe operation. These safety devices reduce the asymmetric thrust to values compatible with airframe structural limitations and controllability.

Pitch lock

The **pitch-lock** mechanism is a speed-sensitive device designed to protect against blade-angle pitch-down in the event of a propeller control system malfunction which results in an overspeed condition. Pitch-lock protection is needed only during governing range operation; hence it is blocked out below 28° coordinator power settings, below 21.5° blade angle, or above 73.5° blade angle.

Mechanical low-pitch stop (MLPS)

The **mechanical low-pitch stop** is designed to prevent the inadvertent entry of the blades into the beta range during flight in the event of propeller control system malfunction. The MLPS with a setting of 18.25 to 18.5° "backs up" the normal hydraulic low-pitch stops.

Hydraulic low-pitch stop (HLPS)

The **hydraulic low-pitch stop** is designed to prevent the propeller hydraulic governor from decreasing the blade angle into the beta range during governing operation. The HLPS has a setting of 20° blade angle from 30 to 68° coordinator. From 68 to 90° coordinator HLPS is scheduled from 20 to approximately 31.5° blade angle. This scheduling of the HLPS is called **beta follow-up** and means that the propeller pitch cannot decrease below 20 or 30° during constant-speed operation controlled by the governor.

Negative torque signal system

The **NTS system** operates by signals from the reduction-gear assembly. The stationary ring gear is mounted in the gear case with helical splines, and if torque on the ring is opposite to normal operation, the ring moves and actuates switches to produce the negative torque signal. The device functions at a specified torque as mentioned previously. If sufficient negative torque is produced when the propeller tends to drive the engine owing to "lean" fuel schedules at flight idle power settings, air gusts on the propeller, loss of engine power, temporary fuel interruptions, or similar conditions, a signal will be produced. The propeller responds to this signal by increasing blade angle as necessary to limit the negative torque. The NTS system within the propeller is blocked out below 21 to 24° coordinator power setting.

Manual feather

Manual feather is accomplished by depressing the FEATHER button in the cockpit. When this is done, the propeller is signaled to feather by the feather solenoid, the electric feather pump motor is energized for approximately 60 sec by a timer, and fuel flow is stopped via an electrical fuel-cutoff actuator on the engine. Thus, the propeller will feather and the engine will stop running when the FEATHER button is depressed. If this button is depressed when operating below a 21 to 24° coordinator power settings, fuel flow will be stopped but the propeller will not feather because the NTS system is blocked out of operation.

Auto feather

The **auto-feather** control system is incorporated in the engine reduction-gear assembly. Whenever the propeller thrust is greater than positive 500 lb, the auto-feather system cannot function. When propeller thrust is less than positive 500 lb, the auto-feather control system will produce auto feather if the auto-feather system is armed. The arming circuit of any given engine auto-feather system includes several switches in series with each other. These switches are a cockpit manually positioned switch, a 75° coordinator power lever switch, and necessary feather button switches. On a four-engine installation, an engine auto-feather circuit is armed by a switch in each of the other engine feather buttons. On a two-engine installation, the feather circuit is armed by a switch in the opposite engine feather button.

The auto-feather system operates in conjunction with signals from the thrust-sensitive signal (TSS) system which is contained in the engine reduction-gear assembly. The TSS system is designed to provide an auto-feather signal in case of power loss during takeoff. The TSS system is independent of the NTS system, since the TSS has a minimum positive **thrust** setting while the NTS system has a negative **torque** setting. If the thrust developed by the propeller is in excess of a positive 500 lb, two switches (parallel) in the thrust-sensitive switch assembly on the reduction-gear assembly are open. In the event of an engine failure on takeoff, the propeller thrust decreases. When it drops below a positive 500 lb, the thrust-sensitive switch assembly switches are closed. Thus, if this switch assembly is properly armed and engine failure occurs, the auto-feather circuitry is energized to effect a feather shutdown.

Emergency feather

Emergency feathering is accomplished by manually pulling the emergency handle. When this handle is pulled, switches are tripped and mechanical linkage is moved which signals the propeller to feather and fuel flow to stop. The switches control electrical circuits which pull the feather button into its feather position via a "pull-in" coil. Thus, pulling the emergency handle effects engine shutdown electrically and mechanically. Emergency feathering can be accomplished under any condition of the engine operation regardless of the power setting.

Solenoid stop

The principal function of the solenoid stop is to prevent a loose or disconnected condition control lever from entering the beta range inadvertently and scheduling low blade angles which would cause excessive drag during flight.

Synchronizing and phase synchronizing

There are five major components which make up the synchronizing and the phase synchronizing systems: (1) propeller alternator, (2) rotary actuator, (3) solenoid valve, (4) electronic synchronizer module, and (5) electronic phase synchronizer module. The effect of these components on the hydraulic system is considered with reference to the following factors of operation:

K1   Speed error, hydraulic
K2   Acceleration sensitivity
K3   Rate of change of trim on hydraulic governor with respect to speed error
K4   Rate of change of trim on hydraulic governor with respect to phase error

The normal propeller governing is obtained by means of a hydromechanical speed-sensitive governor in the regulator. This governor, utilizing the K1 factor of operation, provides satisfactory stability for all normal operation. No external accessories are required for K1 operation.

To obtain optimum stability, it is necessary to use a control factor which is proportional to the acceleration of the engine. Acceleration intelligence, or the K2 factor, is obtained from the engine-driven propeller alternator and the electronic circuits in the phase synchronizer module. The resulting voltage is used to power the solenoid valve in the regulator. Since governors are speed-sensitive devices, some rpm variation (±25 engine rpm) is to be expected when only the K1 factor is utilized. The solenoid valve biases or trims the flow of fluid from the hydraulic governor as required to quicken the recovery from offspeed by dampening out any overcorrection made by the hydraulic governor.

The synchronizing function, K3 factor, requires that the governing rpm of the slave propeller be reset to the governing rpm of the master propeller. This is accomplished by the slave and master propeller alternators sending speed intelligence to the slave synchronizer module. This module compares the speed of the slave relative to master and pulses the slave rotary actuator accordingly. The rotary actuator, when pulsed, actuates the necessary mechanical controls to effect a governing rpm change on the slave propeller. When the rpm of the slave propeller is the same as the rpm of the master propeller, the propellers are synchronized.

The phase synchronizing function, K4 factor, establishes the proper phase relationship by resetting the slave governor at a constant rate whenever the propellers are not at the optimum phase angle. This is accomplished by the slave and master propeller alternators sending phase-angle intelligence to the slave synchronizer module. The synchronizer module sends the phase error information to the slave phase synchronizer module, which converts this phase error information into the proper K4 signal voltage. This control voltage is mixed with the K2 voltage already present. The result is that the solenoid valve is pulsed so that it biases or trims the flow from the hydraulic governor for effective reset action to provide the optimum phase relationship between the slave and master propellers.

Anti-icing and deicing system

The propeller has components on which ice would form during icing conditions in flight. It is necessary either to anti-ice or deice these components if icing conditions are encountered. **Anti-icing** is a term used to identify components which are heated continuously, while **deicing** is a term used to identify components which are heated in sequence by a timer. "Runback" from an anti-iced component could result in undesirable ice formations. Components immediately aft of the anti-iced areas are deiced. Thus, deicing is used to prevent accumulation of these undesirable ice formations by heating the components long enough to remove the ice but not long enough to produce runback. Approximately the front two-thirds of the spinner is anti-iced. The deiced components consist of blade cuffs, spinner islands, and that part of the spinner which is not anti-iced. Refer to Fig. 19·11 for anti-icing and deicing circuits.

Propeller control schedule

The basic requirement for any aircraft powerplant is to provide controllable thrust throughout the range of operating conditions. In a turboprop installation, the major problem becomes one of matching the extreme shp variations of a gas-turbine engine in such a manner as to provide reliably controlled thrust at all times.

For flight operation, a gas-turbine engine is demanded to deliver power within a relatively narrow band of operating rotational speeds. This requires the control system to extract from the propeller controllable thrust within close rpm limits. During flight, the speed-sensitive governor of the propeller automatically controls the blade angle as required to maintain a constant rpm of 13,820 on the engine.

Three factors tend to vary the rpm of the engine during operation. These factors are **shp, airspeed,** and **air density.** If the rpm is to remain constant, the blade angle must vary directly with shp, directly with airspeed, and inversely with air density. The speed-sensitive governor provides the means by which the propeller can adjust itself automatically to varying power and flight conditions while converting the shp to thrust.

To maintain a reasonable thrust schedule for ground operation, adequate control cannot be obtained in the region of 0 to 20 percent thrust with a pure shp scheduling system as used in governing. For ground operation controllable thrust can be obtained by scheduling and coordinating fuel flow and blade angle according to the dictates of the power lever while allowing the engine to remain within rpm limitations.

The ground range of operation of the propeller is called the beta range and extends from 0 to 30 percent coordinator power setting. In this range a definite blade angle is scheduled by the power lever. This angle is from −4 to +20° at the 42-in. station. The governing range of the propeller extends from 30 to 90° coordinator power setting during which the propeller blade angle may increase to more than 40°. In this range the hydraulic governor of the propeller automatically controls the blade angle as required in order to maintain a constant engine rpm of 13,820 and a propeller rpm of 1020.

The power lever taxi range (0 to 34° coordinator) is used only for ground operation. The power lever flight range (34 to 90° coordinator) is used for all flight operation, ground power checks, and takeoff.

As previously explained, the propeller system incorporates safety features to prevent any possibility of the propeller entering into the beta range of operation while the aircraft is airborne. This is necessary because beta range blade angles in flight would result in extremely high drag, making directional control of the aircraft difficult if not impossible.

If the power lever is retarded rapidly to flight idle, a small amount of coordinator pointer overtravel may occur but the propeller remains in the governing range down to 30° coordinator. The 4° of coordinator pointer difference between the propeller governing range and the power lever flight range is a "safety cushion" against the propeller's transitioning into the beta range of operation as a result of rapid power lever movement to flight idle.

The function of the **solenoid stop** is to prevent the propeller condition control from moving into the beta range if the engine linkage to this lever becomes disconnected in flight. The electrical circuit which controls the solenoid stop includes a 34° power-lever-actuated switch that is in series with a landing-gear scissor switch. The solenoid stop is deenergized any time the power lever is above 34° or when there is no weight on the landing gear. Thus the solenoid stop is never energized in flight. If the linkage should become disconnected, the condition control lever tends to "free fall" into the beta range but it cannot enter the beta range because the solenoid stop is contacted at 31.5° coordinator. At this lever position the propeller remains in governing range, the propeller operation remains normal, and the flight crew would be unaware of the condition.

If there is weight on the landing gear, the solenoid stop will be energized when the power lever is retarded below 34° coordinator. Thus, normally the solenoid stop is positioned so that the flight crew can easily move the power lever and consequently the condition control lever below 31.5 coordinator. In the event that a malfunction occurs which results in the solenoid stop not being energized, the solenoid stop is contacted at 31.5 coordinator. If this occurs, the flight crew can exert a little extra force on the power lever to override the stop and move the condition control lever into the beta range.

Summary of turbopropeller features

Because of the many intricate details involved in the construction and operation of the Allison Model A6441FN-606 propeller, it is well to summarize the principal features of this propeller.

1. The propeller is a full-feathering constant-speed four-blade unit capable of converting more than 4500 shp into thrust. It is designed for an SAE 60 propeller shaft.
2. A complete hydraulic system with four pressure pumps is included in the hub section of the propeller to provide the power for the various ranges of operation from maximum reverse thrust to takeoff power. Hydraulic fluid is carried in the rotating regulator section and in the feathering reservoir.
3. The constant-speed feature is provided by means of a speed-sensitive governor. In the governing range the unit is set to provide an engine rpm of 13,820 and a propeller rpm of 1020. The speed-sensitive element of the governor is balanced between centrifugal force and spring pressure. When overspeed occurs, the governor provides for hydraulic fluid under pressure to be directed to the blade torque units.
4. The blade torque units consist of pistons mounted in helical splines. When fluid pressure is applied to one side of a piston, it moves outward or inward in the helical splines, thus producing a rotation of the blade. The four torque units are synchronized by means of a master gear.
5. The principal cockpit controls for the propeller are the Power Lever, Feather Button, Emergency Handle, and synchronizing controls. The power lever is used to set the range of operation through the coordinator and the condition control lever. The coordinator signals the fuel-control unit as required for all ranges of operation in accordance with the movement of the power lever.

   The feather button is used for manual feathering of the propeller through the NTS system. It provides for complete feathering and stopping the engine when the NTS system is not blocked out.

   The emergency handle is used to stop the engine at any time it is deemed necessary. It provides for feathering of the propeller and shutting off fuel in any of the operating ranges.
6. The propeller is provided with a negative torque signal system to reduce propeller drag in case of engine power loss. This system begins to feather the propeller when negative torque on the propeller shaft reaches −300 to −420 shp.
7. A thrust-sensitive signal activates an automatic feathering system if positive thrust decreases below positive 500 lb. This is to reduce drag in case of engine failure on takeoff.
8. The propeller is controlled through the power lever to operate in two principal ranges. These are the **beta range,** from 0 to 30° power-lever setting, and the **governing range,** from 30 to 90° power-lever setting. In the beta range the power lever controls propeller blade angle and fuel flow through the coordinator. In the propeller governing range, the governor in the propeller controls engine speed at 13,820 rpm and the power lever provides for fuel scheduling through the coordinator and the fuel-control unit.
9. The propeller has a **maximum reverse** setting to provide for reverse thrust after landing. Maximum reverse is produced by moving the power lever to the 0° position. This causes rotation of the propeller blades to a negative pitch setting and applied engine power through the fuel control.

A drawing of the complete propeller system is shown in Fig. 19·12. This illustration shows how the power lever and the emergency handle both operate through the coordinator to move the condition control lever at the propeller. It can also be observed that the NTS signal comes from the reduction-gear section of the engine and is delivered through the NTS feather lever to the propeller.

REVIEW QUESTIONS

1. Give a brief description of the counterweight-type constant-speed propeller.
2. When a propeller control in the cockpit is placed in the DEC RPM position, what takes place with respect to pitch?

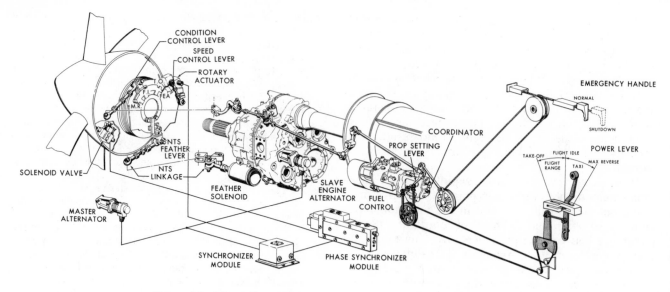

Figure 19·12 *Drawing of complete propeller control system. (Allison)*

3. Describe the pitch-changing mechanism of the hydromatic reversing propeller.
4. How is reverse pitch obtained?
5. Describe the feathering operation of the hydromatic propeller.
6. Explain the operation of the propeller governor.
7. What is the function of a *master* engine with respect to engine synchronizing?
8. What is the purpose of the *governor step motor* in the synchronizing system?
9. Briefly describe the synchronization system for the Hamilton Standard reversing propeller.
10. What is meant by the *beta range* in the operation of the Allison turbopropeller?
11. Describe the physical features of the Allison turbopropeller.
12. Give the number of hydraulic pumps in the system, and tell how they are driven.
13. What is the propeller rpm at governing speed?
14. Describe the construction of the propeller blades.
15. At what position of the power lever does the governing range begin?
16. At what position of the power lever is the engine started?
17. Describe the *regulator* assembly.
18. Where is the hydraulic fluid for the propeller hydraulic system stored?
19. Describe a *torque unit.*
20. What forces act on the governor to produce speed control?
21. What is the function of the master gear?
22. Describe the method by which control is transmitted from the nonrotating engine to the rotating propeller.
23. Describe the feather reservoir assembly.
24. Explain the purpose of the *negative torque signal* system.
25. Through what means is electrical power transferred to the rotating propeller assembly?
26. How would you stop the engine and propeller quickly if the NTS system were blocked out?
27. What is the purpose of the *thrust-sensitive signal?*
28. How is hydraulic fluid added to the propeller supply?
29. Explain the purpose of the *solenoid stop.*
30. What is the function of the *coordinator?*

CHAPTER **20**

Principles of Jet Propulsion

BACKGROUND OF JET PROPULSION

Discovery of the jet-propulsion principle

No one knows who first discovered the jet-propulsion principle, but the honor is sometimes given to a man named Hero, who lived in Alexandria, Egypt, about 150 B.C. He invented a toy whirligig turned by steam, as illustrated in Fig. 20·1 and called his invention an **aeolipile,** but apparently he did not discover any very useful purpose for his discovery.

The historical records are not very definite in describing the aeolipile. If it resembled the picture in Fig. 20·1, it was a primitive form of a jet or reaction engine. On the other hand, some authorities describe it as being operated by hot air instead of steam. The heating of air in a vertical tube induced a flow of air in several tubes arranged radially around a horizontal wheel, and rotation resulted from the creation of an impulse effect if this version of the story is accepted. In that case, Hero's invention was a gas turbine.

In 1550, Leonardo da Vinci, who was a successful Jack-of-all-trades, sketched a device that could be placed in a chimney where the upward movement of hot gases would turn a spit for roasting meat. In 1629, Giovanni Branca, another Italian, perfected a steam turbine that applied the jet principle and could be used to operate primitive machinery.

Figure 20·2 is a drawing of an invention called **Newton's carriage,** which was a jet-propelled steam carriage, although Newton himself may have supplied only the idea, for there are authorities who attribute the design of the carriage to a Dutchman, Willem Jako Gravesande.

Turbine development

The first patent covering a gas turbine was granted to John Barber of England in 1791. It included all the essential elements of the modern gas turbine except that it had a reciprocating-type compressor. In 1808, a patent was granted in England to John Bumbell for a gas turbine which had rotating blades but no stationary, guiding elements. Thus the advantages gained today by the multistage type of turbine were missed.

In 1837, a Frenchman named Bresson was granted a patent for a machine in which a fan delivered air under pressure to a combustion chamber where the air was mixed with a gaseous fuel and burned. The hot products of combustion were then cooled by excess air and

Figure **20·1** Hero's aeolipile.

Figure **20·2** Newton's steam carriage.

405

directed in the form of a jet against a turbine wheel. This was essentially a gas turbine, but there is apparently no record of its practical application.

In 1850, W. F. Fernihough was granted a patent in England for a turbine operated by both steam and gas, but as long as steam was used, the development of a true gas turbine was held back. However, a man named Stolze designed what was probably the first true gas turbine in 1872 and tested working models in the years between 1900 and 1904. Stolze used both a multistage reaction gas turbine and a multistage axial compressor.

Sir Charles Parsons, the great English inventor, obtained a patent in 1884 for a steam turbine, in which he advanced the theory that a turbine could be converted into a compressor by driving it in an opposite direction with an external source of power. Parsons believed that compressed air could be discharged into a furnace or combustion chamber, fuel injected, and the products of combustion expanded through a turbine. This idea of a compressor was essentially the same as that which we have today except for the shape of the blades.

Charles G. Curtis is generally credited with the filing of the first patent application in the United States for a complete gas turbine. His application was filed in 1905, although previously, in 1902, he filed an application for a rotary compressor, blower, and pump combination and actually obtained the patent in 1914. There is some argument about how much Curtis did to develop the gas turbine, but he is credited, without dispute, with the invention of the Curtis steam engine, and he was one of the pioneers in the development of steam turbines.

We come to one of the great names in jet-propulsion development. Dr. Sanford A. Moss, who eventually became one of the leading engineers of the General Electric Company, completed his thesis on the gas turbine in 1900 and submitted it to the University of California in application for his master's degree. The contributions of Dr. Moss to the development of engines of all types are so extensive that to describe them completely would fill several volumes. However, a few of his outstanding contributions will be mentioned. Figure 20·3 is a sketch of Dr. Moss drawn shortly before his death.

In 1902, experiments were conducted at Cornell University with what was probably the first gas turbine developed in the United States. A combustion chamber designed by Dr. Moss was used with a steam-turbine bucket wheel, which functioned as the gas-turbine rotor. A steam-driven compressor supplied compressed air to the combustion chamber. The engine was not a success from the practical viewpoint because the power required to drive the compressor was greater than the power delivered by the gas turbine, but from the experiments Dr. Moss learned enough to enable him to start the General Electric Company's gas-turbine project the next year.

In the following years there were various turbine inventions and developments in the United States and in Europe, but the next outstanding was the construction of the first General Electric turbosupercharger by

Figure **20·3** Dr. Sanford A. Moss.

Dr. Sanford Moss during World War I. The products of combustion of the engine exhaust drove a turbine wheel at constant pressure, and the turbine wheel, in turn, drove a centrifugal compressor that supplied the supercharging.

Strictly speaking, the first General Electric turbo-supercharger was based on French patents by Rateau; hence Dr. Moss and the General Electric Company are entitled to credit for developing the running model, although the credit for the idea behind it belongs to Rateau of France.

It is interesting to consider that the turbosupercharger was developed as an offshoot of a gas turbine, the turbosupercharger then went through a long stage of development, and finally the engineers took the knowledge they acquired from working with the turbosupercharger and applied it to jet propulsion.

Frank Whittle began work on gas turbines while he was still an RAF air cadet. He applied for a patent in England in 1930 for a machine having a blower compressor mounted at the forward end and a gas turbine at the rear end of the same shaft, supplied by energy from the combustion chamber. Discharge jets were located between the annular housings of the rotary elements and in line with several combustion chambers distributed around the circumference.

On May 14, 1941, flight trials began with a Gloster E28/39 experimental airplane equipped with Whittle's engine which was known as the W1. The flight tests were successful, thus greatly increasing the interest of both government and manufacturers and setting the

Figure 20·4 Air Commodore Frank Whittle.

by a change of momentum, and this force is equal to the time rate of change of momentum. The **momentum** of a body is defined as the product of its mass and velocity. From this law it is apparent that, if we change the velocity of a body, a force is required. In equation form, this principle is expressed $F = dM/dt$, where F is the force, M is the momentum, and t is the time. This equation means that the force created by a change in the velocity of a body is equal to the amount of change in velocity divided by the change in time, when appropriate units of measurement are used.

Another equation which expresses the same operation is

$$F = \frac{m}{g}(V_2 - V_1)$$

where M = mass rate of flow, lb per sec
V_2 = final velocity, ft per sec
V_1 = initial velocity, ft per sec
g = acceleration of gravity, 32.2 ft per sec^2

Another expression of Newton's second law is: **Force is proportional to the product of mass and acceleration.** This statement is clearly shown by the two equations given above.

In order to demonstrate the use of the latter of the two equations, we compute the thrust of a jet engine mounted in an airplane flying at 900 ft per sec. The engine takes in 200 lb per sec of air and burns 4 lb per sec of fuel. The velocity of the jet exhaust is 2100 ft per sec with respect to the engine.

Applying the equation,

$$F = \frac{204(2100 - 900)}{32.2}$$

$$= 7600 \text{ lb (approximately)}$$

Converting thrust to horsepower

Because power is determined by using the product of a force and a distance, it is not possible to make a direct comparison of thrust and horsepower in a jet engine. When the engine is driving an airplane through the air, however, we can compute the equivalent horsepower being developed. When we convert the foot-pounds per minute of 1 hp to mile-pounds per hour, we obtain the figure of 375. That is, 1 hp is equal to 33,000 ft-lb per min or 375 mile-lb per hr. Thrust horsepower (thp) is then obtained by using the following formula:

$$\text{thp} = \frac{\text{thrust (lb)} \times \text{airspeed (mph)}}{375}$$

If a jet engine is developing 10,000 lb thrust and is driving an airplane at 600 mph, the thp is found thus:

$$\text{thp} = \frac{10,000 \times 600}{375} = 16,000$$

Effects of reaction

In its simplest form, the jet-propulsion engine may be considered as a device for taking in air, adding energy to that air (by burning fuel), and producing thrust from the accelerated gases. Whether this is con-

stage for the tremendous progress which was to come.

While Whittle and his associates were working on the development of the W1 engine in England, the Heinkel Aircraft Company in Germany was also busy with a similar task. The German company was successful in making the first known jet-propelled flight on August 27, 1939, with a Heinkel He 178 airplane powered by a Heinkel HeS 3B turbojet engine having a thrust of 880 to 1100 lb.

The pioneer jet-propelled fighter planes built in England by the Gloucester (Gloster) Aircraft Company, Ltd., and in the United States by the Bell Aircraft Corporation were powered by a combustion, gas-turbine, jet-propulsion powerplant system developed from Frank Whittle's designs and built by the General Electric Company. Today, Air Commodore Frank Whittle, whose picture appears in Fig. 20·4, is internationally recognized as one of the great leaders in his field.

Only a few of the many important inventors and engineers who contributed to the modern jet-engine program have been mentioned, but the work of every one of them has been based fundamentally on Sir Issac Newton's laws of motion.

REACTION PRINCIPLES

Newton's laws of motion

The thrust produced by a jet engine may be explained by Newton's second and third laws of motion. The second law may be stated thus: **A force is created**

sidered from the momentum standpoint, the pressure standpoint, or the energy standpoint is not too important for the beginner.

An example of reaction is a boy in a boat. If the boy rows the boat toward the shore, steps on the bow, and then attempts to leap ashore, the force with which he drives himself forward reacts and pushes the boat backward. The boy usually misses the shore and lands in the water, simply because a person stands on something fixed which resists this acting force if he wants to leap successfully.

In a similar manner, the end of a garden hose lying on the lawn is driven backward by the reaction of the water when the water is turned on and it shoots forth from the nozzle.

Another example is the reaction of water against the arms of a swimmer or the oars of a boat. The reaction of the water against the propellers of a steam vessel makes the ship move. The reaction of the air against the wings of a bird enables it to fly. The reaction of the air against the propellers of an airplane as they drive the airplane forward and the reaction against the airplane itself follow Newton's second law of motion.

When a pistol or a rifle is fired, it recoils in accordance with Newton's third law of motion, and although it might seem at first thought that this recoil results from the push of the expelled gases on the surrounding air, this is an erroneous assumption. The kick of the gun, whether the bullet breaks through some dense substance or flies through ordinary atmosphere or shoots through a vacuum which has no density at all, is exactly the same in each case.

If the jet of a jet-propelled airplane is regarded as having the same effect as a stream of millions of bullets in multiple force, then the continuous kick which propels the airplane does not result from the jet pushing against the air behind it but follows Newton's second law of motion.

The application of jet powerplants to aircraft has made flying faster than the speed of sound, which was once considered impossible, commonplace. The principal limiting factor to the speed of aircraft at present is the heating effect caused by the friction of air against the surface of the aircraft.

Thrust developed by a conventional propeller

The fixed blades of a conventional propeller are continually swooping air from the front and throwing it to the rear. In effect, the propeller is boring its way through the atmosphere like a giant disk. It is the reaction to the mass of air being thrown violently to the rear that drives the airplane forward. However, the conventional propeller reaches a limit in the speed at which it can revolve. In order to explain how jet propulsion breaks through this limitation, we shall redesign, in theory, a conventional piston engine and propeller combination.

Theoretical conversion of the conventional powerplant into a jet engine

If the conventional airplane engine and propeller are enclosed in a nacelle, thus narrowing down the stream

of air which reacts to the propeller, we have created one form of jet propulsion, as illustrated in Fig. 20·5. Next, the large propellers of conventional design are replaced with a small compressor, the purpose of which is to produce a large mass of compressed air, as shown in Fig. 20·6. A combustion chamber is installed, and fuel is injected to expand the compressed air and increase its velocity as indicated in the diagram of Fig. 20·7. Finally, the external source of power, which is the airplane engine of conventional form, is removed, and in the path of the exhaust gases a turbine is installed to drive the compressor, as shown in Fig. 20·8. In principle, at least, the conventional engine and propeller have been converted in this manner into a jet engine. The principal difference in operation is that the conventional engine and propeller accelerate a large volume of air a small amount while the jet engine accelerates a smaller volume of air a large amount.

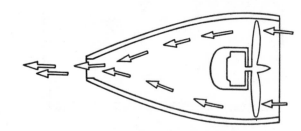

Figure 20·5 Jet propulsion from a propeller.

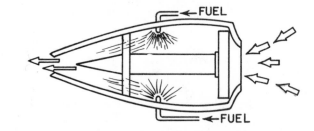

Figure 20·6 Propeller replaced by a compressor.

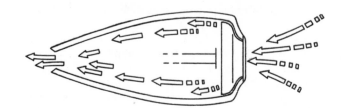

Figure 20·7 Burning fuel used to expand gases.

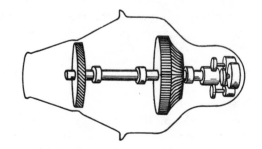

Figure 20·8 Turbine to drive the compressor.

FACTORS AFFECTING THRUST

Air density

The **density** of air is expressed as the weight per unit volume. For example, 1 cu ft of dry air at standard sea-level pressure (29.92 in. Hg) and temperature (59°F) weighs 0.076475 lb. From this we can determine that 13 cu ft of air weighs approximately 1 lb. Since the weight (mass) of air consumed by a jet engine is a primary factor in determining thrust, any condition which affects the weight (density) of the air consumed by the jet engine will also affect the thrust.

The conditions affecting the weight of a given volume of air are **pressure, temperature,** and **humidity.** At a constant temperature, the density of air will vary in proportion to absolute pressure; that is, as pressure increases, density also increases. On the other hand, density decreases as temperature increases.

The effect of humidity is not so pronounced as the effects of pressure and temperature; however, humidity must be taken into account when an accurate evaluation of thrust is required. This is particularly true during operation at or near sea level in areas where humidity is likely to be high. The effect of increased humidity is to decrease air density.

Engine rpm

For any particular engine, the thrust increases rapidly as the rpm approaches the maximum design speed of the engine. Among the reasons for this are the design of the compressor and turbine, the increase in mass airflow, and the increase in the difference between intake velocity V_a and jet nozzle velocity V_j.

Airspeed

As intake airspeed increases, thrust decreases because there is a decrease in the difference between V_a and V_j. However, when an aircraft is in flight, the increase in airspeed is accompanied by ram effect. For this reason the net change in thrust is small because the ram effect offsets the effect of change in airspeed.

Altitude

The decrease in air density due to lower pressures at high altitudes results in a decrease in thrust. Because of the decrease in drag at altitude, the performance of the aircraft is actually improved even though net thrust decreases.

When all factors are combined, it is found that the jet aircraft performs most efficiently at high speeds and high altitudes.

TYPES OF TURBOJET ENGINES

The centrifugal-flow jet engine

A cross-sectional drawing of a centrifugal turbojet engine is shown in Fig. 20 · 9. The term **centrifugal** means that the compressor is of the centrifugal type and that the air is compressed by centrifugal force. The air enters near the center of the impeller and is thrown

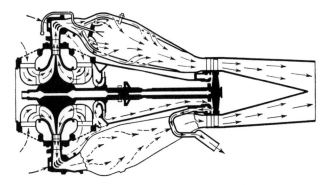

Figure 20 · 9 Cross section of a centrifugal turbojet engine.

outward to the **diffuser** as the impeller rotates. The diffuser converts the kinetic energy of the air leaving the compressor into potential energy (pressure) by exchanging velocity for pressure.

The early jet engine was equipped with a starter, fuel pumps, an overspeed governor, a fuel control, and other accessories. The ducting at the front of the engine allows air to flow into the compressor and thence through the diffuser section to the combustion chambers into which fuel is introduced through nozzles. This arrangement is shown in the drawing of Fig. 20 · 9. The high-velocity gases resulting from the fuel combustion enter a nozzle diaphragm which directs the flow against the blades (buckets) of the turbine wheel. Since the turbine is mounted on a common shaft with the compressor, the compressor is driven by the turbine.

In operation, first the starter motor rotates the compressor and turbine and brings the compressor to a speed which drives a large volume of air through the combustion chambers. When the airflow is sufficient, fuel is injected into the chambers through the spray nozzles and ignited by means of igniter plugs. It should be understood that the jet engine is not an alternate firing engine. The spark igniters are used only for the initial firing, and the fuel in all the combustion chambers burns continuously like a blowtorch as indicated in the drawing of Fig. 20 · 10.

The turbojet engine actually burns only a small percentage of the air taken into the compressor. The larger volume of air flows around the outside of the burning flame and serves as a cooling blanket to prevent the high temperature from burning the combustion chamber. The design of a combustion chamber is shown in Fig. 20 · 11.

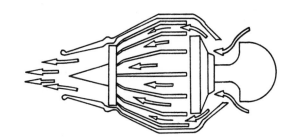

Figure 20 · 10 Continuous burning in a turbojet engine.

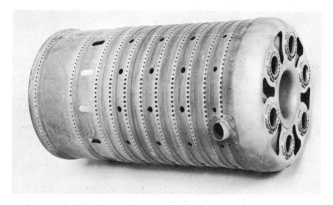

Figure **20 · 11** A combustion chamber.

The axial-flow turbojet engine

In an **axial-flow** jet engine the air flows axially, that is, in a relatively straight path in line with the axis of the engine, as shown in the drawing of Fig. 20·12. The principle of operation of the axial-flow turbojet engine is the same as that of the centrifugal-flow engine; however, the axial-flow engine has a number of advantages. Among these are: (1) The air flows in an almost straight path through the engine, hence less energy is lost as a result of changing direction; (2) the pressure ratio (ratio of compressor inlet pressure to compressor discharge pressure) is greater because the air can be compressed through as many stages as the designer wishes; and (3) the engine frontal area can be smaller for the same volume of air consumed.

A cutaway illustration of a typical axial-flow turbojet engine is shown in Fig. 20·13. This is the Westing-

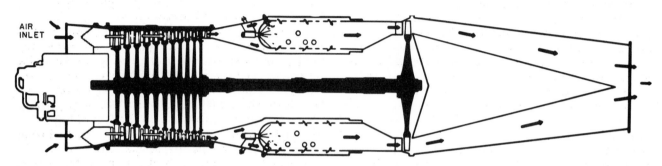

Figure **20 · 12** Drawing to illustrate the axial-flow turbojet engine.

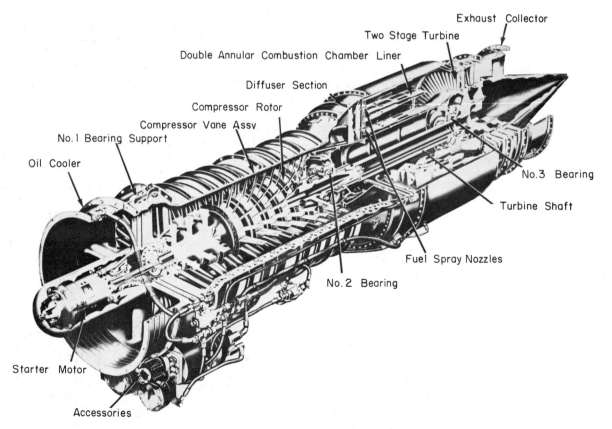

Figure **20 · 13** Westinghouse J-34 turbojet engine.

410

house J-34 engine which was used for many years in Navy aircraft. The principal parts of the engine are shown with proper nomenclature.

The J-34 engine has a 11-stage axial compressor which discharges into a double annular combustion chamber. An **annular** chamber consists of one burning compartment which surrounds the turbine shaft. The fuel nozzles are arranged in a ring at the forward end to provide for a uniform quantity of fuel spray around the chamber. In the double annular chamber, there are two concentric rings of fuel spray nozzles separated by the combustion chamber liner.

The dual-compressor axial-flow engine

A dual-compressor jet engine utilizes two separate compressors, each with its own driving turbine. This type of engine is also called a "twin-spool" or "split-compressor" engine.

A drawing to illustrate the construction of the dual-compressor engine is shown in Fig. 20 · 14. The forward compressor section is called the low-pressure compressor, and the rear section is the high-pressure compressor. It will be observed from the drawing that the low-pressure compressor is driven by a two-stage turbine mounted on the rear end of the inner shaft and the high-pressure compressor is driven by a single-stage turbine mounted on the outer coaxial shaft. The high-pressure rotor turns at a higher speed than the low-pressure rotor.

One of the principal advantages of the split compressor is greater flexibility of operation without danger of stall. The low-pressure compressor can operate at the best speed for the accommodation of the low-pressure, low-temperature air at the forward part of the engine. The high-pressure compressor is speed-governed to operate at the proper speeds for the most efficient performance in compressing the high-temperature, high-pressure air toward the rear of the compressor section. The use of the dual compressor makes it possible to attain pressure ratios of more than 13:1, whereas the single axial compressor produces pressure ratios of 6 or 7:1 unless variable stator vanes are employed.

Turbofan engines

A **turbofan** engine may be considered a cross between a turbojet engine and a turboprop engine. The turboprop engine drives a conventional propeller through reduction gears to provide a speed suitable for the propeller. The propeller accelerates a large volume of air in addition to that which is being accelerated by the engine itself. The turbofan engine accelerates a smaller

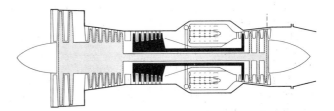

Figure **20 · 15** *Drawing of a forward turbofan engine.*

volume of air than the turboprop engine but a larger volume than the turbojet engine.

A drawing to illustrate the arrangement of a forward turbofan engine with a dual compressor is shown in Fig. 20 · 15. During operation the air from the fan section of the forward blades is carried outside the engine through ducting. It may either be dumped overboard or be carried to the rear of the engine and mixed with the exhaust. The effect of the turbofan design is to greatly increase the power/weight ratio of the engine and to improve the thrust specific fuel consumption (TSFC).

Turbofan engines may be constructed with a forward fan as in the Pratt & Whitney JT-3D or with an aft fan as in the General Electric CJ-805-23 engine. The GE aft fan is a one-stage, counterrotating free turbine mounted in a housing attached to the main turbine casing. The turbine is driven by the engine exhaust and has fan extensions on each blade. These fan blades extend into a coaxial duct which surrounds the main engine exhaust cone. Airflow enters the forward end of the duct and is expelled coaxially with the engine exhaust to produce additional thrust.

PRINCIPAL PARTS OF A JET ENGINE

The compressor

As previously mentioned, there are two types of compressors with respect to airflow, the **centrifugal** type and the **axial** type. Many of the early engines

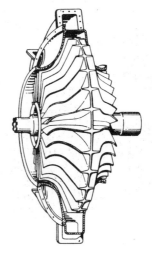

Figure **20 · 16** *Centrifugal-flow compressor.*

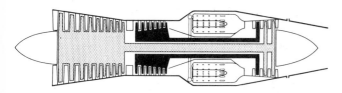

Figure **20 · 14** *Drawing of a dual-compressor engine.*

utilized centrifugal compressors; however, present designs are mostly of the axial-flow type.

The configuration of a centrifugal-flow compressor is shown in Fig. 20·16. This is a double-sided turbine with air inlets at both the front and the rear. Air reaches the rear inlet of the compressor by flowing between the compressor outlet adapters, as shown in the drawing of Fig. 20·9.

Although the centrifugal compressor is not so expensive to manufacture as the axial-flow compressor, its lower efficiency eliminates the advantage of lower cost. Among the successful centrifugal engines manufactured in the United States was the Allison J-33 engine shown in Fig. 20·17.

The compressor rotor and one-half the stator case for an axial-flow turbojet engine are shown in Fig. 20·18. The parts shown are designed for the Westinghouse J-34 turbojet engine. It will be observed that the compressor blades are shaped like small airfoils and that they become smaller in each stage moving from the front of the compressor to the rear. The stator blades are also shaped like small airfoils, and they too become smaller toward the high-pressure end of the compressor. The purpose of the stator blades is to change the direction of the airflow as it leaves each stage of the compressor rotor and give it proper direction for entrance to the next stage. The ends of the stator blades are fitted with shrouds to prevent the loss of air from stage to stage and to the interior of the compressor rotor.

During the operation of the compressor the air pressure increases as it passes each stage, and at the outlet into the diffuser it reaches a value several times that of the atmosphere, the actual pressure being over 70 psi.

The arrangement of a dual axial compressor is shown in Fig. 20·19. This compressor design, as explained previously, makes it possible to obtain extremely high pressure ratios with reduced danger of compressor stall because the low-pressure compressor is free to operate at its best speed and the high-pressure compressor rotor is speed-regulated by means of the fuel-control unit. Compressor stall occurs when the air velocity in the first compressor stages is reduced to a level where the angle of attack of the compressor blades reaches a stall value. This condition is aggravated during acceleration owing to air "choke" at the outlet.

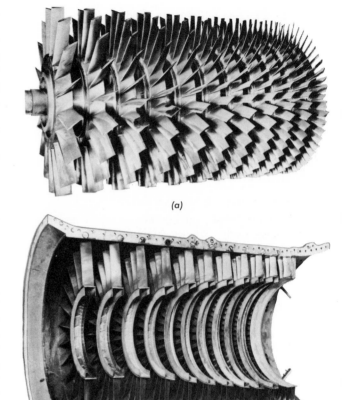

(a)

(b)

Figure **20·18**   Rotor (a) and stator (b) of an axial-flow compressor.

In the dual compressor engine, the compressor drive shafts are coaxial; that is, one shaft is mounted on bearings inside the other. The high-pressure compressor rotor is driven by a single turbine mounted on the aft end of the outer drive shaft, and the low-pressure compressor rotor is driven by a two-stage turbine which is mounted on the end of the inner drive shaft aft of the first turbine.

Important features of compressor design developed by the General Electric Company for the J-79 (CJ-805) and the J-85 (CJ-610) engines are the **variable inlet guide vanes and variable stator vanes.** These vanes are automatically regulated in pitch angle by means of the fuel-control unit. The regulating factors are compressor inlet temperature and engine speed. The effect of the variable vanes is to provide a means for controlling the direction of compressor interstage airflow, thus assuring a correct angle of attack for the compressor blades and reducing the possibility of compressor stall. A more extensive description of the variable vanes will be given in the section describing the CJ-805 engine.

The diffuser

The **diffuser** for a typical gas-turbine engine is that portion of the air passage between the compressor and

Figure **20·17**   Allison J-33 turbojet engine.

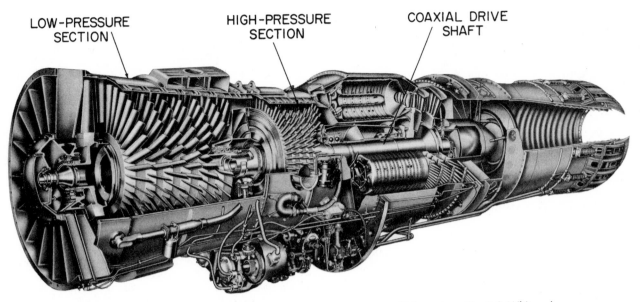

LOW-PRESSURE SECTION   HIGH-PRESSURE SECTION   COAXIAL DRIVE SHAFT

Figure **20·19**   *Arrangement of a dual-axial compressor, JT-3 engine. (Pratt & Whitney)*

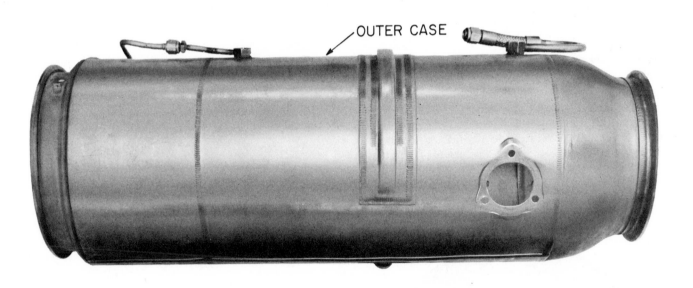

OUTER CASE

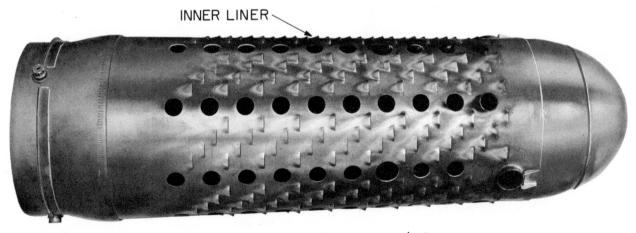

INNER LINER

Figure **20·20**   *A single can-type combustor.*

the combustion chamber or chambers. The purpose of the diffuser is to reduce the velocity of the air and prepare it for entry to the combustion area. As the air velocity decreases, its static pressure increases in accordance with Bernoulli's law. As the static pressure increases, the ram pressure decreases.

Combustion chambers

The combustion section of a turbojet engine may consist of individual combustion chambers ("cans"), an annular chamber which surrounds the turbine shaft, or a combination consisting of individual "cans" within an annular chamber. The latter type of combustor is called the **can-annular** type or simply the **cannular** type.

A typical can-type combustion chamber consists of an outer shell and a removable liner with openings to permit compressor discharge air to enter from the outer chamber. A fuel nozzle is located at the front end of the combustion chamber through which fuel is sprayed into the inner liner. The flame burns in the center of the inner liner and is prevented from burning the liner by a blanket of excess air which enters through holes in the liner and surrounds the flame. All burning is completed before the gases leave the chamber. Figure 20 · 20 is an illustration of a single can-type combustor.

Turbine nozzle diaphragm

The **turbine nozzle diaphragm** is a series of airfoil-shaped vanes arranged in a ring at the rear of the combustion section of a gas-turbine engine. Its function is to control the speed, direction, and pressure of the hot gases as they enter the turbine. A nozzle diaphragm is shown in Fig. 20 · 21. The vanes of the nozzle diaphragm must be designed to provide the most effective gas flow for the particular turbine used in the engine.

Turbines

A turbojet engine may have a single-stage turbine or a multistage arrangement. The function of the turbine is to extract kinetic energy from the high-velocity gases leaving the combustion section of the engine. The energy is converted to shaft horsepower for the purpose of driving the compressor. Approximately three-fourths of the energy available from the burning fuel is required for the compressor. If the engine is used for driving a propeller or a power shaft, up to 90 percent of the energy of the gases will be extracted by the turbine section.

Turbines are three types: the **impulse** turbine, the **reaction** turbine, and a combination of the two called a **reaction-impulse** turbine. Turbojet engines normally employ the reaction-impulse type.

The difference between an impulse turbine and a reaction turbine is illustrated in Fig. 20 · 22. The pressure and speed of the gases passing through the impulse turbine remain essentially the same, the only change being in the direction of flow. The turbine absorbs the energy required to change the direction of the high-speed gases. A reaction turbine changes the speed and

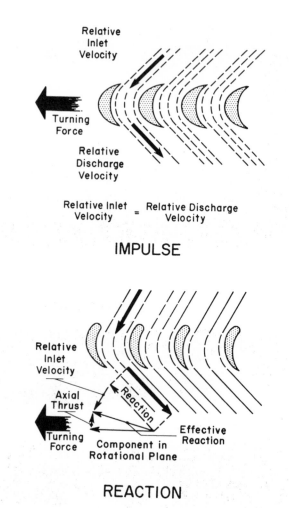

Figure **20 · 22** *Comparison of impulse and reaction turbines.*

Figure **20 · 21** *A nozzle diaphragm.*

414

pressure of the gases. As the gases pass between the turbine blades, the cross-sectional area of the passage decreases and causes an increase in the gas velocity. This increase in velocity is accompanied by a decrease in pressure according to Bernoulli's law. In this case the turbine absorbs the energy required to change the velocity of the gases. Typical turbines are illustrated in Fig. 20·23.

The exhaust nozzle

The normal function of the exhaust nozzle or cone is to control the velocity and temperature of the exhaust gases. Although a certain amount of thrust would be produced even if there were no exhaust nozzle, the thrust would be comparatively low and the direction of flow would not be properly controlled. When a convergent nozzle is used, the velocity of the gases is increased and the flow is directed so the thrust is in line with the engine.

The cross-sectional area of the nozzle outlet is most critical. If the area is too large, the engine will not develop maximum thrust, and if the area is too small, the exhaust temperature will be excessive at full-power conditions and will damage the engine. On some gas-turbine engines, the exhaust nozzle area is adjusted by means of small fittings called "mice." These are installed at the nozzle exit as required to give the correct nozzle area.

If the exhaust gases of a turbojet engine reach supersonic speed it is necessary to employ a conver-

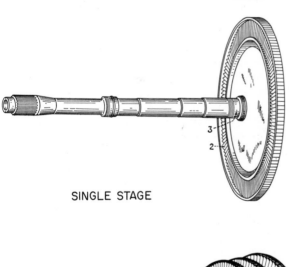

SINGLE STAGE

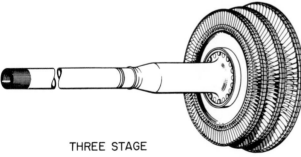

THREE STAGE

Figure **20·23** *Turbines.*

gent-divergent (C-D) exhaust duct in order to obtain maximum thrust. To ensure that a constant weight or volume of a gas will flow past any given point after sonic velocity is reached, the rear part of a supersonic duct must be enlarged to accommodate the additional weight or volume that will flow at supersonic speeds. The rate of increase in area in a divergent duct is just sufficient to allow for the increase in the rate of change in volume of the gases after they become sonic.

Exhaust nozzles on modern airliners usually include thrust-reversing devices and noise supressors. The **thrust reversers** are equipped with vanes and deflectors by which the exhaust gases are deflected outward and forward and are controlled through the thrust lever in the cockpit. After the airplane has landed, the pilot moves the levers to the rear of the idle position. This causes the deflecting vanes to move into the main stream of the exhaust gases and reverse their direction. At the same time fuel flow to the engine is increased in accordance with the position of the thrust lever.

Noise suppressors are special types of exhaust nozzles which break up the main single stream of exhaust gases to many smaller streams. The result is that the frequencies of the sound are increased to a point where some are above the audible level, and those that are still audible are more quickly attenuated by the surrounding air. Thus the noise at a distance from the engine is considerably reduced.

GAS-TURBINE ENGINE SYSTEMS

We shall briefly mention here the principal systems necessary for the operation of gas-turbine engines and shall describe these systems more fully when we deal with specific types of engines. The systems normally associated with gas-turbine engines are the lubrication system, fuel and fuel-control system, ignition system, starter system, and the air-bleed and -supply system.

Lubrication systems

The lubrication systems for gas-turbine engines are similar in many respects to lubrication systems for piston engines. An oil-supply tank is mounted on or near the engine, and the oil is supplied to the bearings and gears in the engine under pressure from the main pressure pump. The system includes pressure-relief valves to prevent excessive pressures and a filter to remove foreign particles from the lubricant. Inside the engine the oil is drained to one or more sumps where it is picked up by scavenge pumps and returned to the oil tank. On many engines the oil is routed through fuel-oil coolers which serve to heat the fuel and cool the oil. The hot oil is passed through one set of passages, and the cold fuel flows through adjacent passages so the heat of the oil can pass through the walls to the fuel.

The lubricant used with the majority of modern high-performance engines is of the synthetic type which will withstand much higher temperatures than will the petroleum-type lubricants previously used. Specifications for two of the synthetic lubricants are MIL-L-7808 and MIL-L-9236.

Fuel and fuel-control systems

The fuel system for a turbojet engine incorporates boost pumps, engine-driven pumps, filters, flow indicators, shutoff valves, fuel ice indicators, drain valves, fuel heater, main fuel-control unit, fuel nozzles, and an afterburner fuel control for those engines equipped with afterburners.

The most critical part of the fuel system is the **fuel-control unit.** Among the parameters (measurements or quantities) fed to the fuel-control unit are power lever (throttle) position, compressor inlet temperature (CIT), engine speed, compressor discharge pressure (CDP) which may also be burner pressure, exhaust gas temperature (EGT), and possibly some others. The fuel-control unit integrates the values of these parameters and adjusts the fuel-metering orifice accordingly. The fuel flow to the nozzles is therefore controlled according to all the conditions of operation so excess fuel cannot be supplied to the engine regardless of the throttle position. If the throttle is moved from the idle position to the full-power position, the fuel control unit will schedule fuel only as it can be properly used by the engine. As engine speed and airflow increase, the fuel flow increases to provide a proper rate of acceleration without danger of overheating the engine or causing a "rich blowout."

When the throttle is moved to the idle position from a cruise or full-power position, the fuel flow will decrease gradually to prevent a "lean flameout."

The fuel nozzle in the combustion chamber is designed to furnish a fine spray of fuel under all conditions of flow. In order to produce a good spray pattern for both high and low pressures, a fuel nozzle is often designed with a flow divider. The flow divider routes the fuel to two concentric spray outlets when the fuel pressure is high, but it cuts off the fuel to the outer passage when the fuel pressure drops below a certain level. The discharge nozzle has spin chambers at the outlets to give the fuel a whirling motion as it leaves the nozzle. This provides a good spray pattern and aids in atomizing the fuel.

It must be noted that fuel nozzles and other components of fuel systems vary in design, and it is only by reference to the manufacturer's instruction manual that the features of a particular model can be ascertained.

Ignition systems

Ignition systems for gas-turbine engines are not designed for continuous operation and therefore differ considerably from those manufactured for piston engines. The spark produced by the gas-turbine ignition system has many times the energy provided by a piston-engine system. One of the reasons this is necessary is that the mixture of fuel and air in a gas-turbine combustor is moving at a high velocity and it is not uniformly distributed. The ignition system is therefore designed to produce a large, flaming spark.

The spark igniters (spark plugs) for a jet engine are usually located at two positions. If the combustion chamber is of the can type or the cannular type, the spark igniters are located in a position to ignite the fuel in two of the cans. The flame is then carried to the other chambers through flame tubes.

The high-energy spark for ignition is produced by a system which utilizes capacitors, transformers, and gas diode tubes. The system shown in Fig. 20·24 is used in the General Electric CJ-805 engine and is representative of a high-energy system.

During operation, a power source of 100-volt 400-cycle alternating current is connected to the ignition units. The current passes through a filter L_1 and C_1 which grounds out radio-frequency noise pulses and prevents the ignition unit from affecting the operation of other aircraft electronic equipment.

From the filter, current passes through the primary of the voltage doubler transformer T_1. This transformer boosts the a-c voltage to 3500 volts across the secondary winding. Tube V_{1-2} conducts during the first half cycle of the secondary current, charging the capacitor C_2 to almost the full potential of the transformer secondary. Tube V_{1-1} conducts on the second half of the transformer secondary cycle, and since the polarity of the voltage during the second half of the secondary cycle is the same as the polarity of the charge on capacitor C_2, the voltages add together to double the voltage across storage capacitor C_3.

The control gap V_3 releases a portion of the stored energy in C_3 when a predetermined value of voltage is reached. When the control gap V_3 breaks down, it becomes effectively a short circuit. This means that the voltage drop across it may be considered as practically zero. The resistor R_3, in parallel with C_4, may be ignored because of its high resistance compared with C_4 and the primary of the transformer T_2 at the instant that V_3 breaks down. When this happens, the current path is through the primary of trigger transformer T_2 and trigger capacitor C_4. At the beginning of this instant of time when V_3 breaks down, C_4 is completely discharged and therefore presents a very small resistance. The sum of the voltage drops must, of course, equal the voltage source (C_3 in this case), which means that at this instant the entire storage capacitor voltage across C_3 must appear across the primary of the trigger transformer T_2. The voltage across the primary causes an even higher voltage to be generated in the secondary of T_2. This voltage breaks down the control gap V_2 and supplies a trigger voltage to the igniter plug. If the igniter plug fires during the first pulse of the trigger

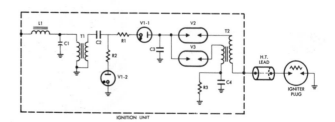

Figure 20·24 Ignition system.

416

transformer primary as is proper, the entire chain of events changes because the current then stored in C_3 immediately starts to flow through the trigger transformer secondary. This current saturates the transformer core, and no flux change can be initiated by the trigger transformer primary winding.

The function of the trigger capacitor C_4 is to block the d-c component from following this path to ground instead of flowing through the igniter plug. The charge placed on the capacitor eventually is dissipated through the resistor R_3, ensuring that the trigger capacitor is completely discharged before the onset of the next spark. The resistor also provides a means of dissipating the ignition unit energy in the event of a failure of the high-tension ignition lead to the igniter plug.

The purpose of the trigger transformer is to provide a voltage boost above the level provided by the voltage doubler. This ensures reliability in the ignition system to compensate for increases in the normal igniter plug ionizing potential during its service life.

The high voltages developed in high-energy ignition systems for gas-turbine engines can be fatal. It is therefore of utmost importance that service personnel avoid coming into contact with the high-voltage leads when power is turned on. Furthermore, if a high-voltage lead is disconnected within a short time after operation, the lead should be grounded to discharge any voltage that may remain stored in a capacitor.

Starting systems

Gas-turbine engine starting systems have been discussed in the chapter on "Engine Starting Systems." However, we shall briefly review some of the principal points to be remembered.

Gas-turbine engines utilize a variety of starting systems. However, the pneumatic-type starter is most commonly used on large engines in commercial use. Pneumatic starters may be supplied with air from a ground cart or from a high-pressure bottle mounted in the aircraft. Basically, the air-turbine starter is a turbine which may be engaged to the engine through a reduction gear and clutch assembly. The operation of the air valves which control the air to the starters is accomplished by means of switches in the cockpit.

In some cases, the air-turbine starter is arranged for a solid-fuel cartridge power supply. In this case, a solid-fuel cartridge is placed in a gas chamber which is connected to the inlet of the turbine. When the cartridge is fired, the gases generated are sufficient to accelerate the engine to starting speed. A new cartridge is required for each start.

Fuel/air combustion starters are operated on the gases derived from the combustion of fuel and air. The turbine is similar to the air turbine. However, the gas generator, which burns petroleum fuel and air, provides the energy for driving the turbine.

Small gas-turbine engines are often started by means of electric starter generators, which are motors that also operate as generators after the engine is started. This type of starter is both economical and convenient for the small gas turbine.

Air-bleed and -supply systems

Compressed air from the compressor section of the gas-turbine engine is used for a number of purposes. It must be understood that the compression of the air as it moves through the compressor causes a substantial rise in temperature. For example, the air at the last stage of the compressor may reach a temperature of over 650°F as a result of compression. This heated air is routed through the compressor inlet struts to prevent icing, and it is also used for various other heating tasks, such as operation of the fuel heater, aircraft heating, thermal anti-icing, etc.

Some engines are provided with automatic air bleeds which operate during the starting of the engine to prevent air from piling up at the high-pressure end of the compressor and "choking" the engine. This permits easier starting and accelerating without the danger of compressor stall.

Compressor air is also utilized within the engine to provide cooling for the turbine wheel and the turbine nozzle vanes. These vanes are hollow to provide passages for the cooling air which is carried through the engine from the compressor to the area surrounding the nozzle diaphragm. Even though the compressed air is heated by compression well above its initial temperature, it is still much cooler than the burning exhaust gases and can therefore provide cooling.

The airflow from the compressor is also used within the engine to pressurize internal areas and control oil flow through the labyrinth seals and around bearings. By application of pressure in the proper areas, the oil flow can be caused to move toward the sumps, where it is picked up by the scavenge pumps and returned to the main oil tank.

The engine compressors often supply pressure for the operation of accessories within the airplane. This air is called customer air supply. It can be used for operating a variety of pneumatic devices.

TURBOPROP AND TURBOSHAFT ENGINES

Turboprop and **turboshaft** engines are similar to turbojet engines; however, they are designed to extract power from the exhaust gas stream to drive propeller shafts and mechanical power shafts. This is accomplished by installing additional turbines in the exhaust gas stream.

Turboprop engine

A **turboprop** engine is shown in Fig. 20·25. This is the T-34 engine manufactured by Pratt & Whitney. This engine incorporates a 13-stage axial-flow compressor, a cannular combustion chamber, and a three-stage turbine. The propeller is driven through a reduction gear providing gear ratios of 0.354:1 and 0.257:1, making a total reduction of 11:1. The reduction-gear assembly is of the combination spur and planetary type.

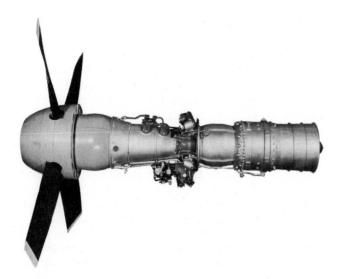

Figure **20·25**   *The Pratt & Whitney T-34 turboprop engine.*

A turboprop engine such as that shown in Fig. 20·25 produces up to 90 percent of its thrust by means of the power extracted from the exhaust stream with the turbine. From 10 to 20 percent of the thrust is obtained from the exhaust jet.

Turboshaft engine

A turboshaft engine designed for use in a helicopter is shown in Fig. 20·26. This is the General Electric T-64 turboshaft engine rated at about 2,850 shp. This engine has a 14-stage compressor with the first six rows of stator vanes variable. The combustion chamber is of the annular type with a basket liner.

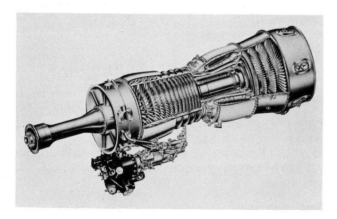

Figure **20·26**   *The General Electric T-64 turboshaft engine. (General Electric)*

The first two of the four turbine stages drive the compressor, and the last two furnish power for the drive shaft which passes through the hollow compressor drive shaft.

REVIEW QUESTIONS

1. Describe Hero's aeolipile.
2. Discuss the contributions of Dr. Sanford Moss to the development of the turbine engine.
3. How did Frank Whittle's developments contribute to the growth of the gas-turbine industry in the United States?
4. When and in what country was the first known jet-aircraft flight made?
5. What laws explain the development of thrust in a jet engine?
6. What factors must be known to determine the theoretical thrust of a particular engine?
7. Give some examples of reaction forces.
8. How can the thrust of a jet engine be converted to horsepower?
9. Compare jet engine thrust with propeller thrust.
10. Explain how air density affects the thrust of a jet engine.
11. Describe the construction of a centrifugal jet engine.
12. Explain the operation of an axial-flow compressor.
13. Describe the arrangement of a dual compressor.
14. Compare the speed of rotation of the low-pressure rotor and the high-pressure rotor in a dual compressor.
15. What is the function of the diffuser?
16. What prevents overheating and burning of the combustion chamber liners?
17. Explain the function of the nozzle diaphragm.
18. What is the purpose of the turbine in a jet engine?
19. Name the two principal types of turbine design.
20. Explain the importance of turbine nozzle area.
21. Name the components of a jet-engine lubrication system.
22. Why is it necessary to use synthetic lubricants in many gas-turbine engines?
23. What indications are sensed by the fuel-control unit in order to provide proper fuel regulation?
24. Compare the ignition system of a gas-turbine engine with that of a piston engine.
25. What safety precaution must be observed with respect to the high-energy ignition system of a jet engine?
26. What type of device is used to apply starting torque to a jet engine?
27. What gas- or air-pressure sources are used to operate the starter?
28. Describe the uses of compressed air bled from the compressor of a jet engine.
29. How is power extracted from the exhaust of a turboprop engine to drive the propeller?
30. Approximately how much jet thrust is produced by a turboprop engine in comparison with the propeller thrust?

CHAPTER 21

Turbojet Engines

THE PRATT & WHITNEY JT-3 ENGINE

General description

The Pratt & Whitney Model JT-3 turbojet engine is the commercial model of the military J-57. This engine has been manufactured with many modifications, and no attempt will be made to discuss all of them in this text. We shall examine details common to all models and provide an overall knowledge of the JT-3 series engine.

The general specifications of the JT-3 engine are as follows:

Thrust rating, takeoff	12,000 lb
Thrust rating, cruising	9,500 lb
Weight	3,500 lb
Power/weight ratio	3.43 lbt/lb
Fuel consumption (sfc)	0.76 lb/lbt/hr
Oil consumption	3.1–4.0 lb/hr

Figure 21·1 is a cutaway view of a JT-3 (J-57) engine equipped with an afterburner. A careful study of this drawing will provide a good understanding of the construction of this engine.

The JT-3 engine is an axial-flow gas turbine incorporating a split compressor, eight annular combustion chambers in a single annular chamber to form a "cannular" unit, and a three-stage reaction turbine. The first-stage turbine drives the rear compressor section through the outer coaxial shaft, while the rear two stages drive the forward compressor section.

The engine is divided into three or four sections, depending upon whether it is equipped with an afterburner. Figure 21·2 is a diagram to show how the four sections are designated. The accessory section is located under the wasp waist of the compressor section, thereby providing minimum frontal interference.

Compressor section

As shown in Fig. 21·1, the compressor for the JT-3 engine is made up of two sections. The forward section (N_1) is the low-pressure section and comprises nine stages of titanium-alloy blades mounted on a rotor consisting of nine titanium-alloy disks and driven by the rear two turbine stages through the inner turbine shaft. The front compressor rotor is free to rotate at its own best speed, thus providing greater flexibility and improved part-load operation. A drawing of this section is shown in Fig. 21·3.

The rear (N_2) compressor is the high-pressure section and consists of seven stages of steel blades mounted on a seven-disk rotor driven by the forward turbine through the outer turbine shaft. The smaller, high-pressure rotor is geared to the starter drive, thereby minimizing the size and weight of the starter and the torque necessary to start the engine. The rear compressor speed is governed by the fuel-control unit, while the front compressor rotor is turned by its turbine at the rpm ensuring optimum flow of air through the compressor. The components adjust themselves to part-load operation with a minimum of interstage bleeding needed to prevent surge. A cross-sectional drawing of the high-pressure compressor is shown in Fig. 21·4. The pressure ratio across the two compressor sections is 13:1 with a mass flow of air at the rate of 183 lb per sec at 9550 rpm N_2 speed.

The compressor casing consists of a titanium front **compressor case** made in two sections and a one-piece conical **rear compressor case** made of steel. The compressor vanes, or stator blades, are mounted in rings inside the compressor cases. There are eight rows of vanes for the front compressor and six for the rear compressor. The compressor vane ring assemblies are made in two sections to provide for easy disassembly.

A set of guide vanes is located between the front and rear compressors to give proper direction to the air as it enters the rear compressor. These vanes are welded into the forward end of the **compressor intermediate case.**

The **compressor intermediate case,** which is integral with the **rear compressor case,** contains supports for the front compressor rear bearing and the rear compressor front bearing together with necessary seal housings. Front compressor bleed air passes through slots in the outer shroud and into the chamber formed by the inner diameter of the rear compressor outer case and the outer diameter of the rear compressor case. Compressor bleed valves mounted on the outer case permit the bleeding of this chamber. An oil tube in the six o'clock vane of the intermediate case supplies pressure oil to the front compressor rear bearing and the rear compressor front bearing. A breather connector is mounted on the intermediate case, and the oil pump and accessory drive housing are secured to the bottom of the case.

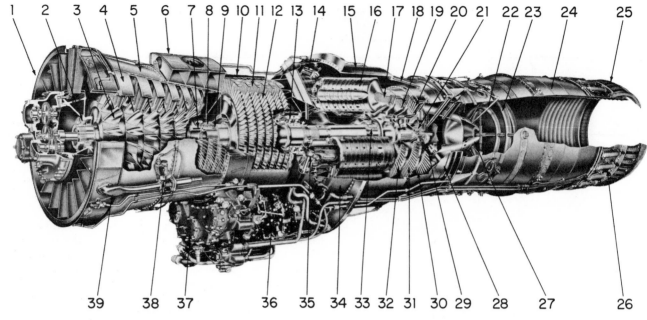

1. Compressor inlet guide vane and shroud
2. Front compressor front bearing
3. Front compressor rotor (N1)
4. Front compressor vane and shroud
5. Front compressor front case
6. Oil tank
7. Front compressor drive turbine shaft coupling
8. Front compressor rear bearing
9. Rear compressor front bearing
10. Rear compressor outer case
11. Rear compressor vane and shroud
12. Rear compressor rotor (N2)
13. Rear compressor rear bearing
14. Fuel manifold
15. Combustion chamber outer front case
16. Combustion chamber
17. Turbine nozzle
18. Combustion chamber outer rear case
19. Second-stage turbine nozzle
20. Third-stage turbine nozzle

21. Turbine rear bearing
22. Turbine rear bearing support rod
23. Flameholder
24. Afterburner cooling air duct
25. Variable-area nozzle
26. Nozzle actuating air cylinder
27. Turbine exhaust cone
28. Turbine exhaust case
29. Turbine rear bearing oil suction pump
30. Third-stage turbine
31. Second-stage turbine
32. First-stage turbine
33. Turbine front bearing
34. Diffuser case
35. Angled accessory drive shaftgear
36. Fuel control unit
37. Starter drive pad
38. Anti-icing regulator and valve
39. Anti-icing air tube

Figure 21·1 Cutaway view of Pratt & Whitney JT-3 engine with afterburner. (Pratt & Whitney Aircraft)

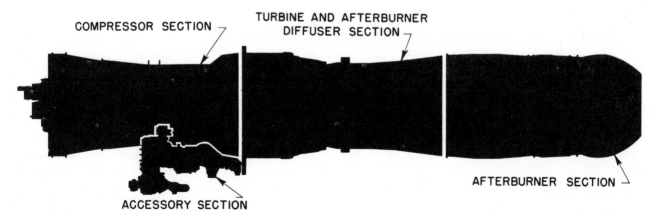

Figure 21·2 Principal sections of the JT-3 engine.

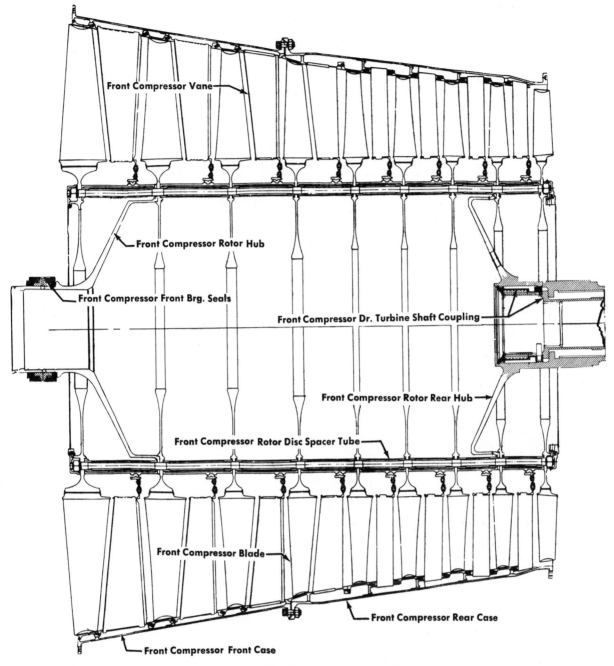

Figure 21·3   *Front compressor section.*

The **front compressor rear bearing** consists of two ball-type bearings mounted adjacent to each other. To the rear of this bearing assembly is the **rear compressor front bearing,** which is of the roller type.

The front hub of the rear compressor rotor is supported by the rear compressor front bearing, the inner race and rollers of which are mounted on the **front compressor rear hub.** The rear compressor front bearing void is sealed from the engine airflow by oil seals on the front hub. The rear hub is supported by a double ball-bearing assembly, which is secured in the bearing housing in the diffuser case. The **rear compressor rear**

bearing void is sealed from the engine airflow by oil seals on the rear hub. Power to drive the engine accessories is derived from the rear hub accessory drive gear which is splined onto the rear hub.

Diffuser case

The **diffuser case** serves to diffuse the airflow discharged from the high-pressure compressor and prepare it for entry into the combustion chambers. Exit guide vanes are welded into the diffuser inner inlet duct to receive the air from the compressor and give it proper direction as it flows toward the combustion

421

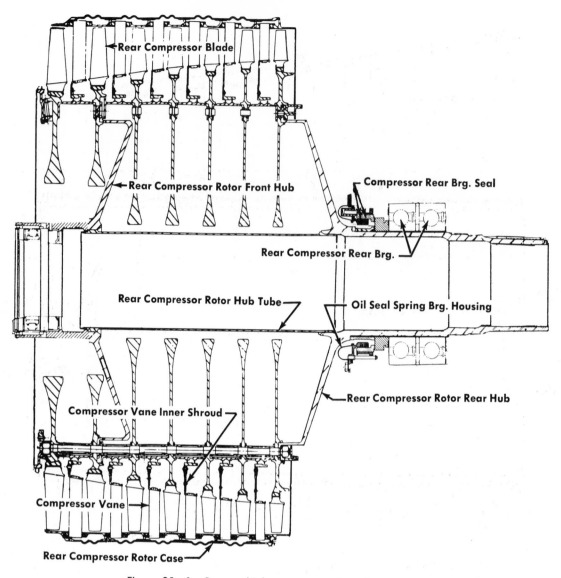

Figure 21·4   Rear or high-pressure section of compressor.

section. As explained previously the purpose of a diffuser is to reduce the velocity of the air before it reaches the burner section.

Near its greatest diameter the diffuser case provides support for the fuel manifold and nozzles. Contained in the diffuser case are the rear compressor rear bearing seal housing, the bearing housing, and the diffuser inner inlet duct. Mounted over the inner end of the six o'clock strut is the angled accessory drive shaftgear with its bearings and housing. A drawing of this arrangement is shown in Fig. 21·5.

Splined in the shaftgear is the oil suction pump drive shaftgear which drives the compressor rear and turbine front bearing oil suction pump. This pump is mounted in the diffuser case adjacent to the angled accessory drive shaftgear. The angled accessory drive long shaft is located in the six o'clock strut and splines into the angled accessory drive shaftgear. The pressure oil tube is located in the four o'clock strut, and the

scavenge oil tube is located in the eight o'clock strut. Bosses on the outside of the diffuser case provide for breather pressurization and anti-icing air. The front flange of the diffuser case is bolted to the rear flange of the rear compressor outer case. A mounting pad for the accessory drive adapter and housing is located at the bottom of the diffuser case. Around the outside of the diffuser case is mounted the diffuser heat shield, which is connected with two inlet ports in approximately the five and seven o'clock locations. These ports are connected to tubes that admit ambient air in between the inner wall of the heat shield and the outer wall of the diffuser case.

Combustion section

The combustion section shown in Fig. 21·6 includes the **combustion chamber outer front case, combustion chambers, turbine front bearing support, fuel manifold, combustion chamber outer rear case,** and the **turbine**

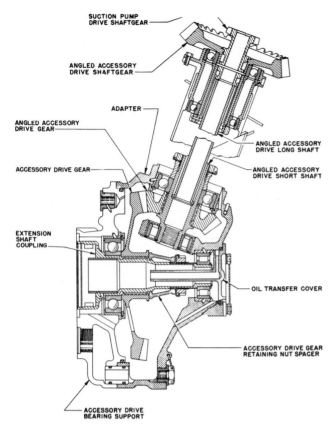

Figure 21·5 Sectional view of angled accessory drive shaftgear.

the turbine front bearing oil pressure and oil suction lines. The **turbine front bearing housing,** the **turbine front bearing seal housing,** and the **turbine front bearing friction damping support** are attached to the rear of the support.

The **combustion chamber outer rear case** is attached to the combustion chamber outer front case and houses the turbine rotor disk and the turbine nozzle. Bosses on the outer diameter of the case provided for pressure probes and thermocouples.

The **turbine nozzle** consists of the **turbine nozzle inner case,** the **turbine nozzle outer case,** and 70 vanes secured between the inner case and the segmented turbine nozzle outer shroud. The nozzle vanes serve to increase the velocity of the gases and give them proper direction to enter the first-stage turbine. The turbine nozzle assembly also includes the outlet ducts which receive the rear ends of the combustion chambers and carry the burning gases to the turbine nozzle. The turbine nozzle is secured at its inner diameter to the turbine front bearing support.

Turbine section

The **rear compressor drive turbine** includes the turbine drive shaft and the first-stage turbine disk. The

nozzle. The combustion chamber outer front case is secured at the front flange to the rear flange of the diffuser case. It houses the eight combustion chambers which are radially located within the case. The forward face of each combustion chamber has six apertures which align the six nozzles of the corresponding fuel nozzle cluster. The eight combustion chambers are interconnected by means of projecting welded flame tubes which serve to ignite the chambers not equipped with spark igniters. Each combustion chamber contains a central bullet-shaped perforated liner. Cutouts for spark igniters are provided in the Nos. 4 and 5 combustion chambers. The combustion chambers are supported at the aft end by eight outlet ducts in the turbine nozzle assembly. Two fuel drain valves are located at the bottom of the combustion chamber outer front case.

The **fuel manifold** assembly may be a one-piece type or a two-piece split type. Each manifold assembly consists of a primary and a secondary fuel manifold and eight clusters of six fuel nozzles, thus making a total of 48 nozzles. Each cluster of six nozzles supplies one combustion chamber with fuel. The manifold incorporates mounting lugs in the inner and outer diameter which are secured to the rear face of the diffuser case.

The **turbine front bearing support** is secured to the rear face of the diffuser case and contains passages for

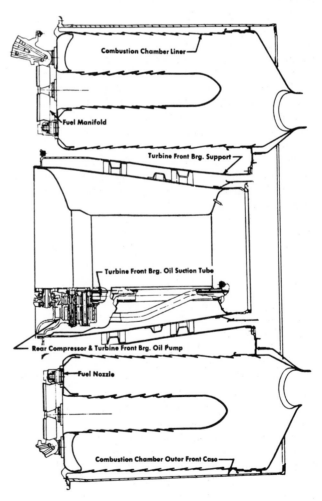

Figure 21·6 Sectional view of combustion section.

423

turbine disk is bolted to the hub of the turbine shaft and has 113 blades held in the outer rim of the disk by means of fir-tree serrations. The blades are secured in the serrations by rivets. The turbine front bearing inner race and rollers are located forward of the disk and secured on the shaft by a nut, a tab washer, and a lock ring. At assembly the turbine shaft splines onto the rear hub of the rear compressor rotor and is secured to the rotor hub by the **rear compressor drive turbine shaft coupling.** The outer race of the **turbine intershaft bearing** is located inside the turbine shaft. The purpose of the intershaft bearing is to support the **front compressor turbine drive shaft** which rotates inside the rear compressor turbine shaft.

In order to control and give proper direction to the gases leaving the first-stage turbine, a **second-stage turbine nozzle** is mounted between the first-stage and second-stage turbines. The second-stage turbine nozzle consists of the turbine nozzle case, the turbine nozzle inner shroud and shroud support, and the turbine nozzle inner seal and seal support. There are 102 vanes secured between the inner shroud and the turbine nozzle case. Seal rings on the inner diameter of the inner seal form an air around the hub of the rear compressor drive turbine shaft hub. The second-stage turbine nozzle is secured to the turbine nozzle.

The **third-stage turbine nozzle** serves the same purpose as the other nozzles and consists of the turbine nozzle case, the turbine nozzle inner seal and seal support, and 88 vanes secured between the inner shroud and the turbine nozzle case. The smooth surface of the inner seal base forms an air seal with the seal rings on the turbine disk spacer. The third-stage turbine nozzle is located between the second- and third-stage turbine disks and is secured to the second-stage nozzle.

The **front compressor drive turbine rotor** consists of the **turbine shaft,** the **second-stage turbine disk,** the **turbine disk spacer,** the **third-stage turbine disk,** and the **turbine rear hub.** The turbine disks, separated by the spacer, and the rear hub are secured to the turbine shaft by means of tie rods, which are long bolts. The second-stage turbine disk has 87 blades in the fir-tree serrations on the outer periphery of the disks. The blades are secured by rivets. The third-stage turbine disk has 79 blades held in the disk in like manner. Inside the turbine shaft is located the turbine shaft bearing oil tube shield which supplies pressure oil to the turbine intershaft bearing. The turbine intershaft bearing inner race and rollers are located on the turbine shaft midway between the second-stage turbine disk and the forward end of the shaft. The rear hub is supported by the turbine rear bearing, and the rotor is secured to the front compressor rear hub by the front compressor drive turbine shaft coupling.

The **turbine exhaust case** contains the turbine exit vanes and shrouds assembly, which consists of 24 vanes radially located and equally spaced between an inner and outer shroud. Aft of the turbine exit vanes and shrouds assembly are eight turbine exhaust struts positioned radially around the inside of the turbine

exhaust case and held in position by the turbine exhaust strut rear tubes. These struts house the turbine rear bearing support rods. The tube extending through the twelve o'clock strut contains the breather tube and also serves as a support for the turbine rear bearing sump. The turbine rear bearing oil drain tube is integral with the strut in the eight o'clock position, and the turbine rear bearing oil pressure tube is integral with the strut in the four o'clock position. Both tubes also serve as a support for the turbine rear bearing sump. The turbine rear bearing support is held firmly in place in the center of the case by the eight support rods extending radially from the support through the struts. These rods are secured in journals on the outer diameter of the turbine exhaust case. Secured to the front of the support is the turbine shaft gas seal, and attached to the rear of the support is the turbine rear bearing sump. The turbine rear bearing seal housing is located in the center bore of the support, and the turbine rear bearing outer race is inside the seal housing. The turbine rear bearing oil suction pump is secured inside the turbine rear bearing sump and is driven by a pinion secured to the rear of the turbine rear hub. The turbine rear bearing void is sealed from the air system by seals on the rear hub. Bosses for pressure probes are provided on the outside of the turbine exhaust case. The turbine exhaust cone is attached to the rear face of the turbine exhaust inner duct weldment.

The afterburner

An **afterburner** consists of a duct attached to the exhaust section of a turbojet engine to provide thrust augmentation. Fuel nozzles are installed in the forward part of the duct to spray large quantities of fuel into the hot exhaust gases. Since there is still a large percentage of unburned oxygen in the exhaust gases as they leave the turbine, there is an adequate supply of oxygen for the burning of additional fuel. Because of the high velocity of the gases, it is necessary to install **flameholders** in the afterburner to prevent the flame from being blown out. The flameholders create areas of turbulence in which the flame can burn. The burning of fuel in the exhaust expands the gases and adds mass to the gas flow, with the result that the engine thrust is increased by 50 to 70 percent.

The afterburner for the J-57 engine, which is the military version of the JT-3, is composed of the **afterburner diffuser** and the **afterburner duct and nozzle assembly.** The entire afterburner is cantilevered from the engine. The diffuser contains 24 equally spaced spray nozzles located radially around the inner wall of the case. The nozzles are mounted individually on the outside periphery of the afterburner diffuser duct and project into the case, extending to a position near the exhaust cone. Metered fuel is supplied to the spray nozzles from the afterburner fuel meter.

Aft of the spray nozzles are circular flameholders concentrically mounted and supported by four tie rods that project in through the wall of the duct. Two of the tie rods are in line in a horizontal position, and

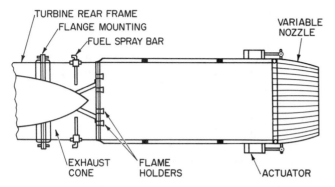

TURBINE REAR FRAME
FLANGE MOUNTING
FUEL SPRAY BAR
VARIABLE NOZZLE
EXHAUST CONE
FLAME HOLDERS
ACTUATOR

Figure 21·7   An afterburner.

the remaining two are in line in a vertical position. The flameholders are concave-convex in design with the concave side toward the rear of the engine.

The afterburner **duct and nozzle assembly** is composed of a double-walled duct, with the inner wall serving as a liner which is perforated at the forward end, and the afterburner exhaust nozzle. The perforated area of the inner liner allows the engine turbine exhaust gases to flow through the outer annulus formed by the double-wall construction and serve as cooling air during afterburner operation. The exhaust nozzle is opened and closed by diffuser case air pressure, which is routed to double-acting pistons mounted around the afterburner duct just forward of the nozzle. The air to the pistons is controlled by signals from the afterburner fuel system. There are two types of nozzles: (1) the iris type with 24 individual overlapping segments and pistons and (2) the flap type with eight pie-shaped flaps and eight pistons. An afterburner is shown in Fig. 21·7.

Lubrication system

The lubrication system serving the engine is of self-contained high-pressure design. It consists of a pressure system which supplies lubrication to the main engine bearings and to the accessory drives and a scavenge system by which oil is withdrawn from the engine and returned through an oil cooler to the fuel-coolant oil cooler and thence to the oil tank. The fuel-coolant oil cooler is regulated by a thermovalve. The engine oil tank, which is mounted on the engine, is connected to the inlet side of the pressure oil pump, thereby completing the oil-flow cycle. A breather system connecting the individual bearing compartments and the oil tank with the breather pressurizing valve completes the engine lubricating system. The oil used in the JT-3 engine conforms to MIL-L-7808. This is a synthetic lubricant capable of withstanding the high temperatures in a modern gas-turbine engine.

The oil pressure pump is located in the upper left-hand section of the oil pump and accessory drive housing. It consists of a single-section gear pump of sufficient capacity to provide the required oil flow under all engine operating conditions. An oil pressure-relief valve is provided beyond the oil pressure strainer

and bearing takeoffs downstream of the pump and is adjusted to maintain a proper pressure differential across the oil metering jets in the engine. A pressure differential of 45 plus or minus 5 psi is reached at approximately 75 percent of normal rated thrust. The pressure-relief valve points in the aft direction and is located on the upper left-hand section of the oil pump and accessory drive housing. It is accessible for adjustment.

The **scavenge oil system** of the engine includes six gear-type pumps which scavenge the main bearing voids and accessory drives and then deliver the scavenged oil to the oil cooler. Two of the pumps are located in the right-hand side of the oil pump and accessory drive housing, two are located in the No. 4 bearing compartment in the diffuser case, one is attached to the front accessory drive rear support in the inlet vane and shroud, and the sixth is located in the turbine rear bearing oil sump.

An **oil strainer assembly** equipped with a bypass valve assembly located on the left side of the oil sump and accessory drive housing assures a clean supply of oil to the lubrication system. The valve permits the oil to bypass the strainer in the event that the strainer becomes clogged.

The strainer assembly is composed of a series of screens in disk form, separated alternately by stamped inlet and outlet spacers and assembled around a perforated tube. The strainer assembly is easily removed for disassembly and cleaning.

An **oil tank** is provided around the upper left-hand quadrant of the front compressor rear case. The oil filler is located in a scupper and is provided with a drain connection for attaching a line overboard. The oil-tank capacity is 5.5 gal, which is considered adequate for a 5-hr flight.

As an integral part of the oil tank, a deaerator is provided which separates the air from the oil as it reenters the oil tank after passing through the coolers. The deaerator is of the can type with oil entering tangentially, and the air released is carried out through the vent system from the top of the oil tank.

On the Pratt & Whitney JT-3D engine mounted on the Boeing 720 airplane, the engine oil tank is located on the right side of the engine aft of the fan air outlet duct. This location takes advantage of the narrow section of the engine.

To ensure proper oil flow from the main bearing oil jets, the pressures in the bearing compartments are regulated by means of a **breather pressurizing system.** Breather tubes in the compressor inlet case, the oil tank, the diffuser case, and the turbine exhaust case are connected to external tubing at the top of the engine. By means of this tubing, the vapor-laden atmospheres of the various bearing compartments and the oil tank are brought together in the compressor intermediate case annulus.

The pressure within the system is controlled by means of the **breather pressurizing valve,** which consists of an aneroid-operated valve and a spring-loaded blowoff valve. Pressurization is provided by seal leak-

425

age air which enters the oil system. The pressurizing valve closes as altitude increases to maintain adequate pressure under all conditions.

The fuel system

The fuel system of the J-57 engine consists of a number of major accessory components plus their associated plumbing and electrical connections. On an engine equipped with an afterburner, the fuel pump handles fuel for normal engine operation and also afterburner operation. The other fuel system components are the fuel-pump transfer valve, the hydro-mechanical fuel-control unit, the fuel flowmeter, the fuel coolant oil cooler, the fuel pressurizing and dump valve, the engine fuel manifold, the afterburner fuel control, the afterburner mechanical shutoff valve, the afterburner igniter fuel valve, the exhaust nozzle actuator control, and the afterburner fuel manifold.

Fuel is supplied to the main engine and afterburner systems by the fuel pump, which has a gear stage for each system. The inlet of both stages is fed by a common centrifugal boost stage. In the fuel-pump transfer valve body an automatic emergency transfer valve is provided which will divert fuel flow from the afterburner stage of the pump to the main fuel system in the event of failure of the main pump stage.

The heart of a turbojet fuel system is the **fuel-control unit.** This rather complex device schedules fuel flow to the engine burners as required by the operating conditions of the engine and at the same time ensures that the engine is protected against "hot" starts, rich blowout, lean blowout, compressor stall, overtemperature, and overspeed.

Typical of hydromechanical fuel-control units for the JT-3 engine is the Hamilton Standard JFC12-11 control. This control may be considered as having a **fuel metering system** and a **computing system** designed to select the rate of fuel flow to be applied to the engine burners in accordance with the percentage of thrust available to the pilot but subject to engine operating limitations as scheduled by the computing system and monitored by the pilot.

The schematic diagram of Fig. 21·8 illustrates the operating principles of the JFC12-11 fuel-control unit. This unit is designed for a JT-3 engine which is not equipped with an afterburner. The description of the control operation in this section refers to the diagram of Fig. 21·8.

The **metering system** of the control may be considered to include those components which actually control the fuel flow from the engine pump to the fuel outlet for the engine. High-pressure fuel is supplied to the control inlet (shown in the lower left portion of the schematic drawing) by engine-driven fixed-displacement pumps. The fuel is routed first to the **coarse filter,** and from there a small portion is passed to the **fine filter** on its way to the computing system, while the main flow passes on to the **main metering valve.** The coarse filter is provided to stop any contaminants which would clog the metering system or the engine fuel nozzles, and the fine filter is designed to

protect the computing system from contamination. Either filter will be moved from its seat to pass fuel directly in the event that clogging causes a substantial pressure drop across the filter. The main metering valve is encountered next on the direct line from the pumps to the nozzles and is made up of a contoured plunger movable axially with respect to a sharp-edged orifice. The function of this valve is to set a fuel flow for each axial position of the plunger, where the axial position represents the output signal of the computer system. The **pressure-regulating valve** provides a constant pressure head across the main metering valve by sensing metering down-stream pressure and balancing the downstream pressure plus a spring force against the main metering valve upstream pressure to define the position of a bypass valve. All fuel in excess of that required to maintain the selected constant-pressure head across the main metering valve is bypassed to the second-stage pump inlet. The result of maintaining a constant-pressure head across the main metering valve is a direct relationship of the flow to the area of the opening between the orifice and the plunger and thus a direct relationship of the flow to the axial position of the plunger. An adjustable **minimum flow stop** is provided on the plunger in order to set a minimum metering area and minimum flow to prevent engine lean blowout.

The final component to act upon the metered flow prior to its discharge from the fuel control into the manifold is the **minimum pressure and shutoff valve.** This valve is designed to shut off hydraulically the flow of metered fuel to the engine when the pilot moves his shutoff lever to the OFF position. This moves the **throttle-operated pilot valve** downward to place high fuel pressure on the spring side of the shutoff valve and force it down against its seat, thus shutting off the flow of fuel to the engine. When the shutoff lever is moved into the ON position, the high-pressure signal is replaced by pump inlet pressure, and when metered fuel pressure has increased sufficiently to overcome the spring force, the valve opens and fuel is allowed to flow to the engine. The minimum pressure and shutoff valve will thus ensure that adequate pressure is always available for operation of the computer system before any fuel is supplied to the engine.

The computing system positions the main metering valve and thereby selects a fuel flow for each condition of engine operation, whether steady state or transient. This is accomplished by the use of the ratio W_f/P_B as a control parameter (variable quantity). W_f is the weight flow of fuel, and P_B represents the total pressure at the engine burners.

In the Model JFC12-11 control, the position of the **governor servo,** shown below and to the right of the main metering valve, represents the proper W_f/P_B ratio for the operating conditions existing at any given time. This position may be taken as an ordinate which, together with an abscissa supplied by the P_B servo, defines a point which represents the fuel flow W_f. Looking at the detailed mechanism involved, the governor servo position W_f/P_B is multiplied by the

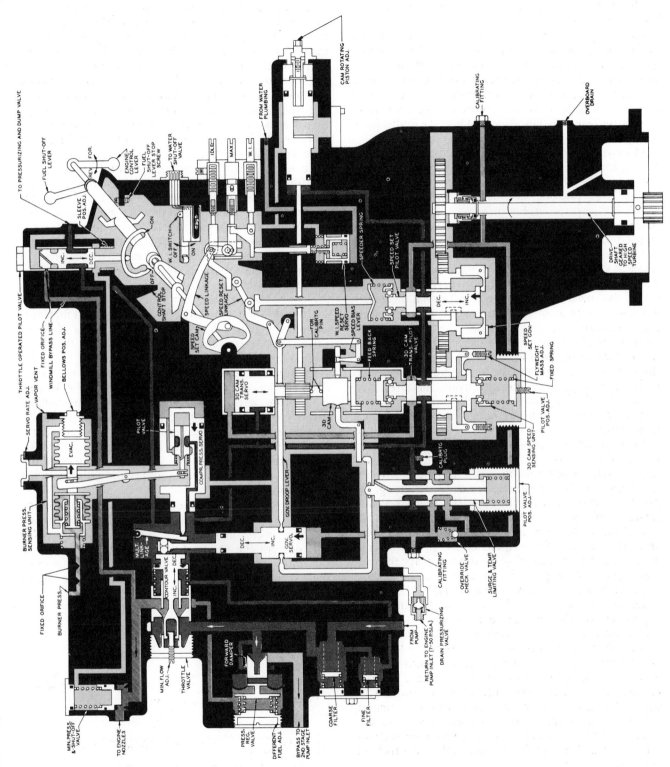

Figure 21·8   Diagram of a fuel-control unit.

427

burner pressure servo P_B to obtain a metering valve position W_f. The rollers at the end of the governor servo extension arm position the metering valve in accordance with their vertical position and the angle of the multiplying lever, which is established by the burner pressure servo.

The P_B signal is an absolute-pressure signal obtained by balancing burner pressure in one bellows against an evacuated bellows and spring to position a pilot valve within the **burner pressure servo piston.** If there should be a change of P_B, the piston then moves to match its position to the new position of the pilot valve, thus introducing the new P_B signal into the multiplying linkage.

The control operates on the basis of curves wherein W_f/P_B is plotted as a function of N (engine rpm) for acceleration and W_f/P_B is plotted as a function of power lever position or selected engine speed for steady-state operation. For steady-state operation, the power lever calls for a W_f/P_B value by setting a speeder spring force on the **speed-setting governor.** The governor in turn generates a position of the governor servo which is supplied to the multiplying linkage as a roller position representing W_f/P_B. If the speed of the engine varies, the speed-setting governor will signal the governor servo to raise or lower this value, thus effecting the correction required to return the engine to the desired steady-state speed. For rapid acceleration, within limitations imposed by control design features, the power lever calls for the maximum W_f/P_B ratio which the engine can use effectively for any given engine speed, taking into account the limitations necessary to prevent compressor surge and turbine overtemperature.

Acceleration is initiated by compressing the speed set governor speeder spring to call for a higher W_f/P_B ratio, which would ordinarily result in rapid downward movement of the governor servo by draining the governor servo fluid out through the **speed set pilot valve.** It will be noted, however, that this fluid must pass through the **surge and temperature-limiting valve** and that the rate of movement of the governor servo may be limited by restricting the drain passage through that valve. The surge and temperature-limiting valve is positioned by the three-dimensional (3D) cam in order to set a maximum W_f/P_B ratio for any given engine speed. The cam has a particular position for each condition of engine speed, since it is translated by a flyweight type of speed sensor and servo system. The result is that a power lever movement toward a higher power, for example, will cause an immediate increase in the ratio to a maximum value for the existing engine speed. As the ratio increases, engine rpm is increased, and the ratio is varied along a maximum curve dictated by the 3D cam until a speed is reached where the proportional-type governor again takes control for steady-state operation.

Deceleration fuel flows are determined by a minimum W_f/P_B ratio obtained by positioning the governor servo against an upper limit. The minimum ratio exists until a fixed minimum weight flow is reached, as set by the mechanical stop on the main metering valve.

To provide optimum engine performance in all regimes of engine operation and to provide fuel-control simplicity, the 3D cam position is bench set by rotating so as to present a single optimum maximum acceleration schedule. The preset schedule is designed to permit the engine to operate within the limits imposed by engine stall during maximum acceleration.

Thrust reversal is provided for by the incorporation of a reverse power engine contour on the speed-set cam to schedule higher engine speeds as the power lever is retarded beyond the idle position into reverse. The contours for increased speed are shown on the speed-set cam in the diagram.

To summarize the action of the JFC12-11 fuel control, the unit maintains a constant fuel pressure across the **main metering valve** (shown in the diagram as **contour valve**). The position of this valve is controlled by burner pressure, power lever setting, engine speed, and rate of acceleration. Increasing the speed requirement by moving the power lever increases the pressure on the speeder spring of the speed-set governor. The flyweight-controlled valve moves down and allows servo pressure to bleed from the **governor servo.** The servo piston moves down, and in so doing, it increases the spring force tending to open the **main metering valve.** The reverse process takes place when the power lever is moved toward a lower power setting.

In any change of power, the engine is prevented from accelerating too rapidly by means of the **3D cam** mechanism and the **surge and temperature-limiting valve.** The 3D cam is adjusted by means of flyweights which control servo pressure to servo pistons. These servos provide rotation and linear motion of the 3D cam, which regulates the surge and temperature-limiting valve and provides additional control to the governor servo valve.

As engine speed increases, burner pressure increases, and this permits the flow of additional fuel. This action and the reverse action of the **burner pressure sensing unit** prevent the engine from receiving a quantity of fuel too great for the flow of air through the engine; that is, fuel is scheduled to the burners as the engine can properly consume the fuel.

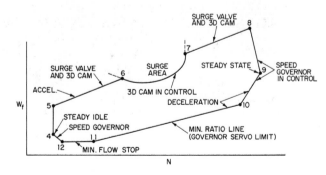

Figure **21·9** *Fuel-flow curve for JFC12-11 fuel control.* (Hamilton Standard)

A typical fuel-flow curve for the JFC12-11 control is shown in Fig. 21·9. The ordinate W_f represents fuel flow valves, and the abscissa N is engine rpm. At point 4 the engine is idling. When the power lever is moved forward, the fuel increases as permitted by the speed governor to point 5, where the surge valve and 3D cam take control of fuel flow. As the engine speed increases, fuel flow is also permitted to increase to point 6. From 6 to 7 is the surge area, and the 3D cam reduces fuel flow sufficiently to prevent surge. From point 7 to point 8 the scheduling is controlled by the 3D cam and the surge valve. At 8 the maximum speed has been reached and the speed governor takes control to reduce fuel flow for steady-state operation at the desired rpm. This condition is attained at point 9. When the power lever is moved to idle, the fuel flow is decreased by the speed governor to point 10, which is the **minimum ratio line.** The fuel flow schedule then follows the line from 10 to 11 as the engine decelerates. From 12 to 13 the speed governor increases fuel flow slightly to maintain idle speed after deceleration.

Figure 21·10 is a schematic diagram of the fuel system for a JT-3D turbofan engine. This engine is not equipped with an afterburner. This diagram shows the relative positions of the fuel-control unit, pressurizing and dump valve, air/fuel heat exchanger, pumps, filters, etc. The normal flow of fuel is from the main fuel tank via the boost pump through the filter, flowmeter, engine-driven pumps, fuel control, pressurizing and dump valve and to the fuel nozzles in the engine.

Ignition system

The fuel/air mixture in a turbojet engine does not present the ideal condition found in the cylinder of a reciprocating engine; hence it is necessary to provide an ignition system which will ignite the mixture even under the conditions of high air velocity, turbulence, and unvaporized fuel existing in the forward part of the combustion chamber. The JT-3D turbofan engines employ a high-energy, capacitor-discharge ignition system with an electrical energy output of 20 joules. This type of ignition system produces an exceptionally hot spark which covers a relatively large area and ignites the fuel/air mixture even though the igniter plug is wet with fuel and fouled with carbon.

The ignition system consists of two identical circuits, one connected to each of the two igniter plugs. Figure 21·11 is a diagram of one of these circuits. When the ignition is turned on at the time of starting, 28-volt d-c power is fed through the **filter** to the **vibrator** in the exciter unit. The vibrator sets up a rapidly intermittent current in the primary coil, thus producing an expanding and collapsing field which induces a high voltage in the secondary winding. This voltage drives the current through the **rectifier tubes** to the **storage capacitors,** thus building up the total charge on the capacitors. When the stored voltage reaches the required value, the gap breaks down in the **discharger tube** and allows the high-voltage current to flow through the primary of the **trigger transformer** to the **trigger capacitor.** This pulse of electrical energy through the primary induces a voltage in the **secondary** of the trigger transformer sufficiently high to break down the gap across the **igniter plug.** When this occurs, the igniter gap is ionized and the energy stored in the storage capacitors discharges through the secondary of the trigger transformer. During this time the trigger capacitor has retained its initial charge and no additional current can flow to it. Furthermore, the bleeder resistors have a value which prevents all but a very small amount of current from flowing through them. The major portion of the energy stored in the storage capacitors therefore passes through the trigger transformer secondary to the igniter plug gap. The spark discharge occurs about twice every second; hence the spark at the gap appears to be almost constant.

Because of the high-energy discharge of the ignition system, it is important that the system be shut off as soon as possible after the engine is started. A reliable timing mechanism must be incorporated in the air start switch circuit to limit the time that the ignition system is energized. One method for accomplishing this for both ground and air starts is to install a cutoff switch on the power lever assembly to turn off the ignition circuit when the power lever is advanced during an acceleration from the idle position.

Great care must be taken in working with a high-energy ignition system to avoid a fatal shock. For this reason, all switches must be turned off and the system discharged by grounding before service work is started.

Anti-icing air system

To reduce the possibility of dangerous icing on the inlet air surfaces, the JT-3 engine is provided with an anti-icing system. The system bleeds hot air from both sides of the high-pressure compressor discharge and pipes the air forward through automatic flow regulators and control valves. The heated air is then introduced into the engine through the hollow inlet guide vanes and through other passages until it is finally spilled into the air inlet stream.

The two control valves are electrically operated and are actuated by a single manual cockpit switch. The automatic flow regulator functions entirely on air temperature acting upon a bimetallic coil secured to an inner valve. Heat expanding the coil causes the valve to close and restrict the flow of air. At 54°C the regulator permits a maximum flow of air, and at 327°C it permits a minimum flow. One control valve and one automatic flow regulator mounted adjacent to each other are provided with each anti-icing tube assembly. The valves and regulators are mounted on the flange between the front compressor front case and the front compressor rear case.

Air-bleed system

The JT-3 engine is normally equipped with an air-bleed system which automatically operates to prevent surge and stall. When the combination of compressor

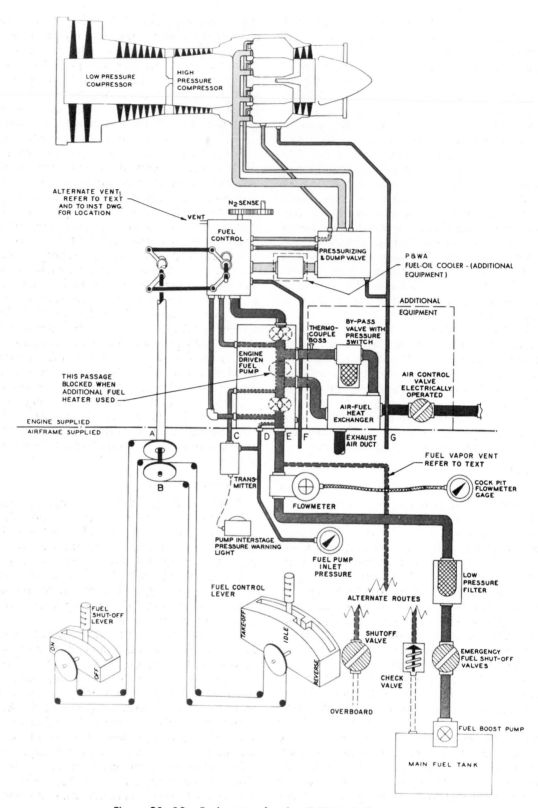

Figure 21·10   Fuel system for the JT-3D turbofan engine.

rotor rpm and air pressure and temperature is such that stall or surge could occur, the bleeds are automatically opened through the action of the **bleed valve governor.**

The speed range of low-pressure compressor surge varies with compressor inlet temperature and inlet pressure. When inlet temperatures T_{t2} decrease and inlet pressure P_{t2} increase, surge-free operation of the

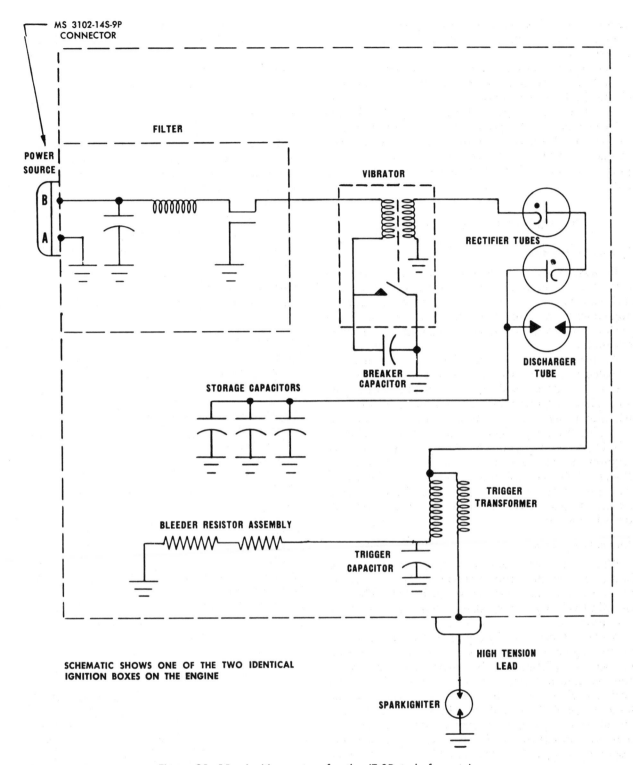

MS 3102-14S-9P
CONNECTOR

FILTER

POWER
SOURCE

VIBRATOR

B

A

RECTIFIER TUBES

DISCHARGER
TUBE

BREAKER
CAPACITOR

STORAGE CAPACITORS

TRIGGER
TRANSFORMER

BLEEDER RESISTOR ASSEMBLY

TRIGGER
CAPACITOR

HIGH TENSION
LEAD

SCHEMATIC SHOWS ONE OF THE TWO IDENTICAL
IGNITION BOXES ON THE ENGINE

SPARKIGNITER

Figure 21·11 Ignition system for the JT-3D turbofan engine.

low compressor with bleed valves closed becomes possible at lower speed of the N_1 rotor. An increase in compressor inlet temperature with a decrease in compressor inlet pressures requires a higher N_1 speed to attain surge-free operation of the low-pressure compressor with bleed valves closed.

The bleed valves are open during starting and

ground idle. They remain open during acceleration until the region of surge-free high-pressure compressor operation is reached as determined by the bleed valve governor, which receives low-pressure rotor speed and compressor inlet temperature and pressure signals. Then the bleed valves close and remain closed at all higher speeds. On deceleration the bleed valves open again as low-pressure compressor speed falls to the region where surging would occur with bleed valves closed.

The two compressor bleed valves are set to operate at different low rotor speeds so that the resulting change in thrust will not occur all at once but rather in two distinct steps. Operation of the right-hand bleed valve occurs at an N_1 speed 500 rpm lower than that of the left-hand valve. Each bleed valve has its own actuator which is operated by high-pressure compressor air P_{t4} and is controlled by the bleed valve governor.

TRIMMING THE ENGINE

Reason for trimming

Because of manufacturing tolerances and changes in performance during the operating life of a turbojet or turbofan engine, it is necessary to make fuel-control adjustments from time to time to assure maximum performance from the engine. This adjustment is called **trimming.**

At the time of manufacturing test, the engine is adjusted to produce its exact rated thrust. The engine speed to produce this thrust is stamped on the engine data plate in terms of actual rpm and percentage of maximum rpm. This is the **trim speed.**

Engine trimming is performed on Pratt & Whitney JT-3D engines at part power setting and is a necessary requirement on newly installed engines or following a change of fuel control unit or tail pipe. Periodic trim may also be necessary during the life of the engine to restore normal "cushion" between takeoff and full-throttle position.

Trimming procedure

When one is preparing to trim an engine installed in an airplane, the airplane should be headed directly into the wind. The engine must not be trimmed when the wind velocity is more than 25 mph or when icing conditions exist.

A check sheet should be prepared to list data and record engine trim and thrust results. The outside air temperature (OAT), true barometric pressure, engine and fuel data, and target exhaust pressure (P_{t7}) should be listed before the engine trim check run is begun. The target value of P_{t7} for different thrust settings is determined from appropriate trim charts. The exhaust pressure ratio (EPR or P_{t7}/P_{t2}) reading which corresponds to target P_{t7} values should be noted to allow a check between the pilot's EPR instrument and the engine P_{t7} test instrument.

The actual trim adjustment of the engine is accomplished by running the engine at the speed (idle) attained with the part power trim stop attached to the fuel-control unit and adjusting the fuel control for the correct speed and EPR. As mentioned previously, the EPR is the ratio of exhaust pressure P_{t7} to engine inlet pressure P_{t2}. After the engine has been checked at the idle trim speed, it is checked again at full throttle.

THE GENERAL ELECTRIC CJ-805-23 TURBOFAN ENGINE

General description

The General Electric CJ-805-23 engine, shown in the cutaway photograph of Fig. 21·12, is an axial-flow, aft-fan (turbofan), jet-propulsion powerplant designed for use in modern jet airliners. The engine incorporates a 17-stage axial-flow compressor driven by a 3-stage reaction turbine; a cannular combustion section; a free-floating, single-stage aft fan; a fixed area, concentric exhaust section; and an integrated control system.

The CJ-805-23 aft-fan engine is a modification of the CJ-805-3 turbojet engine. The gas generator section (compressor and combustion sections) is the same for both engines.

Engine specifications

The specifications for the CJ-805-23 engine are as follows:

Thrust	16,100 lb
Diameter	
Basic engine	32 in.
Aft fan	53 in.
Weight	3800 lb
Overall length with reverser	150 in.
Pressure ratio	
Basic engine	13:1
Aft fan	1.6:1
Bypass ratio	1.54:1
RPM	
Basic engine	7310
Aft fan	5560
Airflow	
Basic engine	170 lb/sec
Aft fan	258 lb/sec
Specific fuel consumption (cruise)	0.518 lb/lbt/hr
Oil consumption	1.5 lb/hr
Power/weight ratio	4.24 lbt/lb

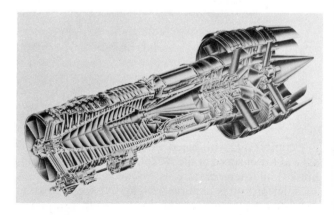

Figure 21·12 Cutaway illustration of General Electric CJ-805-23 aft-fan engine. (General Electric Co.)

ENGINE DESCRIPTION

Compressor section

The compressor section of the engine consists of the **front frame**, the **compressor rotor** and **stator**, and the **rear frame**. These parts are shown in the drawing of Fig. 21 · 13. Air enters the engine at the front frame and passes through a row of variable **inlet guide vanes** (IGV). It then flows through 17 stages of compressor **rotor blades** and **stator vanes** and one row of **outlet guide vanes**. The exit passages from the compressor section are designed to control the velocity of the air as it enters the combustion section.

The compressor front frame is the forward structural member of the engine and forms the air inlet to the engine. It houses the No. 1 bearing, which supports the forward end of the compressor rotor. Trunnion mounts, by which the engine may be supported in ground handling equipment, are provided on the outer shell. This section also provides mounting bosses for the ignition units, the **compressor inlet temperature sensor probe,** the **transfer gearbox,** and the airframe-furnished nose cone fairing.

The frame, a magnesium-alloy casting, consists of an inner hub connected to an outer casing by eight stream-lined, hollow struts. Twenty hollow IGVs are mounted

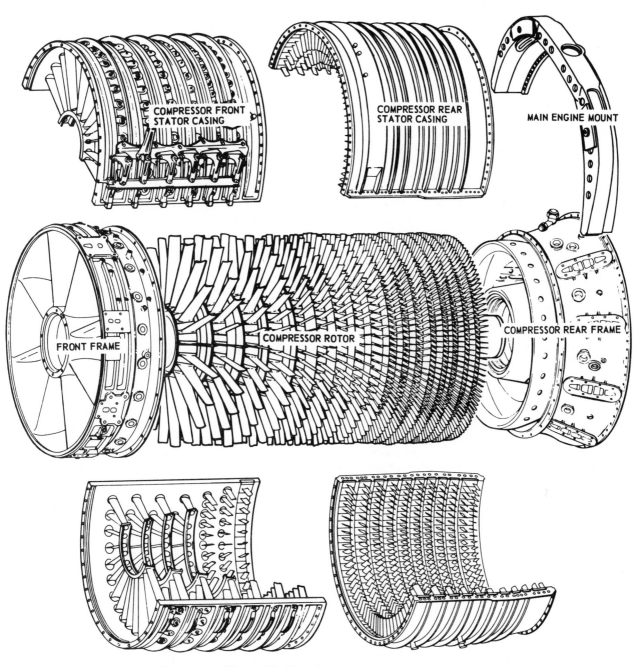

Figure 21 · 13   Compressor section.

433

to a support ring aft of the struts. The hub houses the front gearbox, the No. 1 bearing, and the bearing air and oil seals. The hollow struts and the IGVs are anti-iced with compressor discharge air. The struts house the bearing oil supply and scavenge lines, the sump vent line, and the vertical drive shaft.

The primary function of the **compressor stator** is to direct the flow of air through the compressor. In addition, it forms the load-carrying outer skin between the compressor front frame and the compressor rear frame.

The compressor stator consists of a forward and a rear casing, both split along the horizontal center line; 18 rows of stator vanes; and the actuating linkage for the variable vanes. Six stages of variable vanes, the first four of which are shrouded at their inner ends, and one stage of fixed vanes are housed in the forward half of the casing.

The variable IGVs and the six stages of variable stator vanes are automatically adjusted through the action of the **variable stator servo section** in the fuel control. This action occurs as a result of the integration of the parameters of engine speed and compressor inlet temperature (CIT). The operation of the variable stator vanes is such that they are wide open when engine speed is above 90 percent. At lower speeds they move toward the closed (high-angle) position, and at idle they are at or near the fully closed position. Operation of the variable stator vanes assures optimum performance over a wide range of flight conditions.

The rear compressor houses 10 rows of fixed stator vanes and 2 rows of outlet guide vanes. The airfoil-shaped stationary vanes are mounted in fabricated bases. These mounting bases slide into grooves on the inner surface of the stator casing.

The **compressor rear frame** serves as a diffuser passage for air entering the combustion section and as the mid-support structure of the engine. It houses the No. 2 bearing, which supports the aft end of the compressor rotor and the forward end of the turbine rotor.

The rear frame is a sheet-steel weldment consisting of an outer shell and an inner diffuser or hub connected by 10 equally spaced struts. The No. 2 bearing housing support is supported by the **inner diffuser.** Thrust loads, both radial and axial, applied to the ball-bearing assembly are transmitted to the outer shell through the struts. The main engine mount is attached to the front flange and transmits the thrust, vertical, side, and torque loads to the aircraft structure. The struts also serve as passageways for oil-supply lines, oil scavenge lines, sump pressurization lines, sump vent lines, compressor leakage air, and seventeenth-stage bleed air.

The **compressor rotor** assembly consists of a front and rear stub shaft, 17 disks with associated blades, air ducts, spacers, and torque cones. The rotor blades are of stainless steel, and the remaining components are made of low-alloy-steel forgings.

Power to drive the compressor rotor is transmitted to the rear stub shaft through a splined coupling with the turbine rotor. Torque is then transmitted forward through spacers or torque cones located between the disks to the front stub shaft. The front stub shaft contains a female spline through which power is delivered to the front gearbox. The shrouds of stator vane stages 1 through 4 act as interstage seals for the first four stages of the rotor, and the spacers between the disks perform this function in the remaining stages.

Air flows through holes in the spacer between the seventh- and eighth-stage disks and through ducts in the center of the rotor. A portion of this air bleeds through holes in the ducts into the area between the rotor disks to reduce the pressure differential across the disks and spacers. The remaining air flows through the front stub shaft to pressurize the seals around the No. 1 bearing and through the rear stub shaft into the interior of the turbine rotor, where it is used as cooling air.

Combustion section

The **combustion section** for the CJ-805 engine is of the cannular type; that is, the main chamber is annular and contains 10 combustion liners, or "cans." The combustion section, illustrated in Fig. 21·14, is attached to the compressor section at the compressor rear frame. The inner and outer casings, combustion liners, and transition liners are shown in the drawing. Air from the compressor section flows into the combustion section, with a portion of the air entering the combustion liners where it is mixed with fuel and burned. The remaining air forms a cooling blanket over the inner and outer casings. As the gaseous mixture in the liners is burned, it expands, thus increasing the velocity of the gases. The high-velocity gases are then ejected through the transition liner, where they are transformed from ten individual streams to one annular stream.

The **inner combustion casing** forms the inner wall of the air passage through the combustion section and provides radial support for the transition liner. The casing is fabricated from a chromium-molybdenum-vanadium steel, sometimes called Chromoloy alloy.

The ten **combustion liners** receive a portion of the air entering the combustion section and fuel from the fuel nozzles. The fuel and air are mixed and burned in the combustion liners, and the resulting hot gases then pass through the transition liner as previously explained. An excess of air, both inside and outside the liners, prevents the liner walls from burning.

Each liner is a sheet-metal fabrication with louvers and holes arranged to promote optimum mixing of the fuel and air. A fuel nozzle is inserted into the forward end of each liner. Igniter plugs, located in the Nos. 4 and 5 liners, ignite the fuel/mixture, and the flame is propagated to the remaining liners through cross-fire tubes. The combustion liners are made of a high-temperature alloy.

The **transition liner,** as mentioned previously, converts the ten streams of hot gases from the combustion liners to a single annular stream. It also supports the aft end of the combustion liners. The material for the transition liner is a steel alloy called Incoloy.

The **outer combustion casing** forms the outer boundary of the air passages through the combustion section.

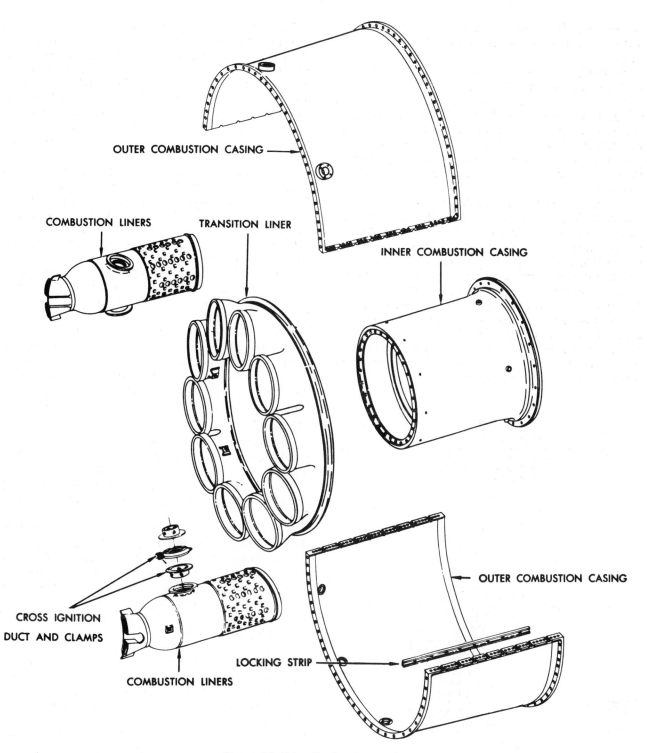

OUTER COMBUSTION CASING

COMBUSTION LINERS

TRANSITION LINER

INNER COMBUSTION CASING

CROSS IGNITION
DUCT AND CLAMPS

COMBUSTION LINERS

OUTER COMBUSTION CASING

LOCKING STRIP

Figure **21·14** *Combustion section.*

It also serves as part of the load-carrying outer skin of the engine. The casing is a sheet-steel component fabricated from Chromoloy. It is split along the horizontal center line, and the two halves are bolted together and sealed with a locking strip. Two bosses are provided on the lower half for mounting the igniter plugs, and two ports are provided for draining the combustion section following a prestart check or false start. Two ports are provided on the top half for supplying air to anti-ice the fan outlet guide vanes.

Turbine section

The **turbine section** of a jet engine is designed to extract power from the gas stream to drive the compressor rotor and the gearbox-mounted accessories. The turbine section of the CJ-805 engine includes the first-stage turbine nozzle, the turbine rotor, and the turbine stator assembly. These are illustrated in Fig. 21 · 15.

As the gas stream flows into the turbine section, it flows through the first-stage turbine nozzle and impinges on the first-stage turbine rotor buckets (blades). It then continues through the remaining two stages of turbine stator nozzles and rotor buckets. The resulting rotation of the turbine rotor turns the compressor rotor and the accessory drives. The gas stream then flows into the inner passage of the aft fan assembly.

The **first-stage turbine nozzle** directs gas from the transition liner so that the gases strike the first-stage turbine blades at the proper angle for the most effective power extraction. The nozzle is a sheet-metal fabrication formed from Hastelloy and Stellite.

The **turbine stator** directs the flow of combustion gases through the turbine rotor buckets and forms part of the load-carrying outer skin of the engine. The stator is designed to provide turbine bucket containment. That is, if a turbine blade should rupture and come loose from the turbine wheel, the outer casing of the stator would prevent the blade from being thrown radially from the engine.

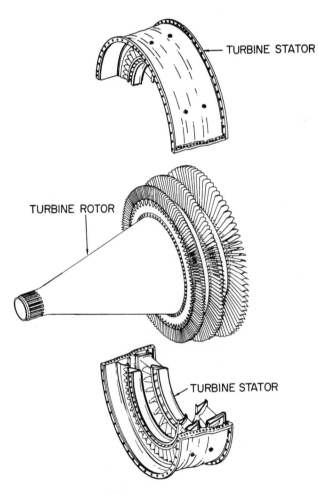

TURBINE STATOR

TURBINE ROTOR

TURBINE STATOR

Figure 21 · 15   Turbine section.

The stator assembly consists of an outer casing, two turbine nozzles, and three honeycomb turbine shrouds. The assembly is split along the horizontal center line. The casing, the honeycomb shrouds, and the third-stage nozzle are stainless-steel fabrications, where the second-stage nozzle is made of Hastelloy and Stellite sheet stock. The stationary portions of the two interstage air seals, while part of the stator assembly, are not split into halves and are assembled with the turbine rotor.

The **turbine rotor** assembly consists of a conical hollow forward shaft, three disks with associated buckets, two torque rings, two air baffles, and the rotating portion of the No. 3 bearing forward air seal. The spline on the forward end of the turbine shaft mates with the female spline of the compressor rotor rear stub shaft. The two shafts are held together with a self-locking bolt and are supported by the No. 2 bearing. The turbine rotor rear stub shaft, which is an integral part of the third-stage disk, is supported by the No. 3 bearing located in the **fan front frame.**

A portion of the seventh-stage air from the interior of the compressor rotor flows through the turbine rotor shaft. The air baffles in the turbine rotor distribute the cooling air over the face of the disks and the inner surfaces of the torque rings. The air then flows through the hollow turbine rotor rear stub shaft.

Aft-fan section

The **aft-fan section** is attached to the turbine stator casing rear flange. It consists of a single-stage free-floating rotor, which is part compressor and part turbine, and a front frame incorporating concentric annular-flow passages. This section is shown in Fig. 21 · 16.

Gases flowing aft from the turbine section flow into the inner passage of the fan front frame and through the partitions of the fan turbine nozzle. The nozzle directs the gases at the correct angle to the turbine airfoil of the fan rotor blades. The gases impart energy to the blades to drive the fan rotor and then flow through the inner passage of the fan rear frame and into the exhaust section.

Secondary air is ducted into the fan inlet and the outer air passage of the fan front frame and flows to the outer sections of the fan rotor blades. The compressor airfoils compress the air at a ratio of 1.6:1. The air then flows through a row of outlet guide vanes, which straighten the direction of flow, and through the outer passage of the fan rear frame to the exhaust section. Secondary airflow through the fan is 1.5 times that of the primary airflow.

The **fan front frame** forms the air inlet to the fan section. It also serves as a support structure because the No. 3 bearing, which supports the aft end of the turbine rotor, and the No. 4 bearing, which supports the forward end of the fan rotor, are housed in the fan front frame hub. A link-pin engine mount is provided on the outer shell. Eight thermocouples are mounted in the diffuser and extend into the primary airstream passage.

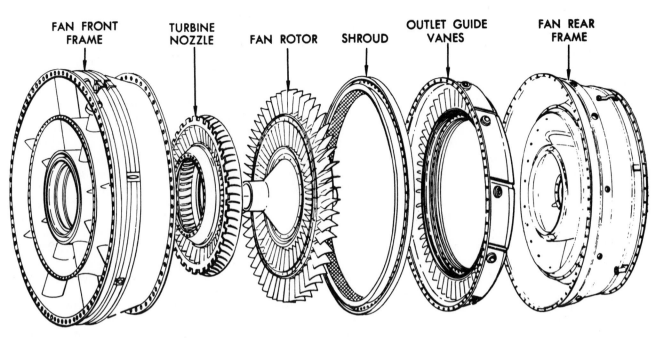

Figure **21·16** Aft-fan section.

Concentric-flow passages are formed by the outer shell, the inner diffuser, and the hub. The hub and outer shell are connected by eight equally spaced struts. A small portion of the primary gas flow is routed out through the struts to anti-ice the portion of the struts that extend through the secondary airstream. The struts also serve as passageways for oil service piping to the bearings, for air to pressurize the bearing sumps, and for the venting of turbine cooling air. The stationary portion of the fan front air seal and the fan turbine nozzle complete the fan front frame assembly.

The **fan rear frame** serves as a diffuser passage for the two airstreams from the fan rotor. The segmented honeycomb shroud ensures that all the secondary air flows through the fan blades. A row of outlet guide vanes straightens the gas flow from the fan rotor compressor airfoil, while baffles around the inner portion of the rear frame struts perform this function in the primary gas stream. The frame also serves as the aft support structure of the engine, since the No. 5 bearing, which supports the aft end of the fan rotor, is housed in the rear frame hub. The inner cone is assembled to the inner flange of the frame and is designed to provide a smooth flow into the exhaust section. The outer shell, inner diffuser, and hub are connected by eight equally spaced struts and are constructed to form the concentric flow passages. The struts serve as passageways for oil and air service lines.

The **fan rotor** consists of two conical shafts and a rotor disk with associated blades. The rotor blades, consisting of two airfoil sections separated by a dividing platform, are mounted to the rotor disk by inserting the blade bases into dovetails in the outer rim of the disk. Projections on the mid platforms interlock the blades, preventing deflection on the blade tips.

Serrations on the front and aft sides of the platform mate with honeycomb segments on the aft side of the turbine nozzle and the forward side of the outlet guide vanes, forming a labyrinth-type air seal to separate the two airstreams. The rotor is supported at the forward end by the No. 4 bearing, a ball-type thrust bearing, and at the aft end by the roller-type No. 5 bearing.

ENGINE SYSTEMS

In order to perform properly through all ranges of power and speed, every turbojet or turbofan engine must be provided with a variety of operating systems. The principal systems for the CJ-805-23 turbofan engine are the airflow system, fuel and control system, lubrication system, electrical system, drain system, and exhaust system. These will be dealt with briefly one at a time.

Airflow system

Turbojet engines and turbofan engines generally utilize some of the air compressed by the engine to cool engine parts, to pressurize certain areas where additional air pressure is desirable, and to anti-ice those areas where ice is likely to occur. In the CJ-805-23 engine, seventh-stage air bleeds into the inside of the compressor rotor. From this point it flows both ways to reduce the pressure differential across the wheels and spacers of the rotor stages. A small amount of the air bleeds through holes in the compressor front stub shaft to pressurize the area between the No. 1 bearing air and oil seals. The flow of air across the air seal prevents loss of oil, and since part of the air flows into the gearbox areas, it provides a positive head for the scavenge pumps.

437

The remaining air flows through the center of the compressor rotor rear stub shaft and into the interior of the turbine rotor. Here the air cools the fore and aft faces of the first- and second-stage disks and the forward face of the third-stage disk. The air is then routed through the turbine rotor rear stub shaft and into the fan front frame. Here the air flows outward through all struts (except strut No. 5) and into the hat section of the outer circumference of the frame. The air heats the hat section, thus decreasing the amount of thermal stress created by the difference in temperature of the two airstreams through the frame.

Ninth-stage air bleeds through holes in the upper half of the compressor rear casing and into a manifold. This air is used to pressurize areas between bearings to control oil flow and to provide positive pressure for scavenge pumps.

Seventeenth-stage air is also used for control of oil flow and to reduce pressure differential across the spacers, torque cones, and disks of the compressor rear stages. This aids in reducing stress on the No. 2 bearing and contributes to its longer life. Air from the seventeenth stage is also utilized for anti-icing.

Fuel system and control

The CJ-805-23 fuel-control establishes engine speed by metering the fuel flow for starting, acceleration, deceleration, and steady-state operation. Since the fan rotor is aerodynamically coupled to the engine rotors, the fuel control indirectly controls fan rotor speed. In addition to fuel flow, the system controls the direction and velocity of the air flowing through the compressor by varying the position of the inlet guide vanes and the first six stages of stator vanes. Besides being used for combustion, fuel is used as servo fluid within the fuel control, as hydraulic fluid for positioning the variable stator actuators, as a coolant for engine and constant-speed drive oil, and to establish reference pressure in the pressurizing and drain valve.

The system consists of a two-element gear pump with an integral centrifugal boost element, a fuel heater, filter, bypassing-type control, two fuel-oil coolers, a pressurizing and drain valve, 10 fuel nozzles, and two variable stator actuators. The fuel system is shown in Fig. 21 · 17.

Fuel-flow path

The aircraft fuel boost pump delivers fuel to the inlet of the engine fuel pump where the boost element steps up the pressure 15 to 45 psi. The fuel flows from the boost element to the two gear-type high-pressure elements which increase the pressure 100 to 850 psig, depending upon engine speed and flight conditions. Fuel from the pump flows to the fuel heater, which uses compressor discharge air to maintain the fuel temperature above freezing. This prevents the formation of ice crystals in the fuel and removes any ice crystals that may have formed before the fuel reaches the heater. Fuel from the heater passes to the fuel-control unit.

The hydromechanical fuel control operates in a manner similar to those previously explained. It meters the flow of fuel to the combustion chambers by varying the area of the metering orifice and, at the same time, maintaining a constant pressure drop across the orifice. The inputs to the fuel control are power lever angle, engine speed, compressor inlet temperature (CIT), and compressor discharge pressure (CDP). The control integrates these parameters to establish the area of the metering orifice and thus schedule the proper fuel flow for any operating condition.

The fuel pump always delivers more fuel to the control than is required to sustain the engine at any given condition. The control uses some of this excess fuel to operate its servo mechanisms and some to position and cool the variable stator actuators. The remainder of unused fuel is returned (bypass flow) to the inlet side of the high-pressure elements of the fuel pump.

Metered fuel from the fuel control flows through the engine fuel-oil cooler, the constant-speed drive fuel-oil cooler, and the airframe-furnished fuel-flow transmitter. In the coolers fuel is used as the coolant for the oil provided that the fuel temperature remains below 127°C (260°F). Each of the coolers has a temperature sensor which may cause the cooler to bypass its oil flow.

From the fuel-flow transmitter, metered fuel is routed to the pressurizing and drain valve. The pressurizing portion of the valve is closed until sufficient pressure is built up to operate the servo assemblies in the control. The pressurizing valve opens when metered fuel pressure is sufficient to overcome the reference pressure, which is directed to the back side of the pressurizing valve from the control bypass flow and the valve spring force. When the engine is shut down, the drain section of the valve opens, draining the fuel manifold to prevent post-shutdown fires but maintaining the upstream portion of the fuel system primed to permit faster starting.

Fuel from the pressurizing and drain valve flows into the 10 fuel discharge nozzles. The nozzles spray atomized fuel into the combustion chambers, where it is mixed with air and burned.

Lubrication system

The lubrication system for the CJ-805-23 turbofan engine requires the use of a high-temperature lubricating oil conforming to Specification MIL-L-7808. As explained previously, this lubricant is a synthetic type which can withstand the high temperatures encountered in gas-turbine engines.

The lubrication system may be divided into three principal subsystems: (1) the oil-supply subsystem, (2) the scavenge subsystem, and (3) the pressurization subsystem. A diagram of the complete system is shown in Fig. 9 · 22.

The oil-supply subsystem delivers oil at the required pressure to the five main bearing areas, the transfer and rear gearboxes, and the damper bearing. The oil

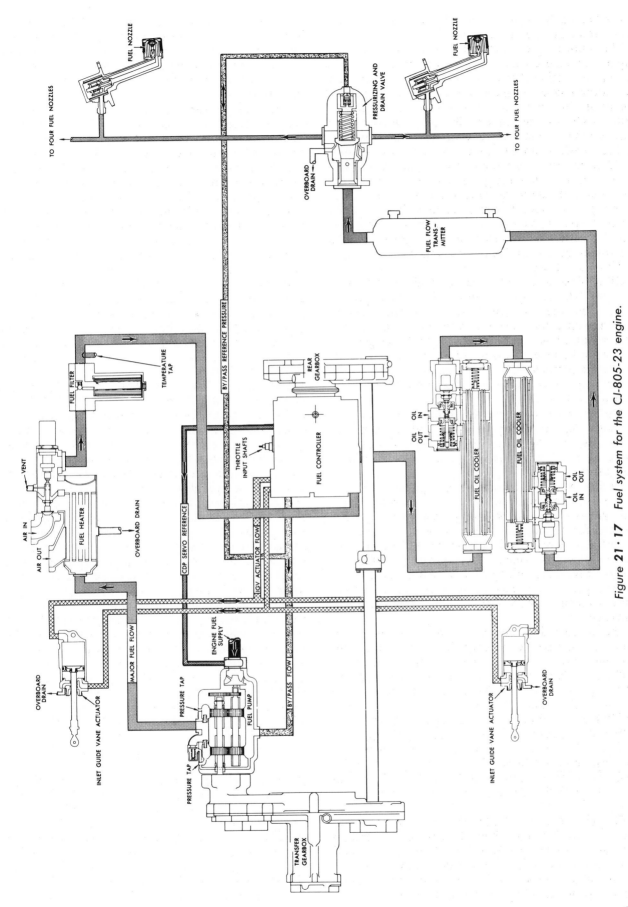

Figure 21·17 Fuel system for the CJ-805-23 engine.

FUEL NOZZLE

FUEL NOZZLE

TO FOUR FUEL NOZZLES

TO FOUR FUEL NOZZLES

PRESSURIZING AND DRAIN VALVE

OVERBOARD DRAIN

FUEL FLOW TRANSMITTER

TEMPERATURE TAP

FUEL FILTER

BY/PASS REFERENCE PRESSURE

REAR GEARBOX

OIL IN

OIL OUT

VENT

AIR IN

AIR OUT

OVERBOARD DRAIN

FUEL HEATER

CDP SERVO REFERENCE

IGV ACTUATOR FLOW

THROTTLE INPUT SHAFTS

FUEL CONTROLLER

FUEL OIL COOLER

FUEL OIL COOLER

OIL OUT

OIL IN

OVERBOARD DRAIN

INLET GUIDE VANE ACTUATOR

MAJOR FUEL FLOW

PRESSURE TAP

ENGINE FUEL SUPPLY

BY/PASS FLOW

PRESSURE TAP

FUEL PUMP

INLET GUIDE VANE ACTUATOR

OVERBOARD DRAIN

TRANSFER GEARBOX

is discharged through jet nozzles onto the bearings, gears, and other mating surfaces in these areas.

The lubricating oil is stored in a two-compartment engine-mounted oil tank. One compartment supplies oil for the engine thrust reverser control system and the aircraft constant-speed drive system. The other compartment supplies oil to the engine oil-supply subsystem. Oil to the engine oil-supply subsystem is gravity fed to the lubricating elements of the lubricant and scavenge pump. The pump raises the oil pressure to 12 to 60 psig, depending upon engine speed, and discharges the oil through an antileak check valve mounted in the discharge port of the pump. From the pump, the oil flows through the lube filter to a tee which divides the flow to supply the inlet gearbox and No. 1 bearing, the transfer and rear gearboxes, the horizontal drive shaft damper bearing, and the Nos. 2, 3, 4, and 5 bearings.

Oil is piped to the inlet gearbox and No. 1 bearing area through a passage in strut No. 5 of the compressor front frame where five jets distribute oil. Three jets are on a tube assembly mounted in the inlet gearbox, one jet is a drilled hole in the oil passage of the inlet gearbox casing, and one jet is a drilled hole in the oil passage of the front frame. Oil to the gearboxes and to the other bearings is distributed in a similar manner as shown in Fig. 9·22.

The **scavenge oil subsystem** returns oil from the bearing sumps, the damper bearing, and the gearboxes to the engine section of the oil tank. The oil is filtered and cooled so that it is ready for reuse in the supply oil subsystem.

During all flight attitudes scavenge oil from the No. 1 bearing sump and the front gearbox drains through strut No. 5 of the compressor front frame to the transfer gearbox. This oil, plus the oil in the transfer gearbox, is returned by one element of the transfer gearbox scavenge pump. The scavenge flow from the damper bearing is piped to the second element of the transfer gearbox scavenge pump. Discharge flow from both elements of the scavenge pump is routed to the scavenge filter.

The combination lubricating and scavenge pump contains two separate scavenge elements. One element scavenges oil from the No. 3 bearing through strut No. 4 of the fan front frame. The remaining element draws oil through strut No. 6 of the fan front frame from the No. 4 bearing sump. The oil from both elements is manifolded and routed to the scavenge oil filter.

The two-element No. 5 bearing scavenge oil pump is mounted on the rear face of the fan tachometer and scavenges oil from the No. 5 bearing sump and the fan tachometer. The scavenge oil is discharged through strut No. 5 of the fan rear frame to the scavenge oil filter.

Filtered scavenge oil flows to the engine fuel-oil cooler where it is cooled by the engine fuel flowing through the cooler core. However, at oil inlet temperatures below 100°F a pressure-relief valve opens to bypass oil around the cooler core. A fuel temperature sensor opens the oil bypass valve when the fuel temperature reaches 241° to prevent further transfer of heat from the scavenge oil to the fuel. Scavenge oil is returned from the cooler to the engine compartment of the oil tank. Here the entrained air is separated from the oil, and the oil is ready for reuse in the supply oil subsystem.

The **sump-pressurizing subsystem** regulates the pressure in the oil tank, gearboxes, and bearing sumps. These units are pressurized primarily to ensure a positive pressure at the inlet to the lubricating and scavenge pumps. However, a second and equally important function is to minimize loss of oil by establishing the proper pressure differential across the bearing seals.

Seventh- and ninth-stage air from the engine compressor is allowed to enter the pressurized areas within the oil system through various passages. Since the scavenge pumps are capable of pumping a greater volume of oil than is in the sumps, they make up the difference by pumping air. This air is entrained in oil and carried to the tank, thus increasing the pressure. The sump-pressurizing valve releases pressure of more than 3 to 6 psi above ambient pressure, thus maintaining this level of pressure in the system.

Ignition system

The ignition system for the CJ-805-23 engine is illustrated in the diagram of Fig. 21·18. This is a high-energy system of a type similar to those previously described. Alternating-current power enters the system through the filter and flows through the primary of the transformer T_1. The voltage is stepped up to about 3500 volts and is then effectively doubled by the action of the gas-filled diodes V_1 and V_2. During one half cycle V_1 will conduct, and during the next half cycle V_2 will conduct. The capacitor C_2 stores the energy, and when the voltage is high enough to discharge through the gap of V_4, a surge of current flows through the primary of the trigger transformer T_2. This causes an even higher voltage to be inducted in the secondary of T_2, thus breaking down the gap in V_3 and discharging the energy across the gap of the igniter plug. Since the gaps are ionized, the entire charge of energy is able to flow from the storage capacitor C_2. The current through the secondary of the trigger transformer saturates the core, and no flux change can be initiated by the primary winding. The capacitor C_3 blocks the d-c component from following the path through the primary instead of passing through the igniter plug.

REVIEW QUESTIONS

1. Briefly describe the configuration of the basic JT-3 engine.
2. Describe the arrangement of the two-spool compressor.
3. What is the pressure ratio across the compressor of the JT-3 engine?
4. At maximum rpm, what is the weight of air pumped by the JT-3 compressor per second?
5. Describe the construction of the compressor vane rings.
6. Name the principal components of the diffuser case assembly for the JT-3 engine.

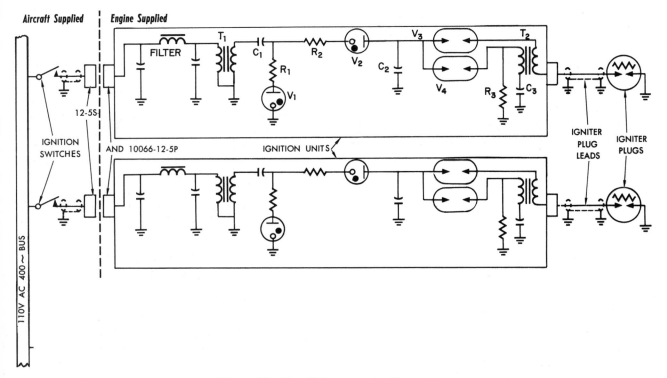

Figure **21·18** *High-energy ignition system.*

7. Describe the method by which the main accessories for the JT-3 engine are driven.

8. Describe the arrangement of the fuel nozzles and manifold.

9. What is the function of the turbine intershaft bearing in the JT-3 engine?

10. Describe the front compressor drive turbine rotor.

11. By what means is the turbine rear bearing supported?

12. What type of lubricant is required for the JT-3 engine?

13. At what oil pressure does the lubrication system operate?

14. Describe the scavenge oil system.

15. What is the function of the breather pressurizing valve?

16. What unit in the fuel control regulates engine speed?

17. Explain how burner pressure affects fuel flow.

18. What unit of the fuel control prevents too rapid acceleration?

19. Give a brief explanation of the ignition system operation for a JT-3 engine.

20. What precaution must be observed in working with the high-energy ignition system?

21. Explain what is meant by *trimming* the engine.

22. By what means are the variable stator vanes actuated on the General Electric CJ-805-23 engine?

23. What is the advantage of variable stator vanes?

24. In what position are the torque cones for the compressor rotor located?

25. What means is employed to reduce the pressure differential across the compressor rotor disks and spacers in the CJ-805 engine?

26. Describe the combustion section for the CJ-805 engine.

27. By what means is the turbine rotor assembly cooled?

28. Describe the aft-fan arrangement for the CJ-805-23 engine.

29. How is compressor air utilized in the CJ-805 engine, other than for combustion of fuel?

30. What are the input parameters for the fuel-control unit used with the CJ-805 engine?

31. What is the range of operating pressures for the oil system of the CJ-805 engine?

32. Trace the flow of engine oil from the oil tank, through the engine, and back to the oil tank.

441

CHAPTER 22

Turboprop Engines

INTRODUCTION

The gas-turbine engine in combination with a reduction gear assembly and a propeller has been in use for over 15 years and has proved to be a most efficient power source for aircraft operating in speed ranges of 300 to 450 mph. These engines provide the best specific fuel consumption of any gas-turbine engine, and they perform well from sea level to comparatively high altitudes (over 20,000 ft).

Although a variety of names has been applied to gas-turbine and propeller combinations, the most widely used name is **turboprop,** and this name will generally be used in this section. Another popular name at the present time is "prop-jet."

The power section of a turboprop engine is similar to that of a turbojet engine; however, there are some important differences. The most important difference is the turbine section. In the turbojet engine the turbine section is designed to extract only enough energy from the hot gases to drive the compressor and accessories. The turboprop engine, on the other hand, has a turbine section which extracts as much power as possible to drive the propeller. For example, the Allison Model 501 engine extracts 3460 hp for the propeller and produces 726 lb thrust. The total equivalent shp (shp plus thrust) is given as 3750 ehp. This means, of course, that the turbine section will usually have more stages than that of the turbojet engine and that the turbine blade design is such that the turbines will extract more energy from the hot gas stream of the exhaust.

Another important feature of the turboprop engine is the reduction-gear assembly through which the propeller is driven. The gear reduction from the engine to the propeller is of a much higher ratio than that used for reciprocating engines because of the high rpm of the gas-turbine engine. For example, the gear reduction for the Rolls-Royce Dart engine is 10.75:1 and the gear reduction for the Allison Model 501 engine is 13.54:1.

Because of the propeller which must be driven by the turboprop engine, a rather complex propeller control system is necessary to adjust the propeller pitch for the power requirements of the engine. At normal operating conditions, both the propeller speed and engine speed are constant. The propeller pitch and the fuel flow must then be coordinated in order to maintain the constant-speed condition; that is, when fuel flow is decreased, propeller pitch must also decrease.

THE ALLISON MODEL 501-D13 ENGINE

General information

The Allison Model 501-D13 turboprop (prop-jet) engine is the commercial version of the Allison T-56 engine which is used for military aircraft. The 501-D13 engine is rated at 3750 eshp (equivalent shaft horsepower) at standard day conditions with an rpm of 13,820 and a turbine inlet temperature of 971°C (1780°F). The engine consists of a **power section,** a **reduction gear,** and a **torquemeter assembly.** The power section and reduction gear are connected and aligned by the torquemeter assembly, and added rigidity is provided by two struts. The propeller is mounted on a single rotation SAE 60A propeller shaft. Figure 22·1 illustrates the configuration and general construction of the engine.

The following definitions apply to the engine:

Front. The propeller end.

Top. Determined by the breather located at the forward end of the power section.

Right and left. Determined by standing at the rear of the engine and facing forward.

Rotation. The direction of rotation is determined when standing at the rear of the engine and facing forward. The power section rotor turns in a counterclockwise direction, and the propeller rotation is clockwise.

Accessories rotation. Determined by facing the mounting pad of each accessory.

Combustion liner numbering. The combustion liners are numbered from 1 through 6 in a clockwise direction when the engine is viewed from the rear. The No.1 liner is at the top vertical center line.

Compressor and turbine stages numbering. Numbered beginning from the forward end of the power section and progressively moving rearward. The compressor has 1 through 14 stages, and the turbine 1 through 4 stages.

Main rotor bearings numbering. Numbered beginning at the forward end of the power section, moving rearward, with the No. 1 being at the forward end of the compressor rotor, No. 2 at the rear end of the com-

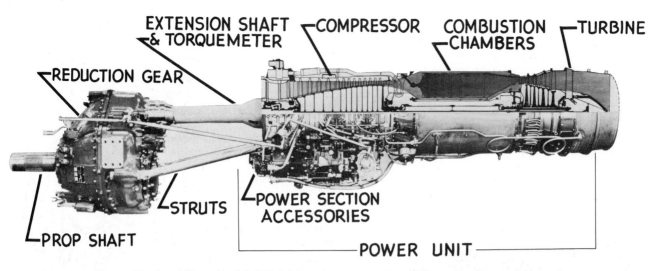

Figure 22·1 Allison Model 501-D13 turboprop engine. (Allison Div. General Motors)

pressor rotor, No. 3 at the forward side of the turbine rotor, and No. 4 at the rear of the turbine rotor.

Igniter plug location. There are two igniter plugs installed in the engine, one in combustion liner No. 2 and one in combustion liner No. 5.

Engine performance

The performance of the Allison 501-D13 engine is far superior to a conventional reciprocating engine of the same weight, and its fuel consumption per horsepower is comparable to that of a reciprocating engine. The following performance data emphasize the value of this engine as a powerplant for commercial aircraft:

Power output	3750 ehp, or 3460 shp + 726 lbt at 13,820 rpm
Max continuous power	2170 ehp, or 1820 shp + 145 lbt at 13,820 rpm
Weight without propeller	1756 lb
Power/weight ratio	2.14 ehp/lb
Fuel consumption (sfc, cruise)	0.55 lb/ehp/hr
Oil consumption	3.0 lb/hr

ENGINE DESCRIPTION

Compressor assembly

The compressor assembly consists of a **compressor air inlet housing assembly, compressor housing, compressor rotor assembly, diffuser,** and **diffuser scavenge oil pump assembly.**

The compressor air inlet housing is a magnesium-alloy casting and is designed to direct and distribute air into the compressor rotor. It also provides the mounting location for the **front compressor bearing,** the **engine breather,** the **accessories drive housing assembly,** the **anti-icing air valves,** the **torquemeter housing,** and the **inlet anti-icing vane assembly.**

The inlet anti-icing vane assembly is mounted on the aft side of the air inlet housing and is utilized to impart the proper direction and velocity to the airflow as it enters into the first stage of the compressor rotor. These vanes may "ice up" under ideal icing conditions; hence provisions are made to direct heat to each of the vanes. Air which has been heated by compression may be extracted from the outlet of the compressor (diffuser) and directed through two tubes to the anti-icing valves mounted on the compressor air inlet housing. The inlet anti-icing vanes are hollow and mate with inner and outer annuli (passages) into which the hot air is directed. From the annuli the air flows through the vanes and exits into the first stage of the compressor through slots which are provided in the trailing edge of the vanes. The construction of the compressor air inlet housing is shown in Fig. 22·2.

The compressor rotor is an axial-flow type and consists of 14 stages. It is supported at the forward end by a roller bearing (bearing No. 1) and at the rear by a ball bearing (bearing No. 2). The illustration of Fig. 22·3 shows the arrangement of the compressor rotor, and Fig. 22·4 shows an inspector checking the seal diameter with a dial gage.

The entire compressor housing assembly is fabricated from steel and consists of four quarters permanently bolted together in halves. The split lines of the housing are located 45° from a vertical center line. The compressor vane assemblies are installed in channels in the compressor housing and are securely located and held in position by bolts. The inner ring of the vane assemblies supports the interstage air seals which form a labyrinth seal, thus preventing air from one stage bleeding back to the previous stage. Between each row of vane assemblies (stator blades) the housing is coated with a special type of sprayed aluminum to provide a minimum compressor rotor blade clearance, thus increasing compressor efficiency. The outlet vane assembly consists of an inner and an outer ring supporting two complete circles of vanes. These are used

443

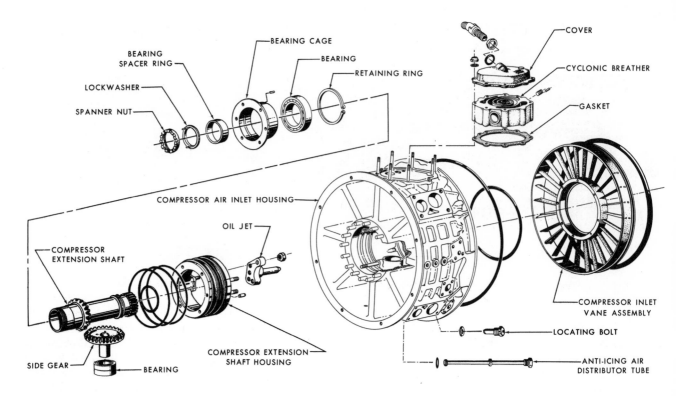

Figure 22·2   Compressor air inlet housing.

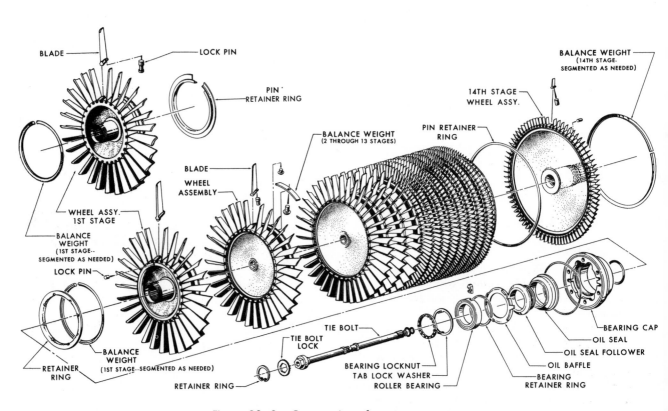

Figure 22·3   Construction of compressor rotor.

Figure 22·4 Inspector checking seal diameter of rotor.

to straighten airflow prior to its entering the combustion section. The compressor housing is ported around the circumference to provide for air bleed. Four bleed air valves are mounted on the outside of the compressor housing at the fifth stage and four at the tenth stage. Those valves at the fifth stage are manifolded together as are those at the tenth stage. These valves are used to unload the compressor during the start and acceleration or when operating at low-speed taxi idle.

The **compressor diffuser,** which is of welded-steel construction, is bolted to the flange at the aft end of the compressor housing assembly and forms the mid-structural member of the engine. One of three engine-to-aircraft mountings is located at this point. Six airfoil struts form passages which conduct compressed air

from the outlet of the fourteenth stage of the compressor to the forward end of the combustion liners. These struts also support the inner cone which provides the mounting for the rear compressor bearing, the seals, the rear compressor bearing oil nozzle, the diffuser scavenge oil pump, and the forward end of the inner combustion chamber. Air is extracted from ports on the diffuser for anti-icing and operation of the fifth- and tenth-stage bleed air valves. Bleed air is also extracted from this point by the airframe manufacturer for aircraft anti-icing, for cross-feeding from one engine to another for engine starter operation, and for operation of the oil cooler augmentor during ground operation. The six fuel nozzles are mounted on and extend into the diffuser. A fire shield is provided at the rear split line to protect the cooler portions of the engine from the high-temperature sections.

The combustion assembly

The combustion section of the 501-13 engine, illustrated in Fig. 22·5, consists of an outer and an inner combustion casing that form an annular chamber in which six **combustion liners** ("cans") are located. These liners are spaced evenly around the center axis of the engine and serve to contain the flame of the burning fuel. Fuel is sprayed continuously from a nozzle during operation into the forward end of each combustion liner. During the starting cycle, two igniter plugs, located in combustion liners 2 and 5, ignite the fuel/air mixture. All six liners are interconnected near their forward ends by **crossover tubes.** Thus, during the starting cycle after ignition has taken place in Nos. 2 and 5 combustion liners, the flame propagates to the

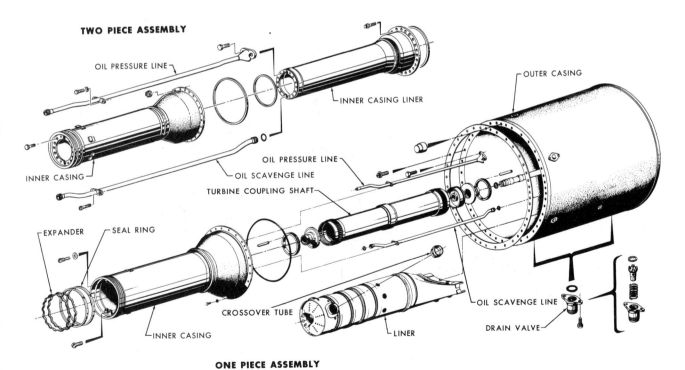

Figure 22·5 Combustion section.

remaining liners. Liners which do not utilize an igniter plug have at the same location a **liner support assembly** which positions the combustion liner and retains it axially. The outer combustion chamber casing provides the supporting structure between the diffuser and the turbine section. Mounted on the bottom of the outer combustion chamber casing are two combustion chamber drain valves which drain fuel after a false start and at engine shutdown.

Turbine unit assembly

The **turbine unit assembly** includes six major components. These are (1) **turbine inlet casing,** (2) **turbine rear bearing support,** (3) **turbine rotor,** (4) **turbine scavenge oil pumps,** (5) **turbine vane casing,** and (6) the **turbine vane assemblies.**

The turbine inlet casing is attached at its forward end to the outer and inner combustion chamber casings. It is designed to locate and house the forward turbine bearing, the seal assembly, front turbine oil jet, and the turbine front scavenge oil pump. The casing is divided into six equal passages by six air-foil struts. Each of these passages provides the means of locating and supporting the aft end of a combustion liner. Located around the outer casing are 18 holes with one thermocouple assembly mounted in each. Thus, three thermocouple assemblies are available at the outlet of each combustion liner. These 18 thermocouple assemblies are dual, and thus two complete and individual circuits are available. One is used to provide a temperature indication, referred to as turbine inlet temperature (TIT), to the cockpit, and the other is used to provide

a signal to the electronic fuel-trimming system. The circuits measure the average temperature of all 18 thermocouples, thus providing an accurate indication of the gas temperature entering the turbine at all times.

The **turbine rotor assembly,** shown in Fig. 22·6, consists of four turbine wheels which are splined on a turbine shaft. The entire assembly is supported by a roller bearing at the forward end and a roller bearing at the aft end. A turbine coupling shaft assembly connects the turbine rotor to the compressor rotor, thus transmitting the power extracted by the four-stage turbine assembly to the compressor, driven accessories, reduction-gear assembly, and the propeller. All four stages of blades are attached to the wheel rims in broached serrations of five-tooth fir-tree design. The first-stage turbine wheel has the smallest blade area, with each succeeding stage becoming larger.

The **turbine vane casing** encases the turbine rotor assembly and retains the four stages of turbine vane assemblies. It is the structural member for supporting the turbine rear bearing support. The vanes are airfoil design and serve two basic functions. They increase the gas velocity prior to each turbine wheel stage and also direct the flow of gases so that they will impinge upon the turbine blades at the most effective angle. Figure 22·7 shows the installation of vane assembly sections.

The **turbine rear bearing support** attaches to the aft end of the turbine vane casing. It houses the turbine rear bearing, the turbine rear scavenge oil pump and support, and the inner exhaust cone and insulation. It also forms the exhaust nozzle for the engine.

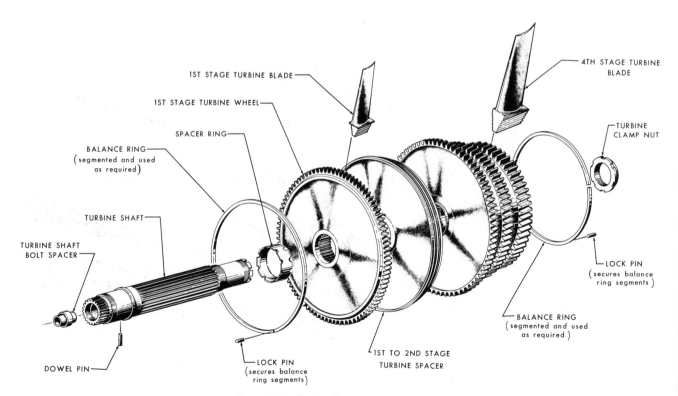

Figure 22·6   Turbine rotor assembly.

Figure **22·7** *Installing vanes in the turbine section.*

Accessories drive housing assembly

The **accessories drive housing assembly** is a magnesium-alloy casting mounted on the bottom of the compressor air inlet housing. It includes the necessary gear trains for driving all power section driven accessories at their proper rpm in relation to engine rpm. Power for driving the gear trains is taken from the

compressor extension shaft by a vertical shaftgear. The accessories driven through this assembly are the **speed-sensitive control**, **speed-sensitive valve**, **oil pump**, **fuel control**, and the **fuel pump**.

REDUCTION-GEAR ASSEMBLY

The principal function of the reduction-gear **assembly** is to provide a means of reducing power section rpm to the range of efficient propeller rpm. It also provides pads on the rear of the case for mounting the starter, cabin supercharger, alternator, tachometer generator, propeller alternator, hydraulic pump, d-c generator, and an oil pump.

The reduction gear has an independent lubrication system which includes a pressure pump and two scavenge pumps. The oil supply is furnished from the oil tank, which also supplies the main engine.

The reduction-gear assembly is remotely located from the power section, as illustrated in Fig. 22·1, and is attached to the power section by the torque-meter shaft and two tie struts. The remote location of the reduction-gear assembly offers the following advantages: (1) better air inlet ducting which increases engine efficiency and performance, (2) the opportunity of readily mounting the gearbox offset up or down for high- or low-wing aircraft, (3) the advantage of additional space for mounting driven accessories without affecting frontal area, (4) containing the engine in the minimum frontal area, and (5) the ability to utilize an electronic torquemeter.

The reduction-gear assembly, illustrated in Fig. 22·8, has an overall reduction-gear ratio of 13.54:1,

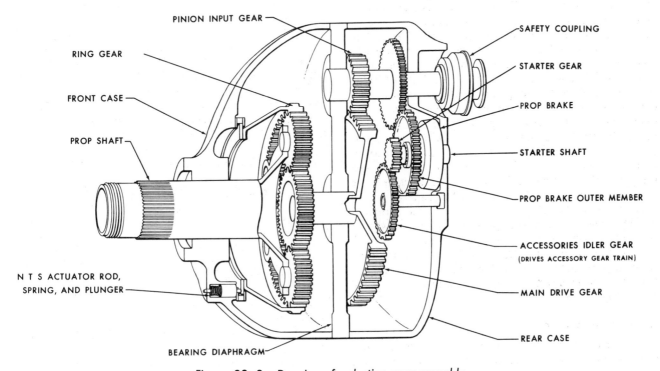

Figure **22·8** *Drawing of reduction-gear assembly.*

and this is accomplished through a two-stage step-down gear train. The primary step-down is accomplished by a spur gear train having a ratio of 3.125:1, and the secondary step-down is provided by a planetary gear train with a ratio of 4.333:1. The propeller shaft rotates in a clockwise direction when viewed from the rear of the engine. In addition to the reduction gears and accessories drives, the reduction-gear assembly includes four other major components. These are (1) the **propeller brake,** (2) the **negative torque signal** (NTS) system, (3) the **thrust-sensitive signal** (TSS), and (4) the **safety coupling.**

Propeller brake

The **propeller brake** is designed to prevent the propeller from windmilling when it is feathered in flight and to decrease the time for the propeller to come to a complete stop after ground shutdown. It is a friction-type brake consisting of a stationary inner member and a rotating outer member which, when locked, acts upon the primary stage reduction gearing. During normal engine operation reduction-gear oil pressure holds the brake in the released position. This is accomplished by oil pressure which holds the outer member away from the inner member. When the propeller is feathered or at engine shutdown, reduction-gear oil pressure drops off and the effective hydraulic pressure decreases, thus allowing a spring force to move the outer member into contact with the inner member.

Negative torque system

The **negative torque system** (NTS) was explained in the section describing the turbopropeller; however, a brief summary of the operation will be given here. As mentioned before, the NTS system is designed to prevent the aircraft from encountering excessive propeller drag when the air is driving the propeller. The system is a part of the reduction-gear assembly, is completely mechanical in design, and is automatic in operation. A negative torque value in the range of 250 to 370 hp, transmitted from the propeller to the reduction gear, causes the planetary ring gear to move forward and overcome a calibrated spring force. As the ring gear moves forward, it actuates two rods which move forward through openings in the reduction-gear front case. Only one rod is used to actuate the propeller NTS linkage. When actuated, the propeller increases blade angle until the abnormal propeller drag and resultant excessive negative torque are relieved. The propeller will never go to the feather position when actuated by the NTS system but will modulate through a small blade-angle range such that it will not absorb more than approximately 250 to 370 hp. As the negative torque is relieved, the propeller returns to normal governing.

Thrust-sensitive signal

The **thrust-sensitive signal** (TSS) provides for initiating automatic feathering at takeoff in case of engine failure. The system must be armed prior to takeoff if it is to function, and a blocking circuit is provided to prevent automatic feathering of more than one propeller. The system is armed by the **auto feather arming switch** and a power-lever-actuated switch. The setting of the power lever switch is such that, if operation is normal, the propeller will be developed considerably more than 500 lb positive thrust. This prevents auto feather except when engine failure occurs.

The system is designed to operate (if armed) when the propeller is delivering less than 500 lb positive thrust. The propeller shaft tends to move in a forward axial direction as the propeller produces positive thrust. Axial travel is limited by a mechanical stop applied to the ball thrust bearing outer race. When the propeller is producing normal thrust of more than 500 lb, a spring in front of the thrust bearing is compressed. When thrust decreases to below 500 lb, the spring can expand and move the thrust bearing forward. This movement is multiplied through mechanical linkage and transmitted mechanically to a pad on the left side of the reduction-gear front case. An electrical switch assembly mounted on the case energizes the feathering circuit.

Safety coupling

The **safety coupling** could readily be classified as a "backup" device for the NTS system. The coupling has a negative torque setting of approximately 1700 hp, and in the event that the NTS system or propeller fails to function properly, the coupling disengages the reduction gear from the power section. This results in a considerable reduction in drag. The safety coupling is located and attached to the forward end of the torquemeter shaft which transmits power from the engine to the reduction gear. During normal operation the safety coupling connects the torquemeter shaft to the reduction gear by helical splines, straight splines, and an intermediate member. When the negative torque is sufficient, the force developed by the helical splines moves the intermediate member against the force of five washerlike circular springs and permits the intermediate member to disengage its helical splines from the inner member. The splines remain disengaged with a ratcheting action until the negative torque is reduced and the splines can reengage.

TORQUEMETER ASSEMBLY AND TIE STRUTS

The torquemeter housing, illustrated in Fig. 22·9, provides alignment and two tie struts provide the necessary rigidity between the power section and the reduction-gear assembly. The tie struts are adjustable through two eccentric pins which are located at the reduction-gear end. These pins are splined to provide a positive locking method after proper alignment is established by the torquemeter housing. The torquemeter provides the means of accurately measuring shaft horsepower input into the reduction-gear assembly. It has an indicated accuracy of ±35 hp from 0 to

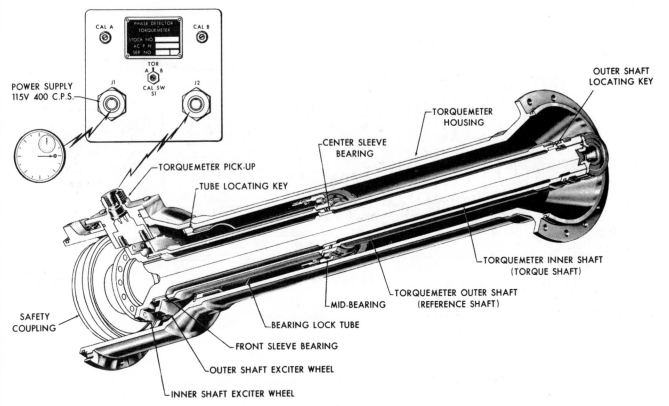

Figure 22·9 Diagram of torquemeter assembly.

maximum allowable power which represents ±1 percent actual horsepower at standard day static takeoff power. The torquemeter consists of the following major parts: (1) the **torquemeter inner shaft,** which is the torque shaft; (2) the **torquemeter outer shaft,** which is the reference shaft; (3) the **torquemeter pick-up assembly** consisting of a magnetic pickup; (4) the **torquemeter housing;** (5) the **phase detector;** and (6) the **indicator.**

The principal operation of the torquemeter is that of measuring electronically the angular deflection (twist) which occurs in the torque shaft relative to the zero reference shaft. The actual degree of angular deflection is sensed by the pickup assembly and transmitted to the phase detector. The phase detector converts the pickup signal into an electrical signal and directs it to the indicator located on the instrument panel.

The torquemeter functions because of the arrangement of the torque shaft, which twists in proportion to torque inside the reference shaft. The reference shaft is a tube surrounding and rigidly attached to the torque shaft at the power section end. At the reduction-gear end the reference tube is free to rotate outside the torque shaft, and a displacement of the magnetic pickup occurs to produce the torque signal. It can be seen from the diagram of Fig. 22·9 that a torque force applied at the power end of the shaft assembly will cause the torque shaft to twist. Since there is no torque on the reference shaft, the twist of the inner shaft will evidence itself as an angular displacement between the flanges at the drive end.

LUBRICATION SYSTEMS

The Model 501-D13 engine power section and reduction-gear assembly have separate and independent lubrication systems which utilize a common oil supply from the engine oil tank. This tank is designed and manufactured by the airplane manufacturer.

The engine manufacturer supplies the airframe manufacturer with information regarding the amount of oil flow required by the reduction-gear assembly and the power section and also the heat rejection from the reduction gear and the power section. The airframe manufacturer then designs an aircraft oil-supply system which will provide the required volume of oil flow and the necessary oil cooling. The airframe manufacturer also supplies the following indications in the cockpit: (1) power section oil pressure, (2) reduction-gear oil pressure, (3) oil inlet temperature, and (4) oil quantity.

Power section lubrication system

Figure 22·10 is a schematic diagram of the engine oil system in the power section. This system includes the following units with their locations as indicated:

1. **Main oil pump.** This includes the pressure pump, a scavenge pump, and the pressure-regulating valve, which is located on the forward side of the accessories drive housing assembly.
2. **Oil filter.** Located on the forward side of the accessories drive housing.

449

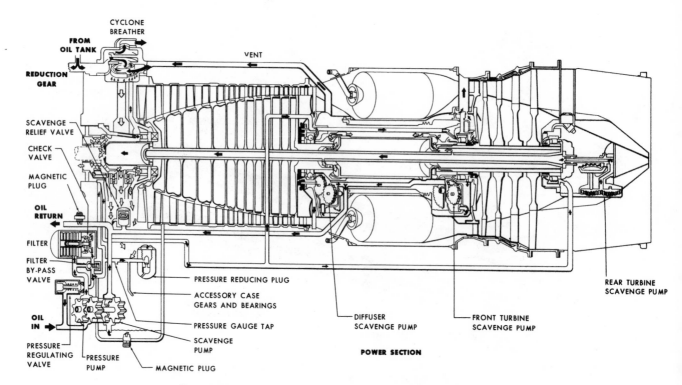

Figure **22·10** *Lubrication system for Allison 501-D13 engine.*

3. **Check valve.** Located in the oil-filter assembly.
4. **Bypass valve** (filter). Located in the accessories drive housing assembly.
5. **Three scavenge pumps.** Located in the diffuser, turbine inlet casing, and the turbine rear bearing support.
6. **Scavenge relief valve.** Located in the accessories drive housing assembly.
7. **Breather.** Located on top of the air inlet housing.

Oil is supplied from the aircraft tank to the inlet of the pressure pump whence it passes through the oil filter before being delivered to other parts of the engine. System pressure (filter outlet pressure) is regulated to 50 to 75 psi by the pressure-regulating valve. A bypass valve is incorporated in the system in the event that the filter becomes clogged sufficiently to restrict oil flow. A check valve prevents oil from seeping into the power section whenever the engine is not running.

The scavenge pump, which is incorporated in the main oil pump, and the three independent scavenge pumps are so located that they will scavenge oil from the power section in any normal attitude of flight. The scavenge pump located in the main oil pump scavenges oil from the accessories drive housing. The other three scavenge pumps scavenge oil from the diffuser and from the front and rear sides of the turbine. The outputs of the diffuser scavenge pump and the front turbine scavenge pumps join that of the main scavenge pump. The output of the rear turbine scavenge pump is delivered to the interior of the turbine-to-compressor tie bolt and the compressor rotor tie bolt. This oil is directed to the splines of the turbine coupling shaft assembly and to the splines of the compressor extension shaft. Thus, the output of the rear turbine scavenge

pump must be rescavenged by the other three scavenge pumps. A scavenge relief valve is located so that it will prevent excessive pressure build-up in the power section scavenge system. The combined flows of scavenged oil from the power section and reduction-gear scavenge systems must be cooled and returned to the supply tank. A magnetic plug is located on the bottom of the accessories drive housing, and another at the scavenge oil outlet on the forward side of the main oil pump assembly. The purpose of these plugs is to attract and hold steel particles which may be in the oil. If particles of appreciable size are found on the plugs at inspection, it is an indication of internal failure and requires that the engine be checked thoroughly to locate the source of the steel.

Reduction-gear lubrication system

The reduction-gear oil system is a dry sump system which feeds from the same oil-supply tank used for the power section system. The system includes the following items, with each of their respective locations as indicated:

1. **Pressure pump.** Located on the left rear side of the reduction gear.
2. **Filter.** Located in the pump body assembly.
3. **Filter bypass valve.** Located in the pump body assembly.
4. **Check valve.** Located in the pump body assembly.
5. Two **scavenge pumps.** One located in the bottom of the rear case and the other in the front case below the prop shaft.
6. Two **pressure-relief valves.** One for the pressure system and the other for the scavenge system. The scavenge relief valve is located in the common outlet of the scavenge pumps, and the other is in the rear case housing near the oil filter outlet.

450

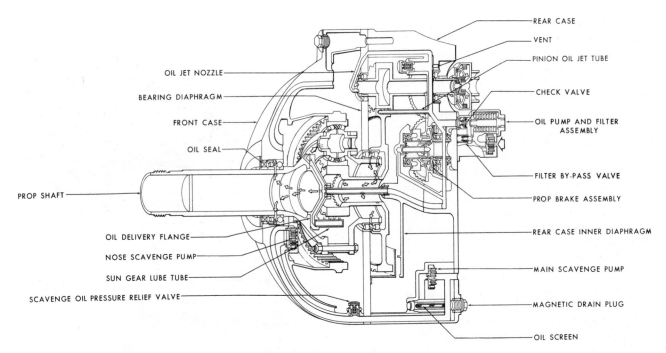

Figure **22·11**   *Reduction-gear oil system.*

The foregoing components of the reduction-gear oil system can be located in the diagram of Fig. 22·11. Oil flows from the pressure pump through a filter and to all parts within the reduction gear which require lubrication. In addition, oil pressure is used as hydraulic pressure for the operation of the propeller brake assembly. A filter bypass valve ensures continued oil flow in the event that the filter becomes clogged. A check valve prevents oil flow by gravity into the reduction gear after engine shutdown. A relief valve which is set at 180 psi to begin opening and to be fully open at 250 psi prevents excessive system pressure. This valve is not to be construed as being a regulating valve, since its only function is that of limiting pressure.

The location of the scavenge pumps provides for scavenging in any normal attitude of flight. The output of the two scavenge pumps returns the oil by a common outlet to the aircraft system. A relief valve, which is set at the same values as the one in the reduction-gear pressure system, limits the maximum scavenge pressure. A magnetic plug is installed on the bottom rear of the reduction-gear assembly to provide a means for draining the case and to detect possible failure in the gear system.

AIR BLEED-OFF SYSTEMS

The Allison Model 501-D13 engine is provided with two air bleed systems, one for use in anti-icing and the other to reduce the compressor load during reduced speed operations. These have been mentioned previously; however, a more detailed description is given here.

Anti-icing system

The **anti-icing system** consists of necessary lines and valves to permit heated compressor air to flow through the air inlet units requiring heat for anti-icing. The system is manually controlled and is turned on by means of a switch in the cockpit. When the switch is turned on, the **anti-icing solenoid** is deenergized to cause anti-icing airflow to the inlet-anti-icing vane assembly, the compressor air inlet housing struts, the fuel-control temperature probe deicer, and the upper half of the torquemeter housing shroud. Note that the solenoid is **deenergized** when anti-icing air is on. The purpose of this arrangement is to provide a "fail-safe" system. In case 24-volt d-c power fails, the anti-icing system will operate to furnish protection even though it may not be needed.

Acceleration bleed system

The **acceleration bleed system** is also called the fifth- and tenth-stage bleed air system because the system bleeds air from the fifth and tenth stages of the compressor during engine start and acceleration and at low-speed taxi. The system unloads the compressor from 0 to 13,000 rpm in order to prevent engine stall and surge. It includes four pneumatically operated bleed air valves located at the fifth stage and four located at the tenth stage, a speed-sensitive valve mounted on the forward side of the accessories housing assembly, and the necessary manifolding and plumbing. The bleed air valves at the fifth stage are manifolded together with the outlet being provided through the nacelle forward of the engine spray baffle assembly. The tenth-stage bleed air valves empty into another manifold, which is ducted to the aft side of the engine spray baffle assembly. The speed-sensitive valve is a flyweight type which responds to engine rpm. When the engine is running at less than 13,000 rpm, the valve is so positioned that all bleed air valve piston heads are vented to the atmosphere. This allows the compressor fifth- and tenth-stage pressures to move the pistons to their open position, thus bleeding air overboard. When the engine is running at 13,000 rpm or more, the speed-sensitive valve directs fourteenth-stage air to the bleed valve piston heads. Since fourteenth-stage pressure is always greater than fifth- or tenth-stage pressures, the bleed air valve pistons move to the closed position, thus preventing air bleed from the fifth and tenth stages. During low-speed taxi operation the fifth- and tenth-stage bleed air valves will be in the open position because engine rpm at this time is below 13,000.

SPEED-SENSITIVE CONTROL

The **speed-sensitive control,** shown in Fig. 22·12, is a flyweight-type unit used to actuate three microswitches which control certain engine functions at predetermined speeds. The control is mounted on the forward side of the accessories drive housing assembly and is driven from the accessory gear train. The control actuates the microswitches to provide for the following actions to take place at 2200, 9000, and 13,000 rpm.

At 2200 rpm

1. The fuel-control cutoff-valve actuator opens the cutoff valve at the outlet of the fuel control to provide fuel for starting the engine.
2. Ignition is turned on.
3. The drip valve is energized to the closed position.
4. The fuel-pump paralleling valve is closed to place the fuel pumps in parallel. The engine fuel-pump light should go on to show operation of the secondary pump.
5. The primer valve opens if the primer button is held in the ON position.

At 9000 rpm

1. The ignition turns off.
2. The drip valve is deenergized but remains closed because of fuel pressure.
3. The paralleling valve opens and places the fuel pumps in series.

At 13,000 rpm

1. The electronic fuel-trimming system is changed from temperature limiting with a maximum temperature of 830°C to temperature limiting with a maximum temperature of 978°C (1792°F).
2. The maximum possible "take" of fuel by the temperature datum valve is reset to 20 percent rather than the previous 50 percent.

IGNITION SYSTEM

The Model 501-D13 engine utilizes a Bendix TCN-24 high-energy ignition system of the capacitor discharge type and operates on 14 to 30 volts d-c input. The operation of these systems has been described previously for other gas-turbine engines. The system includes an exciter and an ignition relay which are

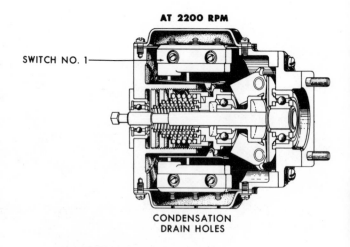

SWITCH NO. 1 — AT 2200 RPM

CONDENSATION DRAIN HOLES

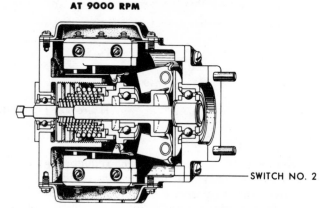

AT 9000 RPM

SWITCH NO. 2

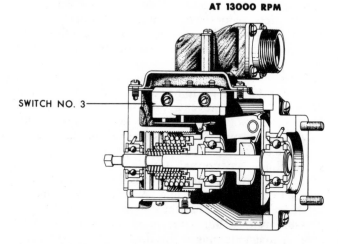

AT 13000 RPM

SWITCH NO. 3

Figure 22·12   Speed-sensitive control.

mounted on the top of the compressor housing, the lead assemblies, and two igniter plugs. The complete system consists of two identical circuits, one for each of the two igniter plugs. During the starting cycle as rpm reaches 2200, the speed-sensitive control automatically completes an electrical circuit to the ignition relay. This closes the circuit to the exciter, thus providing electrical energy to the igniter plugs. When engine rpm reaches 9000, the ignition circuits are deenergized through the action of the speed-sensitive control. Operation of the ignition system requires that the fuel and ignition switch in the cockpit be in the ON position.

THE FUEL SYSTEM

The fuel system for the Model 501-D13 engine includes all the units illustrated in Fig. 22·13 together with associated components. The principal units of the system will be described in this section.

The engine operates on gas-turbine kerosene conforming to Allison Specification EMS-64A or JP4 (MIL-F-5624a), which is similar in characteristics.

The fuel system must deliver metered fuel to the six fuel nozzles of the engine as required to meet all possible conditions of engine operation either on the ground or in flight. This imposes a number of requirements on the fuel system and its controlling units. Some of these requirements are as follows:

1. The capability of starting under all ambient conditions.
2. Adjustment for rapid changes in power.
3. A means of limiting the maximum allowable turbine inlet temperature (TIT).
4. A system which will enable the operator to select a desired power setting (determined by TIT) and have it automatically maintained regardless of altitude, free air temperature, forward speed, and fuel Btu content.
5. A system which incorporates an rpm-limiting device in the event of propeller governor malfunction.
6. A system which must control fuel flow during the rpm range in which the engine compressor is susceptible to stall and surge.

7. A system which coordinates propeller blade angle with fuel flow during ground operation.
8. A system which is capable of operating, if necessary, on the hydromechanical fuel control. However, if this is necessary, closer monitoring of power lever and engine instruments will be necessary.

Fuel pump and low-pressure fuel filter

Fuel from the aircraft fuel system is supplied to the engine fuel pump where it enters into a boost element and is then directed to the **low-pressure filter.** This filter is a paper-cartridge type incorporating two bypass valves (relief valves) which open in the event that the filter becomes clogged from fuel contamination. The paper cartridge is of the type that must be replaced at certain specified inspection intervals.

The fuel-pump assembly includes, in addition to the boost element, two spur-gear-type high-pressure pumps. These are commonly referred to as the **primary** and **secondary** elements. During normal operation these pumps are in series. However, during engine starting (2200 to 9000 rpm) the pumps are placed in parallel by the action of a paralleling valve in the high-pressure filter. The paralleling of the pumps is used to increase the fuel flow during low rpm. Failure of either the primary or secondary pump will not affect normal operation because either pump has sufficient capacity of fuel flow for takeoff power.

High-pressure fuel filter

The **high-pressure fuel filter** assembly consists of two check valves, a paralleling valve, a fuel filter, a pressure

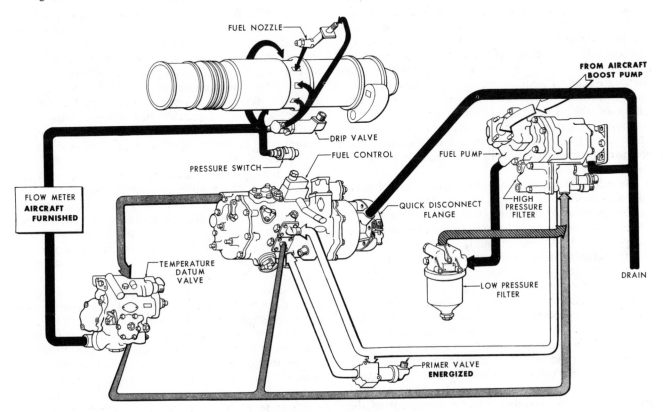

Figure **22·13** *Fuel system.*

switch, and a bypass valve. The high-pressure fuel filter accomplishes six principal functions: (1) It filters the output of the primary and secondary pumps, (2) connects the two pumps in parallel during the starting cycle, (3) connects the two pumps in series during normal operation with the primary pump supplying high-pressure fuel flow to the power section, (4) automatically enables the secondary pump to "take over" upon failure of the primary pump, (5) provides a means of checking primary and secondary pump operation during the starting procedure, and (6) provides a means of indicating primary pump failure with the engine fuel-pump light.

Fuel-control unit

The fuel control for the Allison Model 501-D13 engine is a Bendix AP-B3 hydromechanical unit which senses air density, acceleration, rpm, TIT, and power lever position and schedules fuel accordingly to provide proper operation without surge, stall, excessive temperatures, etc. It supplies a controlled fuel flow for starting and maintains a proper rate of flow for acceleration. The control actually schedules 20 percent more fuel than is normally required for engine operation in order to provide the temperature datum control with fuel for trim purposes. The operation of the temperature datum valve will be described later.

As shown in the diagram of Fig. 22 · 14, fuel enters the control through the **bypass valve** assembly which bypasses the excess fuel delivered to the control and establishes a pressure differential of fuel-pump discharge pressure P_1 minus metered fuel pressure P_2 across the metering valve. This differential ($P_1 - P_2$) remains practically constant during all operation. The position of the bypass valve is determined by the differential forces acting on the flexible diaphragm of the valve. When the bypass valve is stablized, the opening force of P_1 equals the closing force of P_2 plus the spring force. Therefore $P_1 - P_2$ = spring force. The length of the spring is a function of bypass valve position, and spring force is a function of spring length. Thus, when the bypass valve moves to assume a new position, the spring length will vary, causing the spring force to change slightly.

The **relief valve** establishes the maximum fuel pressure within the fuel control and thus establishes the maximum possible fuel flow from the fuel control. It is set to open when P_1 exceeds P_0 (low-pressure filtered fuel pressure) by a preset amount.

The **metering valve** meters all fuel flow to the temperature datum valve in accordance with variations in engine rpm, power lever setting, and compressor air inlet temperature and pressure. The metering valve also provides protection from overspeed by reducing the fuel flow when a certain overspeed rpm is exceeded. The size of the metering valve orifice may be changed by either rotation or linear movement of the valve. Rotation of the valve is caused by changes in compressor air inlet pressure applied through the **inlet pressure actuator assembly.** Linear movement of the valve is caused by changes in rpm, power lever settings, and compressor air inlet temperature.

The metering valve linear opening force is a spring. The **cam assembly** establishes the linear position and hence the size of the metering orifice during normal operation. The **governor spring** force is established by the governor setting lever, which is controlled either by a cam and cam follower positioned by the throttle or by the solenoid-operated governor reset mechanism. When the solenoid is energized, the governor reset mechanism positions the **governor setting lever** so that the governor spring is set for $10,000 + 300 - 100$ rpm low-speed taxi operation. When the solenoid of the governor reset solenoid assembly is deenergized, the reset mechanism positions the **governor setting lever** so the governor spring is set for the overspeed rpm of the taxi and flight ranges. The solenoid is controlled by the cockpit low-speed taxi switch.

The force of the governor weights serves as a closing force for the metering valve. During low-speed taxi operation, the linear position of the metering valve is established by a balance of two forces, the governor spring force and the governor weight force. The cam assembly does not position the metering valve in low-speed taxi operation. During high-speed taxi and flight operation, the governor spring force is greater than the governor weight force. Thus, the governor spring tends to move the metering valve fully open. However, the maximum linear opening of the metering valve will be established by the cam assembly. In the event of overspeeding, the governor weight force increases with rpm. When governor weight force overcomes the governor spring force, the metering valve moves to decrease its linear opening and reduces fuel flow from the fuel control. This limits engine speed at a definite speed above 13,820 rpm, the rpm for which the propeller is set. During an overspeed condition the cam assembly has no control over the linear position of the metering valve because the governor weight force moves the metering valve away from the cam assembly. When the overspeed is corrected, the governor weight force decreases and the governor spring begins to move the metering valve open. Then the cam assembly again determines the maximum linear opening of the metering valve.

The **inlet pressure actuator** assembly senses compressor air inlet pressure changes by means of a pressure probe in the left horizontal air inlet housing strut. The inlet pressure actuator initiates an action which causes the metering valve to rotate and provide a corrected fuel flow required by any air-pressure variation. A partially evacuated bellows, sensitive to pressure changes, repositions the pressure actuator servo valve by means of a lever action whenever compressor air inlet pressure changes. The position of the pressure actuator servo valve establishes servo pressure P_x', which, in turn, establishes the position of the pressure piston and the pressure actuator rack. When the air pressure changes, the pressure actuator servo valve causes P_x' to change. This moves the pressure piston and pressure actuator rack and results in the pressure actuator servo being moved to a stabilized position. When the pressure actuator rack moves, the metering valve drive gear causes the metering valve to rotate by

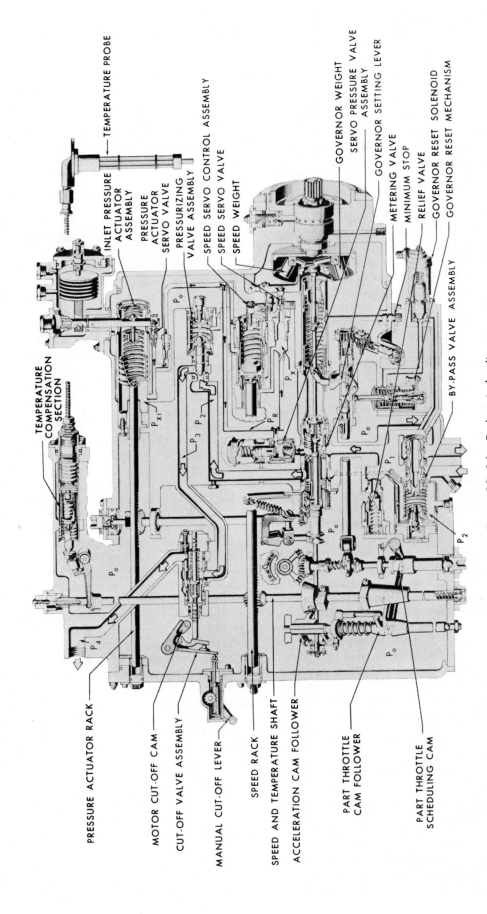

TEMPERATURE PROBE

INLET PRESSURE ACTUATOR ASSEMBLY

PRESSURE ACTUATOR SERVO VALVE

PRESSURIZING VALVE ASSEMBLY

SPEED SERVO CONTROL ASSEMBLY

SPEED SERVO VALVE

SPEED WEIGHT

GOVERNOR WEIGHT

SERVO PRESSURE VALVE ASSEMBLY

GOVERNOR SETTING LEVER

METERING VALVE

MINIMUM STOP

RELIEF VALVE

GOVERNOR RESET SOLENOID

GOVERNOR RESET MECHANISM

BY-PASS VALVE ASSEMBLY

TEMPERATURE COMPENSATION SECTION

PRESSURE ACTUATOR RACK

MOTOR CUT-OFF CAM

CUT-OFF VALVE ASSEMBLY

MANUAL CUT-OFF LEVER

SPEED RACK

SPEED AND TEMPERATURE SHAFT

ACCELERATION CAM FOLLOWER

PART THROTTLE CAM FOLLOWER

PART THROTTLE SCHEDULING CAM

P_o P_R P_X P_{X1} P_3 P_2 P_1 P_4

Figure 22·14 Fuel-control unit.

455

means of a bevel gear. Any change in air pressure results in the rotational movement of the metering valve.

The speed servo control assembly senses rpm changes and initiates an action which causes the metering valve to move linearly and monitor fuel flow to prevent compressor surges during engine accelerations. The position of the speed servo valve establishes servo pressure P_x, which, in turn, establishes the position of a speed piston and speed rack. When rpm increases, the speed weights actuate linkage to move the speed servo valve toward a closed position, causing P_x to increase. Thus, the speed piston moves the speed rack and linkage to stabilize the speed servo valve. Movement of the speed rack rotates the **speed and temperature shaft,** which has two cams, an **acceleration cam** and a **part-throttle cam.** Each of these cams has a follower called, respectively, the **acceleration cam follower** and the **part-throttle cam follower.** The acceleration and part-throttle cams are designed so that, during rpm changes, the acceleration cam positions the acceleration cam follower and, when there is no rpm change, the part-throttle cam positions the part-throttle cam follower, its shaft, and the acceleration cam follower. The position of the acceleration cam follower establishes the linear position of the metering valve and thus the flow of metered fuel from the fuel control. Any change in rpm results in linear movement of the metering valve.

The temperature-compensation section senses compressor air inlet temperature changes by means of a probe inserted through the air inlet housing beneath the left horizontal strut. The **temperature-compensation section** initiates an action which causes the metering valve to move linearly to provide a corrected fuel flow required by any air-temperature variation. The action can be followed on the diagram of Fig. 22·14.

The **temperature probe** and a bellows are filled with alcohol, and any change in air temperature causes the volume of the alcohol to change. Thus the length of the bellows is dependent upon the sensed air temperature. When air temperature changes, the temperature-compensation section causes the **speed and temperature shaft,** with the two cams, to move linearly. Either the acceleration or the part-throttle cam, whichever is in control of the acceleration cam follower at the time of the air-temperature change, will reposition the acceleration cam follower. This causes the metering valve to move linearly to provide a corrected fuel flow. The corrected fuel flow is such that, as air temperature increases, fuel flow is decreased. A return spring always retains the speed and temperature shaft in contact with the bellcrank of the temperature-compensation section. Another bellows in this section is used to prevent any change in P_0 fuel temperature or pressure from moving the speed and temperature shaft. The fuel control compensates for variations only in air temperature and never for fuel-temperature changes.

The **part-throttle scheduling cam** is positioned by the power lever, and when the power lever is moved, the part-throttle scheduling cam moves its followers.

The power lever gears can be seen in the diagram at the upper end of the part-throttle scheduling cam shaft just below the **speed rack.** The part-throttle scheduling cam follower moves the part-throttle cam follower linearly on its shaft. This changes the relative position of the part-throttle cam. The control of the part-throttle cam causes the part-throttle cam follower to pivot slightly. The shaft of the part-throttle cam follower then moves the acceleration cam follower. The acceleration cam follower moves the metering valve linearly to schedule fuel flow as required by the power lever movement.

The **servo pressure valve assembly** establishes and maintains the regulated servo pressure P_R at a predetermined value above P_0. P_R is used by the **inlet pressure actuator assembly** and the **speed servo control assembly,** along with servo valves to establish P_x and P_x' required by the assemblies. The position of the servo pressure valve is determined by P_R, the closing force, and P_0 plus a spring force, the opening force. The **pressurizing valve** causes metered pressure P_2 to build up to a predetermined value before it opens to allow metered fuel pressure P_3 to flow to the cutoff valve assembly. This causes P_1 to build up before fuel can flow from the fuel control and results in quicker stabilization of the fuel-control components during the initial phases of an engine start. The pressurizing valve is not designed to have any metering effect on the fuel, but there is a small decrease in pressure across the pressurizing valve. This is the reason for indicating a P_2 and P_3 metered fuel pressure. The opening force on the pressurizing valve is P_2, and the closing force is P_0 plus spring force.

The **cutoff valve assembly** provides the means by which fuel flow to the engine is started or stopped. Electrical actuation of the cutoff valve is desirable for automatic engine starts and normal shutdowns. Since the possibility of an electrical failure exists, mechanical actuation of the cutoff valve is required for emergency shutdowns. Therefore the cutoff valve may be moved to the closed position, either electrically or mechanically. The cutoff valve must be permitted to open both electrically and mechanically during the engine start. The only time the cutoff valve will be mechanically held closed is when the emergency shutdown handle is pulled to the **emergency** position. Pulling the emergency handle causes the normal cutoff lever to move so that a bellcrank and lever move a plunger to compress a spring within the cutoff valve. When the force of this spring exceeds the force of an opposing spring, the cutoff valve moves against its seat to stop fuel flow. Energizing the cutoff-valve actuator motor causes the cutoff cam to move the bellcrank, lever, and plunger to compress the spring and close the valve. When the cutoff valve is closed, P_3 is ported to P_0. The cutoff valve is not designed to have any metering action, but a small decrease in pressure does occur across the valve. This is the reason for indicating a P_3 and P_4 metered pressure.

Engine lubricating oil is used to lubricate the drive bearings of the fuel control. This oil is supplied and scavenged by the lubricating system of the power section. Internal components of the fuel control are lubricated by the fuel which flows through the fuel control.

Primer valve and manifold switch

The fuel primer system includes a primer valve which is solenoid actuated, a manifold pressure switch, and necessary aircraft wiring and primer button. This system may be used during the starting cycle if desired to provide an increased initial fuel flow. This is accomplished by permitting fuel to flow through the primer valve, bypassing the metering section of the fuel control and entering prior to the fuel-control cutoff valve. An electrical interlock in the control system prevents energizing of the primer system after the engine is started.

Coordinator

The **coordinator** has been discussed previously in connection with the propeller. However, we shall discuss it here as a part of the engine fuel-control system because it coordinates the fuel control, propeller, and the electronic fuel-trimming systems. The operation of the coordinator is controlled by mechanical linkage from the flight deck, normally through the power lever and for special conditions by the emergency shutdown handle.

The coordinator includes a discriminating device, microswitch assembly, a temperature datum control scheduling potentiometer, and the necessary gears and electrical wiring. Power lever movement controls the main shaft of the coordinator, which, in turn, controls the following:

1. Amount of fuel flowing from the fuel control.
2. Propeller blade angle during all ground operations.
3. Scheduling of TIT.
4. Microswitch assembly which transfers the electronic fuel-trimming system from temperature limiting to temperature control and arms the temperature trim switch which permits locking of the temperature datum valve brake. This enables the operator to "lock in" a fuel correction with any power setting above 65°.
5. Propeller beta follow-up mechanism from 68 to 90°.
6. NTS system blockout below 21°.

The discriminating device permits the use of the same mechanical linkage between the coordinator and the propeller for power lever or emergency shutdown handle operation. The discriminator allows the power lever to position the propeller linkage at all times other than emergency shutdown. When the emergency shutdown handle is pulled, the propeller linkage will always be actuated to feather by means of the discriminator regardless of power lever setting.

Electronic fuel-trimming system

The principal units which actuate the **electronic fuel-trimming system** are the **temperature datum valve, temperature datum control, thermocouples, coordinator, speed-sensitive control,** and the **power lever.**

The principal function of the electronic fuel-trim system is to permit the engine to operate at near maximum temperature without danger of overtemperature conditions developing. The engine may operate on several different fuels without making special adjustments of the fuel control because the system makes the adjustments automatically. The system is enabled to carry out its function because an excess of 20 percent is scheduled through the temperature datum valve by the fuel control and the datum valve utilizes this fuel margin to add to the fuel flow if necessary or to take additional fuel from the fuel line to the engine fuel nozzles. The temperature datum valve normally bypasses 20 percent of the fuel passing through it when no adjustment is required; hence the correct amount of fuel flows to the fuel nozzles. However, if additional fuel is required, the temperature datum valve bypasses less than 20 percent of the fuel, thus putting additional fuel into the engine. This is a "put" situation. If the engine needs a smaller amount of fuel than the normal amount, the datum valve "takes" fuel from the system by bypassing more than 20 percent.

When the system is operating in the **temperature-limiting** condition, the power lever is between 0 and 65° of coordinator quadrant travel. At this time the temperature datum valve and the temperature datum control, in coordination with other control units, limit TIT to either 830 or 978°C, depending upon engine speed and position of air-bleed valves.

When the power lever is above 65° (coordinator quadrant), the system operates by **temperature control;** that is, the power lever may be used to schedule a desired turbine inlet temperature. Temperature control requires an rpm in excess of 13,000 with the temperature trim switch in the controlled position. If it is desired, a "locked-in" fuel correction may be used above the 65° setting of the power lever, and in this case the electronic fuel-trimming system operates by **temperature limiting.**

In order for the electronic fuel-trimming system to function, the temperature datum control must receive a temperature signal and a reference signal. The temperature signal always comes from the 18 thermocouples at the turbine inlet. The reference signal can be from one of three sources: (1) **start** (830°C) from a potentiometer in the temperature datum control, (2) **normal** (978°C) from a potentiometer in the temperature datum control, or (3) from a variable potentiometer in the coordinator (approximately 760 to 971° TIT). The third of these signals is developed when the power lever is at 65 to 90° on the coordinator quadrant during temperature-control operation. The variable potentiometer in the coordinator is positioned by movement of the power lever on the flight deck. When the temperature signal (from the thermocouples) is less than the reference signal, the temperature datum control sends no signal to the temperature datum valve. Hence the valve remains in the "null" position and bypasses 20 percent of the fuel. If the temperature signal is greater than the reference signal, the temperature datum control sends a signal to the temperature datum valve to "take" fuel; that is, it bypasses more than 20 percent of the fuel scheduled.

457

During temperature-control operation, if the temperature signal exceeds the reference signal from the coordinator potentiometer, the temperature datum control sends a signal to the temperature datum valve to "take" fuel. If the signal is less than the reference signal, the temperature datum control sends a "put" signal to the temperature datum valve and less than 20 percent of the fuel is bypassed.

Temperature datum valve

The **temperature datum valve** is an electrically operated fuel-trimming device. It is located in the fuel system so that all the fuel flowing from the fuel control to the nozzles must pass through it. The valve operates on a-c power fed from the temperature datum control. Fuel in excess of that required by the engine is bypassed and returned with excess fuel from the fuel control to the inlet of the primary and secondary fuel pumps. To provide for the "put" and "take" of fuel, a solenoid-operated control valve is incorporated in the temperature datum valve. The solenoid is energized by 24 volts direct current through the speed-sensitive control when the engine is operating in the 0- 13,000-rpm range. At 13,000 rpm, the solenoid is deenergized, and this resets the "take" stop to 20 percent of the nominal fuel-flow requirements. A solenoid-operated brake is also included in the temperature datum to hold the valve in the locked position, that is, when the pilot has set the system for a fixed fuel correction. This is when the trim switch is placed in the locked position and the power lever is in the range of 65 to 90°. In the event that an overtemperature condition occurs while the switch is in the locked position, the control system automatically unlocks the brake and the valve bypasses more fuel in order to prevent overtemperature.

Temperature datum control

The **temperature datum control** is an electronic control operated on 115-volt 400-cycle alternating current. The control may be considered as a comparator in that it compares actual with desired or limited turbine inlet temperature signals. If an out-of-balance condition exists, the control signals the temperature datum valve to increase ("put") or decrease ("take") fuel flow as required to bring the temperature back to that which is scheduled. Operation of the temperature datum control requires having the engine temperature datum control switch in the normal position.

The temperature datum control contains four potentiometers, the necessary electrical wiring, and four external adjustments. The external adjustments are referred to as the "bias," "slope," "start limiting," and "normal limiting." The bias and slope adjust the temperature schedule for engine operation between 65 and 90° (coordinator quadrant), which is known as the control range. The other two adjust the start limiting temperature and the normal limiting temperature.

Thermocouples

There is a total of 18 dual thermocouples installed around the **turbine inlet casing** to sense the temperature of the gases entering the turbine nozzle (TIT). These thermocouples form two individual circuits, one providing TIT to the flight deck instrument and the other providing temperature indication to the temperature datum control. The temperature indication is an average signal from all 18 thermocouples.

Fuel nozzles

The fuel nozzles are of the duplex type as shown in Fig. 22·15. The six nozzles are mounted in the diffuser section of the engine and are so mounted that each nozzle end extends into the forward end of one of the combustion liners. The fuel nozzle provides a controlled pattern of fuel flow and also a maximum degree of atomization. At the tip of the nozzle an air shroud surrounds the dual orifice. The air shroud contains a number of air holes through which air is circulated at high velocity to prevent the formation of carbon around the orifices.

Drip valve

The **drip valve** is located at the lowest point in the fuel manifold. It is designed to drain the manifold at engine shutdown, thus preventing fuel from draining into the combustion liners after the fuel-control cutoff valve is closed. The drip valve is a solenoid-operated valve which is closed by completion of the electrical circuit through the 2200-rpm switch in the speed-sensitive control. At 9000 rpm the electrical circuit is broken and fuel manifold pressure acting upon the valve continues to hold it in the closed position. At engine shutdown, when fuel manifold pressure drops to a value of 8 to 10 psi, the valve opens because of spring force.

Drain valves

There are two drain valves installed in the engine, one at the forward end on the bottom of the outer combustion chamber and one at the rear end. These valves are set at 2 to 4 psi air pressure and are held closed by combustion chamber pressure during all engine operations. At engine shutdown the valves open and thus prevent an accumulation of fuel in the outer combustion chamber after a false start or after engine shutdown. If fuel were to remain in the combustion area, serious damage would probably be inflicted on the engine when the next start was made.

THE ROLLS-ROYCE DART TURBOPROP ENGINE

General description

The Rolls-Royce Dart engine has been in use for many years on a variety of aircraft including the Vickers Viscount and the Fairchild F-27 Friendship. The engine has proved to be rugged, dependable, and economical with overhaul periods extending to more than 2000 hr.

The Dart engine utilizes a single-entry two-stage centrifugal compressor, a can-type through-flow com-

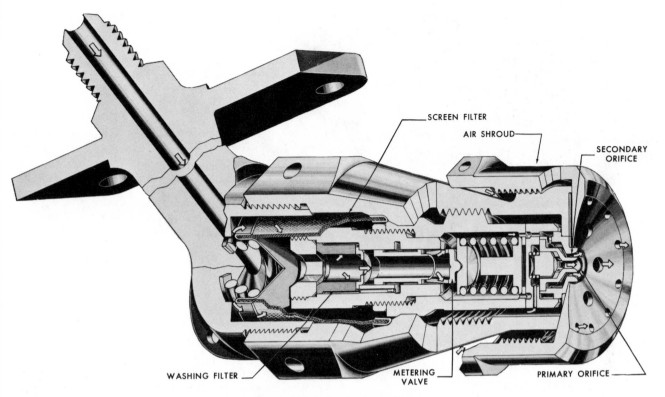

SCREEN FILTER

AIR SHROUD

SECONDARY
ORIFICE

WASHING FILTER

METERING
VALVE

PRIMARY ORIFICE

Figure **22·15** *Fuel nozzle.*

bustion section, and a three-stage turbine. The general design of the engine can be seen in the drawing of Fig. 22·16. This drawing shows the arrangement of the propeller, reduction gear, air inlet, compressor impellers, combustion chambers, turbine, and exhaust.

An external view of the Dart engine is shown in Fig. 22·17. This view shows the propeller shaft, air intake casing, oil cooler, compressor casings, combustion chambers, turbine casing, and exhaust unit. The engine is approximately 45 in. in diameter and 98 in. in length.

Engine data

The general data and performance for the Dart Model 528 engine are as follows:

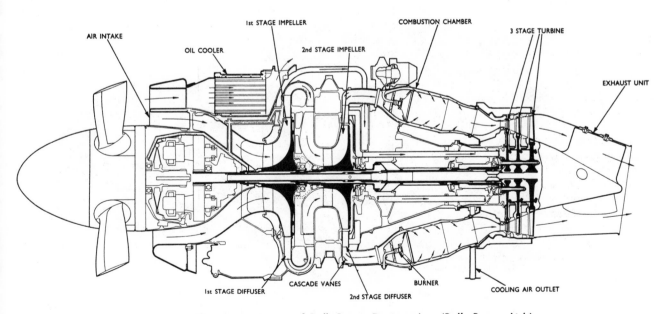

AIR INTAKE

OIL COOLER

1st STAGE IMPELLER

2nd STAGE IMPELLER

COMBUSTION CHAMBER

3 STAGE TURBINE

EXHAUST UNIT

1st STAGE DIFFUSER

CASCADE VANES

2nd STAGE DIFFUSER

BURNER

COOLING AIR OUTLET

Figure **22·16** *Arrangement of Rolls-Royce Dart engine. (Rolls Royce, Ltd.)*

Figure 22·17   External view of Dart engine.

Power output	1835 shp plus 485 lbt
Compression ratio	5.62:1
Engine rpm	15,000
Weight (without propeller)	1415 lb
SFC	0.57 lb/ehp/hr
Power/weight ratio	1.51 ehp/lb

Internal features

The cutaway photograph of the Dart engine shown in Fig. 22·18 reveals the internal construction of the engine. At the forward end is the **reduction-gear assembly** which reduces the propeller shaft speed to 0.093 of the speed of the engine. The reduction-gear housing is integral with the **air intake casing.**

Immediately to the rear of the reduction-gear assembly is the compressor section, which includes two centrifugal impellers. Both impellers are clearly visible in the illustration. Accessory drives are taken from the reduction-gear assembly and through a train of gears aft of the second-stage compressor impeller.

Seven interconnected **combustion chambers** are located between the compressor section and the turbine. These combustion chambers are skewed or arranged in a spiral configuration to shorten the engine and take advantage of the direction of airflow as it leaves the compressor.

A **three-stage turbine** is located to the rear of the combustion chambers. As in other turboprop engines, this turbine is designed to extract as much energy as possible from the high-velocity exhaust gases.

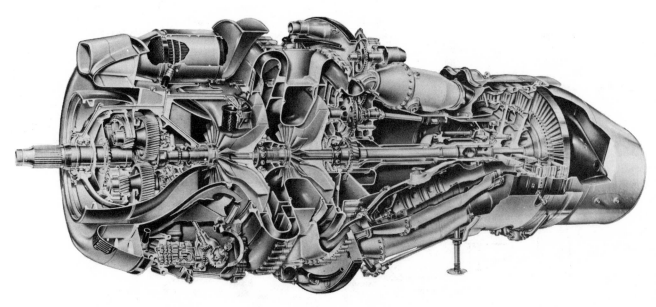

Figure 22·18   Cutaway view of the Dart engine. (Rolls Royce, Ltd.)

Reduction-gear assembly

The **reduction-gear assembly** shown in Fig. 22·19 is of the compound type having high-speed and low-speed trains. The high-speed train consists of a high-speed pinion connected to the main shaft and driving three layshafts through helical gear teeth. To isolate the main shaft couplings from propeller vibrations, a torsionally flexible shaft is used to couple the high-speed pinion to the main shaft. The three layshafts are mounted in roller bearings supported by panels in the gear casing.

The **low-speed gear train** consists of helical gears formed on the front end of the layshafts which drive the internal helically toothed **annulus gear.** This annulus gear is bolted to the propeller shaft driving disk. As a result of driving through the helical gears, the layshafts tend to move axially. This movement is limited by limit shafts mounted coaxially within the layshafts. Each limit shaft is prevented from moving by a ball thrust race at the rear.

The **propeller shaft** is supported by roller bearings housed in the front panel and the domed front casing. Axial thrust is taken on a ball bearing mounted behind the front roller bearing. A labyrinth-type seal assembly, pressurized by compressed air, surrounds the propeller shaft where it passes through the front cover and prevents loss of lubricating oil to the atmosphere.

To permit propeller oil to be transferred from the stationary casing to the rotating propeller shaft, a transfer seal assembly is used. It consists of babbitt lined with bronze bushings fitting closely around an adapter located inside the rear end of the propeller shaft. Tubes screw into the adapter and convey the oil to the pitch-control mechanism.

Torquemeter

Under normal operating conditions, the helical teeth of the gear train produce a forward thrust in each layshaft which is proportional to the propeller shaft torque. This load is hydraulically balanced by oil pressure acting on a piston assembly incorporated in the forward end of each layshaft. The necessary oil pressure is obtained by boosting engine oil pressure with a gear pump mounted on the layshaft front bearing housing and driven from a gear attached to the propeller shaft.

The forward thrust of the layshafts resulting from the greater torque of the low-speed gear train is partially balanced by the rearward thrust produced by the lesser torque of the high-speed gear train. The residual forward thrust is balanced by the torquemeter oil pressure. A gage in the cockpit indicates this pressure, which is a measure of the torque transmitted by the gear. The engine power is calculated from the reading of the gage.

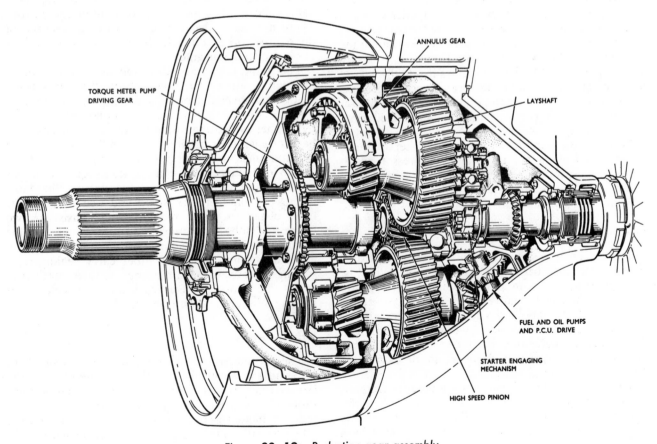

Figure **22·19** *Reduction-gear assembly.*

Auxiliary drives

The auxiliary drives receive power from a bevel gear splined to the rear of the lower limit shaft which meshes with another bevel gear supported in plain bearings in the rear panel of the reduction-gear case. Through the auxiliary drives the oil pumps, fuel pumps, and the propeller control unit are driven.

The compressor

The compressor for the Dart engine comprises two stages, one immediately to the rear of the other as shown in Fig. 22·18. The first-stage impeller is 20 in. in diameter and has 19 blades, while the second-stage impeller is 17.6 in. in diameter with 19 blades.

The compressor casings include the **front compressor casing,** the **intermediate casing,** and the **second-stage outlet casing.** The front compressor casing and the second-stage casing carry the diffuser vane rings, and the intermediate casing carries the interstage guide vanes internally and the engine mounting points externally.

Each rotating assembly consists of an impeller and rotating guide vanes (RGVs). The assemblies are splined onto separate shafts and individually balanced. The split shaft facilitates bearing alignment and makes it unnecessary to disturb the balance during engine build-up. The guide vanes and impellers are locked to the shafts by nuts and cup washers.

Passages are machined through the first-stage rotating guide vanes and between the impeller vanes to permit water/methanol injection. The first-stage shaft is supported at the front by a roller bearing and at the rear by a ball bearing. The second-stage shaft is supported at the front by helical splines inside the rear of the first-stage shaft and at the rear by a ball bearing.

Surrounding each rotating assembly is a **diffuser vane ring.** Each ring consists of a number of fixed vanes forming divergent channels.

Between the compressor stages is a set of guide vanes. Air leaving the first-stage compressor passes between these vanes before entering the second-stage RGVs. The vanes are so angled that they impart a whirling velocity to the airstream.

Combustion section

The combustion section consists of seven individual combustion chambers such as that shown in Fig. 22·20, arranged in an inward spiral (skewed) with respect to the engine main shaft to shorten the engine and promote a smooth gas flow. The chambers are numbered counterclockwise, viewed from the rear, with No. 1 being at the top. Each combustion chamber consists of an **expansion chamber,** an **air casing,** the **flame tube,** and **interconnectors.**

The expansion chambers, forming the forward ends of the combustion chambers, are fitted to the compressor outlet elbows by two link bolts, the seating between the chamber and elbow being formed by a spherical joint ring. At the rear they are attached to

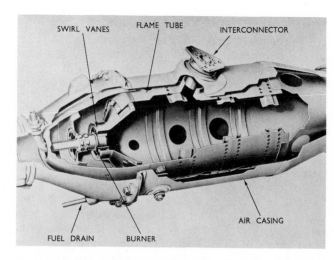

Figure 22·20   Combustion chamber.

the air casing on a bolted flange. Each expansion chamber provides the location for a fuel burner (nozzle), and provision is made for fuel drain connections where necessary. High-energy igniter plugs are carried in the Nos. 3 and 7 chambers.

The air **casings** are bolted to the expansion chambers at the front; however, they are inserted in the discharge nozzles at the rear with a slip fit sealed by piston rings. This permits expansion and contraction of the casings. Each air casing carries two interconnectors, three flame-tube locating pins, and fuel drain connections where necessary. Because of the various positions of interconnectors and fuel drain connections, the casings are not interchangeable.

The flame tubes are fabricated in sections from a high-temperature metal-alloy sheet, the joints being welded and riveted. The tube is located at the front in the air casing by three pins and is supported at the rear by a spherical seating inside the discharge nozzle. The head of each tube carries a set of fixed swirl vanes to assist in efficient mixing of fuel and air.

The **interconnectors** are necessary to equalize the gas pressure and provide a means of passing the flame during light-up from the Nos. 3 and 7 chambers to the other chambers. Each interconnector consists of two concentric tubes to connect the air casings and the flame tubes by independent passages. To provide an expansion joint, the outer tubes carry sealing rings seating in bores in the air casings. A three-bolt flange forms the joint between each interconnector connecting adjacent combustion chambers.

Turbine section

The turbine section of the Dart engine consists of three **turbine wheels** fitted with blades and the **nozzle-box** assembly which contains three sets of **nozzle guide vanes** (NGVs). The compressor drive shaft and the inner reduction-gear drive shaft are coaxial and are attached with bolted flanges to the three turbine wheels.

The nozzle box is a welded two-piece casing into

which are fitted the seven combustion chamber discharge nozzles. It is surrounded by a heat shield. On the front flange of the nozzle box is fitted the nozzle-box mounting drum, which, together with the inner cone and turbine bearing housing, is bolted to the intermediate casing. Flanges on the inside of the nozzle box and inner cone and interstage labyrinth seal platforms provide the location of the nozzle guide vanes.

The nozzle guide vanes form a series of nozzles in which the gases are accelerated. They are of airfoil section and cast hollow to maintain as nearly as possible a constant sectional thickness to reduce thermal stress.

There are 70 high-pressure (HP) vanes which are hooked into flanges machined on the inner cone and nozzle-box outer casing, and 14 of these are used as locators. The inner location is provided by slots in the flange of the inner cone, and the outer location is via locating pegs fitted through the nozzle-box casing and engaging in the guide vane outer platforms.

Fifty-six intermediate pressure (IP) vanes are supported in grooves in the nozzle-box outer casing by the tongues on the outer platforms hooking into the grooves in the nozzle box. They are positioned axially by two rings, and the turbine inter-stage seal is carried on their inner platforms. At the leading edge of 12 of the vanes provision is made for fitting the thermocouples. Twenty-eight of the vanes are used for locators.

The three turbine wheels are secured to the turbine and inner drive shaft by taper bolts. Each wheel consists of a steel disk to which is fitted Nimonic turbine blades, and each blade carries its own shroud. To reduce losses at the blade tips, seals are formed on the shrouds of the HP and IP blades. The root of each blade is of fir-tree shape and fits into a corresponding slot broached in the rim of the disk. The blades are locked to the disk by locking tabs. Labyrinth-type seals are fitted between the stages of the turbine to control the disk cooling airflows.

Exhaust unit

The **exhaust unit** which is bolted to the nozzle box consists of two concentric cones joined by three support fairings. Each fairing is secured by setscrews to a sole plate on the outer cone. The interior of the inner cone is vented to the exhaust gas stream by three circumferentially positioned holes called **pressure balance holes.** Fuel drain holes are incorporated in the assembly to prevent the accumulation of fuel.

When the engine is installed, the exhaust unit is arranged within a conical shroud with its discharge end centrally located in the jet pipe inlet. An annular gap formed between the discharge end of the unit and the jet pipe inlet creates an ejector effect which draws air into the stream. This air is drawn from the combustion compartments between the exhaust unit outer cone and its surrounding shroud. A flow of cooling air is thus provided over the whole combustion compartment.

The oil system

The oil system for the Dart engine is shown in Fig. 22·21. The oil tank is an integral part of the engine, consisting of the annular chamber surrounding the first-stage air inlet. The oil cooler is mounted at the top of the tank as shown. During operation oil is drawn from the standpipe at the bottom of the tank to flow past an oil-temperature bulb and thence to the pressure pump. The pump applies pressure to the oil and forces it to all parts of the engine requiring lubrication.

There are four scavenge pumps in the engine oil system. These pumps scavenge oil from the reduction-gear section, the interstage bearing, second-stage compressor rear bearing, and accessory gearbox drive gears and from the turbine bearings. Oil from the scavenge pumps is delivered by a common external pipe on the left side of the air intake casing to the oil cooler. The oil cooler discharges into the oil tank where the oil is directed over a deaerator tray which spreads it out thinly to permit release of included air.

Air released from the oil in the tank passes through a hollow intake web into the reduction-gear section. From there it passes through the hollow high-speed pinion shaft and compressor shafts to the compressor-turbine coupling and out to the auxiliary gearbox drive housing. The first gear of the auxiliary gearbox drive carries a centrifugal breather. The air released by the breather passes to atmosphere through a cast pocket in the top of the rear compressor casing. Any air in the compressor interstage bearing housing is passed to the breather through the holes in the compressor shaft.

High-pressure oil with a maximum of 70 psi is taken to the propeller control unit (PCU), where the pressure is increased to 670 psi maximum by the PCU pump. The increased pressure supply is directed by the control-valve assembly of the PCU to the **pitch change and stop withdrawal** mechanism of the propeller. The pitch change and stop withdrawal oil supplies are transferred by drilled passages in the air intake casing and reduction gear to the propeller shaft. In the propeller shaft are spring-loaded sealing bushings to maintain the flow separation on transfer to the concentric oil tubes in the shaft.

The oil system includes those features considered standard for engine oil systems such as filters, pressure-relief valves, oil-quantity indicator (dipstick), scavenge oil filters, oil cooler, oil-pressure transmitter, oil-temperature bulb, and oil-pressure warning light.

Fuel system

The fuel system for the Dart engine is designed to satisfy the basic requirements of the engine for all types of operation. The system must provide full atomization of the fuel over the complete range of fuel flow, control fuel flow according to engine demand, provide engine overspeeding control, ensure a specific flow for a given throttle position, compensate fuel flow for altitude conditions, limit flow to suit the engine power rating, provide a correct idling fuel flow, and provide for

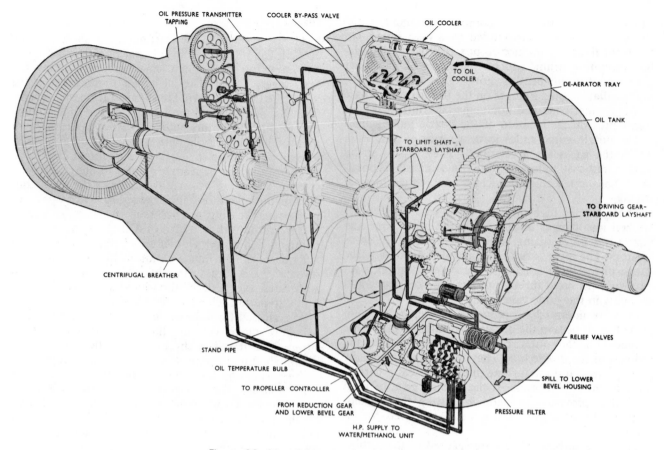

Figure 22·21 *Oil system for the Dart engine.*

complete fuel shutoff when it is desired to stop the engine.

The operation of the fuel pump and fuel-control unit can be understood by examining the diagram of Fig. 22·22. The fuel pump consists of an engine-driven rotor carrying seven plungers spring loaded against a circular cam plate. The output of the pump is varied by changing the angle of the cam plate relative to the rotor through the action of a servo piston. The piston assembly is carried in an alloy body which incorporates the inlet and outlet ports. These communicate with the revolving rotor through a fixed valve plate containing two kidney-shaped ports.

As the rotor of the pump revolves around the cam plate, each plunger in turn is extended and receives low-pressure fuel. It then delivers the fuel at high pressure as the plunger is pushed in during its rotation around the inclined face of the cam plate. Since the pump is driven at a fixed ratio to engine speed, the pump output at maximum stroke is proportional to engine speed. Since, for any given rpm, the engine fuel requirement does not coincide with the maximum pump output, the pump stroke must be varied independently of rpm. This variation in fuel flow to suit engine demand is attained by altering the cam plate angle.

The pump servo, consisting of a spring-loaded piston

in a cylinder connected to the cam plate, is integral with the pump. Movement of the servo piston alters the cam-plate angle and the plunger stroke, thus changing fuel flow. The servo piston receives high fuel pressure on both sides, that on the spring side first passing through an orifice. Fuel flow from the spring side of the piston is controlled by a **spill valve.** When the spill valve is open, the fuel pressure is relieved and the pressure on the opposite side of the piston moves the piston in a direction to reduce the angle of the cam plate. This decreases the pump output.

Engine overspeed is controlled by the diaphragm-type governor in the fuel pump. As shown in the diagram, the pump rotor contains passages through which fuel flows into the pump body by centrifugal force. This being true, it is apparent that the pressure within the pump body will vary according to engine rpm. Since the governor diaphragm is exposed on one side to the pump centrifugal pressure, the diaphragm will move when pressure becomes excessive. This is the case when the engine reaches an overspeed condition. As the diaphragm moves, it pushes a lever which releases a spill valve controlling fuel pressure on the spring side of the servo piston and thus reduces the pump cam plate angle which, in turn, reduces fuel flow. The reduction in fuel flow continues until the

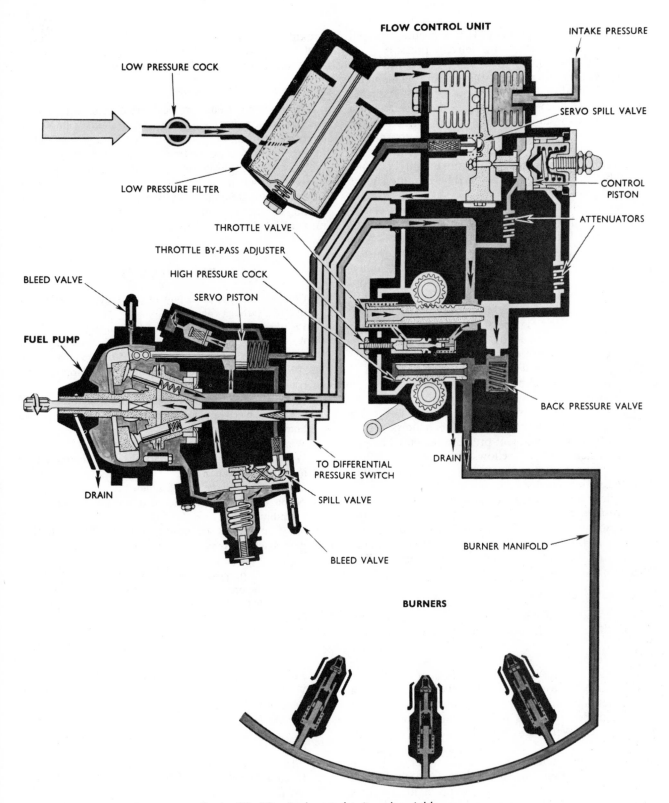

FLOW CONTROL UNIT

INTAKE PRESSURE

LOW PRESSURE COCK

SERVO SPILL VALVE

LOW PRESSURE FILTER

CONTROL PISTON

THROTTLE VALVE

ATTENUATORS

THROTTLE BY-PASS ADJUSTER

BLEED VALVE

HIGH PRESSURE COCK

SERVO PISTON

FUEL PUMP

BACK PRESSURE VALVE

TO DIFFERENTIAL PRESSURE SWITCH

DRAIN

DRAIN

SPILL VALVE

BURNER MANIFOLD

BLEED VALVE

BURNERS

Figure 22·22   Fuel-control unit and variable pump.

engine speed stabilizes at the predetermined overspeed rpm set by the tension spring.

A secondary function of the overspeed governor spill valve is to prevent excessive fuel pressures in the system. Thus it acts as a relief valve. The overspeed governor spill valve rocker arm is loaded by a spring which, through its leverage, will maintain the spill valve in a closed position unless there is an excessive

465

rise in pump delivery pressure. If this occurs, the spill valve opens and reduces pump delivery pressure.

In the fuel flow-control unit a spill valve controls the pump servo according to throttle position. This valve is kept informed of the throttle position by a spring-loaded control piston which senses the fuel flow via pressure signals from upstream and downstream of the throttle valve. Attenuators in the pressure-sensing lines dampen out any pressure fluctuation from the fuel pump. The control piston movement is transmitted by a pushrod to the flexibly mounted lever housing the spill valve.

Under stabilized conditions the fuel-pressure differential across the control piston balances the control piston spring force. The spill valve position is thus automatically adjusted so that the pump servo piston selects the correct pump stroke for fuel flow. When the throttle is opened, the pressure differential across the throttle valve decreases and the control piston senses this decrease. The piston moves to close the spill valve, thus causing the pump output to increase until fuel flow is correct for the new throttle setting. The system then stabilizes in the new position.

Fuel-flow adjustment for variations in altitude is accomplished through the action of the intake pressure aneroid bellows shown in the diagram. As altitude increases, the bellows exert pressure on the spill valve which reduces the pump output. The bellows are so designed that, when ambient pressure reaches 14.7 psi, no further action of the bellows to increase fuel flow can take place. This is to prevent the engine from being provided with excessive fuel.

Fuel flow from the control unit passes through the high-pressure cock and thence to the burners in the combustion chambers. These burners or nozzles are designed to provide a hollow conical spray of fuel at the forward end of each combustion chamber. The burners include thread-type filters.

Water/methanol system

In operation under high ambient temperature conditions, there is a reduction in engine mass airflow and the fuel flow is reduced by trimming in order to maintain the turbine working temperatures within acceptable limits. This results in a reduction of engine shp which can be restored to takeoff level by injecting a water/methanol mixture into the first-stage compressor through drilled passages in the rotating guide vanes and impeller. Water and methanol from the aircraft tank are fed by a tank pump and electrically operated feed cock to the metering valve of the water/methanol unit. The cockpit selector switch operates both the feed cock and tank pump, and a cockpit light indicates when water and methanol are being supplied. The feed cock is interconnected with the propeller feathering system so that, when the propeller is feathered, the water/methanol supply is automatically shut off.

The water/methanol mixture used in the Dart engine consists of water containing between 36 and 38 percent of methanol (methyl alcohol) by weight. This is approximately equivalent to 43.8 volumes of methanol and 56.2 volumes of water. The water and methanol must meet rigid specifications of quality and purity.

Starting and ignition systems

The starter system for the Dart engine is typical of electric-motor starter systems. The starter motor is energized through relays controlled by a starter switch in the cockpit. The system is interconnected with a vibrator-type high-energy ignition system to provide for ignition when the engine is started. Overspeed and safety relays are placed in the system to provide for cutoff of the system when the starter reaches the maximum allowable speed.

REVIEW QUESTIONS

1. Compare the power section of a turboprop engine with that of a turbojet engine.
2. List three advantages of a turboprop engine.
3. Describe the construction and explain the function of the compressor air inlet housing for the 501-D13 engine.
4. What provision is made to prevent ice from forming in the compressor air inlet housing?
5. Describe the construction of the compressor rotor.
6. Why are bleed air valves required in the compressor housing?
7. What is the function of the combustion liners?
8. What are the two principal functions of the thermocouples in the turbine section?
9. Describe the turbine rotor assembly.
10. Name the accessories mounted on the reduction-gear assembly.
11. What advantages are gained by locating the reduction-gear assembly remotely from the power section of the engine?
12. What is the purpose of the propeller brake?
13. Explain the operation of the negative torque system.
14. Under what condition does the thrust-sensitive signal take effect?
15. Describe the operation of the torquemeter.
16. Name the components of the power section lubrication system.
17. Explain the functions of the speed-sensitive control.
18. What type of mechanism in the fuel-control unit is used to sense engine speed?
19. List the conditions of engine operation which are sensed by the fuel-control unit in order to provide correct fuel flow.
20. What is the purpose of the coordinator?
21. Discuss the functions of the temperature datum control and temperature datum valve.
22. What feature of the fuel nozzle prevents the formation of carbon at the tip?
23. Explain the need for drip valves and drain valves.
24. Describe the compressor of the Rolls-Royce Dart engine.
25. What type of combustion section is employed in the Dart engine?
26. Name the principal parts of the combustion chamber.

27. What provision is made for expansion and contraction of the combustion chambers?

28. What material is used for the turbine blades of the Dart engine?

29. Describe the arrangement of the oil tank for the Dart engine.

30. Describe the operation of the fuel pump.

31. Through what unit is the water/methanol mixture injected into the engine?

32. What type of starting system is employed for the Dart engine?

Rocket Engines

CHAPTER 23

INTRODUCTION

No discussion of powerplants for aerospace vehicles would be complete without consideration of the rocket engine and its essential applications in space research and space travel. The field of rocketry and space exploration has at last become a vital and extensive segment of our economy and now represents one of the largest single efforts of the United States government.

The first known use of rockets for military purposes occurred in China in the thirteenth century when "Fire Arrows" were used effectively in the siege of Kaifeng. These were solid-fuel (gunpowder) rockets, and this concept of rocket design continued from that time until early in the twentieth century when liquid-propellant rockets first became a reality. In 1258 rockets were used at Cologne in Europe, and from that time to the present the use of rockets as weapons has waxed and waned, depending partly upon the effectiveness of cannon. Among notable battles in which rockets were employed as weapons were the battles of Seringapatam in India in 1722 and 1799; the attacks on Boulogne in 1806, Danzig in 1806, and Copenhagen in 1807; and, of course, the British attack on Fort McHenry.

During World War II multiple-rocket launchers were used effectively by the United States as well as other nations. The rockets used by the Russians in the Battle of Stalingrad were obtained from the United States under "lend-lease" during World War II.

Liquid-propellant rockets were developed in the United States by Prof. Robert H. Goddard, who struggled for many years to get his ideas accepted and to obtain the financial backing he needed. With the help of Charles Lindbergh, Goddard was able to obtain grants from the Guggenheim Foundation and finally developed a number of successful liquid-propellant rockets which burned gasoline and liquid oxygen. At about the same time German rocket scientists under the leadership of Hermann Oberth were also working on the development of liquid rocket engines. Assisting in this work was Wernher von Braun, who is now a leading American rocket scientist. The effectiveness of the German effort was quite apparent when the V-2 missiles began to fall on Great Britain during the last part of World War II.

Today a wide variety of rockets is employed in many types of operations. They are used in all types of missiles including air to air (AAM), surface to air (SAM), air to surface (ASM), surface to surface (SSM), and other miscellaneous types. Among other designations for missiles are guided air missile (GAM), guided air rocket (GAR), intermediate-range ballistic missile (IRBM), and intercontinental ballistic missile (ICBM).

The rocket engines used for missiles are both solid-propellant types and liquid-propellant types. Their power ranges vary from a few hundred pounds thrust to millions of pounds. For spacecraft, many of the same rocket engines used in missiles are found to be suitable. Of particular interest is the mighty F-1 rocket engine built for the Saturn vehicle to start the Apollo space ship on its trip to the moon. This engine was designed and built by the Rocketdyne Division of North American Aviation, Inc, and produces a thrust of 1,500,000 lb. A cluster of five of these monster engines is used to boost the Saturn-Apollo on the first stage of its flight. A model of the F-1 engine is shown in the photograph of Fig. 23 · 1. Beside the F-1 is the smaller H-1 engine.

PRINCIPLES OF ROCKET PROPULSION

Reaction and formulas

The force which drives a rocket is essentially the same reaction force explained in the discussion of turbojet engine theory. The principal difference be-

Figure 23 · 1   Model of the F-1 rocket engine. (Rocketdyne Div., North American Aviation, Inc.)

468

tween a turbojet engine and a rocket engine is that the turbojet requires oxygen from the atmosphere in order to burn its fuel while the rocket engine carries its own supply of oxygen or other oxidizer. This is why rocket engines are used for space travel.

In the liquid-propellant rocket engine, the liquid fuel and oxidizer is fed into a chamber and burned. An opening at one end of the chamber allows the expanded gases to escape, thus producing thrust in accordance with Newton's second and third laws of motion. In a rocket chamber the force of reaction is equal to the area of the opening (nozzle throat) in the combustion chamber multiplied by the pressure inside the chamber. For example, if burning fuel and oxidizer develop a pressure of 80 psi inside the chamber and the area of the nozzle throat on one end is 2 sq in., the force of reaction will be $2 \times 80 = 160$ lb. This can be expressed by the short form of the **general thrust equation,** thus:

$$F = P_c A_t$$

where F = force, psi
$\quad P_c$ = pressure in the chamber, psi
$\quad A_t$ = area of the throat, sq in.

It must be emphasized here that rocket thrust is not the result of the rocket exhaust pushing against the air outside the rocket engine. As mentioned previously, thrust will be about the same regardless of whether the reaction takes place in the atmosphere or in a vacuum. This is why the rocket is the only suitable powerplant for space travel.

The actual thrust produced by a rocket engine is dependent to some extent upon the design of the expansion nozzle around the exit of the exhaust. An examination of modern rocket engines usually reveals an expansion nozzle shaped as shown in the diagram of Fig. 23·2. The thrust coefficient of the nozzle C_f is dependent upon the ratio of throat area to exit area. This coefficient is multiplied by the theoretical thrust obtained from the basic equation to find the total thrust of the engine. The equation in this case is

$$F = P_c A_t C_f$$

As explained in the discussion on jet-engine thrust,

the thrust force is proportional to the product of mass and acceleration in accordance with Newton's second law. This is shown by the basic equation

$$F = ma$$

where F = force, lb
$\quad m$ = mass, slugs
$\quad a$ = acceleration, ft per sec^2

To use this same equation for rocket thrust we modify it to fit rocket operation, thus:

$$F = \frac{\dot{W}}{g} v_e + (P_e - P_{am}) A_e$$

where F = force, lb
$\quad \dot{W}$ = mass flow rate, lb per sec
$\quad g$ = acceleration of gravity
$\quad v_e$ = velocity of gases at nozzle exit, ft per sec
$\quad P_e$ = gas pressure at nozzle exit
$\quad P_{am}$ = ambient pressure
$\quad A_e$ = area of exit nozzle, sq in.

In the foregoing **fundamental thrust equation,** the term $(P_e - P_{am}) A_e$ is the thrust resulting from the difference in exit nozzle pressure and ambient pressure. The term $(\dot{W}/g) v_e$ is the same as mass times acceleration.

Specific impulse

Specific impulse I_s is a term used to provide an indication of rocket-engine performance. It may be defined as the thrust in pounds obtained from burning one pound of propellant per second. For example, if a rocket engine develops 250 lb thrust per pound of propellant per second, the specific impulse is 250 sec. Instead of using the term pound per pound propellant per second, the unit is merely shortened to seconds. The formula for specific impulse is

$$I_s = \frac{F}{\dot{W}}$$

where F = force, lb
$\quad \dot{W}$ = weight of propellant consumed, lb per sec

Specific propellant consumption is the reciprocal of specific impulse. That is,

$$\dot{W}_{sp} = \frac{1}{I_s}$$

Specific propellant consumption is defined as the weight of propellant consumed per second per pound of thrust. For example, if a rocket engine consumes 1 ton per sec of propellants and produces 520,000 lb thrust, the specific propellant consumption is 0.00384. The formula may also be given as

$$\dot{W}_{sp} = \frac{\dot{W}}{F}$$

Effective exhaust velocity

Effective exhaust velocity is defined as a fictitious exhaust velocity that would give the same jet thrust as that actually obtained. A formula may be derived from the specific impulse formula or by using portions of the

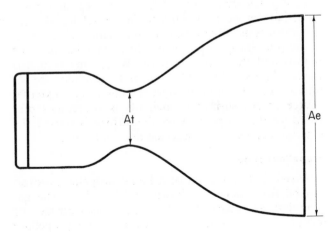

Figure 23·2   Rocket expansion nozzle.

thrust formula. In the first instance, the formula for effective exhaust velocity c or V_{eff} is

$$c = I_s g$$

and in the second instance it is

$$c = V_e \frac{+(P_e - P_a)A_e g}{\dot{W}}$$

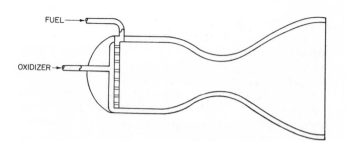

FUEL →

OXIDIZER →

Figure **23·4** *Diagram of a regenerative cooling system.*

LIQUID-PROPELLANT ROCKET-ENGINE SYSTEM

Basic rocket engine

A simplified diagram of a rocket engine is shown in Fig. 23·3. The **injector** is the rear portion of the combustion chamber through which the propellants are injected into the chamber. The injector usually has a number of openings for each of the propellants, and these openings, or "orifices," are designed to direct the fuel and oxidizer in streams so that they will impinge and break up into small particles. Good mixing of the fuel and oxidizer is essential to efficient combustion.

The **combustion chamber** is the space in which the propellants are burned. Extremely high temperatures are developed, and these would cause burning of the chamber material except for a boundary layer of cooler gases which appear to cling to the inner surface of the chamber. If additional cooling is needed, the chamber walls are cooled by means of fuel which is passed between double chamber walls and through the tubes which compose the expansion chamber walls. The use for cooling is called **regenerative cooling.**

The **nozzle** of the rocket engine includes the convergent section at the rear of the combustion chamber, the throat, and the divergent section from the throat to the exit. The most commonly used nozzle design is called the de Laval nozzle, named after the Swedish engineer Dr. Gustaf Patrick de Laval. This is typically a convergent-divergent design.

Nozzle cooling

On modern high-performance rocket engines it is necessary to utilize the regenerative cooling method to keep the nozzles from being destroyed by the extremely high temperatures. A diagram of a regenerative cooling system is shown in Fig. 23·4. In this system the fuel is

pumped through the tubes of the nozzle before it goes to the injector. This system has two advantages: (1) The nozzle is cooled, and (2) heat energy is added to the fuel, thus increasing the specific impulse of the engine. The nozzle wall tubes are made of a heat-resistant high-nickel alloy or similar material.

On rocket engines equipped with nozzle skirts to provide the most effective nozzle expansion ratio (ratio of nozzle-throat cross-sectional area to nozzle-exit cross-sectional area), it is necessary to provide cooling for the skirt. This is accomplished by flowing the turbine exhaust through the double walls of the skirt. Figure 23·5 shows the turbine exhaust shroud joining the skirt of the rocket engine.

Propellant pump

The propellant pump for a rocket engine usually consists of a gas turbine driving two centrifugal pumps which are mounted on the same turbine shaft. In some cases the pumps are mounted on opposite ends of the shaft with the turbine in the middle, and in others the turbine is on one end with the fuel pump in the middle and the oxidizer pump on the outer end. Diagrams of these arrangements are shown in Fig. 23·6.

The material used for the gas turbine and manifold assembly is a high-temperature nickel alloy capable of withstanding the temperature of the gases by which the turbine is driven. The propellant pump cases and impellers may be made of cast-aluminum alloy to provide reduced weight.

The **gas generator** for the turbopump is similar to a rocket-engine combustion chamber in that it utilizes an injector with regeneratively cooled walls. The burned gases are conducted to the inlet of the turbine by means of heat-resistant tubing. Fuel for the gas generator is usually taken from the main rocket supply by tapping into the propellant feed lines between the pumps and the rocket injector. When this system is used, it is necessary that a means be provided for rotating the turbopump to start the engine. An external source of pressurized propellants is sometimes provided for this purpose. After the turbine is started, the external supply is disconnected automatically.

Propellant system

A schematic diagram of a liquid-propellant rocket-engine fuel system is shown in Fig. 23·7. The gas cylinders are charged with a inert gas (nitrogen or helium) which is used to pressurize the propellant

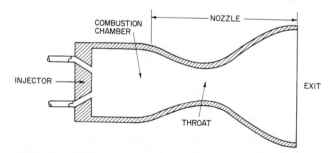

COMBUSTION CHAMBER — NOZZLE

INJECTOR →

EXIT

THROAT

Figure **23·3** *Diagram of a liquid-propellant rocket engine.*

470

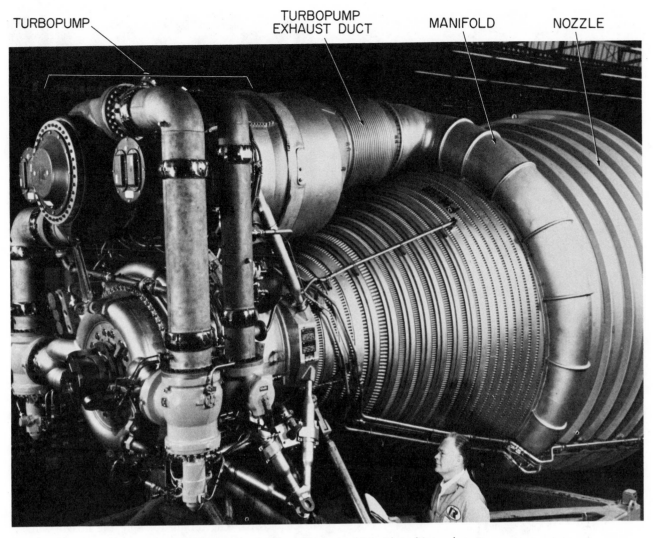

TURBOPUMP   TURBOPUMP EXHAUST DUCT   MANIFOLD   NOZZLE

Figure **23·5** *Cooling of nozzle skirt with turbine exhaust.*

tanks. Fuel and oxidizer are stored in the two large tanks which are connected to the two propellant pumps driven by the turbine. Electrically operated valves are installed in the propellant lines to turn on or shut off the flow of propellants to the pumps. Fuel is directed from the fuel pump to the nozzle walls, where it is used for cooling before it flows to the injector. Propellant-control valves are installed between the pumps and the injector for additional control of the propellants.

Ignition system

The ignition system for a liquid-propellant rocket engine may be an electric spark system, a powder charge with an electrically fired igniter (squib), or a hypergolic system in which a hypergolic chemical is injected to ignite automatically when it comes in contact with liquid oxygen. The type of ignition system used is designed to produce the most immediate and effective ignition of the propellants possible to provide for complete and steady combustion.

Injectors

Injectors are designed in many configurations; however, the principal purpose of the design is to accomplish as thorough a mixing of the fuel and oxidizer as possible. Some injectors are designed so that the fuel and oxidizer streams will impinge upon each other as they enter the combustion chamber. This method usually provides for good mixing and breaking up the propellants into small particles. Another design provides for the propellants to splash against surfaces raised on the face of the injector. The propellants mix as they rebound from the surfaces.

TYPICAL LIQUID-PROPELLANT ROCKET ENGINE

Typical of modern liquid-propellant rocket engines is the Rocketdyne H-1 engine shown in Fig. 23 · 8. This engine is an outgrowth of the earlier engine designed

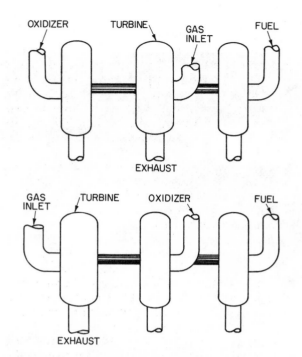

OXIDIZER   TURBINE   GAS INLET   FUEL

EXHAUST

GAS INLET   TURBINE   OXIDIZER   FUEL

EXHAUST

Figure **23·6** Turbopump arrangements.

Figure **23·8** Rocketdyne H-1 liquid-propellant rocket engine.

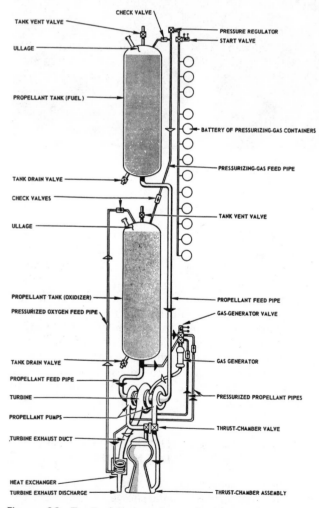

TANK VENT VALVE
CHECK VALVE
ULLAGE
PRESSURE REGULATOR
START VALVE
PROPELLANT TANK (FUEL)
BATTERY OF PRESSURIZING-GAS CONTAINERS
PRESSURIZING-GAS FEED PIPE
TANK DRAIN VALVE
CHECK VALVES
ULLAGE
TANK VENT VALVE
PROPELLANT TANK (OXIDIZER)
PROPELLANT FEED PIPE
PRESSURIZED OXYGEN FEED PIPE
GAS-GENERATOR VALVE
TANK DRAIN VALVE
GAS GENERATOR
PROPELLANT FEED PIPE
TURBINE
PRESSURIZED PROPELLANT PIPES
PROPELLANT PUMPS
THRUST-CHAMBER VALVE
TURBINE EXHAUST DUCT
HEAT EXCHANGER
TURBINE EXHAUST DISCHARGE
THRUST-CHAMBER ASSEMBLY

Figure **23·7** Fuel system for a liquid-propellant rocket engine. (Aero Publishers, Inc.)

472

for the Thor and Jupiter missiles. The H-1 is designed for the Saturn I booster. Eight of these engines are used in a cluster, four being stationary in the center portion of the cluster and the four outer engines mounted in gimbals to provide for directional control.

The propellants for the H-1 engine are RP-1 (kerosene) and liquid oxygen. The propellant system includes two propellant tanks, two turbine-driven pumps driven by one gas turbine, a gas generator for the turbine which utilizes the rocket propellants, and necessary plumbing, valves, and control elements.

The engine has a thrust chamber formed of thin, lightweight metal tubes through which fuel is forced at high speed before it enters the combustion chamber to be burned. The tubing forming the nozzle walls is made of a heat-resistant alloy and is arranged as shown in Fig. 23·8.

The H-1 engine develops 188,000 lb, and the cluster of eight engines used on the Saturn I booster produces 1,500,000 lb.

LIQUID PROPELLANTS

A large variety of fuels and oxidizers is available for liquid-propellant engine; however, the characteristics of the propellants differ considerably. Among the oxidizers are liquid oxygen, fluorine, hydrogen peroxide, red fuming nitric acid (RFNA), white fuming nitric acid (WFNA), and chlorine. Fuels include kerosene (RP-1), JP-4, gasoline, ammonia, hydrazine, hydrogen, alcohol, aniline, and numerous others.

As mentioned previously, some propellant combinations are **hypergolic**. For example, the oxidizer fluorine provides a hypergolic combination with ammonia, hydrazine, or hydrogen. When it is desired that a rocket engine ignite without the aid of a special ignition system, hypergolic combinations are used.

Handling liquid propellants

The technician or rocket-engine servicer who is responsible for handling liquid rocket propellants must be thoroughly trained in the techniques to be employed in carrying out his duties. First, the nature of the individual propellants must be understood. For example, liquid oxygen is always at an extremely low temperature and will freeze any organic material almost instantly. For this reason, it must never be allowed to come in contact with the skin because the resulting injury will be similar to a severe burn. Liquid or gaseous oxygen must not come into contact with greases, oils, or similar substances because of the possibility of spontaneous combustion.

Hydrogen peroxide is extremely unstable and will decompose in the presence of almost any impurity. When this occurs, high-temperature steam is generated; hence severe burns will be caused if the substance comes into contact with the skin.

Many of the propellants are highly toxic, corrosive, and otherwise dangerous when handled improperly; hence they must be used within strict limits. For a particular propellant, the tanks, fluid lines, and valves must be made of a metal or other material with which the propellant will not react chemically. It must be noted also that liquid propellants are pumped and pressurized at very high pressures (up to 3000 psi or more), and for this reason the plumbing must be of the best possible quality.

Persons assigned to the handling of propellants must wear the correct type of protective clothing. Usually such a person must be completely covered from head to foot with clothing which will prevent the propellants from coming into contact with his body. A high-pressure water shower is generally provided for use in case a dangerous propellant is splashed on personnel in the vicinity of fueling operations.

The following are some of the safety rules to be followed in the handling of propellants:

1. Be sure that you understand the nature of the propellants with which you are working.
2. Wear the proper type of protective clothing.
3. Do not permit any propellant to be spilled. If any should be spilled, see that it is immediately removed and neutralized.
4. Do not permit any propellants to be mixed.
5. Make sure that containers, tanks, plumbing, and valves are scrupulously clean, are of the proper material, and are properly assembled before being filled with a propellant.
6. Follow all rules established by the contractor or government agency for the handling of propellants.

SOLID-PROPELLANT ROCKETS

From the time of the earliest known rockets until the present century, all rockets were of the solid-propellant type. The early rockets were filled with gunpowder made of saltpeter (sodium nitrate), sulfur, and charcoal. The composition of the mixture was usually such that burning was not sufficiently rapid to cause an explosion.

Solid propellants

A solid propellant consists of a fuel and oxidizer combined in such a manner that the molecules of each are in contact to the extent that complete chemical combination can take place as the mixture is burned. One combination used for solid-propellant rockets is potassium perchlorate and asphalt with a small amount of petroleum oil. These ingredients were mixed while hot and then poured into the liner to form a solid mass. Amateur rocketeers often use a mixture of powdered zinc and sulfur called "micrograin" as the propellant.

There are many combinations of oxidizers and fuels suitable for solid-propellant rocket engines, and the particular materials used depend upon the characteristics required by the designer of the engine. Solid propellants are usually made up in one piece of a size to fit the engine case. The propellant is called the **grain,** regardless of its size. The grain must be comparatively hard, durable, and safe to handle. Its configuration depends upon the rate of burning and the chamber pressure desired. A grain which is made as a solid cylinder is called **end-burning** because it burns progressively from one end to the other.

It is usually necessary to provide a **restriction** around the grain to prevent the grain from burning the combustion chamber or burning unevenly. It is also common practice to mix an inhibiting material with the grain to control the rate of burning.

Grains are also made in tubular form, that is, with a hollow cylinder-shaped center. The **cruciform** has the hollow center of the grain in the form of a cross, and the **star** grain has a star-shaped center. These are shown in Fig. 23·9. There are many other configurations; however, the foregoing shapes will serve to indicate the possibilities.

Solid-propellant rocket engine

A typical solid-propellant rocket engine is shown in Fig. 23·10. This diagram shows the **case** (chamber), **liner, nozzle, propellant, grain, igniter,** and **restriction.** These are the principal components of a solid-propellant rocket engine.

Solid-propellant rocket engines are used to power the Polaris submarine-launched missile, the Nike Hercules and Zeus missiles, and the Minuteman ICBM. Solid propellants are used in order to make the missiles immediately available for firing in case of an attack warning when it is known that enemy missiles have been launched against targets in this country. With the use of solid propellants, it is not necessary to

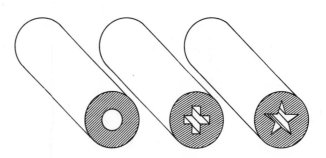

Figure **23·9**   Shapes for solid-propellant grains.

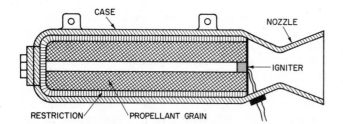

Figure 23·10   A solid-propellant rocket engine.

Figure 23·11   Launching a Nike Hercules missile. (Douglas Aircraft Co.)

fuel the missiles before firing, since the propellants are already in place and ready to be fired.

The launching of a Nike Hercules missile is shown in Fig. 23·11. The booster of this missile consists of a cluster of four solid-propellant rocket engines. A second-stage solid-propellant engine sustains the missile in flight. The purpose of this missile is to intercept high-flying supersonic aircraft or missiles. It has a range of more than 75 miles and operates at altitudes in excess of 150,000 ft.

REVIEW QUESTIONS

1. Compare rocket-engine thrust with jet-engine thrust.
2. Why is a rocket engine the only type suitable for space travel?
3. How can the thrust of a rocket engine be determined?
4. In what way does the expansion nozzle affect rocket thrust?
5. Give the *fundamental thrust equation*.
6. Explain *specific impulse* and *specific propellant consumption*.
7. Describe the principal components of a liquid-propellant rocket engine.
8. Explain how regenerative cooling is accomplished.
9. What fuel is normally used for the turbopump gas generator?
10. Describe the use of turbine exhaust for cooling the nozzle skirt.
11. Give three methods for igniting the propellant mixture.
12. What is the principal function of the injector?
13. List precautions required in the handling of liquid propellants.
14. Describe the propellant *grain* for a solid-propellant rocket engine.
15. What is the principal advantage of a solid-propellant rocket engine?

Index

476